P9-BUI-271

Handbook of Steel Construction

THIRD EDITION

FIRST PRINTING DECEMBER 1980
SECOND PRINTING APRIL 1981

Canadian Institute of Steel Construction

201 Consumers Road, Suite 300
Willowdale, Ontario M2J 4G8

Copyright © 1980

by

Canadian Institute of Steel Construction

All rights reserved. This book or any part thereof must not be reproduced in any form without the written permission of the publisher.

Third Edition
First printing December 1980
Second printing April 1981

IBSN 0-88811-045-6

PRINTED IN CANADA
by
Universal Offset Limited,
Markham, Ontario

CONTENTS

Foreword   v
Preface   vi
Designations   vii
General Nomenclature   viii

Part One
CAN3-S16.1-M78 — "Steel Structures for Buildings — Limit States Design"

Part Two
CISC Commentary on CAN3-S16.1-M78

Part Three
Connections and Tension Members

Part Four
Compression Members

Part Five
Flexural Members

Part Six
Properties and Dimensions

Part Seven
Miscellaneous Data

Part Eight
Properties and Dimensions in Imperial Units

Part Nine
Limit States Design Tables in Imperial Units

Part Ten
General Index

FOREWORD

The Canadian Institute of Steel Construction is the national trade association representing the structural steel, open-web steel joist and steel plate fabricating industries in Canada. Formed in 1930 and granted a Federal charter in 1942, the CISC functions as a non-profit organization promoting the efficient and economic use of fabricated steel in construction.

As a member of the Canadian Steel Construction Council, the Institute has a general interest in all uses of steel in construction. The CISC supports and actively participates in the work of the Canadian Standards Association, the Associate Committee on the National Building Code and numerous other organizations, in Canada and other countries, involved in research work and the preparation of codes and standards.

Preparation of engineering plans is not a function of the CISC. The Institute does provide technical information through the services of its professional engineering staff, through the preparation and dissemination of publications of various types, through the medium of seminars, conferences and other types of meeting, and in many other ways. Architects, engineers and others interested in steel construction are encouraged to make use of CISC services.

The Head Office of the CISC is located at 201 Consumers Road, Suite 300, Willowdale Ontario M2J 4G8. Regional Offices are situated in Vancouver, Calgary, Winnipeg, Toronto, Montreal and Halifax.

PREFACE

This handbook has been prepared and published by the Canadian Institute of Steel Contruction. It is an important part of a continuing effort to provide current, practical information to assist educators, designers, fabricators and others interested in the use of steel in construction.

The First Edition of the "CISC Handbook of Steel Construction" appeared in 1967 and the Second Edition in 1970. In 1977 CISC prepared and published "Limit States Design Steel Manual", based on the requirements of CSA Standard S16.1-1974.

With the introduction, in 1978, of a new series of W (Wide Flange) and HP (H-Pile) structural steel shapes by North American steel mills and CSA Standard CAN3-S16.1-M78, "Steel Structures for Buildings — Limit States Design", in SI units, both the Handbook and the Manual became obsolete. "Metric Structural Steel Design Data" was published, in 1978, to provide essential handbook material for designers and others, while the third edition of the Handbook was being prepared.

This Third Edition of the Handbook is based primarily on CSA Standard CAN3-S16. 1-M78 and is predominately in SI units. For those still dealing with plans in Imperial units, Part Eight provides the properties and dimensions of structural steel shapes in Imperial units and Part Nine provides Limit States Design tables in Imperial units based on the requirements of CSA Standard S16.1-1974 (the Imperial units version of CAN3-S16.1-M78). It is hoped that this enlarged Edition with its expanded coverage of many topics will be welcomed by users.

Permission to reprint portions of their publications, granted by the Canadian Standards Association and the American Institute of Steel Construction, Inc., is gratefully acknowledged. The contributions of many individuals who helped to make publication of this book possible are sincerely appreciated.

Although no effort has been spared in an attempt to ensure that all data is factual at the time of printing and that numerical values are accurate to a degree consistent with current design practices the Canadian Institute of Steel Construction does not assume responsibility for errors or oversights resulting from use of the information contained herein. All suggestions for improvements of this publication will receive full consideration for future printings.

M.I. Gilmor
Editor

December, 1980

DESIGNATIONS

When designating structural steel products on drawings, it is desirable that a standard method of abbreviation be employed which will identify the product without reference to the manufacturer. For SI, the new nomenclature, incorporated in the list below, should be used in future on design drawings, for detailing, and for ordering material from the mill.

Shape	Example
Welded Wide Flange Shapes	
— Beams	WWF900×169
— Columns	WWF450×201
W Shapes	W610×113
	W150×30
Miscellaneous M Shapes	M200×9.7
	M100×19
Standard Beams (S Shapes)	S380×64
Standard Channels (C Shapes)	C230×30
Structural Tees	
— cut from WWF Shapes	WWT250×138
— cut from W Shapes	WT155×43
— cut from M Shapes	MT100×25.5
Bearing Piles (HP Shapes)	HP130×110
Equal Leg Angles (leg dimensions x thickness, all in mm)	L 65 x 65 x 8
Unequal Leg Angles (leg dimensions x thickness, all in mm)	L 125 x 90 x 13
Plates (thickness x width, both in mm)	PL 8 x 500
Square Bars (side, in mm)	Bar 25 □
Round Bars (diameter, in mm)	Bar 30 ϕ
Flat Bars (thickness x width, both in mm)	Bar 5 x 60
Round Pipe (outside diameter x thickness, both in mm)	Pipe — 324 OD x 9.5
Square Hollow Structural Sections (outside dimensions x thickness, both in mm; G40.20-M class)	HSS — 101.6 x 101.6 x 4.78 Class H (or Class C)
Round Hollow Structural Sections (outside diameter x thickness, both in mm; G40.20-M class)	HSS — 60.3 OD x 3.18 Class H (or Class C)
Steel Pipe Piles (outside diameter x thickness both in mm)	Pipe Piles — 324 OD x 9.5
Rectangular Hollow Structural Sections (outside dimensions x thickness, both in mm; G40.20-M class)	HSS — 203.2 x 101.6 x 6.35 Class H (or Class C)

GENERAL NOMENCLATURE

Explanations of the nomenclature used in many sections of this book appear in those specific sections. In addition, the following symbols are included here for convenience. See also pages 1-17 to 1-20, inclusive.

A	Area
A_b	Cross-sectional area of one bolt based on nominal diameter
A_f	Flange area
A_w	Web area; shear area; effective throat area of weld
a	Centre-to-centre distance between transverse web stiffeners, depth of concrete compression zone
a/h	Aspect ratio, ratio of distance between stiffeners to web depth
B_f	Bearing force in a member or component under factored load
B_r	Factored bearing resistance of a member or component
B_x	Bending factor with respect to axis x-x
B_y	Bending factor with respect to axis y-y
b	Width of stiffened or unstiffeneed compression elements; design effective width of concrete or cellular slab
C_e	Euler buckling load = 1 970 000 $A/(KL/r)^2$
C_f	Compressive force in a member or component under factored load; factored axial load
C_r	Factored compressive resistance of a member or component; factored compressive resistance of steel acting at the centroid of that part of the steel area in compression
C'_r	Compressive resistance of concrete acting at the centroid of the concrete area in compression
C_w	Warping torsional constant
C_y	Axial compressive load at yield stress
c	Distance from neutral axis to outer fibre of structural shape
D	Outside diameter of circular sections; diameter of rocker or roller; stiffener factor; fillet weld size (millimetres)
d	Depth; overall depth of a section; diameter of bolt or stud
E	Elastic modulus of steel (200 000 MPa assumed)
E_c	Elastic modulus of concrete
e	End distance; lever arm between the compressive resistance, C_r, and tensile resistance, T_r
e'	Lever arm between the compressive resistance, C'_r, of concrete and tensile resistance, T_r, of steel
F_{cr}	Critical plate buckling stress
F_s	Ultimate shear strength
F_u	Specified minimum tensile strength (Megapascals)
F_y	Specified minimum yield stress, yield point or yield strength
f'_c	Specified compressive strength of concrete at 28 days (Megapascals)
g	Transverse spacing between fastener gauge lines (gauge distance)
h	Clear depth of web between flanges; height of stud
I	Moment of inertia
I_x	Moment of inertia about axis x-x
I_y	Moment of inertia about axis y-y
J	St. Venant's torsion constant
K	Effective length factor
K_x	Effective length factor with respect to axis x-x
K_y	Effective length factor with respect to axis y-y

KL	Effective length
k	Distance from outer face of flange to web toe of fillet of rolled shapes
L	Length
L_{cr}	Maximum unbraced length adjacent to a plastic hinge
L_u	Maximum unsupported length of compression flange for which no reduction in factored moment resistance, M_r, is required
L_x	Unsupported length with respect to axis x-x
L_y	Unsupported length with respect to axis y-y
M_f	Bending moment in a member or component under factored load
M_{f1}	Smaller factored end moment of a beam-column; factored bending moment at a point of concentrated load
M_{f2}	Larger factored end moment of a beam-column
M_p	Plastic moment = ZF_y
M_r	Factored moment resistance of a member or component
M'_r	Factored moment resistance of a member of a given unbraced length greater than L_u
M_{rc}	Factored moment resistance of composite beam
M_y	Yield moment = SF_y
m	Number of faying surfaces or shear planes in a bolted joint, equal to 1 for bolts in single shear and 2 for bolts in double shear
N	Length of bearing of an applied load
P	Concentrated load
Q_r	Sum of the factored resistances of all shear connectors between points of maximum and zero moment
q_r	Factored resistance of a shear connector
R	End reaction of concentrated transverse load applied to a flexural member
r	Radius of gyration
r_t	Radius of gyration, about its axis of symmetry, of a T section comprising the compression flange and 1/6 of the web
r_u	Radius of gyration with respect to axis u-u
r_v	Radius of gyration with respect to axis v-v
r_x	Radius of gyration with respect to axis x-x
r_y	Radius of gyration with respect to axis y-y
r_z	Radius of gyration with respect to axis z-z
S	Elastic section modulus
S_x	Elastic section modulus with respect to axis x-x
S_y	Elastic section modulus with respect to axis y-y
s	Centre-to-centre spacing (pitch) between successive fastener holes in line of stress
T_f	Tensile force in a member or component under factored load
T_r	Factored tensile resistance of a member or component; factored tensile resistance of the steel acting at the centroid of that part of the steel area in tension
t	Thickness
U	Amplification factor for stability analysis of beam-columns
V_f	Shear force in a member or component under factored load
V_r	Factored shear resistance of a member or component
V_s	Slip resistance of a bolted joint
W	Total uniformly distributed load; concentrated load
w	Web thickness; load per unit of length
Z	Plastic section modulus of a steel section

α	Load factor
β	Value used in bolt interaction equation
γ	Importance factor
λ	Non-dimensional slenderness ratio in column formula
μ	Coefficient related to the slip resistance of a bolted joint
ϕ	Performance factor
ψ	Load combination factor
ω	Coefficient used to determine equivalent uniform bending effect in beam-columns
Δ	Deflection of a point of a structure
ASTM	American Society for Testing and Materials
CISC	Canadian Institute of Steel Construction
CPMA	Canadian Paint Manufacturers' Association
CSCC	Canadian Steel Construction Council
CSA	Canadian Standards Association
SSRC	Structural Stability Research Council

PART ONE
CAN3-S16.1-M78, "STEEL STRUCTURES FOR BUILDINGS – LIMIT STATES DESIGN"

General

This Standard is reprinted with the permission of the Canadian Standards Association and contains all revisions approved at the time of printing. Included are: Amendments Numbers 1 and 2 and erratum issued by CSA in November 1979; Amendments to Clause 13.3, Axial Compression, and to Clauses 17.3.6 and 17.4, approved by CSA for printing in Supplement No. 1-1981.

CSA Standards are subject to periodical review and amendments will be published from time to time by CSA.

STEEL STRUCTURES FOR BUILDINGS — LIMIT STATES DESIGN

Prepared by
CANADIAN STANDARDS ASSOCIATION

Approved by
STANDARDS COUNCIL OF CANADA

ISSN 0317-5669
PUBLISHED, DECEMBER, 1978 BY CANADIAN STANDARDS ASSO-
CIATION, 178 REXDALE BOULEVARD, REXDALE, ONTARIO, CANADA
M9W 1R3

COPYRIGHT © CANADIAN STANDARDS ASSOCIATION—1978

ALL RIGHTS RESERVED—NO PART OF THIS PUBLICATION MAY BE
REPRODUCED IN ANY FORM, IN AN ELECTRONIC RETRIEVAL
SYSTEM OR OTHERWISE, WITHOUT THE PRIOR PERMISSION OF
THE PUBLISHER.

Contents

Page

1-9   **Technical Committee on Steel Structures for Buildings**

1-10   **Preface**

1-12   **Reference Publications**

Standard

1-15   **1. Scope**

1-15   **2. Application**

1-15   **3. Definitions and Symbols**
1-16   3.1 Definitions
1-17   3.2 Symbols

1-20   **4. Drawings**
1-20   4.1 Design Drawings
1-21   4.2 Shop Drawings
1-21   4.3 Erection Drawings

1-21   **5. Material: Standards and Identification**
1-21   5.1 Standards
1-21   *5.1.1 General*
1-21   *5.1.2 Structural Steel*
1-21   *5.1.3 Sheet Steel*
1-21   *5.1.4 Cast Steel*
1-21   *5.1.5 Forged Steel*
1-22   *5.1.6 Bolts*
1-22   *5.1.7 Welding Electrodes*
1-22   *5.1.8 Studs*
1-22   5.2 Identification
1-22   *5.2.1 Methods*
1-22   *5.2.2 Unidentified Structural Steel*
1-22   *5.2.3 Tests to Establish Identification*
1-23   *5.2.4 Affidavit*

1-23   **6. Design Requirements**
1-23   6.1 General
1-23   6.2 Requirements Under Specified Loads
1-23   *6.2.1 Deflections*
1-23   *6.2.2 Camber*
1-23   *6.2.3 Dynamic Effects*
1-24   *6.2.4 Resistance to Fatigue*
1-24   *6.2.5 Prevention of Permanent Deformation*
1-24   6.3 Requirements Under Factored Loads
1-24   *6.3.1 Strength*
1-24   *6.3.2 Overturning*

1-24   6.4 Other Requirements
1-24   *6.4.1 Expansion and Contraction*
1-25   *6.4.2 Corrosion Protection*

1-25   **7. Loads and Safety Criterion**
1-25   7.1 Specified Loads
1-26   7.2 Safety Criterion and Effect of Factored Loads

1-27   **8. Analysis of Structure**
1-27   8.1 General
1-27   8.2 Continuous Construction
1-27   8.3 Simple Construction
1-27   8.4 Elastic Analysis
1-28   8.5 Plastic Analysis
1-28   8.6 Stability Effects

1-29   **9. Design Lengths of Members**
1-29   9.1 Simple Span Flexural Members
1-29   9.2 Continuous Span Flexural Members
1-29   9.3 Compression Members

1-30   **10. Slenderness Ratios**
1-30   10.1 General
1-30   10.2 Maximum Slenderness Ratio

1-30   **11. Width-Thickness Ratios: Compression Elements**
1-30   11.1 Classification of Sections
1-30   11.2 Maximum Width-Thickness Ratios of Elements Subject to Compression
1-30   11.3 Width and Thickness

1-31   **12. Gross and Net Areas**
1-31   12.1 Application
1-31   12.2 Gross Area
1-31   12.3 Net Area
1-34   12.4 Pin-Connected Tension Members

1-34   **13. Member and Connection Resistance**
1-34   13.1 General
1-34   13.2 Axial Tension
1-35   13.3 Axial Compression
1-36   13.4 Shear
1-36   *13.4.1 Elastic Analysis*
1-37   *13.4.2 Plastic Analysis*
1-38   *13.4.3 Maximum Slenderness*
1-38   *13.4.4 Gusset Plates*
1-38   *13.4.5 Pins*
1-38   *13.4.6 Combined Shear and Moment in Girders*
1-38   13.5 Bending — Laterally Supported Members
1-39   13.6 Bending — Laterally Unsupported Members
1-40   13.7 Lateral Bracing for Members in Structures Analysed Plastically
1-41   13.8 Axial Compression and Bending
1-41   *13.8.1 Member Strength and Stability — Class 1 and Class 2 Sections*
1-41   *13.8.2 Member Strength and Stability — Class 1 and Class 2 Sections of I-Shaped Members*
1-42   *13.8.3 Member Strength and Stability — Class 3 and Class 4 Sections*

1-42   *13.8.4 Values of ω*
1-43   13.9 Axial Tension and Bending
1-43   13.10 Load Bearing
1-44   13.11 Bolts in Bearing-Type Connections
1-44   *13.11.1 General*
1-44   *13.11.2 Bolts in Shear*
1-44   *13.11.3 Bolts in Tension*
1-44   *13.11.4 Bolts in Combined Shear and Tension*
1-44   13.12 Bolts in Slip-Resistant (Friction-Type) Connections
1-45   *13.12.1 General*
1-45   *13.12.2 Shear Connections*
1-45   *13.12.3 Connections in Combined Shear and Tension*
1-45   13.13 Welds

1-47   **14. Fatigue**
1-47   14.1 General
1-47   14.2 Life
1-47   14.3 10 000 Cycles of Load
1-47   14.4 Over 10 000 Cycles of Load
1-47   14.5 Allowable Range of Stress in Fatigue

1-51   **15. Beams and Girders**
1-51   15.1 Proportioning
1-51   15.2 Rotational Restraint at Points of Support
1-51   15.3 Reduced Moment Resistance of Girders With Thin Webs
1-51   15.4 Flanges
1-52   15.5 Bearing Stiffeners
1-52   15.6 Intermediate Transverse Stiffeners
1-54   15.7 Lateral Forces
1-54   15.8 Web Crippling
1-54   15.9 Stability of Thin Webs
1-54   15.10 Openings
1-55   15.11 Torsion

1-55   **16. Open-Web Steel Joists**
1-55   16.1 Scope
1-56   16.2 Definitions
1-56   16.3 Materials
1-56   16.4 Drawings
1-56   *16.4.1 Building Design Drawings*
1-57   *16.4.2 Joist Design Drawings*
1-57   16.5 Design
1-57   *16.5.1 Loading for Open-Web Steel Joists*
1-57   *16.5.2 Loading for Special Open-Web Joists*
1-57   *16.5.3 Design Assumptions*
1-58   *16.5.4 Verification of Joist Manufacturer's Design*
1-58   *16.5.5 Member and Connection Resistance*
1-58   *16.5.6 Width-Thickness Ratios*
1-58   *16.5.7 Tension Chord*
1-58   *16.5.8 Compression Chord*
1-59   *16.5.9 Webs*
1-59   *16.5.10 Spacers and Battens*
1-59   *16.5.11 Connections and Splices*
1-60   *16.5.12 Bearings*
1-60   *16.5.13 Anchorage*
1-61   *16.5.14 Deflection*

1-61	*16.5.15 Camber*
1-61	*16.5.16 Vibration*
1-61	*16.5.17 Welding*
1-62	16.6 Stability During Construction
1-62	16.7 Bridging
1-62	*16.7.1 General*
1-62	*16.7.2 Installation*
1-62	*16.7.3 Types*
1-62	*16.7.4 Diagonal Bridging*
1-62	*16.7.5 Horizontal Bridging*
1-62	*16.7.6 Attachment of Bridging*
1-62	*16.7.7 Anchorage of Bridging*
1-63	*16.7.8 Bridging Systems*
1-63	*16.7.9 Spacing of Bridging*
1-63	16.8 Decking
1-64	16.9 Shop Painting
1-64	16.10 Manufacturing Tolerances
1-65	16.11 Inspection and Quality Control
1-65	*16.11.1 Inspection*
1-65	*16.11.2 Identification and Control of Steel*
1-65	*16.11.3 Quality Control*
1-65	16.12 Handling and Erection
1-65	*16.12.1 General*
1-65	*16.12.2 Erection Tolerances*
1-66	**17. Composite Beams and Columns**
1-66	17.1 Application
1-66	17.2 Definitions
1-67	17.3 Composite Beams
1-67	*17.3.1 General*
1-67	*17.3.2 Design Effective Width of Concrete*
1-67	*17.3.3 Slab Reinforcement*
1-68	*17.3.4 Composite Action With Cellular Steel Deck*
1-68	*17.3.5 Interconnection*
1-68	*17.3.6 Shear Connectors*
1-69	*17.3.7 Ties*
1-69	17.4 Design of Composite Beams With Shear Connectors
1-71	17.5 Design of Composite Beams Without Shear Connectors
1-71	17.6 Unshored Beams
1-72	17.7 Beams During Construction
1-72	17.8 Design of Composite Columns (Concrete-Filled Hollow Structural Sections)
1-72	**18. General Requirements for Built-Up Members**
1-72	18.1 General Requirements for Compression Members
1-75	18.2 General Requirements for Tension Members
1-75	18.3 General Requirements for Open Box-Type Beams and Grillages
1-75	**19. Stability of Structures and Individual Members**
1-75	19.1 General
1-76	19.2 Stability of Columns
1-76	19.3 Stability of Beams, Girders and Trusses
1-76	**20. Connections**
1-76	20.1 Alignment of Members
1-76	20.2 Unrestrained Members

1-77	20.3 Restrained Members
1-77	20.4 Connections of Tension or Compression Members
1-78	20.5 Bearing Joints in Compression Members
1-78	20.6 Lamellar Tearing
1-78	20.7 Placement of Fasteners and Welds
1-78	20.8 Fillers
1-78	20.9 Welds in Combination
1-79	20.10 Fasteners and Welds in Combination
1-79	20.11 High-Strength Bolts (in Slip-Resistant Joints) and Rivets, in Combination
1-79	20.12 Connections Requiring High-Strength Bolts or Welds
1-79	20.13 Special Fasteners
1-79	**21. Bolting Details**
1-79	21.1 High-Strength Bolts
1-79	21.2 A307 Bolts
1-79	21.3 Effective Bearing Area
1-80	21.4 Long Grips
1-80	21.5 Minimum Pitch
1-80	21.6 Minimum Edge Distance
1-80	21.7 Maximum Edge Distance
1-80	21.8 Minimum End Distance
1-80	21.9 Slotted Holes
1-81	**22. Structural Joints Using ASTM A325 or A490 Bolts**
1-81	22.1 General
1-81	22.2 Bolts, Nuts, and Washers
1-82	22.3 Bolted Parts
1-83	22.4 Installation
1-84	22.5 "Turn-of-Nut" Tightening
1-84	22.6 Tightening by Use of a Direct Tension Indicator
1-84	22.7 Inspection
1-87	**23. Welding**
1-87	23.1 Arc Welding
1-87	23.2 Resistance Welding
1-87	23.3 Fabricator and Erector Qualification
1-88	**24. Column Bases**
1-88	24.1 Loads
1-88	24.2 Finishing
1-88	**25. Anchor Bolts**
1-88	**26. Fabrication**
1-88	26.1 General
1-88	26.2 Straightness of Material
1-88	26.3 Gas Cutting
1-88	26.4 Sheared or Gas Cut Edge Finish
1-89	26.5 Holes for Bolts or Other Mechanical Fasteners
1-89	26.6 Bolted Construction
1-89	26.7 Welded Construction
1-89	26.8 Finishing of Bearing Surfaces
1-90	26.9 Tolerances
1-90	**27. Cleaning, Surface Preparation and Priming**
1-90	27.1 General Requirements

1-91   27.2 Requirements for Special Surfaces
1-91   27.3 Surface Preparation
1-92   27.4 Primer
1-92   27.5 One-Coat Paint

1-92   **28. Erection**
1-92   28.1 General
1-92   28.2 Temporary Loads
1-92   28.3 Adequacy of Temporary Connections
1-92   28.4 Alignment
1-92   28.5 Surface Preparation for Field Welding
1-93   28.6 Field Painting
1-93   28.7 Erection Tolerances

1-93   **29. Inspection**
1-93   29.1 General
1-93   29.2 Co-operation
1-94   29.3 Rejection
1-94   29.4 Inspection of High-Strength Bolted Joints
1-94   29.5 Inspection of Welding
1-94   29.6 Identification of Steel by Marking

1-95   **Appendix A — Standard Practice for Structural Steel for Buildings**

4-22   **Appendix B — Effective Lengths of Compression Members in Frames**

4-24   **Appendix C — Criteria for Estimating Effective Column Lengths in Continuous Frames**

1-96   **Appendix D — Graph Showing Unit Compressive Resistance Versus Slenderness Ratio**

1-97   **Appendix E — Margins of Safety**

4-108   **Appendix F — Columns Subject to Biaxial Bending**

5-169   **Appendix G — Guide for Floor Vibrations**

1-98   **Appendix H — Wind Sway Vibrations**

1-99   **Appendix I — Recommended Maximum Values for Deflections**

4-20   **Appendix J — Guide to Calculation of Stability Effects**

1-101   **Appendix K — Fatigue**

Technical Committee on Steel Structures for Buildings

D.J.L. Kennedy *(Chairman)*
University of Windsor,
Windsor, Ontario

M.I. Gilmor *(Secretary)*
Canadian Institute of Steel
Construction,
Willowdale, Ontario

P.F. Adams
University of Alberta,
Edmonton

D.E. Allen
National Research Council,
Ottawa, Ontario

W.W. Baigent
Canron Limited,
Rexdale, Ontario

J.T. Biskup
Canadian Welding Bureau,
Toronto, Ontario

H. Caratin *(CSA Liaison, Non-voting)*
Canadian Standards Association,
Rexdale, Ontario

D.A. Currie
Algoma Steel Corporation, Limited,
Sault Ste. Marie, Ontario

T.M. DeVroom
Department of Public Works,
Ottawa, Ontario

J.C. Draper
Canadian Pacific Limited,
Montreal, Quebec

Y-M. Giroux
Laval University,
Quebec, Quebec

N.L. Hunter
Armco Canada Ltd.,
Guelph, Ontario

A.B. Johns
Morrison, Hershfield, Burgess &
Huggins, Ltd.,
Toronto, Ontario

J.K. Komocki
Department of National Defence,
Ottawa, Ontario

H.A. Krentz *(Alternate)*
Canadian Institute of Steel
Construction,
Willowdale, Ontario

G.L. Kulak
University of Alberta,
Edmonton

S.L. Lipson
The University of British Columbia,
Vancouver

W. Moroz
The Steel Company of Canada,
Limited,
Hamilton, Ontario

E.J. Rohacek
Norr Group,
Toronto, Ontario

S. Skaberna
Canadian National Railways,
Montreal, Quebec

J. Springfield
C.D. Carruthers & Wallace,
Rexdale, Ontario

D.C. Stringer
Dominion Bridge Company Limited,
Montreal, Quebec

D.L. Tarlton
Canadian Sheet Steel Building
Institute,
Willowdale, Ontario

G.A. Webster
Dominion Foundries and Steel,
Limited,
Hamilton, Ontario

Preface

This is the first edition of CSA Standard CAN3-S16.1-M, Steel Structures for Buildings — Limit States Design.

This Standard, along with CSA Standard S16.1-1974, takes its place beside CSA Standard S16-1969, Steel Structures for Buildings, which is based on working stress design and supersedes previous editions of 1965, 1961, 1954, 1940, 1930 and 1924. CSA Standard S16-1969 will continue to provide engineers with a working stress design standard for some time.

CAN3-S16.1-M is the first such standard for steel structures in Canada prepared in SI units (Le Système internationale d'unités). In limit states design, the designer compares the effect of factored loads to the minimum likely developable resistance; no longer does he compute working stresses to compare with allowable values. Limit states define the various types of collapse and unserviceability that are to be avoided and the object of design is to keep the probability of a limit state being reached below a certain value previously established. This is achieved by applying load factors to the specified loads and performance factors to the specified resistances. These factors replace the single factor of safety used in other design standards. The factors used in this Standard have been determined by calibration with the existing CSA Standard S16-1969. By the use of different factors, for example, for different loads, a more uniform level of safety is obtained.

A considerable number of technical changes, reflecting the latest research developments, have also been incorporated in this Standard. These are based on an increased understanding of the behaviour of steel structures, members and elements, and of steel as a structural material.

As in CSA Standard S16-1969, the clauses relating to fabrication and erection show that design cannot be considered by itself but that it is part of the design and construction sequence.

This Standard sets out minimum requirements for steel structures as outlined in the Scope and, it is expected, will only be used by engineers competent in this field.

CSA Standard S16.1-1974, on which this Standard is based, has been adopted by the Associate Committee on the National Building Code as the reference standard, along with the seventh edition of S16-1969, for Section 4.6 of the National Building Code for 1977. It is expected that CAN3-S16.1-M will be adopted in the next revision of the National Building Code.

This Standard was prepared by the Technical Committee on Steel Structures for Buildings under the jurisdiction of the Standards Steering Committee on Structures and was approved by these Committees. This Standard has been approved as a National Standard by the Standards Council of Canada.

Rexdale, December, 1978

Note: *CSA Publications are subjected to periodic review in order to keep them abreast of progress in the industries concerned. Suggestions for improvement will be welcomed at all times. They will be recorded and in due course brought to the attention of the appropriate Committee for consideration.*

Also, requests for interpretation will be accepted by the Committee. They should be worded in such a manner as to permit a simple "yes" or "no" answer based on the literal text of the requirement concerned.

All enquiries regarding this Standard should be addressed to Canadian Standards Association, 178 Rexdale Boulevard, Rexdale, Ontario M9W 1R3.

Reference Publications

This Publication refers to the following and the year dates shown indicate the latest issues available at the time of printing:

CSA Standards

CAN3-A23.1-M77,
Concrete Materials and Methods of Concrete Construction;

B95-1962,
Surface Texture (Roughness, Waviness, and Lay);

G28-1968,
Carbon-Steel Castings for General Application;

G38-1953,
Heavy Steel Shaft Forgings;

G40.20-M1977,
General Requirements for Rolled or Welded Structural Quality Steel;

G40.21-M1977,
Structural Quality Steels;

G189-1966,
Sprayed Metal Coatings for Atmospheric Corrosion Protection;

S16-1969,
Steel Structures for Buildings;

S37-1976,
Antenna Towers and Antenna Supporting Structures;

S136-1974,
Cold Formed Steel Structural Members;

W47.1-1973,
Certification of Companies for Fusion Welding of Steel Structures;

W48.1-1976,
Mild Steel Covered Arc-Welding Electrodes;

W48.3-1976,
Low-Alloy Steel Arc-Welding Electrodes;

W48.4-1978,
Solid Mild Steel Electrodes for Gas Metal-Arc Welding;

W48.5-1970,
Mild Steel Electrodes for Flux Cored Arc Welding;

W48.6-1977,
Bare Mild Steel Electrodes and Fluxes for Submerged-Arc Welding;

W55.2-1957,
Resistance Welding Practice;

W55.3-1965,
Resistance Welding Qualification Code for Fabricators of Structural Members Used in Buildings;

W59-1977,
Welded Steel Construction (Metal-Arc Welding);

ANSI* Standards
B18.2.1-1972,
Square and Hex Bolts and Screws;

B18.2.2-1972,
Square and Hex Nuts;

ASTM† Standards
A27-77,
Mild- to Medium-Strength Carbon-Steel Castings for General Application;

A36-77a,
Structural Steel;

A108-73,
Steel Bars, Carbon, Cold-Finished, Standard Quality;

A148-73,
High-Strength Steel Castings for Structural Purposes;

A307-76b,
Carbon Steel Externally and Internally Threaded Standard Fasteners;

A325-76c,
High-Strength Bolts for Structural Steel Joints, Including Suitable Nuts and Plain Hardened Washers;

A440-77,
High-Strength Structural Steel;

A486-74,
Steel Castings for Highway Bridges;

A490-77,
Quenched and Tempered Alloy Steel Bolts for Structural Steel Joints;

A514-77,
High-Yield-Strength, Quenched and Tempered Alloy Steel Plate, Suitable for Welding;

A521-76,
Steel, Closed-Impression Die Forgings for General Industrial Use;

A525-77,
Steel Sheet, Zinc-Coated (Galvanized) by the Hot-Dip Process, General Requirements;

A570-75,
Hot-Rolled Carbon Steel Sheet and Strip, Structural Quality;

A668-77,
Steel Forgings, Carbon and Alloy, for General Industrial Use;

CGSB‡ Standards
1-GP-14e-1971,
Primer: Red Lead in Oil;

1-GP-40d-1968,
Primer: Structural Steel, Oil Alkyd Type;

1-GP-81e-1972,
Primer, Alkyd, Air Drying and Baking, for Vehicles and Equipment;

1-GP-140c-1968,
Primer: Red Lead, Iron Oxide, Oil Alkyd Type;

1-GP-166a-1968,
Primer: Basic Lead Silico-Chromate, Oil Alkyd Type;

CISC/CPMA§ Standards
1-73a,
A Quick-Drying One-Coat Paint For Use On Structural Steel;

2-75,
A Quick-Drying Primer For Use On Structural Steel;

Canadian Institute of Steel Construction
Code of Standard Practice for Structural Steel for Buildings;

National Building Code of Canada, 1977;
Metric Values for Use with the National Building Code, 1977;

SSPC** Specifications
PS 12.00-68T,
Guide to Zinc-Rich Coating Systems;

PT 3-64,
Basic Zinc Chromate — Vinyl Butyral Washcoat;

SP 2-63,
Hand Tool Cleaning;

SP 3-63,
Power Tool Cleaning;

SP 4-63,
Flame Cleaning of New Steel;

SP 5-63,
White Metal Blast Cleaning;

SP 6-63,
Commercial Blast Cleaning;

SP 7-63,
Brush-Off Blast Cleaning;

SP 10-63T,
Near-White Blast Cleaning.

Structural Stability Research Council
Guide to Stability Design Criteria for Metal Structures;

*American National Standards Institute.
†American Society for Testing and Materials.
‡Canadian Government Specifications Board.
§Canadian Institute of Steel Construction/Canadian Paint Manufacturers'
 Association
**Steel Structures Painting Council.

CAN3-S16.1-M78

Steel Structures for Buildings — Limit States Design

1. **Scope**

1.1 This Standard provides rules and requirements for the design, fabrication, and erection of steel structures for buildings where the design is based on limit states. The term "steel structures" relates to structural members and frames which consist primarily of structural steel components, including the detail parts, welds, bolts, or other fasteners required in fabrication and erection.

1.2 This Standard does not cover the design, fabrication, and erection of steel structures other than for buildings except as permitted by the authority having jurisdiction.

1.3 Where reference is made to other publications, such reference shall be considered to refer to the latest edition or any revision thereto approved by the organization issuing that publication.

1.4 When designing structures under this Standard, no use shall be made of CSA Standard S16-1969, Steel Structures for Buildings, except that open web steel joists and special open web steel joists not participating in lateral force-resisting frames may be designed in accordance with Clause 20 of CSA Standard S16-1969 as revised in Supplement No. 1-1975 provided that all such joists in the structure are so designed.

2. **Application**

2.1 This Standard applies unconditionally to steel structures for buildings except as noted in Clause 2.2.

2.2 Supplementary rules or requirements may be necessary for unusual types of construction and for steel structures which:

(a) Have great height;

(b) Are required to be movable or be readily dismantled;

(c) Are exposed to severe environmental conditions;

(d) Are required to satisfy aesthetic, architectural, or other requirements of a non-structural nature;

(e) Employ materials or products not listed in Clause 5;

(f) Have other special features that could affect design, fabrication, or erection.

2.3 A rational design based on theory, analysis, and engineering practice, acceptable to the authority having jurisdiction, may be used in lieu of the formulae provided in this Standard. In such cases the design shall provide nominal margins (or factors) of safety at least equal to those intended in the provisions of this Standard (see Appendix E).

3. **Definitions and Symbols**

3.1   **Definitions**
The following definitions apply to this Standard:

General

Approved means approved by the authority having jurisdiction;

Authority having jurisdiction means the professionally qualified representative of the purchaser or the responsible officials with legal authority to control building construction, as applicable;

Limit states means those conditions of a structure in which the structure ceases to fulfil the function for which it was designed. Those states concerning safety are called the ultimate limit states and include exceeding of load-carrying capacity, overturning, sliding, fracture and fatigue. Those states which restrict the intended use and occupancy of the structure are called serviceability limit states and include deflection, vibration and permanent deformation.

Loads

Gravity load (newtons) is equal to the mass of the object (kilograms) being supported multiplied by the acceleration due to gravity, g (9.81 m/s²);

Specified loads (D, L, Q and T) means those loads prescribed by the authority having jurisdiction (see Clause 7.1);

Factored load means the product of a specified load and its load factor.

Factors

Load factor, α, means a factor, given in Clause 7.2, applied to a specified load for the limit states under consideration to take into account the variability of the loads and load patterns and analysis of their effects;

Load combination factor, ψ, means a factor, given in Clause 7.2, applied to factored loads other than dead load to take into account the reduced probability of a number of loads from different sources acting simultaneously;

Importance factor, γ, means a factor, given in Clause 7.2, applied to factored loads to take into account the consequences of collapse as related to the use and occupancy of the structure;

Performance factor, ϕ, means a factor, given in the appropriate clauses of this Standard, applied to a specified material property or the resistance of a member, connection or structure, which, for the limit state under consideration, takes into account the variability of material properties, dimensions, workmanship, type of failure, and uncertainty in prediction of member resistance. To maintain simplicity of design formulae in this Standard, the type of failure and uncertainty in prediction of member resistance have been incorporated in the expressions of member resistance. (See Appendix E for a more detailed discussion.)

Resistance

Resistance, R, of a member, connection or structure is calculated in accordance with this Standard based on the specified material properties and nominal dimensions;

Factored resistance, ϕR, means the product of the resistance and the appropriate performance factor.

Tolerances

Camber means the deviation from straightness of a member or any portion of a member with respect to its major axis. Frequently camber is specified and produced in a member to compensate for deflections that will occur in the member when loaded. (See Clause 6.2.2.) Unspecified camber is sometimes referred to as bow;

Sweep means the deviation from straightness of a member or any portion of a member with respect to its minor axis;

Mill tolerances means variations allowed from the nominal dimensions and geometry with respect to cross-sectional area, non-parallelism of flanges and out-of-straightness such as sweep or camber in the product as manufactured and are given in CSA Standard G40.20-M, General Requirements for Rolled or Welded Structural Quality Steel;

Fabrication tolerances means tolerances allowed from the nominal dimensions and geometry such as the cutting to length, finishing of ends, cutting of bevel angles, and for fabricated members, out-of-straightness such as sweep and camber (see Clause 26);

Erection tolerances means tolerances related to the plumbness, alignment, level, *of the piece as a whole.* The deviations are determined by considering the *locations of the ends of the piece* with respect to the positions stipulated on the drawings.

3.2   Symbols
The following symbols are used throughout this Standard. Deviations from them, and additional nomenclature, are noted where they appear. Dimensions in millimetres and forces in newtons are assumed unless otherwise noted.

A = Area;

A_b = Cross-sectional area of one bolt based on nominal diameter;

A_f = Flange area;

A_g = Gross area;

A_m = Area of fusion face;

A_n = Critical net area;

A_r = Area of reinforcing steel;

A_s = Area of steel section including cover plates; area of bottom (tension) chord of steel joist; area of stiffener or pair of stiffeners;

A_{sc} = Area of steel shear connector;

A_w = Web area; shear area; effective throat area of weld;

a = Centre-to-centre distance between transverse web stiffeners, depth of concrete compression zone;

a' = Length of cover plate termination;

a/h = Aspect ratio, ratio of distance between stiffeners to web depth;

B = Bearing force in a member or component under specified load;

B_f = Bearing force in a member or component under factored load;

B_r = Factored bearing resistance of a member or component;

b = Width of stiffened or unstiffened compression elements; design effective width of concrete or cellular slab;

C = Compressive force in a member or component under specified load; axial load;

C_e = **Euler buckling strength = 1 970 000A/(KL/r)², (newtons)**

C_f = Compressive force in a member or component under factored load; factored axial load;

C_r = Factored compressive resistance of a member or component; factored compressive resistance of steel acting at the centroid of that part of the steel area in compression;

C_r' = Compressive resistance of concrete acting at the centroid of the concrete area in compression;

C_w = Warping torsional constant;

C_y = Axial compressive load at yield stress;

D = Outside diameter of circular sections; diameter of rocker or roller; also stiffener factor;

d = Depth; overall depth of a section; diameter of bolt or stud;

d_b = Depth of beam;

E = Elastic modulus of steel (200 000 MPa assumed);

E_c = Elastic modulus of concrete;

e = End distance; lever arm between the compressive resistance, C_r, and tensile resistance, T_r;

e' = Lever arm between the compressive resistance, C_r', of concrete and tensile resistance, T_r, of steel;

F = Strength or stress (MPa unless noted);

F_{cr} = Critical plate buckling stress;

F_s = Ultimate shear strength;

F_{sr} = Allowable range of stress in fatigue;

F_{st} = Factored axial force in the stiffener;

F_u = Specified minimum tensile strength;

F_y = Specified minimum yield stress, yield point or yield strength;

F_{yr} = Specified yield strength of reinforcing steel;

f_c' = Specified compressive strength of concrete at 28 days;

G = Shear modulus of steel (77 000 MPa assumed);

g = Transverse spacing between fastener gauge lines (gauge distance);

h = Clear depth of web between flanges; height of stud;

h_d = Depth of cellular steel deck;

I = Moment of inertia;

J = St. Venant's torsion constant;

K = Effective length factor;

KL = Effective length;

k = Distance from outer face of flange to web toe of fillet of I-shaped sections;

k_b = Buckling coefficient;

k_v = Shear buckling coefficient;

L = Length;

L_c = Length of channel shear connector;

L_{cr} = Maximum unbraced length adjacent to a plastic hinge;

M = Bending moment in a member or component under specified load;

M_f = Bending moment in a member or component under factored load;

M_{f1} = Smaller factored end moment of a beam-column; factored bending moment at a point of concentrated load;

M_{f2} = Larger factored end moment of a beam-column;

M_p = Plastic moment = ZF_y;

M_r = Factored moment resistance of a member or component;

M_{rc} = Factored moment resistance of composite beam;

M_u = Moment resistance of a member subject to lateral buckling;

M_y = Yield moment = SF_y;

m = Number of faying surfaces or shear planes in a bolted joint, equal to 1 for bolts in single shear and 2 for bolts in double shear;

N = Length of bearing of an applied load;

n = Number of bolts; number of shear connectors required between the point of maximum positive bending moment and adjacent point of zero moment;

n' = Number of shear connectors required between any concentrated load and nearest point of zero moment in a region of positive bending moment;

P = Concentrated load;

Q_r = Sum of the factored resistances of all shear connectors between points of maximum and zero moment;

q_r = Factored resistance of a shear connector;

R = End reaction of concentrated transverse load applied to a flexural member; resistance of a member, connection or structure;

r = Radius of gyration;

r_t = Radius of gyration about its axis of symmetry of a tee section comprising the compression flange and one-sixth of the web;

r_y = Radius of gyration of the member about its weak axis;

S = Elastic section modulus of a steel section;

s = Centre-to-centre spacing (pitch) between successive fastener holes in line of stress;

T = Tensile force in a member or component under specified load;

T_f = Tensile force in a member or component under factored load;

T_r = Factored tensile resistance of a member or component; factored tensile resistance of the steel acting at the centroid of that part of the steel area in tension;

T_y = Axial tensile load at yield stress;

t = Thickness;

t_c = Concrete or cellular slab thickness;

t_f = Flange thickness, average flange thickness of channel shear connector;

t_w = Web thickness of channel shear connector;

V = Shear force in a member or component under specified load;

V_f = Shear force in a member or component under factored load;

V_h = Total horizontal shear to be resisted at the junction of the steel section or joist and the slab or cellular steel deck;

V_r = Factored shear resistance of a member or component;

V_s = Slip resistance of a bolted joint;

V_{st} = Factored shear force in column web to be resisted by stiffener;

w = Web thickness;

w_d = Average width of flute of cellular steel deck;

X_u = Ultimate strength as rated by the Electrode Classification number.

x = Subscript relating to strong axis of a member;

y = Subscript relating to weak axis of a member;

Z = Plastic section modulus of a steel section;

α = Load factor;

β = Value used in bolt interaction equation;

γ = Importance factor;

λ = Non-dimensional slenderness ratio in column formula;

μ = Coefficient related to the slip resistance of a bolted joint;

ϕ = **Performance factor (see definition under Factors, in Clause 3.1);**

ψ = Load combination factor;

ω = Coefficient used to determine equivalent uniform bending effect in beam-columns.

4. Drawings

4.1 Design Drawings

4.1.1 Design drawings shall be drawn to a scale adequate to convey the required information. The drawings shall show a complete design of the structure with members suitably designated and located, including such dimensions and detailed description as necessary to permit the preparation of shop and erection drawings. Floor levels, column centres, and offsets shall be dimensioned.

4.1.2 Design drawings shall designate the design standards used, show clearly the type or types of construction as defined in Clause 8 to be employed, and shall designate the material or product Standards, applicable to the members and details depicted (see Clause 5). Drawings shall be supplemented by data concerning the governing loads, shears, moments, and axial forces to be resisted by all members and their connections when needed for the preparation of shop drawings. (See also Clause 19.1.2.)

4.1.3 Where high-strength bolted joints are required to resist shear between connected parts, the design drawings shall indicate the type of joint, slip-resistant (friction) or bearing, to be provided (see Clause 22).

4.1.4 If required, camber of beams, girders, and trusses shall be called for on the design drawings.

4.2 **Shop Drawings**

Shop drawings giving complete information necessary for the fabrication of the various members and components of the structure, including the required material and product standards and the location, type and size of all mechanical fasteners and welds, shall be prepared in advance of fabrication, and submitted for approval when so specified. Shop drawings shall distinguish clearly between mechanical fasteners and welds required for shop fabrication and those required in the field.

4.3 **Erection Drawings**

Erection drawings shall show the principal dimensions of the structure, piece marks and sizes of the members, where necessary for approval, elevation of the column bases, all necessary dimensions and details for setting anchor bolts and all other information necessary for the assembly of the structure. (See also Clause 19.1.3.)

5. **Material: Standards and Identification**

5.1 **Standards**

5.1.1 **General**

Acceptable material and product standards and specifications (latest editions) for use under this Standard are listed in Clauses 5.1.2 to 5.1.7 inclusive. Materials and products other than those listed also may be used if approved. Approval shall be based on published specifications which establish the properties, characteristics, and suitability of the material or product to the extent and in the manner of those standards which are listed.

5.1.2 **Structural Steel**

CSA G40.21-M,
Structural Quality Steels.

5.1.3 **Sheet Steel**

ASTM A570, Hot-Rolled Carbon Steel Sheet and Strip, Structural Quality.

Other standards for structural sheet are listed in CSA Standard S136, Cold Formed Steel Structural Members. Only structural quality sheet standards which specify chemical composition and mechanical properties will be acceptable for use under CSA Standard S16.1-M. Mill test certificates which list the chemical composition and the mechanical properties shall be available, upon request, in accordance with Clause 5.2.1(a).

5.1.4 **Cast Steel**

CSA G28,
Carbon-Steel Castings for General Application;

ASTM A27,
Mild- to Medium-Strength Carbon-Steel Castings for General Application;

ASTM A148,
High-Strength Steel Castings for Structural Purposes;

ASTM A486,
Steel Castings for Highway Bridges.

5.1.5 **Forged Steel**

CSA G38,
Heavy Steel Shaft Forgings;

ASTM A521,
Steel, Closed-Impression Die Forgings for General Industrial Use;

ASTM A668,
Steel Forgings, Carbon and Alloy, for General Industrial Use.

5.1.6 Bolts

ASTM A307,
Carbon Steel Externally and Internally Threaded Standard Fasteners;

ASTM A325,
High-Strength Bolts for Structural Steel Joints, Including Suitable Nuts and Plain Hardened Washers;

ASTM A490,
Quenched and Tempered Alloy Steel Bolts for Structural Steel Joints.

5.1.7 Welding Electrodes

CSA W48.1,
Mild Steel Covered Arc-Welding Electrodes;

CSA W48.3,
Low-Alloy Steel Arc-Welding Electrodes;

CSA W48.4,
Solid Mild Steel Electrodes for Gas Metal-Arc Welding;

CSA W48.5,
Mild Steel Electrodes for Flux Cored Arc Welding;

CSA W48.6,
Bare Mild Steel Electrodes and Fluxes for Submerged-Arc Welding.

5.1.8 Studs

ASTM A108,
Steel Bars, Carbon, Cold-Finished, Standard Quality, Grades 1015 and 1018.

5.2 Identification

5.2.1 Methods

The materials and products used shall be identified as to specification, including type or grade, if applicable, by one of the following means, except as provided in Clauses 5.2.2 and 5.2.3:

(a) Mill Test Certificates or Producer's Certificates satisfactorily correlated to the materials or products to which they pertain;

(b) Legible markings on the material or product made by its Producer in accordance with the applicable material or product standard.

5.2.2 Unidentified Structural Steel

Unidentified structural steel shall not be used, unless approved. If the use of unidentified steel is authorized, F_y shall be taken as 210 MPa and F_u shall be taken as 380 MPa.

5.2.3 Tests to Establish Identification

Unidentified structural steel may be tested to establish identification when permitted by the authority having jurisdiction. Testing shall be done by an approved testing agency in accordance with CSA Standard G40.20-M, General Requirements for Rolled or Welded Structural Quality Steel. The test results, taking into account both mechanical properties and chemical composition, shall form the basis for classifying the steel as to specification.

5.2.4   Affidavit
The fabricator, if requested, shall provide an affidavit stating that the materials and products which he has used in fabrication conform to the applicable material or product standards called for by the design drawings or specifications.

6.   Design Requirements

6.1   General
As set out in this Standard, steel structures for buildings shall be designed to be serviceable during the useful life of the structure and safe from collapse during construction and during the useful life of the structure. Limit states define the various types of collapse and unserviceability that are to be avoided; those concerning safety are called the ultimate limit states (strength, overturning, sliding, fatigue) and those concerning unserviceability are called the serviceability limit states (deflections, vibration, permanent deformation). The object of limit state design calculations is to keep the probability of a limit state being reached below a certain value previously established for the given type of structure. This is achieved in this Standard by the use of load factors, applied to the specified loads (see Clause 7) and performance factors applied to the specified resistances (e.g., Clause 13). These factors replace the single safety factors used in other design standards. The various limit states are set out in this Clause. Some of these relate to the specified loads and others to the factored loads. Camber, provisions for expansion and contraction and corrosion protection are further design requirements related to serviceability and durability. All limit states shall be considered in the design.

6.2   Requirements Under Specified Loads

6.2.1   Deflections

6.2.1.1   Steel members and frames shall be proportioned so that deflections are within acceptable limits for the nature of the materials to be supported and the intended use and occupancy.

6.2.1.2   In the absence of a more detailed evaluation see Appendix I for recommended values for deflections.

6.2.1.3   Roofs with insufficient slope to prevent ponding shall be designed to withstand any loads likely to occur as a result of ponding.

6.2.2   Camber

6.2.2.1   Camber of beams, trusses or girders, if required, shall be called for on the design drawings. Generally trusses and crane girders of 25 000 mm or greater span should be cambered for approximately the dead-plus-half-live-load deflection (see also Clause 16 for requirements for open-web joists).

6.2.2.2   Any special camber requirements necessary to bring a loaded member into proper relation with the work of other trades shall be stipulated on the design drawings.

6.2.3   Dynamic Effects

6.2.3.1   Suitable provision shall be made in the design for the effect of live load which induces impact or vibration, or both. In severe cases, such as structural supports for heavy machinery which causes substantial impact or vibration when in operation, the possibility of harmonic resonance, fatigue, or unacceptable vibration shall be investigated.

6.2.3.2 Special consideration shall be given to floor systems susceptible to vibration, such as large open floor areas free of partitions, to ensure that such vibration is acceptable for the intended use and occupancy. (A guide on floor vibrations is contained in Appendix G of this Standard.)

6.2.3.3 Unusually flexible structures (generally those whose ratio of height to effectively resisting width exceeds 4:1) shall be investigated for lateral vibrations under dynamic wind load. Lateral accelerations of the structure shall be checked to ensure that such accelerations are acceptable for the intended use and occupancy. (Information on lateral accelerations under dynamic wind loads can be found in Appendix H.)

6.2.4 Resistance to Fatigue
Structural steelwork shall be designed to resist the effects of fatigue under the specified loads in accordance with Clause 14.

6.2.5 Prevention of Permanent Deformation

6.2.5.1 For composite beams, unshored during construction, the stresses in the tension flange of the steel beam, due to the loads applied before the concrete strength reaches $0.75f'_c$, plus the stresses at the same location, due to the remaining specified loads considered to act on the composite section shall not exceed $0.90F_y$.

6.2.5.2 Slip-resistant (friction) joints, in which the design load is assumed to be transferred by the slip resistance of the clamped faying surfaces, shall be proportioned, using the provisions of Clause 13.12, to resist without slipping, the moments and forces induced by the specified loads (see Clause 22).

6.3 Requirements Under Factored Loads

6.3.1 Strength
Structural steelwork shall be proportioned to resist moments and forces resulting from application of the factored loads acting in the most critical combination, taking into account the importance of the building, as specified in Clause 7 and taking into account the performance factors as specified in the appropriate clauses of this Standard.

6.3.2 Overturning
The building or structure shall be designed to resist overturning resulting from application of the factored loads acting in the most critical combination, taking into account the importance of the building as specified in Clause 7, and taking into account the performance factors as specified in the appropriate clauses of this Standard (see Clause 7).

6.4 Other Requirements

6.4.1 Expansion and Contraction
Suitable provision shall be made for expansion and contraction commensurate with the service and erection conditions of the structure.

6.4.2   **Corrosion Protection**

6.4.2.1   Steelwork shall have sufficient corrosion protection to minimize any corrosion likely to occur in the service environment.

6.4.2.2   Corrosion protection shall be provided by means of suitable alloying elements in the steel, by protective coatings or by other effective means, either singly or in combination.

6.4.2.3   Localized corrosion likely to occur from entrapped water, excessive condensation, or from other factors shall be minimized by suitable design and detail. Where necessary, positive means of drainage shall be provided.

6.4.2.4   If the corrosion protection specified for steelwork exposed to the weather, or to other environments in which progressive corrosion can occur, is likely to require maintenance or renewal during the service life of the structure, the steelwork so protected shall have a minimum thickness of 4.5 mm (exclusive of fill plates and shims).

6.4.2.5   The minimum required thickness of steelwork situated in a non-corrosive environment and therefore not requiring corrosion protection is governed by the provisions of Clause 11.

6.4.2.6   Interiors of buildings conditioned for human comfort may be generally assumed to be non-corrosive environments; however, the need for corrosion protection shall be assessed and protection shall be furnished in those where it is deemed to be necessary.

6.4.2.7   Corrosion protection of the inside surfaces of enclosed spaces permanently sealed from any external source of oxygen is unnecessary.

7.   **Loads and Safety Criterion**

7.1   **Specified Loads**

7.1.1   Except as provided for in Clauses 7.1.2 and 7.1.3, the following loads and influences as specified by the authority having jurisdiction shall be considered in the design of a building and its structural steelwork:

    D — Dead loads, including the mass of steelwork and all permanent materials of construction, partitions and stationary equipment multiplied by the acceleration due to gravity to convert mass to force, and the forces due to prestressing;

    L — Live loads, including loads due to intended use and occupancy of the building, movable equipment, snow, rain, soil or hydrostatic pressure, impact, and any other live loads stipulated by the applicable building by-law or the authority having jurisdiction;

    Q — Wind or earthquake loads;

    T — Influences resulting from temperature changes, shrinkage or creep of component materials, or from differential settlement.

7.1.2   If it can be shown by engineering principles, or if it is known from experience, that neglect of some or all of the effects due to T does not affect the structural safety or serviceability, they need not be considered in the calculations.

7.1.3   Suitable provision shall be made for loads imposed on the steel structure during its erection. During subsequent construction of the building, suitable provision shall be made to support the construction loads on the steel structure with an adequate margin of safety.

7.2   **Safety Criterion and Effect of Factored Loads**

7.2.1   **Safety Criterion**
A building and its structural steelwork shall be designed to have sufficient strength or stability, or both, such that:

Factored Resistance $\geq$ Effect of Factored Loads

where Factored Resistance is determined in accordance with other clauses of this Standard and Effect of Factored Load is determined in accordance with Clauses 7.2.2 through 7.2.5. In cases of overturning, uplift and stress reversal, no positive anchorage is required if the stabilizing effect of dead load multiplied by a load factor less than one given in Clause 7.2.3 is greater than the effect of loads tending to cause overturning, uplift and stress reversal multiplied by load factors greater than one given in Clause 7.2.3.

7.2.2   Effect of factored loads, in force units, is the structural effect due to the specified loads multiplied by load factors α defined in Clause 7.2.3, a load combination factor ψ defined in Clause 7.2.4, and an importance factor γ defined in Clause 7.2.5. The factored load combinations shall be taken as follows:

$$\alpha_D D + \gamma\psi\,(\alpha_L L + \alpha_Q Q + \alpha_T T)$$

7.2.3   Load factors, α, shall be taken as follows:

α_D = 1.25, or, in cases of overturning, uplift and stress reversal, 0.85.
α_L = 1.50; α_Q = 1.50; α_T = 1.25.

7.2.4   The load combination factor, ψ, shall be taken as follows:

(a) When only one of L, Q and T act, ψ = 1.00;

(b) When two of L, Q and T act, ψ = 0.70;

(c) When all of L, Q and T act, ψ = 0.60.

The most unfavourable effect shall be determined by considering L, Q and T acting alone with ψ = 1.00 or in combination with ψ = 0.70 or 0.60.

7.2.5   Unless otherwise specified, the Importance Factor, γ, shall be taken as follows:

(a) 1.00 for all buildings except as noted in Item (b);

(b) Not less than 0.80 for:

   (i) Farm buildings having low human occupancy, defined as having an occupant density no greater than one person per 50 000 000 mm² during normal periods of use of 4 hours or longer;

   (ii) Buildings for which it can be shown that collapse is not likely to cause injury or other serious consequences.

8.   Analysis of Structure

8.1   General

8.1.1   In proportioning the structure to meet the various design requirements of Clause 6, the methods of analysis given in this Clause shall be used. The distribution of internal forces and bending moments shall be determined, both under the specified loads to satisfy the requirements of serviceability and fatigue in Clause 6 and under the factored loads as required to satisfy strength and overturning requirements in Clause 7.

8.1.2   Two basic types of construction and associated design assumptions, designated "Continuous" and "Simple", are permitted for all or part of a structure under this Standard. The distribution of internal forces and bending moments throughout the structure will depend on the type or types of construction chosen and the forces to be resisted.

8.2   Continuous Construction
In continuous construction, the beams, girders and trusses are rigidly framed, or are continuous over supports. Connections are generally designed to resist the bending moments and internal forces computed by assuming that the original angles between intersecting members remain unchanged as the structure is loaded.

8.3   Simple Construction

8.3.1   Simple construction assumes that the ends of beams, girders and trusses are free to rotate under load in the plane of loading. Resistance to lateral loads, including sway effects, shall be ensured by a suitable system of bracing or shear walls or by the design of part of the structure as continuous construction, except as provided in Clause 8.3.2.

8.3.2   A building frame designed to support gravity loads on the basis of simple construction may be proportioned to resist lateral loads due to wind or earthquake by distributing the moments resulting from such loading among selected joints of a frame by a recognized empirical method provided that:

(a) The connection and connected members are proportioned to resist the moments and forces caused by lateral loads;

(b) The connected members have solid webs;

(c) The beam or girder can support the full gravity load when assumed to act as a simple beam;

(d) The connection has adequate capacity for inelastic rotation when subjected to the factored gravity and lateral loads;

(e) The mechanical fasteners or welds of the connection are proportioned to resist 1.5 times the moments and forces produced by the factored gravity and lateral loads; and

(f) In assessing the stability of the structure, the flexibility of the connection is considered.

8.4   Elastic Analysis
Under a particular loading combination, the forces and moments throughout all or part of the structure may be determined by an analysis which assumes that individual members behave elastically.

8.5 **Plastic Analysis**

Under a particular loading combination, the forces and moments throughout all or part of the structure may be determined by a plastic analysis provided that:

(a) The steel used has $F_y \leq 0.80F_u$ and exhibits the load-strain characteristics necessary to achieve moment redistribution;

(b) The width-thickness ratios meet the requirements of Class 1 sections as given in Clause 11.2;

(c) The members are braced laterally in accordance with the requirements of Clause 13.7;

(d) Web stiffeners are supplied on a member at a point of load application where a plastic hinge would form;

(e) Splices in beams or columns are designed to transmit 1.1 times the maximum computed moment under factored loads at the splice location or $0.25M_p$, whichever is greater;

(f) Members are not subject to repeated heavy impact or fatigue;

(g) The influence of inelastic deformation on the strength of the structure shall be taken into account. (See also Clause 8.6.)

8.6 **Stability Effects**

8.6.1 The analyses referred to in Clauses 8.4 and 8.5 shall include the sway effects produced by the vertical loads acting on the structure in its displaced configuration, unless the structure is designed in accordance with the provisions of Clause 8.6.3.

For certain types of structures where the vertical loads are small, where the structure is relatively stiff and where the lateral load resisting elements are well distributed, the sway effects may not have a significant influence on the design of the structure (see Clause 9.3.2(b)).

8.6.2 For structures in which the sway effects have been included in the analysis to determine the design moments and forces (see Appendix J) the effective length factors for members shall be based on the side-sway prevented condition (see Clause 9.3.2(a)) and,

(a) Where a loading combination produces significant relative lateral displacements of the column ends, the sway effects shall include the effect of the vertical loads acting on the displaced structure;

(b) However the sway effects shall be not less than those produced by the vertical loads acting on the structure assumed displaced an amount equal to the maximum out-of-plumbness consistent with the erection tolerances specified in Clause 28.7.1;

(c) A deflected configuration in which the erection tolerances are opposite in sense in adjacent storeys, may produce sway effects which govern the design of beam-to-column connections, diaphragms and other elements.

8.6.3 For structures in which the sway effects have not been included in the analysis, the use of effective length factors greater than 1.0 (side-sway permitted case) for the design of columns, provides an approximate method of accounting for the sway effects in moment resisting frames (see Clause 9.3.3). This provision shall not be used for structures analysed in accordance with Clause 8.5.

9. Design Lengths of Members

9.1 Simple Span Flexural Members

Beams, girders, and trusses may be designed on the basis of simple spans whose length may be taken as the distance between centres of gravity of supporting members. Alternatively, the span length of beams and girders may be taken as the actual length of such members measured centre-to-centre of end connections. The length of trusses designed as simple spans may be taken as the distance between the extreme working points of the system of triangulation employed. In all cases the design of columns or other supporting members shall provide for the effect of any significant moment or eccentricity arising from the manner in which a beam, girder, or truss may actually be connected or supported.

9.2 Continuous Span Flexural Members

Beams, girders, or trusses having full or partial end restraint due to continuity or cantilever action, shall be proportioned to carry all moments, shears, and other forces at any section assuming the span, in general, to be the distance between centres of gravity of supporting members. Supporting members shall be proportioned to carry all moments, shears, and other forces induced by the continuity of the supported beam, girder, or truss.

9.3 Compression Members

9.3.1

Compression members shall be designed on the basis of their effective length (KL), the product of effective length factor (K), and unbraced length (L). Unless otherwise specified in this Standard the unbraced length (L) shall be taken as the length of the compression member centre-to-centre of restraining members. The unbraced length may differ for different cross-sectional axes of the compression members. At the bottom storey of a multi-storey structure, or for a single-storey structure, (L) shall be taken as the length from the top of the base plate to the centre of restraining members at the next higher level.

9.3.2

The effective length factor (K) shall be taken as 1.0 for compression members of frames unless the degree of rotational restraint afforded at the ends of the unbraced lengths shows that a value of K less than 1.0 is applicable. (For recommended values of K and a method of computing K, based on rotational restraint, see Appendices B and C respectively, side-sway prevented case.)

(a) In which sway effects (see Clause 8.6.2) have been included in the analysis used to determine the design moments and forces; or

(b) In which the sway effects in addition to the lateral loads are resisted by bracing or shear walls.

9.3.3

For structures with moment resisting frames in which sway effects have not been included in the analysis used to determine the design moments and forces (see Clause 8.6.3), the effective length factor shall be determined from the degree of rotational and translational restraint afforded at the ends of the unbraced length, but shall be not less than 1. (For recommended values of K and a method of computing K, see Appendices B and C respectively, side-sway permitted case.)

9.3.4 Compression Members in Trusses

Unless otherwise specified in this Standard or unless analysis shows that a smaller value is applicable, the effective length factor (K) shall be taken as 1.0 for compression members in trusses.

10. Slenderness Ratios

10.1 General

The slenderness ratio of a compression member shall be taken as the ratio of effective length (KL) to the corresponding radius of gyration (r). The slenderness ratio of a tension member shall be taken as the ratio of unbraced length (L) to the corresponding radius of gyration.

10.2 Maximum Slenderness Ratio

10.2.1 The slenderness ratio of a compression member shall not exceed 200.

10.2.2 The slenderness ratio of a tension member shall not exceed 300. This limit may be waived if other means are provided to control flexibility, sag, vibration, and slack in a manner commensurate with the service conditions of the structure or if it can be shown that such factors are not detrimental to the performance of the structure or of the assembly of which the member is a part.

11. Width-Thickness Ratios: Compression Elements

11.1 Classification of Sections

11.1.1 For the purposes of this Standard, structural sections shall be designated as Class 1, 2, 3 or 4 depending on the maximum width-thickness ratios of their elements subject to compression, and as otherwise specified in Clause 11.1.3.

11.1.2 **Class 1** sections (plastic design sections) will permit attainment of the plastic moment and subsequent redistribution of bending moment.

Class 2 sections (compact sections) will permit attainment of the plastic moment but need not allow for subsequent moment redistribution.

Class 3 sections (non-compact sections) will permit attainment of the yield moment.

Class 4 sections will generally have local buckling of elements in compression as the limit state of structural capacity.

11.1.3 Class 1 sections shall, when subject to flexure, have an axis of symmetry in the plane of loading and shall, when subject to axial compression, be doubly symmetric. Class 2 sections shall, when subject to flexure, have an axis of symmetry in the plane of loading unless the effects of asymmetry of the section are included in the analysis.

11.2 Maximum Width-Thickness Ratios of Elements Subject to Compression

The width-thickness ratio of elements subject to compression shall not exceed the limits given in Table 1 for the specified section classification.

11.3 Width and Thickness

11.3.1 For elements supported along one edge only, parallel to the direction of compressive force, the width shall be taken as follows:

(a) For plates, the width (b) is the distance from the free edge to the first row of fasteners or line of welds;

(b) For legs of angles, flanges of channels and zees, and stems of tees, the width (b) is the full nominal dimension;

(c) For flanges of beams and tees, the width (b) is one-half the full nominal dimension.

11.3.2 For elements supported along two edges parallel to the direction of compressive force the width shall be taken as follows:

(a) For flange or diaphragm plates in built-up sections the width (b) is the distance between adjacent lines of fasteners or lines of welds;

(b) For flanges of rectangular hollow structural sections the width (b) is the clear distance between webs less the inside corner radius on each side;

(c) For webs of built-up sections the width (h) is the distance between adjacent lines of fasteners or the clear distance between flanges when welds are used;

(d) For webs of hot rolled sections the width (h) is the clear distance between flanges.

11.3.3 The thickness of elements is the nominal thickness. For tapered flanges of rolled sections, thickness is the nominal thickness halfway between a free edge and the corresponding face of the web.

12. Gross and Net Areas

12.1 **Application**
In general, tension members shall be proportioned on the basis of net area and compression members on the basis of gross area. (For beams and girders see Clause 15.)

12.2 **Gross Area**
Gross area shall be computed by summing the products of the thickness and gross width of each element, as measured normal to the axis of the member.

12.3 **Net Area**

12.3.1 Net area shall be computed by summing the products of the thickness and the net width of each element, as measured normal to the axis of the member. Net width and area of parts containing holes shall be computed in accordance with Clause 12.3.3.

12.3.2 **Dimensions of Holes**
In computing net area the width of the bolt holes normal to the axis of the member shall be assumed 2 mm larger than the hole dimension specified.

12.3.3 For a series of holes extending across a part of any diagonal or zigzag line, the net width of the part shall be computed by deducting from the gross width the sum of all hole widths in the series and adding for each gauge distance (g) in the series the quantity:

$$\frac{s^2}{4g}$$

where
s = longitudinal spacing (pitch) in millimetres of any two successive holes

g = transverse spacing (gauge) in millimetres of the same two holes

Table 1
Width-Thickness Ratios: Compression Elements

Description of Element	Section Classification			
	Class 1 Plastic Design	Class 2 Compact	Class 3 Non-compact	Class 4* Slender
Legs of angles and elements supported along one edge, except as noted	—	—	$\dfrac{b}{t} \leq \dfrac{200}{\sqrt{F_y}}$	See Clause 13
Angles in continuous contact with other elements; plate girder stiffeners	—	—	$\dfrac{b}{t} \leq \dfrac{260}{\sqrt{F_y}}$	See Clause 13
Stems of T sections	$\dfrac{b}{t} \leq \dfrac{145\dagger}{\sqrt{F_y}}$	$\dfrac{b}{t} \leq \dfrac{170\dagger}{\sqrt{F_y}}$	$\dfrac{b}{t} \leq \dfrac{340}{\sqrt{F_y}}$	See Clause 13
Flanges of I or T sections; plates projecting from compression elements; outstanding legs of pairs of angles in continuous contact‡	$\dfrac{b}{t} \leq \dfrac{145}{\sqrt{F_y}}$	$\dfrac{b}{t} \leq \dfrac{170}{\sqrt{F_y}}$	$\dfrac{b}{t} \leq \dfrac{260}{\sqrt{F_y}}$	See Clause 13
Flanges of channels	—	—	$\dfrac{b}{t} \leq \dfrac{260}{\sqrt{F_y}}$	See Clause 13
Flanges of rectangular hollow structural sections	$\dfrac{b}{t} \leq \dfrac{420}{\sqrt{F_y}}$	$\dfrac{b}{t} \leq \dfrac{525}{\sqrt{F_y}}$	$\dfrac{b}{t} \leq \dfrac{670}{\sqrt{F_y}}$	See Clause 13
Flanges of box sections, flange cover plates and diaphragm plates, between lines of fasteners or welds	$\dfrac{b}{t} \leq \dfrac{525}{\sqrt{F_y}}$	$\dfrac{b}{t} \leq \dfrac{525}{\sqrt{F_y}}$	$\dfrac{b}{t} \leq \dfrac{670}{\sqrt{F_y}}$	See Clause 13

Perforated cover plates	—	—	$\frac{b}{t} \leq \frac{840}{\sqrt{F_y}}$	—
Webs in axial compression	$\frac{h}{w} \leq \frac{670}{\sqrt{F_y}}$	$\frac{h}{w} \leq \frac{670}{\sqrt{F_y}}$	$\frac{h}{w} \leq \frac{670}{\sqrt{F_y}}$	See Clause 13
Webs in flexural compression	$\frac{h}{w} \leq \frac{1100}{\sqrt{F_y}}$	$\frac{h}{w} \leq \frac{1370}{\sqrt{F_y}}$	$\frac{h}{w} \leq \frac{1810}{\sqrt{F_y}}$	See Clause 13
Webs in combined flexural and axial compression	$\frac{h}{w} \leq \frac{1100}{\sqrt{F_y}}\left(1 - 1.40\frac{C_f}{C_y}\right)$ §	when $\frac{C_f}{C_y} \leq 0.15$, $\frac{h}{w} \leq \frac{1370}{\sqrt{F_y}}\left(1 - 1.28\frac{C_f}{C_y}\right)$ when $\frac{C_f}{C_y} > 0.15$, $\frac{h}{w} \leq \frac{1180}{\sqrt{F_y}}\left(1 - 0.43\frac{C_f}{C_y}\right)$	when $\frac{C_f}{C_y} \leq 0.15$, $\frac{h}{w} \leq \frac{1810}{\sqrt{F_y}}\left(1 - 1.69\frac{C_f}{C_y}\right)$ when $\frac{C_f}{C_y} > 0.15$, $\frac{h}{w} \leq \frac{1470}{\sqrt{F_y}}\left(1 - 0.54\frac{C_f}{C_y}\right)$	See Clause 13
Circular hollow sections	$\frac{D}{t} \leq \frac{13\,000}{F_y}$	$\frac{D}{t} \leq \frac{18\,000}{F_y}$	$\frac{D}{t} \leq \frac{23\,000}{F_y}$	—

* Class 4 includes all sections not otherwise specified.
† See Clause 11.1.3.
‡ Can be considered as Class 1 or Class 2 sections if angles are continuously connected by adequate mechanical fasteners or welds and there is an axis of symmetry in the plane of loading.
§ $\frac{h}{w}$ need not be less than $\frac{670}{\sqrt{F_y}}$

12.3.4 The critical net area of the part is obtained from that series of holes which gives the least net width; however, net area taken through one or more holes shall not be assumed to exceed the following limits:

(a) $0.85A_g$ when $\quad\quad F_y/F_u \leq 0.75$

(b) $0.90A_g$ when $0.75 < F_y/F_u \leq 0.85$

(c) $0.95A_g$ when $0.85 < F_y/F_u$

12.3.5 For angles the gross width shall be the sum of the widths of the legs minus the thickness. The gauge for holes in opposite legs shall be the sum of the gauges from the heel of the angle minus the thickness.

12.3.6 In computing the net area across plug or slot welds the weld metal shall not be taken as adding to the net area.

12.4 **Pin-Connected Tension Members**

12.4.1 In pin-connected tension members, the net area across the pin hole, normal to the axis of the member, shall be at least 1.33 times the cross-sectional area of the body of the member. The net area of any section on either side of the axis of the member measured at an angle of 45° or less to the axis of the member, shall be not less than 0.9 times the cross-sectional area of the body of the member.

12.4.2 The distance from the edge of the pin hole to the edge of the member, measured transverse to the axis of the member, shall not exceed 4 times the thickness of the material at the pin hole.

12.4.3 The diameter of a pin hole shall be not more than 1 mm larger than the diameter of the pin.

13. **Member and Connection Resistance**

13.1 **General**
To meet the strength requirements of this Standard, all factored resistances, as determined in this Clause, shall be greater than or equal to the effect of factored loads determined in accordance with Clause 7.2 and ϕ shall be taken as 0.90 unless otherwise specified.

13.2 **Axial Tension**
The factored tensile resistance, T_r, developed by a member subjected to an axial tension force shall be taken as:

(a) The lesser of

(i) $T_r = \phi A_n F_y$ when $A_n/A_g \geq F_y/F_u$

$$= \phi\left(F_u\,\frac{A_n}{A_g}\right)\cdot A_n \text{ when } A_n/A_g < F_y/F_u$$

(ii) $T_r = 0.85\phi A_n F_u$

(b) On net area at pin connections

$$T_r = 0.75\phi A_n F_y$$

13.3   **Axial Compression**

13.3.1   The factored axial compressive resistance for W shapes and for hollow structural sections manufactured according to CSA Standard G40.20 — M1978, Class C (cold formed non-stress relieved) and conforming to the requirements of Clause 11 of this Standard for Class 1, 2 or 3 sections, shall be taken as*;

(a) $0 \leqslant \lambda \leqslant 0.15,$ $C_r = \phi A F_y$

(b) $0.15 < \lambda \leq 1.0,$ $C_r = \phi A F_y \, (1.035 - 0.202\lambda - 0.222\lambda^2)$

(c) $1.0 < \lambda \leq 2.0,$ $C_r = \phi A F_y \, (-0.111 + 0.636\lambda^{-1} + 0.087\lambda^{-2})$

(d) $2.0 < \lambda \leq 3.6,$ $C_r = \phi A F_y \, (0.009 + 0.877\lambda^{-2})$

(e) $3.6 < \lambda,$ $C_r = \phi A F_y \, \lambda^{-2} = \phi A \left[\dfrac{1\,970\,000}{(KL/r)^2} \right]$

where

$$\lambda = \frac{KL}{r} \sqrt{\frac{F_y}{\pi^2 E}}$$

These expressions are applicable to the W shapes normally rolled in Canada and can be assumed to be valid for other doubly symmetric Class 1, 2 or 3 sections, except for solid round non-stress relieved cold straightened bars greater than 50 mm diameter (refer to CSA Standard S37, Antenna Towers and Antenna Supporting Structures). Welded H-shapes should have flange edges flame cut. Singly symmetric, asymmetric or cruciform sections should be checked as to whether torsional-flexural buckling is critical.

13.3.2   The factored axial compressive resistance for hollow structural sections manufactured according to CSA Standard G40.20 — M1978, Class H (hot formed or cold formed stress relieved) and conforming to the requirements of Clause 11 of this Standard for Class 1, 2 or 3 sections, shall be taken as;

(a) $0 \leqslant \lambda \leqslant 0.15,$ $C_r = \phi A F_y$

(b) $0.15 < \lambda \leqslant 1.2,$ $C_r = \phi A F_y \, (0.990 + 0.122\lambda - 0.367\lambda^2)$

(c) $1.2 < \lambda \leqslant 1.8,$ $C_r = \phi A F_y \, (0.051 + 0.801\lambda^{-2})$

(d) $1.8 < \lambda \leqslant 2.8,$ $C_r = \phi A F_y \, (0.008 + 0.942\lambda^{-2})$

(e) $2.8 < \lambda,$ $C_r = \phi A F_y \, \lambda^{-2} = \phi A \left[\dfrac{1\,970\,000}{(KL/r)^2} \right]$

where

$$\lambda = \frac{KL}{r} \sqrt{\frac{F_y}{\pi^2 E}}$$

Values of $\sqrt{\dfrac{F_y}{\pi^2 E}}$ and $\dfrac{F_y}{\pi^2 E}$ to compute λ and λ^2 respectively are given in Table 2.

Table 2

Values of $\sqrt{\dfrac{F_y}{\pi^2 E}}$ and $\dfrac{F_y}{\pi^2 E}$

F_y	$\sqrt{\dfrac{F_y}{\pi^2 E}}$	$\dfrac{F_y}{\pi^2 E}$
230	0.0108	0.000 116
260	0.0115	0.000 132
300	0.0123	0.000 152
350	0.0133	0.000 177
380	0.0139	0.000 192
400	0.0142	0.000 203
480	0.0156	0.000 243
700	0.0188	0.000 355

13.3.3 The factored compressive resistance, C_r, developed by a member subject to an axial compressive force and designated as a Class 4 section according to Clause 11 shall be calculated in accordance with Clause 12 of CSA Standard S136, Cold Formed Steel Structural Members, except that the capacity so calculated shall not exceed that given by Clause 13.3.1 or 13.3.2, as applicable, when multiplied by the local buckling factor Q as given in CSA Standard S136. The calculated value, F'_y applicable to cold formed members, that may be used in Clause 12 of CSA Standard S136 shall be determined by using only the values for F_y and F_u that are specified in the relevant structural steel material standard.

13.4   **Shear**

13.4.1   **Elastic Analysis**
Except as noted in Clause 13.4.2, the factored shear resistance, V_r, developed by the web of a flexural member subjected to shear shall be taken as:

$$V_r = \phi A_w F_s$$

where

A_w = shear area ("dw" for rolled shapes and "hw" for girders)

F_s is as follows:

(a) $\dfrac{h}{w} \leq 439 \sqrt{\dfrac{k_v}{F_y}}$ . . . . $F_s = 0.66 F_y$

(b) $439 \sqrt{\dfrac{k_v}{F_y}} < \dfrac{h}{w} \leq 502 \sqrt{\dfrac{k_v}{F_y}}$ . . . $F_s = \dfrac{290 \sqrt{F_y k_v}}{(h/w)}$

(c) $502 \sqrt{\dfrac{k_v}{F_y}} < \dfrac{h}{w} \leq 621 \sqrt{\dfrac{k_v}{F_y}}$ . . . $F_s = \left(\dfrac{290 \sqrt{F_y k_v}}{(h/w)} \right) \tau + \eta F_y$

(d) $621 \sqrt{\dfrac{k_v}{F_y}} < \dfrac{h}{w}$ . . . . $F_s = \left(\dfrac{180\ 000\ k_v}{(h/w)^2} \right) \tau + \eta F_y$

where

F_s = ultimate shear stress (MPa)

k_v = shear buckling coefficient

$\quad = 4 + \dfrac{5.34}{(a/h)^2}$ when $a/h < 1$

$\quad = 5.34 + \dfrac{4}{(a/h)^2}$ when $a/h \geq 1$

$\tau = 1 - \dfrac{0.866}{\sqrt{1 + (a/h)^2}}$

$\eta = \dfrac{0.50}{\sqrt{1 + (a/h)^2}}$

a/h = aspect ratio, ratio of distance between stiffeners to web depth

For unstiffened webs, $a/h = \infty$ and $\tau = 1$, $\eta = 0$, $k_v = 5.34$.

The values given in Table 3 may be used. The gross area of a web shall be taken as the product of the web depth (h) and the web thickness (w), except that for rolled shapes the overall depth (d) may be substituted for h.

Table 3
Coefficients for Shear Formulae

a/h	τ	η	k_v
0.25	0.160	0.485	89.4
0.33	0.178	0.475	52.2
0.50	0.225	0.447	25.4
0.67	0.280	0.415	16.0
0.75	0.307	0.400	13.5
1.00	0.388	0.354	9.34
1.25	0.459	0.312	7.90
1.50	0.520	0.277	7.12
1.75	0.570	0.248	6.65
2.00	0.613	0.224	6.34
2.25	0.648	0.203	6.13
2.50	0.678	0.186	5.98
2.75	0.704	0.171	5.87
3.00	0.726	0.158	5.78
Infinity	1.000	0	5.34

13.4.2 Plastic Analysis

In structures designed on the basis of a plastic analysis, as defined in Clause 8.5 the factored shear resistance, V_r, developed by the web of a flexural member subjected to shear shall be taken as:

$V_r = 0.55 \phi w d F_y$

13.4.3 **Maximum Slenderness**
The slenderness ratio (h/w) of a web shall not exceed:

$83\,000/F_y$

where
F_y = specified minimum yield point of the compression flange steel (see Clause 15.3).

This limit may be waived if analysis indicates that compression flange buckling into the web will not occur at factored load.

13.4.4 **Gusset Plates**
The total factored shear resistance of the gross area of gusset plates shall be taken as:

$V_r = 0.50\phi A_g F_y$

13.4.5 **Pins**
The total factored shear resistance of the nominal area of pins shall be taken as:

$V_r = 0.66\phi A F_y$

13.4.6 **Combined Shear and Moment in Girders**
Transversely stiffened girders depending on tension-field action to carry shear, with $h/w > 502\sqrt{k_v/F_y}$, shall be proportioned in such a way that the following limits are observed:

$$\frac{V_f}{V_r} \leq 1.0$$

$$\frac{M_f}{M_r} \leq 1.0$$

$$0.727\,\frac{M_f}{M_r} + 0.455\,\frac{V_f}{V_r} \leq 1.0$$

where

V_r is established according to Clause 13.4 and M_r is established according to Clause 13.5 or Clause 13.6 as applicable.

13.5 **Bending — Laterally Supported Members**
The factored moment resistance, M_r, developed by a member subjected to bending moments, where continuous lateral support is provided to the compression flange shall be taken as:

(a) For Class 1 and Class 2 sections:

$M_r = \phi Z F_y = \phi M_p$

(b) For Class 3 sections:

$M_r = \phi S F_y = \phi M_y$

(c) For Class 4 sections:

(i) When both the web and the compression flange fall within Class 4 of Table 1, the value M_r shall be determined in accordance with Clause 12 of CSA Standard S136, Cold Formed Steel Structural Members. The calculated value, F'_v, applicable to cold formed members, shall be determined by using only the values for F_y and F_u that are specified in the relevant structural steel material standard;

(ii) For beams or girders whose flanges meet the requirements of Class 3 and whose webs exceed the limits for Class 3, see Clause 15;

(iii) For beams or girders whose webs meet the requirements of Class 3 and whose flanges exceed the limits for Class 3:

$$M_r = \phi S F_{cr}$$

where

F_{cr} = the critical stress corresponding to local buckling of compression elements and is given by:

When $b/t \leq 520 \sqrt{\dfrac{k}{F_y}}$

$$F_{cr} = F_y \left[1.46 - 0.0015 \sqrt{\frac{F_y}{k}} \, (b/t) \right]$$

When $b/t > 520 \sqrt{\dfrac{k}{F_y}}$

$$F_{cr} = \frac{181\,000k}{(b/t)^2}$$

in which

k = 0.43 for legs of angles
= 0.70 for flanges of I, channels, and T-sections (i.e., elements supported along one edge parallel to direction of stress)
= 1.28 for stems of T-sections
= 5.0 for flange or diaphragm plates or portions thereof supported along two edges parallel to direction of stress

13.6   **Bending — Laterally Unsupported Members**
Where continuous lateral support is not provided to the compression flange of a member subjected to bending, the factored moment resistance, M_r, may be taken as:

(a) For Doubly Symmetric Class 1 and Class 2 Sections:

(i) When $M_u > \dfrac{2}{3} M_p$

$$M_r = 1.15\phi M_p \left(1 - \frac{0.28M_p}{M_u} \right) \text{ but not greater than } \phi M_p$$

(ii) When $M_u \leq \dfrac{2}{3} M_p$

$$M_r = \phi M_u$$

where

$$M_u = \frac{\pi}{\omega L} \sqrt{EI_y GJ + \left(\frac{\pi E}{L} \right)^2 I_y C_w}$$

For I-shaped members bent about the major axis, M_u may be taken as:

$$M_u = \frac{S}{\omega} \sqrt{\sigma_1{}^2 + \sigma_2{}^2}$$

$$\sigma_1 = \frac{140\ 000}{Ld/A_f}$$

$$\sigma_2 = \frac{1\ 700\ 000}{(L/r_t)^2}$$

where

ω = $0.6 + 0.4M_{f1}/M_{f2}$ for members bent in single curvature

ω = $0.6 - 0.4M_{f1}/M_{f2}$ for members bent in double curvature, but not less than 0.4

L = unsupported length of compression flange in millimetres

C_w = 0 for hollow structural sections

in which

M_{f1} is the smaller and M_{f2} the larger bending moment at the ends of the unsupported length, taken about the strong axis of the member

ω = 1.0 when the bending moment at any point within the unsupported length is larger than M_{f2} or when there is no effective lateral support for the compression flange at one of the ends of the unsupported length

(b) For Doubly Symmetric Class 3 and Class 4 Sections and for Channels Prevented from Twisting:

(i) When $M_u > \frac{2}{3}M_y$

$$M_r = 1.15\phi M_y \left(1 - \frac{0.28M_y}{M_u}\right)$$

but not greater than ϕM_y for Class 3 sections and ϕSF_{cr} for Class 4 sections;

(ii) When $M_u \leq \frac{2}{3} M_y$

$$M_r = \phi M_u$$

where

$$M_u = \frac{\pi}{\omega L} \sqrt{EI_y GJ + \left(\frac{\pi E}{L}\right)^2 I_y C_w}$$

For I-shaped members and channels M_u may be taken as:

$$M_u = \frac{S}{\omega} \sqrt{\sigma_1^2 + \sigma_2^2}$$

where
σ_1 and σ_2 are as defined in Clause 13.6(a)
σ_2 = 0 for channels

(c) For unsymmetric shapes a rational method of analysis such as given in the Structural Stability Research Council's "Guide to Stability Design Criteria for Metal Structures" should be used.

13.7   **Lateral Bracing for Members in Structures Analysed Plastically**
Members in structures or portions of structures in which the distributions of moments and forces have been determined by a plastic analysis shall be braced to resist lateral and torsional displacement at all hinge locations. The

laterally unsupported distance, L_{cr}, from such braced hinge locations to the nearest adjacent point on the frame similarly braced shall not exceed:

$$L_{cr} = 550r_y / \sqrt{F_y} \text{ for } \frac{M_{f1}}{M_{f2}} > 0.5$$

$$L_{cr} = 980r_y / \sqrt{F_y} \text{ for } \frac{M_{f1}}{M_{f2}} \le 0.5$$

where

$\dfrac{M_{f1}}{M_{f2}}$ is equal to the ratio of the smaller moment to the larger moment at opposite ends of the unbraced length, in the plane of bending considered; positive when the member is bent in single curvature and negative when bent in double curvature.

$$-1.0 \le \frac{M_{f1}}{M_{f2}} \le 1.0$$

Both bracing requirements should be checked and the more severe shall govern the location of the braced point. Bracing is not required at the location of the last hinge to form in the failure mechanism assumed as the basis for proportioning the structure. Except for the regions specified above, the maximum unsupported length of members in structures analysed plastically need be not less than that which would be permitted for the same members in structures analysed elastically.

13.8   **Axial Compression and Bending**[*]

13.8.1   **Member Strength and Stability — Class 1 and Class 2 Sections**
Members required to resist bending moments and an axial compressive force shall be proportioned so that:

(a) In a state of complete yielding (partly in tension, partly in compression) the section is capable of holding in equilibrium the factored moments and axial load. Conservatively, this requirement is satisfied if the section meets the requirements of Clause 13.8.3(a);

$$(b) \quad \frac{C_f}{C_r} + \frac{\omega_x M_{fx}}{M_{rx}\left(1 - \dfrac{C_f}{C_{ex}}\right)} + \frac{\omega_y M_{fy}}{M_{ry}\left(1 - \dfrac{C_f}{C_{ey}}\right)} \le 1.0$$

where

M_{rx} is defined in Clause 13.6(a) and M_{ry} is defined in Clause 13.5(a).

[*]*More detailed methods of determining the resistance of columns subject to biaxial bending are given in Appendix F.*

13.8.2   **Member Strength and Stability — Class 1 and Class 2 Sections of I-Shaped Members**
Members required to resist bending moments and an axial compressive force shall be proportioned so that:

$$(a) \quad \frac{M_{fx}}{M_{rx}} + \frac{M_{fy}}{M_{ry}} \le 1.0$$

where

M_r is defined in Clause 13.5(a)

(b) $\dfrac{C_f}{C_r} + \dfrac{0.85M_{fx}}{M_{rx}} + \dfrac{0.60M_{fy}}{M_{ry}} \leq 1.0$

where

$C_r = \phi A F_y$

M_r is defined in Clause 13.5(a)

(c) $\dfrac{C_f}{C_r} + \dfrac{\omega_x M_{fx}}{M_{rx}\left(1 - \dfrac{C_f}{C_{ex}}\right)} + \dfrac{\omega_y M_{fy}}{M_{ry}\left(1 - \dfrac{C_f}{C_{ey}}\right)} \leq 1.0$

where

C_r is defined in Clause 13.3.1

M_{rx} is defined in Clause 13.6(a)

M_{ry} is defined in Clause 13.5(a)

13.8.3 **Member Strength and Stability — Class 3 and Class 4 Sections**
Members required to resist bending moments and an axial compressive force shall be proportioned so that:

(a) $\dfrac{C_f}{C_r} + \dfrac{M_{fx}}{M_{rx}} + \dfrac{M_{fy}}{M_{ry}} \leq 1.0$

where

$C_r = \phi A F_y$

M_r is defined in Clause 13.5(b) or 13.5(c)(i) and (c)(iii)

(b) $\dfrac{C_f}{C_r} + \dfrac{\omega_x M_{fx}}{M_{rx}\left(1 - \dfrac{C_f}{C_{ex}}\right)} + \dfrac{\omega_y M_{fy}}{M_{ry}\left(1 - \dfrac{C_f}{C_{ey}}\right)} \leq 1.0$

where

C_r is defined in Clause 13.3

M_{rx} is defined in Clause 13.6(b)

M_{ry} is defined in Clause 13.5(b) or 13.5(c)(i) and (c)(iii)

13.8.4 **Values of ω**
Unless otherwise determined by analysis, the following values shall be used for ω:

(a) Members not subjected to transverse loads between supports:

   (i) For members of frames analysed in accordance with Clause 8.6.2,
   $\omega = 0.6 + 0.4M_{f1}/M_{f2}$ for members bent in single curvature
   $\omega = 0.6 - 0.4M_{f1}/M_{f2}$ for members bent in double curvature, but not less than 0.4

   where

   M_{f1}/M_{f2} = ratio of the smaller moment to the larger moment at opposite ends of the unbraced length, in the plane of bending considered;

(ii) For members of frames analysed in accordance with Clause 8.6.3,
ω = 0.85 for members bent in double curvature or subject to moment at one end
ω = 1.0 for members bent in single curvature due to moments at both ends

(b) Members subjected to distributed load or series of point loads between supports:
$\omega = 1.0$

(c) Members subjected to a concentrated load or moment between supports: $\omega = 0.85$.

For the purpose of design, members subjected to concentrated load (or moment) between supports (e.g., crane columns) may be considered to be divided into two segments at the point of load (or moment) application. Each segment shall then be treated as a member which depends on its own flexural stiffness to prevent side-sway in the plane of bending considered and ω shall be taken as 0.85. In computing the slenderness ratio KL/r, for use in Clause 13.8, the total length of the member shall be used.

13.9   Axial Tension and Bending
Members required to resist both bending moments and an axial tensile force shall be proportioned so that:

(a) $\dfrac{T_f}{T_r} + \dfrac{M_f}{M_r} \leq 1.0$

where

$M_r = \phi M_p$ for Class 1 and Class 2 sections

$M_r = \phi M_y$ for Class 3 and Class 4 sections

(b) $\dfrac{M_f}{M_r} - \dfrac{T_f Z}{M_r A} \leq 1.0$ for Class 1 and Class 2 sections

or $\dfrac{M_f}{M_r} - \dfrac{T_f S}{M_r A} \leq 1.0$ for Class 3 and Class 4 sections

where

M_r is defined in Clause 13.5(c) or 13.6

13.10   Load Bearing
The factored bearing resistance, B_r, developed by a member or portion of a member, subjected to bearing shall be taken as:

(a) On the contact area of machined, accurately sawn or fitted parts

$B_r = 1.50 \phi F_y A$

(b) On expansion rollers or rockers

$B_r = 0.000\,13 \phi D L F_y^2$

where

B_r is in newtons

ϕ is taken as 0.90

D and L are the diameter and length respectively of roller or rocker

F_y is the specified minimum yield point of the weaker part in contact

(c) In bearing-type connections

$B_r = \phi tneF_u \leq 3\phi tdnF_u$

where

ϕ is taken as 0.67

F_u is the tensile strength of the plate

The ratio of end distance to bolt diameter shall meet the requirements of Clause 21.8.

13.11 Bolts in Bearing-Type Connections

13.11.1 General
For bolts in bearing-type connections ϕ shall be taken as 0.67 to ensure that the connection will not fail before the member.

13.11.2 Bolts in Shear
The factored resistance developed by a bolted joint subjected to shear shall be taken as the lesser of:

(a) The factored bearing resistance, B_r, given in Clause 13.10(c); or

(b) The factored shear resistance of the bolts taken as:

$V_r = 0.60\phi nmA_bF_u$*

When the bolt threads are intercepted by any shear plane, the factored shear resistance of any joint shall be taken as 70 per cent of V_r.

For joints longer than 1300 mm the shearing resistance shall be taken as 80 per cent of the above values.

For A325 bolts 1 inch or less in diameter F_u is 825 MPa and for A325 bolts greater than 1 inch in diameter F_u is 725 MPa. For A490 bolts F_u is 1035 MPa.

ASTM Standards A325 and A490 are written in Imperial Units. Accordingly, bolt diameters are shown in the Imperial System.

13.11.3 Bolts in Tension
The factored tensile resistance developed by a bolted joint, T_r, subjected to tension, T_f, shall be taken as:

$T_r = 0.75\phi nA_bF_u$

13.11.4 Bolts in Combined Shear and Tension
A bolt in a joint required to develop resistance to both tension and shear shall be proportioned so that the following relationship is satisfied:

$$\frac{V_f^2}{m^2} + \beta T_f^2 \leq 0.56\phi^2\beta(A_bF_u)^2$$

where
β = an interaction factor derived from test results
    = 0.69 for A325 bolts, shear plane through shank
    = 0.41 for A325 bolts, shear plane through threads
    = 0.56 for A490 bolts, shear plane through shank
    = 0.30 for A490 bolts, shear plane through threads

Except that V_f shall not exceed V_r given in Clause 13.11.2.

13.12 Bolts in Slip-Resistant (Friction-Type) Connections

13.12.1   General

The requirement for a slip-resistant connection is that under the forces and moments produced by specified loads, slip of the assembly shall not occur. In addition the effect of factored loads shall not exceed the bearing and shear resistance of the connection as given in Clause 13.11.

13.12.2   Shear Connections

The slip resistance, V_s, of a bolted joint, subjected to shear, V, shall be taken as:

$$V_s = 0.26\mu mnA_bF_u$$

where μ, a function of slip probability, is expressed as a function of bolt type and condition of the faying surfaces of the parts. Representative values corresponding to a 5 per cent probability of slip are given in Table 4.

Table 4
Values of μ

Steel Surface Treatment	A325 Bolts	A490 Bolts
Tightly adhering clean mill scale except for quenched and tempered steels	0.59	0.51
Blast cleaned G40.21-M, Grade 300W, 300T A36, A440	0.99	0.87
Blast cleaned A514	0.69	0.60
Hot-dip galvanized G40.21-M, Grade 300W, 300T A36, A440	0.31	0.27
Galvanized, then wire-brushed or blasted G40.21-M, Grade 300W, 300T A36, A440	0.76	0.66
Vinyl treated G40.21-M, Grade 300W, 300T A36	0.62	0.54

13.12.3   Connections in Combined Shear and Tension

Bolts in a joint required to develop resistance to both tension and shear shall be proportioned so that the following relationship is satisfied for the specified loads:

$$\frac{V}{V_s} + 1.9\ \frac{T}{nA_bF_u} \leq 1.0$$

where

V_s = slip resistance as defined in Clause 13.12.2. Except that the factored tension T_f shall not exceed T_r given in Clause 13.11.3.

13.13   Welds

13.13.1   The factored resistance of welds shall be as shown in Table 5.

13.13.2   In no case shall the strength of the weld be taken in excess of the capacity of the connected base metal.

13.13.3 The compression strength of joints utilizing partial joints penetration groove welds shall be based on the effective throat area of the welds plus the effective area of the base metal fitted in intimate contact.

13.13.4 The vector sum of factored longitudinal and transverse shear loads shall not exceed the factored resistances given in Table 5.

13.13.5 Plug and slot welds shall be considered only to provide shear resistance in the plane of the connected parts.

Table 5
Factored Resistance of Welds

Type of Weld	Type of Load and Orientation	Factored Resistance
Complete Joint Penetration Groove Welds	Tension or compression parallel to axis of weld*	Same as for base metal
	Tension normal to effective throat	
	Compression normal to effective throat	
	Shear on effective throat	The smaller of (a) base metal $\quad V_r = 0.66\phi A_m F_y$ or (b) weld metal $\quad V_r = 0.50\phi A_w X_u$
Partial Joint Penetration Groove Welds	Tension or compression parallel to axis of weld*	Same as for base metal
	Compression normal to effective throat	
	Tension other than parallel to axis of weld	The smaller of (a) base metal $\quad V_r = 0.66\phi A_m F_y$ or (b) weld metal $\quad V_r = 0.50\phi A_w X_u$
	Shear on effective throat	
Fillet Welds	Tension or compression parallel to axis of the weld*	Same as for base metal
	Tension or compression other than parallel to axis of weld	The smaller of (a) base metal $\quad V_r = 0.66\phi A_m F_y$ or (b) weld metal $\quad V_r = 0.50\phi A_w X_u$
	Shear on effective throat	
Plug and Slot Welds	Shear on effective throat	

where X_u = ultimate strength as rated by the Electrode Classification number.

No load transfer occurs.

14.   Fatigue

14.1   General

14.1.1   In addition to meeting the requirements of Clause 14, for fatigue, any member or connection shall also meet the requirements for the static load conditions using the factored loads.

14.1.2   Members and connections subjected to fatigue loading shall be designed, detailed and fabricated so as to minimize stress concentrations and abrupt changes in cross-section.

14.1.3   Specified loads for the design of members or connections shall be used for all fatigue calculations.

14.1.4   A specified load less than the maximum specified load but acting with a greater number of cycles may govern and shall be considered.

14.1.5   Plate girders with $h/w > 3150/\sqrt{F_y}$ shall not be used under fatigue conditions.

14.1.6   Slotted holes shall not be used in bolted connections in members subject to fatigue.

14.2   Life
For guidance in determining the number of cycles the life of the building should be assumed to be not less than 50 years unless otherwise stated.

14.3   10 000 Cycles of Load
When a load is expected to be applied not more than 10 000 times during the life of the structure, no special considerations beyond those in Clause 14.1.2 need apply.

14.4   Over 10 000 Cycles of Load
When a load is expected to be applied more than 10 000 times in the life of the structure, the loaded members, connections, bolts, and welds shall be proportioned so that the probability of fatigue failure is acceptably small. In such cases the design should be based on the best available information as to the fatigue characteristics of the materials and components to be used. In the absence of more specific information, Clause 14.5 provides guidance in proportioning members and parts. Fatigue resistance shall be provided only for those loads considered to be repetitive and hence contributing to fatigue. Often the magnitude of a repeated load is less than the maximum static load which the member or part would be designed to sustain.

14.5   Allowable Range of Stress in Fatigue
When this Clause is used as the basis for design, the members, connections, bolts and welds shall be proportioned so that the computed range of stress does not exceed the allowable range of stress F_{sr} given in Table 6(a) for the appropriate type and location of material shown in Table 6(b). The range of stress is defined as the algebraic difference between the maximum stress and the minimum stress. Tension stress is considered to have the opposite albegraic sign from compression stress. Members subject to a range of stress involving only compression need not be designed for fatigue. The information in Tables 6(a) and 6(b) is shown diagramatically in Appendix K.

Table 6(a)
Allowable Range of Stress in Fatigue

Category (see Table 6(b))	F_{sr} (MPa)			
	For 100 000 Cycles	For 500 000 Cycles	For 2 000 000 Cycles	Over 2 000 000 Cycles
A	415	250	165	165
B	310	190	125	110
C	220	130	90	70*
D	185	110	70	48
E	145	85	55	32
F	95	55	36	18
W	115	85	65	48

Except for transverse stiffener welds on girder webs or flanges, where 83 MPa should be used.

Table 6(b)
Description of Design Conditions for Various Joint Classifications

General Condition	Situation	Stress Category (see Table (a))	Illustrative Example No. (see Figure K2)
Plain Material	Base metal with rolled or cleaned surfaces. Flame cut edges with a surface roughness not exceeding 1000 (25 μm) as defined by CSA Standard B95.	A	1, 2
Built-Up Members	Base metal and weld metal in members without attachments, built-up of plates or shapes connected by continuous complete or partial penetration groove welds or by continuous fillet welds, parallel to the direction of applied stress.	B	3, 4, 5, 7
	Calculated flexural stress at toe of transverse stiffener welds on girder webs or flanges.	C	6
	Base metal at end of partial length welded cover plates having square or tapered ends, with or without welds across the ends		
	Flange thickness $\leq$20 mm	E	7
	Flange thickness >20 mm	F	7
Complete Joint Penetration Grooves	Base metal and weld metal at complete penetration groove welded splices of rolled and welded sections having similar profiles when welds are ground flush and weld soundness established by non-destructive examination.	B	8, 9, 13

(Continued)

Table 6(b) (Continued)
Description of Design Conditions for Various Joint Classifications

General Condition	Situation	Stress Category (see Table 6(a))	Illustrative Example No. (see Figure K2)
Complete Joint Penetration Grooves	Base metal and weld metal in or adjacent to complete penetration groove welded splices at transitions in width or thickness, with welds ground to provide slopes no steeper than 1 to 2½, with grinding in the direction of applied stress, and weld soundness established by non-destructive examination.	B	10, 11
	Base metal and weld metal in or adjacent to complete penetration groove welded splices, involving equal widths or thicknesses of material, or both, or involving transitions having slopes no greater than 1 to 2½ when reinforcement is not removed and weld soundness is established by non-destructive examination.	C	8, 9, 10, 11
	Base metal at details attached by groove welds subjected to transverse or longitudinal loading regardless of detail length, or both, except as modified in (e) and *asterisked footnote.		
	(a) When provided with transition radius less than 50 mm;	E	13
	(b) When provided with transition radius less than 150 mm but not less than 50 mm and weld end ground smooth;	D	13
	(c) When provided with transition radius less than 600 mm but not less than 150 mm and weld ends ground smooth;	C	13
	(d) When provided with transition radius equal to or greater than 600 mm with welds and weld ends ground smooth;	B	13
	(e) Base metal at details attached by groove welds subject to longitudinal loading only when the detail length, L, parallel to the line of stress is between 50 mm and 12 times the plate thickness, but less than 100 mm, and the transition radius R is less than 50 mm.	D	12, 13
Fillet Welded Connections	Base metal at intermittent fillet welds	E	6, 14, 15, 16
	Base metal adjacent to fillet welded attachments with length L in direction of stress less than 50 mm and stud-type shear connectors.	C	

(Continued)

Table 6(b) (Continued)
Description of Design Conditions for Various Joint Classifications

General Condition	Situation	Stress Category (see Table (a))	Illustrative Example No. (see Figure K2)
Fillet Welded Connections	Base metal at details attached by fillet welds subjected to transverse or longitudinal loading, or both, regardless of length (shear stress on the throat of fillet welds governed by stress category W) except as modified in (e) and *asterisked footnote.		
	(a) When provided with transition radius less than 50 mm;	E	13
	(b) When provided with transition radius less than 150 mm but not less than 50 mm and weld ends ground smooth;	D	13
	(c) When provided with transition radius less than 600 mm but not less than 150 mm and weld ends ground smooth;	C	13
	(d) When provided with transition radius equal to or greater than 600 mm and weld ends ground smooth;	B	13
	(e) Base metal at details attached by fillet welds with detail length L in direction of stress between 50 mm and 12 times the plate thickness but less than 100 mm and the transition radius is less than 50 mm.	D	13, 14, 15
Fillet Welds	Shear stress on throat of fillet welds.	W	8a
Mechanically Fastened Connections	Base metal at gross section of high-strength bolted slip-resistant connections, except axially loaded joints which induce out-of-plane bending in connected material.	B	17
	Base metal at net section of high-strength bolted bearing-type connections and other mechanically fastened joints.	B	17

*For connections to the **flange**, subjected to **transverse loading**, the condition of the welded joint (relative thicknesses of the parts joined and whether or not reinforcing is removed) may require the use of a lower stress category than that permitted by the size of the transition radius used. See Example 13 in Figure K2 of Appendix K for details. For connections to the **web**, and unequal thickness flange connections subjected to **transverse loading**, Category E must be used regardless of transition radius used (see Example 13 of Appendix K, Figure K2).

15.   **Beams and Girders**

15.1   **Proportioning**
Beams and girders consisting of rolled shapes (with or without cover plates), hollow structural sections, or fabricated sections shall be proportioned on the basis of the properties of the gross section or the modified gross section as noted below. No deduction shall be made for fastener holes in webs or flanges unless the reduction of flange area by such holes exceeds 15 per cent of the gross flange area, in which case the excess shall be deducted. The effect of openings other than holes for fasteners shall be considered in accordance with Clause 15.10.

15.2   **Rotational Restraint at Points of Support**
Beams and girders shall be restrained against rotation about their longitudinal axes at points of support.

15.3   **Reduced Moment Resistance of Girders With Thin Webs**
When the web slenderness ratio, h/w, exceeds $1810\sqrt{M_f/\phi S}$ the flange must meet the width-thickness ratios of Class 3 sections of Clause 11 and the factored moment resistance of the beam or girder, M'_r, shall be determined by:

$$M'_r = M_r\left[1.0 - 0.0005\frac{A_w}{A_f}\left(\frac{h}{w} - 1810/\sqrt{M_r/\phi S}\right)\right]$$

where
M_r = factored moment resistance determined by Clause 13.5 or 13.6 but not to exceed ϕM_y

15.4   **Flanges**

15.4.1   Flanges of welded girders preferably shall consist of a single plate or a series of plates joined end-to-end by complete penetration groove welds.

15.4.2   Flanges of bolted girders shall be proportioned so that the total cross-sectional area of cover plates does not exceed 70 per cent of the total flange area.

15.4.3   Fasteners or welds connecting flanges to webs shall be proportioned to resist horizontal shear forces due to bending combined with any loads which are transmitted from the flange to the web other than by direct bearing. Spacing of fasteners or intermittent welds in general shall be in proportion to the intensity of the shear force and shall not exceed the maximum for compression or tension members as applicable, in accordance with Clause 18.

15.4.4   Partial length flange cover plates shall be extended beyond the theoretical cut-off point and the extended portion shall be connected with sufficient fasteners or welds to develop a force in the cover plate at the theoretical cut-off point not less than:

$$P = \frac{AM_{fc}y}{I_g}$$

where
P   = required force to be developed in cover plate

A   = area of cover plate

M_{fc} = moment due to factored loads at point of theoretical cut-off

y   = distance from centroid of cover plate to neutral axis of cover-plated section

I_g = moment of inertia of cover-plated section

Additionally, for welded cover plates, the welds connecting the cover plate termination to the beam or girder shall be designed to develop the force P defined above within a length a' measured from the actual end of the cover plate, determined as follows:

(a) a' = the width of cover plate when there is a continuous weld equal to or larger than three-fourths of the cover plate thickness across the end of the plate and along both edges in the length a'

(b) a' = 1.5 times the width of cover plate when there is a continuous weld smaller than three-fourths of the cover plate thickness across the end of the plate and along both edges in the length a'

(c) a' = 2 times the width of cover plate when there is no weld across the end of the plate but continuous welds along both edges in the length a'

15.5   Bearing Stiffeners

15.5.1   Pairs of bearing stiffeners on the webs of single-web beams and girders shall be required at points of concentrated loads and reactions wherever the bearing resistance on the web is exceeded (see Clause 15.8). Bearing stiffeners shall be required also at unframed ends of single-web girders having web slenderness ratios greater than $1100/\sqrt{F_y}$. Box girders may employ diaphragms designed to act as bearing stiffeners.

15.5.2   Bearing stiffeners shall bear against the flange or flanges through which they receive their loads, and shall extend approximately to the end of the flange plates or flange angles. They shall be designed as columns in accordance with Clause 13.3, assuming the column section to comprise the pair of stiffeners and a centrally located strip of the web equal to not more than 25 times its thickness at interior stiffeners, or a strip equal to not more than 12 times its thickness when the stiffeners are located at the end of the web. The effective column length, KL, shall be taken as not less than three-fourths of the length of the stiffeners in computing the ratio KL/r. Only that portion of the stiffeners outside of the angle fillet or the flange-to-web welds shall be considered effective in bearing. Angle bearing stiffeners shall not be crimped. Bearing stiffeners shall be connected to the web so as to develop the full force required to be carried by the stiffener into the web or vice versa.

15.6   Intermediate Transverse Stiffeners

15.6.1   Intermediate transverse stiffeners when used shall be spaced to suit the shear resistance determined from the formula given in Clause 13.4; except that at girder end panels or at panels containing large openings, the smaller panel dimension, a or h, shall not exceed $1150w/\sqrt{V_f/\phi A_w}$ where V_f is the largest shear in the panel.

15.6.2   The maximum distance between stiffeners, when stiffeners are required, shall not exceed the values shown in Table 7. Closer spacing may be required in accordance with Clause 15.6.1.

Table 7
Maximum Intermediate Transverse Stiffener Spacing

Web Slenderness Ratio (h/w)	Maximum Distance Between Stiffeners (a) in Terms of Clear Web Depth (h)
Up to 150	3h
Over 150	$\dfrac{67\ 500h}{(h/w)^2}$

15.6.3 Intermediate transverse stiffeners may be furnished singly or in pairs. Width-thickness ratios shall conform to Clause 11. The moment of inertia of the stiffener, or pair of stiffeners if so furnished, shall be not less than $(h/50)^4$ mm^4 taken about an axis in the plane of the web. The gross area of intermediate stiffeners, or pairs of stiffeners if so furnished, shall be given by the expression

$$A_s \geq \frac{aw}{2}\left[1 - \frac{a/h}{\sqrt{1 + (a/h)^2}}\right]CYD$$

where

a = distance centre-to-centre of adjacent stiffeners (i.e., panel length)

w = web thickness

h = web depth

C = $1 - \dfrac{310\ 000k_v}{F_y(h/w)^2}$ but not less than 0.10

Y = ratio of specified minimum yield point of web steel to specified minimum yield point of stiffener steel

D = stiffener factor

= 1.0 for stiffeners furnished in pairs

= 1.8 for single angle stiffeners

= 2.4 for single plate stiffeners

k_v = shear buckling coefficient (see Clause 13.4.1)

F_y = specified minimum yield point of web steel

When the greatest shear, V_f, in an adjacent panel is less than that permitted by Clause 13.4.1, this gross area requirement may be reduced in like proportion by multiplying by the ratio V_f/V_r.

15.6.4 Intermediate transverse stiffeners shall be connected to the web for a shear transfer per pair of stiffeners (or per single stiffener when so furnished), in newtons per millimetre of web depth (h), not less than $1 \times 10^{-4}h\ F_y^{3/2}$; except that when the largest computed shear V_f in the adjacent panels is less than V_r computed by Clause 13.4.1 this shear transfer may be reduced in the same proportion. However the total shear transfer shall in no case be less than the value of any concentrated load or reaction required to be transmitted to the web through the stiffener. Fasteners connecting intermediate transverse stiffeners to the web shall be spaced not more than 300 mm on centre. If intermittent fillet welds are used, the clear distance between welds shall not exceed 16 times the web thickness or 4 times the weld length.

15.6.5 When intermediate stiffeners are used on only one side of the web, the stiffeners shall be attached to the compression flange. Intermediate stiffeners used in pairs shall have at least a snug fit against the compression flange. When stiffeners are cut short of the tension flange the distance cut short shall be equal to or greater than 4 times but not greater than 6 times the girder web thickness. Stiffeners preferably shall be clipped to clear girder flange-to-web welds.

15.7 **Lateral Forces**
The flanges of beams and girders supporting cranes or other moving loads shall be proportioned to resist any lateral forces produced by such loads.

15.8 **Web Crippling**
Bearing stiffeners shall be provided where the factored concentrated load or reactions exceed the factored compressive resistances of webs of rolled beams and welded plate girders at the web toe of the flange-to-web fillets computed as follows:

(a) For interior loads
$B_r = 1.25\phi w \, (N + 2k)F_y$
(b) For end reactions
$B_r = 1.25\phi w \, (N + k)F_y$

where
w = web thickness
N = length of bearing (N shall be not less than k for end reactions)
k = distance from outer face of flange to web toe of flange-to-web fillet

15.9 **Stability of Thin Webs**
The sum of all loads on the compression edge of the web plate resulting from concentrated and distributed loads bearing directly, or through a flange plate, and not supported by bearing stiffeners, shall not exceed the factored resistances as calculated below:

(a) When the flange is restrained against rotation

$$B_r = \phi \, \frac{115\,000}{(h/w)^2} \left[5.5 + \frac{4}{(a/h)^2} \right] A$$

(b) When the flange is not restrained against rotation

$$B_r = \phi \, \frac{115\,000}{(h/w)^2} \left[2 + \frac{4}{(a/h)^2} \right] A$$

where for distributed loads A is equal to the panel length times the web thickness and for concentrated loads and loads distributed over partial length of a panel, A equals the web thickness times the lesser panel dimension, a or h.

15.10 **Openings**

15.10.1 Except as provided in Clause 15.1, the effect of all openings in beams and girders shall be considered in the design. At all points where the factored shear or moments at the net section would exceed the capacity of the member at that point adequate reinforcement shall be added to the member to provide the required strength and stability.

15.10.2   Unreinforced circular openings may be located in the web of unstiffened prismatic compact beams or girders without considering net section properties provided that:

(a) The specified design load for the member is uniformly distributed;

(b) The section has an axis of symmetry in the plane of bending;

(c) The openings are located within the middle third of the depth and the middle half of the span of the member;

(d) The spacing between the centres of any two adjacent openings, measured parallel to the longitudinal axis of the member, is a minimum of 2.5 times the diameter of the larger opening;

(c) The factored maximum shear at the support does not exceed 50 per cent of the factored shear resistance of the section.

15.10.3   If the forces at openings are determined by an elastic analysis, the procedure adopted shall be in accordance with published, recognized principles acceptable to the authority having jurisdiction. The forces determined by such elastic analysis shall not exceed the factored resistances, given in Clause 13 and if applicable, Clause 14.

15.10.4   The strength and stability of the member in the vicinity of openings may be determined on the basis of assumed locations of plastic hinges, such that the resulting force distributions satisfy equilibrium, provided that the analysis is carried out in accordance with Clauses 8.5(a), (b), and (f). However, for I-type members the width-thickness ratio of the flanges may meet the requirements of Class 2 sections, provided the webs meet the width-thickness limit of Class 1 sections.

15.11   **Torsion**

15.11.1   Beams and girders subjected to torsion shall have sufficient strength and rigidity to resist the torsional moment and forces in addition to other moment or forces. The connections and bracing of such members shall be adequate to transfer the reactions to the supports.

15.11.2   Members subjected to torsional deformations required to maintain compatability of the structure need not be designed to resist the associated torsional moments provided that the structure satisfies the requirements of equilibrium.

15.11.3   For all members subjected to loads causing torsion, the torsional deformations under specified loads shall be limited in accordance with the requirements of Clause 6.2.1.1.

16.   **Open-Web Steel Joists**

16.1   **Scope**
Clause 16 provides requirements for the design, manufacture, transport and erection of open-web steel joists used in construction of buildings. Joists intended to act compositely with the deck shall be designed using the requirements of Clause 17 in conjunction with the requirements of this Clause. This Clause shall not be used for the design of joists not having an axis of symmetry in the plane of the joist.

16.2   Definitions
The following definitions apply to Clause 16:

Open-web joists or joists means simply supported steel trusses of relatively low mass with parallel or slightly pitched chords and triangulated web systems proportioned to span between masonry walls, or structural supporting members, or both, and provide direct support for floor or roof deck.

Open-web steel joists are flexural members whose design is governed by the loading given in Clause 16.5.1. This definition does not include primary trusses supporting joists, other secondary members, and special joists.

Special open-web steel joists or special joists means:

(a) Joists subjected to the loads stipulated in Clause 16.5.2; and

(b) Cantilever joists, continuous joists and joists having special support conditions; and

(c) Joists having other special requirements.

In general open web steel joists and special open-web steel joists are manufactured on a production-line basis employing jigs, certain details of the members being standardized by the individual manufacturer.

Deck or decking means the structural floor or roof element spanning between adjacent joists and directly supported thereby. The terms deck and decking include cast-in-place or precast concrete slabs, profiled metal deck, wood plank or plywood and other relatively rigid elements suitable for floor or roof construction;

Tie joist means a joist which has at least one end connected to a column to facilitate erection and is designed to resist gravity loads only unless otherwise specified;

Span of an open-web steel joists means the distance centre-to-centre of joists bearings.

16.3   Materials
Steel for joists shall be of a structural quality, suitable for welding, meeting the requirements of Clause 5.1.1. Yield levels reported on mill test certificates or determined according to Clause 8.3 of CSA Standard S136, Cold Formed Steel Structural Members, shall not be used as the basis for design.

16.4   Drawings

16.4.1   Building Design Drawings
The building design drawings prepared by the building designer shall show:

(a) The uniformly distributed specified live and dead gravity loads, the unbalanced loading condition and the concentrated load conditions given in Clause 16.5.1 or 16.5.2 and any special loading conditions such as non-uniform snow loads, horizontal loads, end moments, net uplift, and allowances for mechanical equipment;

(b) Maximum joists spacing and where necessary camber, maximum joist depth and shoe depth;

(c) Where joists are not supported on steel members, maximum bearing pressures or sizes of bearing plates;

(d) Anchorage requirements in excess of the requirements of Clause 16.5.13;

(e) Bracing as may be required by Clause 16.8.1.

Note: *It is recommended that the building design drawings include a note warning that attachments for mechanical, electrical and other services shall be made by using approved clamping devices or u-bolt type connectors and that no drilling or cutting shall be done unless approved by the building designer.*

16.4.2 Joist Design Drawings

Joist design drawings prepared by the joist manufacturer shall show, at least, specified loading, factored member loads, material specification, member sizes, dimensions, spacers, welds, shoes, anchorages, bearings, field splices, bridging locations and camber.

16.5 Design

16.5.1 Loading for Open-Web Steel Joists

Unless otherwise specified by the building designer (in accordance with Clause 16.5.2), the factored moment and shear resistances of an open-web steel joist at every section shall be not less than the moment and shear due to the following factored load conditions, considered separately:

(a) A uniformly distributed load equal to the total dead and live load;

(b) An unbalanced load with 100 per cent of the total dead and live load on any continuous portion of the joist and 25 per cent of total dead and live loads on the remainder to produce the most critical effect on any component;

(c) A concentrated factored load applied at any panel point of 13.5 kN for floor joists for office or similar occupancy or 2 kN for roof joists.

16.5.2 Loading for Special Open-Web Steel Joists

The factored moment and shear resistance of special open-web steel joists at every section shall be not less than the moment and shear due to the loading conditions specified by the building designer in Clause 16.4.1(a) nor due to the factored dead load plus the following factored live load conditions (a), (b), or (c) considered separately:

(a) For floor joists, an unbalanced live load applied on any continuous portion of the joist to produce the most critical effect on any component;

(b) For roof joists, an unbalanced loading condition with 100 per cent of the snow load plus other live loads applied on any continuous portion of the joist and 50 per cent of the snow load on the remainder of the joist to produce the most critical effect on any component;

(c) The appropriate factored concentrated load from Table 4.1.6.B of the National Building Code of Canada; applied at any one panel point to produce the most critical effect on any component.

16.5.3 Design Assumptions

Open-web steel joists shall be designed for loads acting in the plane of the joist applied to the compression chord which is assumed to be prevented from lateral buckling by the deck.

For the purpose of determining axial forces in all members the loads may be replaced by statically equivalent loads applied at the panel points.

16.5.4 **Verification of Joist Manufacturer's Design**
When the adequacy of the design of a joist cannot be readily demonstrated by a rational analysis based on accepted theory and engineering practice, the joist manufacturer may elect to verify the design by test. The test shall be carried out to the satisfaction of the building designer. The test loading shall be 1.10/0.9 times the factored loads used in the design.

16.5.5 **Member and Connection Resistance**
Member and connection resistance shall be calculated in accordance with the requirements of Clause 13 except as otherwise specified in Clause 16.

16.5.6 **Width-Thickness Ratios**

16.5.6.1 **General**
Width-thickness ratios of compression elements of hot formed sections shall be governed by Clause 11. Width thickness ratios of compression elements of cold formed sections shall be governed by CSA Standard S136, Cold Formed Steel Structural Members.

16.5.6.2 **Compression Elements Supported Along One Edge**
For purposes of determining the appropriate width-thickness ratio, any stiffening effect of the deck or the joist web shall be neglected.

16.5.7 **Tension Chord**
The tension chord shall be continuous and may be designed as an axially loaded tension member unless subject to eccentricities in excess of those permitted under Clause 16.5.11.4 or to applied load between panel points. The governing radius of gyration of the tension chord or any component thereof shall be not less than 1/240 of the corresponding unsupported length. For joists with the web in the y-plane the unsupported length of chord for computing L_x/r_x shall be taken as the panel length centre-to-centre of panel points and the unsupported length of chord for computing L_y/r_y shall be taken as the distance between bridging lines connected to the tension chord. Joist shoes, when anchored, may be assumed to be equivalent to bridging lines. When net uplift is specified, the tension chord shall be designed for the resulting load reversal. Where shown on the drawings, bottom chords of joists shall be designed for end moments. Moments due to concentrated loads shall be included in the design.

16.5.8 **Compression Chord**

16.5.8.1 The compression chord shall be continuous and may be designed for axial compressive force alone when the panel length does not exceed 610 mm, when concentrated loads are not applied between the panel points, and when not subjected to eccentricities in excess of those permitted under Clause 16.5.11.4. When the panel length exceeds 610 mm the compression chord shall be designed as a continuous member subject to combined axial and bending forces.

16.5.8.2 The slenderness ratio (KL/r) of the compression chord, or of its components, shall not exceed 90 for interior panels nor 120 for end panels where the governing (KL/r) shall be the maximum value determined by the following:

(a) For x-x (horizontal) axis, L_x shall be the distance centre-to-centre of panel points. K = 0.9;

(b) For y-y (vertical) axis, L_y shall be the distance centre-to-centre of the attachments of the deck. The spacing of attachments shall be not more than the design slenderness ratio of the top chord times the radius of gyration of the top chord about its vertical axis nor more than 1000 mm. K = 1.0;

(c) For z-z (skew) axis of individual components, L_z shall be the distance centre-to-centre of panel points or spacers, or both. Decking shall not be considered to fulfil the function of batten plates or spacers for top chords consisting of two separated components. K = 0.9.

where
r = the appropriate radius of gyration

16.5.8.3   Compression chords of joists in panel lengths exceeding 610 mm shall be proportioned such that:

$$\frac{C_f}{C_r} + \frac{M_f}{M_r} \leq 1.0$$

where
M_r is given in Clause 13.5 and C_r is given in Clause 13.3.

At the panel point C_r may be taken as $\phi A F_y$ and Clause 13.5(a) may be used to determine M_r provided that the chord meets the requirements of a Class 2 section and $M_f/M_p < 0.25$.

The chord shall be assumed to be pinned at the joist supports.

16.5.9   **Webs**

16.5.9.1   Webs shall be designed in accordance with the requirements of Clause 13 to resist the shear at any point due to the factored loads given in Clause 16.5.1 or 16.5.2. Particular attention shall be paid to possible reversals of shear.

16.5.9.2   The length of a web member shall be taken as the distance between the intersections of the axes of the web and the chords. For buckling in the plane of the web the effective length factor shall be taken as 0.9 if the web consists of individual members. For all other cases the effective length factor shall be taken as 1.0.

16.4.9.3   **Web Members in Tension**
The slenderness ratio of a web member in tension need not be limited.

16.5.9.4   **Web Members in Compression**
The slenderness ratio of a web member in compression shall not exceed 200.

16.5.10   **Spacers and Battens**
Compression members, consisting of two or more sections, shall be interconnected so that the slenderness ratio of each section computed using its least radius of gyration is less than or equal to the design slenderness ratio of the built-up member. Spacers or battens shall be an integral part of the joist.

16.5.11   **Connections and Splices**

16.5.11.1   Component members of joists shall be connected by welding, bolting or other approved means.

16.5.11.2   Connections and splices shall develop the factored loads required by this Standard without exceeding the factored member resistances given in

Clause 16. Butt-welded splices shall develop the factored tensile resistance, T_r of the member.

16.5.11.3 Splices may occur at any point in chord or web members.

15.5.11.4 Eccentricity Limits

Members connected at a joint preferably shall have their gravity axes meet at a point. Where this is impractical and eccentricities are introduced such eccentricities may be neglected if they do not exceed:

(a) **For continuous web members** — The greater of the two distances measured from the neutral axis of the chord member to the extreme fibres of the chord member;

(b) **For non-continuous web members** — The distance measured from the neutral axis to the back (outside face) of the chord member.

When the eccentricity exceeds these limits, provision shall be made for the effects of total eccentricity.

Eccentricities assumed in design shall be those at maximum fabrication tolerances which shall be stated on the shop drawings.

16.5.12 Bearings

16.5.12.1 Bearings at ends of joists shall be proportioned so that the factored bearing resistance of the supporting material is not exceeded.

16.5.12.2 Where a joist bears, with or without a bearing plate on solid masonry or concrete support, the end of the bearing shall extend at least 90 mm beyond the face of support.

16.5.12.3 Where a joist bears on a member of the structural steel frame the end of the bearing shall extend at least 65 mm beyond the face of the support except that when the available bearing area is restricted, this distance may be reduced provided that the bearing is adequately anchored to the support and the factored bearing resistance is not exceeded.

16.5.12.4 The bearing detail and the end panels of the joist shall be proportioned to include the effect of the eccentricity between the centre of bearing and the intersection of the axes of the chord and the end diagonal.

16.5.13 Anchorage

16.5.13.1 Joist ends shall be properly anchored to withstand the effect of factored loads:

(a) In no case shall the anchorage to masonry be less than:
(i) For floor joists, a 10 mm diameter rod at least 300 mm long embedded horizontally;

(ii) For roof joists, a 20 mm diameter anchor bolt 300 mm long embedded vertically with a 50 mm—90° hook;

(b) The anchorage to steel shall be a connection capable of withstanding a horizontal load not less than 10 per cent of the end reaction of the joist but not less than one 20 mm diameter bolt or a pair of fillet welds satisfying the minimum size and length requirements of CSA Standard W59, Welded Steel Construction (Metal-Arc Welding).

16.5.13.2 Tie Joists

Tie joists may have their top and bottom chords connected to a column. Unless otherwise specified, tie joists shall have top and bottom chord connections each at least equivalent to those required by Clause 16.5.13.1. Either top or bottom connection shall be by means of a mechanical fastener.

16.5.13.3 Frame Action

Where joists are used as a part of a frame, the joist to column connection shall be designed to carry the moments and forces due to the factored loads (see Clause 7.2).

16.5.14 Deflection

16.5.14.1 General

Steel joists shall be proportioned so that deflection due to specified loads is within acceptable limits for the nature of the materials to be supported and the intended use and occupancy. Such deflection limits shall be as given in Clause 6.2 unless otherwise specified by the building designer.

16.5.14.2 Deflection Calculations

The deflection may be established by test or may be computed assuming a moment of inertia equal to the gross moment of inertia of the chords about the centroidal axis of the joist and multiplying the calculated deflection derived on this basis by 1.10.

16.5.15 Camber

Unless otherwise specified by the building designer the nominal camber in millimetres shall be equal to 0.07 times the square of the span expressed in metres. For tolerances see Clause 16.10.9.

16.5.16 Vibration

The building designer shall give special consideration to floor systems where unacceptable vibration may occur. The joist manufacturer when requested shall supply joist properties and details to the building designer. (See Appendix G.)

16.5.17 Welding

16.5.17.1 Arc Welding

Arc welding design and practice shall conform to CSA Standard W59, Welded Steel Construction (Metal-Arc Welding).

16.5.17.2 Resistance Welding

Resistance welding design and practice shall conform to the applicable requirements of CSA Standard W55.2, Resistance Welding Practice.

16.5.17.3 Fabricator and Erector Qualification

Fabricators and erectors of welded construction covered by this Standard shall be certified by the Canadian Welding Bureau in Division 1 or 2 to the requirements of CSA Standard W47.1, Certification of Companies for Fusion Welding of Steel Structures, or CSA Standard W55.3, Resistance Welding Qualification Code for Fabricators of Structural Members Used in Buildings, or both, as applicable.

16.5.17.4 The factored resistances of welds shall be equal to those given in Table 5.

16.5.17.5 Field Welding

When field welding joists to supporting members, surfaces to be welded shall be free of coatings which are detrimental to achieve an adequate weldment.

16.5.17.6 Removal of Flux and Slag

Flux and slag shall be removed from all welds.

16.6 Stability During Construction

Means shall be provided to support joist chords against lateral movement and to hold the joist in the vertical or specified plane during construction.

16.7 Bridging

16.7.1 General

Bridging transverse to the span of joists may be used to meet the requirements of Clause 16.6 and also to meet the slenderness ratio requirements for chords. Bridging is not to be considered "bracing" as defined under Clause 19.3.1.

16.7.2 Installation

All bridging and bridging anchors shall be completely installed before any construction loads are placed on the joists except for the weight of the workmen necessary to install the bridging.

16.7.3 Types

Unless otherwise specified or approved by the building designer the joist manufacturer shall supply bridging which may be either the diagonal or horizontal type.

16.7.4 Diagonal Bridging

Diagonal bridging consisting of crossed members running from top chord to bottom chord of adjacent joists shall have a slenderness ratio (L/r) of not more than 200 where "L" is the length of the diagonal bridging member, or one-half this length when crossed members are connected at their point of intersection, and "r" is the least radius of gyration. All diagonal bridging shall be connected adequately to the joists by bolts or welds.

16.7.5 Horizontal Bridging

A line of horizontal bridging shall consist of a continuous member attached to either the top chord or the bottom chord. Horizontal bridging members shall have a slenderness ratio of not more than 300.

16.7.6 Attachment of Bridging

Attachment of diagonal and horizontal bridging to joist chords shall be by welding or mechanical means capable of resisting an axial load of at least 3 kN in the attached bridging member. These welds should meet the minimum length requirements stipulated in CSA Standard W59, Welded Steel Construction (Metal-Arc Welding).

16.7.7 Anchorage of Bridging

Each line of bridging shall be adequately anchored at each end to sturdy walls or to main components of the structural frame, if practicable. If not practicable, diagonal and horizontal bridging shall be provided in combination between adjacent joists near the ends of bridging lines.

The ends of joists designed to bear on their bottom chords shall be held adequately in position by attachments to the walls or to the structural frame or by lines of bridging located at the ends except where such ends are built into masonry or concrete walls.

16.7.8   Bridging Systems
Bridging systems, including sizes of bridging members, and all necessary details, shall be shown on the erection drawings. If a specific bridging system is required by the design, the design drawings shall show all information necessary for the preparation of shop and erection drawings.

16.7.9   Spacing of Bridging
Diagonal and horizontal bridging, whichever is furnished, shall be spaced so that the unsupported length of the chord between bridging lines, or between laterally supported ends of the joist and adjacent bridging lines, does not exceed:

(a) For compression chords, 170r;

(b) For tension chords, 240r;

where
r = the applicable chord radius of gyration about its axis in the plane of the web

Ends of joists anchored to supports may be assumed to be equivalent to bridging lines. If not so anchored before installing deck, the distance from the face of the support to the nearest bridging member in the plane of the bottom chord shall not exceed 120r. In no case shall there be less than one line of horizontal or diagonal bridging attached to each joist spanning 4000 mm or more. If only a single line of bridging is required, it shall be placed at the centre of the joist span. If bridging is not used on joists less than 4000 mm in span, the ends of such joists shall be anchored to the supports so as to prevent overturning of the joist during placement of the deck.

16.8   Decking

16.8.1   Decking to Provide Lateral Support
Decking shall bear directly on the top chord of the joist and shall be sufficiently rigid to provide lateral support to the compression chord of the joist. In special cases where the decking is incapable of furnishing the required lateral support, the compression chord of the joist shall be braced laterally in accordance with the requirements of Clause 19.3.

16.8.2   Attachments of decking considered to provide lateral support shall be capable of staying the top chords laterally. Attachments shall be deemed to fulfil this requirement when the attachments as a whole are adequate to resist a force in the plane of the decking of not less than 5 per cent of the maximum force in the top chord and assumed to be uniformly distributed along the length of the top chord. The spacing of attachments shall be not more than the design slenderness ratio of the top chord times the radius of gyration of the top chord about its vertical axis nor more than 1000 mm.

16.8.3   Diaphragm Action
Where decking is used in combination with joists to form a diaphragm for the purpose of transferring lateral applied loads to vertical bracing systems, special attachment requirements shall be fully specified on the building design drawings.

16.8.4   Cast-in-place slabs used as decking shall have a minimum thickness of

50 mm. Forms for cast-in-place slabs shall not cause lateral displacement of the top chords of joists during installation of the forms or the placing of the concrete. Non-removable forms shall be positively attached to top chords by means of clips, ties, wedges, fasteners, or other suitable means at intervals not exceeding 1000 mm; however, there shall be at least two attachments in the width of each form at each joist. Forms and their method of attachment shall be such that the cast-in-place slab, after hardening, is capable of furnishing lateral support to the joist chords.

16.9 **Shop Painting**

Joists shall have one shop coat of protective paint of a type standard with the manufacturer unless otherwise specified.

16.10 **Manufacturing Tolerances**

16.10.1 The tolerance on the specified depth of the manufactured joist shall be ± 7 mm.

16.10.2 The maximum deviation from the design location of a panel point measured along the length of a chord shall be 13 mm. In joists in which an individual end diagonal is attached to the bottom chord or in which the end diagonal is a continuation of an upturned bottom chord the gravity axes of the members in such a joint should meet at a point. (See Clause 16.5.11.4.)

16.10.3 The maximum deviation from the design location of a panel point measured perpendicular to the longitudinal axis of the chord and in the plane of the joist shall be 7 mm.

16.10.4 The connections of web members to chords shall not deviate laterally more than 3 mm from that assumed in the design.

16.10.5 The maximum sweep of a joist or any portion of the length of the joist upon completion of manufacture shall be 1/500 of the length on which the sweep is measured.

16.10.6 The maximum tilt of bearing shoes shall be 1 in 50 measured from a plane perpendicular to the plane of the web and parallel to the longitudinal axis of the joist.

16.10.7 The tolerance on the specified shoe depth shall be ± 3 mm.

16.10.8 The tolerance on the specified length of the joint shall be ± 7 mm. The connection holes in a joist shall not vary from the detailed location by more than 2 mm for members 10 000 mm or less in length or by more than 3 mm for members over 10 000 mm in length.

16.10.9 The tolerance on the nominal or specified camber shall be

$$\pm \left(6 \text{ mm} + \frac{\text{Span, in mm}}{4\ 000} \right) \text{mm}.$$

The resulting actual minimum camber in a joist to be +3 mm except that the maximum range in camber for joists of the same span shall be limited to 20 mm.

16.11 Inspection and Quality Control

16.11.1 Inspection
Material and workmanship at all times shall be subject to inspection by qualified inspectors representing the authority having jurisdiction. Random in-process inspection shall be carried out by the manufacturer and all joists shall be thoroughly inspected by the manufacturer before shipping.

16.11.2 Identification and Control of Steel
Steel used in the manufacture of joists shall at all times, in the manufacturers' plant be marked to identify its specification (and grade, where applicable). This shall be done by suitable markings or by recognized colour coding or by any system devised by the manufacturer that will ensure to the satisfaction of the authority having jurisdiction that the correct material is being used.

16.11.3 Quality Control
Upon request of the authority having jurisdiction the manufacturer shall provide evidence of having suitable quality control measures to ensure that the joists meet all requirements specified. When testing is part of the manufacturer's normal quality control program, the loading criteria shall be 1.0/0.9 times the factored loads for the materials used in the joists.

For resistance welding the quality control procedures outlined in CSA Standard W55.3, Resistance Welding Qualification Code for Fabricators of Structural Members Used in Buildings, shall be met. For arc-welding quality control, the requirements of CSA Standard W59, Welded Steel Construction (Metal-Arc Welding), shall be met.

16.12 Handling and Erection

16.12.1 General
Care shall be exercised to avoid damage during strapping, transport, unloading, site storage and piling, and erection. Dropping of joists shall not be permitted. Special precautions shall be taken when erecting long, slender joists and preferably hoisting cables shall not be released until the member is stayed laterally by at least one line of bridging. Joists shall have all bridging attached and be permanently fastened into place before the application of any loads. Heavy construction loads shall be adequately distributed so as not to exceed the capacity of any joist. Field welding shall not cause damage to joists, bridging, deck and supporting steel members.

16.12.2 Erection Tolerances

16.12.2.1 The maximum sweep of a joist or a portion of the length of a joist upon completion of erection shall not exceed the requirements of Clause 16.10.5, and shall be in accordance with the general requirements of Clause 28.

16.12.2.2 All members shall be free from twists, sharp kinks and bends.

16.12.2.3 Location of Joist
When joists are finally fastened in position in the field, the maximum deviation from the location shown on the erection drawings shall be 15 mm.

16.12.2.4 The deviation, normal to the specified plane of the web of a joist, shall not exceed 1/50 of the depth of the joist.

17. Composite Beams and Columns

17.1 Application

17.1.1 The provisions of Clause 17 apply to:

(a) Composite beams consisting of steel sections or joists interconnected with either a reinforced concrete slab or a cellular steel deck with concrete cover slab;

(b) Composite columns consisting of steel hollow structural sections completely filled with concrete.

17.1.2 For any requirement not covered in Clause 17 the design shall conform to the provisions of this Standard.

17.2 Definitions

Cellular steel deck means a load-carrying steel deck formed from zinc-coated sheet steel, consisting of either:

(a) A single fluted element, or

(b) A two element section comprising a fluted element in conjunction with a flat sheet.

The maximum depth of the deck shall be 80 mm and the average width of the minimum flute shall be 50 mm. Cellular steel deck may be of a type intended to act compositely with the cover slab in supporting applied load;

Concrete means Portland cement concrete in accordance with CSA Standard CAN3-A23.1, Concrete Materials and Methods of Concrete Construction:

Slab means a reinforced cast-in-place concrete slab at least 65 mm in effective thickness. The area equal to the design effective width times effective slab thickness shall be free of voids or hollows except for those specifically permitted in the definition of effective slab thickness;

Cover slab means the concrete above the flutes of cellular steel deck. All flutes shall be filled with concrete;

Effective cover slab thickness, t, means the minimum thickness of concrete measured from the top of the cover slab to the top of the cellular steel deck. This thickness shall be not less than 65 mm unless the adequacy of a lesser thickness has been established by appropriate tests;

Effective slab thickness, t, means the overall slab thickness, provided that;

(a) The slab is cast with a flat underside; or

(b) The slab is cast on corrugated steel forms having an amplitude of corrugation not greater than 0.25 times the overall slab thickness; or

(c) The slab is cast on ribbed steel forms whose profile meets the following requirements. The minimum clear distance between ribs (the part of the form profile which projects into the concrete) shall be 125 mm; the maximum rib height shall be 40 mm but not more than 0.4 times the overall slab thickness; the average width of a rib shall not exceed 0.25 times the overall slab thickness nor 0.2 times the minimum clear distance between ribs.

In all other cases, effective slab thickness means the overall slab thickness minus the height of form rib or corrugation;

Steel joist means an open web steel joist suitable for composite design;

Steel section means a steel structural section with a solid web, or webs, suitable for composite design. Web openings are permissible only on condition that their effects are fully investigated and accounted for in the design.

17.3 Composite Beams

17.3.1 General

17.3.1.1 Calculation of deflections shall take into account creep of concrete, increased flexibility resulting from partial shear connection, and the effect, if any, of the fluted profile of cellular steel deck. Where values are not established by test or analysis, computed elastic deflections which neglect the above effects shall be increased by a minimum of 15 per cent for each effect which would apply.

17.3.1.2 The web area of steel sections or web system of steel joists shall be proportioned to carry the total vertical shear V_f.

17.3.1.3 End connections of steel sections or joists shall be proportioned to transmit the total end reaction of the composite beam.

17.3.2 Design Effective Width of Concrete

17.3.2.1 Slabs or cover slabs extending on both sides of the steel section or joist shall be deemed to have a design effective width, b, equal to the least of:

(a) 0.25 times the composite beam span;

(b) 16 times the overall slab thickness, or overall cover slab and cellular steel deck thickness, plus the width of the top flange of the steel section or top chord of the steel joist;

(c) The average distance from the centre of the steel section or joist to the centres of adjacent parallel supports.

17.3.2.2 Slabs or cover slabs extending on one side only of the supporting section or joist shall be deemed to have a design effective width, b, not greater than the width of top flange of the steel section, or top chord of the steel joist, plus the least of:

(a) 0.1 times the composite beam span;

(b) 6 times the overall slab thickness or overall cover slab and cellular steel deck thickness;

(c) 0.5 times the clear distance between the steel section or joist and the adjacent parallel support.

17.3.3 Slab Reinforcement
Slabs shall be adequately reinforced to support all specified loads and to control cracking both parallel and transverse to the composite beam span. Reinforcement parallel to the span of the beam in regions of negative bending moment of the composite beam shall be anchored by embedment in concrete which is in compression. The reinforcement of slabs which are to be continuous over the end support of steel sections or joists fitted with flexible end connections shall be given special attention.

The possibility of longitudinal cracking due to composite action, directly over the steel section or joist, shall be controlled by the provision of additional transverse reinforcement or other effective means unless it is known from experience that cracking due to composite action is unlikely. Such additional reinforcement shall be placed in the lower part of the slab and anchored so as to develop the yield strength of the reinforcement. The area of such reinforcement shall be not less than 0.005 times the concrete area in the longitudinal direction of the beam and shall be uniformly spaced along the composite beam span.

17.3.4 Composite Action With Cellular Steel Deck

Cover slabs intended to act compositely with cellular steel deck shall have reinforcement transverse to the span of the composite beam as required. Reinforcement shall be not less than that required by the specified fire resistance design of the assembly.

17.3.5 Interconnection

17.3.5.1 Except as permitted by Clauses 17.3.5.2 and 17.3.5.4 interconnection between steel sections or joists and slabs or cellular steel deck with cover slabs shall be attained by the use of shear connectors as prescribed in Clause 17.3.6.

17.3.5.2 Unpainted steel sections or joists supporting slabs and totally encased in concrete do not require interconnection by means of shear connectors provided that:

(a) A minimum of 50 mm of concrete covers all portions of the steel section or joist, except as noted in Item (c);

(b) The cover in Item (a) is reinforced to prevent spalling; and

(c) The top of the steel section or joist is at least 40 mm below the top and 50 mm above the bottom of the slab.

17.3.5.3 Studs may be welded through a maximum of two steel sheets, each not more than 1.7 mm in thickness, including zinc coating to a maximum of G90 (ASTM A525, Steel Sheet, Zinc-Coated (Galvanized) by the Hot-Dip process, General Requirements). Otherwise holes through the sheet are required for placing studs. The welding of studs shall meet the requirements of CSA Standard W59, Welded Steel Construction (Metal-Arc Welding).

17.3.5.4 Other methods of interconnection which have been adequately demonstrated by test and verified by analysis may be used to effect the transfer of forces between the steel section or joist and the slab or cellular steel deck with cover slab. In such cases the design of the composite member shall conform to the design of a similar member employing shear connectors, insofar as practicable.

17.3.5.5 The diameter of a welded stud shall not exceed 2.5 times the thickness of the part to which it is welded, unless test data satisfactory to the authority having jurisdiction is provided to establish the capacity of the stud as a shear connector.

17.3.6 Shear Connectors

The factored shear resistance, q_r, of a shear connector shall be established by tests acceptable to the authority having jurisdiction, except that the following values shall be acceptable without further verification and where ϕ_{sc}, the performance factor for shear connectors, is taken as 0.80:

(a) **End welded studs, headed or hooked with h/d ≥ 4**

$$q_r = 0.5\phi_{sc} A_{sc} \sqrt{f'_c E_c} \leq 450\phi_{sc} A_{sc} \text{ (newtons)}$$

This value is limited to design incorporating a solid concrete slab; or designs incorporating a cellular steel deck with concrete cover slab in which the flute average width is at least twice the height of the cellular steel deck and the projection of the stud, based on its length prior to welding, is at least two stud diameters above the top surface of the cellular steel deck;

(b) **End welded studs, headed, in selected cases** — Table 8 gives values of q_r for selected cases of composite beams incorporating cellular steel deck not covered by Item (a). Cover slabs shall consist of normal density concrete (2300 kg/m³) with $f'_c \geq 20$ MPa.

(c) **Channel connectors**

$$q_r = 36.5\phi_{sc} (t_f + 0.5t_w)L_c \sqrt{f'_c} \text{ (newtons)}$$

This formula is limited to design incorporating a solid concrete slab of normal density concrete (2300 kg/m³) with $f'_c \geq 20$ MPa.

Table 8
Factored Shear Resistances of Studs for Selected Cases

Height of Cellular Steel Deck (mm)	Flute Average Width, Minimum (mm)	Depth of Cover Slab (mm)	Stud Size d x h (mm x mm)	No. of Studs per Flute	Factored Shear Resistance* q_r (newtons)
40	50	65	14 x 75	1	24 000ϕ_{sc}
40	50	65	20 x 75	1	50 000ϕ_{sc}
				2	76 000ϕ_{sc} per pair
40	50	90	20 x 100	1	79 000ϕ_{sc}
				2	113 000ϕ_{sc} per pair

Factored shear resistances given in Table 8 are derived from test and reflect the influence of flute geometry and stiffness on the useful capacity of the studs.

17.3.7 Ties

Mechanical ties shall be provided between the steel section or joist and the slab or cellular steel deck to prevent separation. Shear connectors may serve as mechanical ties if suitably proportioned. The maximum spacing of ties shall not exceed 1000 mm and the average spacing in a span should not exceed 600 mm nor be greater than that required to achieve any specified fire resistance rating of the composite assembly.

17.4 Design of Composite Beams With Shear Connectors

17.4.1 The composite beam shall consist of steel section or joist, shear connectors, ties, and slab or cellular steel deck with cover slab.

17.4.2 The properties of the composite section shall be computed neglecting any concrete area in tension within the maximum effective area equal to effective width times effective thickness. If a steel joist is used the area of its top chord shall be neglected in determining the properties of composite section and only Clause 17.4.3(a) is applicable.

17.4.3 The factored moment resistance, M_{rc}, of the composite section with the slab or cover slab in compression shall be computed as follows, where $\phi = 0.90$ and ϕ_c, the performance factor for concrete, $= 0.67$:

(a) **Case 1** — Full shear connection and plastic neutral axis is in the slab that is $Q_r \geqslant \phi A_s F_y$ and $\phi A_s F_y \leqslant 0.85 \phi_c btf'_c$ where Q_r equals the sum of the factored resistances of all shear connectors between points of maximum and zero moment.

$$M_{rc} = T_r e' = \phi A_s F_y e'$$

where e' = the lever arm and is computed using

$$a = \frac{\phi A_s F_y}{0.85 \phi_c bf'_c}$$

(b) **Case 2** — Full shear connection and plastic neutral axis in the steel section that is $Q_r \geqslant 0.85 \phi_c btf'_c$ and $0.85 \phi_c btf'_c < \phi A_s F_y$

$$M_{rc} = C_r e + C'_r e'$$

$$C'_r = 0.85 \phi_c bt f'_c$$

$$C_r = \frac{\phi A_s F_y - C'_r}{2}$$

(c) **Case 3** — Partial shear connection that is $Q_r < 0.85 \phi_c btf'_c$ and $< \phi A_s F_y$

$$M_{rc} = C_r e + C'_r e'$$

$$C'_r = Q_r$$

$$C_r = \frac{\phi A_s F_y - C'_r}{2}$$

where e' = the level arm and is computed using

$$a = \frac{C'_r}{0.85 \phi_c bf'_c}$$

17.4.4 No composite action shall be assumed in computing flexural strength when Q_r is less than 0.5 times the lesser of $0.85 \phi_c btf'_c$ and $\phi A_s F_y$. No composite action shall be assumed in computing deflections when Q_r is less than 0.25 times the lesser of $0.85 \phi_c btf'_c$ and $\phi A_s F_y$.

17.4.5 For full shear connection, the total horizontal shear, V_h, at the junction of the steel section or joist and the concrete slab or cellular steel deck, to be resisted by shear connectors distributed between the point of maximum bending moment and each adjacent point of zero moment, shall be:

$$V_h = \phi A_s F_y$$

for Case 1 and

$$V_h = 0.85 \phi_c btf'_c$$

for Case 2 as defined in Clause 17.4.3(a) and (b), where $Q_r \geq V_h$.

17.4.6 For partial shear connection, the total horizontal shear as defined in Clause 17.4.3(c) shall be:

$$V_h = Q_r$$

17.4.7 Composite beams employing steel sections and concrete slabs may be designed as continuous members. The factored moment resistance of the composite section, with the concrete slab in the tension area of the composite section shall be the factored moment resistance of the steel section alone except that when sufficient shear connectors are placed in the negative moment region, suitably anchored concrete slab reinforcement parallel to the steel sections and within the design effective width of the concrete slab may be included in computing the properties of the composite section. The total horizontal shear, V_h, to be resisted by shear connectors between the point of maximum negative bending moment and the adjacent point of zero moment shall be taken as:

$$V_h = \phi A_r F_{yr}$$

17.4.8 The number of shear connectors to be located each side of the point of maximum bending moment (positive or negative, as applicable) and distributed between that point and the adjacent point of zero moment shall be not less than:

$$n = \frac{V_h}{q_r}$$

Shear connectors may be spaced uniformly except that in a region of positive bending, the number of shear connectors required between any concentrated load applied in that region and the nearest point of zero moment shall be not less than n'

$$n' = n \left(\frac{M_{f1} - M_r}{M_f - M_r} \right)$$

where

M_{f1} = positive bending moment under factored load at concentrated load point

M_r = factored moment resistance of the steel section alone

M_f = maximum positive bending moment under factored load

17.5 Design of Composite Beams Without Shear Connectors

17.5.1 Unpainted steel sections or joists supporting concrete slabs and encased in concrete in accordance with Clause 17.3.5.2 may be proportioned on the basis that the composite section supports the total load.

17.5.2 The properties of the composite section for determination of load-carrying capacity shall be computed by ultimate strength methods, neglecting any area of concrete in tension.

17.5.3 As an alternative method of design, encased simple span steel sections or joists may be proportioned on the basis that the steel section or joist alone supports 0.90 times the total load.

17.6 Unshored Beams

For composite beams, unshored during construction, the stresses in the tension flange of the steel section or joist, due to the loads applied before the concrete strength reaches $0.75f'_c$ plus the stresses at the same location, due to the remaining specified loads considered to act on the composite section shall not exceed $0.90F_y$.

17.7   **Beams During Construction**
The steel section or joist alone shall be proportioned to support all factored loads applied prior to hardening of the concrete without exceeding its calculated capacity under the conditions of lateral support or shoring, or both, to be furnished during construction.

$$M_f \leq M_r$$

17.8   **Design of Composite Columns (Concrete-Filled Hollow Structural Sections)**

17.8.1   Hollow structural sections completely filled with concrete may be assumed to carry compressive load as composite columns.

17.8.2   The factored compressive resistance of a composite column shall be taken as:

$$C_{rc} = C_r + C'_r$$

where
C'_r = compressive resistance of concrete area (A_c) of the column
F_c shall be taken as noted below using a value for ϕ_c of 0.67:

$$\text{for } \frac{KL}{r} \leq \sqrt{\frac{\pi^2 E}{F_y}} \qquad F_c = 0.85 \,\phi_c\, f'_c \left[\left(\sqrt{\frac{\pi^2 E}{F_y}} - \frac{KL}{r} \right) \Big/ \sqrt{\frac{\pi^2 E}{F_y}} \right]$$

$$\frac{KL}{r} > \sqrt{\frac{\pi^2 E}{F_y}} \qquad F_c = 0$$

and the slenderness ratio to be assumed is that of the steel section alone.

17.8.3   Where bending as well as axial compression is to be resisted, the bending shall be assumed to be resisted by the steel section alone. The steel section shall be proportioned as a beam-column to carry the total bending, plus axial compression (C_r) equal to the difference between the total axial compression (C_{rc}) and that portion which can be sustained by the concrete (C'_r).

$$C_r = C_{rc} - C'_r$$

18.   **General Requirements for Built-Up Members**

18.1   **General Requirements for Compression Members**

18.1.1   All components of built-up compression members and the transverse spacing of their lines of connecting bolts or welds shall meet the requirements of Clauses 10 and 11.

18.1.2   All component parts in contact with one another at the ends of built-up compression members shall be connected by bolts spaced longitudinally not more than four diameters apart for a distance equal to 1.5 times the width of the member, or by continuous welds having a length not less than the width of the member.

18.1.3   Unless closer spacing is required for transfer of load, or for sealing inaccessible surfaces, the longitudinal spacing, in line, between intermediate bolts or clear longitudinal spacing between intermittent welds in built-up compression members shall not exceed the following, as applicable:

(a) For compression members composed of two or more rolled shapes in contact or separated from one another by intermittent fillers, the slenderness ratio of any shape between points of interconnection shall not exceed the slenderness ratio of the built-up member. The least radius of gyration of each component part shall be used in computing the slenderness ratio of that part between points of interconnection with other component parts;

(b) $330t/\sqrt{F_y}$ but not more than 300 mm for the outside component of the section consisting of a plate when the bolts on all gauge lines or intermittent welds along the component edges are not staggered, where t = thickness of outside plate;

(c) $525t/\sqrt{F_y}$ but not more than 450 mm for the outside component of the section consisting of a plate when the bolts or intermittent welds are staggered on adjacent lines, where t = thickness of outside plate.

18.1.4 The spacing requirements of Clauses 18.1.3, 18.2.3 and 18.2.4 will not always provide a continuous tight fit between components in contact. When the environment is such that corrosion could be a serious problem, the spacing of bolts or welds may need to be less than the specified maximum.

18.1.5 Open sides of compression members built up from plates or shapes shall be connected to each other by lacing, batten plates, or perforated cover plates.

18.1.6 Lacing shall provide a complete triangulated shear system and may consist of bars, rods or shapes. The spacing of connections of lacing to a main component shall be such that the slenderness ratio of a main component between these points of connection does not exceed the governing slenderness ratio of the member as a whole. Lacing shall be proportioned to resist a shear, normal to the longitudinal axis of the member, of not less than 2.5 per cent of the total axial load on the member plus the shear from transverse loads, if any.

18.1.7 The slenderness ratio of lacing members shall not exceed 140. The effective length for single lacing shall be the distance between connections to the main components; for double lacing connected at the intersections, the effective length shall be 70 per cent of that distance.

18.1.8 Lacing members shall preferably be inclined to the longitudinal axis of the built-up member at an angle of not less than 45°.

18.1.9 Lacing systems shall have diaphragms in the plane of the lacing and as near the ends as practicable and at intermediate points where lacing is interrupted. Such diaphragms may be plates (tie plates) or shapes.

18.1.10 End tie plates used as diaphragms shall have a length not less than the distance between the lines of bolts or welds connecting them to the main components of the member. Intermediate tie plates shall have a length not less than one-half that prescribed for end tie plates. The thickness of tie plates shall be at least 1/60 of the width between lines of bolts or welds connecting them to the main components, and the longitudinal spacing of the bolts or clear longitudinal spacing between welds shall not exceed 150 mm. At least three bolts shall connect the tie plate to each main component, or, alternatively, a total length of weld not less than one-third the length of tie plate shall be used.

18.1.11 Shapes used as diaphragms shall be proportioned and connected to transmit from one main component to the other a longitudinal shear equal to 5 per cent of the axial compression in the member.

18.1.12 Perforated cover plates may be used in lieu of lacing and tie plates on open sides of built-up compression members. The net width of such plates at access holes shall be assumed available to resist axial load provided that:

(a) The width-thickness ratio conforms to Clause 11;

(b) The length of the access hole does not exceed twice its width;

(c) The clear distance between access holes in the direction of load is not less than the transverse distance between lines of bolts or welds connecting the perforated plate to the main components of the built-up member;

(d) The periphery of the access hole at all points has a minimum radius of 40 mm.

18.1.13 Battens consisting of plates or shapes may be used on open sides of built-up compression members which do not carry primary bending in addition to axial load. Battens shall be provided at the ends of the member, at locations where the member is laterally supported along its length and elsewhere as determined by the following spacing requirements:

(a) When the slenderness ratio of the built-up member with respect to the axis perpendicular to the battens is equal to or less than 80 per cent of the slenderness ratio with respect to the axis parallel to the battens, the spacing between battens shall be such that the slenderness ratio of a main component between ends of adjacent batten plates shall not exceed 50, nor shall it exceed 70 per cent of the slenderness ratio of the built-up member with respect to the axis parallel to the battens;

(b) When the slenderness ratio of the built-up member with respect to the axis perpendicular to the battens is more than 80 per cent of the slenderness ratio with respect to the axis parallel to the battens, the spacing between battens shall be such that the slenderness ratio of a main component between ends of adjacent batten plates shall not exceed 40, nor shall it exceed 60 per cent of the slenderness ratio of the built-up member with respect to the axis perpendicular to the battens.

18.1.14 Battens shall have a length not less than the distance between lines of bolts or welds connecting them to the main components of the member and a thickness not less than 1/60 of this distance if the batten consists of a flat plate. Battens and their connections shall be proportioned to resist simultaneously a longitudinal shear force, V_f, and a moment, M_f,

where

$$V_f = \frac{0.025 C_f d}{na} \text{ (newtons)}$$

$$M_f = \frac{0.025 C_f d}{2n} \text{ (N·mm)}$$

d = longitudinal distance centre-to-centre of battens (mm)

a = distance between lines of bolts or welds connecting the batten to each main component (mm)

n = number of parallel planes of battens

18.2   General Requirements for Tension Members

18.2.1   Tension members composed of two or more shapes, plates or bars separated from one another by intermittent fillers shall have the components interconnected at fillers spaced so that the slenderness ratio of any component between points of interconnection shall not exceed 300.

18.2.2   Tension members composed of two plate components in contact or a shape and a plate component in contact shall have the components interconnected so that the spacing between connecting bolts or clear spacing between welds does not exceed 36 times the thickness of the thinner plate nor 450 mm (see Clause 18.1.3).

18.2.3   Tension members composed of two or more shapes in contact shall have the components interconnected so that the spacing between connecting bolts or the clear spacing between welds does not exceed 600 mm, except where it can be determined that a greater spacing would not affect the satisfactory performance of the member (see Clause 18.1.3).

18.2.4   Tension members composed of two separated main components may have either perforated cover plates or tie plates on the open sides of the built-up member. Tie plates including end tie plates shall have a length not less than two-thirds of the transverse distance between bolts or welds connecting them to the main components of the member and shall be spaced so that the slenderness ratio of any component between the tie plates does not exceed 300. The thickness of tie plates shall be at least 1/60 of the transverse distance between the bolts or welds connecting them to the main components and the longitudinal spacing of the bolts or welds shall not exceed 150 mm. Perforated cover plates shall comply with the requirements of Clause 18.1.11(b), (c), and (d).

18.3   General Requirements for Open Box-Type Beams and Grillages

Where two or more rolled beams or channels are used side-by-side to form a flexural member, they shall be connected together at intervals of not more than 1500 mm. Through bolts and separators may be used, provided that in beams having a depth of 300 mm or more, no fewer than two bolts shall be used at each separator location. When concentrated loads are carried from one beam to the other, or distributed between the beams, diaphragms having sufficient stiffness to distribute the load shall be bolted or welded between the beams. The design of members shall provide for torsion resulting from any unequal distribution of loads. Where beams are exposed, they shall be sealed against corrosion of interior surfaces, or spaced sufficiently far apart to permit cleaning and painting.

19.   Stability of Structures and Individual Members

19.1   General

19.1.1   In the design of a steel structure care shall be taken to ensure that the structural system is adequate to resist the forces caused by the factored loads and to ensure that a complete structural system is provided to transfer the factored loads to the foundations, particularly when there is a dependence on walls, floors, roofs acting as shear resisting elements or diaphragms. (See also Clause 8.6.)

Note: The structure should also be checked to ensure that adequate resistance to torsional deformations has been provided.

19.1.2   Design drawings shall indicate all load resisting elements essential to the integrity of the completed structure and shall show details necessary to ensure the effectiveness of the load resisting system. Design drawings shall also indicate the requirements for roofs and floors used as diaphragms.

19.1.3   Erection drawings shall indicate all load resisting elements essential to the integrity of the completed structure. Permanent and temporary load resisting elements essential to the integrity of the partially completed structure shall be clearly specified on the erection drawings.

19.1.4   Where the portion of the structure under consideration does not provide adequate resistance to lateral forces, provision shall be made for transferring the forces to adjacent lateral load resisting elements.

19.2   **Stability of Columns**
Beam-to-column connections shall have adequate strength to transfer the lateral forces produced by possible out-of-plumbness as specified in Clause 28.7.1. These forces shall be computed for the loading cases of Clause 7.2.4 using the appropriate load combination factors.

19.3   **Stability of Beams, Girders and Trusses**

19.3.1   Bracing members assumed to provide lateral support to the compression flange of beams and girders, or to the compression chord of trusses, and the connections of such bracing members, shall be proportioned to resist a force equal to 1 per cent of the force in the compression flange or chord at the point of support.

19.3.2   When bracing of the compression flange or chord is effected by a slab or deck, the slab or deck and the means by which the computed bracing forces are transmitted between the flange or chord and the slab or deck shall be adequate to resist a force in the plane of the slab or deck. This force shall be considered to be uniformly distributed along the length of the compression flange or chord, and shall be taken as at least 5 per cent of the maximum force in the flange or chord, unless a lesser amount can be justified by analysis.

19.3.3   Consideration shall be given to the probable accumulation of forces when a bracing member must transfer forces from one braced member to another.

19.3.4   Members restraining beams and girders designed to resist loads causing torsion shall be proportioned according to the requirements of Clause 15.11. Special consideration shall be given to the connections of asymmetric section such as channels, angles and zees.

20.   **Connections**

20.1   **Alignment of Members**
Axially loaded members meeting at a joint shall have their gravity axes intersect at a common point if practicable; otherwise the results of bending due to the joint eccentricity shall be provided for.

20.2   **Unrestrained Members**
Except as otherwise indicated on the design drawings, all connections of beams, girders, and trusses shall be designed and detailed as flexible and ordinarily may be proportioned for the reaction shears only. Flexible beam connections shall accommodate end rotations of unrestrained (simple)

beams. To accomplish this, inelastic action at the specified load levels in the connection is permitted.

20.3   **Restrained Members**

When beams, girders, or trusses are subject to both reaction shear and end moment due to full or partial end restraint or to continuous or cantilever construction, their connections shall be designed for the combined effect of shear, bending, and axial load. When beams are rigidly framed to the flange of an H-type column, stiffeners shall be provided on the column web as follows:

(a) Opposite the compression flange of beam when

$$B_r = \phi w_c (t_b + 5k)F_{yc} < \frac{M_f}{d_b}$$

except that for members with Class 3 or 4 webs,

$$B_r = \phi \frac{640\ 000}{(h_c/w_c)^2} w_c(t_b + 5k)$$

(b) Opposite the tension flange of beam when

$$T_r = \phi 7t_c^2 F_{yc} < \frac{M_f}{d_b}$$

where

w_c = thickness of column web

t_b = thickness of beam flange

k = distance from outer face of column flange to web toe of fillet, or to web toe of flange-to-web weld in a welded column

F_{yc} = specified yield point of column

d_b = depth of beam

h_c = clear depth of column web

t_c = thickness of column flange

The stiffener or pair of stiffeners opposite either beam flange must develop a force equal to:

$$F_{st} = \frac{M_f}{d_b} - B_r$$

Stiffeners shall also be provided on the web of columns, beams or girders if V_r computed from Clause 13.4.2 is exceeded, in which case the stiffener or stiffeners must transfer a shear force equal to:

$$V_{st} = V_f - 0.55\phi wdF_y$$

In all cases the stiffeners shall be connected so that the force in the stiffener is transferred through the stiffener connection. When beams frame to one side of the column only, the stiffeners need not be longer than one-half the depth of the column.

20.4   **Connections of Tension or Compression Members**

The connections at ends of tension members or compression members not finished to bear shall develop the force due to the factored loads. However the connection shall be designed for not less than 50 per cent of the resistance of the member based on the behaviour of the member in the overall structure, unless otherwise permitted by the authority having jurisdiction.

20.5 Bearing Joints in Compression Members

20.5.1 Where columns bear on bearing plates, or are finished to bear at splices there shall be sufficient fasteners or welds to hold all parts securely in place.

20.5.2 Where other compression members are finished to bear, the splice material and connecting fasteners or welds shall be arranged to hold all parts in place and shall be proportioned for 50 per cent of the computed load.

20.6 Lamellar Tearing
Corner or "T" joint details of rolled structural members or plates involving transfer of tensile forces in the through-thickness direction resulting from shrinkage due to welding executed under conditions of restraint, shall be avoided where possible. If this type of connection cannot be avoided, measures shall be taken to minimize the possibility of lamellar tearing.

20.7 Placement of Fasteners and Welds
Except in members subjected to repeated loads (as defined in Clause 14), disposition of fillet welds to balance the forces about the neutral axis or axes for end-connections of single angle, double angle, or similar types of axially loaded members is not required. Eccentricity between the gravity axes of such members and the gauge lines of bolted end-connections also may be neglected. In axially loaded members subjected to repeated loads, the fasteners or welds in end connections shall have their centre of gravity on the gravity axis of the member unless provision is made for the effect of the resulting eccentricity.

20.8 Fillers

20.8.1 When load-carrying fasteners pass through fillers with a total thickness greater than 6 mm in bearing-type shear connections, the fillers shall be extended beyond the splice material and the filler extension shall be secured by sufficient fasteners to distribute the total force in the member uniformly over the combined section of the member and the filler, or alternatively an equivalent number of fasteners shall be included in the connection.

20.8.2 In welded construction, any filler with a total thickness greater than 6 mm shall extend beyond the edges of the splice plate and shall be welded to the part on which it is fitted with sufficient weld to transmit the splice plate load, applied at the surface of the filler, as an eccentric load. Welds connecting the splice plate to the filler shall be sufficient to transmit the splice plate load and shall be long enough to avoid overloading the filler along the toe of the weld. Any filler 6 mm or less in thickness shall have its edges made flush with the edges of the splice plate and the required weld size shall be equal to the thickness of the filler plate plus the size necessary to transmit the splice plate load.

20.9 Welds in Combination
If two or more of the general types of weld (groove, fillet, plug, or slot) are combined in a single connection, the effective capacity of each shall be separately computed with reference to the axis of the group in order to determine the factored resistance of the combination.

20.10   Fasteners and Welds in Combination

20.10.1   When approved, high-strength bolts in slip-resistant connections may be considered as sharing load with welds in new work.

20.10.2   In making alterations to structures, existing rivets and high-strength bolts may be utilized to carry forces resulting from existing dead loads, and welding may be proportioned to carry all additional loads.

20.11   High-Strength Bolts (in Slip-Resistant Joints) and Rivets, in Combination
In making alterations, rivets and high-strength bolts in slip-resistant joints may be considered as sharing forces due to dead and live loads.

20.12   Connections Requiring High-Strength Bolts or Welds

20.12.1   High-strength bolts or welds shall be used for the following connections unless otherwise permitted by the authority having jurisdiction:

(a) Connections of beams, girders, and trusses on which the bracing of the structure is dependent, and column splices, in structures over 30 000 mm in height;

(b) Roof truss splices, connections of trusses to columns, column splices, column bracing, knee braces, and crane supports in all structures carrying cranes over 50 kN capacity;

(c) Connections for supports of running machinery, or of other live loads which produce impact or cyclic load;

(d) Any other connections so stipulated on the design drawings.

20.12.2   In all cases except those listed in Clause 20.12.1 connections may be made with A307 bolts.

20.12.3   For the purposes of Clause 20.12 height of a tier structure is the distance from curb level to the top of the roof beams in flat roofs or curb level to top of roof beams at mean gable height in the case of sloping roofs. Penthouses may be excluded in determining the height of a structure.

20.13   Special Fasteners
Fasteners of special types may be used when approved.

21.   Bolting Details

21.1   High-Strength Bolts
A325 and A490 high-strength bolts and their usage shall conform to Clause 22.

21.2   A307 Bolts
Nuts on A307 bolts shall be tightened to an amount corresponding to the full effort of a man using a spud wrench. When so specified, nuts shall be prevented from working loose by the use of lock washers, lock nuts, jam nuts, thread burring, welding, or other approved methods.

21.3   Effective Bearing Area
The effective bearing area of bolts shall be the nominal diameter multiplied by the length in bearing. For countersunk bolts half the depth of the countersink shall be deducted from the bearing length.

21.4   **Long Grips**
A307 bolts which carry calculated loads, the grip of which exceeds five diameters, shall have their number increased by 0.6 per cent for each additional 1 mm in the grip.

21.5   **Minimum Pitch**
The minimum distance between centres of bolt holes preferably shall be not less than 3 bolt diameters and in no case less than 2 ⅔ diameters.

21.6   **Minimum Edge Distance**
The minimum distance from the centre of a bolt hole to any edge shall be that given in Table 9.

Table 9
Minimum Edge Distance for Bolt Holes

Bolt Diameter		At Sheared Edge	At Rolled or Gas Cut Edge†
Inches*	Millimetres	Millimetres	Millimetres
⅝	–	28	22
–	16	28	22
¾	–	32	25
–	20	34	26
⅞	–	38‡	28
–	22	38	28
–	24	42	30
1	–	44‡	32
–	27	48	34
1⅛	–	51	38
–	30	52	38
1¼	–	57	41
–	36	64	46
Over 1¼	Over 36	1¾ x Diameter	1¼ x Diameter

ASTM Standards A325 and A490 are written in Imperial Units. Accordingly, bolt diameters are shown in the Imperial System.
†*Gas cut edges shall be smooth and free from notches. Edge distance in this column may be decreased 3 mm when hole is at a point where computed stress under factored loads is not more than 0.3 of the yield stress.*
‡*At ends of beam framing angles this distance may be 32 mm.*

21.7   **Maximum Edge Distance**
The maximum distance from the centre of any bolt to the nearest edge of parts in contact shall be 12 times the thickness of the outside connected part with a maximum of 150 mm.

21.8   **Minimum End Distance**
In the connection of tension members having more than two bolts in a line parallel to the direction of load, the minimum end distance (from centre of end fastener to nearest end of connected part) shall be governed by the edge distance values given in Table 9. In members having either one or two bolts in the line of load, the end distance shall be not less than 1½ bolt diameters.

21.9   **Slotted Holes**
Maximum and minimum edge distance for bolts in slotted or oversize holes

(as permitted in Clause 22.3.2) shall conform to the requirements given in Clauses 21.6, 21.7 and 21.8 assuming that the fastener can be placed at any extremity of the slot or hole.

22. Structural Joints Using ASTM A325 or A490 Bolts

22.1 General

22.1.1 Clause 22 deals with the design, assembly, and inspection of structural joints using ASTM A325 or A490 bolts, or equivalent fasteners, tightened to a specific minimum tension. A325 and A490 bolts are used in holes slightly larger than the nominal bolt size.

22.1.2 Joints required to resist shear between connected parts shall be designated on design and shop drawings as either bearing-type or slip-resistant.

22.1.3 Slip-resistant shear joints, in which specified load is assumed to be transferred by the slip resistance of the clamped faying surfaces, shall be required:

(a) In connections subject to load reversal;

(b) Where slippage into bearing cannot be tolerated.

22.1.4 In bearing-type shear joints due recognition of the presence or absence of threads in the shear planes of the joint shall be made. Where an outside part adjacent to a nut is less than 10 mm thick, threads shall be considered to be present unless special precautions are taken.

22.1.5 **Applied Tension**
Bolts required to support load by direct tension shall be proportioned so that the tensile load on the bolt area, independent of initial tightening force, shall not exceed the factored tensile resistance as given in Clause 13.11.2. The applied load shall be taken as the sum of the external load plus any tension caused by prying action due to deformation of the connected parts. If the connection is subject to repeated loading, prying forces must be avoided.

22.1.6 Joints subject to repeated loads shall be proportioned in accordance with Clause 14.

22.2 Bolts, Nuts, and Washers

22.2.1 Except as provided in Clause 22.2.4, bolts, nuts, and washers shall conform to ASTM Standards A325, High-Strength Bolts for Structural Steel Joints, Including Suitable Nuts and Plain Hardened Washers, and A490, Quenched and Tempered Alloy Steel Bolts for Structural Steel Joints, as applicable.

22.2.2 Except as provided in Clause 22.2.4, bolt dimensions shall be those prescribed by ANSI Standard B18.2.1, Square and Hex Bolts and Screws, Including Hex Cap Screws and Lag Screws, for heavy hex structural bolts; and nut dimensions shall be those prescribed by ANSI Standard B18.2.2, Square and Hex Nuts, for heavy, semi-finished hex nuts. The length of bolts shall be such that the point of the bolt will be flush with, or outside the face of, the nut when completely installed.

22.2.3 If required, A325 bolts, nuts, and washers may be galvanized in accordance with the requirements of ASTM Standard A325, High-Strength Bolts for

Structural Steel Joints, Including Suitable Nuts and Plain Hardened Washers. When installed on a galvanized bolt in a solid steel connection and with three to five threads in the grip, they shall be capable of producing a tensile-type fracture of the bolt and of rotating one full turn from snug before failure.

22.2.4 Other fasteners which meet the chemical composition requirements of ASTM Standard A325, High-Strength Bolts for Structural Steel Joints, Including Suitable Nuts and Plain Hardened Washers, or A490, Quenched and Tempered Alloy Steel Bolts for Structural Steel Joints, and which meet the mechanical requirements of the same Standard in full-size tests and which have body diameter and bearing areas under the head and nut, or their equivalent, not less than those provided by a bolt and nut of the same nominal dimensions prescribed by Clauses 22.2.1 and 22.2.2, may be used. Such alternative fasteners may differ in other dimensions from the prescribed bolt and nut dimensions. When such fasteners are proposed as an alternative to A325 or A490 standard bolts their use shall be subject to the approval of the authority having jurisdiction.

22.2.5 If necessary, washers may be clipped on one side to a point not closer than $7/8$ of the bolt diameter from the centre of the washer hole.

22.2.6 Design drawings shall indicate the type or types of bolt which may be used. Shop and erection drawings shall show the type of bolt to be used.

22.3 **Bolted Parts**

22.3.1 Bolted parts shall fit together solidly when assembled and shall not be separated by gaskets or any other interposed compressible material.

22.3.2 Holes may be punched, sub-punched or sub-drilled and reamed, or drilled, as permitted by Clause 26.5. The nominal diameter of a hole shall be not more than 2 mm greater than the nominal bolt size, except that, where shown in the design drawings and at other locations approved by the designer, enlarged or slotted holes may be used with high-strength bolts 16 mm in diameter and larger. Joints utilizing enlarged or slotted holes shall be proportioned in accordance with the requirements of Clause 22 and Clauses 13.11 and 13.12 and shall meet the following conditions:

(a) Oversize holes are 4 mm larger than bolts 22 mm and less in diameter, 6 mm larger than bolts 24 mm in diameter, and 8 mm larger than bolts 27 mm and greater in diameter. Oversized holes shall not be used in bearing-type connections but may be used in any or all plies of slip-resistant connections. Hardened washers shall be used under the head and the nut;

(b) Short slotted holes are 2 mm wider than the bolt diameter and have a length which does not exceed the oversize diameter provisions of Item (a) by more than 2 mm. They may be used in any or all plies of slip-resistant or bearing-type connections. The slots may be used without regard to direction of loading in slip-resistant connections but shall be normal to the direction of the load in bearing-type connections. Hardened washers shall be used under the head and the nut;

(c) Long slotted holes are 2 mm wider than the bolt diameter and have a length more than allowed in Item (b) but not more than 2.5 times the bolt diameter and may be used:

(i) In slip-resistant connections without regard to direction of loading.

One-third more bolts shall be provided than would be needed to satisfy the requirements of Clause 13.12;

(ii) In bearing-type connections with the long diameter of the slot normal to the direction of loading. No increase in the number of bolts over those necessary in Clause 13.11 is required;

(iii) In only one of the connected parts of either a slip-resistant or bearing-type connection at an individual faying surface;

(iv) Provided that structural plate washers or a continuous bar not less than 8 mm in thickness cover long slots that are in the outer plies of joints. These washers or bars shall have a size sufficient to cover completely the slot after installation.

(d) The above requirement for the nominal diameter of hole may be waived to permit the use of the following bolt diameters and hole combinations in bearing-type or slip-resistant connections:

(i) Either ¾-inch diameter bolt or an M20 bolt in a 22 mm hole;

(ii) Either ⅞-inch diameter bolt or an M22 bolt in a 24 mm hole;

(iii) Either 1-inch diameter bolt or an M24 bolt in a 27 mm hole.

22.3.3 When assembled, all joint surfaces including those adjacent to bolt heads, nuts, and washers shall be free of scale (tight mill scale excepted), burrs, dirt, and foreign material which would prevent solid seating of the parts.

22.3.4 Faying surfaces within slip-resistant joints shall be free of oil, paint, lacquer, or other coatings except as noted below:

(a) Hot-dip galvanizing, provided that faying surfaces are wire brushed or "brush-off" blast-cleaned after galvanizing and prior to assembly;

(b) Sprayed metal coatings applied in accordance with CSA Standard G189, Sprayed Metal Coatings for Atmospheric Corrosion Protection;

(c) Zinc-rich paints as defined in SSPC PS 12.00-68T, Guide to Zinc-Rich Coating Systems, covering zinc-rich paints with organic and inorganic vehicles applied to blast-cleaned surfaces;

(d) Vinyl surface treatment applied in accordance with SSPC PT 3-64, Basic Zinc Chromate — Vinyl Butyral Washcoat, to blast-cleaned surfaces.

Faying surfaces within slip-resistant joints also may be coated by other materials and methods provided that these have been sufficiently tested to establish the performance of full-size similarly coated joints to the satisfaction of the authority having jurisdiction.

22.4 **Installation**

22.4.1 Each bolt shall be tightened to provide, when all bolts in the joint are tight, at least the minimum bolt tension given in Table 11 for the size and type of bolt used.

22.4.2 Threaded bolts shall be tightened in accordance with Clause 22.5 or 22.6. If necessary, tightening may be done by turning the bolt while holding the nut against rotation.

22.4.3 A325 bolts may be installed without a hardened washer except as required by Clause 22.3.2(a), (b), or (c) for oversize or slotted holes, or by Clause 22.7.4 (when inspection involves the use of a torque wrench). A490 bolts shall be installed with a hardened washer. For both A325 and A490 bolts, the hardened washer when used shall be under the element (nut or bolt head) turned in tightening. When A490 bolts are used with steel having a specified minimum yield point of less than 280 MPa a hardened washer shall be placed under the bolt head and under the nut.

22.4.4 Bevelled washers shall be used to compensate for lack of parallelism where, in the case of A325 bolts, an outer face of bolted parts has more than a 5 per cent slope with respect to a plane normal to the bolt axis. In the case of A490 bolts, bevelled washers shall be used to compensate for any lack of parallelism due to slope of outer faces.

22.5 "Turn-of-Nut" Tightening

22.5.1 After aligning the holes in a joint, sufficient bolts shall be placed and brought to a "snug-tight" condition to ensure that the parts of the joint are brought into full contact with each other. "Snug-tight" is the tightness attained by a few impacts of an impact wrench or the full effort of a man using a spud wrench.

22.5.2 Following the initial snugging operation, bolts shall be placed in any remaining open holes and brought to "snug-tightness". Re-snugging may be necessary in large joints.

22.5.3 When all bolts are "snug-tight" each bolt in the joint then shall be tightened additionally by the applicable amount of nut rotation given in Table 12, with tightening progressing systematically from the most rigid part of the joint to its free edges. During this operation there shall be no rotation of the part not turned by the wrench unless the bolt and nut are match-marked to enable the amount of relative rotation to be determined.

22.6 Tightening by Use of a Direct Tension Indicator
Tightening by this means is permitted, provided that it can be demonstrated by an accurate direct measurement procedure that the bolt has been tightened according to Table 10.

22.7 Inspection

22.7.1 When inspection is performed, the inspector shall determine that the requirements of Clauses 22.2, 22.3, 22.4 and 22.5 are met. Installation of bolts shall be observed to ascertain that a proper tightening procedure is employed. The turned element of all bolts shall be visually examined for evidence that they have been tightened. For bearing-type connections with no bolts subject to tensile or combined shear and tensile loads this inspection is all that is required.

22.7.2 Bolts installed by the "turn-of-nut" method may have tensions exceeding those given in Table 11 but this shall not be cause for rejection.

22.7.3 When bolts are installed in accordance with Clause 22.6 the verification that the bolt has been properly tightened is determined by the direct tension indicator.

22.7.4 When the verification of bolt tension is a required part of the inspection procedure, and the requirements of Clause 22.6 are not met, one of the following inspection methods shall be used unless otherwise specified:

(a) **General Method** — This method may be used for bolts in both slip-resistant and bearing-type joints and for bolts subject primarily to applied tension:

(i) The inspector shall use an inspection wrench which shall be a manual or power torque wrench capable of indicating a selected torque value;

(ii) Three bolts of the same grade and diameter as those under inspection, and representative of the lengths and condition of those in the structure, shall be placed individually in a calibration device capable of indicating bolt tension. The surface under the part to be turned in tightening each bolt shall be similar to that under the corresponding part in the structure, i.e., there shall be a washer under the part turned if washers are so used in the structure or, if no washer is used, the material abutting the part turned shall be of the same specification as that in the structure;

(iii) When the inspection wrench is a manual wrench, each bolt specified in Item (ii) shall be tightened in the calibration device by any convenient means to the minimum tension specified for its size in Table 10. The inspection wrench then shall be applied to the tightened bolt and the torque necessary to turn the nut or head 5° in the tightening direction shall be determined. The average torque measured in the tests of three bolts shall be taken as the job inspection torque to be used in the manner specified in Item (v);

(iv) When the inspection wrench is a power wrench it shall be adjusted so that it will tighten each bolt specified in Item (ii) to a tension at least 5 but not more than 10 per cent greater than the minimum tension specified for its size in Table 10. This setting of wrench shall be taken as the job inspection torque to be used in the manner specified in Item (v);

(v) Bolts represented by the sample prescribed in Item (ii) which have been tightened in the structure shall be inspected by applying, with the inspection wrench, in the tightening direction, the job inspection torque to 10 per cent of the bolts but not less than two bolts, selected at random in each connection. If no nut or bolt head is turned by this application of the job inspection torque the connection shall be accepted as properly tightened. If any nut or bolt head is turned by the application of the job inspection torque, this torque shall be applied to all bolts in the connection. If further nuts or bolt heads in the connection are turned by application of the job inspection torque and it appears evident that the bolts have been tightened beyond the snug condition the inspector shall request the fabricator or erector to install in the connection a new bolt of similar size and condition to those previously installed. The new bolt shall be tightened under the observation of the inspector by rotating the turned element the amount from snug given in Table 11, after which the inspector shall apply the job inspection torque to the new bolt. If the nut or bolt head of the new bolt is turned by application of the job inspection torque the inspector shall recalibrate the inspection wrench before proceeding with further inspection. If the nut or bolt head of the new bolt is not turned by application of the job inspection torque all bolts in the connection whose nut or head is turned by the job inspection torque shall be tightened and reinspected. Alternatively, if it appears evident that the bolts in the connection have not been tightened beyond the snug condition, the fabricator or erector shall tighten all the bolts in the connection and then re-submit the connection for inspection. Care shall be exercised by the inspector to ensure that bolts which have been adequately tightened by the fabricator or erector are not subjected to more than 15° of additional rotation of the turned element when being inspected;

(b) **Simplied Method** — This method may be used for bolts in bearing type joints where a washer is used under the turned element. Bolts shall not be galvanized.

(i) The inspector shall use an inspection wrench which shall be a manual or power torque wrench capable of indicating a selected torque value;

(ii) Bolts which have been tightened in the structure shall be inspected by applying with the inspection wrench, in the tightening direction, the applicable job inspection torque given in Table 12 to 10 per cent of the bolts but not less than two bolts, selected at random in each connection. If no nut or bolt head is turned by this application of the job inspection torque, the connection shall be accepted as properly tightened. If any nut or bolt head is turned by the application of the job inspection torque, this torque shall be applied to all bolts in the connection, and all bolts whose nut or head is turned by the job inspection torque shall be tightened and reinspected, or alternatively, the fabricator or erector, at his option may re-tighten all the bolts in the connection and then re-submit the connection for the specified inspection.

Table 10
Bolt Tension

Bolt Diameter Inches	Minimum Bolt Tension* (kN)	
	A325 Bolts	A490 Bolts
$\frac{1}{2}$	53	67
$\frac{5}{8}$	85	107
$\frac{3}{4}$	125	157
$\frac{7}{8}$	174	218
1	227	285
$1\frac{1}{8}$	249	356
$1\frac{1}{4}$	316	454
$1\frac{3}{8}$	378	538
$1\frac{1}{2}$	458	658

*Equal to 70 per cent of specified minimum tensile strength given in ASTM Standards A325 and A490, soft converted to SI units.

Table 11
Nut Rotation* From Snug-Tight Condition

Disposition of Outer Faces of Bolted Parts	Bolt Length‡	Turn
Both faces normal to bolt axis or one face normal to axis and other face sloped 1:20 (bevel washer not used)†	Up To and Including 4 Diameters	$\frac{1}{3}$
	Over 4 Diameters and Not Exceeding 8 Diameters or 200 mm	$\frac{1}{2}$
	Exceeding 8 Diameters or 200 mm	$\frac{2}{3}$
Both faces sloped 1:20 from normal to bolt axis (bevel washers not used)†	For All Lengths of Bolts	$\frac{3}{4}$

*Nut rotation is rotation relative to bolt regardless of the element (nut or bolt) being turned. Tolerance on rotation: 30° over or under. For coarse thread heavy hex structural bolts of all sizes and length and heavy hex semi-finished nuts.
†Bevel washers are necessary when A490 bolts are used.
‡Bolt length is measured from underside of head to extreme end of point.

Table 12
Job Inspection Torque*

Bolt Diameter D Inches	Job Inspection Torque (N·m)†	
	A325 Bolts	A490 Bolts
$\frac{1}{2}$	140	180
$\frac{5}{8}$	280	355
$\frac{3}{4}$	500	625
$\frac{7}{8}$	810	1 020
1	1210	1520
$1\frac{1}{8}$	1495	2135
$1\frac{1}{4}$	2105	3025
$1\frac{3}{8}$	2770	3945
$1\frac{1}{2}$	3665	5265

*To be used in conjunction with Clause 22.7.4(b).
†Equal to 5.334D times bolt tension given in Table 10 rounded to nearest 5 N·m.

23. Welding

23.1 Arc Welding

Arc welding design and practice shall conform to CSA Standard W59, Welded Steel Construction (Metal-Arc Welding).

23.2 Resistance Welding

Resistance welding practice and design shall conform to the applicable requirements of CSA Standard W55.2, Resistance Welding Practice.

23.3 Fabricator and Erector Qualification

Fabricators and erectors eligible to assume full responsibility for welded construction covered by this Standard shall be those certified by the Canadian Welding Bureau to the requirements of CSA Standard W47.1, Certification of Companies for Fusion Welding of Steel Structures, for Division 1 or Division 2 or CSA Standard W55.3, Resistance Welding Qualification Code for Fabricators of Structural Members Used in Building, or both, as applicable. For fusion welded structures, part of the work may be sublet to a Division 3 fabricator or erector; however, full responsibility shall remain with the Division 1 or Division 2 fabricator or erector.

24. Column Bases

24.1 Loads
Suitable provision shall be made to transfer column loads and moments to footings and foundations.

24.2 Finishing
Column bases shall be finished in accordance with the following requirements:

(a) Steel-to-steel contact bearing surfaces of rolled steel bearing plates shall be finished in such a manner that the requirements of Clauses 26.8, 26.9.7 and 28.7.3 are satisfied. In general, rolled steel bearing plates 50 mm or less in thickness may be used without planing provided a satisfactory contact bearing is obtained; rolled steel bearing plates over 50 mm but not over 100 mm in thickness may be straightened by pressing or by planing on all bearing surfaces, to obtain a satisfactory contact bearing; rolled steel bearing plates, over 100 mm in thickness, shall be planed on all bearing surfaces except as noted in Clause 24.2(c);

(b) Column bases other than rolled steel bearing plates shall be planed on all bearing surfaces except as noted in Clause 24.2(c);

(c) The bottom surfaces of bearing plates and column bases which rest on masonry or concrete foundations and are grouted to ensure full bearing need not be planed.

25. Anchor Bolts

25.1
Anchor bolts shall be designed to resist the effect of factored loads determined in accordance with Clause 7.2. They shall provide resistance to tension due to uplift forces and bending moments and, in combination with the friction between the base plate and the foundation unit, they shall provide resistance to shear. The embedment length and arrangement of the anchor bolts in the foundation shall be such that the required load capacity can be developed. Forces present during construction as well as those present in the finished structure shall be resisted.

26. Fabrication

26.1 General
Unless otherwise specified, the provisions of Clause 26 shall apply to both shop and field fabrication.

26.2 Straightness of Material
Prior to layout or fabrication, rolled material shall be straight within established rolling mill tolerances. If straightening is necessary, it shall be done by means that will not injure the material. Sharp kinks and bends shall be cause for rejection.

26.3 Gas Cutting
Gas cutting shall be done by machine where practicable. Gas cut edges shall conform to CSA Standard W59, Welded Steel Construction (Metal-Arc Welding). Re-entrant corners shall be free from notches and shall have the largest practical radii, with a minimum radius of 14 mm.

26.4 Sheared or Gas Cut Edge Finish

26.4.1 Planing or finishing of sheared or gas cut edges of plates or shapes shall not be required unless specifically noted on the drawings or included in a stipulated edge preparation for welding.

26.4.2 The use of sheared edges in the tension area shall be avoided in locations subject to plastic hinge rotation at factored loading. If used, such edges shall be finished smooth by grinding, chipping, or planing.

26.4.3 Burr shall be removed as required in Clause 22.3.3, and when required for proper fit-up for welding, and when burr creates a hazard during or after construction.

26.4.4 The requirements of Clause 26.4.2 shall be noted on design and shop drawings when applicable.

26.5 **Holes for Bolts or Other Mechanical Fasteners**

26.5.1 Unless otherwise shown on design drawings or as specified in Clause 22.3.2, holes shall be made 2 mm larger than the nominal diameter of the fastener. Holes may be punched when the thickness of material is not greater than the nominal fastener diameter plus 4 mm. For greater thicknesses holes shall be drilled from the solid or either sub-punched or sub-drilled and reamed. The die for all sub-punched holes or the drill for all sub-drilled holes shall be at least 4 mm smaller than the required diameter of the finished hole. Holes in CSA Standard G40.21-M (Type 700Q) or ASTM Standard A514 steels over 13 mm in thickness shall be drilled.

26.5.2 In locations subject to plastic hinge rotation at factored loading, fastener holes in the tension area shall be sub-punched and reamed or drilled full size.

26.5.3 The requirements of Clause 26.5.2 shall be noted on design and shop drawings where applicable.

26.6 **Bolted Construction**

26.6.1 Drifting done during assembly to align holes shall not distort the metal nor enlarge the holes. Holes in adjacent parts shall match sufficiently well to permit easy entry of bolts. If necessary, holes, except oversize or slotted holes, may be enlarged to admit bolts by a moderate amount of reaming; however, gross mis-match of holes shall be cause for rejection.

26.6.2 Assembly of high-strength bolted joints shall be in accordance with Clause 22.

26.7 **Welded Construction**
Workmanship and technique shall conform to those prescribed by CSA Standard W59, Welded Steel Construction (Metal-Arc Welding) or CSA Standard W55.2, Resistance Welding Practice, as applicable.

26.8 **Finishing of Bearing Surfaces**
Compression joints which depend on contact bearing shall have the bearing surfaces prepared to a common plane by milling, sawing, or other suitable means. Surface roughness shall have a roughness height rating not exceeding 500 (12.5 μm) as defined in CSA Standard B95, Surface Texture (Roughness, Waviness, and Lay), unless otherwise specified.

26.9 **Tolerances**

26.9.1 Structural members consisting primarily of a single rolled shape shall be straight within the tolerances allowed by CSA Standard G40.20-M, General Requirements for Rolled or Welded Structural Quality Steel, except as specified in Clause 26.9.4.

26.9.2 Built-up bolted structural members shall be straight within the tolerances allowed for rolled wide-flange shapes by CSA Standard G40.20-M, General Requirements for Rolled or Welded Structural Quality Steel, except as specified in Clause 26.9.4.

26.9.3 Dimensional tolerances of welded structural members shall be those prescribed by CSA Standard W59, Welded Steel Construction (Metal-Arc Welding), unless otherwise specified.

26.9.4 Fabricated compression members shall not have a deviation from straightness more than one-thousandth of the axial length between points which are to be laterally supported.

26.9.5 Beams with bow within straightness tolerances shall be fabricated so that after erection the bow due to rolling or fabrication shall be upward.

26.9.6 All completed members shall be free from twists, bends, and open joints. Sharp kinks or bends shall be cause for rejection.

26.9.7 Compression joints which depend upon contact bearing, when assembled during fabrication, shall have at least 75 per cent of the entire contact area in full bearing and the separation of any remaining portion shall not exceed 0.25 mm except adjacent to toes of flanges where a localized separation not exceeding 0.60 mm is permissible.

26.9.8 A variation of 1 mm is permissible in the overall length of members with both ends finished for contact bearing.

26.9.9 Members without ends finished for contact bearing, which are to be framed to other steel parts of the structure, may have a variation from the detailed length not greater than 2 mm for members 10 000 mm or less in length and not greater than 4 mm for members over 10 000 mm in length.

27. **Cleaning, Surface Preparation and Priming**

27.1 **General Requirements**

27.1.1 All steelwork, except as exempted by Clauses 27.1.2, 27.1.3, and 27.2 or unless otherwise noted on design drawings or in the job specifications, shall be given one coat of primer or one-coat paint (see Clause 27.5) applied in the shop. The primer or one-coat paint shall be applied thoroughly and evenly to dry clean surfaces by suitable means.

27.1.2 Steelwork to be subsequently concealed by interior building finish need not be given a coat of primer unless otherwise specified (see Clause 6.4.2).

27.1.3 Steelwork to be encased in concrete need not be given a coat of primer. Steelwork designed to act compositely with reinforced concrete and depending on natural bond for interconnection shall not be given a coat of primer.

27.1.4 Steelwork to be shop-primed shall be cleaned of all loose mill scale, loose rust, weld slag, and flux deposit, dirt, and other foreign matter and excessive weld spatter prior to application of the primer. Oil and grease shall be removed by solvent. The fabricator shall be free to use any satisfactory method to clean the steel and prepare the surface for painting unless a specific method of surface preparation is called for.

27.1.5 Primer shall be dry before loading primed steelwork for shipment.

27.1.6 Steelwork not to be shop-primed after fabrication shall be cleaned of oil and grease by solvent cleaners and shall be cleaned of dirt and other foreign matter.

27.2 **Requirements for Special Surfaces**

27.2.1 Surfaces inaccessible after assembly shall be cleaned, or cleaned and primed, as required by Clause 27.1, prior to assembly. Inside surfaces of enclosed spaces entirely sealed off from any external source of oxygen need not be primed.

27.2.2 In compression members, surfaces finished to bear and assembled during fabrication shall be cleaned before assembly but shall not be primed unless otherwise specified.

27.2.3 Surfaces finished to bear and not assembled during fabrication shall be protected by a corrosion inhibiting coating. The coating shall be of a type that can be readily removed prior to assembly or shall be of a type that makes such removal unnecessary.

27.2.4 Faying surfaces of high-strength bolted slip-resistant joints shall not be primed or otherwise coated except as permitted by Clause 22.

27.2.5 Joints to be field welded and surfaces to which shear connections are to be welded shall be kept free of primer and any other coating which could be detrimental to achieving a sound weldment, except that sheet steel decks may be welded to clean primed steelwork.

27.3 **Surface Preparation**
Unless otherwise specified, or approved, surface preparation shall be in conformance with one of the following applicable specifications of the Steel Structures Painting Council:

SP 2
Hand Tool Cleaning;

SP 3,
Power Tool Cleaning;

SP 4,
Flame Cleaning of New Steel;

SP 5,
White Metal Blast Cleaning;

SP 6,
Commercial Blast Cleaning;

SP 7,
Brush-Off Blast Cleaning;

SP 10,
Near-White Blast Cleaning.

27.4   **Primer**
Unless otherwise specified, or approved, shop primer shall conform to one of the following standards of the Canadian Government Specifications Board:
1-GP-14e,
Primer: Red Lead in Oil;

1-GP-40d,
Primer: Structural Steel, Oil Alkyd Type;

1-GP-81e,
Primer, Alkyd, Air Drying and Baking, for Vehicles and Equipment;

1-GP-140c,
Primer: Red Lead, Iron Oxide, Oil Alkyd Type;

1-GP-166a,
Primer: Basic Lead Silico-Chromate, Oil Alkyd Type;

or CISC/CPMA 2-75,
A Quick-Drying Primer For Use On Structural Steel.

27.5   **One-Coat Paint**
Unless otherwise specified, or approved, one-coat paint intended to withstand exposure to essentially non-corrosive atmosphere for a period of time not exceeding 6 months shall conform to CISC/CPMA Standard 1-73a, A Quick-Drying One-Coat Paint For Use On Structural Steel.

28.   **Erection**

28.1   **General**
The steel framework shall be erected true and plumb within the specified tolerances. Temporary bracing shall be employed wherever necessary to withstand all loads to which the structure may be subject during erection and subsequent construction, including loads due to wind, equipment and operation of same. Temporary bracing shall be left in place undisturbed as long as required for safety (see also Clause 25). The erector shall ensure during erection that an adequate margin of safety exists in the uncompleted structure and members using the factored member resistance computed in accordance with Clause 13. (See also Clause 19.1.3.)

28.2   **Temporary Loads**
Wherever piles of material, erection equipment, or other loads are carried during erection, suitable provision shall be made to ensure that the loads can be safely sustained during their duration and without permanent deformation or other damage to any member of the steel frame and other building components supported thereby.

28.3   **Adequacy of Temporary Connections**
As erection progresses the work shall be securely bolted or welded to take care of all dead load, wind, and erection loads.

28.4   **Alignment**
No permanent welding or bolting shall be done until as much of the structure as will be stiffened thereby has been suitably aligned.

28.5   **Surface Preparation for Field Welding**
The portions of surfaces that are to receive welds shall be thoroughly cleaned of all foreign matter, including paint film.

28.6   **Field Painting**
Unless otherwise specified, the cleaning of steelwork in preparation for field painting, touch-up of shop primer, spot-painting of field fasteners, and general field painting, shall not be considered to be a part of the erection work.

28.7   **Erection Tolerances**

28.7.1   Unless otherwise specified, members of the steel framework shall be considered plumb, level, and aligned if the misalignment does not exceed the following tolerances:

(a) Exterior columns of multi-storey buildings — 1 to 1000; but not more than 25 mm towards nor 50 mm away from the building line in the first 20 storeys plus 2 mm for each additional storey up to a maximum of 50 mm towards or 75 mm away from the building line over the full height of the building;

(b) Columns adjacent to elevator shafts — 1 to 1000; but not more than 25 mm in the first 20 storeys plus 1 mm for each additional storey up to a maximum of 50 mm over the full height of the elevator shaft:

(c) Spandrel beams — 1 to 1000;

(d) All other pieces — 1 to 500.

28.7.2   Shelf angles, sash angles, and lintels specified to be provided with adjustable connections shall be considered within tolerances when each piece is level within a tolerance of 1 to 1000, when adjoining ends of these members are aligned vertically within 2 mm and when the locations of these members vertically and horizontally is within 10 mm of the location established by the dimensions on the drawings.

28.7.3   Column splices and other compression joints which depend upon contact bearing, after alignment shall have at least 65 per cent of the entire contact area in full bearing and the separations of any remaining portions shall not exceed 0.5 mm except locally at toes of flanges where a separation of 0.75 mm is permissible; otherwise corrective measures shall be taken.

28.7.4   The fit-up of joints to be field welded shall be within the tolerances shown on the field assembly drawings before welding is begun.

29.   **Inspection**

29.1   **General**
Material and workmanship at all times shall be subject to inspection by qualified inspectors representing and responsible to the authority having jurisdiction. The inspection shall cover shop work and field erection work to ensure compliance with this Standard.

29.2   **Co-operation**
All inspection insofar as possible shall be made in the fabricator's shop and the fabricator shall co-operate with the inspector, permitting access for inspection to all places where work is being done. The inspector shall co-operate in avoiding undue delay in the fabrication or erection of the steelwork.

29.3   **Rejection**
Material or workmanship not conforming to the provisions of this Standard may be rejected at any time during the progress of work when non-conformance to these provisions is established.

29.4   **Inspection of High-Strength Bolted Joints**
The inspection of high-strength bolted joints shall be performed in accordance with the procedures prescribed in Clause 23.

29.5   **Inspection of Welding**
The inspection of welding shall be in accordance with the applicable clause in CSA Standard W59, Welded Steel Construction (Metal-Arc Welding).

29.6   **Identification of Steel by Marking**
In the fabricator's plant steel used for main components shall at all times be marked to identify its specification (and grade, if applicable). This shall be done by suitable markings or by recognized colour coding except that cut pieces identified by piece mark and contract number need not continue to carry specification identification markings when it has been satisfactorily established that such cut pieces conform to the required material specifications.

Appendix A

Standard Practice for Structural Steel for Buildings

Note: *This Appendix is not a mandatory part of this Standard.*

A1. Matters concerning standard practice not covered by the Standard but pertinent to the fabrication and erection of structural steel, such as a definition of structural steel items, the computation of weights, etc., are to be in accordance with the "Code of Standard Practice for Structural Steel" published by the Canadian Institute of Steel Construction unless otherwise clearly specified in the plans and specifications issued to the bidders.

Note:

See page 4–22 for Appendix B
See page 4–24 for Appendix C
See page 4–108 for Appendix F
See page 5–169 for Appendix G
See page 4–20 for Appendix J
See page 7–3 for CISC Code of Standard Practice.

Appendix D

Graph Showing Unit Compressive Resistance Versus Slenderness Ratio

Note: This Appendix is not a mandatory part of this Standard.

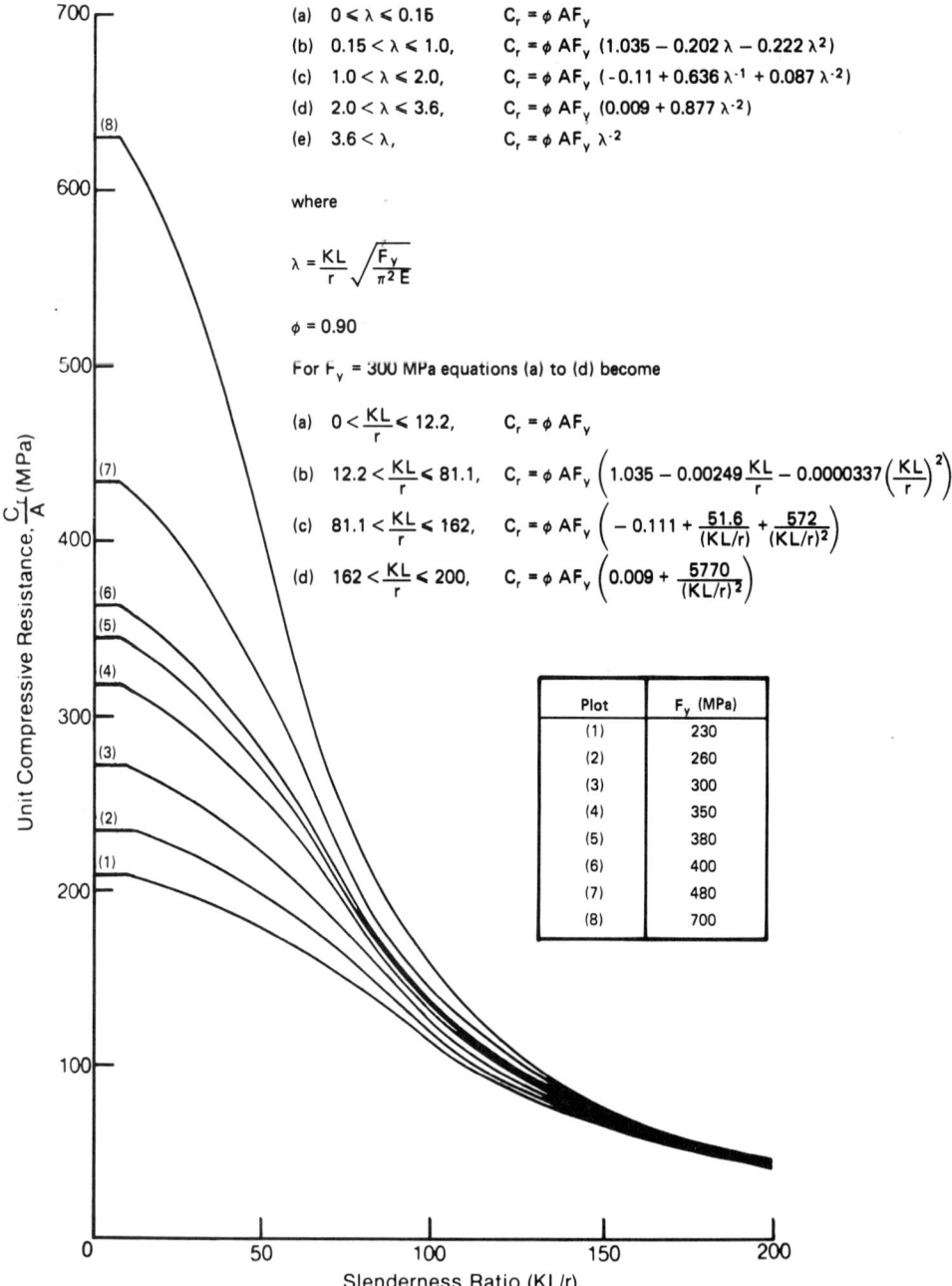

(a) $0 \leqslant \lambda \leqslant 0.15$, $C_r = \phi AF_y$

(b) $0.15 < \lambda \leqslant 1.0$, $C_r = \phi AF_y (1.035 - 0.202\lambda - 0.222\lambda^2)$

(c) $1.0 < \lambda \leqslant 2.0$, $C_r = \phi AF_y (-0.11 + 0.636\lambda^{-1} + 0.087\lambda^{-2})$

(d) $2.0 < \lambda \leqslant 3.6$, $C_r = \phi AF_y (0.009 + 0.877\lambda^{-2})$

(e) $3.6 < \lambda$, $C_r = \phi AF_y \lambda^{-2}$

where

$$\lambda = \frac{KL}{r} \sqrt{\frac{F_y}{\pi^2 E}}$$

$\phi = 0.90$

For $F_y = 300$ MPa equations (a) to (d) become

(a) $0 < \dfrac{KL}{r} \leqslant 12.2$, $C_r = \phi AF_y$

(b) $12.2 < \dfrac{KL}{r} \leqslant 81.1$, $C_r = \phi AF_y \left(1.035 - 0.00249\dfrac{KL}{r} - 0.0000337\left(\dfrac{KL}{r}\right)^2 \right)$

(c) $81.1 < \dfrac{KL}{r} \leqslant 162$, $C_r = \phi AF_y \left(-0.111 + \dfrac{51.6}{(KL/r)} + \dfrac{572}{(KL/r)^2} \right)$

(d) $162 < \dfrac{KL}{r} \leqslant 200$, $C_r = \phi AF_y \left(0.009 + \dfrac{5770}{(KL/r)^2} \right)$

Plot	F_y (MPa)
(1)	230
(2)	260
(3)	300
(4)	350
(5)	380
(6)	400
(7)	480
(8)	700

Figure D1

Note: For the curves plotted, equation (e) applies only to $F_y = 700$ MPa with $KL/r \geqslant 191.2$.

Appendix E

Margins of Safety

Note: This Appendix is not a mandatory part of this Standard.

E1. An advantage of limit states design is that the probability of failure for different loading conditions is made more consistent, by the use of distinct load factors for the different loads to which the structure is subject, than is the case in working stress design where a single factor of safety is used. Furthermore different performance factors can, in a parallel manner, be applied to determine member resistances with a uniform reliability. The combination of the load factor and the inverse of the performance factor gives a number comparable to the traditional factor of safety. In this Standard a performance factor of 0.90 is generally used.

E2. For live loads the load factor of 1.50 multiplied by the inverse of the performance factor 1/0.90 equals 1.67, comparable to the working stress design standard. By using a load factor of 1.25 for dead load, probabilistic studies indicate that consistent probabilities of failure are determined over all ranges of dead to live load ratios. The same probabilistic studies also show that load combination factors of 0.70 and 0.60, (depending on the number of loads taken in combination) applied only to live, wind or earthquake and temperature, and a factor of 0.85 applied to dead load when it is counteractive to live loads, also result in a consistent probability of failure.

E3. Performance factor, see Clause 3.1.3, generally allows for underrun in the member or connection resistance as compared to that predicted. The underrun may arise from variability in material properties, dimensions and workmanship as well as from simplifications in the mathematical derivation of the resistance equation.

For simplicity in some cases in this Standard uncertainty in the formulation of the theoretical member resistance has been incorporated directly in the expression for member resistance rather than using a lower value for the performance factor. This is the case for the column curve where the curve predicting the ultimate strengths as a function of slenderness ratio has been derived statistically taking into account residual stresses and initial out-of-straightness.

E4. For bolts a performance factor of 0.67 is used to ensure that connector failures will not occur before general failure of the member as a whole. For long bolted joints and for the case where shear planes intersect the threads, reduction factors are applied to the resistance formulations. As for bolts, a performance factor of 0.67 is desirable for welds. The numerical modifier (0.50) in the expressions for weld resistance contains a component which reduces the nominal performance factor used in that section (0.90) to the value of 0.67.

E5. The expressions for resistance for welds are based on CSA Standard W59, Welded Steel Construction (Metal-Arc Welding), and therefore maintain the margins of safety of that Standard.

Appendix H

Wind Sway Vibrations

Note: This Appendix is not a mandatory part of this Standard.

H1. Wind motion of tall buildings or other flexible structures may create annoyance for human occupants, unless measures are taken at the design stage. The main source of annoyance is lateral acceleration, although noise (grinding and wind howl) and visual effects can also cause concern.

H2. For a given wind speed and direction, the motion of a building, which includes vibration parallel and perpendicular to the wind direction and twist, is best predicted by a wind tunnel test. Approximate calculation rules are, however, given in References (1) and (4) of Clause H4.

H3. In cases where wind motion is significant in design, the following should be considered:

(a) Education of occupants that although high winds may occasionally cause motion, the building is safe;

(b) Minimization of noises — detailing of building joints to avoid grinding, design of elevator guides to avoid scraping due to sway;

(c) Minimization of twist by symmetry of layout, bracing or outer walls (tube concept). Twist vibration also creates a magnified visual effect of relative motion of adjacent buildings;

(d) Possible introduction of mechanical damping to reduce wind vibration.

H4. **References**

(1) Supplement No. 4 to the National Building Code of Canada, 1977, Commentary on Wind Loads.

(2) Hansen, R.J., Reed, J.W. and Van Marcke, E. H. Human Response to Wind-Induced Motion of Buildings, Journal of the Structural Division, ASCE, Vol. 99, No. ST7, July 1973, p. 1589—1605.

(3) Chen, P.W. and Robertson, L.E. Human Perception Thresholds of Horizontal Motion. Journal of the Structural Division, ASCE, Vol. 98, No. ST8, August 1972, p. 1681—1695.

(4) Davenport, A.G. New Approaches to Design Against Wind Action. In Press.

(5) Reed, J.W. Wind-Induced Motion and Human Discomfort in Tall Buildings. Department of Civil Engineering Research Report R71-42. Massachusetts Institute of Technology, November 1971.

(6) Hogan, M. The Influence of Wind on Tall Building Design. Faculty of Engineering Science Research Report BLWT-4-71, University of Western Ontario, March 1971.

Appendix I

Recommended Maximum Values for Deflections

Note: *This Appendix is not a mandatory part of this Standard.*

For Specified Design Live and Wind Loads[*]

		Due to:		
Industrial Type Buildings	**Vertical Deflection**	Live Load	Simple span members supporting inelastic roof coverings	$\frac{1}{240}$ of span
		Live Load	Simple span members supporting elastic roof coverings	$\frac{1}{180}$ of span
		Live Load	Simple span members supporting floors	$\frac{1}{300}$ of span
		Maximum Wheel Loads (no impact)	Simple span crane runway girders for crane capacity of 225 kN and over	$\frac{1}{800}$ of span
		Maximum Wheel Loads (no impact)	Simple span crane runway girders for crane capacity under 225 kN ..	$\frac{1}{600}$ of span
	Lateral Deflection	Crane Lateral Force	Simple span crane runway girders	$\frac{1}{600}$ of span
		Crane Lateral Force OR Wind	Building column sway†	$\frac{1}{400}$ to $\frac{1}{200}$ of height

(Continued)

For Specified Design Live and Wind Loads* (Continued)

All Other Buildings	**Vertical Deflection**	Live Load	Simple span members of floors and roofs supporting construction and finishes susceptible to cracking	$\frac{1}{360}$ of span
		Live Load	Simple span members of floors and roofs supporting construction and finishes not susceptible to cracking	$\frac{1}{300}$ of span
	Lateral Deflection	Wind	Building sway, due to all effects	$\frac{1}{400}$ of bldg. height
		Wind	Storey drift, (relative horizontal movement of any two consecutive floors due to the shear effects) in buildings with cladding and partitions without special provision to accommodate building frame deformation	$\frac{1}{500}$ of storey height
		Wind	The same, with such provision	$\frac{1}{400}$ of height

*Since some building materials augment the rigidity provided by the steelwork, the wind load assumed carried by the steelwork, for calculating deflections can be somewhat reduced from the design wind used in strength and stability calculations. The more common structural elements contributing to the stiffness of a building are masonry walls, certain types of curtain walls, masonry partitions and concrete around steel members. The **maximum** suggested amount of this reduction is 15 per cent. In tall and slender structures (height greater than **4 times** the width) it is recommended that the wind effects be determined by means of dynamic analysis, or wind tunnel tests.

†Permissible sway of industrial buildings varies considerably depending on factors such as wall construction, building height, effect of deflection on the operation of crane, etc. Where the operation of the crane is sensitive to the lateral deflections, a permissable lateral deflection less than 1/400 of the height may be required.

Appendix K

Fatigue

Note: *This Appendix is not a mandatory part of this Standard.*

K1.   Figure K1 is a plot of the design curves for the allowable stress range for categories A to F of Tables 6(a) and (b).

K2.   Figure K2 gives illustrative examples of the various fatigue categories described in Table 6(b).

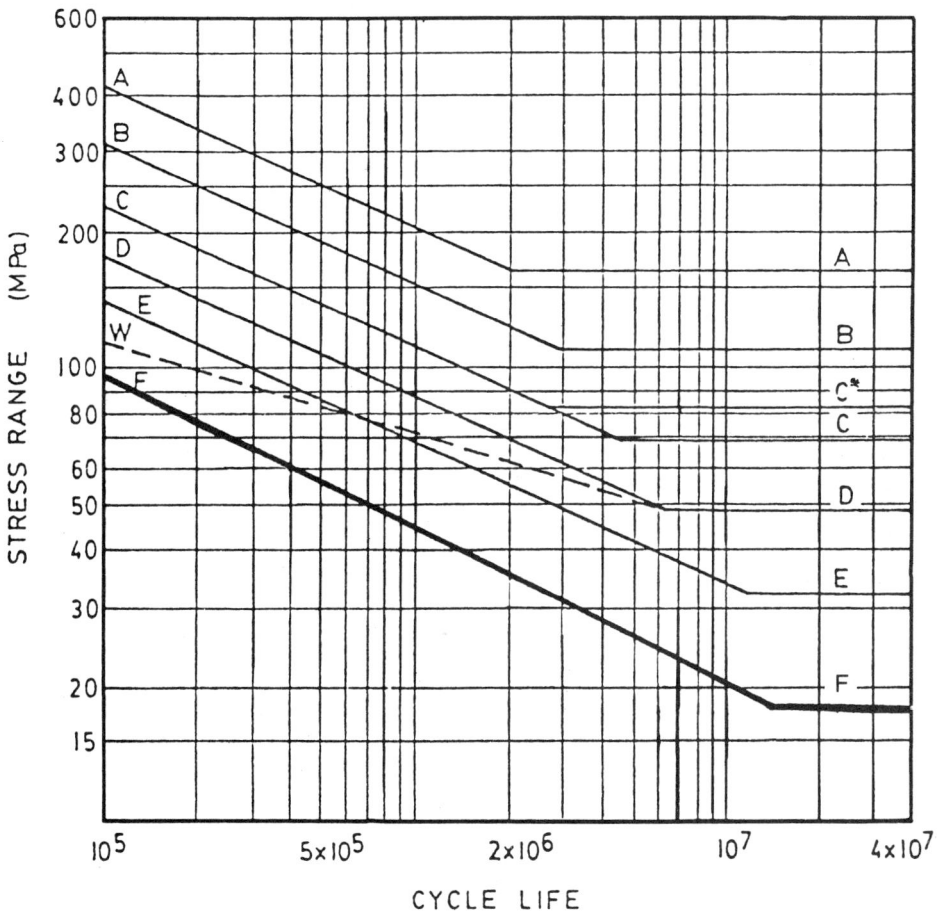

Except for transverse stiffener welds on girder webs or flanges where 83 M Pa should be used.

Figure K1
Design Curves for the Allowable Stress Range for Categories A to F

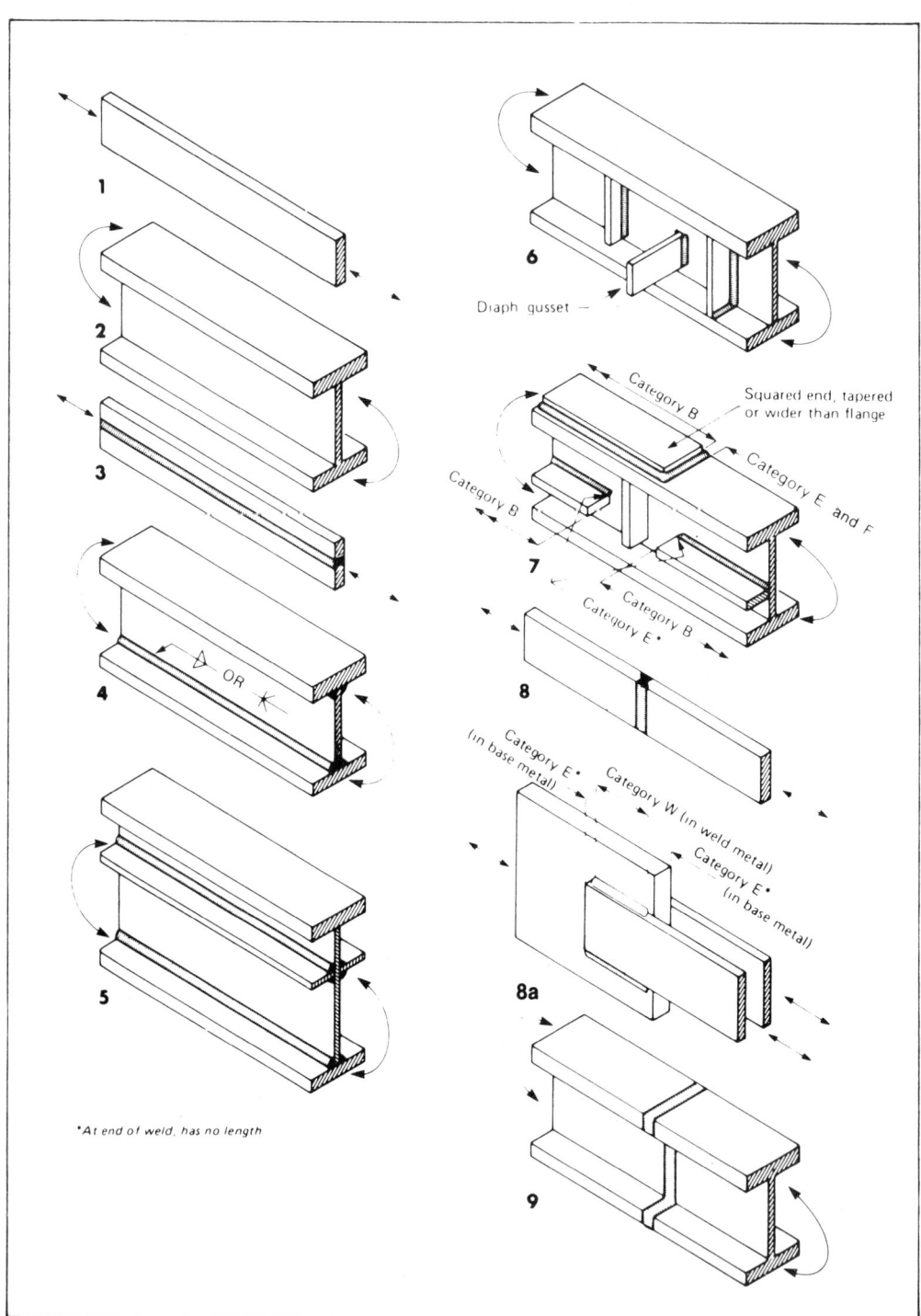

Figure K2
Illustrative Examples of Various Fatigue Categories

Note: *The numbers below each Figure are referenced in Table 6(b).*

(Continued)

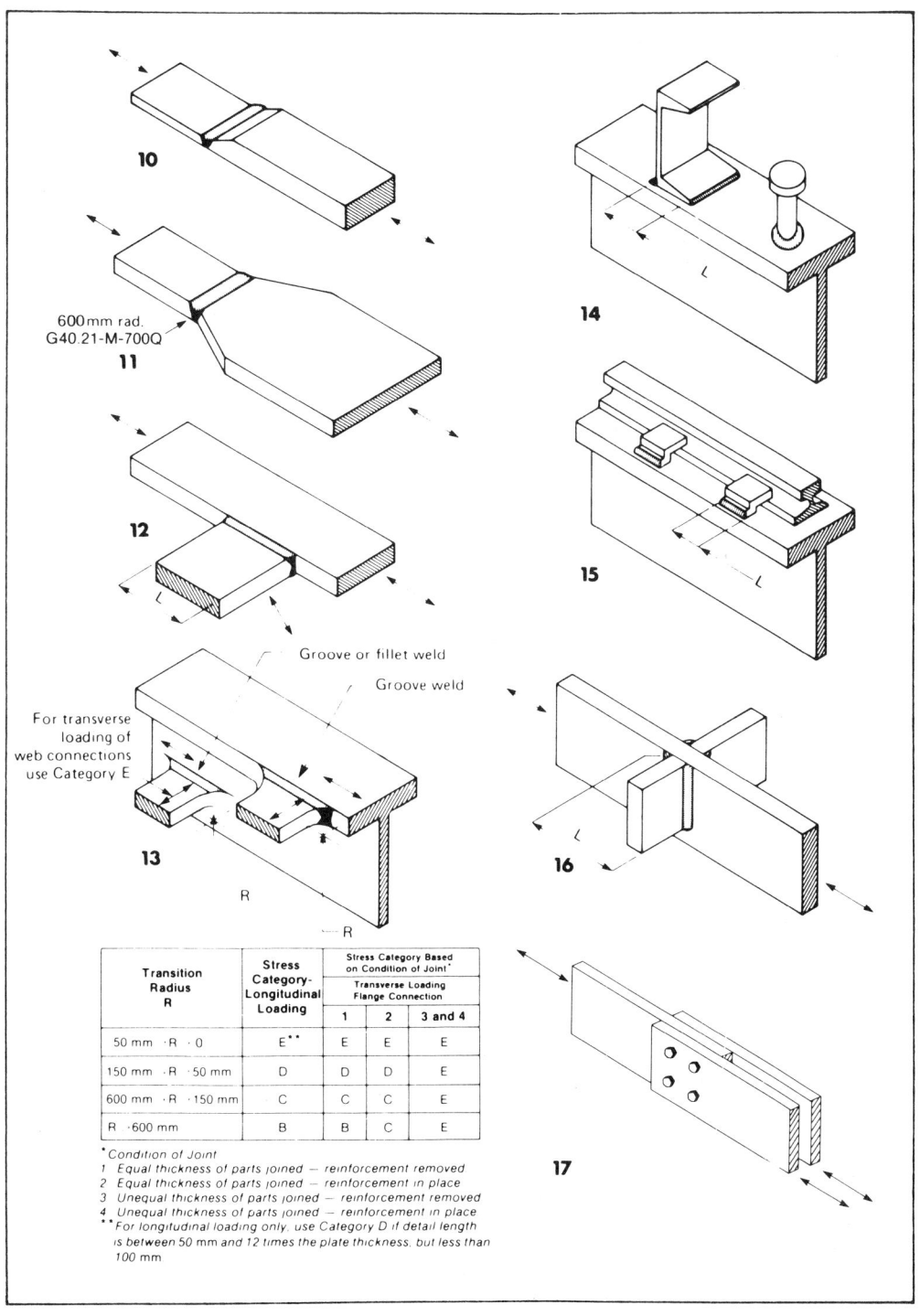

10

11 600mm rad. G40.21-M-700Q

12 L

13 For transverse loading of web connections use Category E

Groove or fillet weld
Groove weld

R
R

14 L

15 L

16 L

17

Transition Radius R	Stress Category-Longitudinal Loading	Stress Category Based on Condition of Joint*		
		Transverse Loading Flange Connection		
		1	2	3 and 4
50 mm · R · 0	E**	E	E	E
150 mm · R · 50 mm	D	D	D	E
600 mm · R · 150 mm	C	C	C	E
R ·600 mm	B	B	C	E

*Condition of Joint
1 Equal thickness of parts joined — reinforcement removed
2 Equal thickness of parts joined — reinforcement in place
3 Unequal thickness of parts joined — reinforcement removed
4 Unequal thickness of parts joined — reinforcement in place
** For longitudinal loading only, use Category D if detail length is between 50 mm and 12 times the plate thickness, but less than 100 mm

Figure K2 (Continued)

Note: *The numbers below each Figure are referenced in Table 6(b).*

PART TWO
CISC COMMENTARY ON CAN3-S16.1-M78

Preface

This Commentary has been prepared by the Canadian Institute of Steel Construction in order to clarify the intent of various provisions of the National Standard of Canada, written by CSA, CAN3-S16.1-M78, "Steel Structures for Buildings — Limit States Design". This standard is the SI (metric) edition of the Limit States Standard first published by CSA as S16.1-1974. This Commentary and the information contained in the over one hundred references cited herein provide an extensive backdrop to the development of the Standard and its technical requirements.

The Institute gratefully acknowledges the efforts of Dr. G. L. Kulak in the preparation of the SI Commentary and of Drs. P. F. Adams, D. E. Allen, Y. M. Giroux and D.J.L. Kennedy and Messrs. H. A. Krentz, J. Springfield, D. L. Tarlton and D. K. Turner for their valuable contributions to the Commentary.

The explanations and opinions expressed in this Commentary are those of the Institute and are not intended to be considered the opinion of the CSA Committee responsible for the preparation of the Standard nor to detract from this Committee's duties insofar as interpretation and revision of the Standard is concerned.

M. I. Gilmor
Editor

Introduction

In 1974 the Canadian Standards Association introduced the new standard S16.1-1974, "Steel Structures for Buildings — Limit States Design". This represented a significant departure from previous standards concerned with the design of steel structures for buildings in North America and, particularly, in Canada. In 1978 CSA produced the National Standard of Canada CAN3-S16.1-M78. This standard is the one referred to in this Commentary and is the basis of the tables and other descriptive material provided in Parts 3 to 5 of the Handbook. For the most part, S16.1-M78 is simply the reformulation of the previous standard S16.1-1974 into SI (Systéme International) units. There are some changes of substance, however, as improvements in S16.1-1974 became apparent or as new information about member and structure behavior became available.

Standards based on working stress, with the exception of a few clauses on plastic design, require the calculation of stresses at various points in the structure and comparison of these stresses with allowable stresses. The allowable stresses are usually established as some portion of the yield point of the material. Elements or members subjected to compression are examined for stability, usually expressed as an allowable compressive stress. A limit states standard takes a different approach. To serve their intended purposes, all building structures must meet the following requirement — to prevent, with sufficiently small probability, the occurrence of various types of collapse or unserviceability. Limit states are those conditions of the structure corresponding to the onset of the various types of collapse or unserviceability. The conditions associated with collapse are called ultimate limit states; those associated with unserviceability are called serviceability limit states.

In limit states design, the capacity or performance of the structure or its components is checked against the various limit states at certain load levels. For the ultimate limit states of strength and stability, the structure must retain its load carrying capacity up to the factored load levels. For serviceability limit states, the performance of the structure at specified load levels must be satisfactory. (Specified loads are those prescribed by the authority having jurisdiction over the building. A factored load is the product of a specified load and its load factor.) Examples of the serviceability requirement include prevention of damage to non-structural elements, and restrictions on deflections, permanent deformations, fatigue cracking, slip in slip-resistant (friction-type) connections, and acceleration under vibratory motion.

Because both the loads acting on a structure and the resistance of a member can only be defined statistically, the "factor of safety", commonly used in working stress standards, is divided, in limit states standards, into two parts — a load factor and a performance factor. A load factor (α) is applied to the specified load to take into account the fact that loads higher than those anticipated may exist and also to take into account approximations in the analysis of the load effects. A performance factor (ϕ) is applied to the theoretical member strengths, or resistances (R), to take into account that the resistance of the member due to variability of the material properties, dimensions and workmanship may be less than anticipated, and also to take into account the type of failure and uncertainty in the prediction of the resistance. An advantage, therefore, of limit states design is that the factors assigned to loads arising from different sources can be related to their uncertainty of prediction, and the factors assigned to different members can be related to their reliability and to the different types of failure. Thus, a greater degree of consistency against failure can be obtained[1,2,3].

For the failure of structural steel members by yielding, the performance factor was taken to be 0.90[112] To maintain simplicity in design, the resistance formulas for buckling or other types of member failure were adjusted so that a uniform performance factor, $\phi = 0.90$, could be used and yet provide the necessary safety required in the definition of the performance factor. For example, the resistance formula for tension, clause 13.2(a)(i), provides a higher safety factor for members which fracture across the net sec-

FIGURE 2-1

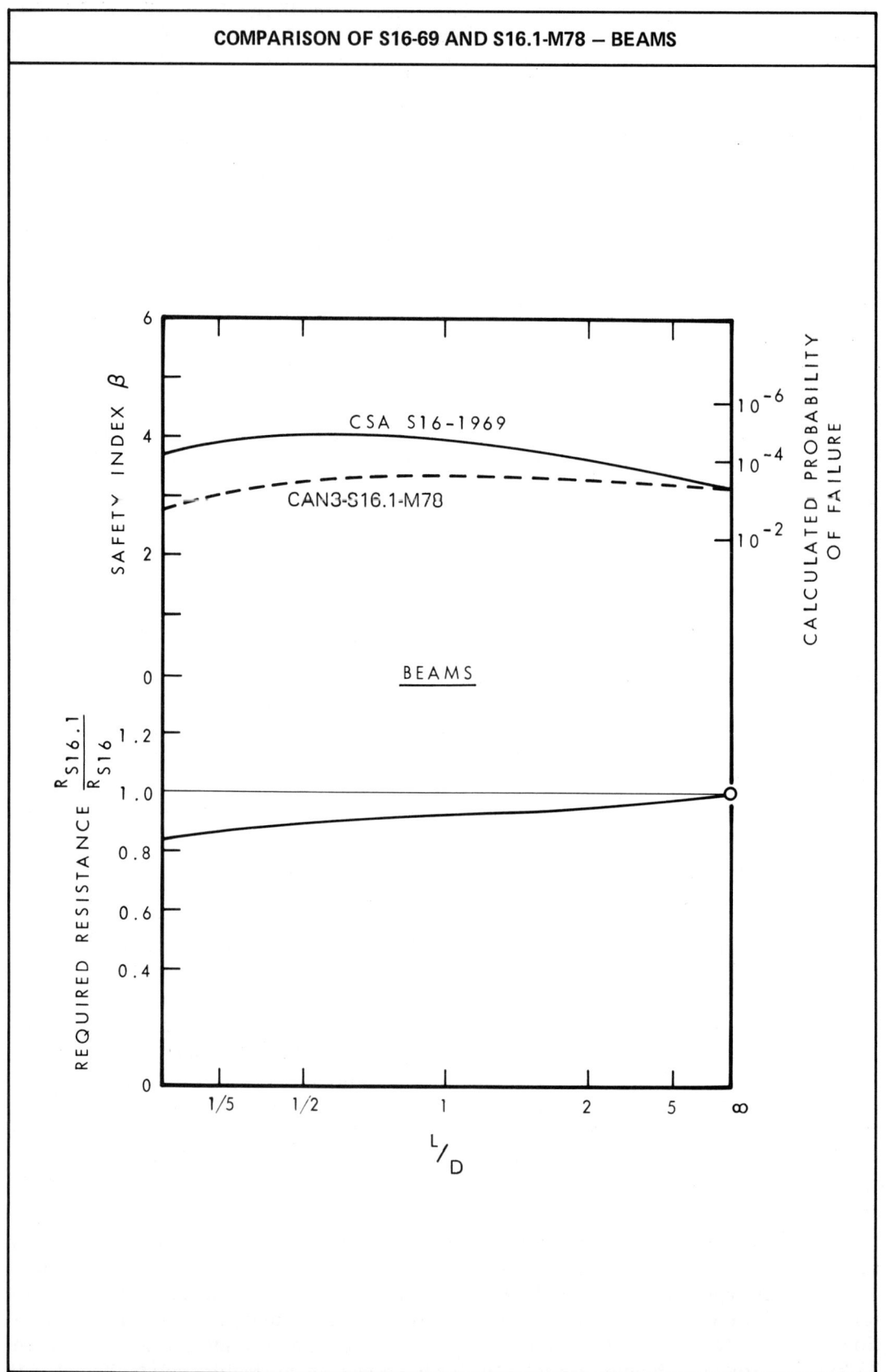

COMPARISON OF S16-69 AND S16.1-M78 — BEAMS

FIGURE 2-2

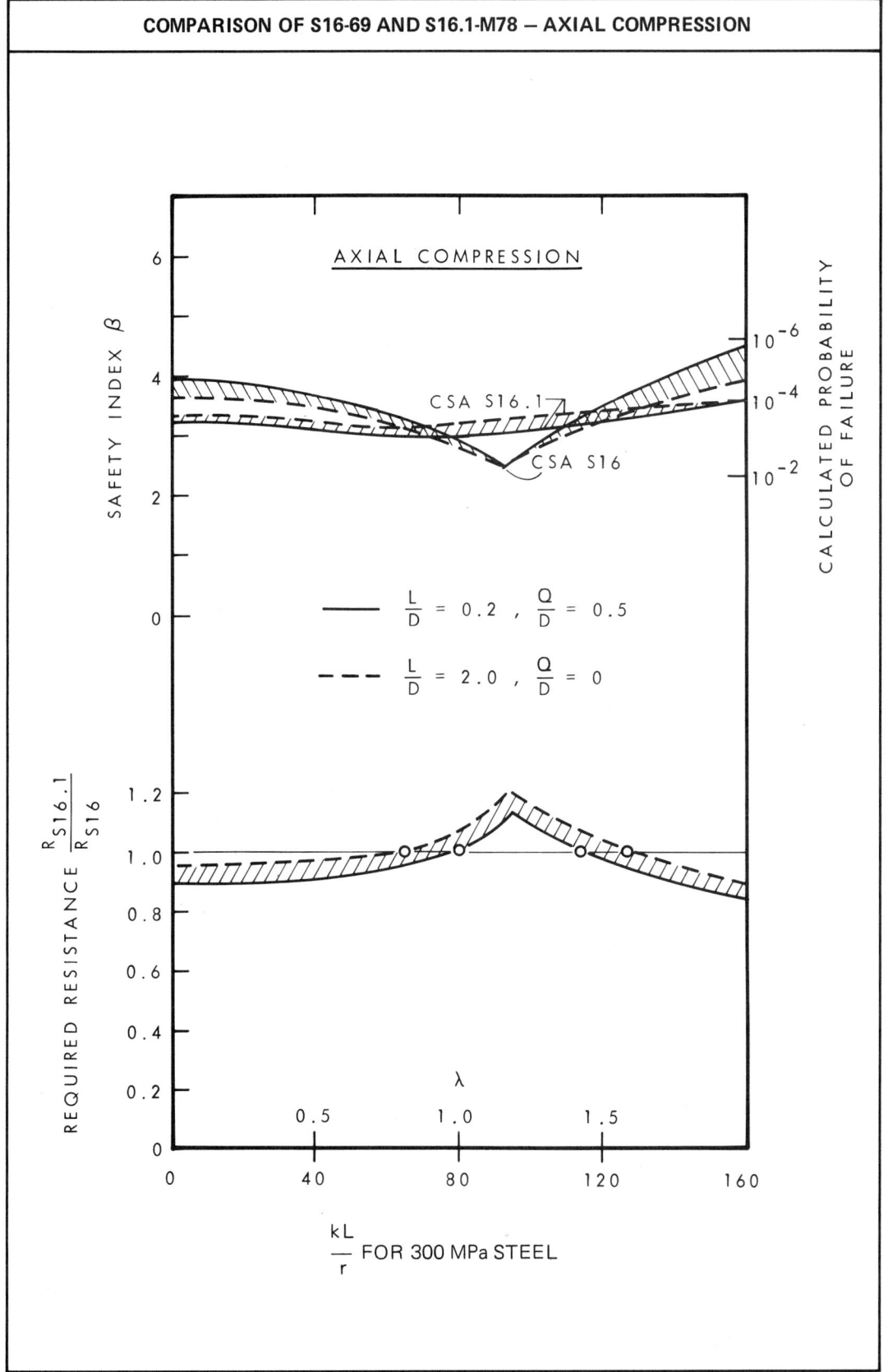

COMPARISON OF S16-69 AND S16.1-M78 — AXIAL COMPRESSION

AXIAL COMPRESSION

CSA S16.1

CSA S16

$\dfrac{L}{D} = 0.2 \; , \; \dfrac{Q}{D} = 0.5$

$\dfrac{L}{D} = 2.0 \; , \; \dfrac{Q}{D} = 0$

SAFETY INDEX β

CALCULATED PROBABILITY OF FAILURE

REQUIRED RESISTANCE $\dfrac{R_{S16.1}}{R_{S16}}$

λ

$\dfrac{kL}{r}$ FOR 300 MPa STEEL

tion before the member can yield in the gross section. For columns, a substantial change was made to the column formula, since the previous formula gave inconsistent safety levels for different slenderness ratios. The only exceptions to $\phi = 0.90$ are:

(1) Bolts in bearing type connections, where $\phi = 0.67$, to ensure that the connectors will be stronger than the members being joined;

(2) Crushing resistance of concrete (for composite construction), $\phi_c = 0.67$ to take into account the greater strength variability and type of failure associated with concrete.

(3) Shear connectors (for composite construction), $\phi_{sc} = 0.80$.

Probabilistic studies[2] show that consistent probabilities of failure are determined for all dead-to-live load ratios when a dead load factor of 1.25 and a live load factor of 1.50 are used. The live load factor of 1.50, when divided by the performance factor of 0.90, gives a factor of 1.67 which is the nominal factor of safety in the working stress design standard, CSA S16-1969, "Steel Structures for Buildings"[56]. Thus, the limit states design standard, S16.1-M78 is calibrated to the working stress design standard S16-1969, which has a long history of successful application.

Figures 2—1 and 2—2 compare S16.1-M78 and S16-1969 for beams, and for columns in axial compression. The safety index, β, which is a measure of the probability of failure[2], is plotted in the upper part of the Figures. It is seen that S16.1 gives more uniform safety, $2.9 < \beta < 3.5$, for these cases than does S16, $2.5 < \beta < 4.5$. The ratio of resistances required by the two standards is plotted in the lower part of the figures. The circles identify cases when both standards give the same required resistance. These occur for beams subject to live load only and for intermediate columns. Assuming that design is governed by strength, the figures indicate roughly a 10 percent decrease in material for beams and short columns carrying mainly dead load and an increase of 0 to 10 percent for intermediate to long columns. Overall a material saving of roughly 5 percent is expected.

The saving in material is essentially due to a reduction in the load factor for dead load compared to previous standards. The justification for this is that dead loads can be predicted more closely both in magnitude and distribution and can be controlled more closely than the variable loads.

References 1 and 2 provide considerably more information on the type of probabilistic, calibration and design studies that were performed while developing the limit states standard. Reference 4 contains a more extensive discussion on limit states design in the National Building Code of Canada. Reference 112 provides information on the statistical determination of the performance factor (ϕ).

It is expected that the use of National Standard of Canada CAN3-S16.1-M78 will lead to some economic advantage in the construction of steel structures and will help many designers to develop an improved understanding of the behaviour of structures. At the same time, a more uniform degree of safety against failure of steel structural members should be achieved.

In the Commentary clauses that follow, the numbers and headings used refer to the relevant clause numbers and headings of National Standard of Canada CAN3-S16.1-M78. For simplicity, this will be referred to as S16.1-M78.

1. SCOPE

When structures are designed using S16.1-M78, no use shall be made of CSA Standard S16-1969. In S16-1969 only specified loads are used for determining the strength of members, while in S16.1-M78, both specified and factored loads are used. Thus, by staying within one standard the possibility of confusion as to which loads are being considered is reduced. Furthermore, some of the technical requirements in the new standard are more stringent and therefore have a counter effect to the changes resulting from the new load factors.

An exception is made for open web steel joists not participating in lateral force-resisting frames provided that they are designed in accordance with Supplement 1-75 of S16-1969 since, by this Supplement, the joist clauses of S16-69 were revised in keeping with those of S16.1-1974.

2. APPLICATION

Clause 2.3 of this section notes that the designer has the freedom (subject to approval from the authority having jurisdiction) to use methods of design or analyses in lieu of the formulae given in the Standard. It is required, of course, that the same margins of safety that are in the Standard be provided in the alternate.

5. MATERIALS: STANDARDS AND IDENTIFICATION

The design requirements contained in S16.1-M78 have been developed on the assumption that the materials and products which will be used are those listed in clause 5. These materials and products are all covered by standards prepared by the Canadian Standards Association (CSA) or the American Society for Testing and Materials (ASTM).

The standards listed provide controls over manufacture and delivery of the materials and products which are necessary to ensure that the materials and products will have the characteristics assumed when the design provisions of S16.1-M78 were prepared. The use of materials and products other than those listed is permitted, but the designer should assure himself, when this option is used, that the materials and products have the characteristics required to perform satisfactorily in the structure. In particular, ductility is often as important as the strength of the material. Weldability and toughness may also be required in many structures.

6. DESIGN REQUIREMENTS

This clause clearly distinguishes between those requirements which must be checked using specified loads (serviceability limit states) and those which must be checked using factored loads (ultimate limit states). Many of the serviceability requirements (deflections, vibrations, etc.) are stipulated qualitatively and guidance, in quantitative form, is provided in Appendices. Thus, the designer is permitted to use the best information available to him in order to satisfy the serviceability requirements, but is also provided with information that the S16 Committee considers to be generally suitable, when used with competent engineering judgement.

Since the S16.1-M78 Standard was published, additional useful information on vibrations of floor systems (clause 6.2.3.2) has been published[5,6,7,118].

7. LOADS AND SAFETY CRITERION

This clause sets forth the fundamental safety criterion that must be met, namely;

Factored Resistance $\geq$ Effect of Factored Loads

The expression for the Effect of Factored Loads,

$$\alpha_D D + \gamma \psi (\alpha_L L + \alpha_Q Q + \alpha_T T)$$

is identical with that given in Part 4 of the National Building Code of Canada[8] as are the values given for the various load factors (α), load combination factors (ψ) and importance factors (γ). This data has been included in clause 7 for the convenience of designers using S16.1-M78.

The Factored Resistance is given by the product ϕ R, where ϕ is the performance factor discussed in the introduction to this Commentary and R is the theoretical member strength, or resistance. The Factored Resistances of various types of members are given in clauses 13, 15, 16, 17 and 20.

8. ANALYSIS OF STRUCTURE

Clause 8 permits the use of two basic types of construction — "continuous" and "simple" — and each type is defined. In recognition of previous successful practice, a special form of "simple" construction is permitted. In this form of construction, a building frame may be designed to support gravity loads on the basis of "simple" construction and to support lateral loads due to wind or earthquake through the provision of moment-resisting joints. A number of limitations are imposed in clause 8.3.2 if this method is used.

The limitations are intended to ensure that the moment-resisting joints designed nominally for wind or earthquake moments alone have both the strength and ductility necessary to accommodate the "overload" which will result if factored gravity and lateral loads act concurrently. It is assumed that if the connection has adequate capacity for inelastic rotation when subjected to the first application of factored gravity and lateral loading, under subsequent loading cycles the connection will behave elastically although it will have a permanent inelastic deformation[9,10]. Such an assumption is valid except in joints where load fluctuation would create alternating plasticity in the connection[11].

Clause 8 also permits the use of two general methods of analysis — elastic and plastic. Methods of elastic analysis are familiar to most designers. A brief explanation of the plastic analysis requirements of clause 8.5 in S16.1-M78 follows.

8.5 Plastic Analysis

The use of plastic analyses at the factored load levels to determine the forces and moments throughout a structure implies that the structure achieves its limit of usefulness when sufficient plastic hinges have developed to transform the frame into a mechanism. During the hinging process, the structure develops an increased load-carrying capacity above that corresponding to the formation of the initial plastic hinge. On the other hand, the members in which the early-forming hinges occur must be sufficiently stocky and well braced so that inelastic deformations can occur without loss of moment capacity.

Deflections at the specified load level are limited in accordance with clause 6.2.1. This is based on the premise that where deflections are important the same limitations should apply regardless of the method of analysis. Plastically designed structures are usually "elastic" at specified load levels so the deflections would be computed on the basis of an elastic analysis.

8.5(a) Material. The plastic method relies on certain basic assumptions for its validity[12] and this Standard imposes the necessary restrictions in order to preserve the applicability of the plastic theory. The basic restriction pertains to the steel itself and is contained in clause 8.5(a) which states, in effect, that the steel specified shall be characterized by a plateau in the stress-strain curve at the yield stress level and shall exhibit strain-hardening when the average strain exceeds the plastic strain. The use of steels exhibiting significant amounts of strain-hardening is a first step toward ensuring that satisfactory moment redistribution will occur[13]. This behavior should be evidenced at the temperatures to which the structure will be subjected in service. Also, although not explicitly stated, plastically designed structures usually entail welded fabrication, and therefore the steel specified should also be weldable. At normal temperatures all the steels referred to in clause 5.1.2 should be satisfactory except for CSA G40.21-M, 700 Q and 700 QT steels ($F_y > 0.80 \, F_u$).

8.5(b) Width-Thickness Ratios. In order to preclude local buckling and thus ensure adequate hinge rotation, compression elements in regions of plastic moment must have width-thickness ratios no greater than those specified for Class 1 (plastic design) sections in clause 11.2. Class 1 sections are more restricted in width-thickness ratio requirements than Class 2 sections. Although both are expected to meet the same strength requirement (attainment of the plastic moment), only plastic design sections need the rotation capacity necessary for redistribution of moments.

8.5(c) Lateral Bracing. The lateral bracing requirements are more severe than those for structures designed on the basis of an elastic moment distribution so that adequate rotation capacity of the member is ensured. Two values of L_{cr} are specified, one for the case where the moment gradient is pronounced, the other (more stringent) for the case of uniform, or near uniform moment. The dividing point has been selected as $M/M_p = 0.5$ as this seems to best agree with available test results[14]. Both criteria should be applied and the more severe requirement shall govern the determination of L_{cr}.

Since the final hinge in the failure mechanism does not require rotation capacity the bracing spacing limitations of this clause do not apply and the requirements of clause 13.6.1 may be used.

Lateral bracing is required to prevent both lateral movement and twisting at a braced point. Lateral bracing is usually provided by floor beams or purlins which frame into the beam to be braced. These bracing members must have adequate axial strength and axial stiffness to resist the tendency to lateral deflection. These requirements are indicated in clause 19.3 and further information on the design of bracing members is available in reference 15. When the bracing member contacts the member braced only at the compression flange, it is desirable that the lateral brace possess some bending stiffness about its major axis; however, there are insufficient experimental results to indicate the magnitude required.

A concrete slab into which the compression flange is embedded or to which the compression flange is mechanically connected, as in composite construction, or metal decks welded to the top flange of the beam in the positive moment region, would provide sufficient restraint to lateral and torsional displacements. Reference 107 suggests that the point of contraflexure of the plastic moment diagram may be considered a braced point. If the lateral brace is connected to the tension flange provision must be made for maintaining the shape of the cross-section and for preventing lateral movement of the compression flange.

8.5(d) Web Crippling. Web stiffeners are required on a member at a point of load application where a plastic hinge would form. Stiffeners are also required at beam-to-column connections where the loads delivered by beam flanges would either cripple the column web or, in the case of tension loads, curl the column flange. The rules for stiffener design are given in clause 20.3.

In lieu of pairs of stiffener plates parallel to and approximately in line with the flanges of the member delivering the load, plates parallel to the column web and attached to the toes of the column flanges may be used. Reference should be made to the technical literature[12] for further details of stiffeners and for special requirements pertaining to tapered and curved haunches[16].

When the shear force is excessive, additional stiffening may be required to limit shear deformations. The capacity of an unreinforced web to resist shear is assumed to be that related to an average shear yield stress equal to $F_y/\sqrt{3}$. The effective depth of the web of a rolled shape is taken as 95 per cent of the section depth. This leads to the expression, in clause 13.4.2

$$V_r = 0.95 \, \phi \, d \, w \, F_y/\sqrt{3} = 0.55 \, \phi \, wd \, F_y$$

At beam-to-column connections, if the shear force exceeds that permitted by clause 13.4.2, the deficiency may be overcome by providing doubler plates to increase the web thickness or by providing diagonal stiffeners (Figure 2—3). The force in the beam flange that is transferred into the web as a shear is (approximately)

$$V = M/d_b$$

Equating this to the shear resistance as given in clause 13.4.2 (where now $w = w_c$ and $d = d_c$), and solving for the required web thickness,

$$w_c \geqslant \frac{M}{0.55\phi\ d_c\ d_b\ F_y} \geqslant \frac{2.0\ M}{d_c\ d_b\ F_y}$$

FIGURE 2-3

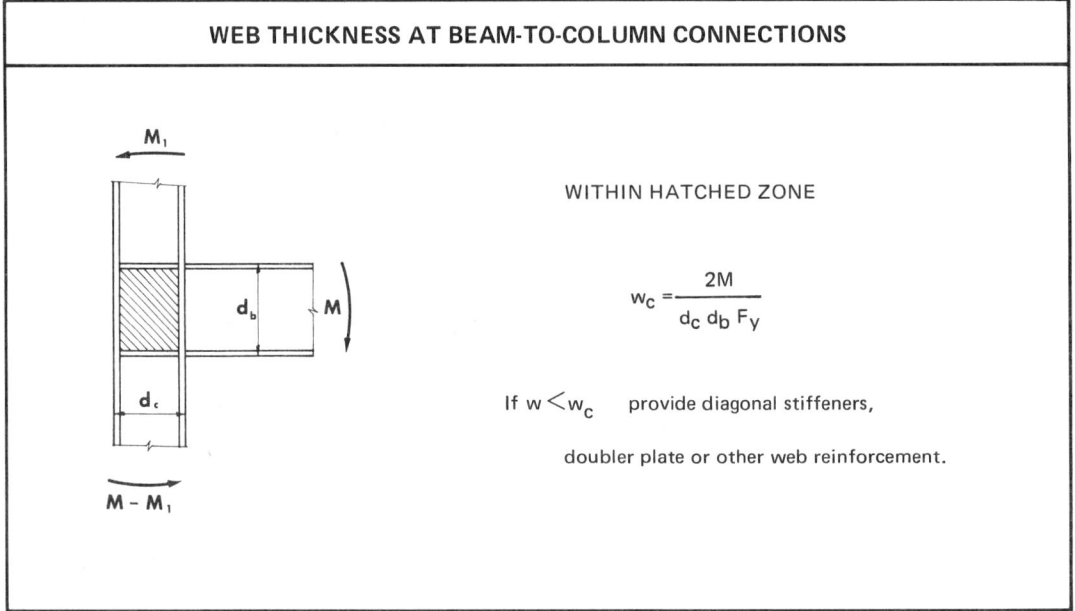

WEB THICKNESS AT BEAM-TO-COLUMN CONNECTIONS

WITHIN HATCHED ZONE

$$w_c = \frac{2M}{d_c\ d_b\ F_y}$$

If $w < w_c$ provide diagonal stiffeners,

doubler plate or other web reinforcement.

If the actual web thickness is less than w_c, the required area of diagonal stiffeners may be obtained by considering the equilibrium of forces at the point where the top flange of the beam frames to the column. The total force to be transmitted ($V = M/d_b$) is assumed to be taken by the web and the horizontal component of the force in the diagonal stiffener:

$$V = M/d_b = 0.55\ \phi\ w_c\ d_c\ F_y + \phi\ F_y\ A_s \cos \theta$$

where

A_s = cross sectional area of diagonal stiffeners

$\theta = \tan^{-1}\ (d_b/d_c)$

The required stiffener area is therefore

$$A_s = \frac{1}{\phi \cos \theta} \left[\frac{M}{F_y\ d_b} - 0.55\ w_c\ d_c \right]$$

8.5(e) Splices. The bending moment diagram corresponding to the failure mechanism reflects the changes in stiffness that occur during the plastic hinging process. For example, points of inflection in the final bending moment distribution may be required to resist significant moments to enable the structure to reach its predicted load-carrying capacity[17]. To ensure that splices have sufficient capacity to enable the structure to act as if continuous up to the ultimate load, a minimum connection requirement of 0.25 M_p is specified in clause 8.5(e). At any splice location, the computed moments corresponding to various factored loading conditions must be increased by 10 percent; the splice is then designed either for these increased moments or for the minimum requirement of 0.25 M_p.

8.5(f) Impact and Fatigue. The use of moment redistribution to develop the strength of the structure corresponding to a failure mechanism implies a ductile type of behavior. Members which may be repeatedly subjected to heavy impact and members which may be subject to fatigue should not be designed on the basis of a plastic analysis since ductile behavior cannot be anticipated under these conditions. Such members, at least for the present, are best proportioned on the basis of an elastic bending moment distribution.

8.5(g) Inelastic Deformations. For continuous beams and certain types of relatively stiff, regular frames, the additional moments produced by the vertical loads acting through the lateral displacements of the structure may be negligible. For other types of structures, in particular multi-storey frames, these secondary effects may have a significant influence on the strength of the structure[12].

FIGURE 2-4

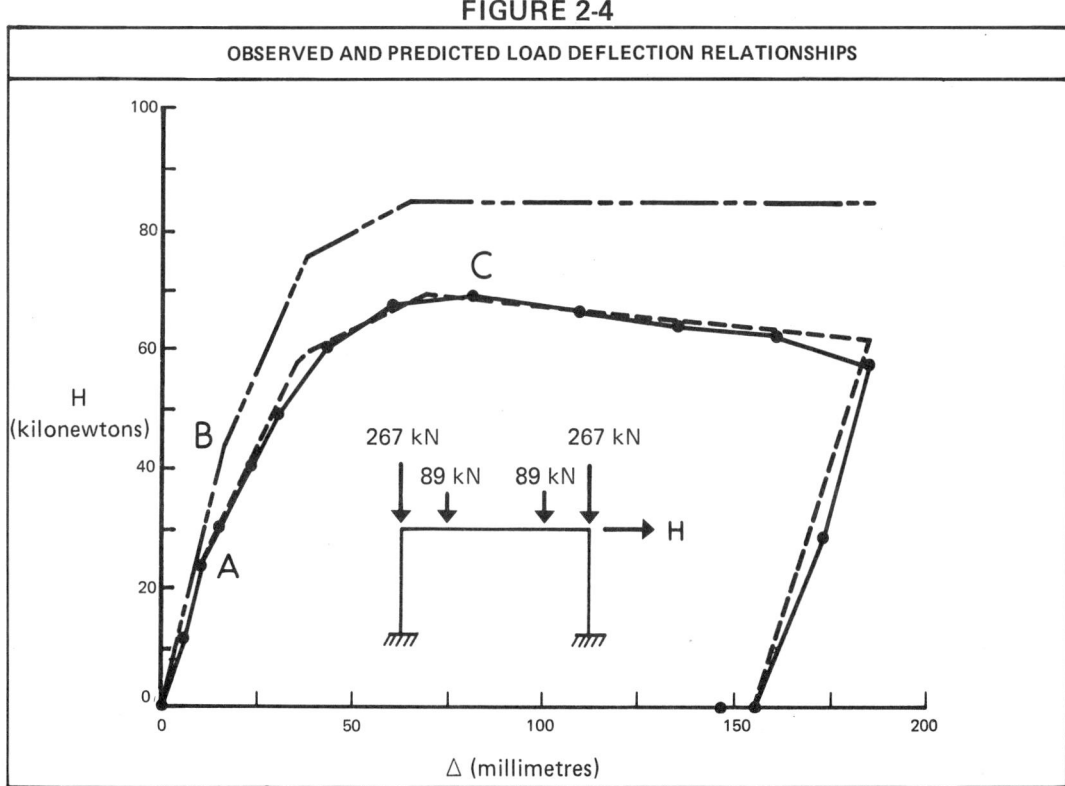

OBSERVED AND PREDICTED LOAD DEFLECTION RELATIONSHIPS

For example, in the structure shown in the inset of Figure 2—4, the secondary effects have reduced the ultimate strength by approximately 25%[12,18]. In this structure the first plastic hinge formed at stage A while the ultimate strength (considering moment redistribution) was not attained until stage C. The inelastic deformations between these two stages have a serious influence on the strength of the structure. Clause 8.6.1 requires that the sway effects produced by the vertical loads be accounted for in design. The specific purpose of clause 8.5(g) is to ensure that, in a structure analyzed on the basis of a plastic moment distribution, the additional effects produced by inelastic sway deformations are accommodated. In most cases the actual strength of the structure can only be predicted by tracing the complete load-deflection relationship for the structure or for selected portions[19]. Methods are available to perform this type of design. For braced multi-storey frames, however, simpler techniques have also been developed[20].

8.6 Stability Effects

8.6.1 The basic thrust of clause 8.6.1 is the recognition that all structures are subjected to sway deformations. The vertical loads acting through the deformed shape of the structure produce secondary bending moments in the case of a moment resisting frame or additional forces in a vertical truss system. These additional moments or forces (the stability effects) reduce the strength of the structure, as shown for a moment-resistant frame in Figure 2—4. In addition, bending moments and deflections which exceed those predicted by a first order analysis are produced at all stages of loading[18]. Similar effects are produced in structures containing a vertical bracing system, as shown in Figure 2—5 where the steel frame is linked to a reinforced concrete shear wall[18].

FIGURE 2-5

LOAD — DEFLECTION RELATIONSHIPS

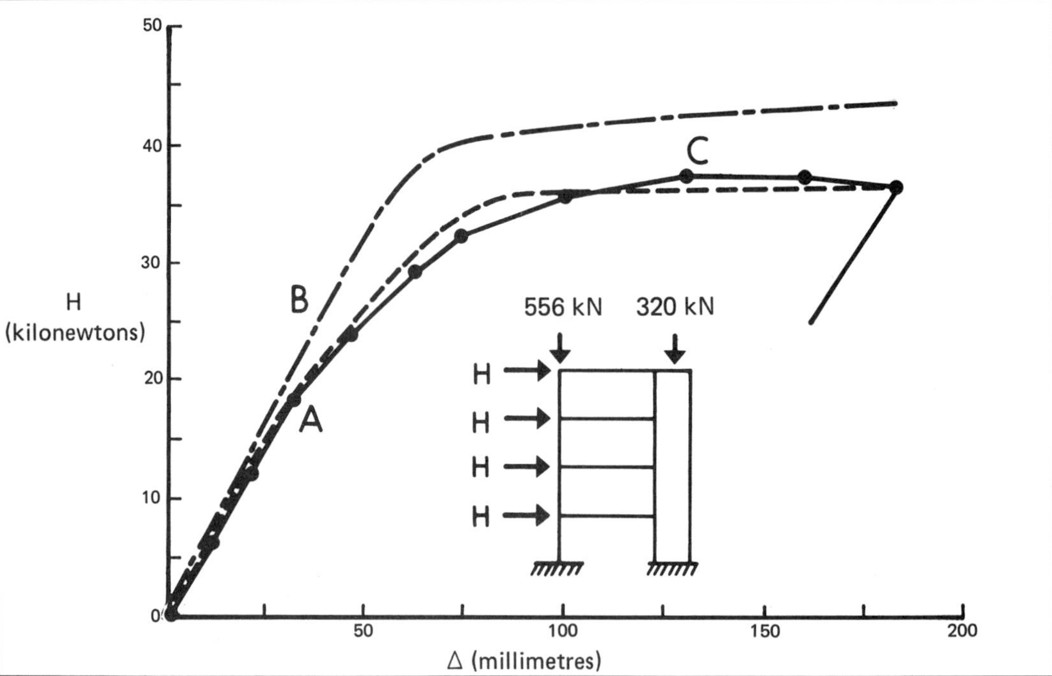

To account for these stability effects, two different approaches are possible. The approach recommended in S16.1-M78 is to perform analyses which include the stability effects. This type of analysis is termed a second-order analysis, since equilibrium is formulated on the deformed structure. In this way the additional moments or forces generated by the vertical loads are accommodated directly. An alternative approach is provided through the use of clause 8.6.3.

In some cases these secondary effects are small and may be ignored by the designer. Presumably this will be the case for relatively stiff structures subjected to relatively small vertical loads and having a reasonably uniform distribution of lateral load resisting elements. Studies are in progress to determine the types of structures that would fall into this category; however, the results are not yet available. The onus is clearly on the designer to assure himself that the secondary effects are negligible if they are not to be included in the design process.

8.6.2 To determine the magnitude of the stability effects two approaches are suggested. Computer programs are available, based on equilibrium of the deformed structure[21,22]. The use of this type of program ensures that the additional moments or forces generated by the vertical loads acting through the displaced structural shape (the so-called P∆ effect) will be taken into account. In addition, most second-order programs also account for the reduction in column stiffnesses, caused by their axial loads[22].

The second approach, outlined in Appendix J of S16.1-M78, is simply to modify the results of first-order analysis to include the P∆ effects. It is implied in this approach that the reduction in individual member stiffnesses will be negligible, although a simple check may be used to ensure that this assumption is justified[18].

In Appendix J a technique is outlined whereby the deflections computed by a first-order analysis may be used to compute artificial sway forces[18]. These forces are then added to the original forcing system and the structure is reanalyzed. The final moments or forces then include an allowance for the P∆ effects.

Appendix J calls for an iterative process to be used to ensure that the P-∆ effects are not underestimated. As an alternative, estimated deflections may be used to calculate initial sway forces[92]. The structure is then analyzed under the lateral load caused by wind or earthquake plus the sway forces. If the resulting deflections are less than those assumed for the initial estimate of the P∆ effects then these effects have been over-estimated and (if the designer is satisfied that the situation is acceptable) the iterative process is not required.

FIGURE 2-6

LOAD-MOMENT RELATIONSHIP

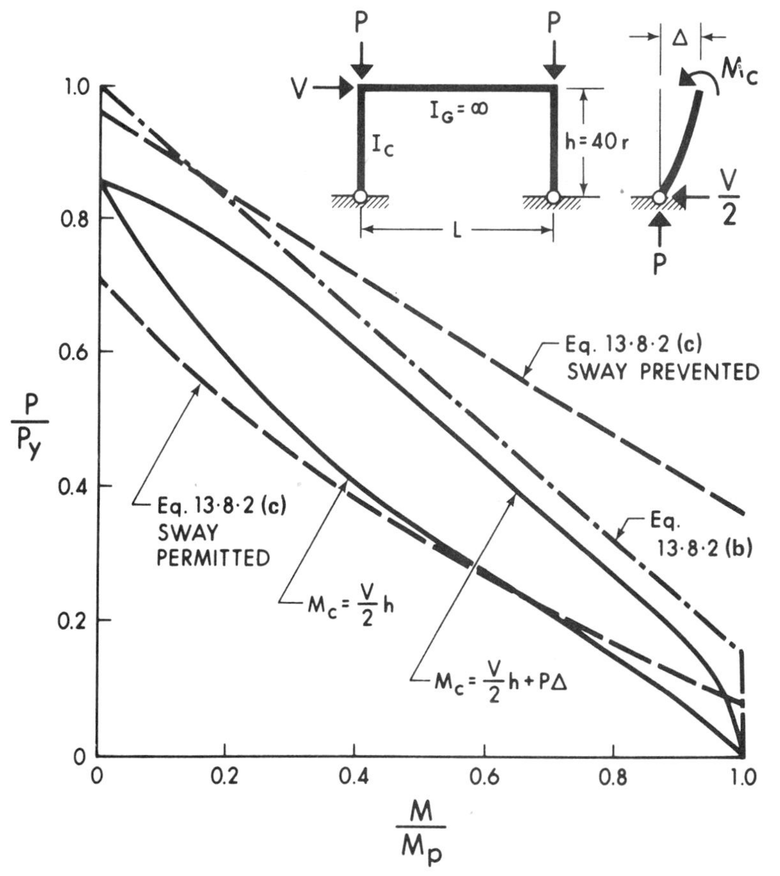

2-13

In this direct procedure a check on the flexibility of the structure (as required by step 6 of Appendix J) is not achieved. It has been observed[25], however, that most regular structures meeting reasonable deflection limits under the specified loads will be adequately designed using the PΔ approach.

Those structures for which the PΔ effects have been included in the analysis, or for which these effects are negligible, may be designed on the basis of the sway-prevented condition. The basis for this is shown in Figure 2—6 where the ultimate strengths are plotted for the frame shown in the inset. The results plotted as the solid curves relate the maximum value of the column top moment, M_c, to the axial load ratio, P/P_y. The primary bending moment $\left(M_c = \dfrac{Vh}{2}\right)$ is shown as the lower solid curve while the total bending moment $\left(M_c = \dfrac{Vh}{2} + P\Delta\right)$ is shown as the upper solid curve. The difference in moments between the two curves is then a measure of the PΔ effect.

The stability interaction equation, 13.8.2(c), based on sway-prevented conditions and the strength interaction equation, 13.8.2(b), are again plotted as the upper dashed line and the broken line in Figure 2—6. The envelope provided by these two relationships predicts the full moment capacity of the member. In this case, however, the prediction is slightly unconservative.

FIGURE 2-7

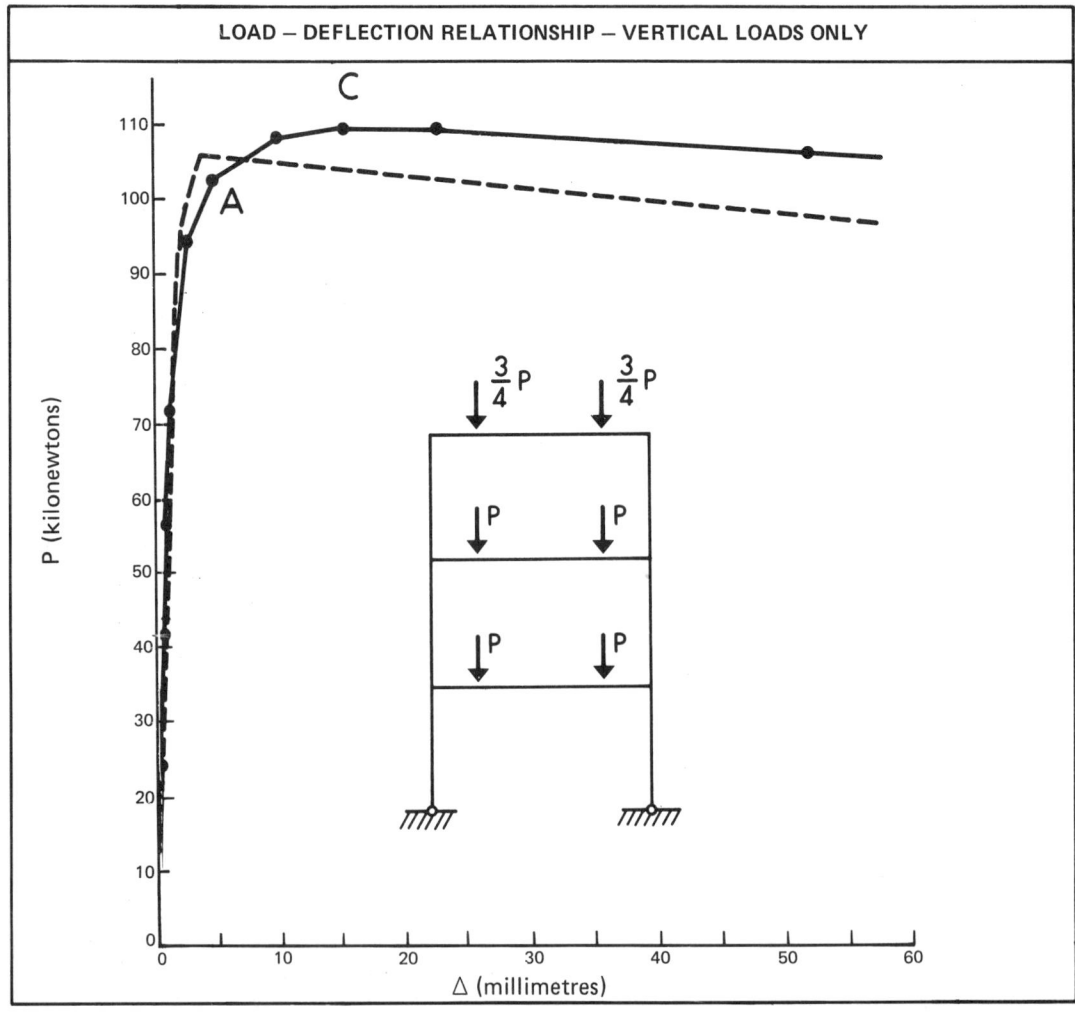

LOAD — DEFLECTION RELATIONSHIP — VERTICAL LOADS ONLY

Clause 8.6.2 requires that the calculated PΔ effects be based on the deflections produced by the applied loads (clause 8.6.2(a)) magnified by the flexibility of the frame. In some cases, particularly for combinations of vertical loads only, significant lateral deflections will not be developed.

For these cases, however, the PΔ effects are still important, as shown in Figure 2—7. The frame, shown in the inset to the figure, is subjected to vertical load only. As the loads are increased, the PΔ effects produced by the vertical loads acting through the lateral displacements caused by fabrication lead to failure through instability, much the same as the combined loading cases shown in Figures 2—4 and 2—5.

To simulate this condition, clause 8.6.2(b) requires that the PΔ effects be based on the initial out-of-plumbs produced during the erection process. The corresponding tolerances are specified in clause 28.7.1 and references 18, 23 and 92 illustrate the calculation of the PΔ effects.

Note that the more severe of the requirements of clause 8.6.2(a) or 8.6.2(b) will govern the design. It is not considered necessary to add the two effects together[18].

Clause 8.6.2(c) emphasizes the fact that out-of-plumbs which are different in sense in adjacent storeys may lead to the more severe requirements for the design of beam-to-column connections, etc.

In dealing with the forces produced by out-of-plumbs, the conservative position was taken, namely that all columns in a given story will be deflected into this position causing the most severe effect. More recently information on the actual, statistical out-of-plumbs has become available[109].

8.6.3 As an alternative to the above approach, the analysis used by the designer may be a first-order analysis, in other words the moments produced by the PΔ effect are not computed. The stability interaction equation, Equation 13.8.2(c), based on sway-permitted conditions, is plotted as the lower dashed line in Figure 2—6. It is apparent that the stability interaction equation used in this fashion does not predict the full capacity of the member. Rather, the equation limits the capacity available to the designer to only that portion used by the primary bending moment. The remaining member capacity is then available to resist the PΔ effect (which is presumably not computed nor included in the analysis).

In CSA Standard S16-1969 it is assumed that if the structure contains a stiff vertical truss or shear wall translation is effectively prevented and the columns can be designed as sway-prevented members; in the absence of this stiff vertical element, the columns are to be designed as if sway is permitted. The real distinction between the sway-permitted case and the sway-prevented case, however, is that in the latter the interaction equations permit the designer to utilize the full moment capacity of the column while, if the column is designed as sway-permitted, the designer is able to use only a part of the full capacity.

The S16.1-M78 Standard requires the use of the interaction equations based on the sway-permitted conditions if the PΔ effects have not been included in the analysis. It should be noted that this approach is not recommended for structures having columns of significantly differing stiffnesses and is not permitted for structures resisting lateral loads by vertical truss or shear wall systems[24].

9. DESIGN LENGTH OF MEMBERS

9.1 For design purposes it is usually convenient to consider the length of a member as equal to the distance between centres of gravity of supporting members. In most instances the difference resulting from considering a member to be that length rather than its actual length centre-to-centre of end connections is small. In some cases, however, there is sufficient difference to merit computing the actual length. Regardless of the length used for design, the actual connection detail may cause an eccentric load, or moment, to act on the supporting member and this effect must be taken into account.

9.3 Compression members are designed on the basis of effective length (KL) which is the product of the actual unbraced length times the appropriate effective length factor. Both the unbraced length and the effective length factor may vary with respect to the cross-sectional axis of the member under consideration.

The concept of effective length (KL) is used in computing the slenderness ratio of compression members, and hence, in determining the resistance of compression members. Much information about effective lengths is contained in technical literature[25,26] and some guidance for the designer is provided in Appendices B and C of the Standard. The CISC-CSCC Column Selection Program 3 (a computer program available to designers)[27] contains routines for computing effective lengths, based on the principles outlined in Appendix C.

The major difference between CSA Standard S16-1969 and the requirement of clause 9.3 of S16.1-M78 is the distinction made between the conditions for which the effective length factor should be computed on the basis of a sway-prevented model and those for which the sway-permitted model is appropriate. The commentary on clause 8.6 provides some guidance on this question.

10. SLENDERNESS RATIOS

The maximum slenderness ratio of 200 for compression members, stipulated in clause 10.2.1, has been included in S16.1-M78 for practical reasons. As illustrated in Appendix D of S16.1, the strength, or resistance, of a compression member becomes quite small as the slenderness ratio increases beyond about 150, and the member becomes relatively inefficient. In addition, as the slenderness ratio increases, the effects of initial imperfections become more significant and the reliability of accurately predicting these effects becomes more questionable. Accordingly, a limiting permissible slenderness ratio of 200 was established for S16.1.

In theory, from considerations of strength, no limiting slenderness ratio is required for a tension member. Again, however, considerations of serviceability resulted in the imposition of a slenderness ratio limit of 300, with permission to waive this limit under specified conditions.

11. WIDTH-THICKNESS RATIOS: COMPRESSION ELEMENTS

Clause 11.1 identifies four categories of cross-section, Class 1 through Class 4, based upon the width-to-thickness ratios of the elements of the cross-section in compression. The ratios given in Table 1 of clause 11 for Classes 1, 2, or 3 ensure that the respective ultimate limit states will be attained prior to local buckling of the plate elements. These ultimate limit states are: Class 1 — attainment of the plastic moment capacity (beams) or the plastic moment capacity reduced for the presence of axial load (beam-columns) along with rotation capacity sufficient to fulfill the assumption of plastic analysis; Class 2 — attainment of the plastic moment capacity as above for beams and beam-columns but with no requirement for rotation capacity; Class 3 — attainment of the yield moment for beams or the yield moment reduced for the presence of axial load for beam-columns.

With respect to axially loaded members such as columns or struts, the distinction based on moment capacity does not exist. Table 1 simply shows the same limit for each of Classes 1, 2, and 3 for webs in axial compression. The flange limit for columns should be taken as that for Class 3 beam flanges, that is, $260/\sqrt{F_y}$.

Figure 2—8 illustrates the requirements for Classes 2 and 3; these sections will be those most used in practice.

FIGURE 2-8

WIDTH – THICKNESS RATIOS FOR COMPRESSION ELEMENTS

CLASS 2 SECTIONS		CLASS 3 SECTIONS	
NOTE: Class 2 sections must have an axis of symmetry in plane of bending. Sections marked * are considered Class 2 only for bending about x-x.		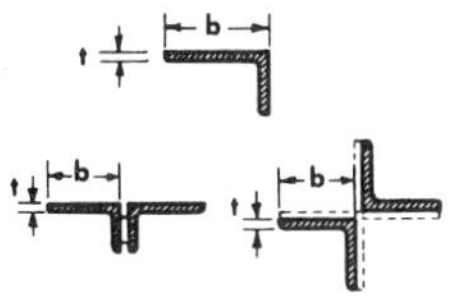	$\frac{b}{t} \leqslant \frac{200}{\sqrt{F_y}}$ 'b' is the longer leg length
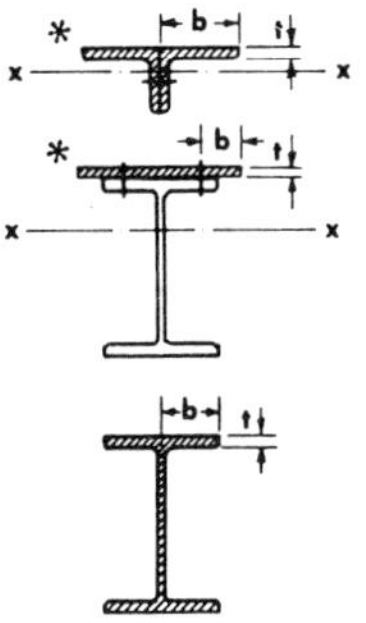	$\frac{b}{t} \leqslant \frac{170}{\sqrt{F_y}}$	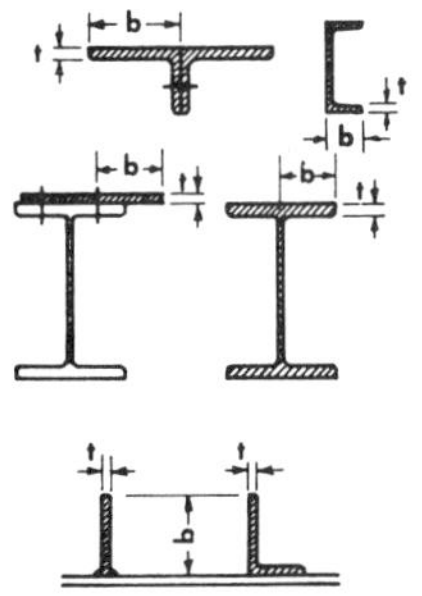	$\frac{b}{t} \leqslant \frac{260}{\sqrt{F_y}}$
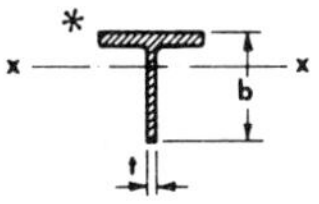	$\frac{b}{t} \leqslant \frac{170}{\sqrt{F_y}}$	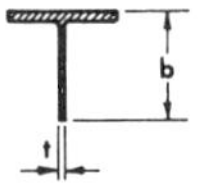	$\frac{b}{t} \leqslant \frac{340}{\sqrt{F_y}}$
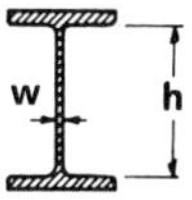	$\frac{h}{w} \leqslant \frac{1\,370}{\sqrt{F_y}}$ bending only $\frac{h}{w} \leqslant \frac{670}{\sqrt{F_y}}$ axial comp^n. (See Clause 11 S16.1-M78)	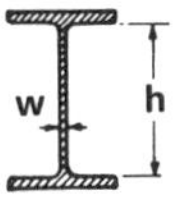	$\frac{h}{w} \leqslant \frac{1\,810}{\sqrt{F_y}}$ bending only $\frac{h}{w} \leqslant \frac{670}{\sqrt{F_y}}$ axial comp^n. (See Cl. 11, S16.1-M78)
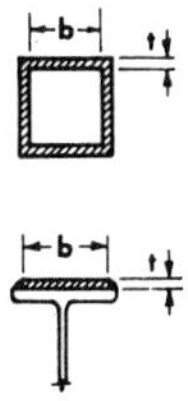	$\frac{b}{t} \leqslant \frac{525}{\sqrt{F_y}}$	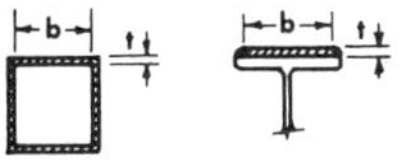	$\frac{b}{t} \leqslant \frac{670}{\sqrt{F_y}}$
		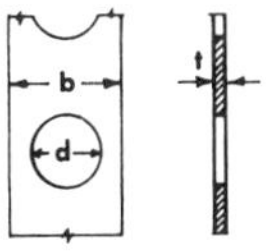	$\frac{b}{t} \leqslant \frac{840}{\sqrt{F_y}}$ Effective Area = (b – d) t
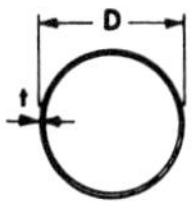	$\frac{D}{t} \leqslant \frac{18\,000}{F_y}$	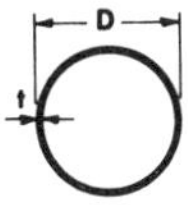	$\frac{D}{t} \leqslant \frac{23\,000}{F_y}$

Cl. 11, S16.1-M78

The bases of the requirements, particularly those for W-shapes, come from a background of both experimental and theoretical studies. For example, the restrictions on flanges have both a theoretical basis (see, for instance, Ch. 6 of Ref. 29 or Art. 6.2 of Ref. 12 or Ch. 4 of Ref. 25) and an extensive experimental background[30,31,32]. The restrictions for webs in flexural compression come from both theory and tests for Class 1[30] but mostly from test results for Classes 2 and 3[33,34].

Figure 2—9 plots the requirements for the case of webs under both axial compression and compression due to bending. Since the amount of web under compression varies from complete (columns) to one-half (beams), the depth-to-thickness limits will vary as a function of the amount of axial load. The basis for Class 1 beam-columns is derived from early work on plastic design[30] while the limits for Classes 2 and 3 come mostly from experimental studies[35,36]. At the time the S16.1-1974 Standard was written, the work on Class 3 was not completed and the slenderness limits established were the same as those given for Class 2 for all values of $C_f/C_y > 0.15$. Standard S16.1-M78 now prescribes values of web slenderness for Class 3 which are more liberal than Class 2 throughout the entire range of C_f/C_y.

A study currently underway at the University of Alberta is attempting to unify all of the work in this area respecting W-shapes. The result is expected to be a recommendation for slight upward revision or no change in most categories except for column flanges. Until this work is completed designers are advised not to relax the provision for column flanges.

FIGURE 2-9

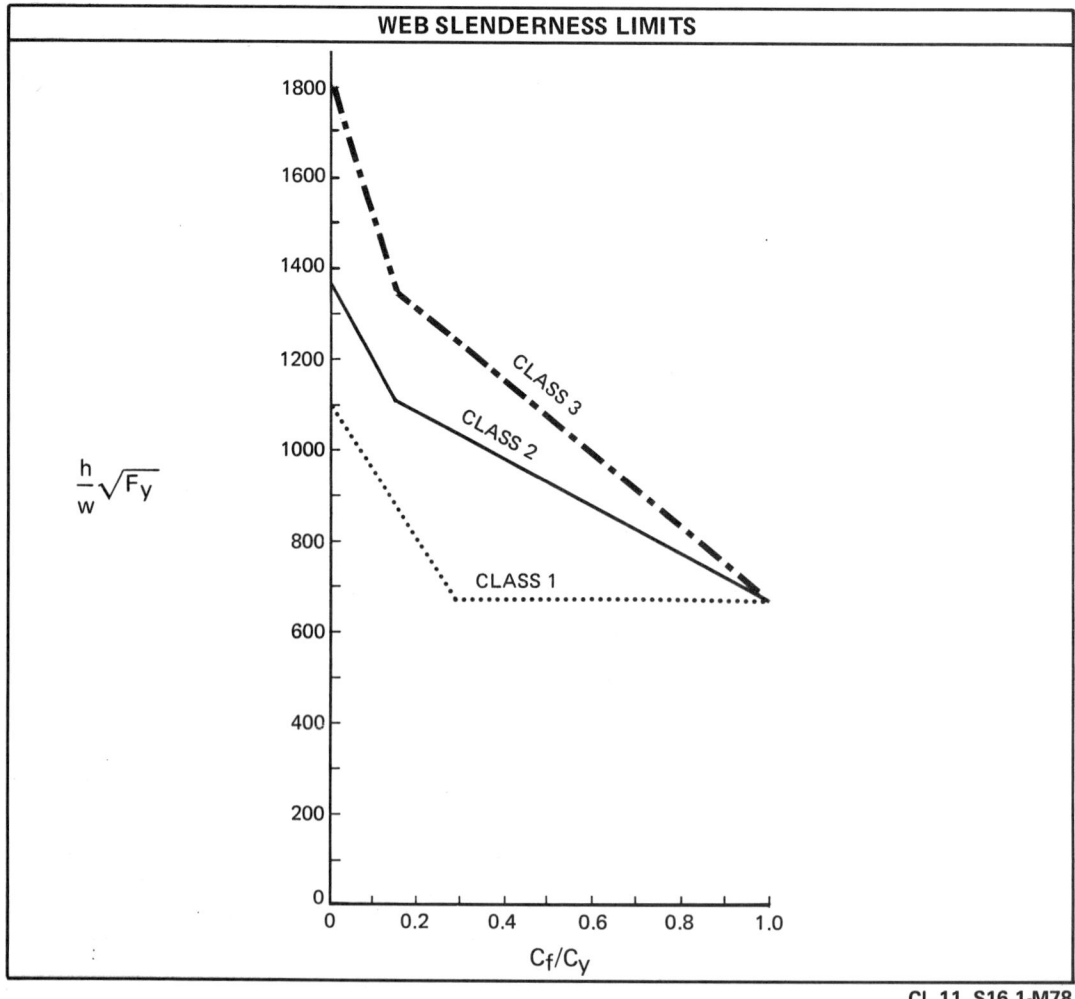

WEB SLENDERNESS LIMITS

Cl. 11, S16.1-M78

Sections used for columns, beams, or beam-columns may be composed of elements whose width-to-thickness ratios exceed those prescribed for Class 3 provided that the resistance equations are adjusted accordingly. These sections, called Class 4, should be evaluated according to the rules given in clause 13.

The requirement for Class 3 circular hollow sections, $D/t \leqslant 23\,000/F_y$ is based on tests[37] which indicates that tubes that satisfy this requirement can reach yield stress without local buckling. The more conservative requirements for Class 1 and Class 2 sections are based on research referred to in reference 28.

12. GROSS AND NET AREAS

12.3 Net Area

In all cases, the net area shall be determined on the assumption that the hole diameter is 2 mm greater than that specified by the designer. This provides an allowance for the distortion that occurs in the metal around a punched hole. (Since holes for fasteners are customarily required to be 2 mm greater than the fastener diameter, clause 22.3.2, this means that the net area is determined on the basis that the holes are 4 mm greater in diameter than the fasteners that will be used.)

The location of the least width of a part may be obvious from inspection. When it is not clear which of several potential tear paths might be critical, the various possibilities must be examined, and the net width established using the "$s^2/4g$" rule (clause 12.3.3).

Both tests and theory show that once any hole or pattern of holes has been introduced into a part, there is an upper limit to the amount of material that will be effective in resisting tensile loads. This limit is principally governed by the ratio of the yield point of the steel to its ultimate strength. For the types of steels most commonly used at present in structural work (e.g., G40.21-M 300W), the maximum net area that can be considered effective is limited to 85% of the gross cross-sectional area (clause 12.3.4.a). Other limits, higher than this value, are specified for higher strength steels.

12.4 Pin-Connected Tension Members

In pin-connected tension members the non-uniform distribution of stress makes it desirable that the net area across the pin hole be at least one third greater than the area of the body of the member[38]. To avoid end splitting, the area beyond the pin hole within a 45 degree arc each side of the longitudinal axis of the member must be at least 90 per cent of the area of the body of the member.

13. MEMBER AND CONNECTION RESISTANCE

13.2 Axial Tension

The resistance of a tensile member is to be established as the lesser of the capacity based on yield strength (clause 13.2(a)(i)) and the capacity based on ultimate strength (clause 13.2(a)(ii)).

The yield load capacity is further distinguished as to the amount of ductility that might be expected to occur in members that use mechanical fasteners rather than welds. In such cases, if the ratio of net area to gross area (A_n/A_g) is greater than the ratio of the yield point of the material to its ultimate strength (F_y/F_u), then the member cross-section will yield on the gross cross-section prior to the time that the ultimate strength is reached at the net cross-section (that is, $A_n F_u > A_g F_y$). Such a member would have considerable reserve of ductility if failure were to occur. Load could possibly be redistributed to other parts of the structure but, in any event, failure would be preceded by ample warning as the result of large deformations.

If the criterion stated above is not met, failure would potentially occur by tearing through the net cross-section before any significant amount of yielding was present (that is, $A_n F_u < A_g F_y$). When fracture might precede yielding, a lower tensile resistance is specified. It varies with the amount of ductility that might be expected, that is, with the ratio A_n/A_g.

Clause 13.2(a)(ii) places a limit on the tensile capacity based on ultimate strength. The limit here is somewhat more stringent than that placed on yield strength because failure at ultimate is absolute. The multiplier 0.85 in the equation given in this clause is introduced to take this into account, and is consistent with past practice, such as in CSA Standard S16-1969, where the nominal factor of safety against failure by yielding is 1.67, and against ultimate tensile capacity is 2.0. (0.85 is approximately equal to the ratio of 1.67 to 2.00).

The resistance provided by a pin-connected member is to be taken as 0.75 times that for a member connected by the usual structural fastener. This reduction recognizes the greater non-uniformity of stress that occurs around a hole that is large relative to the material in which it is formed.

13.3 Axial Compression

Steel columns are conveniently classified as short, intermediate, or long members, and each category has an associated characteristic type of behavior. Loosely speaking, a short column is one which can resist a load equal to the yield load ($C_y = AF_y$). Thus, the maximum strength is governed only by the yield stress of the steel. The failure of long columns is accompanied by a rapid increase in lateral deflection. The member may be slender enough that the load at which this rapid deflection takes place does not produce significant yielding of the cross-section. Thus, the maximum load is not a function of the material strength but depends on the bending stiffness (EI) and length of the member.

Columns in the intermediate range are the most common group in steel buildings and are the most difficult to analyze. Failure is again characterized by a rapid increase in deflection but this takes place at a time when some portions of the cross-section have yielded. The amount of yielding that takes place is greatly influenced by the residual stresses that are present and the strength of the column is influenced both by this and by the magnitude of the initial imperfections. The effect of initial imperfections was not considered explicitly in the working stress standard S16-1969 but was included implicitly by adjusting the value of the safety factors for longer member in which these effects are more severe.

In S16.1-M78 both the effects of residual stress and those caused by initial out-of-straightness are considered in formulating the relationship for the column strength. In the place of the relatively simple tangent modulus theory used to predict the ultimate strength of the perfectly straight column[29], the member must be treated as a beam-column acted upon by an axial force and by bending moments that vary along the length of the member[40].

The behavior of a column predicted by the two different approaches is shown qualitatively in Figure 2—10 where the load, P, is plotted against the mid-height lateral deflection δ. For columns having relatively small initial out-of-straightness, the maximum strengths may be approximately the same as the tangent modulus buckling loads. As the initial out-of-straightness increases however, the maximum strength of the member drops significantly below the tangent modulus buckling load.

This strength reduction may be particularly severe for columns in the "intermediate" range of slenderness ratios. For those members, inelastic action, where some of the stresses due to the axial load plus bending moment added to the compressive residual stresses exceed the yield stress, occurs well before the maximum strength is attained. Thus, the magnitude of the residual stresses as well as the magnitude and shape of the out-of-straight-

FIGURE 2-10

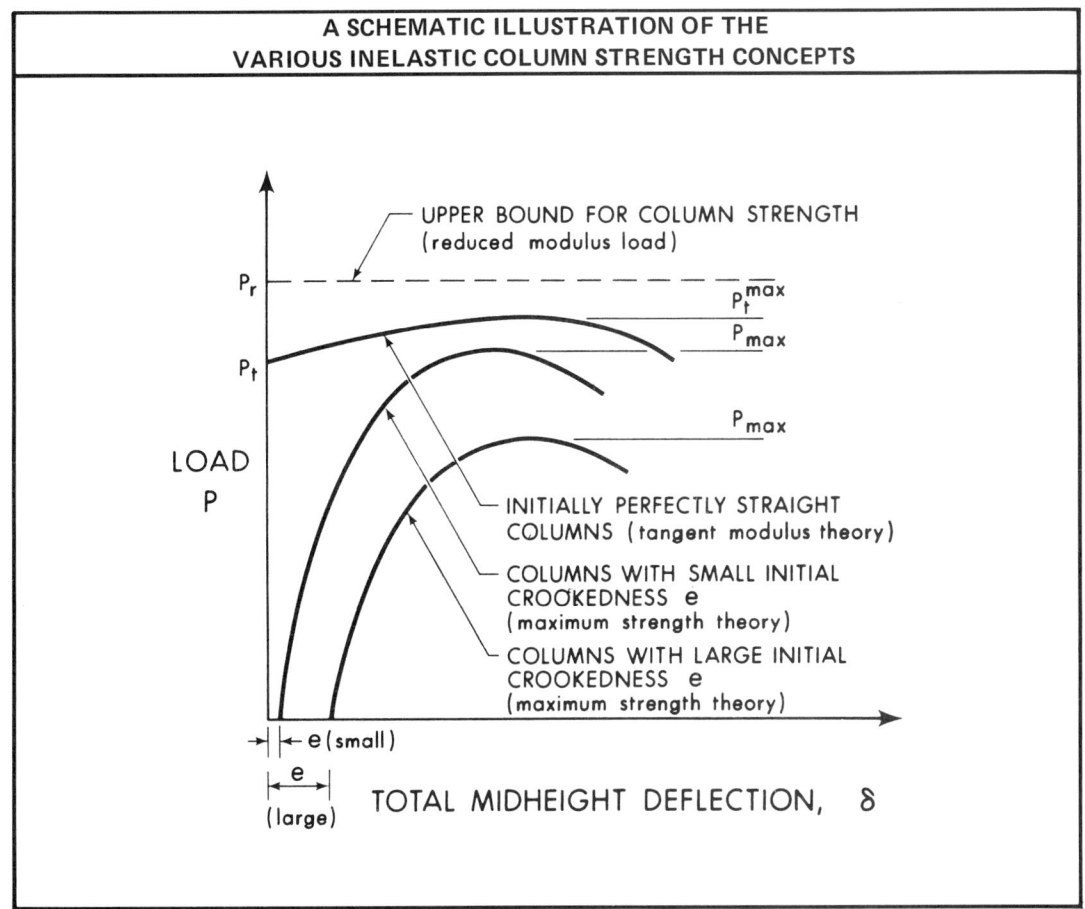

A SCHEMATIC ILLUSTRATION OF THE
VARIOUS INELASTIC COLUMN STRENGTH CONCEPTS

ness significantly influence the results. Figure 2—11 gives some indication of the scatter obtained from analyses of columns having the same out-of-straightness but differing residual stress distribution.

In order to reflect the various factors affecting the maximum strength of columns having various slenderness ratios, column curves proposed by the Structural Stability Research Council[25], have been adopted for use in S16.1-M78. The Council's Column Curve 2 is used as the basis for the description of resistance of W-shapes and for cold-formed non-stress relieved hollow structural sections (Clause 13.3.1). The latter, Class C hollow structural shapes, are included in the Standard for the first time and their introduction is based on work reported in Reference 114.

The footnote to Clause 13.3.1 should be reviewed carefully by designers. The column curve given should be used only for W-shapes rolled in Canada or for other doubly-symmetric Class 1, 2, or 3 sections except that solid round non-stress relieved cold straightened bars are specifically excluded. The curve should be used for welded H-shapes only when the flange edges have been flame cut. (The treatment of other welded H-shapes is discussed below.) Since the expressions for column resistance are for x-axis or y-axis buckling only, singly symmetric, asymmetric, or cruciform sections should also be checked for lateral-torsional buckling.

Because of a more favorable residual stress pattern, hot formed or cold formed stress relieved hollow structural shapes (Class H) have now been assigned the resistance given by Column Curve 1 of the Structural Stability Research Council (Clause 13.3.2).[112]

FIGURE 2-11

**TYPICAL FREQUENCY DISTRIBUTION HISTOGRAMS FOR THE
MAXIMUM STRENGTH OF ALL 112 COLUMN CURVES WITH
INITIAL OUT-OF-STRAIGHTNESS e/L = 1/1000**

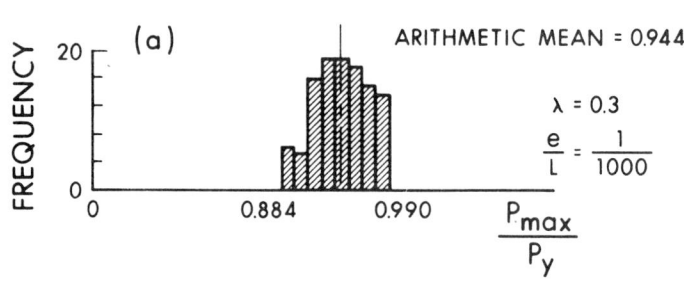

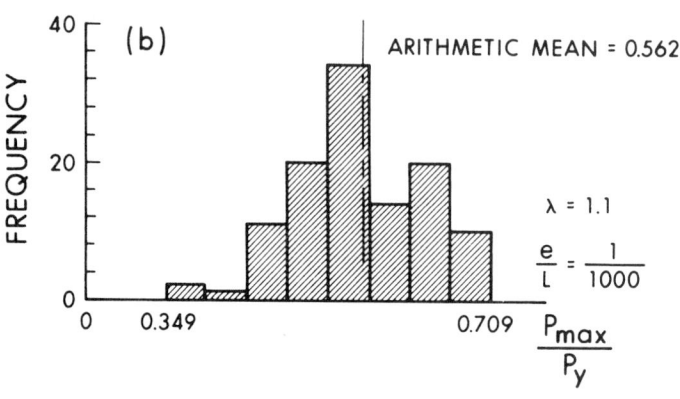

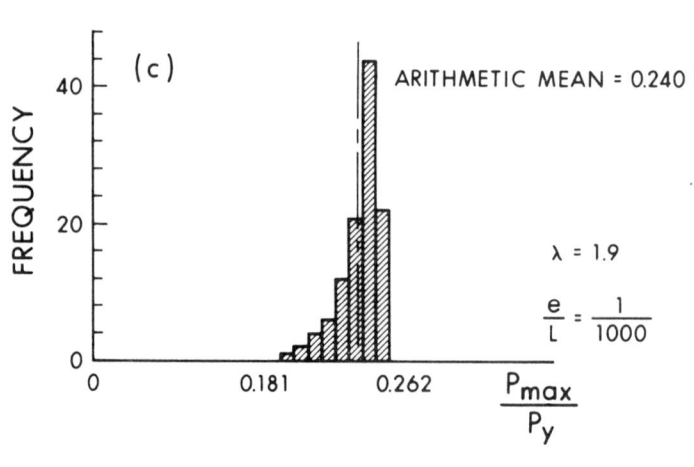

In Canada, many H-shaped columns, usually called WWF shapes, are made by welding together three plate components. The flange to web welds induce large residual stresses which are tensile in the vicinity of the weld and compressive near the flange tips. Unless offsetting tensile residual stresses exist in the plate which comprises the flange tips, before the section is welded, the compressive stresses can be higher than normally occur in rolled shapes, resulting in a section with reduced inelastic buckling strength. Studies have indicated that welded H-shapes which have flange edges flame-cut, contain acceptable residual stresses at the flange tips after the section is welded. Accordingly, clause 13.3.1 notes that if welded H-shapes are to be used, they should be designed in accordance with the formulas in clause 13.3.1 only if the flange edges are comprised of flame cut plate. The WWF sections produced in Canada do use flame cut plate.

For many heavy sections and welded sections fabricated from universal mill plate, the Council's Column Curve 3 could be used, permitting a capacity reduced below that corresponding to Column Curve 2.[25]

Because the column curves are based, in part, on the magnitude and distribution of residual stresses care should be exercised in their application, for example, in determining the capacity of an existing column which is being reinforced in such a manner that there is an increase in compressive residual stresses in the fibres most remote from the centroid. In such a situation a common solution would be to so add material as to greatly reduce the slenderness ratio.

13.4 Shear

13.4.1 Elastic Analysis

Although bending can be present unaccompanied by shear, a transversely loaded beam will always have shear combined with moment. However, in regions where shear predominates, it can be considered to act alone and clause 13.4.1 sets out the appropriate resistance equations. (The interaction of shear and moment is treated in clause 13.4.6.) The shear strength equations are set out for a stiffened plate girder: unstiffened plate girders or stocky rolled beams become special cases of this.

Extensive theoretical and experimental studies of plate girders[42] have indicated the following:

1. At stresses below the proportional limit (taken as 80% of the shear yield stress), buckling is elastic (Euler buckling).

2. At stresses above the proportional limit, buckling is inelastic.

3. A transition is required in the strength descriptions between the region where elastic buckling governs and the region where inelastic buckling controls. This is necessary principally because of the presence of residual stresses.

4. Considerable post-buckling strength is available in stiffened webs through the development of a tension field along the diagonal of a buckled panel.

5. Additional strength due to strain-hardening is attained in stocky webs.

The four ranges of resistance prescribed in clause 13.4.1 correspond to the following modes of behaviour and are illustrated in Figure 2—12.

1. Strain-hardening.

$$\frac{h}{w} \leqslant 439\sqrt{\frac{k_v}{F_y}}$$

2. Transition curve between strain hardening and inelastic buckling. At $\frac{h}{w} = 502\sqrt{\frac{k_v}{F_y}}$,

FIGURE 2-12

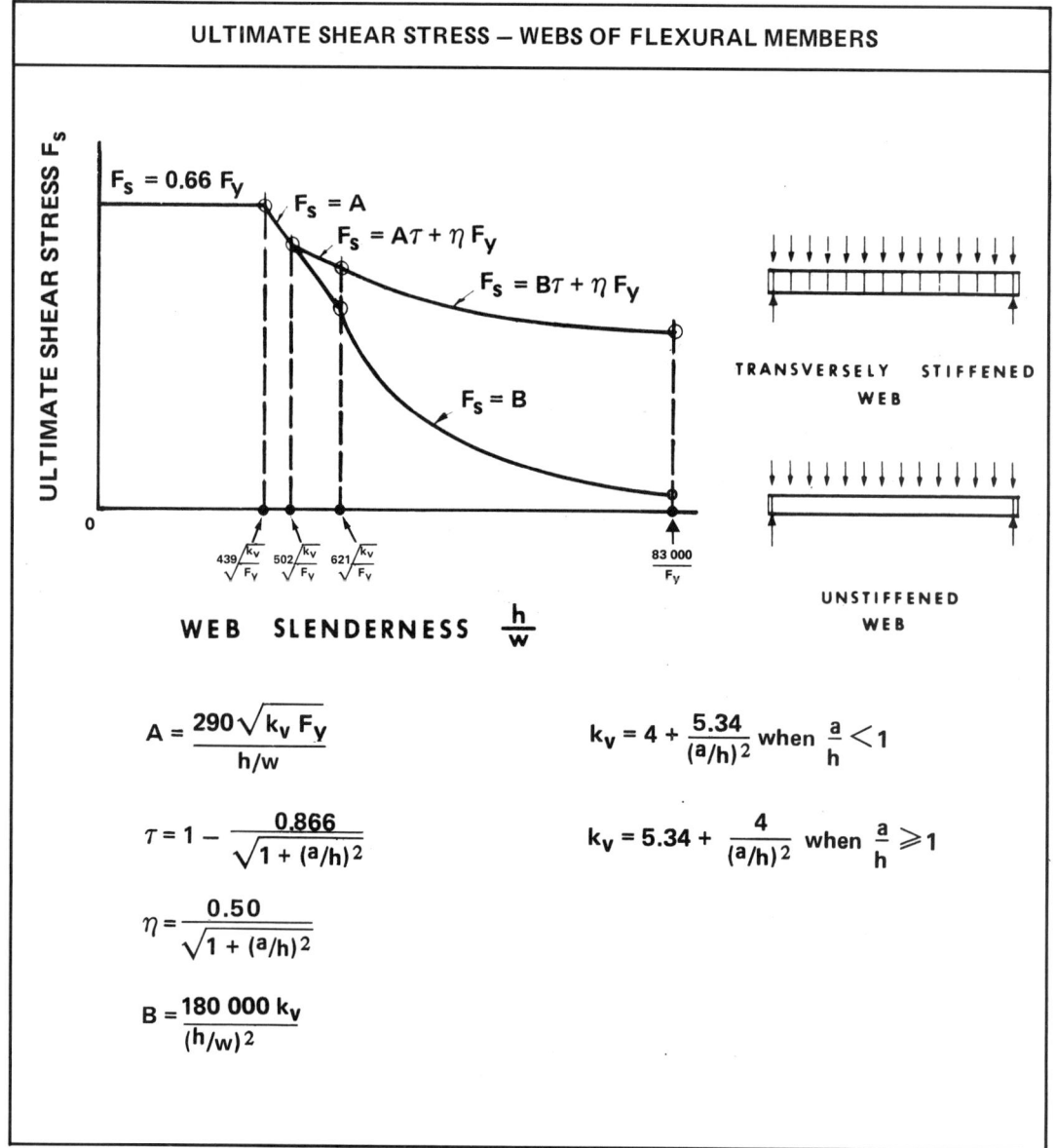

ULTIMATE SHEAR STRESS — WEBS OF FLEXURAL MEMBERS

ULTIMATE SHEAR STRESS F_s

$F_s = 0.66\ F_y$

$F_s = A$

$F_s = A\tau + \eta\ F_y$

$F_s = B\tau + \eta\ F_y$

$F_s = B$

WEB SLENDERNESS $\dfrac{h}{w}$

$439\sqrt{\dfrac{k_v}{F_y}}$ $502\sqrt{\dfrac{k_v}{F_y}}$ $621\sqrt{\dfrac{k_v}{F_y}}$ $\dfrac{83\ 000}{F_y}$

TRANSVERSELY STIFFENED WEB

UNSTIFFENED WEB

$$A = \frac{290\sqrt{k_v\ F_y}}{h/w}$$

$$\tau = 1 - \frac{0.866}{\sqrt{1 + (a/h)^2}}$$

$$\eta = \frac{0.50}{\sqrt{1 + (a/h)^2}}$$

$$B = \frac{180\ 000\ k_v}{(h/w)^2}$$

$$k_v = 4 + \frac{5.34}{(a/h)^2} \quad \text{when } \frac{a}{h} < 1$$

$$k_v = 5.34 + \frac{4}{(a/h)^2} \quad \text{when } \frac{a}{h} \geqslant 1$$

Clause 13.4.1, S16.1-M78

$F_s = 0.575\ F_y$, which is the shear yield stress according to the von Mises-Hencky yield criterion.

$$439\sqrt{\frac{k_v}{F_y}} < \frac{h}{w} \leqslant 502\sqrt{\frac{k_v}{F_y}}$$

3. Inelastic buckling, with post-buckling strength in stiffened webs.

$$502\sqrt{\frac{k_v}{F_y}} < \frac{h}{w} \leqslant 621\sqrt{\frac{k_v}{F_y}}$$

4. Elastic buckling, with post-buckling strength in stiffened webs.

$$621\sqrt{\frac{k_v}{F_y}} < \frac{h}{w}$$

The upper limit of F_s (0.66 F_y) for the load carrying capacity of webs with low slenderness ratios is established by taking into account the beneficial effect of strain-hardening in the web. This limit corresponds to excessive deformation rather than to catastrophic failure and is higher than that derived from rational analysis, 0.55 F_y, as used in clause 13.4.2 for plastic analysis. The value of F_s = 0.66 F_y corresponds to the allowable stress of 0.40 F_y used in S16-1969 and is retained, since the safeguard is against deformation rather than actual failure. The allowable stress limit has been used without difficulties for the last sixty years.

In unstiffened webs, no tension field can develop, and the second and third formulae become identical. In that case, the stiffener spacing "a" is taken as infinity and the significant parameters take the following values: τ = 1, η = 0, k_v = 5.34.

In computing the shear resistance it is assumed that the shear stress is distributed uniformly over the depth of the web. The web area A_w is the product of web thickness (w) and web depth (h) except for rolled shapes where it is customary to use the overall beam depth (d) in place of (h).

13.4.2 Plastic Analysis

The shear resistance of unreinforced webs of flexural members designed on the basis of a plastic analysis is derived from a rational analysis assuming that the shear capacity is attained when the web is stressed uniformly at the level of $F_y/\sqrt{3}$ = 0.575 F_y (von Mises-Hencky yield criterion).

Only 95% of the depth of the web is assumed to be effective, but since it is convenient to work with the nominal web area (dw), this factor is introduced directly into the numerical coefficient, giving:

$$V_r = 0.55 \, \phi \, wd \, F_y$$

As pointed out in the preceding section, this value is lower than that used for elastic analysis; this is related to the strong probability that high shear and high moment will occur simultaneously at a hinge location, competing for the yield resistance of the web. There is enough interaction between the two to warrant retaining this limit until new evidence indicates that it may safely be increased.

13.4.3 Maximum Slenderness

To prevent the web from buckling under the action of the small vertical components of the flange force which arise as the girder is bent in flexure, the web slenderness, h/w, is limited to $\dfrac{83\,000}{F_y}$. This limit is derived from the theoretical limit equal to $\dfrac{0.48E}{\sqrt{F_y(F_y + F_{rc})}}$, assuming F_{rc}, the residual stress in the compression flange, to be approximately $\frac{1}{3} F_y$ [29].

13.4.6 Combined Shear and Moment in Girders

When high shear and high moment occur simultaneously in the web of a transversely stiffened girder, the available resistance to shear and moment must be reduced according to the formula given in clause 13.4.6. The intent is to prevent exceeding the yielding capacity of the web in the vicinity of the flange[44].

Girders are assumed to depend on tension field development only if the web slenderness ratio h/w > $502\sqrt{\dfrac{k_v}{F_y}}$ as defined in clause 13.4.1.

Figure 2—13 illustrates the interaction formula provided in clause 13.4.6.

FIGURE 2-13

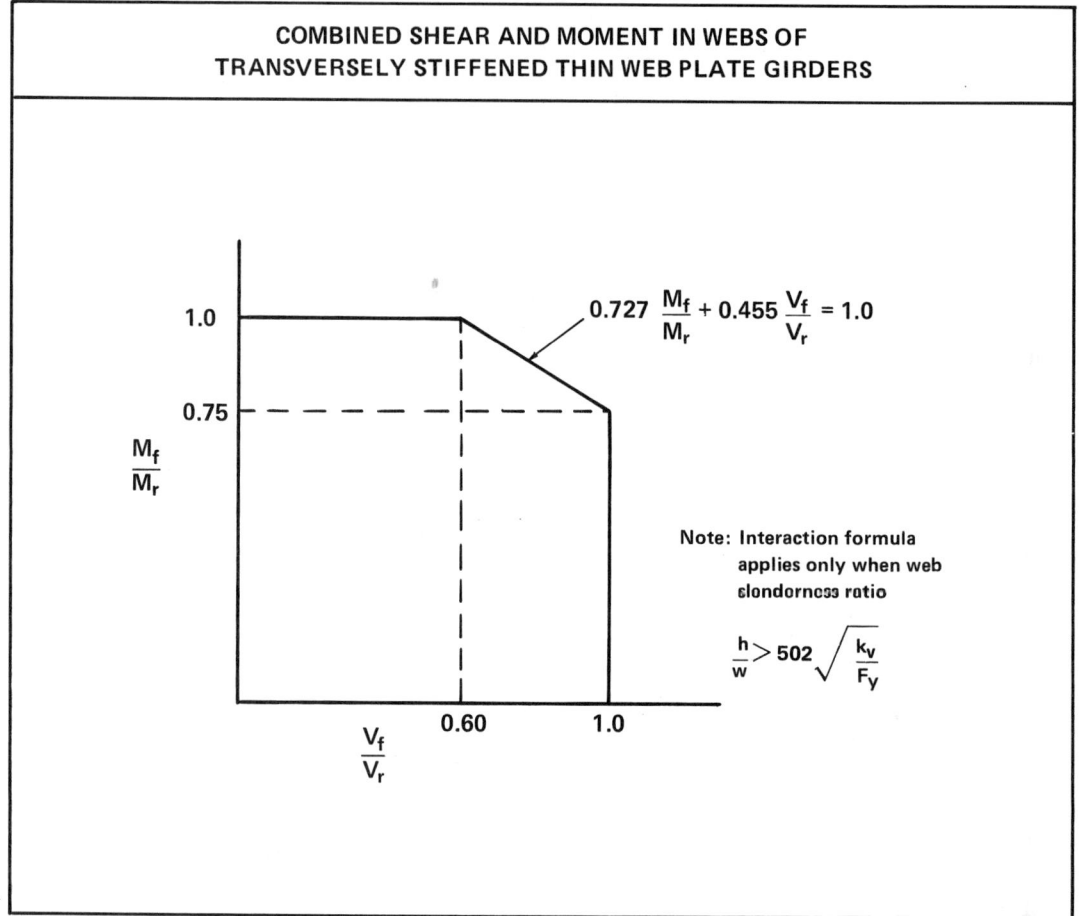

COMBINED SHEAR AND MOMENT IN WEBS OF
TRANSVERSELY STIFFENED THIN WEB PLATE GIRDERS

$$0.727 \frac{M_f}{M_r} + 0.455 \frac{V_f}{V_r} = 1.0$$

Note: Interaction formula
applies only when web
slenderness ratio

$$\frac{h}{w} > 502 \sqrt{\frac{k_v}{F_y}}$$

Clause 13.4.6, S16.1-M78

13.5 Bending — Laterally Supported Members

The moment resistance developed by a laterally supported member subjected to bending is dependent on the width-to-thickness ratios of the plates composing the cross-sections. Excessively slender plates will decrease the resistance of the plate element to buckling and will therefore reduce the moment capacity below the desired capacity, M_p or M_y.

In a beam, local buckling of the compression flange is of primary concern although in built-up plate girders web buckling is also of importance.

In Figure 2–14 the moment resistance (divided by ϕ) is plotted against a characteristic deflection for beams having various plate width-to-thickness ratios. The curve shown as characteristic of Class 1 sections represents ideal behavior for a beam. The moment resistance reaches M_p and increases slightly as the beam continues to deflect. Eventually, after a significant amount of inelastic deflection has occurred, local buckling of either the flange or web may occur, leading to a drop-off in moment capacity. The limitations on width-to-thickness ratios for Class 1 sections are given in clause 11.2 of S16.1 for those sections meeting the requirements of clause 11.1.3. As given in clause 13.5(a), the moment resistance is based on the product of the specified minimum yield point, F_y, and the plastic section modulus, Z. This implies that all fibres of the section are completely yielded but neglects the additional resistance developed due to strain-hardening. This is appropriate since the increase in strength produced by strain-hardening action is very much a function of the loading condition[12].

FIGURE 2-14

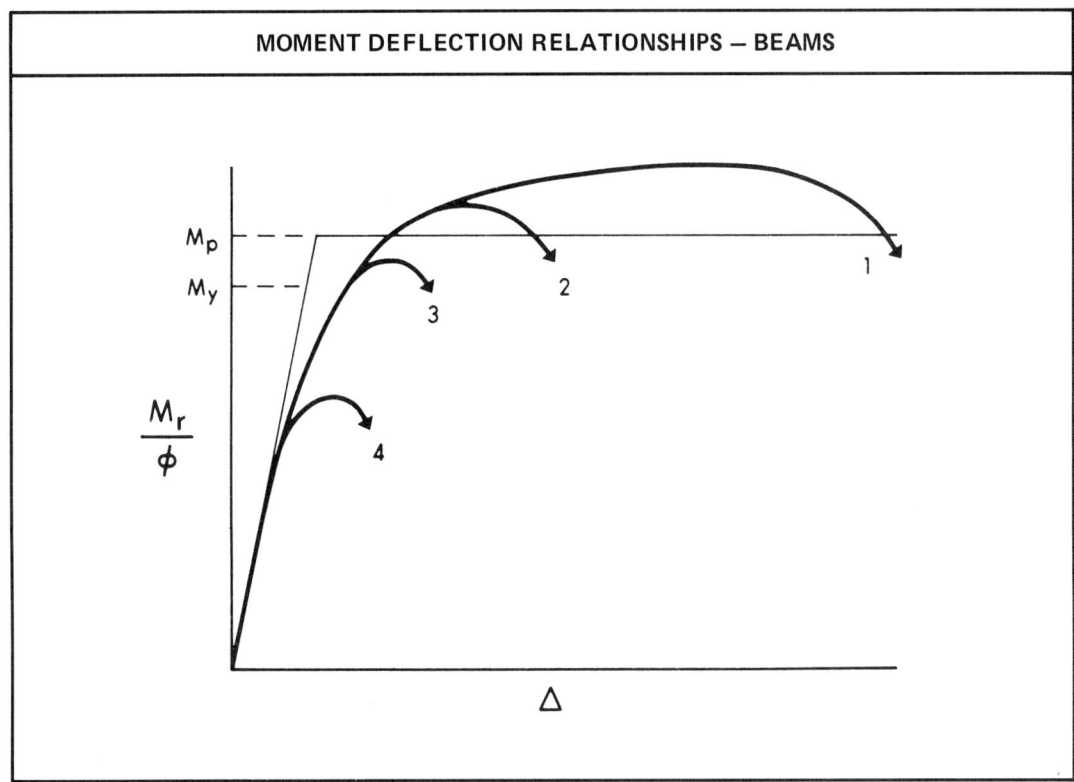

MOMENT DEFLECTION RELATIONSHIPS – BEAMS

The width-thickness ratios specified in clause 11.2 for Class 2 Sections are less restrictive than those for Class 1 since there is no requirement for large inelastic deformations[22]. The maximum moment resistance developed by the Class 2 Section is the same as that of the stockier Class 1 Section, however, and clause 13.5(a) specifies the same factored moment resistance for both types of sections.

The width-to-thickness ratios for Class 3 Sections as specified in clause 11.2 are again less restrictive than those for Class 2. As shown in Figure 2—14, however, the more slender plates may buckle locally before the moment resistance reaches M_p. Nevertheless, the plates are sufficiently stocky so that a moment resistance of $M_y = SF_y$ can be attained.

The reduction in moment resistance from M_p to M_y was reflected in S16-1969 by a reduction in allowable stress from $0.66 \, F_y$ for the so-called "compact" or "plastic design" sections to $0.60 \, F_y$ for the "non-compact" sections. This reduction is appropriate for the W or I shaped members where the moment causing full yielding to occur (M_p) is approximately 10% in excess of that causing nominal yielding in the extreme fibres (M_y).

A second factor, which was included explicitly in S16-1969, is the apparent increase in strength for Class 1 and 2 Sections other than W or I-type shapes, for example, solid sections where the allowable stress for rounds is $0.90 \, F_y$ and for rectangles $0.75 \, F_y$. This factor is also included in S16.1-M78, although in a less obvious form, since the plastic section modulus will be larger (relative to the elastic modulus) for rounds and rectangles than for W or I type shapes and thus the moment resistance will be appropriately increased. It should be noted that the increased moment resistances for shapes other than W or I types, will be greater in S16.1-M78 than in S16-1969.

Sections having plate components that are too slender to meet the requirements for Class 3 Sections are classified as Class 4 Sections. As shown in Figure 2—14 those sections buckle locally at moments less than M_y and their moment resistance must be expressed as a function of the width-to-thickness ratios of the plates composing the section.

Clause 13.5(c) divides Class 4 Sections into three categories. The first category contains those sections having both flange and web plates falling within Class 4. Clause 13.5(c)(i) requires that this type of section be designed to the requirements of CSA S136, "Cold Formed Steel Structural Members", using the material properties appropriate to the structural steel specified.

The second category contains those sections having flanges meeting the requirements of Class 3 but having webs sufficiently slender to place the section in Class 4. Clause 13.5(c)(ii) requires that this type of section be designed according to the requirements of clause 15 which bases the moment resistance on a consideration of the redistribution of load carrying capacity between the portion of the slender web in compression, and the compression flange. These sections are generally referred to as plate girders.

Clause 13.5(c)(iii) treats those Class 4 Sections having web plates meeting the Class 3 requirements but slender compression flanges, falling within Class 4 limits. In this case, the moment resistance is governed by local buckling of the compression elements and is given by SF_{cr}. The term F_{cr} is the critical stress for the local buckling and is a function of the type of compression element considered[26].

The value of $\phi = 0.90$ chosen for beams has been determined by a statistical analysis based on three series of tests where beams under a range of loading and restraint conditions were examined[45,112].

13.6 Bending — Laterally Unsupported Members

If a beam is laterally unsupported, its strength may be governed by lateral buckling of the member before the nominal bending capacity of the cross-section (M_p or M_y) can be attained.

The resistance to lateral buckling depends upon the lateral bending stiffness of the cross-section (EI_y) as well as the resistance developed in pure (St. Venant) and warping torsion. The St. Venant torsional resistance is that resistance developed by the shear stresses in the individual plates making up the cross-section. The St. Venant stiffness is the product GJ where G represents the shear modulus of the material and J is the St. Venant torsional constant.

The warping resistance is generated by cross-bending of the flanges. As the beam twists the cross-section rotates about its centroidal axis and this motion induces lateral bending strains in the flanges. These strains result in the development of flange bending moments and accompanying shear forces. The couple produced by the shear forces makes up the warping torsional resistance and is a function of $EI_y C_w$, where C_w is the warping torsional constant.

For a beam having simply-supported boundary conditions and prevented from twisting about its centroidal axis, the moment at which lateral buckling will occur is given by the equation for M_u in clauses 13.6(a)(ii) and 13.6(b)(ii). This expression assumes that the member is completely elastic at the moment corresponding to lateral buckling.

If the bending moment corresponding to lateral buckling is above approximately $\frac{2}{3}$ of the moment resistance for a laterally supported member, then the assumptions made in deriving the elastic buckling expressions are no longer valid as the compression flange has been considerably softened by yielding at the flange tips. This yielding is caused by the residual strains acting together with those due to the applied load. The moment resistance is therefore reduced according to an empirical equation if the value of M_u is above $\frac{2}{3} M_p$ for Class 1 and 2 sections (Clause 13.6(a)(i)) or $\frac{2}{3} M_y$ for Class 3 and 4 sections (Clause 13.6(b)(i)).

Regardless of the results of the lateral buckling calculations, in no case may the moment resistance exceed that based on the local buckling strength. Thus, $M_r \leqslant \phi M_p$ for Class 1 and 2 sections and $M_r \leqslant \phi M_y$ or ϕSF_{cr} for Class 3 and 4 sections respectively.

The value of $\phi = 0.90$ chosen for laterally unsupported beams has been shown, by statistical analysis, to be generally conservative except for elastic buckling of rolled W shapes where $\phi = 0.84$ (7 percent less) was determined[112]. Since the actual end conditions of a beam in a structure will provide some degree of increased restraint over the laboratory situation, and to avoid the complexities associated with a variable ϕ value, the constant value of $\phi = 0.90$ is used for this type of member.

The requirements of this clause may well be conservative due to the assumptions regarding boundary conditions. Although the requirements specify that L is the length of the beam between lateral supports, it is logical in some cases to take L as the distance

FIGURE 2-15

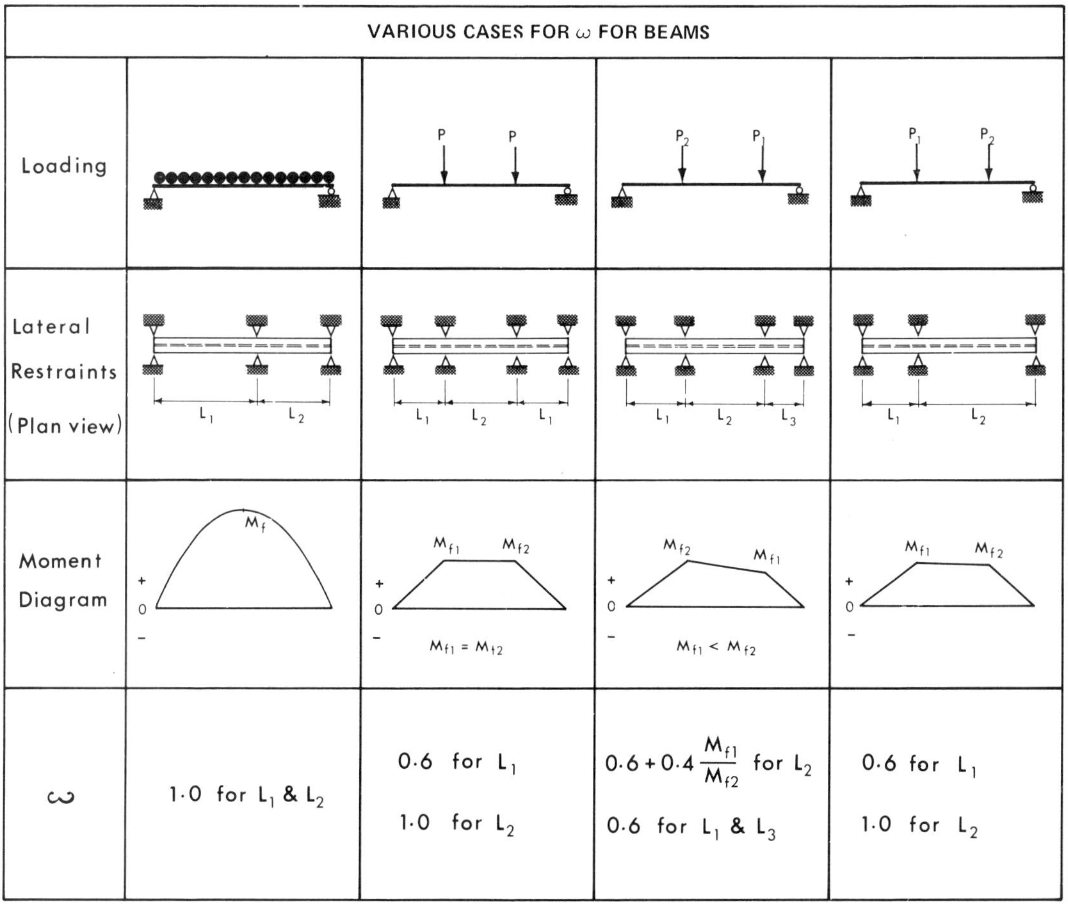

VARIOUS CASES FOR ω FOR BEAMS				
Loading				
Lateral Restraints (Plan view)	L_1 L_2	L_1 L_2 L_1	L_1 L_2 L_3	L_1 L_2
Moment Diagram	M_f	M_{f1} M_{f2} $M_{f1} = M_{f2}$	M_{f2} M_{f1} $M_{f1} < M_{f2}$	M_{f1} M_{f2}
ω	1·0 for L_1 & L_2	0·6 for L_1 1·0 for L_2	$0.6 + 0.4 \dfrac{M_{f1}}{M_{f2}}$ for L_2 0·6 for L_1 & L_3	0·6 for L_1 1·0 for L_2

between points of contraflexure on the laterally buckled shape of the compression flange. In other cases, however, when yielding of adjacent spans may have reduced the restraint, this procedure is not recommended. In view of the difficulty in assessing the various situations, this Standard does not specify any adjustment for end restraint.

The Standard does permit the use of an equivalent moment factor, ω, for use when the bending moment is not uniform over the length of the member. The value of ω used is the same as that for beam-columns. The value of ω determined by clause 13.8.4(a)(i) is applicable only when the moment gradient for the applied loads is linear between the points of lateral support for which the values of M_{f_1} and M_{f_2} are appropriate. Thus, for the common case of a beam supporting a uniformly distributed load, ω always has the value of 1.0. Figure 2—15 illustrates selected cases of ω for various loading and support conditions. Reference 25 recommends values of ω for unusual loading and support conditions.

For I-shaped members the various cross-sectional properties may be approximated (by neglecting the contribution of the web) and M_u can be expressed in terms of parameters σ_1 and σ_2 [22].

Channels prevented from twisting are treated in a manner similar to I-sections except that the lateral flange bending component σ_2 is assumed to be zero.

13.7 Lateral Bracing for Members in Structures Analysed Plastically

This item has been covered in the commentary on clause 8.5(c).

13.8 Axial Compression and Bending

There are three requirements which must be met to ensure the adequacy of any beam-column. As prescribed by clause 11.2 of the standard, the compression elements of the cross-section must be proportioned such that local buckling does not occur prior to attainment of the cross-section strength. In clause 13.8, requirements relating to a strength check of the cross-section and requirements relating to a stability check of the entire member are set forth.

13.8.1 Clause 13.8.1(a) is a statement of the principle involved in the strength check. It may be applied simply as follows. Consider a W-shape subject to moment, M_f, and thrust, C_f (Figure 2—16). If part of the web, taken at yield stress, will just sustain the thrust, C_f, the remainder of the cross-section (flanges plus adjoining web) is available to resist the moment, M_f, at yield stress. Such a principle is relatively easy to apply for uniaxial bending. For W shapes, references 12 and 46 give explicit expressions for the plastic moment capacity, reduced for the presence of axial load.

FIGURE 2-16

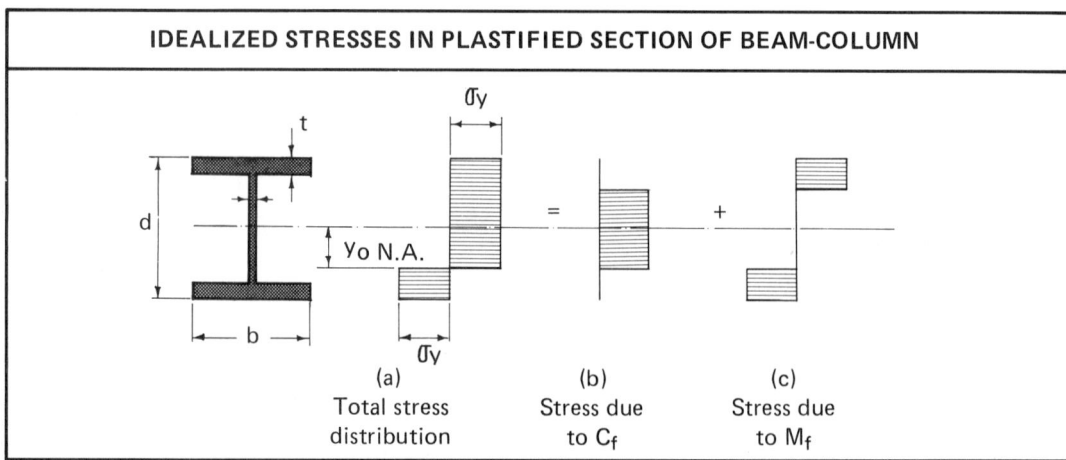

IDEALIZED STRESSES IN PLASTIFIED SECTION OF BEAM-COLUMN

(a) Total stress distribution

(b) Stress due to C_f

(c) Stress due to M_f

For biaxial bending, no simple methods exist for an exact strength check, since both the location and angular disposition of the neutral axis have to be determined. For this reason, interaction expressions have been introduced to predict member strength. Their accuracy tends to be dependent on the complexity of the expression and the shape of the cross-section.

Clause 13.8.1(b) is the general form of the stability interaction expression, applicable to any compact shape. Empirical in origin, it is formula 8.29 from reference 25.

The equivalent moments used in the numerator terms are discussed under clauses 13.8.4 (a), (b) and (c). Amplification factors $(1-C_f/C_e)$ are included in the denominator bending terms to allow for the additional bending caused by the axial load acting in the deformed column. The major axis resisting moment, M_{rx} is determined from the formulas of 13.6(a) to reflect the propensity of the member to fail through lateral-torsional buckling.

13.8.2 Clauses 13.8.2 (a) and (b) are strength checks for I and W Class 1 or 2 shapes. Clause 13.8.2(a) controls when bending is dominant. The following is an explanation of the derivation of Clause 13.8.2(b). Reference 12 gives the following expressions for the plastic moment of resistance, reduced for the presence of axial loads and are shown in Figure 2–17.

$$M_{rcx} = 1.18\ M_{rx}\ (1-C_f/C_y) \leqslant M_{rx}$$

$$M_{rcy} = 1.19\ M_{ry}\ [1-(C_f/C_y)^2\ ] \leqslant M_{ry}$$

FIGURE 2-17

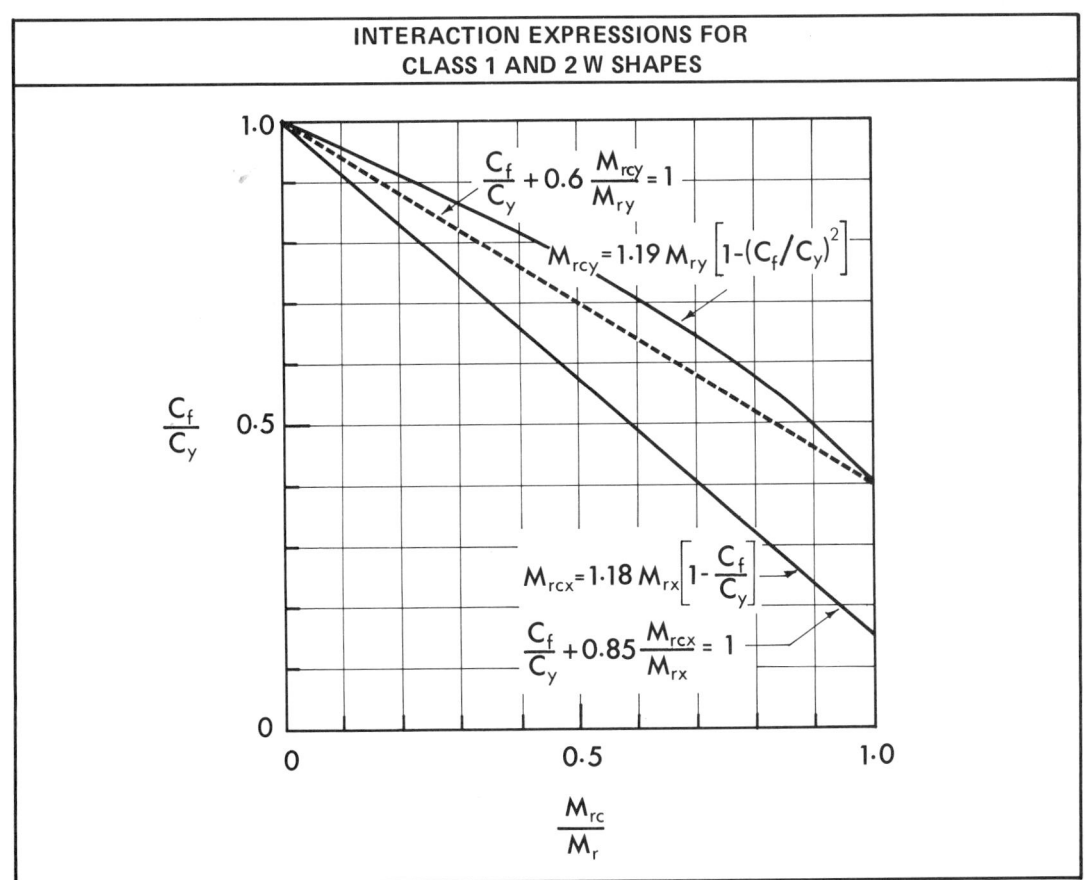

(These expressions are used in Appendix F of S16.1-M78 in which more refined approaches to biaxial bending are developed).

For bending about the X—X axis, the expression may be transposed as follows:

$$\frac{C_f}{C_y} + 0.85 \frac{M_{rcx}}{M_{rx}} \leqslant 1.0$$

The following linear expression has been suggested as a good approximation to the second-order expression for M_{rcy} [47];

$$\frac{C_f}{C_y} + 0.6 \frac{M_{rcy}}{M_{ry}} \leqslant 1.0$$

Clause 13.8.2(b) resulted by combining these expressions.

Clause 13.8.2(c) is identical in form to that of 13.8.1(b). For W and I shapes, the shape factors inherent in M_{rx} and M_{ry} are about 1.12 and 1.55, respectively, whereas a fixed value of 1.10 was used in the stress form of this clause in S16-1969. As in 13.8.1(b), a linear interaction is assumed between all three terms in 13.8.2(c). In the Commentary to Appendix F, it is demonstrated that the economies can be achieved by using slightly more complex non-linear interaction expressions.

13.8.3 For Class 3 sections, clause 13.8.3(a) essentially limits the extreme fibre stress, at the most highly stressed corner of the cross-section, to the nominal yield stress. In fact, because of residual stresses, some yielding may occur at such a fibre if this expression is just satisfied. For Class 4 sections, the stress limit may be less than nominal yield depending on the critical stresses for the particular section.

Again, clause 13.8.3(b) is an empirical linear interaction expression relating the critical axial load ratio and the ratios of applied moment to limiting moment capacity about the two orthogonal axes.

13.8.4 This clause lists values of ω, a coefficient used to compute a uniform bending effect in beam-columns which is intended to be equivalent to the effect of a non-uniform moment effect. This coefficient is explained in more detail in reference 25 where it is called C_m. Figures 2—18 and 2—19 offer guidance in the design of beam-columns subjected to various bending moment effects. Reference 48 contains more guidance on the design of beam-columns subject to concentrated load (or moment) between supports.

13.9 Axial Tension and Bending

A simple, generally conservative, interaction formula is given in 13.9(a) to check the adequacy of members subjected to combined bending and axial tension. In effect, the equation computes the sum of the stresses due to bending and due to axial load and compares the sum to the quantity ϕF_y.

For members subjected predominately to bending, failure may occur by buckling of the compression flange. A check against this is provided by clause 13.9(b). Clause 13.9(b) can be written (for a Class 1 or 2 section) as;

$$\frac{M_f - T_f(Z/A)}{M_r} \leqslant 1.0$$

For Class 3 or 4 sections, Z is replaced by S. By dividing both the numerator and denominator of the left-hand side by Z, the following expression results;

$$\frac{M_f/Z - T_f/A}{M_r/Z} \leqslant 1.0$$

FIGURE 2-18

GUIDE TO DESIGN OF BEAM-COLUMNS
PRISMATIC MEMBERS — MOMENT AT ENDS — NO TRANSVERSE LOADS

Conditions		P–Δ Effects Included	ω	Design Criteria		
				Class 1 and 2 I-shape columns	Class 1 and 2 sections	Class 3 and 4 sections
M_2 / M_1 (single curvature) $M_2 \geqslant M_1$ Single curvature bending		YES	$0.6 + 0.4 \dfrac{M_1}{M_2}$			
		NO	1.0			
M_2 / $M_1 = 0$ $M_1 = 0$ Single curvature bending		YES	0.6	$\dfrac{M_{fx}}{M_{rx}} + \dfrac{M_{fy}}{M_{ry}} \leqslant 1.0$ $\dfrac{C_f}{C_r} + 0.85\dfrac{M_{fx}}{M_{rx}}$ $+ \dfrac{0.60\,M_{fy}}{M_{ry}} \leqslant 1.0$	$\dfrac{C_f}{C_r} + \dfrac{M_{fx}}{M_{rx}}$ $+ \dfrac{M_{fy}}{M_{ry}} \leqslant 1.0$	$\dfrac{C_f}{C_r} + \dfrac{M_{fx}}{M_{rx}}$ $+ \dfrac{M_{fy}}{M_{ry}} \leqslant 1.0$
		NO	0.85	$\dfrac{C_f}{C_r} + \dfrac{\omega_x M_{fx} U_x}{M_{rx}}$ $+ \dfrac{\omega_y M_{fy} U_y}{M_{ry}}$ $\leqslant 1.0$	$\dfrac{C_f}{C_r} + \dfrac{\omega_x M_{fx} U_x}{M_{rx}}$ $+ \dfrac{\omega_y M_{fy} U_y}{M_{ry}}$ $\leqslant 1.0$	$\dfrac{C_f}{C_r} + \dfrac{\omega M_{fx} U_x}{M_{rx}}$ $+ \dfrac{\omega_y M_{fy} U_y}{M_{ry}}$ $\leqslant 1.0$
M_2 / M_1 (double curvature) $M_2 \geqslant M_1$ Double curvature bending		YES	$0.6 - 0.4 \dfrac{M_1}{M_2}$ $\not< 0.4$			
		NO	0.85			

C_f = Factored compressive load
C_r = Factored compressive resistance
M_f = Factored bending moment (x-x or y-y axis)
M_r = Factored moment resistance (x-x or y-y axis)

ω = coefficient used to determine equivalent uniform bending effect (X-X or y-y axis)

U = Amplification factor = $\dfrac{1}{1 - (c_f/c_e)}$ (x-x or y-y axis)

FIGURE 2-19

GUIDE TO DESIGN OF BEAM-COLUMNS PRISMATIC MEMBERS – TRANSVERSE LOADS				
CONDITIONS	M_f	ω*	DESIGN CRITERIA	
$M_2 = 0$ / $M_1 = 0$ Load W distributed uniformly. $M_2 = M_1 = 0$ Max. span moment $M_3 = \dfrac{WL}{8}$	M_3	1.0	For Class 1 and 2 I-shaped columns	
Load W distributed uniformly. $M_2 = \dfrac{WL}{8} \qquad M_1 = 0$ Max. span moment $M_3 = \dfrac{9WL}{128}$	M_2	1.0	$\dfrac{M_{fx}}{M_{rx}} + \dfrac{M_{fy}}{M_{ry}} \leqslant 1.0$ $\dfrac{C_f}{C_r} + \dfrac{0.85\,M_{fx}}{M_{rx}} + \dfrac{0.60\,M_{fy}}{M_{ry}} \leqslant 1.0$	
Load W distributed uniformly. $M_2 = M_1 = \dfrac{WL}{12}$ Max. span moment $M_3 = \dfrac{WL}{24}$	M_2	1.0	$\dfrac{C_f}{C_r} + \dfrac{\omega_x\,M_{fx}\,U_x}{M_{rx}} + \dfrac{\omega_y\,M_{fy}\,U_y}{M_{ry}} \leqslant 1.0$ ——— For Class 1 and 2 sections	
Load P at mid-span. $M_2 = M_1 = 0$ Max. span moment $M_3 = \dfrac{PL}{4}$	M_3	0.85	$\dfrac{C_f}{C_r} + \dfrac{M_{fx}}{M_{rx}} + \dfrac{M_{fy}}{M_{ry}} \leqslant 1.0$ $\dfrac{C_f}{C_r} + \dfrac{\omega_x\,M_{fx}\,U_x}{M_{rx}} + \dfrac{\omega_y\,M_{fy}\,U_y}{M_{ry}} \leqslant 1.0$ ———	
Load P at mid-span. $M_2 = \dfrac{3PL}{16} \qquad M_1 = 0$ Max. span moment $M_3 = \dfrac{5PL}{32}$	M_2	0.85	For Class 3 and 4 sections $\dfrac{C_f}{C_r} + \dfrac{M_{fx}}{M_{rx}} + \dfrac{M_{fy}}{M_{ry}} \leqslant 1.0$	
Load P at mid-span. $M_2 = M_1 = \dfrac{PL}{8}$ Max. span moment $M_3 = \dfrac{PL}{8}$	M_2	0.85	$\dfrac{C_f}{C_r} + \dfrac{\omega_x\,M_{fx}\,U_x}{M_{rx}} + \dfrac{\omega_y\,M_{fy}\,U_y}{M_{ry}} \leqslant 1.0$	
Note: See Clause 13.8.4(c) for alternate procedure for concentrated load cases. *See Article 8.6 of reference 25 for alternate methods of determining ω, (Cm).				

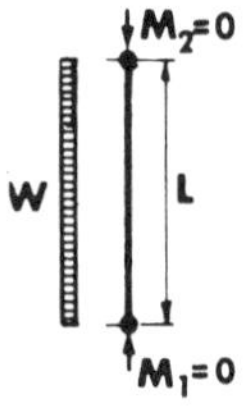

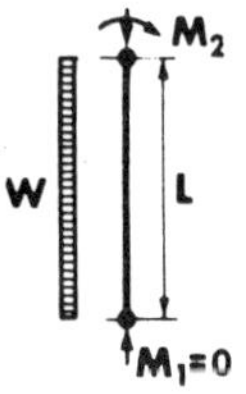

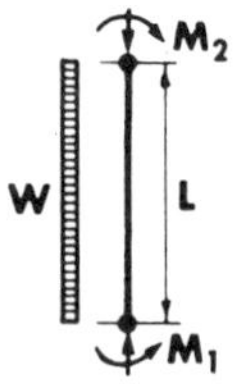

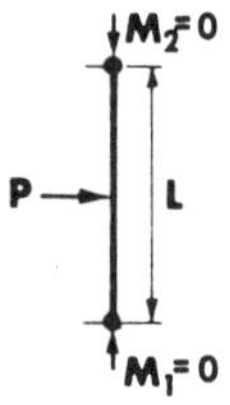

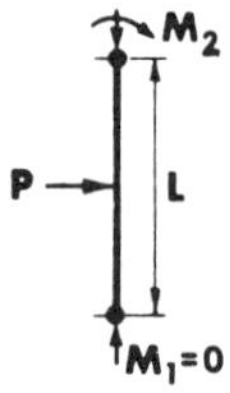

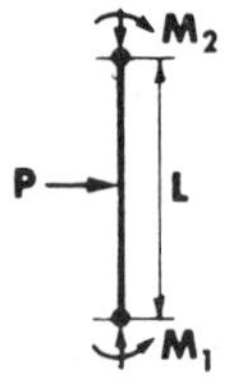

On the left-hand side, the numerator represents the net compressive stress (M_f/Z is the bending compressive stress at factored load and T_f/A is the axial tensile stress at factored load) while the denominator, M_r/Z, is the permissible bending resistance expressed as a stress. Thus, the clause limits the net compressive stress to that which would be permissible for bending alone.

13.10 Load Bearing

The bearing resistance given for machined, accurately sawn or fitted part in contact (clause 13.10(b)) reflects the fact that a triaxial compressive stress state generally exists which restricts yielding of the parts in contact. The value given is based on the previous working stress design standard, which experience has shown to give satisfactory results.

For a cylindrical roller or rocker in contact with a flat surface, the maximum shearing stress developed due to a line load of q kN/mm is

$$\tau_{max} = 0.27 \sqrt{\frac{qE}{\pi D(1-\nu^2)}}$$

where ν is Poisson's ratio[49]. From this the bearing resistance is then

$$\frac{B_r}{\phi} = q\,L = \frac{\pi DL(1-\nu^2)\,(\tau_{max})^2}{0.27^2\,E}$$

Setting $\tau_{max} = \frac{4}{3}\tau_y$ and $\tau_y = \frac{F_y}{\sqrt{3}}$ leads to

$$\frac{B_r}{\phi} = \frac{\pi DL(1-\nu^2)}{0.27^2\,E} \left[\frac{4}{3} \times \frac{F_y}{\sqrt{3}}\right]^2 = 0.000\,13\;DLF_y^2$$

The "Hertz" solution, as reported in reference 50 gives the allowable load as

$$2.86DL\,\frac{(2.7F_y)^2}{E} = 0.000\,10\;DLF_y^2$$

and indicates that the value of 0.000 13 obtained by calibration with the existing standard for a yield stress of about 400 MPa is somewhat conservative.

For bearing-type connections, clause 13.10(c), tests have shown[51,52,53,54] that the ratio of the bearing stress (B_r/dt) to the ultimate tensile strength of the plate (F_u) is in the same ratio as the end distance of the bolt (e) to its diameter (d). Thus,

$$\frac{B_r}{\phi dt} = \frac{e}{d}F_u$$

Or, for n fasteners, $B_r = \phi tneF_u$

As the test results do not provide data for e/d greater than 3, an upper limit of e = 3d is imposed, that is

$$B_r \leqslant 3\phi tdnF_u$$

As for connections in general, the value of ϕ in clause 13.10(c) is to be taken as 0.67. This value has been reduced from 0.90 originally used in S16.1-1974 as a result of a pilot series of tests which indicated that lower failure loads could occur in thin webs of coped beams with compact connections.[115] (See also the commentary to clause 13.11.)

13.11 Bolts in Bearing-Type Connections

13.11.1 It is the initial premise of the resistances developed in this clause that the strength of the structure should be governed by member capacity rather than by that of the connector. Hence, the value of ϕ to be used here is established at a lower value (0.67) than that prescribed for members (0.90). This is applicable to all parts of clause 13.11.

13.11.2 The strength of a bolted connection can be governed by the bearing capacity of the material abutting the fastener (clause 13.10(c)), by the net section capacity if in tension (clause 13.2(a)), or by the shear strength of the fasteners. The latter is the subject of clause 13.11.2.

Based on extensive testing, it has been established that the shear strength of high-strength bolts is approximately 0.60 times the tensile strength of the bolt material. Hence, to obtain the shear resistance of a group of bolts, this quantity is multiplied by the cross-sectional area of one bolt, the number of shear planes in the joint, and the total number of bolts resisting the load ($V_r = 0.60 \phi \, n \, m \, A_b \, F_u$).

Two modifications are necessary in special circumstances. If the bolt thread is intercepted by a shear plane, there is less shear area available than that given above. The ratio of the area through the thread root of a bolt to its shank area is about 0.70 for the usual structural sizes. (In unusual cases, such as thin parts and small bolt diameters, the threaded part of the shank may be intercepted by two shear planes. The designer should further modify the shear strength equation accordingly.)

The second possible modification concerns joint length. It has been well established that, except for the case of two bolts in line, joint strength is not linearly proportional with joint length. The average resistance per fastener decreases with joint length. In the interest of simplicity, S16.1-M78 breaks down joint strength into two cases. Joints less than 1300 mm long require no reduction when calculating the total shear resistance of the bolts while those greater than 1300 mm long are to be taken as 80% of the basic value. This "step" evaluation provides a reasonable approximation to the true case.

13.11.3 It is intended that the designer include an estimate of the force that may be present due to prying action when calculating the tensile force present in a member (T_f). The "Guide to Design Criteria for Bolted and Riveted Joints"[55] gives several recommendations as to how to obtain this force. If the connection is subjected to repeated loading, prying action must be avoided.

The ultimate resistance of a single high-strength bolt loaded in tension by the connected parts is equal to the product of its stress area (a value lying between the gross bolt area and the area taken through the thread roots) and the ultimate tensile strength of the bolt material. For simplicity, the equation given in clause 13.11.2 uses the nominal area of the bolt (A_b) and the multiplier 0.75 to provide an approximate conversion to the stress area.

13.11.4 The expression given in this clause is an elliptical interaction equation developed directly from test results. The value 0.56 is the square of 0.75, the necessary conversion from nominal bolt area to stress area. The empirical parameter β depends upon bolt type and location of the shear plane with respect to the threads.

13.12 Bolts in Slip-Resistant (Friction-Type) Connections

In the design of a slip-resistant joint, the first concern is the probability of slip under specified loads. However, the ultimate strength of the bolted joint, after slip into bearing has occurred, is still dependent upon the bearing and shear resistances as a bearing-type joint.

13.12.2 The slip resistance of a bolted joint is given by the product of the number of faying surfaces, the coefficient of friction of the parts being joined, and the total clamping force provided by the bolts. In addition to these quantities, S16.1-M78 recognizes explicitly that the ideal situation of zero percent probability of slip is not attainable. The designer must choose the slip probability level that he thinks appropriate to the structure being considered.

Both the slip coefficient and the initial clamping force have considerable variation about their mean values. The necessary frequency distributions for these effects are known for a large number of practical cases and they have been used to evaluate the slip probability levels for various situations.

Table 4 gives the values of μ to be used in the equation giving the slip resistance V_s in clause 13.12.2. These values combine the effects of the probable clamping force and the type and condition of the faying surfaces. They have been chosen for the 5% probability level, that is, there is a 5% chance that the joint will slip into bearing under the specified loads. For comparable situations covered by CSA Standard S16-1969 the result will be a slight improvement in economy of a given joint. For connections which are desired to be slip resistant but for which a larger probability of slip is tolerable, a table of μ-values for the 10% level is available in the reference 55.

The numerical modifier in the equation given in clause 13.12.2 (that is, 0.26) includes the necessary relationship between tensile area and nominal bolt area and the relationship between bolt tensile strength and required proof load. It also contains a component that enables the use of the equation as given along with published values of μ in reference 55. In this reference, they are used in conjunction with shear stress values. S16.1-M78 avoids this since bolts in a friction-type connection are, by definition, never acting in shear at specified load levels.

Designers are reminded that the use of high-strength bolts in a friction-type connection should be the exception rather than the rule. They are the preferred solution where cyclic loads or load reversals are present or where the use of the building is such that the small slips that might otherwise occur cannot be tolerated.

13.12.3 This clause considers the case of a friction-type shear connection which also has a component of load parallel to the axes of the bolts. There are no published test results covering this situation and the equation given has been chosen as a matter of judgement.

Taking as a base the case where there is no component of load parallel to the axes of the bolts, it is apparent that the resistance to slip will be reduced as tensile load is applied. This reduction will continue until the parts are on the verge of separation, at which time the slip resistance goes to zero. The interaction relationship given assumes linear response between the end limits of all shear and no tension and all tension and no shear.

The terms in the equation given are all either defined directly or follow from explanations given in the Commentary except for the quantity:

$$\frac{1.9}{n \, A_b \, F_u}$$

which can be broken down as:

$$\frac{1}{0.53 \, n \, A_b \, F_u} = \frac{1}{0.75 \times 0.67 \, n \, A_b \, F_u}$$

$$= \frac{1}{0.75 \, \phi \, n \, A_b \, F_u}$$

$$\equiv \frac{1}{T_r}, \text{ clause } 13.11.3.$$

13.13 Welds

The clauses on welds produce results very comparable to those which would have been obtained under S16-1969. Consistent with previous practice, the major area of consideration is that of the shear resistance of complete or partial penetration groove welds, plug and slot welds, and of fillet welds. The resistances of welds in other categories (tension or compression parallel to axis of complete or partial penetration groove welds and of fillet welds, tension or compression normal to the throat of complete groove welds, and compression normal to the throat of partial penetration groove welds) are taken as the same as those for the base metal. Tension other than parallel to the axis of partial penetration groove welds is considered to be the same as shear.

S16.1-M78 explicitly recognizes that the shear resistance of a weld must be evaluated on the basis of both the resistance of the weld itself and of the base metal adjacent to the weld.

The resistance of the base metal is given as $V_r = 0.66 \, \phi \, A_m \, F_y$. This expression is consistent with that given in clause 13.4.1(a) of S16.1-M78 for the shear resistance of a flexural member with a stocky web. The area of metal (A_m) to be used here is the area of the fusion face. The shear yield of steel is customarily taken to be $F_y/\sqrt{3}$, that is, $0.58 \, F_y$. The increase between this value and that given in the equation above ($0.66 \, F_y$) is attributable to the beneficial effects of strain-hardening. The value of ϕ to be used in evaluating the shear resistance of the base metal will normally be taken as 0.90.

The strength of the weld metal is given as $V_r = 0.50 \, \phi \, A_w \, X_u$. The term A_w is the effective throat area of the weld and X_u is the ultimate tensile strength of the electrode (as given by the electrode classification number).

As has already been stated, both the fastening element (the weld) and the connected material are being considered in this clause. Therefore, in order to avoid confusion, the value of ϕ to be used in calculating the weld resistance is taken as 0.90. However, as was noted when discussing high-strength bolts, it is desirable to ensure that the fasteners will not fail before the member being connected. In that case, ϕ was modified (to 0.67). In the equation for fastener resistance given in this section, the reduction is incorporated into the modifier (0.50). As well, the modifier relates the shear strength of the weld to the electrode tensile strength as obtained from tests. For a load factor of 1.5, the results obtained here will be comparable to those which would have been obtained under S16-1969.

14. FATIGUE

For the few cases where members and connections of building structures are subject to the types of repeated loading which gives rise to fatigue conditions, clause 14 provides the requirements to design these members and connections for the appropriate fatigue life. The Standard defines fatigue as an ultimate limit state but one for which the requirements are checked at specified load levels. However, clause 14.1.1 requires that factored resistances be sufficient for the factored static loads in addition to the fatigue requirements of clause 14.

The most important difference between former standards and this Standard is the use in determining fatigue life of the "stress range" concept. Basically, this concept, reflecting the results of a comprehensive research project,[67,68,69] states that the difference between the maximum applied stress and the minimum applied stress (the stress range) accounts for nearly all the variation in fatigue life for a given steel member or detail. The Standard categorizes an extensive list of design conditions and situations into six stress range categories A to F.

It is important to realize that the concept using stress range means that only live load and impact stresses need to be considered when designing for fatigue, since stress range is the difference between maximum and minimum stress. Also the research conducted indicates that fatigue design need be considered only for regions subjected to tension stresses or stress reversal but not for regions subject only to compressive stresses regardless of their magnitudes. Appendix K provides diagrammatic representations of the allowable stress ranges and various fatigue categories.

To achieve the desired fatigue life (in terms of the appropriate number of cycles of applied load) the steel member or connection must be sized to keep the range of stress within that given in Table 6(a) for the category (A to F) determined using Table 6(b), and the desired number of cycles.

Designers are reminded that secondary stresses can also be a source of fatigue failures[110].

The maximum web slenderness permitted $(3150/\sqrt{F_y})$, is based on research conducted in the United States[117].

15. BEAMS AND GIRDERS

15.1 Proportioning

As in past standards beams and girders can be proportioned on the basis of the properties of their gross section except (a) when the material removed for fastener holes exceeds 15% of the gross flange area[57] and (b) when openings other than holes for fasteners are considered in accordance with clause 15.10.

15.3 Reduced Moment Resistance of Girders With Thin Webs

Plate girders are frequently designed with strong, stubby flanges and relatively thin webs. Such sections would normally be considered as Class 4 sections, by virtue of the slenderness of the web $(\frac{h}{w} > 1810/\sqrt{F_y})$, and the actual bending resistance of the flanges would be underestimated.

The intent of this clause is to allow the efficient use of girders with Class 4 webs and flanges of Class 3, or better, by giving a satisfactory estimate of their bending resistance.

The mechanical behaviour leading to this clause is as follows. When a slender web is sufficiently loaded in compression due to bending, it attempts to relieve itself of load by buckling sidewards. A portion of the share of the bending moment which the web would be assumed to carry according to the elastic theory of distribution of bending stresses must be picked up by the compression flange, which is then overloaded.[43] (Figure 2—20)

FIGURE 2-20

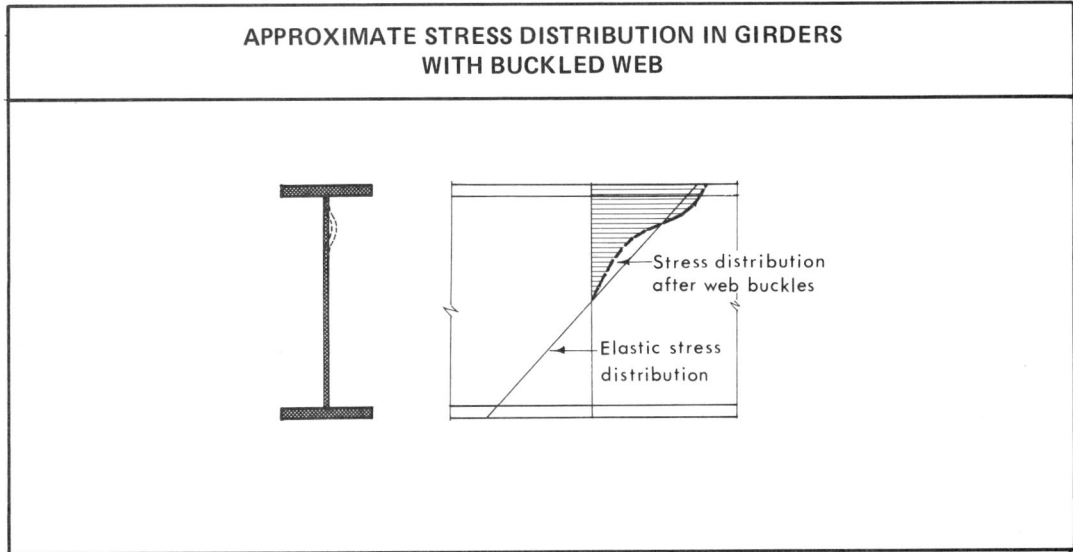

APPROXIMATE STRESS DISTRIBUTION IN GIRDERS
WITH BUCKLED WEB

Stress distribution after web buckles

Elastic stress distribution

Clause 15.3 accommodates the extra flange load by reducing the moment resistance of the girder, which resistance is still estimated on the basis of an elastic linear stress distribution, to M_r'. In most cases the applicable reduction is small. Figure 2—21 illustrates the amount of reduction according to the formula given in the clause.

FIGURE 2-21

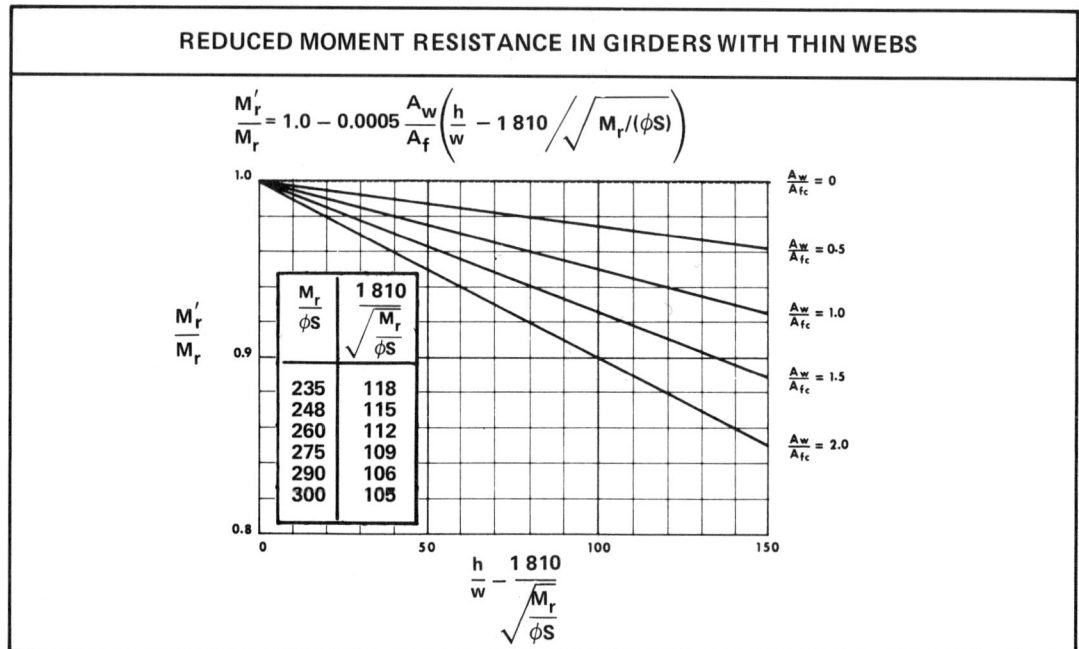

REDUCED MOMENT RESISTANCE IN GIRDERS WITH THIN WEBS

$$\frac{M_r'}{M_r} = 1.0 - 0.0005 \frac{A_w}{A_f}\left(\frac{h}{w} - 1\,810 \left/ \sqrt{M_r/(\phi S)}\right.\right)$$

Clause 15.3, S16.1-M78

The limit of $1810/\sqrt{F_y}$ on the slenderness of a Class 3 web is replaced in this clause by $1810/\sqrt{M_r/(\phi S)}$ to account for the possibility that M_r may already have been reduced in clause 13.5 or 13.6 by consideration of flange instability (lateral flange buckling). The effect of the substitution is to increase the slenderness at which the reduction will be imposed; this is justified by the lower compressive bending stresses present in the web and the consequently decreased possibility of web buckling sidewards.

No data is available to indicate that a partial plastic hinge can develop in a girder with a Class 4 web and so an upper limit of ϕM_y is imposed on the overall bending resistance of a girder.

15.4 Flanges.

Clause 15.4.4 requires partial length cover plates to extend sufficiently beyond the theoretical cut-off point such that the horizontal shear force at the theoretical cut-off point can be developed by the fastener or welds and transmitted to the cover plate. In the case of welded cover plates, theoretical and experimental studies[58] have shown that the horizontal shear force $\left(\dfrac{A\,M_f\,y}{I_g}\right)$ is developed within a specific length (a') from the actual end of the cover plate, where M_f is the factored moment at a distance, a', from the actual end of the cover plate. Because the maximum weld size is limited by the cover plate thickness, it may not be possible to develop the shear force, P, at the theoretical cut-off point. Then the cover plate length must be increased such that the smaller shear force a length a' away from the end of the cover plate can be developed by the terminal welds. Figure 2—22 illustrates this requirement.

15.6 Intermediate Transverse Stiffeners

Spacing the intermediate transverse stiffeners to suit the shear resistance of clause 13.4 permits the proper tension fields to occur in the web panels under load. However,

FIGURE 2-22

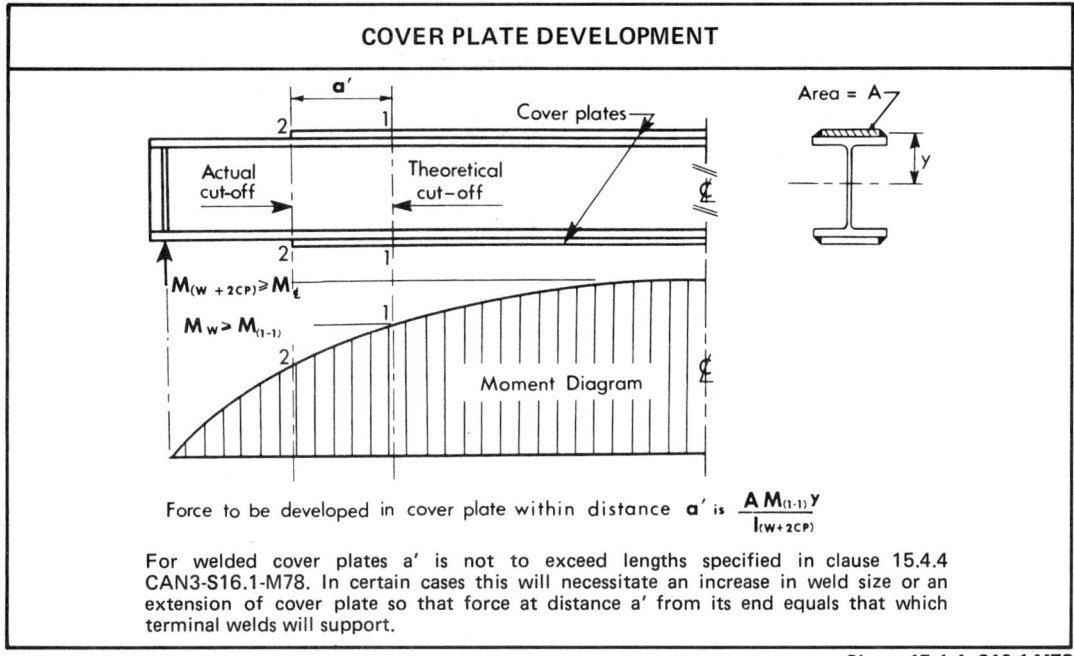

COVER PLATE DEVELOPMENT

Force to be developed in cover plate within distance a' is $\dfrac{A\,M_{(1-1)}\,y}{I_{(w+2CP)}}$

For welded cover plates a' is not to exceed lengths specified in clause 15.4.4 CAN3-S16.1-M78. In certain cases this will necessitate an increase in weld size or an extension of cover plate so that force at distance a' from its end equals that which terminal welds will support.

Clause 15.4.4, S16.1-M78

since a panel with a large opening cannot develop a tension field, it, as well as the end panels which serve to anchor the truss-like action, must remain elastic. Thus, the smaller panel discussion, a or h, is limited to $1150\,w/\sqrt{V_r/\phi A_w}$. This expression is derived directly from clause 13.4.1(d) for $\tau = 1.0$, $\eta = 0$ and $k_v = 7.34$.[42] Figure 2—23 illustrates the action of a thin web girder under load.

FIGURE 2-23

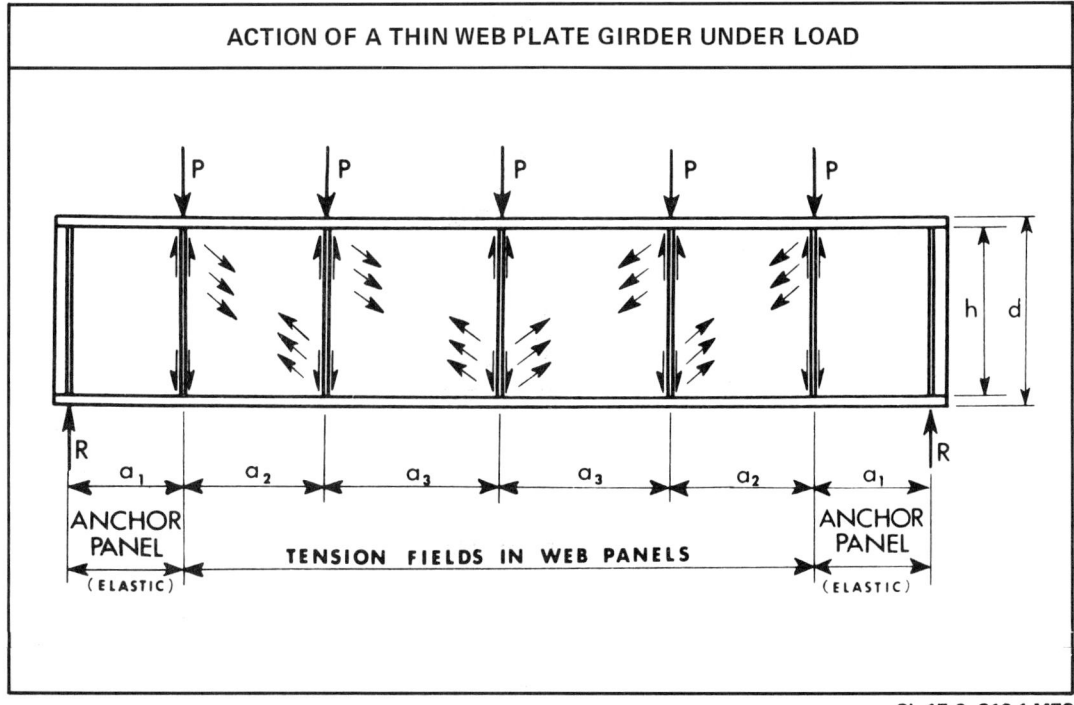

ACTION OF A THIN WEB PLATE GIRDER UNDER LOAD

Cl. 15.6, S16.1-M78

When intermediate transverse stiffeners are required, clause 15.6.2 puts limits on the maximum spacing. Thus, the maximum spacing may be limited by this clause or by shear resistance of the web. Insofar as clause 15.6.2 is concerned, when h/w ⩽ 150 the ratio a/h cannot exceed 3. When h/w > 150, the ratio a/h cannot exceed $\dfrac{67\ 500}{(h/w)^2}$. Figure 2—24 shows the relationship graphically. When a/h exceeds 3 the value of the stiffener is very minor, whereas when h/w > 150 the maximum stiffener spacing is reduced for ease in fabrication and handling.

FIGURE 2-24

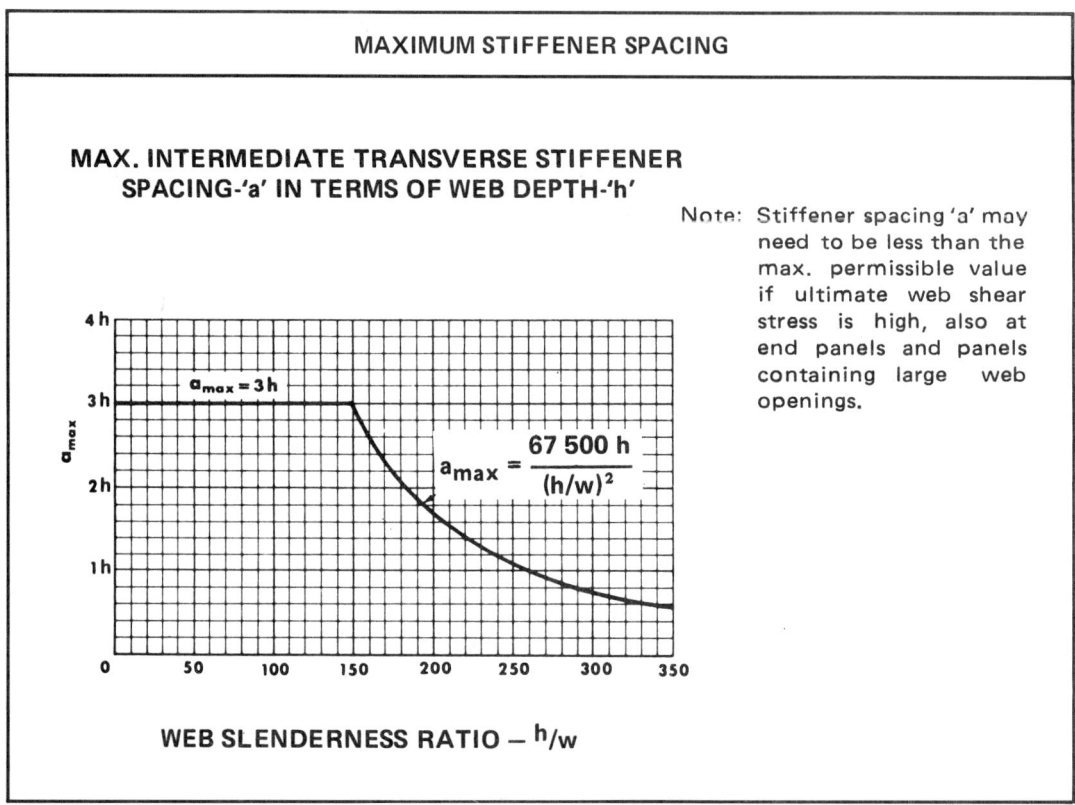

MAXIMUM STIFFENER SPACING

MAX. INTERMEDIATE TRANSVERSE STIFFENER SPACING-'a' IN TERMS OF WEB DEPTH-'h'

Note: Stiffener spacing 'a' may need to be less than the max. permissible value if ultimate web shear stress is high, also at end panels and panels containing large web openings.

Cl. 15.6.2, S16.1-M78

Clause 15.6.3 requires that intermediate transverse stiffeners have both a minimum moment of inertia and a minimum area. The former provides the required stiffness when web panels are behaving in an elastic manner; the latter ensures that the stiffener can sustain the compression to which it is subjected when the web panel develops a tension field. Since stiffeners subject to compression act as columns, stiffeners placed only on one side of the web are loaded eccentrically and are less efficient. The stiffener factor (D) is included in the formula for stiffener area to account for the lowered efficiency of stiffeners furnished singly rather than in pairs.

Clause 15.6.4 requires that a minimum shear be transferred between the stiffener and the web.[42] Intermediate stiffeners furnished singly (rather than in pairs) must be attached to the compression flange so as to assist in preventing the flange from tipping under loads.

15.8 Web Crippling

The equations given in this clause provide a safe estimate of the factored compressive resistance of webs of rolled beams and welded plate girders. They are derived from the equations given in the previous working stress design standard by multiplying those equations by the nominal factor of safety of that standard, 5/3. Experience has shown that the working stress equation has provided a satisfactory margin of safety[59]. In fact, reference 60 recommends that the compressive resistance be computed as the yield stress acting on the web over a length equal to the length of bearing plus 5k. For long bearing lengths (15k) the difference in compressive resistance for interior loads computed by reference 60 and that by clause 15.8 is negligible.

15.9 Stability of Thin Webs

Basler[61] suggested that the critical buckling loads for webs, based on elastic analysis of the buckling of plates, can be computed by

$$B_{cr} = \frac{\pi^2 E}{12(1-\nu^2)(h/w)^2} \left(5.5 + \frac{4}{(a/h)^2}\right) A$$

or

$$B_{cr} = \frac{\pi^2 E}{12(1-\nu^2)(h/w)^2} \left(2 + \frac{4}{(a/h)^2}\right) A$$

for the two cases when the flange is or is not restrained against rotation, respectively. Flange restraint would be provided, for example, when a concrete slab is cast on top of the beam.

For steel, the quantity $\pi^2 E/12(1-\nu^2)$ is equal to 180 760 and the value of 115 000 in equations of clause 15.9 provides an additional margin of about 1.6 to take into account the vulnerability of light webs to instability. This also provides for the possibility of overloading of a small floor area which, over the whole area, is loaded only to the specified value. Figure 2—25 illustrates the application of these formulas.

FIGURE 2-25

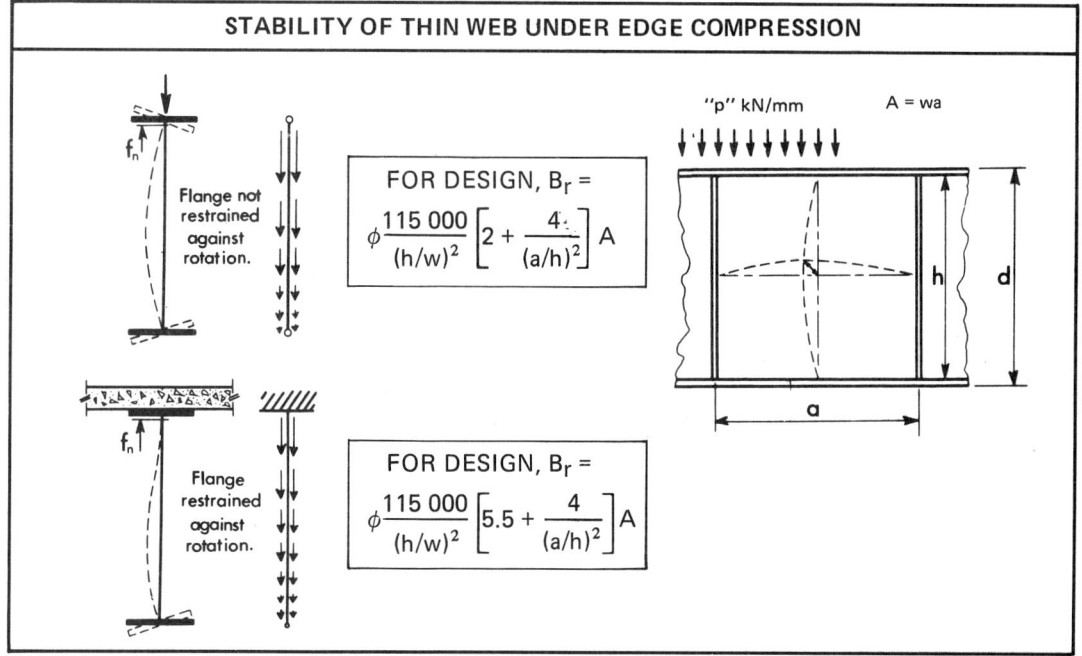

STABILITY OF THIN WEB UNDER EDGE COMPRESSION

Flange not restrained against rotation.

FOR DESIGN, $B_r =$

$$\phi \frac{115\ 000}{(h/w)^2} \left[2 + \frac{4}{(a/h)^2}\right] A$$

Flange restrained against rotation.

FOR DESIGN, $B_r =$

$$\phi \frac{115\ 000}{(h/w)^2} \left[5.5 + \frac{4}{(a/h)^2}\right] A$$

"p" kN/mm   A = wa

15.10 Openings

In general, if the factored moments or shears at the net section exceed the capacity of the member at that point, reinforcement is required. However, research[62] has indicated that unreinforced circular openings may be used in prismatic compact beams or girders without a reduction in their resistance under the conditions listed in clause 15.10.2. Figure 2—26 illustrates the geometrical conditions of clause 15.10.2.

FIGURE 2-26

UNREINFORCED CIRCULAR WEB OPENINGS IN BEAMS

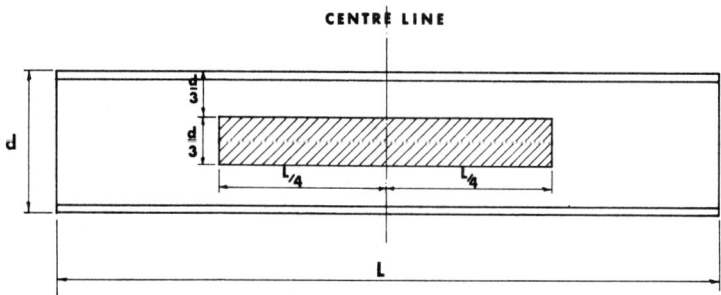

CENTRE LINE

Unreinforced circular holes may be placed anywhere within the hatched zone without affecting the strength of the beam for design purposes, provided:

1. Beam supports uniformly distributed load only.

2. Beam section has an axis of symmetry in plane of bending.

3. Spacing of holes meets the requirements shown below.

SPACING OF HOLES

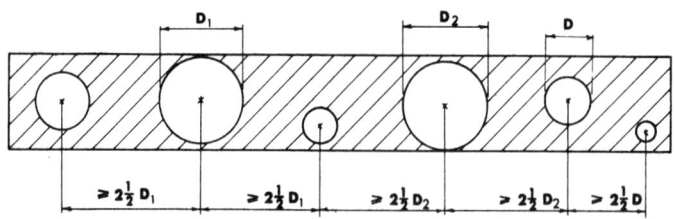

Spacing must be ⩾ 2½ times diameter of the larger opening of any two adjacent openings.

Cl. 15.10, S16.1-M78

The analysis to account for the effect of the opening on a member may be either elastic[63,64] or plastic,[63,65,66]. In the case of plastic analysis the flanges may meet Class 2 requirements but the web must meet the requirements of Class 1 sections.

15.11 Torsion

In many cases beams are not subject to torsion because of the restraint provided by slabs, bracing or other framing members. However, when the forces and moments due to torsion must be resisted by the members, it is in addition to any other moments and forces to which the member is subjected. For guidance, references 70 and 71 should be consulted.

16. OPEN-WEB STEEL JOISTS

16.1 Open-web steel joists (OWSJ) are generally proprietary products whose design, manufacture, transport and erection are covered by the requirements of Clause 16. The Standard clarifies the information to be provided by the building designer (user-purchaser) and the joist manufacturer (joist designer-fabricator).

16.2 Definitions

There are many variations of the simply supported joist which has given rise to the definition for *special open-web joists or special joists.* These joists are those subjected to *specific loading conditions,* cantilever joists, continuous joists and joists having special support conditions. Span is the distance centre-to-centre of joist bearings and may be any length.

16.3 Materials

The use of yield strength levels reported on mill test certificates for the purposes of design is prohibited as this practice may significantly lower the margin of safety by not properly accounting for the statistical distribution of yield levels. Historically all design rules have been, and still are, based on the use of the *specified* minimum yield point or yield strength.

16.4.1 Building Design Drawings

The Standard recognizes that the building designer may not be the joist designer; therefore, building design drawings are required to provide specific information for the design of the joists. Loads such as unbalanced, non-uniform, concentrated, and net up-lift, are to be shown by the building designer. Options, such as attachments for deck when used as a diaphragm, special camber and any other special requirements should also be provided. Although steel joist manufacturers may indicate the maximum clear openings for ducts, etc. which can be accommodated through the webs of each depth of their OWSJ, building designers should, in general, show on the building design drawings the size, location and elevation of openings required through OWSJ. Large ducts may be accommodated by special design. Ducts which require open panels and corresponding reinforcement of the joist, should where possible, be located within the middle half of the joist. This information is required prior to the time of tendering to permit inclusion of an appropriate cost.

16.4.2 Joist Design Drawings

A joist manufacturer's design information may come in varying forms including: design sheets, computer printout, tables, etc. Not all joist manufacturers make "traditional" detail drawings.

16.5 Design

16.5.1 and 16.5.2 Loading

Both OWSJ and special OWSJ are to withstand three loading conditions each considered separately:

(1) uniformly distributed load;

(2) the unbalanced load which would produce the most critical effect on any component; and

(3) an appropriate concentrated load.

For special OWSJ, reference is made to Table 4.1.6B of the National Building Code of Canada (NBCC) for the concentrated load to be used. In this manner S16.1-M78 loading requirements for special OWSJs are tied to the NBCC.

To accommodate load tables in OWSJ catalogues for such purposes as estimating, the Standard provides for specific unbalanced and concentrated loading conditions. The concentrated factored loads given for floor and roof joists are total loads to be applied at a panel point. In a load table under limit states design, it is anticipated that only total factored load will be shown because the ratio of dead-to-live load of the floor system will not be known.

Since the building designer specifies the loading conditions, the design loading for joists should be shown clearly on the drawings. A joist schedule (Figure 2—27) can be used to record all loads on joists.

FIGURE 2-27

JOIST SCHEDULE						
Mark	Depth (mm)	Spacing (mm)	Specified Dead Load	Specified Live Load	Specified Snow (live) Load	Remarks
J1	600	1 300	2.4 kPa*	2.6 kPa*		$\Delta_{live} = \dfrac{span}{320}$
J2	700	2 000	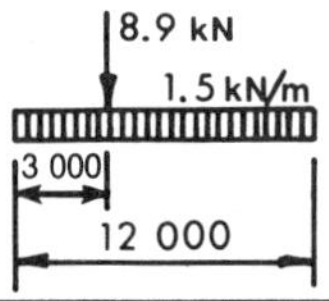 8.9 kN / 1.5 kN/m / 3 000 / 12 000		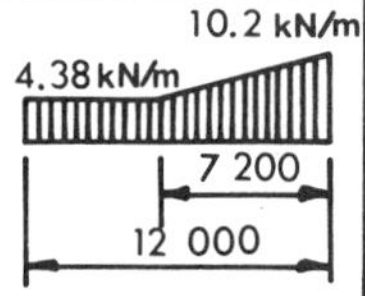 10.2 kN/m / 4.38 kN/m / 7 200 / 12 000	$\Delta_{live} = \dfrac{span}{240}$ suggested I for vibration

* 1 kPa = 1 kN/m^2

On a joist schedule specific joist designations from a manufacturer's catalogue or from the AISC and Steel Joist Institute in the U.S.A. are not appropriate and should not be specified. All heavy concentrated loads such as those resulting from partitions, large pipes, mechanical and other equipment to be supported by OWSJ, should be shown on the structural drawings. Small concentrated loads may be allowed for in the uniform dead load.

Since the depth of the joist supplied may vary slightly for different joist manufacturers, indicate in the remarks column when specified depth is critical. When the importance factor, γ, is not equal to 1.0 it should be specified by the building designer. It is recommended that the building designer insert a suggested moment of inertia, I_x, in the remarks column where vibration of a floor system is a consideration.

16.5.3 Design Assumptions

The loads may be replaced by statically equivalent loads applied at the panel points for the purpose of determining axial forces in all members. It is assumed that any moments induced in the joist chord by direct loading do not influence the magnitude of the axial forces in the members. Tests on trusses[72] have shown that the secondary moments at the joints do not affect the ultimate axial forces determined by a pin-jointed truss analysis.

16.5.4 Verification of Joist Manufacturer's Design

When there is difficulty in analysing the effect of certain specific conditions, for example 1) a particular web-chord connection or 2) a geometric configuration of a cold formed chord, a joist manufacturer can elect to verify the design assumption by a test. The numerical factor of 1.10/0.9 stipulated as a multiplier for the factored loads may be explained as follows:

1) The factor of 1/0.9 is used since the joist manufacturer must provide for the same underrun in resistance as that assumed in the rest of the Standard.

2) The factor of 1.10 provides that the results of one or several tests bear a similar statistical relationship to the entire series of joists that the average yield strength has to the normal design value of F_y, the specified minimum yield strength.

Part 5 of Reference 113 contains a performance testing procedure for OWSJ.

16.5.7 Tension Chord

A minimum radius of gyration is specified for the tension chord members, thus providing a minimum stiffness to facilitate handling and erection. Both net uplift causing load reversal and concentrated loads on the chords must be considered when appropriate.

16.5.8 Compression Chord

When the conditions set out in this clause have been fulfilled, only axial force need be considered when the panel length is less than 610 mm[73]. In these cases the stiffness of the deck tends to effect "panel point" loading of the joist, thus, offsetting the theoretical reduction in chord capacity. When the panel length exceeds 610 mm, a simplified form of the beam-column interaction[73] formula is used. When calculating bending moments in the end panel, it is customary to assume the end of the chord to be pinned even though the joist bearing is welded to its support. Also, when determining the appropriate width-thickness ratio of the compression top chord, the stiffening effect of supported deck or the web is to be neglected (Clause 16.5.6.1).

FIGURE 2-28

JOISTS — LENGTH OF A WEB MEMBER

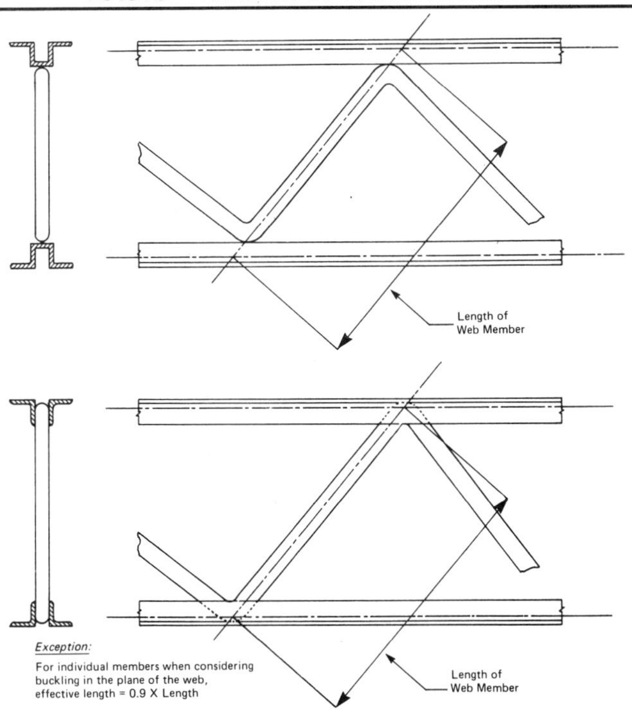

Length of Web Member

Exception:
For individual members when considering buckling in the plane of the web, effective length = 0.9 X Length

Length of Web Member

Cl. 16.5.9.2, S16.1-M78

16.5.9 Webs

The length of web members for design purposes are shown in Figure 2—28. With the exception of web members made of individual members, the effective length factor is always taken as 1.0. For individual members this factor is 0.9 for buckling in the plane of the web, but is 1.0 for buckling perpendicular to the plane of the web.

Web members in tension are not required to meet a limiting slenderness ratio, which is significant when flats are used as tension members, however, attention should be paid to those loading cases where the possibility of shear reversal must be considered. It is likely that tension diagonals (except for end diagonals) may have to resist compression forces due to requirements for concentrated loads.

Prior to the 1975, joists had to be designed for a minimum shear requirement, however, CAN3-S16.1-M78 requires the joist to be checked for a critical unbalanced loading condition.

16.5.10 Spacers and Battens

Spacers and battens can only be omitted when the least radius of gyration of each section is equal to or more than the least radius of gyration of the built-up member. "Integral part" means that an additional element attached to the joist during construction, such as the steel deck, may not serve as a spacer or batten. [Clause 16.5.8.2(c)]

16.5.11 Connections and Splices

Splices are permitted at any point in chord or web members and these splices must be capable of carrying the factored loads by developing the proper factored resistances. As a general rule, it is preferable to have the gravity axes of members meet at a common point within a joint. However, when this is not practical, eccentricities may be neglected if they do not exceed those described in clause 16.5.11.4 (Figure 2—29). A research project at the University of Alberta has shown that the effect of small eccentricities, which are present in joists to be of a minor consequence except for eccentricities, at the end bearing and the intersection of the end diagonal and bottom chord[119]. (See also Clause 16.5.12.4)

16.5.12 Bearings

Special attention is drawn to the possibility of eccentricity between the centre of bearing and the intersection of the axes of the chord and the end diagonal. Since the location of the centre of bearing is dependent on the field support conditions, and their construction tolerances, it may be wise to assume a maximum probable distance centre-to-centre of bearing when designing the bearing detail. Lacking specific information a reasonable assumption might be the overall length of the joist less 65 mm (since the minimum bearing on a steel support is 65 mm). Therefore, the location of the centre of bearing would be 32 mm from the end of the joist (Figure 2—30). When detailing the joists, care must be taken to provide sufficient clearance between the end diagonal and the supporting member or wall (maximum 25 mm). One solution, to obtaining proper bearing, is to increase the depth of the bearing shoe.

If the support is found to be improperly located, such that the span of the joist is increased, the resulting eccentricity may be greater than that assumed. Increasing the length of the bearing shoe to obtain proper bearing may create the more serious problem of increasing the amount of eccentricity. The Standard requires that the bearing detail and the end of the joist be proportioned to include the effect of such eccentricity. Minimum bearing area on concrete and masonry will be calculated from the factored bearing resistance specified by the building designer. The minimum length of bearing on concrete or masonry is 80 mm to avoid interference between the ends of the joists and the outside course of brick or a 200 mm wall. On steel 65 mm is desirable but not mandatory; however, there has to be enough bearing to get minimum anchorage.

FIGURE 2-29

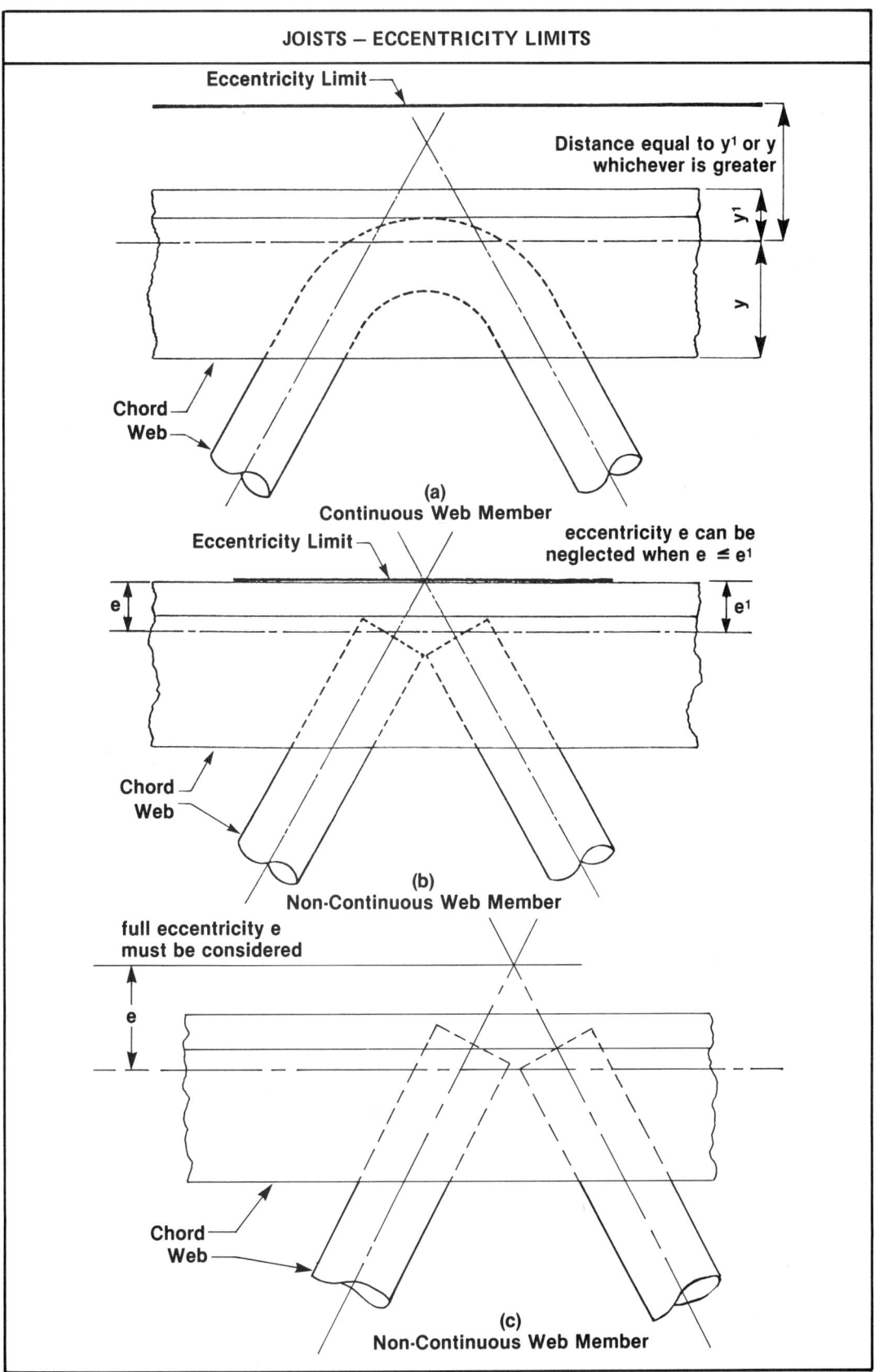

JOISTS — ECCENTRICITY LIMITS

Eccentricity Limit

Distance equal to y^1 or y whichever is greater

y^1

y

Chord

Web

(a)
Continuous Web Member

Eccentricity Limit

eccentricity e can be neglected when $e \leqq e^1$

e

e^1

Chord

Web

(b)
Non-Continuous Web Member

full eccentricity e must be considered

e

Chord

Web

(c)
Non-Continuous Web Member

FIGURE 2-30

JOISTS — BEARING ECCENTRICITY

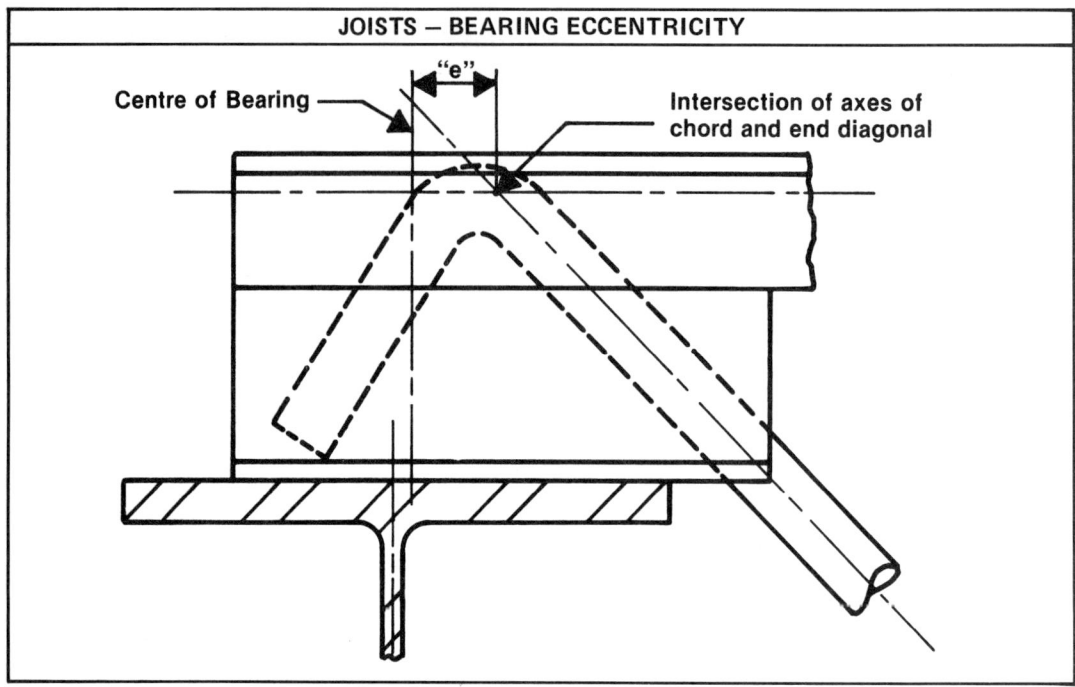

FIGURE 2-31

JOISTS — BEARING ON STEEL

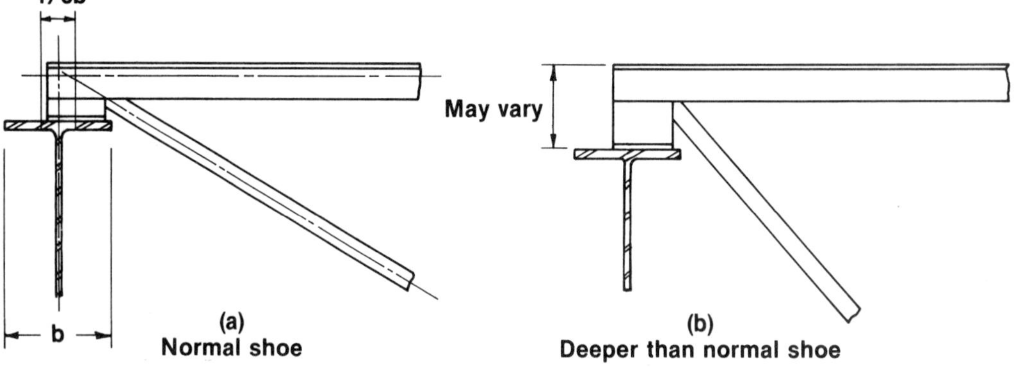

1/3b

May vary

b

(a)
Normal shoe

(b)
Deeper than normal shoe

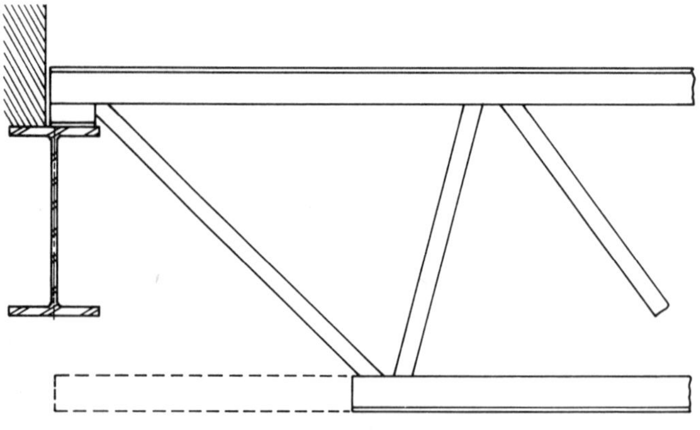

(c)
See Clause 16.5.12.3 when bearing is less than 65 mm

2-50

FIGURE 2-32

JOISTS — BEARING ON STEEL PLATES ANCHORED TO CONCRETE AND MASONRY

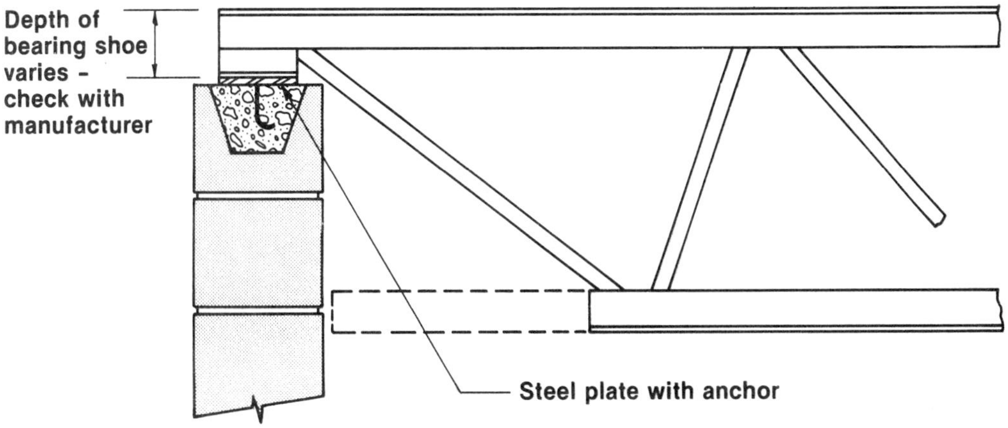

Depth of bearing shoe varies – check with manufacturer

Steel plate with anchor

FIGURE 2-33

TIE JOISTS

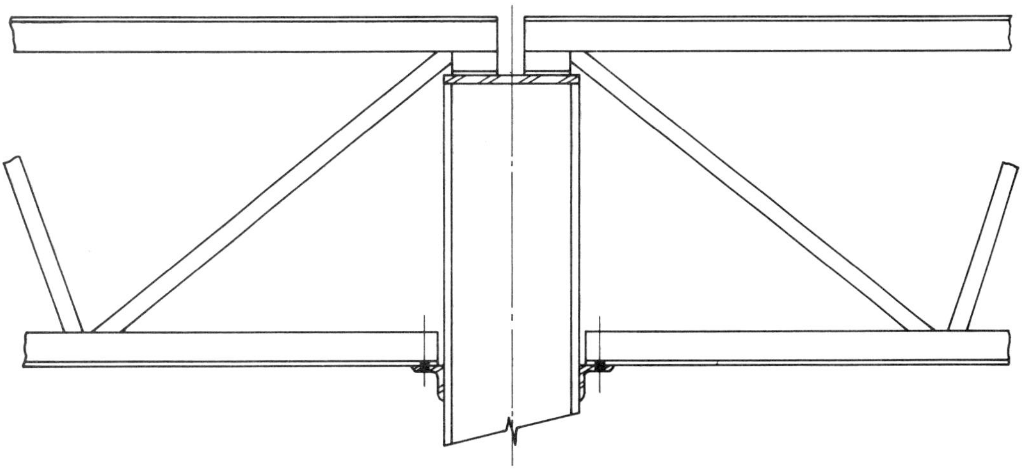

16.5.13.2 Tie Joists

The function of tie joists is to assist in the erection and plumbing of the steel frame. Plumbing cables should be so installed that excessive compressive forces are not introduced into the joists. Top and bottom chords are both attached at the column line. This may be done by bolting either the top or bottom chord; after plumbing the columns, the other chord is then usually welded (Figure 2—33).

Since the joists, by definition, are only to aid in the erection, spacing and plumbing of columns, the ends of at least one chord of these joists must be detailed for connection by mechanical fasteners. Either the top or the bottom chord may be used for this purpose. In most buildings, tie joists remain as installed with both top and bottom chords connected; however, current practices vary throughout Canada with in some cases the bottom chord connections to the columns being made with slotted holes. A research project at McGill University studied the behaviour of tie joist connections and concluded that tie connection may be insufficient to carry lateral loads[120].

For spandrel beams and other beams on which joists frame from one side only, the centre of bearing shoe should be located within the middle third of the flange of the supporting beam. By using a deeper than normal shoe, interference between the support and the end diagonal may be avoided.

16.5.13.3 Frame Action

Where frame action involving joists is desired, the appropriate moments and forces are to be shown on the building design drawings to enable the joist and the joist-to-column connections to be designed by the joist manufacturer.

If joists are to be used also to brace columns or to resist lateral forces on the finished building, the appropriate axial forces, moments and shears should be noted on the structural drawings to facilitate the proper design of these special joists.

16.5.4 Deflections

Deflections are to be computed under specified load levels. The method of computing deflections given in clause 16.5.14.2 has been verified by tests[73].

16.5.15 Camber

Nominal camber can be in accordance with the values tabulated in Table 2—1 according to the expression in Clause 16.5.15 rounded to the nearest millimetre or as specified by the building designer. Specific manufacturing tolerances (both plus and minus) are covered in Clause 16.10.9 and are applicable to either nominal or specified camber. For joists spanning 17 000 mm or greater, a maximum difference in camber has been set at 20 mm to limit the differential camber between two adjacent joists.

Table 2-1

Camber (mm)			
Span	Nominal Camber	Minimum Camber	Maximum Camber
Up to 6 000		3	10
7 000	3	3	11
8 000	4	3	12
9 000	6	3	14
10 000	7	3	16
11 000	8	3	17
12 000	10	3	19
13 000	12	3	21
14 000	14	4	23
15 000	16	6	26
16 000	18	8	28

16.5.16 Vibration

Appendix G of CAN3-S16.1-M78 is a Guide for Floor Vibrations and contains recommendations for floors using steel joists. By increasing the floor thickness (mass), damping will be increased more efficiently than by increasing the moment of inertia (I_x) of the joists.

16.5.17.3 Fabricator and Erector Qualification

A fabricator or erector certified in Division 3 may meet the requirement of the Standard by having the work done under the supervision of a fabricator certified in Division 1 or 2. Many welded joints used in OWSJ are not prequalified under CSA W59, therefore the certified fabricator must have all these welded joints qualified by the Canadian Welding Bureau.

16.5.17 Welding

Flux and slag are removed from all welds to assist in the inspection of the welds as well as to increase the life of the protective coatings applied to the joists.

16.6 Stability During Construction

A distinction is made between bridging, put in to meet the slenderness ratio requirements for top and bottom chords, and the temporary support required by clause 16.6 to hold joists against movement during construction. Permanent bridging, of course, can be used for both purposes.

16.7 Bridging

Figures 2—34 to 2—36 provide illustrations of bridging and details of bridging connections.

FIGURE 2-34

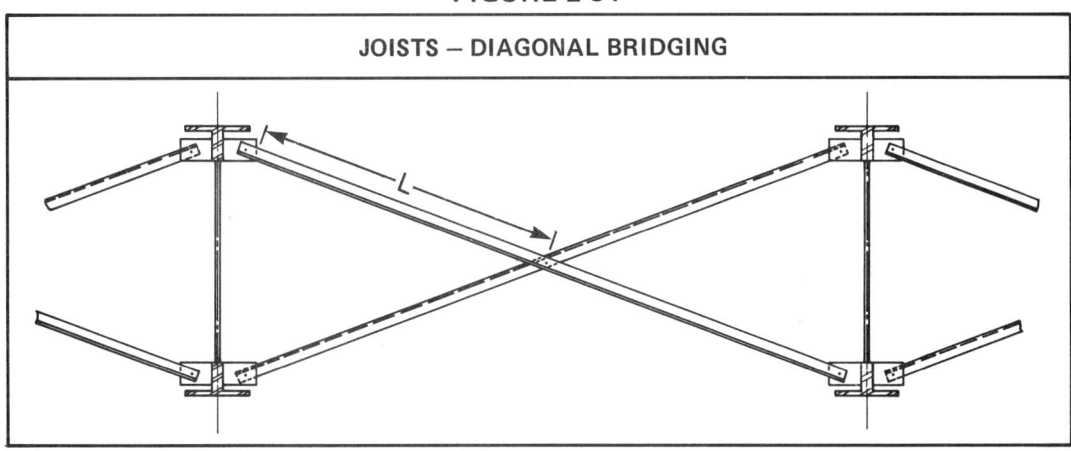

JOISTS — DIAGONAL BRIDGING

FIGURE 2-35

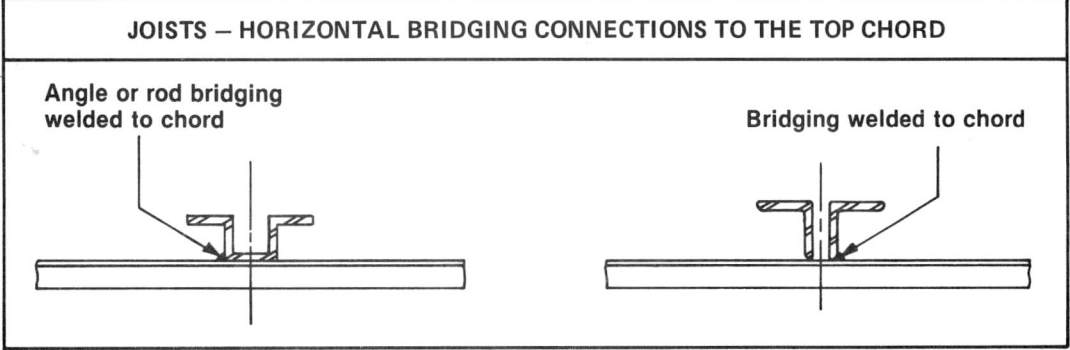

JOISTS — HORIZONTAL BRIDGING CONNECTIONS TO THE TOP CHORD

Angle or rod bridging welded to chord

Bridging welded to chord

FIGURE 2-36

JOISTS — HORIZONTAL BRIDGING CONNECTIONS TO THE BOTTOM CHORD

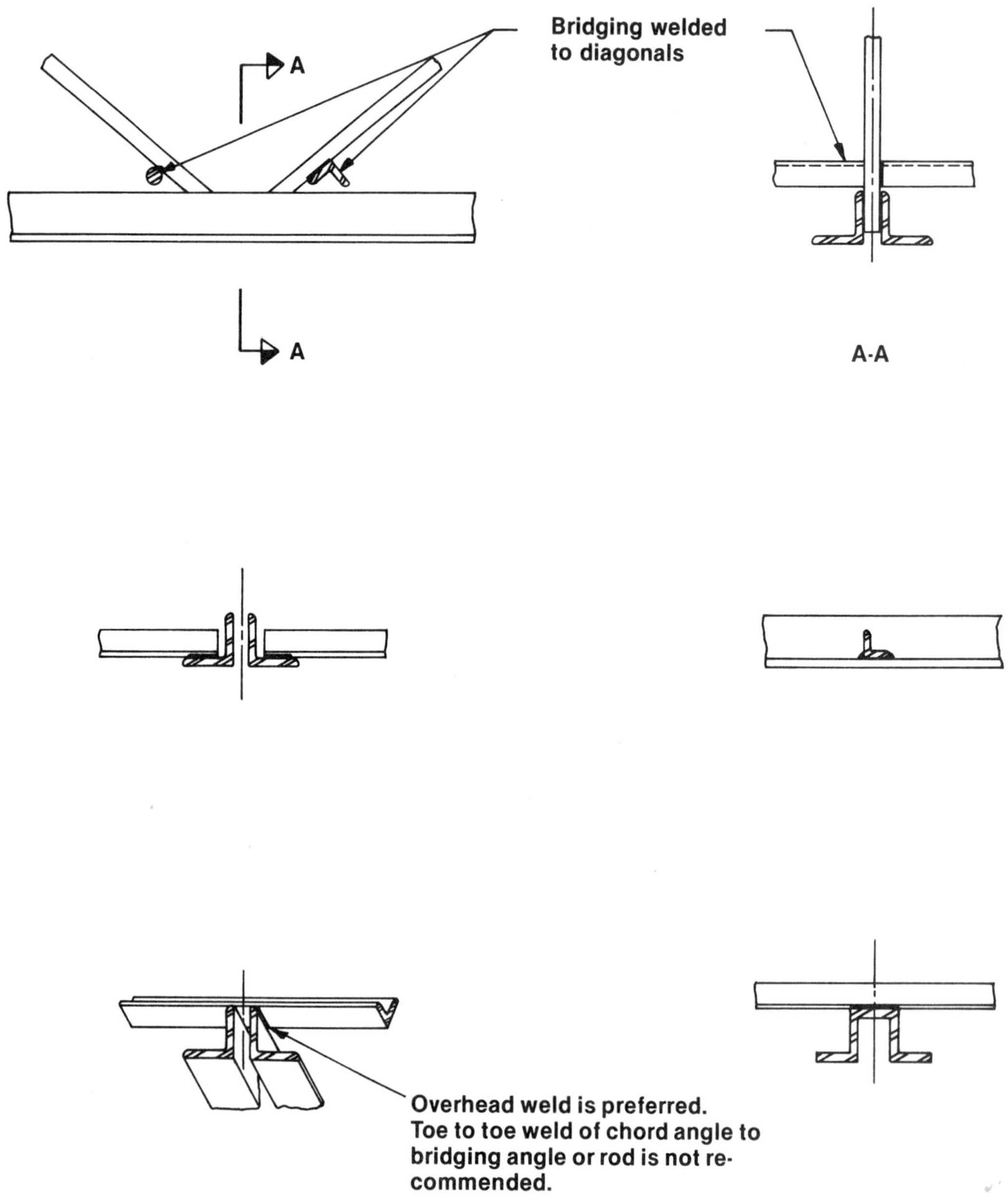

A

Bridging welded to diagonals

A

A-A

Overhead weld is preferred. Toe to toe weld of chord angle to bridging angle or rod is not re- commended.

16.7.7 Anchorage of Bridging

Ends of bridging lines can be anchored to the adjacent steel frame or adjacent concrete or masonry walls as shown in Figure 2—37.

FIGURE 2-37

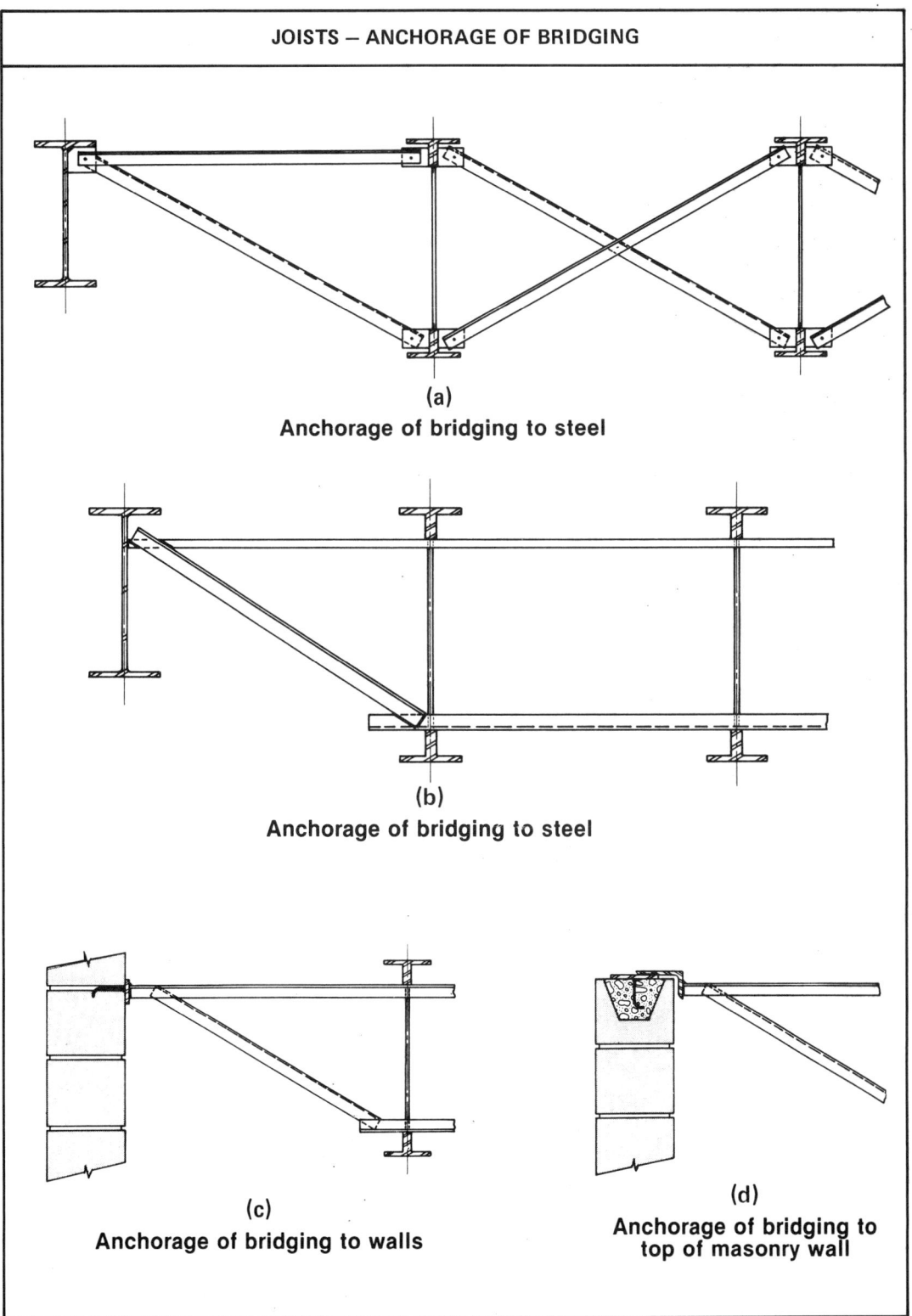

JOISTS — ANCHORAGE OF BRIDGING

(a)
Anchorage of bridging to steel

(b)
Anchorage of bridging to steel

(c)
Anchorage of bridging to walls

(d)
Anchorage of bridging to top of masonry wall

Where attachment to the adjacent steel frame or walls is not practicable, diagonal and horizontal bridging shall be provided in combination between adjacent joists near the ends of bridging lines as shown in Figure 2—38.

Extra lines of bottom chord bridging may be required, and joists should be checked for stress reversals resulting from the cantilevered end.

It is generally considered good practice to install a line of bridging at the first bottom chord panel point as shown in Figure 2—39.

FIGURE 2-38

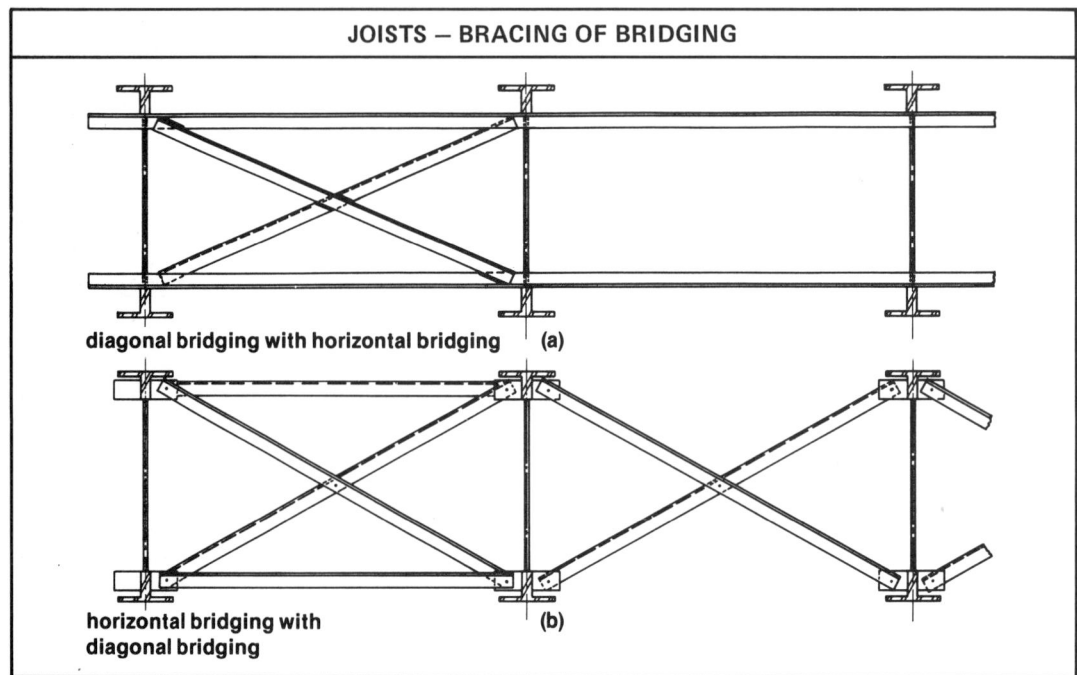

JOISTS — BRACING OF BRIDGING

diagonal bridging with horizontal bridging   (a)

horizontal bridging with
diagonal bridging   (b)

FIGURE 2-39

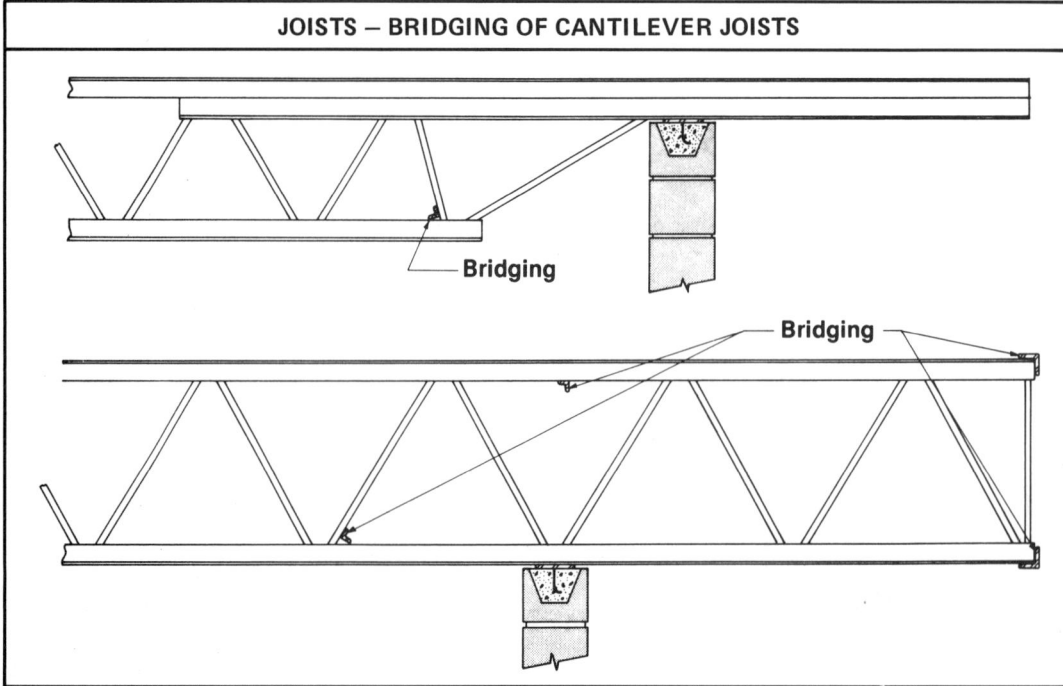

JOISTS — BRIDGING OF CANTILEVER JOISTS

Bridging

Bridging

16.7.9 Spacing of Bridging

Either horizontal or diagonal bridging is acceptable, although, horizontal bridging is generally recommended for shorter spans up to about 15 000 mm and is usually attached by welding. Diagonal bridging is recommended for longer spans and is usually attached by bolting. Bridging need not be attached at panel points and may be fastened at any point along the length of the joists. When horizontal bridging is used, bridging lines will not necessarily appear in pairs as the requirements for support of tension chords are not the same as those for compression chords. Since the ends of joists are anchored, the supports may be assumed to be equivalent to bridging lines. Joists bearing on the bottom chord will require bridging at the ends of the top chord.

16.8 Decking

Decking is assumed to be sufficiently rigid to provide lateral support to the compression chord of the joist. In those special cases where decking is not capable of furnishing the required lateral support, the compression chord is to be braced laterally in accordance with the rules for providing stability to beams, girders and trusses; that is, be proportioned to resist a force equal to 1 percent of the force in the compression chord at the point of support or a total uniformly distributed load equal to 5 percent of the force in the compression chord.

Where the decking complies with clause 16.8 and is sufficiently rigid to provide lateral support to the top (compression) chord, the top chord bridging is no longer required. Bottom (tension) chord bridging is permanently required such that the unsupported length of the chord does not exceed 240 r as defined in clause 16.7.9.

Clause 16.8.3, requires the building designer to show the special attachment requirements on the building design drawings when decking is used in combination with joists to form a diaphragm for the purpose of transferring lateral applied loads to vertical bracing systems.

16.9 Shop Painting

Interiors of buildings conditioned for human comfort are generally assumed to be of a non-corrosive environment and therefore do not require corrosion protection.

OWSJ normally receive one coat of paint suitable for a production line application. This paint is adequate for three months of exposure, which should be ample time to enclose the OWSJ in the finished structure and/or finish painting the joists.

Special coatings and paints with special preparations are expensive because they have to be applied individually to each joist by spraying or other means.

16.10 Manufacturing Tolerances

Figure 2—40 illustrates many of the manufacturing tolerance requirements.

16.11.3 Quality Control

When testing forms part of the manufacturers normal quality control programme, the test shall follow steps 1 to 4 of the loading procedure given in Part 5 of Reference 113.

FIGURE 2-40

JOISTS — MANUFACTURING TOLERANCES

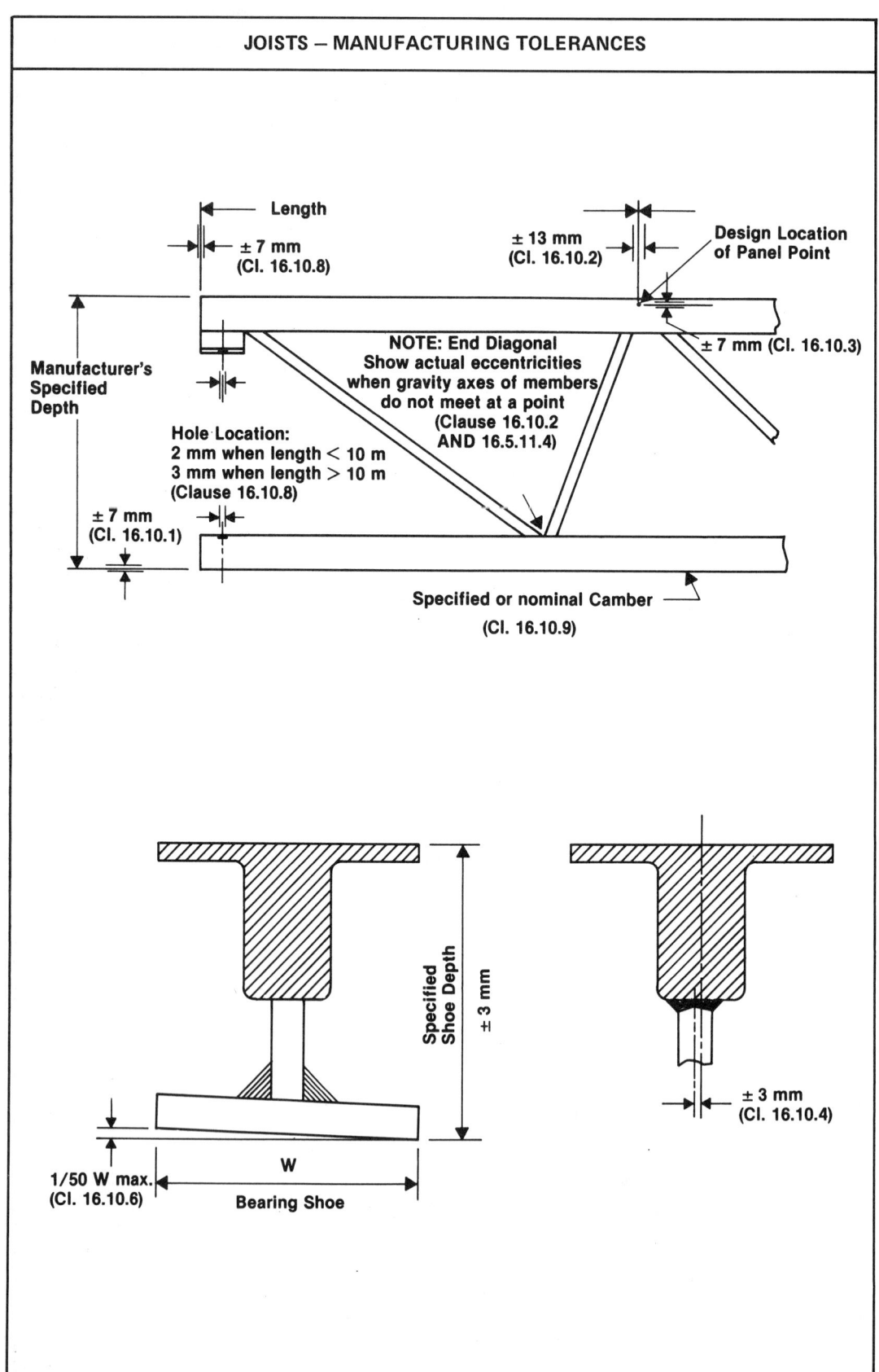

16.12.1 Erection Tolerances

Figure 2—41 illustrates many of the erection tolerance requirements.

FIGURE 2-41

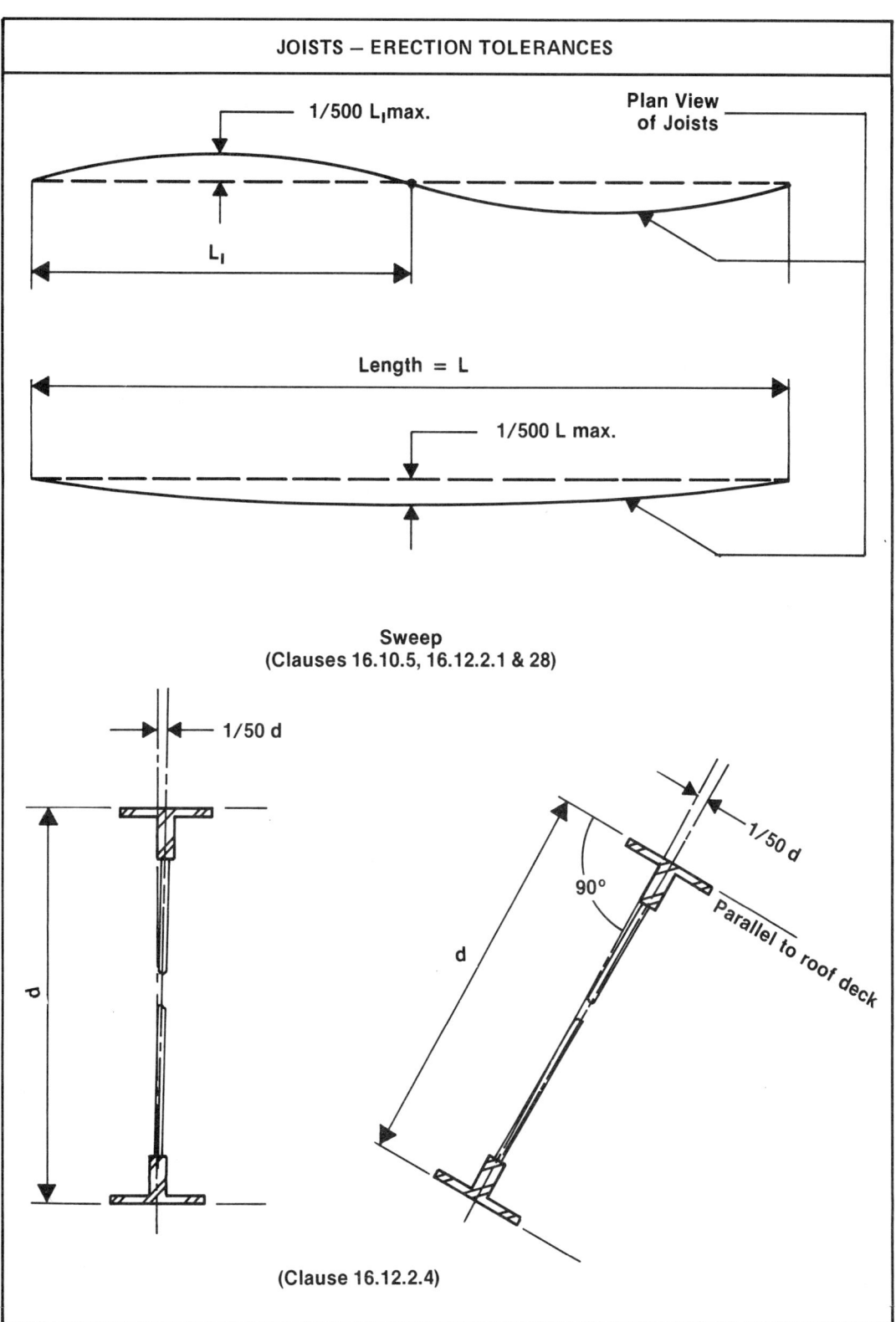

JOISTS — ERECTION TOLERANCES

1/500 L₁max.

Plan View
of Joists

L_I

Length = L

1/500 L max.

Sweep
(Clauses 16.10.5, 16.12.2.1 & 28)

1/50 d

d

1/50 d

90°

Parallel to roof deck

d

d

(Clause 16.12.2.4)

17. COMPOSITE BEAMS AND COLUMNS

Clause 17 provides specific requirements for the design of:

(a) Composite beams consisting of steel sections or joists interconnected by means of shear connectors with either a reinforced concrete slab or cellular steel deck and concrete cover slab;

(b) Composite beams consisting of steel sections or joists fully encased in concrete interacting with a concrete slab;

(c) Composite columns consisting of hollow structural steel sections filled with concrete.

17.2 Definitions

Figure 2—42 illustrates various cases of effective slab and cover slab thickness.

FIGURE 2-42

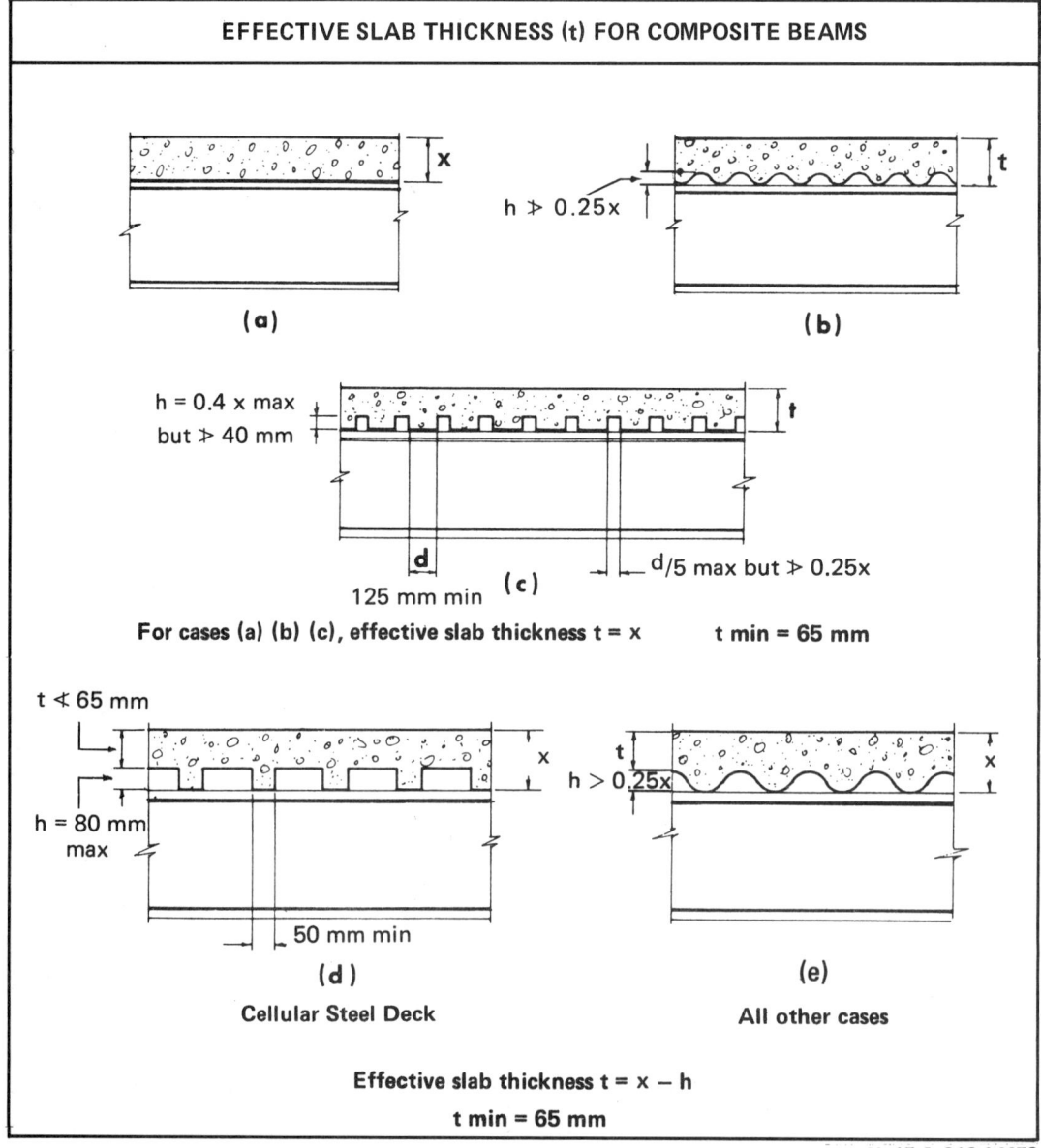

EFFECTIVE SLAB THICKNESS (t) FOR COMPOSITE BEAMS

(a)

(b)

$h \not> 0.25x$

$h = 0.4\ x$ max but $\not> 40$ mm

$d/5$ max but $\not> 0.25x$

125 mm min   (c)

For cases (a) (b) (c), effective slab thickness t = x   t min = 65 mm

$t \not< 65$ mm

$h = 80$ mm max

50 mm min

(d)

Cellular Steel Deck

$h > 0.25x$

(e)

All other cases

Effective slab thickness t = x − h

t min = 65 mm

Cl. 17.2, S16.1-M78

17.3 Composite Beams

17.3.1 General

The arbitrary increases to the elastically computed deflections for the effects of creep, partial shear connections and fluted steel deck profile affords a convenient means to check deflection against any prescribed deflection limit. Other approaches such as tests or analysis[74] are permitted. The deflection due to concrete creep is of concern for "permanent" loads (e.g. dead loads and live loads of long duration). Reference 3 suggests that the 15% increase for partial shear connection could be reduced linearly as the number of shear connectors approached the value for full composite action and the 15% increase for the fluted profile of cellular steel deck be applied when the flute width is less than twice its height.

Since the concrete is not assumed to carry any vertical shear the steel member must carry the total factored vertical shear. Similarly, the end connections must carry the total factored end reaction of the composite beam.

17.3.2 Design Effective Width of Concrete

The width of slab or cover slab deemed to be effective, when computing the concrete force, is the least of the three values given in the clause. These rules were formulated on the basis of elastic conditions (see, for example, Ref. 75). There is more recent evidence[111] that suggests that conditions at ultimate load are different. It appears that the rules may be unconservative for interior girders and conservative for exterior girders.

17.3.3 Slab Reinforcement

The longitudinal shear forces generated by interconnecting concrete slabs to steel sections or joists by means of shear connectors sometimes cause longitudinal cracking of the slab directly over the steel. This is independent of any flexural cracking which may occur due to the slab spanning continuously over supports, although the two effects may combine. Longitudinal shear cracking is more apt to start from the underside of the slab whereas flexural cracking is more apt to start at the top surface of the slab. Some investigation has been carried out[76,77] but a full explanation and corresponding design procedure is, to date, not available.

This phenomenon has not been observed in cover slabs over cellular steel deck, possibly because the steel deck provides a measure of reinforcement. Reinforcement of the cover slab for other reasons, as may be indicated by consideration of flexure, fire resistance, shrinkage or temperature effects may, however, be necessary.

17.3.5 Interconnection

Except in the case of unpainted sections or joists supporting slabs and totally encased in concrete to a depth of 50 mm on sides and soffit, shear connectors are required to effect the interconnection of steel and concrete. While studs are assumed to be the usual method of interconnection and are the subject of most of the specific requirements in subsequent clauses, other means of interconnection which have been shown to be satisfactory may be used instead. Where end-welded steel studs are welded through cellular steel deck both the total sheet thickness and the total amount of zinc coating are limited in accordance with successful field experience to date.

Tests have shown that a shear connector is not fully effective if welded to a support which is too thin or flexible[85]. For this reason the stud diameter is limited to 2.5 times the thickness of the part to which it is welded unless a lesser thickness can be justified.

17.3.6 Shear Connectors

The general intent of this clause is to require the use of shear connector resistances, q_r/ϕ_{sc}, which have been satisfactorily established by test. Certain types of shear connectors (studs, channels) have been extensively tested in the past and therefore permissible values are given which are considered acceptable without further verification.

The performance factor $\phi_{sc} = 0.80$ has been introduced by way of a 1980 revision to S16.1-M78. The application of a performance factor to shear connector resistances means that this section is now consistent with other parts of the Standard, that is, nominal member or connector resistances should be modified to account for possible variations in material strength, dimensions of the part, and so on. In addition, the previous formulation, which did not include the performance factor, led to an anomaly. For certain beam and slab combinations, the strength equations produced a sharp drop in capacity as one moved from the case of 100% shear connection to anything less than 100% shear connection. The introduction of the performance factor removes this anomoly. Designers will find that for the case of the plastic neutral axis in the slab, more shear connectors will be required than formerly. When the neutral axis is in the steel beam, fewer shear connectors will be required.

The values given in clause 17.3.6(a) are based on an extensive research programme[78] involving both normal and lightweight concrete slabs. The limiting value of $450\,\phi_{sc}\,A_{sc}$ represents the tensile strength of the stud times its cross-sectional area (A_{sc}) for as the concrete pushes against the stud, the stud eventually begins to bend over and develop a tensile resistance. The same values may be used in designs incorporating studs passing through the flutes of cellular steel deck into the concrete cover slab above provided that the flute average width is at least twice its height and the stud extends into the cover slab at least 2 diameters.[79] (The designer should confirm that the tensile strength of the stud is at least 450 MPa or the strength equation should be adjusted accordingly.)

Based on work by Robinson and others[75], numerical values are given in Table 8 for studs used in conjunction with cellular steel deck in which the flute average width is less than twice its height. Robinson also found that the value of a pair of studs in a flute was less than twice the value of a single stud and the values given reflect these findings. A similar reduction does not appear to be needed for pairs of studs in solid slabs; in this case the value of a pair is simply assumed to be twice the value of a single stud. It is recommended, however, that where studs are used in pairs the lateral spacing between them be not less than 4 stud diameters measured centre to centre of studs in order to minimize excessive localized stress in the surrounding concrete.

The value assigned to channel connectors[80] is the same as used in CSA S16-1969 except that it has been recast in a limit states format.

17.4 Design of Composite Beams with Shear Connectors.

The factored moment resistance of a composite beam is computed based on the ultimate capacity of the cross-section[26,29,75,81,82,83,84] where the following assumptions are made:

(1) Concrete in tension is neglected.

(2) If a steel joist is used, only the lower chord is considered effective when computing the moment resistance.

(3) Tension and compression forces are in equilibrium about the plastic neutral axis.

(4) Forces are obtained as the product of a limit states stress (ϕF_y for steel and $0.85\,\phi_c F'_c$ for concrete) times the appropriate area.

(5) The performance factor for concrete (ϕ_c) is set at a lower value (0.67) than that used for steel members (0.90). This is to take into account the greater variability in the strength and dimensions of concrete elements.

Three design cases, 1, 2 and 3, are considered where:

(1) Case 1 represents full shear connection and the plastic neutral axis in the slab.

(2) Case 2 represents full shear connection and the plastic neutral axis in the steel section.

(3) Case 3 represents partial shear connection for which the plastic neutral axis is always in the steel section.

When joists are used, only Case 1 is permitted since this provides for an efficient design and a predictable mode of failure. For Case 3, the position of the compressive resistance of the concrete is determined by the expression for "a" as suggested in reference 84.

17.4.4 Where partial shear connection is used, a lower limit of 50 percent of the lesser of $0.85\,\phi_c F'_c bt$ and $\phi A_s F_y$ is imposed for flexural strength considerations. The limit is reduced to 25 percent for deflection considerations. The lower limit for strength evaluation is based on studies which indicate that, at some value below one half the number of shear connectors required for full shear connection, the "flexibility" at the plane of interconnection has increased to the point where the basic assumptions as to an integral composite section may not apply over the whole loading range. The lower limit for deflection design is less stringent because deflection is normally of concern up to the level of specified load rather than the higher level of factored load on which strength design is based.

17.4.5 If the factored resistance provided by the shear connectors is at least equal to the factored horizontal shear force $\phi A_s F_y$, then full shear connection has been provided for Case 1 (plastic neutral axis in the slab). For full shear connection for Case 2 (plastic neutral axis in the steel), the factored resistance provided by the shear connectors must be at least equal to $0.85\,\phi_c\, b\, t\, f'_c$. These values are obtained by considering the forces above or below the plane on which the horizontal force acts, that is, the interface between the steel and the concrete. Since conditions at the location $M = M_{max}$ are implicitly being considered, this total horizontal shear force is the summation of connector resistances between that location and any adjacent point of $M = 0$.

17.4.8 Shear connectors may be spaced uniformly in most cases. An exception is the case where, in a region of positive bending, a concentrated load or loads occurs between the point of zero moment and the point of maximum positive moment. This clause ensures that the moment capacity of the composite section at the point of concentrated load is achieved. If n represents the total number of shear connectors to develop the maximum moment, M_f, and n', the number to develop the moment M_{f_1} at the point of concentrated load, then it might be assumed that $n'/n = M_{f_1}/M_f$. However the steel section alone has a moment capacity, M_r, which is not dependent on the presence or absence of shear connectors. This capacity is subtracted from both M_f and M_{f_1} to obtain the equation given in clause 17.4.8.

17.5 Design of Composite Beams Without Shear Connectors

As a conservative simplification clause 17.5.3 permits the design of encased simple span steel sections or joists as if the steel section or joist alone supported 90 percent of the total load. This is a tacit assumption that the composite section containing the encased steel section or joist will have a moment resistance at least 11 percent greater than the bare steel member. Typically, the moment resistance computed according to clause 17.5.2 would show a larger increase over the bare steel member.

17.6 Unshored Beams

To obtain strains resulting from the application of specified load within the elastic range it is required to limit the stress (as a measure of strain) in the tension flange of the steel section or joist to $0.90\,F_y$ under specified load. This limit is basically the same as that used in CSA S16-1969 $(0.82\,F_y)$[86] modified to account for Class 1 and 2 sections. The state of stress or strain of the bottom fibre of steel at specified loads has no effect whatsoever on the ability of the composite beam to reach its ultimate moment. This clause serves to guard against permanent deformations under specified loads.

17.8 Design of Composite Columns

Where hollow structural sections (HSS) used as columns are completely filled with concrete, advantage may be taken of the increased load capacity, which will be highest for stocky members and minimal for slender members. Many research programmes have demonstrated that composite columns of this type have improved load-carrying ability within a certain range of parameters.[87]

To some extent, the means by which load is transmitted to the column (e.g. via the concrete core or the steel shell) has an influence on load carrying capacity. So does the duration of the load relative to the creep characteristics of concrete. Clause 17.8 permits a conservative but simple approach to the problem of assessing column strength. It is assumed that the hollow steel section carries the same axial load, C_r, as if it were not filled with concrete. The concrete core is assumed to carry additional axial load C_r', ranging linearly from $0.85 \, \phi_c f_c' A_c$ when KL/r (the slenderness ratio of the HSS alone) is zero, down to nil when KL/r is equal to or greater than $\sqrt{\pi^2 E/F_y}$. If bending is present, in addition to axial load, the bending must be resisted by the steel section alone acting as a beam-column.

18. GENERAL REQUIREMENTS FOR BUILT-UP MEMBERS

The term built-up member refers to any structural member assembled from two or more components. Such members may be used to resist compression, tension or bending and the requirements for fastening together the various components vary accordingly.

In compression members it is necessary to prevent local buckling of components at loads less than those which would cause the member to buckle as a whole. In tension members, buckling is not a consideration but it is generally desirable that components be stitched together sufficiently to work in unison and to minimize vibration. With exposed members it is also important that components in contact be fitted together tightly enough to minimize possible corrosion problems. The sketches comprising Figure 2–43 illustrate the main provisions of clause 18.

FIGURE 2-43 (a)

BUILT-UP MEMBER DETAILS

Tension Members	Requirements	Tension Members	Requirements
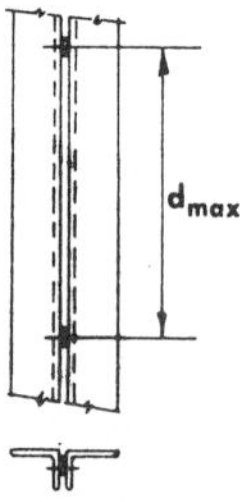 d_{max}	TWO ROLLED SHAPES NOT IN CONTACT d_{max} = 300 × least radius of gyration of one component.	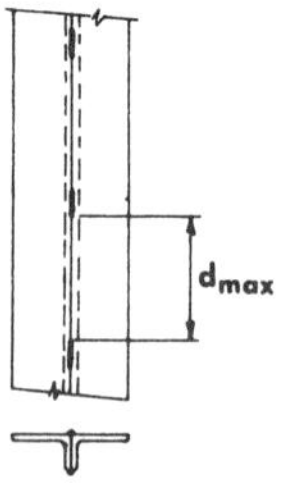 d_{max}	TWO ROLLED SHAPE IN CONTACT d_{max} = 600 mm d_{max} may be increased when justified.
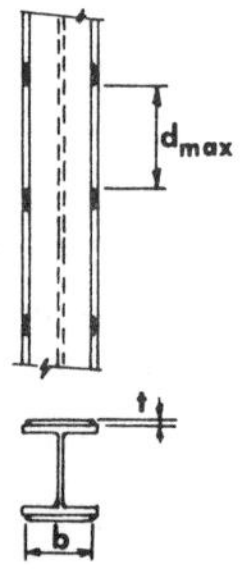 d_{max}	SHAPE AND PLATE IN CONTACT d_{max} = 36 t or 450 mm whichever is lesser.	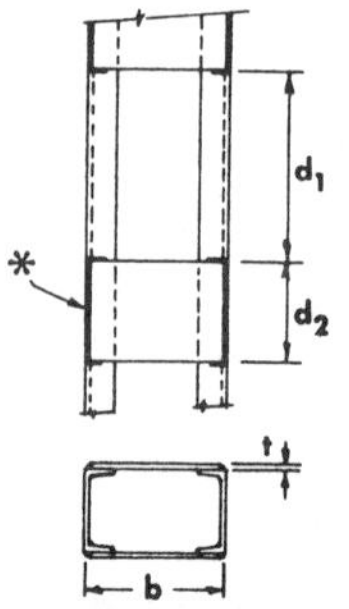 d_1 d_2	BATTENS b ≤ 60 t d_2 ⩾ ⅔ b d_1 ≤ 300 × least radius of gyration of one component. *For intermittent welds or fasteners max pitch = 150 mm

Cl. 18.2, S16.1-M78

FIGURE 2-43 (b)

BUILT-UP MEMBER DETAILS

Compression Members	Requirements	Compression Members	Requirements
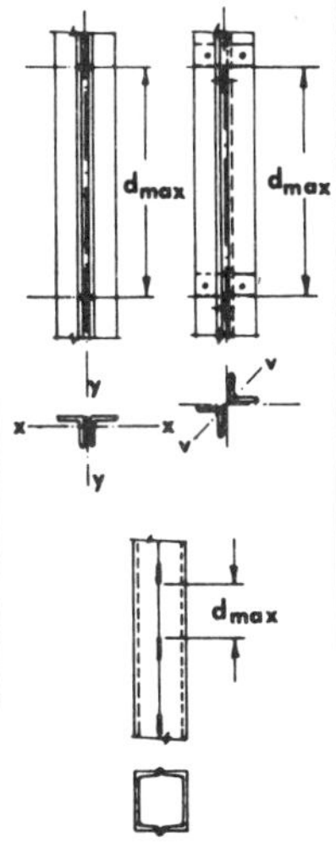	**ROLLED SHAPES** $$d_{max} = \left(\frac{KL}{r}\right) r_{min}$$ $\frac{KL}{r}$ = Design slenderness ratio of member as a whole. r_{min} = Least radius of gyration of one component. 18.1.3		**LACING AND TIE PLATES** $b \leqslant 60\,t$ $d_1 \geqslant \frac{b}{2} \qquad d_2 \geqslant b$ $d_3 \leqslant \frac{KL}{r_1} r_3 \;<\; \frac{KL}{r_2} r_3$ $L_a \leqslant 140 \times$ rad. of gyration of lacing member. $\alpha \geqslant 45°$ KL = Effective length of member referred to appropriate axis 18.1.4-9
	STAGGERED FASTENERS OR WELDS $$d_{max} = \frac{525}{\sqrt{F_y}} \quad \text{or} \quad 450 \text{ mm}$$ t = Outside plate thickness. 18.1.3		**BATTENS** $b \leqslant 60\,t$ $d_2 \geqslant b$ When $\frac{K_y L_y}{r_y} \leqslant 0.8 \frac{K_x L_x}{r_x}$ $\frac{d_1}{r_{y_1}} \leqslant 50 \;\leqslant 0.7 \frac{K_x L_x}{r_x}$ When $\frac{K_y L_y}{r_y} > 0.8 \frac{K_x L_x}{r_x}$ $\frac{d_1}{r_{y_1}} \leqslant 40 \;\leqslant 0.6 \frac{K_y L_y}{r_y}$ 18.1.13
	FASTENERS OR WELDS NOT STAGGERED $$P_{max} = \frac{330}{\sqrt{F_y}} \quad \text{or} \quad 300 \text{ mm}$$ t = Outside plate thickness. 18.1.3		

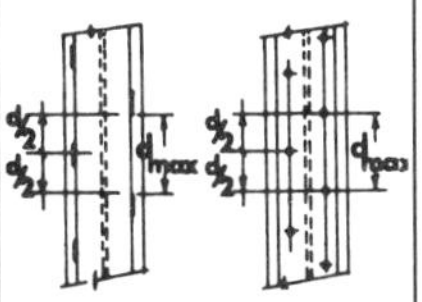

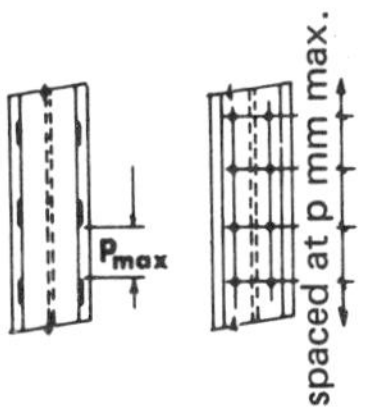

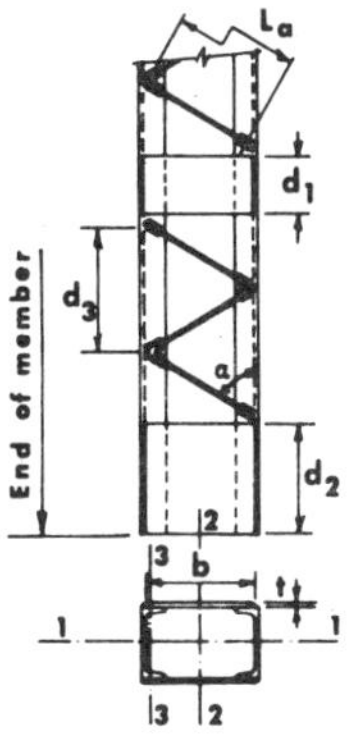

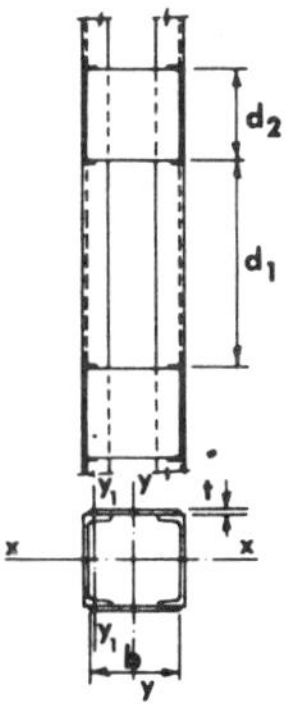

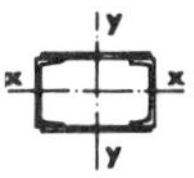

		Beams and Grillages	**Requirements**
	ENDS OF BUILT-UP COLUMNS Welded Connections: $$d_{min} = b$$ Bolted Connections: $$d_{min} = 1.5\,b$$ P_{max} = 4 × diameter of fastener 18.1.2		For non-load-sharing beams only, through bolts and separators may be used. Cl. 18.3 Not less than: One bolt ——— d < 300 mm Two or more bolts — d ≥ 300 mm Centres of separator groups ≤ 1 500 mm
	$b < \dfrac{840}{\sqrt{F_y}}$ Note: For bolted fabrication $b \geqslant 400$ mm is preferred. $L \leqslant 2W$ **PERFORATED COVER PLATES** $D \geqslant b$ $r \geqslant 40$ mm 18.1.12		Diaphragms shall be used for sharing loads. Cl. 18-3 Diaphragms shall have sufficient stiffness to distribute required load. Centres of diaphragms ≤ 1 500 mm

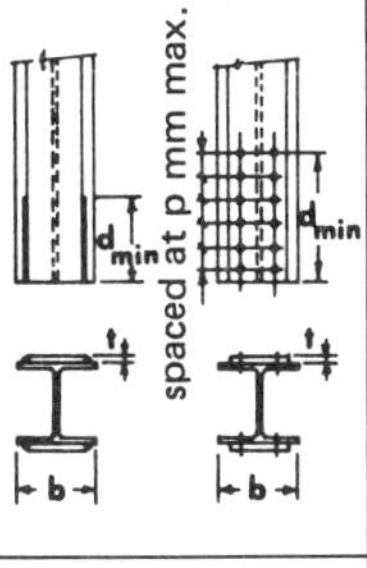

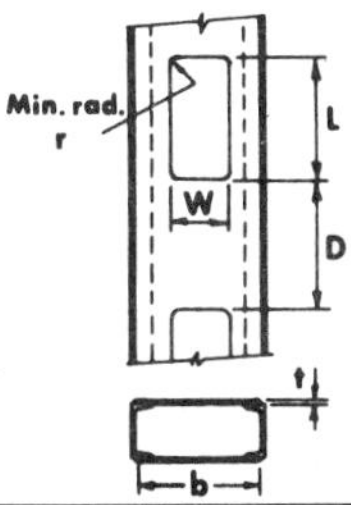

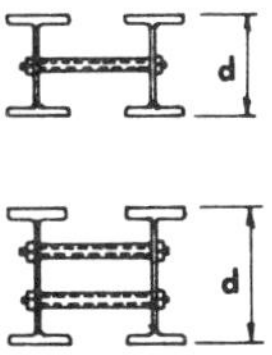

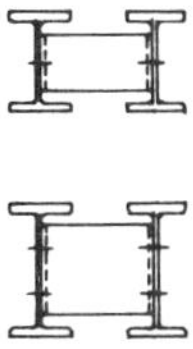

Clauses 18.1 and 18.3, S16.1-M78

19. STABILITY OF STRUCTURES AND INDIVIDUAL MEMBERS

19.1 General

There is increased emphasis in this Standard on the designer's responsibility to ensure stability of the structure and the individual members (see also Commentary on clause 8.6); on the interconnection of various load resisting elements, for example, use of floors or roofs as diaphragms; on proper load transfer, for example, use of one bent to provide resistance to lateral load for several, more flexible, adjacent bents or the use of end walls for lateral load resistance of the central structure, and on the necessity to show information on design and erection drawings.

19.2 Stability of Columns

The clause relates to a local requirement and reminds the designer that the beam-to-column connection may have to be capable of resisting a tensile or compressive component as well as the usual shear or moment. The requirements of this clause are somewhat less severe than those of CSA Standard S16-1969 which called for a force transfer of 2 percent of the axial force in the column. By basing the force requirements on the anticipated out-of-plumb coupled with the flexibility of the structure, a less conservative approach to the problem is anticipated. (See also the Commentary on clause 8.6)

19.3 Stability of Beams, Girders and Trusses

The requirement of clause 19.3.1 is reduced from that required by S16-1969. The previous requirement was based on the early work done by Winter[88] while other approaches show that a less conservative value is more appropriate, especially if the member is subjected to loads producing a moment gradient.[89,90] For members in plastically designed structures under uniform moment conditions the force may be higher than that specified.[91]

When an element in a structure must resist the "bracing forces" from more than one member it is not possible to state explicitly how these forces should be combined, since the out-of-straightness giving rise to the bracing forces may vary both in magnitude and sense. The conservative assumption would be that all forces act in the same sense at the maximum magnitude. Reference 109 provides more guidance in selected cases.

Since the shear centre of an asymmetric section does not coincide with the centroid, this section may be unintentionally loaded so as to produce torsion and biaxial bending. Both the connections and the members providing reactions should be checked.

20. CONNECTIONS

20.3 Restrained Members

When the compressive or tensile force, transmitted by a beam flange to a column (approximately equal to the factored moment divided by the depth of the beam) exceeds the factored bearing or tensile resistance of the web of the column, stiffeners are required to develop the load in excess of the bearing or tensile resistance.

Reference 60 recommends that the length of the column web resisting the compressive force be taken as the thickness of the beam flange plus 5k. This length multiplied by the thickness of the column web and the specified minimum yield point of the column gives the bearing resistance for the column web for Class 1 and 2 webs.

The same reference, using conservative assumptions as to the relative dimensions of beams and columns, computes the column flange bending resistance when subjected to tensile load from the beam flange, to be $7\ t_c^2\ F_{yc}$. Tests have shown that connections proportioned in accordance with this equation have carried the plastic moment of the beam satisfactorily.

For members with Class 3 and 4 webs, the bearing resistance of the web is limited by its buckling strength. The expression for factored bearing resistance is conservatively based on the critical buckling stress for a plate with both edges simply supported.

$$\sigma_{cr} = \frac{\pi^2 E}{12(1-\nu^2)\,(h/w)^2} \quad k = \frac{723\,000}{(h_c/w_c)^2} \quad \text{when } k_{min} = 4$$

The coefficient 640 000, given in clause 20.3(a), reflects a further reduction of about 10 percent to account for uncertainty in the prediction of the member strength and thereby to maintain a more uniform level of probability of failure.

20.4 Connections of Tension or Compression Members.

The 50 percent rule provides for a reasonably sized connection, especially when a member has been designed for stiffness rather than strength.

20.6 Lamellar Tearing

This clause has been included in recognition of the widespread use of welded joints in steel structures for buildings. In cases where shrinkage results as a consequence of welding under highly restrained conditions, very large tensile strains may be set up. If these are transferred across the through-thickness direction of rolled structural members or plates, lamellar tearing may result. If this type of joint cannot be avoided, steps must be taken to minimize the possibility of lamellar tearing[93,94].

20.7 Placement of Fasteners and Welds

Reference 95 has shown that, except for cases of repeated loads, end welds on tension angles and other similar members need not be placed so as to balance the forces about the neutral axis of the member.

20.8 Fillers

In bearing-type shear connections development of the filler before the splice material diminishes bending of the bolt. In slip-resistant joints, tests with fillers up to 1 inch in thickness and with surface conditions comparable to other joint components show that the fillers become an integral part of the joint and they need not be developed before the splice material.[55]

21. BOLTING DETAILS

While clause 13.10(c) specifies the bearing capacity of the plate material as a function of end distance, clause 21.8 specifies the minimum edge distances permitted for connections of tension members with one, two or more bolts for various bolt diameters. Reference 55 contains a comprehensive summary of bearing strengths as a function of end distance and the types of failures that are guarded against.

22. STRUCTURAL JOINTS USING ASTM A325 OR A490 BOLTS

22.1 General

Both A325[97] and A490[98] bolts are produced by quenching and tempering. A325 bolts are somewhat lower in tensile strength than A490 bolts but have greater ductility. Both types of bolts are intended to be initially tensioned to at least 70 percent of their specified minimum tensile strengths and, therefore, exert a high clamping force on the parts which they join. When joints are required to resist shear between connected parts, it is required that the design and shop drawings specify the joints as either slip-resistant or bearing-type. As explained in the Commentary on clause 13.12, the shear transfer in slip-resistant joints results from the action of the clamping forces in the bolts upon the faying surfaces. This shear transfer is to be examined at specified load levels, and it is expected that this type of connection will be used primarily in connections subjected to load reversal or where slip into bearing would result in unacceptable geometry changes in the structure.

Although the load transfer in bearing-type connections will also be by friction at low load levels, slip into bearing will occur well before factored load levels are reached. Thus, the controlling strength elements are shear of the bolt across the shank of the bolt (clause 13.11) and the bearing capacity of the plate adjacent to the bolts (clause 13.10(c)). Since there are few joints in building construction that are subject to load reversal nor are there many situations where a one-time slip into bearing cannot be tolerated, bearing-type joints would be the usual choice.

As a result of normal fabrication, practice, minor misalignment of bolt holes may occur in connections with two or more bolts except when all parts of the connection are match punched or drilled. Such misalignment, if anything, has a beneficial effect[55] in offering a stiffer joint, improved slip resistance and decreased rigid body motion.

22.1.5 Applied Tension

Figure 2—44 illustrates that, when an external tensile force is applied to the connected parts, the applied external force and the internal clamping force in the bolt are not additive. The bolt needs to be proportioned only for the factored tensile load. The illustration (Fig. 2—44) assumes 'stiff" connected material relative to the bolt. Measurement of actual bolt forces in connections of practical sizes has shown that there is an increase in bolt force over that assumed but it is modest, usually about 5-10 percent.

The effect of prying action on bolt tension, illustrated in Figure 2—45, is an important design consideration. Page 278 of the "Guide to Design Criteria for Bolted and Riveted Joints" summarizes the criteria for the design of tension connections when prying action is present. For load reversal or repeated load situations these connections must be proportioned so that prying is avoided.

The Research Council on Structural Connections is currently (1980) considering specific limitations on the allowable tension for different ranges of stress cycles provided the prying forces are less than 60 percent of the external load. These limits are based on an evaluation of available test data. Until more guidance is available designers should consider a conservative design approach to these connections.

22.2 Bolts, Nuts and Washers

The "standard" A325 or A490 bolt has a heavy hex head, restricted thread length, coarse threads and is equipped with a heavy hex nut. Proprietary versions are available which differ from the "standard" type in various aspects, and in some cases may offer one or more advantages. Their use is permissible under the conditions set forth in clause 22.2.4.

Galvanized A325 bolts are permitted by clause 22.2.3; however galvanized A490 bolts are not permitted since they are especially susceptible to stress corrosion and hydrogen stress cracking.[55]

22.3 Bolted Parts

As permitted by clause 22.3.4, the faying surfaces of slip-resistant joints may be hot-dip galvanized or coated with sprayed metal coatings, zinc-rich paints, or a vinyl surface treatment. Other materials and methods may also be used when approved.

22.4 Installation

Even though the Standard divides the design of shear joints into bearing-type and slip-resistant connections, the installation procedure is the same for all bolts. As has already been described, the high initial bolt tension is necessary for slip-resistant joints. Although the ultimate shear strength of a high strength bolt is independent of the initial

FIGURE 2-44

EFFECT OF APPLIED TENSION ON TIGHTENED HIGH-STRENGTH BOLTS

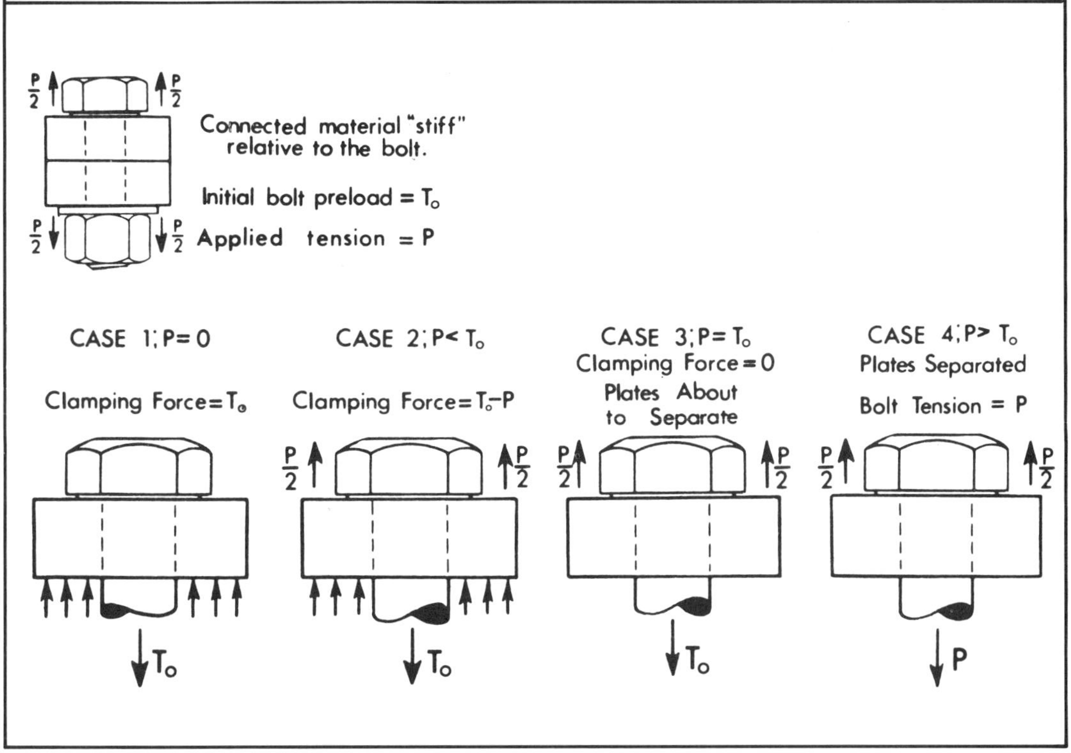

Connected material "stiff" relative to the bolt.

Initial bolt preload = T_o

Applied tension = P

CASE 1; $P = 0$

Clamping Force = T_o

CASE 2; $P < T_o$

Clamping Force = $T_o - P$

CASE 3; $P = T_o$
Clamping Force = 0
Plates About to Separate

CASE 4; $P > T_o$
Plates Separated

Bolt Tension = P

FIGURE 2-45

EFFECT OF PRYING ACTION ON BOLT TENSION

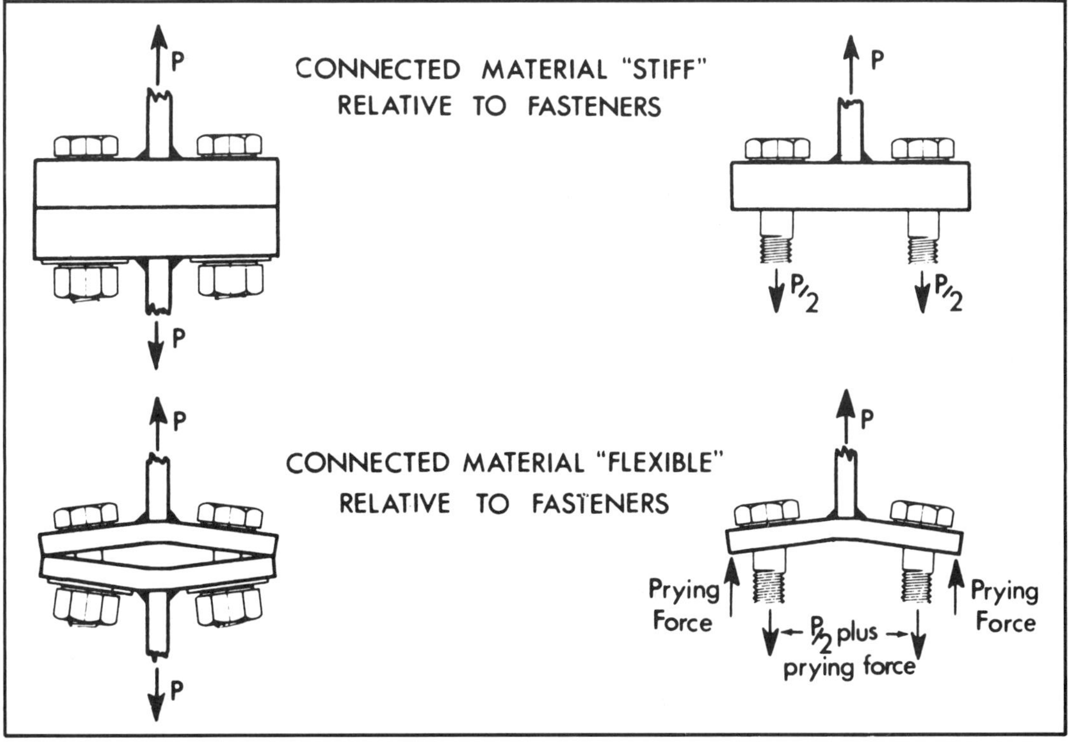

CONNECTED MATERIAL "STIFF" RELATIVE TO FASTENERS

CONNECTED MATERIAL "FLEXIBLE" RELATIVE TO FASTENERS

Prying Force

Prying Force

$P/2$ plus prying force

clamping force[55], the presence of such a force provides a better stress pattern and security against nut loosening for either type of connection. In addition, the use of a consistent procedure for all bolted joints minimizes the potential for errors.

Except when galvanized, A325 bolts may be reused once or twice, providing that proper control on the number of reuses can be established.[55,96] A490 bolts should not be reused.

22.5 "Turn-of-Nut" Tightening.

Any installation procedure used for high strength bolts involves elongating the bolt so as to produce the desired tensile force. Although part of the bolt probably remains elastic (the shank), the threaded portion behaves plastically. It is because the bolt as a whole is tightened into the inelastic range (out onto the flat portion of its load vs. deformation response curve), that the exact location of "snug-tight" is not critical. For the same reason, application of the specified amount of nut rotation will result in preloads which are above those prescribed in Table 10 and which are not greatly variable. There is a reasonable margin against twist-off but the tolerance on nut rotation prescribed in the footnote to Table 11 is good practice, particularly when galvanized A325 bolts or black A490 bolts are used.

22.6 Tightening by Use of a Direct Tension Indicator

The Standard permits use of direct tension indicator bolting systems. All of these are proprietary in nature but all rely on some physical change in some part of the bolt system to indicate when the minimum bolt tension has been achieved. For example, one such system relies on a physical gap being closed down to a specified dimension which can be measured with the appropriate tool.

22.7 Inspection

Bolts, nuts and washers are normally received with a light residual coating of oil. This coating is not detrimental, if fact it is desirable, and should not be removed. Galvanized bolts and/or nuts may be coated with a special lubricant to facilitate tightening. Obviously, this should not be removed.

Bolts tightened by the turn-of-nut method may have the outer face of the nut match-marked with the bolt point before final tightening, thus affording the inspector visual means of noting nut rotation. Such marks can be made with crayon or paint by the wrench operator after the bolts have been snugged.

The sides of nuts or bolt heads tightened with an impact wrench appear slightly peened and thus indicate that the wrench has been applied. For bolts in a bearing-type connection subjected only to shear, this evidence that the nuts have been tightened is sufficient inspection since the ultimate shear strength of the bolt is independent of the amount of preload.

When a torque wrench is used in inspection to verify bolt tension, the procedures to be followed are described in detail in clause 22.7.4. Note that the Simplified Method is recommended primarily for bolts in bearing-type joints. A washer under the turned element is necessary to minimize erratic torque-tension relationships. The Simplified Method is not recommended for the inspection of galvanized bolts because of the more erratic torque-tension relationship likely to occur when threads are zinc-coated.

24. COLUMN BASES

In general the use of base plates bearing directly on grout is preferred to the use of levelling plates interposed between the base plate and the grout. The latter condition may lead to uneven bearing.

APPENDIX F – COLUMNS SUBJECT TO BIAXIAL BENDING

These refined expressions were introduced in an Appendix for two reasons: 1) the desire of the Committee not to further complicate the limit states standard by the mandatory use of new concepts in beam-column design, and 2) at the time the Standard was written, the design procedures had been developed for only a limited group of sections. The range of applicability has been expanded since the Standard was adopted, however.

In the Commentary to clause 13.8, the linearity of interaction expressions presented in that clause was discussed. In fact, the interaction curve relating axial load and the two orthogonal moments is not linear, for either strength or stability.

The simplest demonstration of non-linearity is that used by Ellis and Pillai[99] in their work on HSS. Consider a circular tube subject to eccentric loading about the x and y axes. Since the section properties are uniform about the polar axis, the interaction expressions of clause 13.8 would sum the moment effects as if a moment of $P(e_x + e_y)$ were applied, whereas the actual moment is $P\sqrt{e_x^2 + e_y^2}$. Thus, the interaction curve for a circular tube, is a quadrant of a circle. Finding a similar effect applied to square HSS, Pillai determined that the available test data fitted the expression in clause F3(c) if the sum of the moment terms was modified by the expression

$$\gamma = \frac{e_x^2 + e_y^2}{e_x + e_y}$$

The value of γ is equivalent to ν in clause F3(c).

Chen and his research associates at Lehigh[100,101,102] found that a similar non-linear effect applied to W-shapes. They proposed the expressions in Clause F1(a) and (b) for strength and stability respectively, evaluating the exponents ζ and η from rigorously calculated interaction curves. Chen, et al had shown that for strength, their exponent was valid for cross-sections having b/d ratios from 1.0 to 0.55. This covered most of the practical range of sections used. For stability, only the sections having 'b' approximately equal to 'd' had been investigated. The limit of 0.8 was set to cover the actual b/d ratio of all the nominally square shapes. For simplicity in writing the Appendix, a limiting b/d ratio of 0.8 has been stated first for both strength and stability, but the intent of clause F2 is that b/d ratios down to 0.55 may be designed for strength using the requirements of clause F1(a) and for stability using the requirements of clause 13.8.2(c).

Since the printing of the Standard, further research by Ross and Chen[103] has expanded the applicability of clause F1(b) by the development of exponent expression as follows:

$$\eta = 0.4 + \frac{C_f}{C_r} + \frac{b}{d} \text{ for } \frac{b}{d} \geqslant 0.3$$

and

$$\eta = 1.0 \qquad\qquad \text{for } \frac{b}{d} < 0.3$$

Use of these expressions eliminates the need for clause F2.

The expressions for M_{ox} and M_{oy} have been determined from clause 13.8.1, transposed and applied for uniaxial bending only.

Essentially, the interaction expressions (a) and (b) in clause F1 define an interaction surface relating the boundary conditions on the three perpendicular axes (i.e. axial resistance and moment resistance about each axis). Therefore, the better these values are determined, the better will be the interaction surface.

Unlike W-shapes, significant biaxial bending is imposed on HSS whenever beams frame into the column about two perpendicular axes. The design expressions given in clause F3 for square HSS sections, for both strength and stability, were developed by

Pillai[104,105,116]. Since the form of the expressions is completely different to those for W-shapes research is underway to develop exponents for the curvilinear interaction expressions for both square and rectangular HSS.

Limitations

Significant economy may result in designs according to Appendix 'F', but before adopting these, some general thought should be given to the extent to which yielding under service load is likely and, in view of this, whether further restrictions on the design are necessary. (See the Note to Appendix F.)

The Standard recommends a value of 0.85 for C_m for compression members in frames subject to joint translation (sidesway). This approach should not be used in combination with the method recommended here, the development of which is based on constant end eccentricities up to maximum load. To use the recommended method in sway frames, the end moments should be determined by a second-order analysis, i.e. the $P\Delta$ effects at ultimate load should be included. Springfield has proposed additional precautions in reference 106.

REFERENCES

1. Kennedy, D.J.L., "Limit States Design — An Innovation in Design Standards for Steel Structures". — Can. J. Civ. Eng., Vol. 1, No. 1, Sept., 1974.
2. Allen, D. E., "Limit States Design — A Probabilistic Study" — Can. J. Civ. Eng., Vol. 2, No. 1, Mar., 1975.
3. Kennedy, D.J.L., Allen, D. E., Adams, P. F., Kulak, G. L., Turner, D. K. and Tarlton, D. L., "Limit States Design" — Proc. Can. Struc. Eng. Conf. 1976, Can. Steel Indust. Const. Counc., Willowdale.
4. National Building Code of Canada 1980, The Supplement, Chapter 4, Commentary F, Nat. Res. Counc. Can., Ottawa, Ont.
5. Allen, D. L., "Vibrational Behaviour of Long-Span Floor Slabs" — Can. J. Civ. Eng., Vol. 1, No. 1, Sept., 1974.
6. Murray, T. M., "Design to Prevent Floor Vibrations" — Eng. J. AISC, Third Quarter, 1975.
7. Allen, D. E. and Ranier, J. H., "Vibration Criteria for Long-Span Floors" — Can. J. Civ. Eng., Vol. 3, No. 2, June, 1976.
8. National Building Code of Canada 1980 (clause 4.1.4) — Nat. Res. Counc. Can., Ottawa, Ont.
9. Sourochnikoff, B., "Wind-Stresses in Semi-Rigid Connections of Steel Framework" — Trans. ASCE, 1950.
10. Disque, R. O., "Wind Connections with Simple Framing" — Eng. J., AISC, July, 1964.
11. Popov, E. P. and Pinkney, R. B., "Cyclic Yield Reversal in Steel Building Connections" — Proc. ASCE J. Struc. Div., Vol. 95, No. ST3, Mar., 1969.
12. "Commentary on Plastic Design in Steel" — ASCE Manual of Engineering Practice No. 41, 1971.
13. Adams, P. F. and Galambos, T. V., "Material Considerations in Plastic Design" — Publ. Int. Assoc. for Bridge and Struc. Eng., Vol. 29-II, 1969.
14. Lay, M. G. and Galambos, T. V., "Inelastic Beams Under Moment Gradient" — Proc. ASCE J. Struc. Div., Vol. 93, No. ST1, Feb., 1967.
15. Lay, M. G. and Galambos, T. V., "Bracing Requirements for Inelastic Steel Beams" — Proc. ASCE J. Struct. Div., Vol. 92, No. ST2, April, 1966.
16. Fisher, J. W., Lee, G. C., Yura, J. A., and Driscoll, G. C., "Plastic Analysis and Tests of Haunched Corner Connections" — Welding Res. Counc. Bul. No. 91, Oct., 1963.
17. Hart, W. H. and Milek, W. A., "Splices in Plastically Designed Continuous Structures" — Eng. J., AISC, April, 1965.
18. Adams, P. F., "The Design of Steel Beam-Columns" — Can. Steel Indus. Const. Counc. Willowdale, Ont., April, 1974.
19. Beedle, L. S., Lu, L. W., Lim. L. C., "Recent Developments in Plastic Design Practice" — Proc. ASCE J. Struc. Div., Vol. 95, No. ST9, Sept., 1969.
20. "Plastic Design of Braced Multistorey Steel Frames" — Amer. Iron and Steel Inst., New York, N.Y., 1968.
21. Logcher, R. D., et al., "ICES STRUDL II", Engineering Users Manual — Dept. Civ. Eng., Mass. Inst. Tech., Cambridge, Mass., June, 1969.
22. Galambos, T. V., "Structural Members and Frames" — Prentice-Hall Inc., Englewood Cliffs, N.J., 1968.
23. Wood, B. R., Beaulieu, D., and Adams, P. F., "Column Design by P-Delta Method" — Proc. ASCE J. Struc. Div., Vol. 102, No. ST2, Feb., 1976.
24. Springfield, J. and Adams, P. F., "Aspects of Column Design in Tall Steel Buildings" — Proc. ASCE J. Struc. Div., Vol. 98, No. ST5, May, 1972.
25. "Guide to Stability Design Criteria for Metal Structures, (3rd ed.)" — Struc. Stab. Research Counc. — John Wiley & Sons, Inc., New York, N.Y., 1976.
26. Tall, L. et al., "Structural Steel Design (2nd Ed.)" — The Ronald Press Company, New York, N.Y., 1974.
27. "Column Selection Program 3" — Can. Inst. of Steel Const., Willowdale, Ont., 1977.
28. "Hollow Structural Sections Design Manual for Columns and Beams" — The Steel Company of Canada Limited, Hamilton, Ont., 1973.
29. Adams, P. F., Krentz, H. A., and Kulak, G. L., "Limit States Design in Structural Steel — SI Units", 1979, Can. Inst. of Steel Const., Willowdale, Ont.
30. Haaijer, G. and Thurlimann, B., "On Inelastic Buckling in Steel" — Proc. ASCE J. Eng. Mech. Div., April, 1958.
31. Lay, M. G., "Flange Local Buckling in Wide-Flange Shapes" — Proc. ASCE J. Struc. Div., Vol. 91, No. ST6, Dec., 1965.
32. Lukey, A. F. and Adams, P. F., "Rotation Capacity of Beams Under Moment Gradient" — Proc. ASCE J. Struc. Div., Vol. 95, No. ST6, June, 1969.
33. Holtz, N. and Kulak, G. L., "Web Slenderness Limits for Compact Beams" — Dept. Civ. Eng. Univ. of Alberta, Report No. 43, Mar., 1973.
34. Holtz, N. and Kulak, G. L., "Web Slenderness Limits for Non-Compact Beams" — Dept. Civ. Eng., Univ. of Alberta, Report No. 51, Aug., 1975.
35. Perlynn, M. J. and Kulak, G. L., "Web Slenderness Limits for Compact Beam-Columns" — Dept. Civ. Eng., Univ. of Alberta, Report No. 50, Sept., 1974.
36. Nash, D. S. and Kulak, G. L., "Web Slenderness Limits for Non-Compact Beam-Columns" — Dept. Civ. Eng., Univ. of Alberta, Report No. 53, Mar., 1976.

37. Winter, G., "Commentary on the 1968 Edition of the Specification for the Design of Cold-Formed Steel Structural Members" — Amer. Iron and Steel Inst., New York, N.Y., 1970.

38. Johnston, B. G., "Pin Connected Plate Links" — Trans. ASCE, 1939.

39. Beedle, L. S. and Tall, L., "Basic Column Strength" — Proc. ASCE J. Struc. Div., Vol. 86, No. ST7, July, 1960.

40. Bjorhovde, R., "A Probabilistic Approach to Maximum Column Strength" — Proc. Conf. on Safety and Reliability of Metal Structures, ASCE, Nov., 1972.

41. Keen, R. G. and Cran, J. A., "Implications of Canadian Standards Association Standard G40.20 on the Manufacture of Hollow Structural Sections" — Tech. Bul. 15, The Steel Company of Canada, Limited, Hamilton, Ont., June, 1974.

42. Basler, K., "Strength of Plate Girders in Shear" — Proc. ASCE J. Struc. Div., Vol. 87, No. ST7, Oct., 1961.

43. Basler, K. and Thurlimann, B., "Strength of Plate Girders in Bending" — Proc. ASCE J. Struc. Div., Vol. 87, No. ST6, Aug., 1961.

44. Basler, K., "Strength of Plate Girders Under Combined Bending and Shear" — Proc. ASCE J. Struc. Div., Vol. 87, No. ST7, Oct., 1961.

45. Yura, J. A., Galambos, T. V., and Ravindra, M. K., "The Bending Resistance of Steel Beams" — Proc. ASCE J. Struc. Div., Vol. 104, No. ST9, Sept. 1978.

46. Beedle, L. S., "Plastic Design of Steel Frames" — John Wiley & Sons, New York, N.Y., 1958.

47. Pillai, U. S., "Beam-Columns of Hollow Structural Sections" — Can. J. Civ. Eng., Vol. 1, No. 2, Dec., 1974.

48. Gilmor, M. I., "Choice of Prismatic Crane Column Sections by Computer" — Can. J. Civ. Eng., Vol. 2, No. 3, Sept., 1975.

49. Seeley, F. B. and Smith, J. O., "Advanced Mechanics of Materials (2nd ed.)." — John Wiley & Sons, Inc., New York, N.Y., 1957, pp. 365-367.

50. Manniche, K. and Ward-Hall, G., "Mission Bridge — Design and Construction of the Steel Box Girder" — Can. J. Civ. Eng., Vol. 3, No. 2, June, 1975.

51. Munse, W. H., "The Effect of Bearing Pressure on the Static Strength of Riveted Connections" Bul. No. 454, Eng. Exp. Stn., Univ. of Illinois, Urbana, Ill., July, 1959.

52. Jones, J., "Bearing-Ratio Effect on Strength of Riveted Joints" — Trans. ASCE, Vol. 123, 1958, pp. 964-972.

53. de Back, J. and de Jong, A., "Measurement on Connections with High Strength Bolts, Particularly in View of the Permissible Arithmetical Bearing Stress" — Report 6-68-3, Stevin Lab., Delft Univ. of Tech., Delft, The Netherlands, 1968.

54. Hirano, N., "Bearing Stresses in Bolted Joints" — Soc. of Steel Const. of Japan, Vol. 6, No. 58, Tokyo, 1970.

55. Fisher, J. W. and Struik, J.H.A., "Guide to Design Criteria for Bolted and Riveted Joints" — John Wiley & Sons, New York, N.Y., 1974.

56. CSA Standard S16-1969, "Steel Structures for Buildings" — Can. Stand. Assoc., Rexdale, Ont., 1969.

57. Lilley, S. B., Carpenter, S. T., "Effective Moment of Inertia of a Riveted Plate Girder" — Trans. ASCE, 1940.

58. Subcommittee on Cover Plates, ASCE Task Committee on Flexural Members, "Commentary on Welded Cover-Plated Beams" — Proc. ASCE J. Struc. Div., Vol. 93, No. ST4, Aug., 1967.

59. McGuire, W., "Steel Structures" — Prentice Hall, Englewood Cliffs, N.J., 1968, p. 682.

60. Graham, J. D., Sherbourne, A. N., Khabbaz, R. N., Jensen, C. D., "Welded Interior Beam-to-Column Connections" — AISC, 1959.

61. Besler, K., "New Provisions for Plate Girder Design" — Proc. 1961 Nat. Eng. Conf., AISC, 1961.

62. Redwood, R., McCutcheon, J., "Beam Tests with Unreinforced Web Openings" — Proc. ASCE J. Struc. Div., Vol. 94, No. ST1, Jan., 1968.

63. Redwood, R. G., "Design of Beams with Web Holes" — Can. Steel Ind. Const. Counc., Willowdale, Ont., 1973.

64. Bower, J. E. et al., "Suggested Design Guide for Beams with Web Holes" — Proc. ASCE J. Struct. Div., Vol. 97, No. ST11, Nov., 1971.

65. Redwood, R. G., "Simplified Plastic Analysis for Reinforced Web Holes" — Eng. J. AISC, Vol. 8, No. 4, Oct., 1971.

66. Redwood, R. G., "Tables for Plastic Design of Beams with Rectangular Holes" — Eng. J. AISC, Vol. 9, No. 1, Jan., 1972.

67. National Cooperative Highway Research Program Report 102, "Effect of Weldments on the Fatigue Strength of Steel Beams" — Transportation Research Board, National Academy of Sciences, Washington, D.C.

68. National Cooperative Highway Research Program Report 147, "Fatigue Strength of Steel Beams with Welded Stiffeners and Attachments" — Transportation Research Board, National Academy of Sciences, Washington, D.C.

69. Fisher, J. W., "Guide to 1974 AASHTO Fatigue Specifications" — AISC, New York, N.Y., 1974.

70. "Torsional Analysis of Rolled Steel Sections" — Handbook 1963C, Bethlehem Steel Corp., Bethlehem, Pa., 1967.

71. Brockenbrough, R. L. and Johnston, B. G., "Steel Design Manual" — United States Steel Corp., Pittsburgh, Pa., 1974.

72. Aziz, T.S.A., "Inelastic Nonlinear Behaviour of Steel Triangulated Planar Frames" — Thesis, Carleton Univ., Ottawa, Ont., May, 1972.

73. Kennedy, D.J.L. and Rowan, W.H.D., "Behaviour of Compression Chords of Open Web Steel Joists" — Report to CISC, 1964.

74. Johnson, R. P., and Smith, D.G.E., "Design Rules for the Control of Deflections in Composite Beams" — The Struc. Eng., Vol. 53, No. 9, Sept., 1975.

75. Robinson, H. and Wallace, I. W., "Composite Beams with 1½ inch Metal Deck and Partial and Full Shear Connection" — Trans. CSCE, Vol. 16, No. A—8, published in The Eng. J., EIC, Sept., 1973.

76. Johnson, R. P., "Longitudinal Shear Strength of Composite Beams" — ACI Journal Proc. Vol. 67, June, 1970.

77. El-Ghazzi, M. N., Robinson, H. and Elkholy, I.A.S., "Longitudinal Shear Capacity of Slabs of Composite Beams" — Can. J. Civ. Eng., Vol. 3, No. 4, Dec., 1976.

78. Ollgaard, J. G., Slutter, R. G. and Fisher, J. W., "Shear Strength of Stud Connectors in Light-weight and Normal-Weight Concrete" — Eng. J. AISC, April, 1971.

79. Fisher, J. W., "Design of Composite Beams with Formed Metal Deck" — Eng. J. AISC, July, 1970.

80. Slutter, R. G. and Driscoll, G. C., "Flexural Strength of Steel Concrete Composite Beams" — Proc. ASCE, J. Struc. Div., Vol. 95, No. ST2, April, 1965.

81. Vincent, G. S., "Tentative Criteria for Load Factor Design of Steel Highway Bridges" — Steel Res. Const. Bul., No. 15, AISI, March, 1969.

82. Hansell, W. C. and Viest, I. M., "Load Factor Design for Steel Highway Bridges" — Eng. J. AISC, Vol. 8, No. 4, Oct., 1971.

83. "Standard Specification for Highway Bridges" — American Association of State Highway and Transportation Officials, Washington, D.C., 1977.

84. Robinson, H., "Composite Beam Incorporating Cellular Steel Decking" — Proc. ASCE J. Struc. Div., Vol. 95, No. ST3, March, 1969.

85. Gobel, G., "Shear Strength of Thin Flange Composite Specimens" — Eng. J. AISC, April, 1968.

86. Viest, I. M. et al., "Tentative Recommendations for the Design and Construction of Composite Beams and Girders for Buildings" — Proc. ASCE J. Struc. Div., Vol. 86, No. ST12, Dec., 1960.

87. International Committee for the Study and Development of Tubular Structures (CIDECT), Monograph No. 1, "Concrete Filled Hollow Section Steel Columns Design Manual" — Whitefriars Press Ltd., London, 1970.

88. Winter, G., "Lateral Bracing of Columns and Beams" — Proc. ASCE J. Struc. Div., Vol. 84, No. ST2, Mar., 1958.

89. Massey, C., "Lateral Bracing Forces of Steel I-Beams" — Proc. ASCE Eng. Mech. Div., Vol. 88, EM6, Dec., 1962.

90. Zuk, W., "Lateral Bracing Forces on Beams and Columns" — Proc. ASCE Eng. Mech. Div., Vol. 82, EM3, July, 1956.

91. Lay, M. G. and Galambos, T. V., "Bracing Requirements for Inelastic Steel Beams" — Proc. ASCE, J. Struc. Div., Vol. 92, ST2, April, 1966.

92. Wood, B. R., Beaulieu, D., Adams, P. F., "Further Aspects of Design by P-Delta Method" — Proc. ASCE J. Struc. Div., Vol. 102, No. ST3, Mar., 1976.

93. Thornton, C. H., "Quality Control in Design and Supervision Can Eliminate Lamellar Tearing" — Eng. J. AISC, Fourth Quarter, 1973.

94. "AISC Commentary on Highly Restrained Welded Connections" — Eng. J. AISC, Third Quarter, 1973.

95. Gibson, G. T., Wake, B. T., "An Investigation of Welded Connections for Angle Tension Members" — Welding J. AWS, Jan., 1942.

96. Research Council on Riveted and Bolted Structural Joints, "Specification for Structural Joints Using ASTM A325 or A490 Bolts" — April, 1978.

97. ASTM A325-79, "High-Strength Bolts for Structural Steel Joints, Including Suitable Nuts and Plain Hardened Washers" — Amer. Soc. for Test. and Mat., Standard A325.

98. ASTM A490-79, "Quenched and Tempered Alloy Steel Bolts for Structural Steel Joints" — Amer. Soc. for Test. and Mat., Standard A490.

99. Pillai, U. S. and Ellis, J. S., "Hollow Tubular Beam-Columns in Biaxial Bending" — Proc. ASCE J. Struc. Div., Vol. 97, No. ST5, May, 1971.

100. Chen, W. F., and Atsuta, T., "Interaction Equations for Biaxially Loaded Sections" — Proc. ASCE J. Struc. Div., Vol. 98, No. ST5, May, 1972.

101. Chen, W. F., and Atsuta, T., "Ultimate Strength of Biaxially Loaded Steel H-Columns" — Proc. ASCE J. Struc. Div., Vol. 99, No. ST3, Mar., 1973.

102. Tebedge, N. and Chen, W. F., "Design Criteria for H-Columns Under Biaxial Loading" — Proc. ASCE, J. Struc. Div., Vol. 100, No. ST3, Mar., 1974.

103. Ross, D. A. and Chen, W. F., "Design Criteria for Steel I-Columns under Axial Load and Biaxial Bending" — Can. J. Civ. Eng., Vol. 3, No. 3, Sept., 1976.

104. Pillai, U. S., "Beam-Columns of Hollow Structural Sections" — Can. J. Civ. Eng., Vol. 1, No. 2, Dec., 1974.

105. Pillai, U. S., "Review of Recent Research on the Behaviour of Beam-Columns under Biaxial Bending" — Civ. Eng. Res. Report No. CE 70—1, Royal Military College of Canada, Kingston, Ont., Jan., 1970.

106. Springfield, J., "Design of Columns Subject to Biaxial Bending" — Eng. J. AISC, Vol. 12, No. 3, Third Quarter, 1975.

107. Disque, R. O., "Applied Plastic Design in Steel" — Van Nostrand Reinhold, New York, N.Y., 1971.

108. Beaulieu, D., Perlynn, M., Dunbar, A., Adams, P. F., and Keller, D., "The Effects of Column Out-of-Plumbs on the Stability of Core-Braced Buildings" — Can. J. Civ. Eng., Vol. 3, No. 3, Sept., 1976.

109. Beaulieu, D. and Adams, P. F., "Significance of Structural Out-of-Plumb Forces and Recommendations for Design" — Can. J. Civ. Eng., Vol. 7, No. 1, March, 1980.

110. Fisher, J. W., "Fatigue Cracking in Bridges from Out-of-Plane Displacements" — Can. J. Civ. Eng., Vol. 5, No. 4, Dec., 1978.

111. Heins, C. P., and Fan, H. M., "Effective Composite Beam Width at Ultimate Load" — Proc. ASCE J. Struc. Div., Vol. 102, No. ST11, Nov., 1976.

112. Kennedy, D.J.L., and Gad Aly, M., "Limit States Design of Steel Structures — Performance Factors" — Can. J. Civ. Eng. Vol. 7, No. 1, March, 1980.

113. "Steel Joist Facts" 2nd edition, Can. Inst. of Steel Const., Willowdale, Ont., 1980.

114. Bjorhovde, R. and Birkemoe, P. C., "Limit States Design of HSS Columns" — Can. J. Civ. Eng., Vol. 6, No. 2, June, 1979.

115. Birkemoe, P. C. and Gilmor, M. I., "Behaviour of Bearing Critical Double-Angle Beam Connections", Eng. J., AISC, Fourth Quarter, 1978.

116. Pillai, U. S., and Kurian, V. J., "Tests on Hollow Structural Section Beam-Columns", Can. J. Civ. Eng., Vol. 4, No. 2, June, 1977.

117. Toprac, A. and Natarajan, M., "Fatigue Strength of Hybrid Plate Girders" — Proc. ASCE J. Struct. Div., Vol. 97, No. ST4, April, 1971.

118. Reiner, J. H., "Dynamic Tests on a Steel-Joist Concrete-Slab Floor", Can. J. Civ. Eng., Vol. 7, No. 2, June 1980.

119. Kaliandasani, R. A., Simmonds, S. H. and Murray, D. W., "Behaviour of Open Web Steel Joists", — Dept. Civ. Eng., Univ. of Alberta, Report No. 62, July, 1977.

120. Shrivastava, S. C., Redwood, R. G., Harris, P. J. and Ettehadieh, A. A., "End Moments in Open Web Steel Tie Joists," McGill University, June, 1979.

NOTES

PART THREE
CONNECTIONS AND TENSION MEMBERS

General Information   3-3

Connection Loads   3-4

Bolts

    Bolt Data — Metric and Imperial Series   3-5

    Bolts in Bearing-Type Connections   3-7

    Bolts in Slip-Resistant (Friction-Type) Connections   3-14

    Bolts in Tension and Prying Action   3-18

    Eccentric Loads on Bolt Groups   3-24

Welds

    Weld Data   3-36

    Eccentric Loads on Weld Groups   3-38

Framed Beam Shear Connections   3-52

    Double Angle Beam Connections   3-54

    End Plate Connections   3-60

    Single Angle Beam Connections   3-62

    Tee-Type Beam Connections   3-64

Seated Beam Shear Connections   3-66

    Unstiffened Angle Seat Connections   3-66

    Stiffened Seated Beam Connections   3-70

Moment Connections   3-72

Hollow Structural Section Connections   3-80

Tension Members   3-89

GENERAL INFORMATION

Part 3 contains tables, examples, dimensions and general information of assistance to designers, detailers and others concerned with the design and detailing of connections and tension members according to the requirements of Clauses 13.2, 13.9, 13.10(c), 13.11, 13.13, 20.0, 21.0 and 22.0 of CAN3-S16.1-M78. Information is included for both metric series and Imperial series bolts, though all design data is given in SI units. For convenience Part 3 is divided into seven main sections.

Bolt Data

Pages 3—5 to 3—35 inclusive contain information on size, diameter, area and strength of bolts, including bolt resistances and unit resistances, for evaluating bolts in bearing-type connections, slip-resistant (friction-type) connections, and bolts subjected to tension and prying action. Included also are tables for evaluating eccentric loads on various bolt groups.

Weld Data

Pages 3—36 to 3—51 inclusive contain information on factored resistance of welds, including values for various sizes of fillet welds with a comparison between Imperial and metric sized fillet welds. Included are tables for evaluating eccentric loads on various weld groups and configurations.

Framed Beam Shear Connections

Pages 3—52 to 3—65 inclusive contain information on common types of beam shear connections traditionally considered to be standard in the industry. Included are double angle beam connections, simple end plate connections, single angle beam connections and Tee-Type Beam Connections.

Seated Beam Shear Connections

Pages 3—66 to 3—71 inclusive contain information on un-stiffened and stiffened seated beam shear connections of a type commonly used in practice, where direct framing of the supported beam is either not desirable or possible.

Moment Connections

Pages 3—72 to 3—79 inclusive contain examples of welded and welded-bolted moment connections, and information for the design of stiffeners on supporting columns.

Hollow Structural Section Connections

See page 3—80.

Tension Members

Pages 3—89 to 3—93 contains tables and examples for calculating net area and for evaluating the unit tensile resistance of tension members for various grades of steel and various ratios of net to gross area.

CONNECTION LOADS

Connections are designed and detailed for the member reactions and loads given on the structural steel design drawings by the building designer. Most connections are generally designed for factored loads, however, specified loads are used for the design of connections subject to repeated loading and for calculating the slip resistance of slip-resistant (friction-type) connections.

In evaluating member loads and forces it is preferable to keep different types of load separate to facilitate application of the different load factors and load combination factors specified in Clause 7.2 of CAN3-S16.1-M78 and other governing codes. However, this may not always be convenient, and Figure 3—1 is included to permit an approximate evaluation of either the total specified load or the total factored load when either one is known, and the ratio of the specified dead load to specified live load is known or the unit specified dead load and unit specified live load are both known. The curve is based on load factors α given in Clause 7.2.3 and makes no allowance for possible live load reductions permitted by the applicable building codes.

Example

Given:

The total factored dead and live load reaction at the end of a beam to be designed as a slip-resistant connection is 235 kN and the specified unit dead and live loads are 4.35 kPa and 2.16 kPa respectively. What is the reaction under specified load.

Solution:

Ratio D/L = 4.35/2.16 = 2.0

From Fig. 3—1, for D/L = 2.0, $(L + D)/(\alpha_L L + \alpha_D D)$ = 0.75

Therefore specified load reaction is 0.75 × 235 = 176 kN

FIGURE 3-1

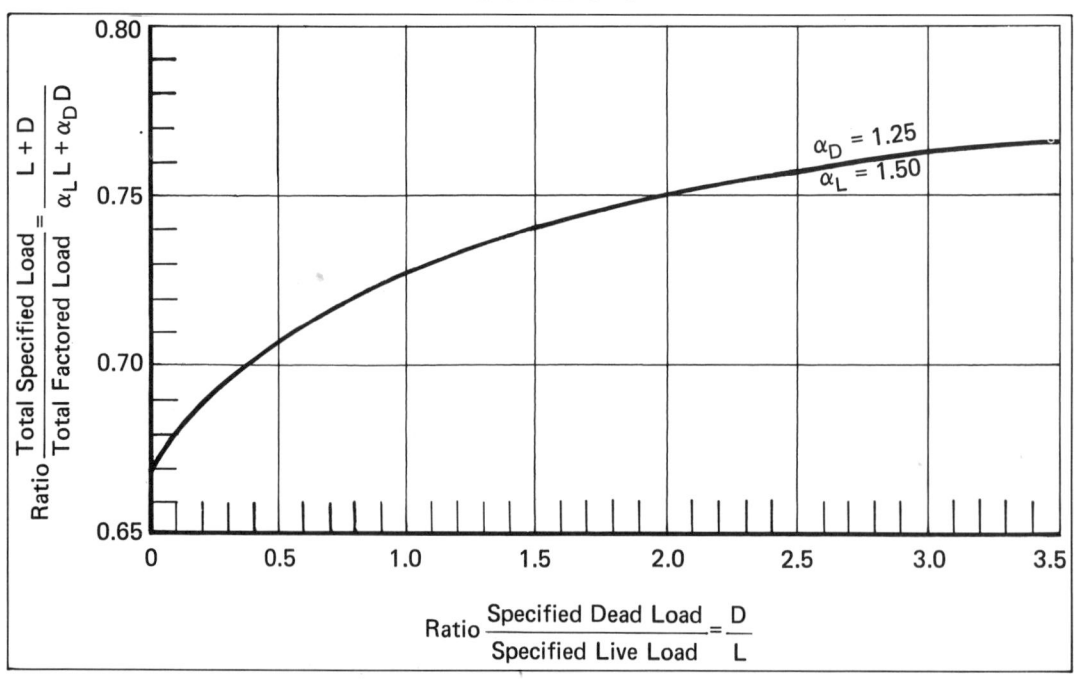

BOLT DATA

General

Tables in this section are based on CAN3-S16.1-M78, and include information for both metric series and Imperial series bolts. Data for the metric series bolts is based on ASTM Specifications A325M and A490M (tentative) and for the Imperial series bolts on ASTM Specifications A325, A490 and A307. Values are tabulated in ascending order of nominal cross-sectional area $A_b(mm^2)$ to facilitate comparison between metric and Imperial sizes. Bold type is used for metric series bolts when both metric sizes and Imperial sizes appear on the same table. This section includes the following:

Bolt Data Metric and Imperial Series

Table 3—1 on page 3—6 lists the size, nominal diameter (mm), nominal area (mm²) and values of $A_b F_u$ for bolt sizes from M16 to M36 and 1/2 inch to 1-1/2 inch diameter.

Bolts in Bearing-Type Connections

Tables 3—2 to 3—7 on pages 3—7 to 3—11 list values of bearing and bolt resistances computed in accordance with Clauses 13.10(c) and 13.11. Tables 3—8 and 3—9 on page 3—13 assist in evaluating combined shear and tension on bolts.

Bolts in Slip-Resistant (friction-type) Connections

Tables 3—10 and 3—11 on page 3—15 list resistances, for use with bolts in slip-resistant connections, computed in accordance with Clause 13.12.

Bolts in Tension and Prying Action

Tables and design aids on pages 3—18 to 3—23 assist in evaluating the effects of prying action on bolts loaded in tension.

Eccentric Loads on Bolt Groups

Tables for evaluating eccentric loads on bolts in bearing-type and slip-resistant connections for various bolt group configurations are given on pages 3—24 to 3—33.

BOLT DATA
Metric and Imperial Series

Table 3-1

Bolt Size		Nominal Diameter of Bolt (mm)	Nominal Area (A_b) (mm²)	$A_b F_u$** (kN)				
Metric*	Imperial			A325M	A490M	A325	A490	A307
	1/2	12.70	127			104	131	
	5/8	15.88	198			163	205	81.9
M16		16.00	201	167	209			
	3/4	19.05	285			235	295	118
M20		20.00	314	261	327			
M22		22.00	380	316	395			
	7/8	22.23	388			320	402	161
M24		24.00	452	375	470			
	1	25.40	507			418	524	
M27		27.00	573	475	595			
	1—1/8	28.58	641			465	664	
M30		30.00	707	587	735			
	1—1/4	31.75	792			574	819	
M36		36.00	1018	845	1060			
	1—1/2	38.10	1140			827	1180	

*The number following the letter M is the nominal bolt diameter in millimetres.
**See Table 3—3 page 3—8 for specified minimum tensile strengths, F_u.

BOLTS IN BEARING-TYPE CONNECTIONS

General

Connections are generally detailed as bearing-type unless specified otherwise by the building designer. Bearing type connections are designed for factored loads, and Tables 3—2 to 3—9 inclusive on the following pages assist in evaluating the requirements of Clause 13.11 of CAN3-S16.1-M78. Clause 22.3.2 lists the size and type of holes permitted with bearing type connections.

Table 3—2, page 3—7, summarises the requirements of Clause 13.11.2 for bolts in shear and Clause 13.11.3 for bolts in tension, and lists expressions for factored resistance and unit factored resistance of bolts in bearing-type connections.

Table 3—3, page 3—8, lists, for A325M, A490M, A325, A490 and A307 bolts, values of the specified minimum tension, F_u, values of unit factored shear resistances, 0.4 F_u and 0.28 F_u, and values of unit factored tensile resistances, 0.5 F_u.

Table 3—4, page 3—8, lists factored shear and tensile resistances in kN/bolt for both metric series and Imperial series bolts.

Table 3—5, page 3—9, lists values of the specified minimum tensile strength, F_u, for the common grades of structural steel, and values of unit factored bearing resistances, 0.67 F_u and 2.0 F_u.

Tables 3—6 and 3—7, pages 3—9 to 3—11 inclusive, list factored bearing resistance in kN/bolt for five different values of F_u for the connected material. Bearing resistances in these tables are given in terms of the material thickness, t, and end distance, e, and are independent of the diameter, d, and grade of the bolt. Maximum bearing values are reached when e = 3d. The shaded areas on each table give the approximate range of end distances for the bolt sizes listed, from the minimum end distance to that of e = 3d, for which the tabulated factored bearing resistances are applicable. The shear values in Table 3—4 govern if less than the bearing values given in Tables 3—6 and 3—7.

For connections consisting of G40.21-M 300W steel (F_u = 450 MPa), see Table 3—6, page 3—9.

Tables 3—8 and 3—9 on page 3—13 assist in evaluating bolts in combined shear and tension according to Clause 13.11.4.

Table 3-2
CAN3-S16.1-M78 SUMMARY
Bearing-Type Connections

Bolt Situation in Joint	Factored Resistance	Unit Factored Resistance (n = m = A_b = 1)	Clause Reference
BOLTS IN SHEAR			13.11.2
Shear on bolts with threads excluded from shear plane	$V_r = 0.60 \phi\, n\, m\, A_b F_u$	$V_r = 0.40\, F_u$	13.11.2(b)
Shear on bolts with threads intercepted by shear plane	$V_r = 0.42 \phi\, n\, m\, A_b F_u$	$V_r = 0.28\, F_u$	
For joints longer than 1300 mm	shear = 0.80 V_r		
Bearing on main material	$B_r = \phi\, t\, n\, e\, F_u$ $\leqslant 3 \phi\, t\, d\, n\, F_u$	$B_r = 0.67\, t\, e\, F_u$ $\leqslant 2.0\, t\, d\, F_u$	13.10(c)
BOLTS IN TENSION	$T_r = 0.75 \phi\, n\, A_b F_u$	$T_r = 0.50\, F_u$	13.11.3

Notes: 1. Oversize holes are not permitted in bearing-type connections (see Clause 22.3.2(a) of CAN3-S16.1-M78)
      2. See Clause 22.3.2(b), (c) of CAN3-S16.1-M78 re use of slotted holes in bearing-type connections.
      3. See Clause 23.3.2(d) of CAN3-S16.1-M78 for hole diameters permitted with M20 or 3/4-inch diameter, M22 or 7/8-inch diameter, and M24 or 1-inch diameter bolts.

UNIT FACTORED SHEAR AND TENSILE RESISTANCES**
$\emptyset = 0.67$

Table 3-3

Bolt Grade	Specified Minimum Tensile Strength, F_u (MPa)	Unit Factored Shear Resistance		Unit Factored Tensile Resistance 0.50 F_u (MPa)
		Threads Excluded 0.40 F_u (MPa)	Threads Intercepted 0.28 F_u (MPa)	
A325M	830	334	234	417
A490M	1040	418	293	523
A325 (d ⩽ 1")	825	332	232	415
A325 (d ⩾ 1−1/8")	725	291	204	364
A490	1035	416	291	520
A307*	414	166	117	208

*Use of A307 bolts in connections is covered in Clause 20.12.2 of CAN3-S16.1-M78.
**Values for Imperial series bolts are based on ASTM specifications A325 and the A490 soft converted to SI units.

FACTORED SHEAR AND TENSILE RESISTANCES (kN PER BOLT)

Table 3-4

Bolt Size		Nominal Area A_b (mm^2)	Factored Shear Resistance[†] — Single Shear**(kN/bolt)						Factored Tensile Resistance, T_r (kN/bolt)		
			Threads Excluded			Threads Intercepted [††]					
Metric*	Imperial		A325 A325M	A490 A490M	A307	A325 A325M	A490 A490M	A307	A325 A325M	A490 A490M	A307
	1/2	127	42.2	52.8		29.5	37.0		52.7	66.0	
	5/8	198	65.7	82.4	32.9	45.9	57.6	23.2	82.2	103	41.2
M16		201	67.1	84.0		47.3	58.9		83.8	105	
	3/4	285	94.6	119	47.3	66.1	82.9	33.4	118	148	59.3
M20		314	105	131		73.5	92.0		131	164	
M22		380	127	159		88.9	111		158	199	
	7/8	388	129	161	64.4	90.0	113	45.4	161	202	80.7
M24		452	151	189		106	132		188	238	
	1	507	168	211		118	148		210	264	
M27		473	191	240		134	168		239	300	
	1−1/8	641	187	267		131	187		233	333	
M30		707	236	296		165	207		295	370	
	1−1/4	792	230	329		162	230		288	412	
M36		1018	340	426		238	298		425	532	
	1−1/2	1140	332	474		233	322		415	593	

* The number following the letter M is the nominal bolt diameter in millimetres.
† For joints longer than 1 300 mm use 80% of the factored shear resistance.
**For double shear multiply tabulated values by 2.0.
††Threads assumed to be intercepted when thickness of part adjacent to nut < 10 mm unless special precautions are taken.

Table 3-5 — UNIT FACTORED BEARING RESISTANCES

Material Standard and Grade		Specified Minimum Tensile Strength, F_u (MPa)	$0.67\,F_u$ (MPa)	Maximum $2.0\,F_u$ (MPa)
CSA G40.21-M	230G	380	255	760
	260W, 260WT	410	275	820
	300W for HSS only	410	275	820
	300W, 350W, 300WT	450	302	900
	350G, 350WT, 350R, 350A, 350AT	480	322	960
	380W and 380WT for HSS only	480	322	960
	400W, 400WT, 400A, 400AT	520	348	1040
	480W, 480WT, 480A, 480AT	590	395	1180
ASTM	A36	400	268	800
	A572 Grade 42	415	278	830
	Grade 50	450	302	900
	A441 F_y = 42	435	291	870
	F_y = 46	460	308	920
	F_y = 50	485	325	970

Table 3-6 — FACTORED BEARING RESISTANCE, B_r* (kN/bolt)

CSA G40.21-M   300W, 350W, 300WT (F_u = 450 MPa)

Material Thickness t (mm)	End Distance**, e (mm)											
	20	25	30	35	40	45	50	60	70	80	90	100
4	24.1	30.1	36.2	42.2	48.2	54.3	60.3	72.4	84.4	96.5	109	121
4.5	27.1	33.9	40.7	47.5	54.3	61.1	67.8	81.4	95.0	109	122	136
5	30.1	37.7	45.2	52.8	60.3	67.8	75.4	90.4	106	121	136	151
6	36.2	45.2	54.3	63.3	72.4	81.4	90.4	109	127	145	163	181
7	42.2	52.8	63.3	73.9	84.4	95.0	106	127	148	169	190	211
8	48.2	60.3	72.4	84.4	96.5	109	121	145	169	193	217	241
9	54.3	67.8	81.4	95.0	109	122	136	163	190	217	244	271
10	60.3	75.4	90.4	106	121	136	151	181	211	241	271	301
11	66.3	82.9	99.5	116	133	149	166	199	232	265	298	332
12	72.4	90.4	109	127	145	163	181	217	253	289	326	362
13	78.4	98.0	118	137	157	176	196	235	274	314	353	392
14	84.4	106	127	148	169	190	211	253	295	338	380	422
15	90.4	113	136	158	181	204	226	271	317	362	407	452
16	96.5	121	145	169	193	217	241	289	338	386	434	482
17	103	128	154	179	205	231	256	308	359	410	461	513
18	109	136	163	190	217	244	271	326	380	434	488	543
19	115	143	172	200	229	258	286	344	401	458	516	573
20	121	151	181	211	241	271	301	362	422	482	543	603
21	127	158	190	222	253	285	317	380	443	507	570	633
22	133	166	199	232	265	298	332	398	464	531	597	663
23	139	173	208	243	277	312	347	416	485	555	624	693
24	145	181	217	253	289	326	362	434	507	579	651	724
25	151	188	226	264	301	339	377	452	528	603	678	754
28		211	253	295	338	380	422	507	591	675	760	844
30		226	271	317	362	407	452	543	633	724	814	904
32		241	289	338	386	434	482	579	675	772	868	965
35		264	317	369	422	475	528	633	739	844		

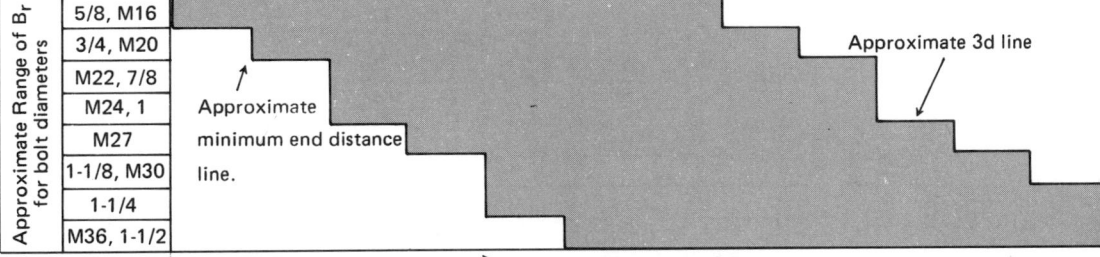

Approximate Range of B_r for bolt diameters	
5/8, M16	
3/4, M20	
M22, 7/8	↑ Approximate minimum end distance line.
M24, 1	
M27	
1-1/8, M30	
1-1/4	
M36, 1-1/2	

Approximate 3d line

* B_r = 0.67 t e F_u ** For e > 3d use B_r value for e = 3d.

Notes: 1. Bolt shear governs if less than bearing. See Table 3-4.
2. Bearing values below dashed horizontal lines exceed single shear bolt values.

FACTORED BEARING RESISTANCE, B$_r$* (kN/bolt) Table 3-7

ASTM A36 (F$_u$ = 400 MPa)

Material Thickness t (mm)	End Distance**, e (mm)											
	20	25	30	35	40	45	50	60	70	80	90	100
4	21.4	26.8	32.2	37.5	42.9	48.2	53.6	64.3	75.0	85.8	96.5	107
4.5	24.1	30.1	36.2	42.2	48.2	54.3	60.3	72.4	84.4	96.5	109	121
5	26.8	33.5	40.2	46.9	53.6	60.3	67.0	80.4	93.8	107	121	134
6	32.2	40.2	48.2	56.3	64.3	72.4	80.4	96.5	113	129	145	161
7	37.5	46.9	56.3	65.7	75.0	84.4	93.8	113	131	150	169	188
8	42.9	53.6	64.3	75.0	85.8	96.5	107	129	150	172	193	214
9	48.2	60.3	72.4	84.4	96.5	109	121	145	169	193	217	241
10	53.6	67.0	80.4	93.8	107	121	134	161	188	214	241	268
11	59.0	73.7	88.4	103	118	133	147	177	206	236	265	295
12	64.3	80.4	96.5	113	129	145	161	193	225	257	289	322
13	69.7	87.1	105	122	139	157	174	209	244	279	314	348
14	75.0	93.8	113	131	150	169	188	225	263	300	338	375
15	80.4	100	121	141	161	181	201	241	281	322	362	402
16	85.8	107	129	150	172	193	214	257	300	343	386	429
17	91.1	114	137	159	182	205	228	273	319	364	410	456
18	96.5	121	145	169	193	217	241	289	338	386	434	482
19	102	127	153	178	204	229	255	306	356	407	458	509
20	107	134	161	188	214	241	268	322	375	429	482	536
21	113	141	169	197	225	253	281	338	394	450	507	563
22	118	147	177	206	236	265	295	354	413	472	531	590
23	123	154	185	216	247	277	308	370	431	493	555	616
24	129	161	193	225	257	289	322	386	450	515	579	643
25	134	167	201	234	268	301	335	402	469	536	603	670
28	150	188	225	263	300	338	375	450	525	600	675	750
30	161	201	241	281	322	362	402	482	563	643	724	804
32		214	257	300	343	386	429	515	600	686	772	858
35		234	281	328	375	422	469	563	657	750	844	938

Approximate Range of B$_r$ for bolt diameters (graphical region)

- 5/8, M16
- 3/4, M20
- M22, 7/8
- M24, 1
- M27
- 1-1/8, M30
- 1-1/4
- M36, 1-1/2

Approximate minimum end distance line →
← Approximate 3d Line.

Material Thickness t (mm)	End Distance**, e (mm)											
	20	25	30	35	40	45	50	60	70	80	90	100
4	22.0	27.5	33.0	38.5	44.0	49.4	54.9	65.9	76.9	87.9	98.9	110
4.5	24.7	30.9	37.1	43.3	49.4	55.6	61.8	74.2	86.5	98.9	111	124
5	27.5	34.3	41.2	48.1	54.9	61.8	68.7	82.4	96.1	110	124	137
6	33.0	41.2	49.4	57.7	65.9	74.2	82.4	98.9	115	132	148	165
7	38.5	48.1	57.7	67.3	76.9	86.5	96.1	115	135	154	173	192
8	44.0	54.9	65.9	76.9	87.9	98.9	110	132	154	176	198	220
9	49.4	61.8	74.2	86.5	98.9	111	124	148	173	198	223	247
10	54.9	68.7	82.4	96.1	110	124	137	165	192	220	247	275
11	60.4	75.5	90.7	106	121	136	151	181	212	242	272	302
12	65.9	82.4	98.9	115	132	148	165	198	231	264	297	330
13	71.4	89.3	107	125	143	161	179	214	250	286	321	357
14	76.9	96.1	115	135	154	173	192	231	269	308	346	385
15	82.4	103	124	144	165	185	206	247	288	330	371	412
16	87.9	110	132	154	176	198	220	264	308	352	396	440
17	93.4	117	140	163	187	210	233	280	327	374	420	467
18	98.9	124	148	173	198	223	247	297	346	396	445	494
19	104	130	157	183	209	235	261	313	365	418	470	522
20	110	137	165	192	220	247	275	330	385	440	494	549
21	115	144	173	202	231	260	288	346	404	461	519	577
22	121	151	181	212	242	272	302	363	423	483	544	604
23	126	158	190	221	253	284	316	379	442	505	569	632
24	132	165	198	231	264	297	330	396	461	527	593	659
25	137	172	206	240	275	309	343	412	481	549	618	687
28	154	192	231	269	308	346	385	461	538	615	692	769
30	165	206	247	288	330	371	412	494	577	659	742	824
32	175	220	264	308	352	396	440	527	615	703	791	879
35	192	240	288	337	385	433	481	577	673	769	865	961
Material Thickness t (mm)	20	25	30	35	40	45	50	60	70	80	90	100

End Distance**, e (mm)

CSA G40.21-M 260W, 260WT (F$_u$ = 410 MPa)

* B$_r$ = 0.67 t e F$_u$ ** For e > 3d use B$_r$ value for e = 3d.

3-10   Notes: 1. Bolt shear governs if less than bearing. See Table 3—4.
2. Bearing values below dashed horizontal lines exceed single shear bolt values.

Table 3-7   FACTORED BEARING RESISTANCE, B$_r$* (kN/bolt)

Material Thickness t (mm)	CSA G40.21-M 350G, 350WT, 350R, 350A, 380W, 380WT (F_u = 480 MPa) End Distance ** , e (mm)											
	20	25	30	35	40	45	50	60	70	80	90	100
4	25.7	32.2	38.6	45.0	51.5	57.9	64.3	77.2	90.0	103	116	129
4.5	28.9	36.2	43.4	50.7	57.9	65.1	72.4	86.8	101	116	130	145
5	32.2	40.2	48.2	56.3	64.3	72.4	80.4	96.5	113	129	145	161
6	38.6	48.2	57.9	67.5	77.2	86.8	96.5	116	135	154	174	193
7	45.0	56.3	67.5	78.8	90.0	101	113	135	158	180	203	225
8	51.5	64.3	77.2	90.0	103	116	129	154	180	206	232	257
9	57.9	72.4	86.8	101	116	130	145	174	203	232	260	289
10	64.3	80.4	96.5	113	129	145	161	193	225	257	289	322
11	70.8	88.4	106	124	142	159	177	212	248	283	318	354
12	77.2	96.5	116	135	154	174	193	232	270	309	347	386
13	83.6	105	125	146	167	188	209	251	293	334	376	418
14	90.0	113	135	158	180	203	225	270	315	360	405	450
15	96.5	121	145	169	193	217	241	289	338	386	434	482
16	103	129	154	180	206	232	257	309	360	412	463	515
17	109	137	164	191	219	246	273	328	383	437	492	547
18	116	145	174	203	232	260	289	347	405	463	521	579
19	122	153	183	214	244	275	306	367	428	489	550	611
20	129	161	193	225	257	289	322	386	450	515	579	643
21	135	169	203	236	270	304	338	405	473	540	608	675
22	142	177	212	248	283	318	354	425	495	566	637	708
23	148	185	222	259	296	333	370	444	518	592	666	740
24	154	193	232	270	309	347	386	463	540	617	695	772
25	161	201	241	281	322	362	402	482	563	643	724	804
28		225	270	315	360	405	450	540	630	720	810	900
30		241	289	338	386	434	482	579	675	772	868	
32		257	309	360	412	463	515	617	720	823	926	
35			338	394	450	507	563	675	788	900		

Approximate Range of B$_r$ for bolt diameters:

| 5/8, M16 |
| 3/4, M20 |
| M22, 7/8 |
| M24, 1 |
| M27 |
| 1-1/8, M30 |
| 1-1/4 |
| M36, 1-1/2 |

Approximate minimum end distance line →

Approximate 3d line. ←

Material Thickness t (mm)	CSA G40.21-M 400W, 400WT, 400A, 400AT (F_u = 520 MPa) End Distance ** , e (mm)											
4	27.9	34.8	41.8	48.8	55.7	62.7	69.7	83.6	97.6	111	125	139
4.5	31.4	39.2	47.0	54.9	62.7	70.6	78.4	94.1	110	125	141	157
5	34.8	43.5	52.3	61.0	69.7	78.4	87.1	105	122	139	157	174
6	41.8	52.3	62.7	73.2	83.6	94.1	105	125	146	167	188	209
7	48.8	61.0	73.2	85.4	97.6	110	122	146	171	195	219	244
8	55.7	69.7	83.6	97.6	111	125	139	167	195	223	251	279
9	62.7	78.4	94.1	110	125	141	157	188	219	251	282	314
10	69.7	87.1	105	122	139	157	174	209	244	279	314	348
11	76.6	95.8	115	134	153	172	192	230	268	307	345	383
12	83.6	105	125	146	167	188	209	251	293	334	376	418
13	90.6	113	136	159	181	204	226	272	317	362	408	453
14	97.6	122	146	171	195	219	244	293	341	390	439	488
15	105	131	157	183	209	235	261	314	366	418	470	523
16	111	139	167	195	223	251	279	334	390	446	502	557
17	118	148	178	207	237	267	296	355	415	474	533	592
18	125	157	188	219	251	282	314	376	439	502	564	627
19	132	165	199	232	265	298	331	397	463	530	596	662
20	139	174	209	244	279	314	348	418	488	557	627	697
21	146	183	219	256	293	329	366	439	512	585	658	732
22	153	192	230	268	307	345	383	460	537	613	690	766
23	160	200	240	280	321	361	401	481	561	641	721	801
24		209	251	293	334	376	418	502	585	669	753	836
25		218	261	305	348	392	435	523	610	697	784	871
28		244	293	341	390	439	488	585	683	780	878	
30		261	314	366	418	470	523	627	732	836	941	
32			334	390	446	502	557	669	780	892		
35			366	427	488	549	610	732	854			
Material Thickness t (mm)	20	25	30	35	40	45	50	60	70	80	90	100

* B$_r$ = 0.67 t e F$_u$ ** For e > 3d use B$_r$ value for e = 3d.

Notes: 1. Bolt shear governs if less than bearing. See Table 3—4.
    2. Bearing values below dashed horizontal lines exceed single shear bolt values.

Bolts in Combined Shear and Tension — Bearing-Type Connections

Clause 13.11.4 of CAN3-S16.1-M78 requires each bolt in a bearing-type joint subject to both shear and tension to satisfy a relationship which can be expressed as $V_f^2 + \beta T_f^2 \leqslant \beta (0.75 \phi A_b F_u)^2$, where V_f is the factored shear load on the bolt and T_f is the factored tensile load on the bolt including prying effects.

This expression can be written as $V_f^2 + \beta T_f^2 = \beta T_r^2$, where T_r is the factored tensile bolt resistance (See Table 3—4, page 3—8). If the shear tension ratio V_f/T_f on the bolts

is X, then solving for V_f and T_f gives, $V_f = XT_f$ and $T_f = [\beta T_r^2/(X^2 + \beta)]^{\frac{1}{2}}$

In practical applications, combined shear and tension is more likely to occur for the threads excluded condition, since a plate or flange which is thin enough to include threads in the shear plane (less than 10 mm) has little capacity to transmit tension. Tables 3—8 and 3—9 give values of V_f and T_f for various shear-tension ratios X, for M20, M22 and M24 A325M and A490M bolts and 3/4, 7/8 and 1-inch A325 and A490 bolts with threads excluded from the shear plane, where β = 0.69 for A325M and A325 bolts and β = 0.56 for A490M and A490 bolts.

Example

Given:

A bracing connection to support an inclined factored load P having a tension component T_f of 800 kN and a shear component V_f of 640 kN has been designed using a Tee section cut from a W410 × 85. Check the number of M20, A325M bolts required assuming 90 mm gauge in the Tee flange and a bolt pitch of 90 mm using G40.21-M 300W steel.

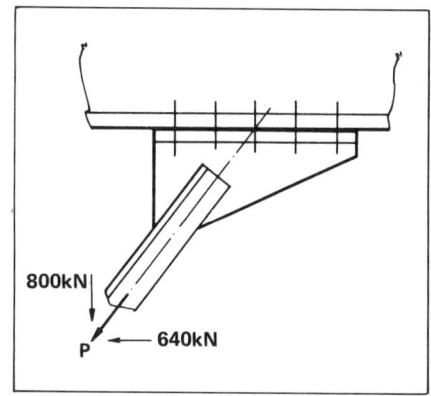

Solution:

Assume no prying action. Shear tension ratio is 640/800 = 0.80.
From Table 3—8, V_f = 75.5 kN, T_f = 94.4 kN per bolt.
Therefore number of bolts required = 640/75.5 = 800/94.4 = 8.48.

When there is no prying action then 10 bolts are required; however, to allow for prying action, assume 12 bolts and check tension on bolts and required flange thickness (see pages 3—18 to 3—23).

Applied tension load per bolt, T_f = 800/12 = 66.7 kN.

For W410 × 85, t = 18.2 mm

$$b = 1/2(90 - 10.9) = 39.6 \text{ mm, } b' = 29.6 \text{ mm}$$
$$a = 1/2(181 - 90) = 45.5 \text{ mm, } a' = 55.5 \text{ mm}$$
$$a' + b' = 85.1 \text{ mm}$$

$\delta = 1 - 22/90 = 0.76$

$$\alpha = \left[\frac{4 \times 66.7 \times 29.6 \times 10^3}{90 \times 300 \times (18.2)^2} - 1\right] \times \frac{55.5}{0.76 \times 85.1} = -0.10, \text{ Use } \alpha = 0.0$$

$B_f = T_f = 66.7 \text{ kN}$

$$\text{Required } t = \sqrt{\frac{4 \times 66.7 \times 29.6 \times 10^3}{90 \times 0.9 \times 300}} = 18.0 \text{ mm} < 18.2 \text{ mm} - \text{OK}$$

Therefore Tee cut from W410 × 85 is adequate with 12 M20 bolts.

Table 3-8 — For A325M and A325 Bolts

Shear Tension Ratio X = V_f/T_f		Bolt Size											
		3/4		M20		M22		7/8		M24		1	
X	1/X	V_f	T_f	V_f	T_f	V_f	T_f	V_f	T_f	V_f	T_f	V_f	T_f
0	T_r	0	118	0	131	0	158	0	161	0	188	0	210
0.10		11.7	117	13.0	130	15.7	157	16.0	160	18.7	187	20.8	208
0.20		23.0	115	25.4	127	30.8	154	31.4	157	36.6	183	40.8	204
0.30		33.3	111	36.9	123	44.7	149	45.3	151	53.1	177	59.4	198
0.40		42.4	106	47.2	118	56.8	142	58.0	145	67.6	169	75.6	189
0.50		50.5	101	56.0	112	67.5	135	69.0	138	80.5	161	90.0	180
0.60		57.4	95.7	63.6	106	76.8	128	78.6	131	91.2	152	102	170
0.70		63.1	90.2	70.0	100	84.7	121	86.1	123	101	144	113	161
0.80		68.0	85.0	75.5	94.4	91.2	114	92.8	116	108	135	121	151
0.90		72.0	80.0	79.9	88.8	96.3	107	98.1	109	115	128	128	142
1.00	1.00	75.4	75.4	83.7	83.7	101	101	103	103	120	120	134	134
1.11	0.90	78.6	70.7	87.1	78.4	105	94.6	107	96.4	126	113	140	126
1.25	0.80	81.6	65.3	90.6	72.5	109	87.4	111	89.1	130	104	145	116
1.43	0.70	84.7	59.3	94.0	65.8	113	79.4	116	80.9	135	94.5	151	106
1.67	0.60	87.7	52.6	97.3	58.4	118	70.5	120	71.8	140	83.9	156	93.7
2.00	0.50	90.6	45.3	100	50.2	121	60.6	124	61.8	144	72.1	161	80.5
2.50	0.40	93.0	37.2	103	41.3	125	49.8	127	50.8	148	59.3	166	66.2
3.33	0.30	94.6	28.5	105	31.7	127	38.2	129	38.9	151	45.5	168	50.8
5.00	0.20	94.6	19.3	105	21.5	127	25.9	129	26.4	151	30.8	168	34.4
10.0	0.10	94.6	9.8	105	10.8	127	13.3	129	13.3	151	15.6	168	17.4
V_r	0	94.6	0	105	0	127	0	129	0	151	0	168	0

$V_f = XT_f$, $T_f = \sqrt{\beta T_r^2/(X^2 + \beta)}$ where $\beta = 0.69$ for threads excluded case.

Table 3-9 — For A490M and A490 Bolts

Shear Tension Ratio X = V_f/T_f		Bolt Size											
		3/4		M20		M22		7/8		M24		1	
X	1/X	V_f	T_f	V_f	T_f	V_f	T_f	V_f	T_f	V_f	T_f	V_f	T_f
0	T_r	0	148	0	164	0	199	0	202	0	238	0	264
0.10		14.7	147	16.3	163	19.7	197	20.0	100	23.6	236	26.2	262
0.20		28.6	143	31.6	158	38.4	192	39.0	195	46.0	230	51.0	255
0.30		41.1	137	45.6	152	55.5	185	56.1	187	66.3	221	73.5	245
0.40		52.4	131	58.0	145	70.4	176	71.2	178	84.0	210	93.2	233
0.50		61.5	123	68.0	136	82.5	165	84.0	168	99.0	198	110	220
0.60		69.0	115	76.8	128	93.0	155	94.8	158	112	186	124	206
0.70		75.6	108	84.0	120	102	145	104	148	122	174	135	193
0.80		80.8	101	89.6	112	109	136	110	138	130	163	144	180
0.90		85.1	94.6	94.5	105	114	127	116	129	137	152	152	169
1.00	1.00	88.7	88.7	98.3	98.3	119	119	121	121	143	143	158	158
1.11	0.90	91.9	82.7	102	91.6	123	111	126	113	148	133	163	147
1.25	0.80	95.0	76.0	105	84.2	128	102	130	104	153	122	170	136
1.43	0.70	98.1	68.7	109	76.1	132	92.3	134	93.7	157	110	176	123
1.67	0.60	101	60.6	112	67.2	136	81.5	138	82.7	163	97.5	180	108
2.00	0.50	104	51.9	115	57.5	139	69.7	142	70.8	167	83.4	185	92.5
2.50	0.40	106	42.4	118	47.0	143	57.1	145	57.9	171	68.2	189	75.7
3.33	0.30	108	32.4	120	35.9	145	43.6	147	44.2	174	52.1	193	57.8
5.00	0.20	110	21.9	122	24.3	148	29.5	150	29.9	176	35.2	196	39.1
10.00	0.10	110	11.0	122	12.2	149	14.9	151	15.1	178	17.8	197	19.7
V_f	0	119	0	131	0	159	0	161	0	189	0	211	0

$V_f = XT_f$, $T_f = \sqrt{\beta T_r^2/(X^2 + \beta)}$ where $\beta = 0.56$ for thread excluded.

BOLTS IN SLIP-RESISTANT (FRICTION-TYPE) CONNECTIONS

General

Slip-resistant connections are generally used only when specified. Joints required to transmit shear are termed slip-resistant joints when it is assumed in the design that the *specified* load is transfered by the slip resistance (friction) of the clamped faying surfaces according to Clause 13.12 of CAN3-S16.1-M78. Clause 22.1.3 requires slip-resistant joints in connections subject to load reversal and where slippage into bearing cannot be tolerated. In addition to the slip resistance, the factored resistance of the joint under factored loads must be checked.

Tables

Tables 3—10 and 3—11 on page 3—15 are based on Clause 13.12.2 of CAN3-S16.1-M78 for bolts in slip-resistant (friction-type) connections.

Table 3—10 lists values μ for 5% probability of slip and values of unit slip resistance ($0.26 \, \mu \, F_u$) for A325M, A490M, A325 and A490 bolt grades for the six surface conditions given in Table 4 of CAN3-S16.1-M78.

Table 3—11 lists slip-resistant values ($V_s = 0.26 \, \mu \, m \, n \, A_b F_u$) for bolted joints with a single faying surface (m = 1), for two surface conditions for M16 to M36 A325M and A490 bolts and 1/2 to 1-1/2 inch A325 and A490 bolts.

Example

Given:

A single shear connection is subject to 380 kN at specified load level and 550 kN at factored load level. Select the number of M20 A325M bolts required for a slip-resistant connection. Steel is G40.21-M 300W and surface is clean mill scale.

Solution:

(a) For specified loads

From Table 3—11, V_s = 40.0 kN (M20 A325M bolt for clean mill scale)

Number of bolts required = 380/40.0 = 9.5 — Use 10

(b) Check connection at factored loads

From Table 3—4, V_r = 105 kN (M20 A325M threads excluded)

Factored shear resistance of joint = 10 × 105 = 1 050 kN > 550 kN — OK

Based upon thicknesses and end distances of the connected material, the factored bearing resistance of the joint at factored loads would also be checked.

Table 3-10

Steel Surface Treatment	Bolt Grade **									
	A325M		A490M		A325 d ≤ 1″		A325 d ≥ 1-1/8″		A490	
	F_u = 830 MPa		F_u = 1040 MPa		F_u = 825 MPa		F_u = 725 MPa		F_u = 1035 MPa	
	$0.26\mu F_u$ (MPa)	μ	$0.26\mu F_u$ (MPa)	μ	$0.26\mu F_u$ (MPa)	μ	$0.26\mu F_u$ (MPa)	μ	$0.26\mu F_u$ (MPa)	μ
Tight clean mill scale except quenched and tempered steels	127	0.59	138	0.51	127	0.59	112	0.59	137	0.51
Blast cleaned carbon and low-alloys steels.	214	0.99	235	0.87	213	0.99	187	0.99	234	0.87
Blast cleaned quenched and tempered steels	149	0.69	162	0.60	148	0.69	130	0.69	161	0.60
Hot-dip galvanized	67	0.31	73	0.27	67	0.31	59	0.31	73	0.27
Hot-dipped, Galvanized and roughened	164	0.76	178	0.66	163	0.76	144	0.76	178	0.66
Vinyl treated	134	0.62	146	0.54	133	0.62	116	0.62	145	0.54

**Values for Imperial series bolts are based on ASTM specifications A325 and A490 soft converted to SI units.

Table 3-11

Bolt Size		Nominal Area A (mm²)	Tight Clean Mill Scale Except for Q & QT Steels		Blast Cleaned Carbon and Low-alloy Steels	
Metric*	Imperial		A325M A325	A490M A490	A325M A325	A490M A490
	1/2	127	16.1	17.4	27.1	29.7
	5/8	198	25.2	27.1	42.2	46.3
M16		201	25.5	27.7	43.0	47.2
	3/4	285	36.2	39.0	60.7	66.7
M20		314	40.0	43.3	67.2	73.8
M22		380	48.3	52.4	81.3	89.3
	7/8	388	49.3	53.2	82.6	90.8
M24		452	57.4	62.4	96.7	106
	1	507	64.4	69.5	108	119
M27		573	72.8	79.1	123	135
	1 1/8	641	71.8	87.8	120	150
M30		707	90.0	97.6	151	166
	1 1/4	792	88.7	109	148	185
M36		1018	129	140	218	239
	1 1/2	1140	128	156	213	267

**These resistances are for use with specified loads in accordance with Clause 13.12 of CAN3-S16.1-M78.
* The number following the letter M is the nominal bolt diameter in millimetres.
† For double shear (m = 2) multiply tabulated values by 2.0.

Bolts in Combined Shear and Tension — Slip-Resistant Connections

Clause 13.12.3 of CAN3-S16.1-M78 requires that bolts in a slip-resistant connection subject to both shear and tension satisfy the following relationship for specified loads

$$\frac{V}{V_s} + 1.9 \frac{T}{n\,A_b\,F_u} \leqslant 1.0$$

The above relationship can be expressed as (See Commentary page 2—37)

$$\frac{V}{V_s} + \frac{T}{T_r} \leqslant 1.0$$

If the shear tension ratio V/T on the bolts is X, then solving for V and T gives $V = XT$ and $T = V_s/(X + V_s/T_r)$

Table 3—12 lists values of V and T for various shear tension ratios X, for the condition of tightly adhering clean mill scale ($\mu = 0.59$) using A325M or A325 bolts in single shear, a common condition occurring in practice. This table can be used to establish directly the number of bolts required to satisfy the interaction equation for slip resistant connections subjected to a combination of shear and tension.

Clause 13.12.3 also requires that the factored tension T_f including any prying forces must not exceed the bolt tensile resistance T_r. For a method of evaluating the prying effect see page 3—18.

Example

Given:

Find the number of M20 A325M bolts required in a slip-resistant connection to resist a specified tension force of 320 kN (factored tension force of 450 kN) and a specified shear force of 400 kN. The single faying surface consists of clean mill scale.

Solution:

Shear tension ratio = 400/320 = 1.25

From Table 3—12 for M20 bolts, V/T = 1.25,

V = 32.1 kN and T = 25.6 kN per bolt

Therefore number of bolts required = 400/32.1 = 12.5

or = 320/25.6 = 12.5

Therefore use 14 bolts

Check factored tensile resistance.

T_f = 450/10 = 45 kN/bolt applied load

T_r (from Table 3—4) = 131 kN > 45 kN — OK

Allowances for prying forces would depend upon the thickness of the connecting material, and the design of the connecting material would have to take this into account (see pages 3—18 to 3—23 inclusive).

The ultimate strength of the joint would also have to be checked for shear and bearing.

Table 3-12
$\mu = 0.59$

Shear Tension Ratio X = V/T		3/4		M20		M22		7/8		M24		1	
X	1/X	V	T	V	T	V	T	V	T	V	T	V	T
0.5		22.4	44.7	24.7	49.4	29.8	59.6	30.4	60.9	35.4	70.9	39.8	79.5
0.6		23.9	39.8	26.4	44.0	31.9	53.1	32.5	54.2	37.9	63.1	42.5	70.8
0.7		25.1	35.9	27.7	39.6	33.5	47.8	34.2	48.8	39.8	56.8	44.6	63.8
0.8		26.1	32.6	28.8	36.0	34.8	43.5	35.5	44.4	41.4	51.7	46.4	58.0
0.9		26.9	29.9	29.8	33.1	35.9	39.9	36.7	40.7	42.7	47.4	47.9	53.2
1.0	1.0	27.6	27.6	30.5	30.5	36.9	36.9	37.6	37.6	43.8	43.8	49.2	49.2
1.11	0.9	28.3	25.5	31.3	28.2	37.8	34.0	38.4	34.7	44.9	40.4	50.3	45.4
1.25	0.8	29.0	23.2	32.1	25.6	38.7	31.0	39.5	31.6	46.0	36.8	51.6	41.3
1.43	0.7	29.8	20.8	32.9	23.0	39.7	27.8	40.5	28.3	47.2	33.0	52.9	37.0
1.67	0.6	30.5	18.3	33.7	20.2	40.7	24.4	41.6	24.9	48.4	29.0	54.3	32.5
2.00	0.5	31.3	15.7	34.7	17.3	41.8	20.9	42.7	21.3	49.7	24.9	55.8	27.9
2.50	0.4	32.2	12.9	35.6	14.2	43.0	17.2	43.9	17.5	51.1	20.4	57.3	22.9
3.33	0.3	33.1	10.0	36.6	11.0	44.2	13.3	45.1	13.5	52.5	15.8	58.9	17.7
5.00	0.2	34.1	6.8	37.7	7.5	45.5	9.1	46.4	9.3	54.0	10.8	60.5	12.1
10.00	0.1	35.1	3.5	38.8	3.9	46.9	4.7	47.8	4.8	55.7	5.6	62.5	6.2
V_s	0	36.2	0	40.0	0	48.3	0	49.3	0	57.4	0	64.4	0

$$V = XT, \quad T = \frac{V_s}{X + V_s/T_r}$$

BOLTS IN TENSION AND PRYING ACTION

General

Connections with fasteners loaded in tension occur in many common situations such as hanger and bracing connections with Tee-type gussets, and end plate moment connections. Clause 22.1.5 of CAN3-S16.1-M78 requires that when bolts are loaded in direct tension, the effects of prying action must be taken into account in proportioning the bolts and connected parts. This clause also requires the connection be proportioned to avoid prying forces when subjected to repeated loading.

The actual stress distribution in the flange of a Tee-type connection is extremely complex and depends on the bolt size and arrangement and on the dimensions of the connecting flange. Various design methods have been proposed in the technical literature for proportioning these connections.

The procedures given in this section are based on the recommendations contained on page 278 of the "Guide to Design Criteria for Bolted and Riveted Joints" by Fisher and Struik.[1] These include Tables 3—13 and 3—14 for preliminary trial design, and sets of formulae for evaluating the bolt forces and required flange thickness.

The trial design tables on pages 3—22 and 3—23 are based on M20 A325M bolts, but they can be used assuming other bolt sizes provided the proportions of the connection are within the practical limits suggested.

For repeated loads special attention must be paid to bolt installation to ensure that the bolts are properly tightened to provide the required clamping force. (Although the Research Council on Structural Connections is currently (1980) considering specific limitations on the allowable tension for different ranges of stress cycles provided the prying forces are less than 60% of the external load, clause 22.1.5 of CAN3-S16.1-M78 requires that prying effects be avoided if bolts in tension are subject to repeated loading. See also Part 2 Commentary page 2—68).

The tables for trial design demonstrate the effects on the prying forces of flange thickness and of gauge distance and edge distance. In general prying effects can be minimized by dimensioning for minimum practical gauge distance and for maximum permissible edge distance. For repeated loading the flange must be made thick enough and stiff enough so that deformation of the flange is virtually eliminated.

The expressions for prying effects are based on tests carried out on Tees. For angles, assuming the distribution of moment shown, the moment equilibrium equation can be derived from statics as

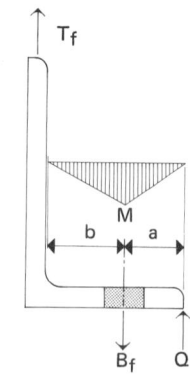

$$Tb = Qa$$

Therefore $Q/T = b/a$

References

1. Fisher, J. W. and Struik, J.H.A., "Guide to Design Criteria for Bolted and Riveted Joints" — John Wiley & Sons, New York, N.Y. 1974.

2. Douty, R. T. and McGuire, W., "High Strength Bolted Moment Connections", ASCE J. of St. Div., April 1965.

3. Nair, R. S., Birkemoe, P. C. and Munse, W. H., "High Strength Bolts Subject to Tension and Prying", Structural Research Series 353, Dept. Civil Eng. U. of Ill., Urbana, Sept. 1969.

Trial Design Tables

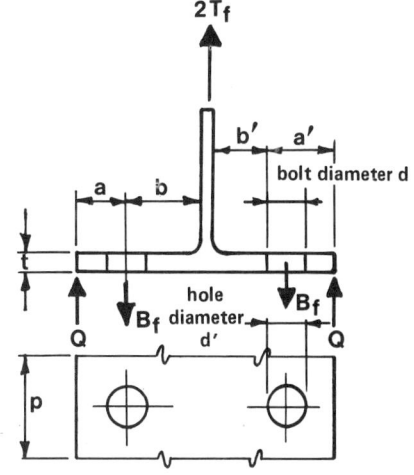

Table 3—13 lists values of R' for different values of b, a, and α according to the relationship:

$$R' = 1 + \frac{\delta\alpha}{1 + \delta\alpha} \times \frac{b'}{a'} \text{ for } 1.0 \geqslant \alpha \geqslant 0$$

where for the table:

$\delta = 0.75, d' = 22$ mm, $d = 20$ mm for M20 bolt,
$\delta = 1 - d'/p$.

Table 3—14 lists values of α for different values of b, a, R' and t according to the relationship:

$$\alpha = \left[\frac{4 \, B \, b'}{p \, F_y \, t^2} - 1 \right] \times \frac{a'}{\delta \, (a' + b')} \text{ for } 1.0 \geqslant \alpha \geqslant 0$$

where for the table:

$F_y = 300$ MPa (300W Material)

$\delta = 0.75$, $d' = 22$ mm, $p = 88$ mm $B = 0.75 \, A_b F_u$

$F_u = 830$ MPa, A_b is for M20 A325M bolts

When α is greater than 1.0, the material governs the connection capacity and the bolts may have excess capacity to resist the applied loads in spite of prying action. The limiting strength condition is reached when the flange bends in double curvature with plastic hinges forming at the bolt line and at the web-flange interface, and t can be calculated using the formula.

$$t = \left(\frac{T_f}{p} \times \frac{2b}{\phi F_y} \right)^{1/2}$$

When α is less than 0.0, the flange is sufficiently thick and stiff so that prying action is substantially reduced and the connection capacity is governed by the tension capacity of the bolts. Minimum t can be calculated using the formula

$$t = \left(\frac{T_f}{p} \times \frac{4b}{\phi F_y} \right)^{1/2}$$

When $1.0 > \alpha > 0$, both the flange material thickness and the tension capacity of the bolts govern simultaneously, with the prying forces varying from a maximum at $\alpha = 1.0$ to a minimum at $\alpha = 0$. The flange thickness t and governing dimensions can be selected using the Tables 3—13 and 3—14.

Tables 3—13 and 3—14 have been developed on the basis of $\delta = 0.75$ assuming the use of M20 bolts, however, they can be used for trial design using larger diameter bolts and other values of δ and will give reasonable results. The bolt pitch, p, should be selected so that p lies between 4 and 5 times the bolt diameter (i.e. $4.0 \, d \leqslant p \leqslant 5.0 \, d$) and p should be kept as small as practicable to reduce any two way action. Also, dimension, a, for design purposes must not exceed 1.25b.

Use of Trial Design Tables

1. Knowing total applied factored load, select preferred number and size of tension bolts and calculate applied load per bolt, and limiting ratio $R' = T_r/T_f$, where T_r is the factored tensile bolt resistance given in Table 3—4 on page 3—8. R' should be > 1.0

2. From Table 3—13, with known maximum R' select b, a and α.

3. From Table 3—14 select t for appropriate b, a and α.

4. Choose a suitable rolled section from table of section properties or plate thickness from table of preferred plate thickness (page 6—105), and check bolt load, B_f, and flange thickness, t, using method outlined below for final design.

Nomenclature

T_f = Applied factored tension load per bolt (kN)

B_f = Load per bolt including prying action at factored load (kN)

Q = Prying force per bolt at factored load (kN). $Q = B_f - T_f$

T_r = Tensile resistance of bolts (kN) = 0.67 x (0.75 $A_b F_u$) = 0.50 $A_b F_u$

F_y = Yield strength of flange material (MPa)

p = Length of flange tributary to each bolt (mm)

t = Required thickness of flange (mm)

b = Distance from bolt line (gauge line) to face of Tee stem (mm)

a = Distance from bolt line to edge of Tee flange, not more than 1.25b (mm)

d = Bolt diameter (mm)

d' = Nominal hole diameter (mm)

b' = $b - d/2$

a' = $a + d/2$

δ = Ratio of net area (at bolt line) to gross area at face of Tee stem.

α = Ratio defined below.

Formulae

$$\delta = 1 - d'/p \qquad (1)$$

$$\alpha = \left[\frac{4\, T_f\, b' \times 10^3}{p\, F_y\, t^2} - 1\right] \times \frac{a'}{\delta\,(a' + b')} \quad , \quad 0 \leqslant \alpha \leqslant 1.0 \qquad (2)*$$

$$B_f = T_f\left[1 + \frac{\delta \alpha}{(1 + \delta \alpha)} \times \frac{b'}{a'}\right] \leqslant T_r \qquad (3)$$

$$\text{Req'd } t = \left\{\frac{4\, B_f\, a'\, b' \times 10^3}{p\, \phi\, F_y\, [a' + \delta \alpha\,(a' + b')]}\right\}^{½} \qquad (4)$$

* If $\alpha > 1.0$, Use $\alpha = 1.0$ in equations (3) and (4)

* If $\alpha < 0.0$, Use $\alpha = 0.0$ in equations (3) and (4)

Example

Given:

Design a tension Tee connection with 4 bolts in tension for a factored load of 500 kN assuming the bolts on a 100 mm gauge with the Tee connected to rigid supports. Use G40.21-M 300W steel.

Solution:

a) *Trial Section*

Applied load per bolt = $500/4 = 125$ kN $= T_f$

Try 4-M22 bolts. T_r (Table 3—4) = 158 kN, therefore max $R' = 158/125 = 1.26$

Assuming 10 mm web, $b = (100 - 10)/2 = 45$ mm

From Table 3—13, for $b = 45$ mm, $R' = 1.26$ a number of selections are possible:

for $a = 50$ mm, $\alpha = > 1.0$, Use $\alpha = 1.0$ or

   $a = 45$ mm, $\alpha = 0.9$ or

   $a = 40$ mm, $\alpha = 0.8$

From Table 3—14, for $b = 45$ and appropriate a and α approximate values of t are:

for $a = 50$ and $\alpha = 1.0$, $t = 21$ mm or

   $a = 45$ and $\alpha = 0.9$, $t = 22$ mm or

   $a = 40$ and $\alpha = 0.8$, $t = 23$ mm

Try a T cut from W530 $\times$ 138: $t = 23.6$ mm, $p = 100$ mm (= approx. 4.5d)

$b = 1/2 (100 - 14.7) = 42.7$ mm; $1.25b = 53.3$ mm

$a = 1/2 (214 - 100) = 57.0$ mm $> 1.25b$, Use 53.3 mm

$a' = 53.3 + 11 = 64.3$ mm; $b' = 42.7 - 11 = 31.7$ mm

$a' + b' = 96$ mm

b) *Final Design Check*

$$\delta \quad = \quad 1 - 24/100 = 0.76 \tag{1}$$

$$\alpha \quad = \quad \left[\frac{4 \times 125 \times 31.7 \times 10^3}{100 \times 300 \times 23.6^2} - 1 \right] \times \frac{64.3}{(0.76 \times 96)} = -0.05, \text{ Use } \alpha = 0.0 \tag{2}$$

$$B_f \quad = \quad 125 \times \left[1 + \frac{0.0}{1.0} \times \frac{31.7}{64.3} \right] = 125 \text{ kN} < T_r - \text{OK} \tag{3}$$

$$\text{Req'd t} \quad = \quad \left\{ \frac{4 \times 125 \times 64.3 \times 31.7 \times 10^3}{100 \times 0.9 \times 300 \left[64.3 + (0.0 \times 96) \right]} \right\}^{1/2} = 24.2 \text{ mm} \simeq 23.6 \text{ mm} \tag{4}$$

For T cut W530 $\times$ 138, flange thickness is within 3% (OK). Alternatively a built-up Tee having a flange thickness cut from 25 mm plate (first preference plate thickness) could be used.

VALUES OF R'

$$R' = \left[1 + \frac{\delta\alpha}{(1+\delta\alpha)} \times \frac{b'}{a'}\right]^{**}$$

Table 3-13

b (mm)	α	a*, (mm) 25	30	35	40	45	50	55	60	65	70
30	1.0	1.24	1.21	1.19	1.17						
	0.9	1.23	1.20	1.18	1.16						
	0.8	1.21	1.19	1.17	1.15						
	0.7	1.20	1.17	1.15	1.14						
	0.6	1.18	1.16	1.14	1.12						
	0.5	1.16	1.14	1.12	1.11						
	0.4	1.13	1.12	1.10	1.09						
	0.3	1.10	1.09	1.08	1.07						
	0.2	1.07	1.07	1.06	1.05						
	0.1	1.04	1.03	1.03	1.03						
	0.0	1.00	1.00	1.00	1.00						
35	1.0	1.31	1.27	1.24	1.21	1.19					
	0.9	1.29	1.25	1.22	1.20	1.18					
	0.8	1.27	1.23	1.21	1.19	1.17					
	0.7	1.25	1.22	1.19	1.17	1.16					
	0.6	1.22	1.19	1.17	1.16	1.14					
	0.5	1.19	1.17	1.15	1.14	1.12					
	0.4	1.16	1.14	1.13	1.12	1.10					
	0.3	1.13	1.11	1.10	1.09	1.08					
	0.2	1.09	1.08	1.07	1.07	1.06					
	0.1	1.05	1.04	1.04	1.03	1.03					
	0.0	1.00	1.00	1.00	1.00	1.00					
40	1.0	1.37	1.32	1.29	1.26	1.23	1.21				
	0.9	1.35	1.30	1.27	1.24	1.22	1.20				
	0.8	1.32	1.28	1.25	1.23	1.20	1.19				
	0.7	1.30	1.26	1.23	1.21	1.19	1.17				
	0.6	1.27	1.23	1.21	1.19	1.17	1.16				
	0.5	1.23	1.20	1.18	1.16	1.15	1.14				
	0.4	1.20	1.17	1.15	1.14	1.13	1.12				
	0.3	1.16	1.14	1.12	1.11	1.10	1.09				
	0.2	1.11	1.10	1.09	1.08	1.07	1.07				
	0.1	1.06	1.05	1.05	1.04	1.04	1.03				
	0.0	1.00	1.00	1.00	1.00	1.00	1.00				
45	1.0	1.43	1.38	1.33	1.30	1.27	1.25	1.23			
	0.9	1.40	1.35	1.31	1.28	1.26	1.24	1.22			
	0.8	1.38	1.33	1.29	1.26	1.24	1.22	1.20			
	0.7	1.34	1.30	1.27	1.24	1.22	1.20	1.19			
	0.6	1.31	1.27	1.24	1.22	1.20	1.18	1.17			
	0.5	1.27	1.24	1.21	1.19	1.17	1.16	1.15			
	0.4	1.23	1.20	1.18	1.16	1.15	1.13	1.12			
	0.3	1.18	1.16	1.14	1.13	1.12	1.11	1.10			
	0.2	1.13	1.11	1.10	1.09	1.08	1.08	1.07			
	0.1	1.07	1.06	1.05	1.05	1.04	1.04	1.04			
	0.0	1.00	1.00	1.00	1.00	1.00	1.00	1.00			
50	1.0	1.49	1.43	1.38	1.34	1.31	1.29	1.26	1.24	1.23	
	0.9	1.46	1.40	1.36	1.32	1.29	1.27	1.25	1.23	1.21	
	0.8	1.43	1.38	1.33	1.30	1.27	1.25	1.23	1.21	1.20	
	0.7	1.39	1.34	1.31	1.28	1.25	1.23	1.21	1.20	1.18	
	0.6	1.35	1.31	1.28	1.25	1.23	1.21	1.19	1.18	1.17	
	0.5	1.31	1.27	1.24	1.22	1.20	1.18	1.17	1.16	1.15	
	0.4	1.26	1.23	1.21	1.18	1.17	1.15	1.14	1.13	1.12	
	0.3	1.21	1.18	1.16	1.15	1.13	1.12	1.11	1.10	1.10	
	0.2	1.15	1.13	1.12	1.10	1.09	1.09	1.08	1.07	1.07	
	0.1	1.08	1.07	1.06	1.06	1.05	1.05	1.04	1.04	1.04	
	0.0	1.00	1.00	1.00	1.00	1.00	1.00	1.00	1.00	1.00	
55	1.0	1.55	1.48	1.43	1.39	1.35	1.32	1.30	1.28	1.26	1.24
	0.9	1.52	1.45	1.40	1.36	1.33	1.30	1.28	1.26	1.24	1.23
	0.8	1.48	1.42	1.38	1.34	1.31	1.28	1.26	1.24	1.23	1.21
	0.7	1.44	1.39	1.34	1.31	1.28	1.26	1.24	1.22	1.21	1.19
	0.6	1.40	1.35	1.31	1.28	1.25	1.23	1.21	1.20	1.19	1.17
	0.5	1.35	1.31	1.27	1.25	1.22	1.20	1.19	1.18	1.16	1.15
	0.4	1.30	1.26	1.23	1.21	1.19	1.17	1.16	1.15	1.14	1.13
	0.3	1.24	1.21	1.18	1.17	1.15	1.14	1.13	1.12	1.11	1.10
	0.2	1.17	1.15	1.13	1.12	1.11	1.10	1.09	1.08	1.08	1.07
	0.1	1.09	1.08	1.07	1.06	1.06	1.05	1.05	1.04	1.04	1.04
	0.0	1.00	1.00	1.00	1.00	1.00	1.00	1.00	1.00	1.00	1.00

* For design a ≤ 1.25b
** δ = 0.75 and d' = 22 mm.

Table 3-14

$$\alpha = \left[\frac{4Bb'}{p\,F_y\,t^2} - 1 \right] \frac{a'}{\delta(a' + b')} \quad **$$

VALUES OF α

b = 30 mm

t (mm)	a = 25	30	35	40
16	1.00	1.00	1.00	
17	0.89	0.93	0.97	1.00
18	0.70	0.74	0.77	0.79
19	0.54	0.57	0.59	0.61
20	0.41	0.43	0.44	0.46
21	0.29	0.31	0.32	0.33
22	0.19	0.20	0.21	0.21
23	0.10	0.11	0.11	0.11
24	0.02	0.03	0.03	0.03
25	0.00	0.00	0.00	0.00

b = 35 mm

t (mm)	a = 25	30	35	40	45
18	1.00	1.00	1.00	1.00	1.00
19	0.82	0.86	0.90	0.94	0.96
20	0.66	0.70	0.73	0.76	0.78
21	0.53	0.56	0.58	0.60	0.62
22	0.41	0.44	0.45	0.47	0.49
23	0.31	0.33	0.34	0.36	0.37
24	0.22	0.23	0.25	0.25	0.26
25	0.14	0.15	0.16	0.16	0.17
26	0.07	0.08	0.08	0.09	0.09
27	0.01	0.01	0.01	0.01	0.01
28	0.00	0.00	0.00	0.00	0.00

b = 40 mm

t (mm)	a = 25	30	35	40	45	50
19	1.00	1.00	1.00			
20	0.88	0.93	0.98	1.00	1.00	1.00
21	0.73	0.77	0.81	0.85	0.88	0.90
22	0.60	0.64	0.67	0.70	0.72	0.74
23	0.49	0.52	0.54	0.57	0.59	0.60
24	0.39	0.41	0.43	0.45	0.47	0.48
25	0.30	0.32	0.34	0.35	0.36	0.38
26	0.23	0.24	0.25	0.26	0.27	0.28
27	0.16	0.17	0.18	0.18	0.19	0.20
28	0.10	0.10	0.11	0.11	0.12	0.12
29	0.04	0.04	0.05	0.05	0.05	0.05
30	0.00	0.00	0.00	0.00	0.00	0.00

b = 45 mm

t (mm)	a = 25	30	35	40	45	50	55
20	1.00	1.00					
21	0.90	0.96	1.00	1.00	1.00	1.00	1.00
22	0.76	0.81	0.86	0.90	0.93	0.96	0.99
23	0.64	0.68	0.72	0.75	0.78	0.81	0.83
24	0.53	0.57	0.60	0.63	0.65	0.67	0.69
25	0.44	0.47	0.49	0.52	0.54	0.56	0.57
26	0.36	0.38	0.40	0.42	0.44	0.45	0.46
27	0.28	0.30	0.32	0.33	0.34	0.36	0.37
28	0.22	0.23	0.24	0.25	0.26	0.27	0.28
29	0.16	0.17	0.17	0.18	0.19	0.20	0.20
30	0.10	0.11	0.11	0.12	0.12	0.13	0.13
31	0.05	0.06	0.06	0.06	0.06	0.07	0.07
32	0.01	0.01	0.01	0.01	0.01	0.01	0.01
33	0.00	0.00	0.00	0.00	0.00	0.00	0.00

b = 50 mm

t (mm)	a = 25	30	35	40	45	50	55	60	65
21	1.00	1.00							
22	0.90	0.97	1.00	1.00	1.00	1.00			
23	0.77	0.83	0.88	0.92	0.96	0.99	1.00	1.00	1.00
24	0.66	0.71	0.75	0.78	0.82	0.85	0.87	0.90	0.92
25	0.56	0.60	0.63	0.66	0.69	0.72	0.74	0.76	0.78
26	0.47	0.50	0.53	0.56	0.58	0.60	0.62	0.64	0.66
27	0.39	0.42	0.44	0.46	0.48	0.50	0.52	0.53	0.54
28	0.32	0.34	0.36	0.38	0.40	0.41	0.42	0.43	0.45
29	0.25	0.27	0.29	0.30	0.32	0.33	0.34	0.35	0.36
30	0.20	0.21	0.22	0.23	0.24	0.25	0.26	0.27	0.28
31	0.15	0.16	0.16	0.17	0.18	0.19	0.19	0.20	0.20
32	0.10	0.10	0.11	0.12	0.12	0.13	0.13	0.13	0.14
33	0.05	0.06	0.06	0.07	0.07	0.07	0.07	0.07	0.08
34	0.02	0.02	0.02	0.02	0.02	0.02	0.02	0.02	0.02
35	0.00	0.00	0.00	0.00	0.00	0.00	0.00	0.00	0.00

b = 55 mm

t (mm)	a = 25	30	35	40	45	50	55	60	65	70
22	1.00	1.00								
23	0.89	0.95	1.00	1.00	1.00					
24	0.77	0.83	0.88	0.92	0.96	1.00	1.00	1.00	1.00	1.00
25	0.66	0.71	0.76	0.80	0.83	0.86	0.89	0.92	0.94	0.97
26	0.57	0.61	0.65	0.68	0.71	0.74	0.77	0.79	0.81	0.83
27	0.48	0.52	0.55	0.58	0.61	0.63	0.65	0.67	0.69	0.71
28	0.41	0.44	0.47	0.49	0.51	0.53	0.55	0.57	0.58	0.60
29	0.34	0.37	0.39	0.41	0.43	0.45	0.46	0.48	0.49	0.50
30	0.28	0.30	0.32	0.34	0.35	0.37	0.38	0.39	0.40	0.41
31	0.23	0.24	0.26	0.27	0.28	0.30	0.31	0.31	0.32	0.33
32	0.18	0.19	0.20	0.21	0.22	0.23	0.24	0.25	0.25	0.26
33	0.13	0.14	0.15	0.16	0.16	0.17	0.18	0.18	0.19	0.19
34	0.09	0.10	0.10	0.11	0.11	0.12	0.12	0.12	0.13	0.13
35	0.05	0.06	0.06	0.06	0.06	0.07	0.07	0.07	0.07	0.08
36	0.02	0.02	0.02	0.02	0.02	0.02	0.02	0.02	0.02	0.02
37	0.00	0.00	0.00	0.00	0.00	0.00	0.00	0.00	0.00	0.00

**Where F_y = 300 MPa, δ = 0.75, d' = 22 mm, p = 88 mm, B = 0.75 $A_b F_u$ (F_u = 830 MPa)

ECCENTRIC LOADS ON BOLT GROUPS

General

A bolted connection is eccentrically loaded when the line of action of the applied load passes outside the centre of rotation of the bolt group. When the bolts are subjected to shear forces only, the effect of this eccentricity is to cause rotation about a single point called the instantaneous centre of rotation. The location of the instantaneous centre is obtained when the connection satisfies the three equilibrium equations for statics, $\Sigma F_x = 0$, $\Sigma F_y = 0$ and $\Sigma M = 0$ about the instantaneous centre.

Calculation of the instantaneous centre described in the references is a trial and error process, and the tables included in this section permit rapid evaluation of different common bolt groups subjected to various eccentricities. All tables are based on symmetrical arrangements of bolts.

Bearing-Type Connections

For bearing type connections, a method of analysis is that described in Reference 2. At the time the ultimate load is reached, it is assumed that the bolt furthest from the instantaneous centre will just reach its failure load. The resistance of each bolt is assumed to act on a line perpendicular to the radius joining the bolt to the instantaneous centre, and is assumed to vary linearly with the length of the radius. The resistance of each bolt is calculated according to the load deformation relationship:

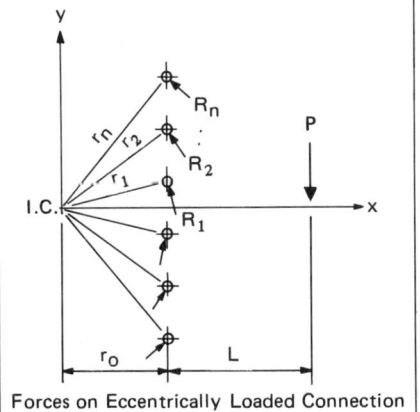

Forces on Eccentrically Loaded Connection

$$R = R_u (1 - e^{-\mu\Delta})^\lambda \ldots \ldots \text{Reference 1}$$

and the ultimate load is reached when $\Delta = \Delta_{max}$ for the bolt furthest from the instantaneous centre

where R = bolt load at any given deformation

R_u = ultimate bolt load

Δ = shearing, bending and bearing deformation of the bolt, and local deformation of the connecting material.

μ,λ = regression coefficients

e = base of natural logarithms

Slip-Resistant (Friction-Type) Connections

For slip-resistant connections, the method of anlaysis is essentially the same as that for bearing-type, except that the limiting slip resistance of the joint is reached when the maximum slip resistance of each individual bolt is reached as expressed by the relationship, $R = V_s = 0.26 \ \mu mn \ A_b F_u$ and the slip resistance of each bolt is assumed to the equal.

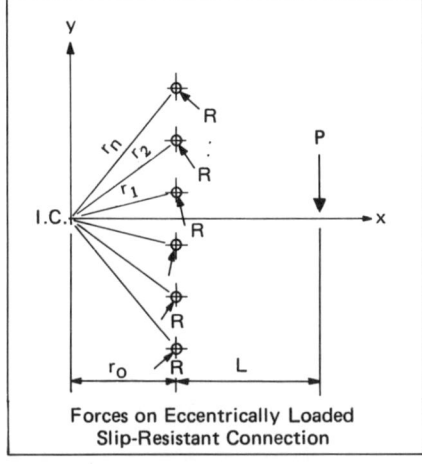

Forces on Eccentrically Loaded
Slip-Resistant Connection

Tables

Tables 3—15 to 3—21 have been developed using the method described for bearing-type connections. Values tabulated are non-dimensional coefficients C and may be used for bolts of any diameter. In determining the coefficients C the following values were used. R_u = 74 kips (329 kN), μ = 10.0, λ = 0.55, Δ_{max} = 0.34 inches (8.64 mm). These values were obtained experimentally for 3/4 inch diameter A325 bolts and are reported in Reference 2.

The ultimate load P for each bolt group and eccentricity was computed and then divided by the maximum value of R (when Δ = Δ_{max}) to obtain the values of C.

The tables may thus be used to obtain the factored resistance of a connection expressed as a vertical load P, by multiplying the coefficient C for any particular bolt group and eccentricity by the factored shear resistance of a single bolt. i.e. $P_f = C \times V_r$.

Coefficients were developed in a similar way for slip-resistant connections, except that the individual bolt resistances for all bolts in the group were assumed to be equal. The coefficients calculated in this way were from 5% to 10% higher than those for bearing-type connections. Thus only one set of tables, based on the bearing-type connections is provided for use with both bearing-type and slip-resistant connections.

Use of Tables

Bearing-Type Connections

1) To obtain the coefficient C required for a given geometry of bolts and eccentricity of load, divide the factored load, P_f, by the factored shear resistance, V_r, of a single bolt for the appropriate shear condition. i.e. $C = P_f/V_r$.

2) To determine the capacity of a given connection, multiply the coefficient C for the bolt group and eccentricity, by the appropriate bolt shear resistance value, V_r, of a single bolt. i.e. $P_f = C \times V_r$.

V_r is the factored shear resistance of the bolt from Table 3—4. Used in this way these tables provide a margin of safety which is consistant with bolts in joints less than 1300 mm long and subjected to shear produced by concentric loads only.

Slip-Resistant (Friction-Type) Connections

Although developed using the method for bearing-type connections, these tables can also be used for slip-resistant connections using the *specified* load, P, and the appropriate slip resistance value, V_s, for the bolt size and condition of the faying surface.

1) Required $C = P/V_s$

2) Capacity $P = C \times V_s$

V_s is the slip resistance determined from Tables 3—10 and 3—11.

References

1. Fisher, J. W., and Struik, J.H.A., "Guide to Design Criteria for Bolted and Riveted Joints", John Wiley and Sons, 1974.

2. Crawford, S. F., and Kulak, G. L., "Eccentrically Loaded Bolted Connections", Journal of the Structural Division, ASCE, Vol. 97, No. ST3, March 1971.

3. Shermer, C. L., "Plastic Behaviour of Eccentrically Loaded Connections", Engineering Journal, AISC, Vol. 8, No. 2, April, 1971.

4. Kulak, G. L., "Eccentrically Loaded Slip Resistant Connections", Engineering Journal, AISC, Vol. 12, No. 2, Second Quarter, 1975.

5. Adams, P. F., Krentz, H. A., Kulak, G. L., "Limit States Design in Structural Steel-SI Units", CISC, 1979.

Example

1. Given:

A double column bracket must be designed to support a factored load of 700 kN at an eccentricity of 400 mm. Find the number of M20, A325M bolts per flange required for a gauge dimension of 120 mm and a pitch of 80 mm assuming a bearing-type connection.

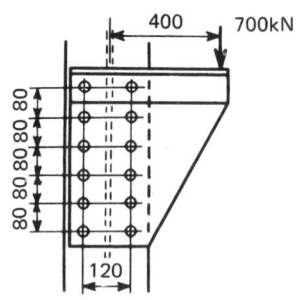

Solution:

P_f = 700/2 = 350 kN, L = 400 mm

V_r = 105 kN (Table 3—4 page 3—8, single shear, threads excluded)

Required C = 350/105 = 3.33

From Tables 3—16 and 3—17 for 2 rows of bolts at 80 mm pitch

6 bolts 80 mm gauge, C = 3.49

320 mm gauge, C = 4.77

Interpolating for 120 mm gauge C = 3.49 + (4.77 − 3.49) × 40/240 = 3.70

Use 6 rows of bolts (total 12 bolts)

Capacity = 3.70 × 105 = 389 kN per side

The bearing capacity of the connected material would also be checked for the various material thicknesses and end distances involved.

2. Given:

Find the number of M22 bolts required for a similar bracket assuming a slip-resistant connection with clean mill scale and a *specified* load of 500 kN.

Solution:

P = 500/2 = 250 kN, L = 400 mm

V_s = 48.3 kN (Table 3—11, page 3—15)

Required C = 250/48.3 = 5.18

From Tables 3—16 and 3—17 for 2 rows of bolts at 80 mm pitch

8 rows 80 mm gauge, C = 5.89

320 mm gauge, C = 7.16

Interpolating for 120 mm gauge, C = 5.89 + (7.16 − 5.89) × 40/240 = 6.10

Use 8 rows of bolts (total 16 bolts)

Capacity = 6.10 × 48.3 = 295 kN per side

The ultimate strength of the joint would also be checked in bearing and shear for factored loads.

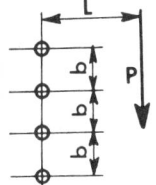

Moment Arm, L, Millimetres												Number of Bolts	Pitch b mm
75	100	125	150	175	200	225	250	300	400	500	600		
0.94	0.74	0.60	0.51	0.44	0.39	0.35	0.31	0.26	0.20	0.16	0.13	2	
1.86	1.49	1.24	1.05	0.90	0.79	0.71	0.64	0.53	0.40	0.32	0.27	3	
2.95	2.50	2.15	1.85	1.62	1.44	1.30	1.18	0.99	0.75	0.60	0.51	4	
4.07	3.56	3.12	2.76	2.44	2.19	1.97	1.79	1.51	1.15	0.92	0.77	5	
5.17	4.67	4.21	3.77	3.37	3.06	2.77	2.53	2.16	1.65	1.34	1.12	6	80
6.25	5.79	5.30	4.82	4.38	4.01	3.66	3.37	2.89	2.23	1.80	1.51	7	
7.34	6.89	6.39	5.91	5.43	5.01	4.62	4.28	3.69	2.88	2.34	1.97	8	
8.40	7.99	7.51	7.02	6.54	6.07	5.64	5.24	4.57	3.60	2.93	2.48	9	
9.45	9.06	8.61	8.12	7.62	7.15	6.69	6.26	5.50	4.37	3.59	3.03	10	
10.5	10.1	9.71	9.23	8.73	8.25	7.75	7.30	6.49	5.20	4.30	3.65	11	
11.5	11.2	10.8	10.3	9.85	9.36	8.85	8.40	7.51	6.09	5.06	4.30	12	
1.01	0.82	0.67	0.57	0.49	0.43	0.39	0.35	0.29	0.22	0.18	0.15	2	
2.00	1.65	1.37	1.17	1.01	0.89	0.79	0.71	0.60	0.45	0.36	0.30	3	
3.11	2.68	2.33	2.04	1.80	1.60	1.44	1.31	1.11	0.84	0.68	0.57	4	
4.22	3.79	3.36	3.00	2.69	2.41	2.19	2.00	1.69	1.29	1.04	0.87	5	
5.31	4.89	4.45	4.06	3.66	3.34	3.05	2.81	2.40	1.85	1.50	1.26	6	90
6.40	5.99	5.58	5.13	4.73	4.35	4.00	3.70	3.20	2.48	2.02	1.69	7	
7.46	7.10	6.68	6.24	5.82	5.40	5.02	4.66	4.06	3.20	2.61	2.20	8	
8.51	8.18	7.77	7.34	6.90	6.48	6.07	5.69	5.00	3.98	3.27	2.76	9	
9.56	9.24	8.87	8.46	8.02	7.57	7.15	6.74	6.00	4.83	3.99	3.39	10	
10.6	10.3	9.95	9.54	9.12	8.69	8.25	7.81	7.02	5.73	4.76	4.06	11	
11.6	11.3	11.0	10.6	10.2	9.80	9.34	8.93	8.07	6.66	5.59	4.78	12	
1.09	0.89	0.74	0.63	0.55	0.48	0.43	0.39	0.33	0.25	0.20	0.16	2	
2.14	1.79	1.50	1.28	1.12	0.98	0.88	0.79	0.66	0.50	0.40	0.33	3	
3.25	2.85	2.50	2.21	1.95	1.76	1.59	1.45	1.22	0.94	0.75	0.63	4	
4.34	3.97	3.57	3.21	2.90	2.63	2.39	2.19	1.87	1.43	1.15	0.96	5	
5.44	5.07	4.69	4.29	3.92	3.60	3.32	3.05	2.63	2.04	1.66	1.39	6	100
6.51	6.16	5.78	5.40	5.01	4.64	4.31	4.01	3.49	2.73	2.23	1.88	7	
7.56	7.25	6.89	6.51	6.11	5.72	5.36	5.01	4.41	3.50	2.88	2.43	8	
8.60	8.32	7.98	7.61	7.22	6.81	6.44	6.07	5.40	4.35	3.59	3.05	9	
9.64	9.37	9.06	8.71	8.31	7.93	7.52	7.15	6.43	5.25	4.37	3.73	10	
10.7	10.4	10.1	9.79	9.42	9.03	8.64	8.24	7.50	6.20	5.21	4.46	11	
11.7	11.5	11.2	10.9	10.5	10.1	9.74	9.35	8.58	7.19	6.09	5.24	12	
1.25	1.02	0.85	0.74	0.65	0.57	0.51	0.46	0.39	0.29	0.24	0.20	2	
2.32	2.00	1.72	1.50	1.31	1.16	1.05	0.95	0.79	0.60	0.48	0.40	3	
3.44	3.11	2.80	2.51	2.25	2.04	1.85	1.69	1.45	1.11	0.90	0.75	4	
4.53	4.22	3.91	3.57	3.27	3.00	2.76	2.54	2.19	1.69	1.37	1.15	5	
5.60	5.32	5.02	4.68	4.37	4.05	3.77	3.50	3.05	2.41	1.96	1.66	6	120
6.65	6.40	6.11	5.78	5.45	5.13	4.82	4.53	4.01	3.20	2.63	2.23	7	
7.69	7.46	7.19	6.89	6.57	6.25	5.91	5.60	5.02	4.07	3.38	2.88	8	
8.72	8.51	8.26	7.98	7.68	7.36	7.01	6.69	6.06	5.00	4.20	3.59	9	
9.75	9.56	9.33	9.06	8.77	8.45	8.12	7.80	7.16	6.00	5.09	4.37	10	
10.8	10.6	10.4	10.1	9.85	9.55	9.24	8.91	8.25	7.02	6.01	5.21	11	
11.8	11.6	11.4	11.2	10.9	10.6	10.3	10.0	9.35	8.09	6.99	6.09	12	
1.45	1.24	1.07	0.94	0.83	0.74	0.66	0.60	0.51	0.39	0.31	0.26	2	
2.57	2.33	2.08	1.86	1.67	1.50	1.36	1.24	1.05	0.79	0.64	0.53	3	
3.66	3.44	3.21	2.95	2.73	2.51	2.32	2.15	1.85	1.45	1.18	0.99	4	
4.72	4.53	4.31	4.07	3.83	3.58	3.35	3.14	2.77	2.19	1.80	1.52	5	
5.77	5.60	5.40	5.17	4.93	4.68	4.44	4.21	3.77	3.06	2.54	2.16	6	160
6.80	6.65	6.47	6.26	6.03	5.79	5.54	5.30	4.83	4.01	3.37	2.89	7	
7.82	7.69	7.52	7.33	7.12	6.89	6.66	6.40	5.92	5.02	4.28	3.70	8	
8.84	8.72	8.57	8.40	8.20	7.98	7.75	7.51	7.02	6.07	5.25	4.58	9	
9.86	9.75	9.61	9.45	9.26	9.06	8.84	8.61	8.12	7.15	6.27	5.51	10	
10.9	10.8	10.6	10.5	10.3	10.1	9.92	9.70	9.23	8.25	7.31	6.50	11	
11.9	11.8	11.7	11.5	11.4	11.2	11.0	10.8	10.3	9.36	8.40	7.51	12	

* See p. 3—24 for more details regarding these tables.

ECCENTRIC LOADS ON BOLT GROUPS

Coefficients C*

Table 3-16

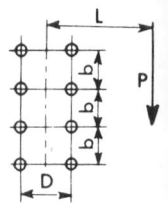

Pitch b mm	Number of Bolts in Each Row	D = 80 mm											
		Moment Arm, L, Millimetres											
		75	100	125	150	175	200	225	250	300	400	500	600
	1	0.69	0.56	0.47	0.41	0.36	0.32	0.29	0.28	0.23	0.18	0.15	0.12
80	2	2.15	1.76	1.49	1.28	1.12	1.03	0.93	0.84	0.71	0.54	0.43	0.36
	3	3.86	3.20	2.76	2.40	2.11	1.89	1.71	1.56	1.32	1.03	0.83	0.69
	4	5.89	5.09	4.46	3.90	3.51	3.14	2.84	2.59	2.20	1.70	1.38	1.15
	5	8.06	7.18	6.36	5.62	5.06	4.55	4.12	3.80	3.24	2.49	2.02	1.71
	6	10.2	9.34	8.40	7.57	6.87	6.22	5.72	5.25	4.49	3.49	2.83	2.38
	7	12.4	11.5	10.5	9.68	8.85	8.06	7.44	6.85	5.92	4.62	3.75	3.16
	8	14.6	13.7	12.8	11.8	10.9	10.1	9.33	8.63	7.50	5.89	4.81	4.07
	9	16.7	15.9	14.9	14.0	13.0	12.1	11.3	10.5	9.22	7.29	5.99	5.06
	10	18.8	18.1	17.1	16.2	15.2	14.3	13.4	12.6	11.1	8.85	7.28	6.18
	11	20.9	20.2	19.3	18.4	17.4	16.5	15.5	14.6	13.0	10.5	8.70	7.40
	12	23.0	22.3	21.5	20.6	19.6	18.6	17.7	16.7	15.0	12.2	10.2	8.70
90	2	2.21	1.87	1.59	1.37	1.20	1.07	0.99	0.90	0.76	0.58	0.46	0.39
	3	4.05	3.44	2.97	2.58	2.28	2.04	1.84	1.68	1.43	1.11	0.90	0.75
	4	6.18	5.46	4.76	4.23	3.76	3.38	3.10	2.83	2.41	1.85	1.51	1.26
	5	8.36	7.58	6.79	6.09	5.46	4.97	4.52	4.14	3.56	2.74	2.23	1.87
	6	10.6	9.75	8.91	8.11	7.40	6.79	6.21	5.71	4.94	3.85	3.13	2.64
	7	12.7	12.0	11.1	10.2	9.44	8.71	8.08	7.46	6.49	5.08	4.16	3.51
	8	14.9	14.1	13.3	12.5	11.6	10.8	10.0	9.37	8.21	6.49	5.34	4.51
	9	17.0	16.3	15.5	14.7	13.8	12.9	12.2	11.4	10.1	8.05	6.63	5.62
	10	19.1	18.4	17.7	16.8	16.0	15.1	14.3	13.5	12.0	9.72	8.07	6.85
	11	21.1	20.5	19.8	19.0	18.2	17.3	16.4	15.6	14.1	11.5	9.60	8.20
	12	23.2	22.6	22.0	21.2	20.4	19.5	18.7	17.8	16.1	13.3	11.2	9.63
100	2	2.34	1.99	1.68	1.46	1.28	1.14	1.05	0.96	0.81	0.61	0.49	0.41
	3	4.29	3.67	3.14	2.77	2.44	2.19	1.98	1.81	1.54	1.18	0.96	0.81
	4	6.45	5.74	5.09	4.50	4.06	3.66	3.32	3.07	2.62	2.01	1.63	1.38
	5	8.65	7.89	7.16	6.48	5.89	5.34	4.90	4.50	3.85	2.99	2.43	2.05
	6	10.8	10.1	9.32	8.58	7.89	7.27	6.68	6.20	5.35	4.19	3.43	2.89
	7	13.0	12.3	11.5	10.7	10.0	9.30	8.66	8.03	7.03	5.56	4.55	3.85
	8	15.1	14.4	13.7	12.9	12.2	11.4	10.7	10.1	8.87	7.09	5.83	4.96
	9	17.2	16.6	15.9	15.2	14.4	13.6	12.9	12.1	10.8	8.75	7.26	6.17
	10	19.2	18.7	18.1	17.4	16.6	15.8	15.0	14.3	12.9	10.5	8.81	7.52
	11	21.3	20.8	20.2	19.5	18.8	18.0	17.2	16.4	15.0	12.4	10.5	8.98
	12	23.3	22.9	22.3	21.7	21.0	20.2	19.5	18.6	17.1	14.4	12.2	10.5
120	2	2.57	2.15	1.88	1.63	1.44	1.28	1.16	1.05	0.91	0.69	0.56	0.47
	3	4.61	4.06	3.55	3.11	2.75	2.49	2.25	2.06	1.75	1.35	1.09	0.93
	4	6.84	6.21	5.59	5.04	4.58	4.15	3.82	3.51	3.00	2.34	1.90	1.59
	5	9.02	8.39	7.75	7.16	6.57	6.05	5.56	5.16	4.47	3.47	2.84	2.39
	6	11.1	10.6	9.98	9.35	8.68	8.11	7.53	7.04	6.16	4.88	4.01	3.39
	7	13.2	12.7	12.2	11.5	10.9	10.3	9.63	9.06	8.02	6.44	5.33	4.53
	8	15.3	14.9	14.3	13.7	13.1	12.4	11.8	11.2	10.0	8.18	6.81	5.82
	9	17.4	17.0	16.5	15.9	15.3	14.7	14.0	13.4	12.1	10.0	8.44	7.23
	10	19.5	19.1	18.6	18.1	17.5	16.9	16.2	15.5	14.3	12.0	10.2	8.79
	11	21.5	21.1	20.7	20.2	19.6	19.0	18.4	17.8	16.5	14.0	12.0	10.5
	12	23.5	23.2	22.8	22.3	21.8	21.2	20.6	20.0	18.7	16.2	14.0	12.2
160	2	2.89	2.51	2.22	1.95	1.76	1.58	1.43	1.30	1.11	0.86	0.69	0.58
	3	5.11	4.63	4.19	3.77	3.38	3.07	2.79	2.55	2.19	1.69	1.38	1.16
	4	7.29	6.85	6.35	5.89	5.44	5.03	4.67	4.32	3.77	2.96	2.42	2.05
	5	9.41	9.02	8.58	8.08	7.60	7.15	6.70	6.29	5.54	4.43	3.65	3.09
	6	11.5	11.2	10.8	10.3	9.83	9.35	8.84	8.41	7.55	6.14	5.12	4.37
	7	13.6	13.3	12.9	12.5	12.0	11.5	11.1	10.6	9.63	8.03	6.78	5.82
	8	15.6	15.3	15.0	14.6	14.2	13.7	13.3	12.8	11.8	10.0	8.57	7.42
	9	17.7	17.4	17.1	16.8	16.4	15.9	15.5	15.0	14.0	12.1	10.5	9.16
	10	19.7	19.5	19.2	18.9	18.5	18.1	17.6	17.2	16.2	14.3	12.5	11.0
	11	21.7	21.5	21.3	20.9	20.6	20.2	19.8	19.4	18.4	16.5	14.6	13.0
	12	23.7	23.5	23.3	23.0	22.7	22.3	21.9	21.5	20.6	18.7	16.8	15.0

* See p. 3—24 for more details regarding these tables.

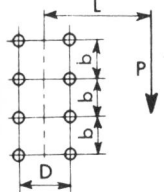

D = 320 mm												Number of Bolts in Each Row	Pitch b mm
Moment Arm, L, Millimetres													
75	100	125	150	175	200	225	250	300	400	500	600		
1.36	1.23	1.12	1.03	0.95	0.88	0.83	0.78	0.69	0.57	0.48	0.42	1	
2.89	2.62	2.41	2.22	2.05	1.91	1.78	1.68	1.49	1.22	1.04	0.89	2	
4.56	4.17	3.81	3.53	3.26	3.03	2.84	2.66	2.38	1.95	1.65	1.43	3	
6.35	5.87	5.38	5.00	4.63	4.34	4.06	3.81	3.41	2.78	2.36	2.04	4	
8.31	7.67	7.10	6.60	6.16	5.74	5.41	5.07	4.52	3.72	3.16	2.72	5	
10.3	9.64	8.95	8.34	7.81	7.34	6.87	6.46	5.80	4.77	4.02	3.49	6	80
12.4	11.6	10.9	10.2	9.58	9.02	8.46	8.00	7.18	5.89	5.00	4.34	7	
14.5	13.7	12.9	12.2	11.5	10.8	10.2	9.64	8.67	7.16	6.08	5.25	8	
16.6	15.8	15.0	14.2	13.4	12.7	12.0	11.4	10.3	8.53	7.22	6.27	9	
18.6	17.9	17.1	16.3	15.4	14.7	13.9	13.2	12.0	9.97	8.49	7.38	10	
20.7	20.0	19.2	18.4	17.5	16.7	15.9	15.2	13.8	11.5	9.85	8.54	11	
22.8	22.1	21.3	20.5	19.7	18.8	18.0	17.1	15.6	13.2	11.3	9.82	12	
2.91	2.66	2.43	2.25	2.08	1.93	1.81	1.71	1.51	1.23	1.05	0.90	2	
4.63	4.23	3.89	3.61	3.34	3.10	2.90	2.72	2.44	1.99	1.69	1.46	3	
6.52	5.99	5.54	5.15	4.78	4.48	4.19	3.94	3.53	2.88	2.44	2.11	4	
8.48	7.87	7.34	6.85	6.36	5.97	5.58	5.28	4.70	3.87	3.26	2.84	5	
10.6	9.88	9.25	8.65	8.10	7.62	7.19	6.76	6.07	5.00	4.22	3.67	6	90
12.6	12.0	11.3	10.6	9.99	9.41	8.89	8.37	7.52	6.21	5.28	4.56	7	
14.7	14.1	13.3	12.6	11.9	11.3	10.7	10.1	9.12	7.59	6.42	5.58	8	
16.8	16.2	15.4	14.7	14.0	13.3	12.6	12.0	10.8	9.03	7.69	6.69	9	
18.9	18.3	17.6	16.8	16.1	15.3	14.6	13.9	12.7	10.6	9.05	7.87	10	
21.0	20.4	19.7	19.0	18.2	17.4	16.6	15.9	14.6	12.3	10.5	9.17	11	
23.0	22.5	21.8	21.1	20.3	19.5	18.8	18.0	16.5	14.0	12.1	10.5	12	
2.95	2.69	2.46	2.28	2.11	1.96	1.83	1.73	1.54	1.25	1.06	0.92	2	
4.71	4.32	3.98	3.66	3.42	3.18	2.97	2.79	2.50	2.04	1.73	1.50	3	
6.64	6.13	5.70	5.27	4.93	4.59	4.33	4.07	3.62	2.97	2.53	2.18	4	
8.66	8.08	7.56	7.04	6.60	6.20	5.80	5.45	4.89	4.03	3.40	2.95	5	
10.7	10.1	9.55	8.93	8.39	7.90	7.46	7.03	6.31	5.21	4.43	3.84	6	100
12.8	12.2	11.6	10.9	10.4	9.78	9.26	8.74	7.87	6.54	5.53	4.81	7	
14.9	14.3	13.7	13.0	12.4	11.8	11.1	10.6	9.57	7.98	6.80	5.91	8	
17.0	16.4	15.8	15.1	14.5	13.8	13.1	12.5	11.4	9.54	8.17	7.08	9	
19.1	18.5	17.9	17.3	16.6	15.9	15.2	14.5	13.3	11.2	9.64	8.40	10	
21.2	20.6	20.1	19.4	18.7	18.0	17.3	16.6	15.3	13.0	11.2	9.78	11	
23.2	22.7	22.2	21.5	20.9	20.2	19.4	18.7	17.3	14.9	12.9	11.3	12	
3.02	2.76	2.53	2.35	2.17	2.02	1.89	1.78	1.58	1.29	1.10	0.94	2	
4.87	4.47	4.13	3.84	3.55	3.33	3.11	2.92	2.60	2.14	1.82	1.57	3	
6.86	6.40	5.95	5.55	5.20	4.88	4.58	4.30	3.86	3.18	2.68	2.33	4	
8.95	8.44	7.94	7.44	7.02	6.58	6.21	5.88	5.25	4.33	3.68	3.18	5	
11.0	10.5	10.0	9.48	8.93	8.48	8.00	7.59	6.84	5.70	4.82	4.19	6	120
13.1	12.7	12.1	11.5	11.0	10.5	9.93	9.45	8.58	7.17	6.11	5.29	7	
15.2	14.8	14.2	13.7	13.1	12.5	12.0	11.4	10.4	8.81	7.53	6.56	8	
17.3	16.9	16.4	15.8	15.3	14.7	14.1	13.5	12.4	10.5	9.07	7.91	9	
19.3	18.9	18.5	17.9	17.4	16.2	16.2	15.6	14.5	12.4	10.7	9.40	10	
21.4	21.0	20.6	20.1	19.5	18.9	18.4	17.8	16.6	14.4	12.5	11.0	11	
23.4	23.1	22.7	22.2	21.7	21.1	20.5	19.9	18.7	16.3	14.4	12.7	12	
3.16	2.90	2.66	2.47	2.29	2.15	2.01	1.89	1.69	1.38	1.17	1.01	2	
5.14	4.78	4.46	4.16	3.86	3.62	3.39	3.20	2.85	2.35	1.99	1.73	3	
7.22	6.84	6.44	6.09	5.73	5.40	5.10	4.81	4.33	3.58	3.04	2.63	4	
9.32	8.96	8.56	8.14	7.74	7.33	6.96	6.61	6.00	4.97	4.23	3.69	5	
11.4	11.1	10.7	10.3	9.82	9.40	8.97	8.57	7.82	6.61	5.65	4.93	6	160
13.5	13.2	12.8	12.4	12.0	11.5	11.1	10.7	9.81	8.37	7.22	6.30	7	
15.5	15.3	14.9	14.5	14.1	13.7	13.2	12.8	11.9	10.3	8.94	7.84	8	
17.6	17.3	17.0	16.7	16.3	15.8	15.4	15.0	14.0	12.3	10.8	9.53	9	
19.6	19.4	19.1	18.8	18.4	18.0	17.6	17.1	16.2	14.4	12.7	11.3	10	
21.7	21.4	21.2	20.8	20.5	20.1	19.7	19.3	18.4	16.5	14.7	13.2	11	
23.7	23.5	23.2	22.9	22.6	22.2	21.8	21.4	20.5	18.7	16.8	15.2	12	

* See p. 3—24 for more details regarding these tables.

ECCENTRIC LOADS ON BOLT GROUPS

Coefficients C*

Table 3-18

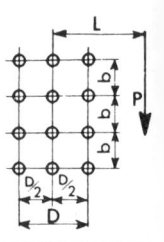

Pitch b mm	Number of Bolts in Each Row	D = 160 mm											
		Moment Arm, L, Millimetres											
		75	100	125	150	175	200	225	250	300	400	500	600
	1	1.49	1.26	1.11	0.96	0.84	0.77	0.69	0.62	0.52	0.39	0.31	0.26
80	2	3.52	3.05	2.63	2.30	2.09	1.87	1.69	1.54	1.30	1.02	0.82	0.69
	3	6.06	5.18	4.61	4.07	3.63	3.27	3.03	2.77	2.35	1.84	1.48	1.24
	4	8.94	7.86	7.00	6.22	5.65	5.11	4.65	4.26	3.70	2.85	2.31	1.97
	5	12.1	10.9	9.72	8.77	7.90	7.17	6.63	6.10	5.25	4.11	3.34	2.81
	6	15.3	14.0	12.6	11.5	10.5	9.68	8.88	8.19	7.13	5.56	4.57	3.85
	7	18.5	17.2	15.9	14.6	13.4	12.4	11.4	10.6	9.18	7.25	5.94	5.05
	8	21.8	20.5	19.0	17.7	16.4	15.2	14.1	13.2	11.5	9.12	7.53	6.37
	9	25.0	23.7	22.4	20.9	19.6	18.3	17.1	15.9	14.1	11.2	9.25	7.88
	10	28.1	27.0	25.6	24.2	22.8	21.4	20.1	18.9	16.8	13.5	11.2	9.55
	11	31.3	30.2	28.9	27.5	26.0	24.6	23.3	22.0	19.6	15.9	13.2	11.3
	12	34.4	33.4	32.1	30.8	29.4	27.9	26.5	25.1	22.6	18.5	15.5	13.3
90	2	3.64	3.16	2.73	2.39	2.18	1.95	1.76	1.61	1.36	1.07	0.86	0.72
	3	6.26	5.46	4.77	4.29	3.84	3.46	3.15	2.93	2.50	1.92	1.58	1.32
	4	9.30	8.31	7.35	6.63	5.96	5.47	4.99	4.58	3.92	3.07	2.49	2.09
	5	12.6	11.4	10.3	9.30	8.48	7.72	7.07	6.52	5.67	4.41	3.63	3.06
	6	15.7	14.6	13.4	12.2	11.2	10.4	9.52	8.87	7.68	6.06	4.96	4.21
	7	19.0	17.8	16.6	15.4	14.3	13.2	12.2	11.4	10.0	7.88	6.51	5.50
	8	22.2	21.1	19.9	18.6	17.4	16.3	15.2	14.2	12.5	9.99	8.23	7.01
	9	25.4	24.3	23.1	21.9	20.6	19.4	18.2	17.1	15.2	12.3	10.2	8.65
	10	28.5	27.5	26.4	25.1	23.9	22.7	21.4	20.2	18.1	14.7	12.3	10.5
	11	31.6	30.7	29.6	28.5	27.2	25.9	24.6	23.4	21.1	17.4	14.5	12.5
	12	34.7	33.9	32.9	31.7	30.5	29.2	27.9	26.6	24.3	20.1	17.0	14.6
100	2	3.77	3.28	2.84	2.49	2.27	2.03	1.84	1.68	1.42	1.12	0.90	0.76
	3	6.54	5.72	5.00	4.44	4.04	3.66	3.33	3.05	2.65	2.03	1.67	1.40
	4	9.62	8.66	7.78	7.03	6.34	5.75	5.32	4.89	4.20	3.29	2.68	2.25
	5	12.9	11.8	10.8	9.81	8.98	8.19	7.58	6.99	6.10	4.76	3.92	3.30
	6	16.1	15.1	14.0	12.9	11.9	11.0	10.2	9.48	8.29	6.56	5.38	4.57
	7	19.3	18.3	17.2	16.1	15.0	14.0	13.0	12.2	10.7	8.54	7.07	5.99
	8	22.5	21.6	20.5	19.4	18.3	17.1	16.1	15.1	13.5	10.8	8.97	7.65
	9	25.7	24.8	23.8	22.6	21.5	20.4	19.3	18.2	16.3	13.3	11.0	9.44
	10	28.8	28.0	27.0	26.0	24.8	23.7	22.5	21.4	19.3	15.9	13.3	11.4
	11	31.9	31.1	30.2	29.2	28.1	27.0	25.8	24.7	22.4	18.7	15.8	13.6
	12	35.0	34.2	33.4	32.4	31.4	30.3	29.1	27.9	25.6	21.6	18.4	15.9
120	2	4.02	3.45	3.06	2.70	2.40	2.21	2.00	1.83	1.56	1.19	0.99	0.83
	3	6.99	6.18	5.50	4.88	4.39	4.04	3.69	3.39	2.90	2.27	1.84	1.57
	4	10.2	9.29	8.48	7.66	7.01	6.45	5.92	5.46	4.76	3.71	3.05	2.57
	5	13.4	12.5	11.7	10.7	9.89	9.16	8.50	7.87	6.88	5.45	4.47	3.80
	6	16.6	15.8	14.9	14.0	13.1	12.2	11.4	10.7	9.41	7.51	6.22	5.27
	7	19.8	19.1	18.2	17.2	16.3	15.3	14.5	13.7	12.1	9.81	8.16	6.94
	8	22.9	22.2	21.4	20.5	19.6	18.6	17.7	16.8	15.1	12.3	10.4	8.88
	9	26.0	25.4	24.6	23.8	22.9	21.9	21.0	20.0	18.2	15.1	12.8	11.0
	10	29.1	28.5	27.8	27.0	26.1	25.2	24.3	23.3	21.4	18.0	15.3	13.3
	11	32.2	31.7	31.0	30.2	29.4	28.5	27.5	26.6	24.6	21.1	18.1	15.7
	12	35.3	34.8	34.1	33.4	32.6	31.7	30.8	29.9	27.9	24.2	21.0	18.4
160	2	4.38	3.87	3.45	3.07	2.79	2.52	2.30	2.11	1.83	1.41	1.15	0.98
	3	7.60	6.92	6.30	5.72	5.17	4.75	4.35	4.01	3.50	2.73	2.25	1.89
	4	10.9	10.2	9.54	8.82	8.22	7.59	7.06	6.61	5.76	4.58	3.78	3.20
	5	14.1	13.5	12.8	12.1	11.4	10.7	10.0	9.45	8.41	6.74	5.59	4.77
	6	17.2	16.7	16.1	15.4	14.7	14.0	13.3	12.6	11.3	9.27	7.79	6.68
	7	20.3	19.8	19.3	18.7	18.0	17.2	16.6	15.8	14.5	12.1	10.2	8.79
	8	23.4	23.0	22.5	21.9	21.2	20.6	19.9	19.1	17.7	15.1	12.9	11.2
	9	26.4	26.1	25.6	25.1	24.5	23.8	23.2	22.4	21.0	18.2	15.8	13.8
	10	29.5	29.2	28.7	28.2	27.7	27.1	26.4	25.7	24.3	21.4	18.8	16.6
	11	32.5	32.2	31.8	31.4	30.9	30.3	29.7	29.0	27.6	24.7	21.9	19.5
	12	35.6	35.3	34.9	34.5	34.0	33.5	32.9	32.2	30.9	28.0	25.1	22.5

* See p. 3—24 for more details regarding these tables.

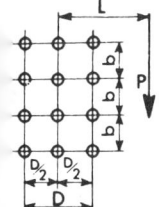

D = 320 mm												Number of Bolts in Each Row	Pitch b mm
Moment Arm, L, Millimetres													
75	100	125	150	175	200	225	250	300	400	500	600		
1.97	1.78	1.63	1.49	1.37	1.28	1.18	1.11	0.98	0.77	0.62	0.53	1	
4.22	3.79	3.47	3.17	2.90	2.71	2.50	2.32	2.05	1.63	1.35	1.14	2	
6.66	6.04	5.49	5.07	4.66	4.30	4.03	3.75	3.32	2.66	2.18	1.87	3	
9.41	8.57	7.86	7.20	6.69	6.19	5.74	5.41	4.74	3.81	3.18	2.69	4	
12.3	11.3	10.4	9.63	8.88	8.24	7.74	7.22	6.42	5.18	4.33	3.67	5	
15.4	14.2	13.1	12.2	11.4	10.6	9.89	9.33	8.23	6.67	5.58	4.79	6	80
18.5	17.3	16.1	15.0	14.0	13.1	12.3	11.6	10.3	8.39	7.04	6.00	7	
21.7	20.4	19.2	18.0	16.9	15.9	14.9	14.0	12.5	10.2	8.59	7.40	8	
24.8	23.6	22.4	21.1	19.8	18.8	17.6	16.7	14.9	12.3	10.4	8.88	9	
27.9	26.8	25.6	24.3	23.0	21.7	20.5	19.5	17.5	14.4	12.2	10.5	10	
31.1	30.0	28.8	27.5	26.1	24.8	23.6	22.4	20.2	16.8	14.2	12.3	11	
34.2	33.2	32.0	30.7	29.4	28.0	26.7	25.4	23.1	19.3	16.4	14.2	12	
4.24	3.85	3.52	3.21	2.94	2.74	2.54	2.36	2.08	1.66	1.38	1.16	2	
6.81	6.18	5.61	5.14	4.78	4.42	4.14	3.85	3.41	2.74	2.25	1.93	3	
9.61	8.77	8.06	7.46	6.87	6.42	5.96	5.56	4.93	3.97	3.31	2.81	4	
12.6	11.7	10.8	9.97	9.27	8.60	8.02	7.56	6.66	5.44	4.51	3.87	5	
15.7	14.7	13.6	12.8	11.9	11.1	10.4	9.75	8.69	7.06	5.92	5.05	6	90
18.9	17.8	16.7	15.7	14.7	13.8	13.0	12.2	10.9	8.87	7.45	6.42	7	
22.1	21.0	19.9	18.8	17.6	16.7	15.7	14.8	13.3	10.9	9.21	7.89	8	
25.2	24.2	23.1	21.9	20.7	19.7	18.6	17.6	15.8	13.1	11.1	9.57	9	
28.3	27.4	26.3	25.1	24.0	22.8	21.6	20.5	18.6	15.5	13.1	11.3	10	
31.5	30.5	29.5	28.4	27.2	25.9	24.7	23.7	21.6	18.0	15.3	13.3	11	
34.6	33.7	32.7	31.5	30.4	29.2	28.0	26.8	24.5	20.7	17.7	15.4	12	
4.29	3.90	3.53	3.26	2.99	2.79	2.58	2.39	2.12	1.69	1.40	1.18	2	
6.91	6.28	5.75	5.27	4.90	4.53	4.21	3.96	3.47	2.79	2.32	1.99	3	
9.83	9.04	8.33	7.65	7.11	6.59	6.18	5.77	5.13	4.14	3.46	2.93	4	
12.9	12.0	11.1	10.3	9.60	8.97	8.36	7.83	6.98	5.66	4.74	4.07	5	
16.1	15.1	14.1	13.2	12.4	11.5	10.9	10.2	9.09	7.46	6.22	5.35	6	100
19.2	18.3	17.2	16.2	15.3	14.4	13.6	12.8	11.5	9.41	7.93	6.79	7	
22.4	21.4	20.5	19.4	18.4	17.4	16.4	15.6	14.0	11.6	9.78	8.44	8	
25.5	24.6	23.7	22.6	21.6	20.5	19.5	18.5	16.8	13.9	11.8	10.2	9	
28.6	27.8	26.8	25.8	24.8	23.6	22.6	21.5	19.7	16.5	14.1	12.2	10	
31.7	30.9	30.0	29.0	28.0	26.9	25.8	24.7	22.7	19.2	16.4	14.3	11	
34.8	34.1	33.2	32.3	31.2	30.1	29.0	27.9	25.8	22.0	19.0	16.5	12	
4.41	4.02	3.64	3.36	3.08	2.88	2.66	2.47	2.19	1.75	1.44	1.23	2	
7.17	6.58	5.99	5.53	5.11	4.77	4.44	4.14	3.68	2.96	2.47	2.09	3	
10.2	9.46	8.79	8.16	7.55	7.07	6.58	6.21	5.48	4.44	3.71	3.19	4	
13.4	12.6	11.7	11.0	10.3	9.66	9.03	8.51	7.56	6.21	5.18	4.45	5	
16.5	15.7	14.9	14.1	13.2	12.5	11.8	11.1	9.95	8.20	6.91	5.92	6	120
19.7	18.9	18.1	17.2	16.4	15.5	14.7	13.9	12.6	10.4	8.82	7.63	7	
22.8	22.1	21.3	20.4	19.5	18.7	17.8	17.0	15.4	12.9	11.0	9.49	8	
25.9	25.3	24.5	23.7	22.8	21.9	21.0	20.1	18.4	15.5	13.3	11.5	9	
29.0	28.4	27.7	26.9	26.0	25.1	24.2	23.3	21.5	18.3	15.8	13.8	10	
32.1	31.5	30.9	30.1	29.3	28.4	27.5	26.5	24.7	21.3	18.5	16.2	11	
35.2	34.6	34.0	33.3	32.5	31.6	30.7	29.8	27.9	24.3	21.3	18.7	12	
4.64	4.23	3.89	3.55	3.30	3.05	2.86	2.66	2.33	1.87	1.56	1.32	2	
7.62	7.05	6.55	6.06	5.64	5.23	4.88	4.61	4.07	3.30	2.77	2.38	3	
10.8	10.2	9.57	8.99	8.42	7.92	7.46	7.00	6.26	5.11	4.30	3.70	4	
14.0	13.4	12.7	12.1	11.5	10.9	10.3	9.72	8.77	7.21	6.10	5.27	5	
17.1	16.6	16.0	15.3	14.7	14.0	13.3	12.7	11.5	9.68	8.23	7.13	6	160
20.2	19.7	19.2	18.6	17.9	17.2	16.6	15.9	14.6	12.4	10.6	9.21	7	
23.3	22.9	22.4	21.8	21.2	20.5	19.8	19.1	17.7	15.2	13.2	11.5	8	
26.4	26.0	25.5	25.0	24.4	23.7	23.1	22.4	21.0	18.3	16.0	14.1	9	
29.4	29.1	28.6	28.1	27.6	27.0	26.3	25.6	24.2	21.4	18.9	16.8	10	
32.5	32.2	31.7	31.3	30.7	30.2	29.5	28.9	27.5	24.7	22.0	19.6	11	
35.5	35.2	34.8	34.4	33.9	33.4	32.7	32.1	30.8	27.9	25.1	22.6	12	

* See p. 3—24 for more details regarding these tables.

ECCENTRIC LOADS ON BOLT GROUPS

Coefficients C*

Table 3-20

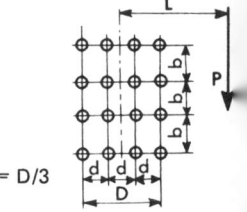

d = D/3

Pitch b mm	Number of Bolts in Each Row	D = 240 mm											
		Moment Arm, L, Millimetres											
		75	100	125	150	175	200	225	250	300	400	500	600
	1	2.31	2.02	1.79	1.56	1.41	1.26	1.14	1.05	0.89	0.69	0.56	0.47
80	2	5.12	4.52	3.97	3.58	3.20	2.89	2.63	2.46	2.10	1.62	1.31	1.13
	3	8.33	7.41	6.57	5.96	5.36	4.93	4.50	4.13	3.60	2.78	2.26	1.90
	4	12.1	10.8	9.77	8.78	8.05	7.33	6.71	6.27	5.40	4.26	3.47	2.92
	5	16.1	14.6	13.3	12.1	11.0	10.1	9.37	8.66	7.57	5.91	4.88	4.12
	6	20.4	18.7	17.0	15.6	14.4	13.3	12.3	11.4	10.0	7.94	6.50	5.55
	7	24.6	22.9	21.2	19.5	18.1	16.8	15.5	14.5	12.7	10.1	8.40	7.11
	8	28.9	27.2	25.4	23.6	22.1	20.6	19.1	17.9	15.8	12.7	10.5	8.94
	9	33.1	31.5	29.7	27.9	26.2	24.5	22.9	21.6	19.1	15.4	12.8	11.0
	10	37.4	35.8	34.0	32.1	30.4	28.6	27.0	25.4	22.7	18.3	15.3	13.1
	11	41.6	40.1	38.4	36.5	34.7	32.9	31.1	29.4	26.4	21.6	18.1	15.5
	12	45.7	44.3	42.7	40.9	39.0	37.1	35.3	33.5	30.2	25.0	21.0	18.1
90	2	5.23	4.55	4.07	3.61	3.29	2.98	2.71	2.48	2.17	1.67	1.36	1.16
	3	8.63	7.67	6.83	6.20	5.59	5.07	4.71	4.32	3.70	2.91	2.37	2.00
	4	12.5	11.2	10.1	9.24	8.38	7.74	7.10	6.55	5.73	4.46	3.69	3.11
	5	16.7	15.3	13.9	12.7	11.7	10.7	9.88	9.24	8.01	6.35	5.19	4.42
	6	20.9	19.3	17.9	16.4	15.2	14.1	13.0	12.2	10.7	8.49	7.03	5.95
	7	25.2	23.7	22.1	20.6	19.2	17.8	16.6	15.5	13.7	11.0	9.06	7.73
	8	29.5	28.0	26.4	24.7	23.3	21.8	20.4	19.2	17.0	13.7	11.4	9.70
	9	33.7	32.3	30.8	29.1	27.5	25.9	24.4	23.0	20.6	16.6	13.9	11.9
	10	37.9	36.6	35.1	33.5	31.8	30.1	28.6	27.1	24.3	19.9	16.7	14.3
	11	42.0	40.8	39.4	37.8	36.1	34.5	32.8	31.2	28.3	23.3	19.7	17.0
	12	46.2	45.0	43.7	42.1	40.6	38.9	37.2	35.5	32.4	27.0	22.9	19.8
100	2	5.35	4.66	4.17	3.71	3.39	3.06	2.79	2.56	2.24	1.73	1.40	1.18
	3	8.83	7.84	7.09	6.36	5.83	5.30	4.92	4.52	3.88	3.06	2.49	2.10
	4	12.9	11.7	10.6	9.59	8.82	8.06	7.49	6.92	6.06	4.74	3.92	3.30
	5	17.2	15.8	14.5	13.3	12.2	11.3	10.5	9.71	8.53	6.78	5.55	4.74
	6	21.4	20.0	18.7	17.2	16.0	14.9	13.9	12.9	11.4	9.11	7.56	6.41
	7	25.7	24.4	22.9	21.5	20.0	18.8	17.5	16.5	14.6	11.7	9.78	8.35
	8	29.9	28.7	27.2	25.7	24.3	22.9	21.6	20.4	18.1	14.7	12.3	10.5
	9	34.1	32.9	31.6	30.1	28.6	27.1	25.8	24.4	21.8	18.0	15.1	12.9
	10	38.3	37.2	35.9	34.5	33.0	31.5	30.0	28.6	25.9	21.4	18.1	15.6
	11	42.4	41.4	40.2	38.8	37.4	35.8	34.3	32.8	30.0	25.1	21.3	18.4
	12	46.5	45.6	44.4	43.1	41.7	40.2	38.7	37.2	34.2	28.9	24.7	21.4
120	2	5.52	4.90	4.40	3.92	3.53	3.25	2.97	2.73	2.38	1.84	1.50	1.26
	3	9.31	8.42	7.59	6.85	6.22	5.75	5.28	4.87	4.25	3.35	2.73	2.30
	4	13.6	12.4	11.4	10.4	9.57	8.88	8.19	7.59	6.66	5.29	4.34	3.70
	5	17.9	16.7	15.5	14.4	13.3	12.4	11.5	10.7	9.48	7.58	6.29	5.33
	6	22.1	21.0	19.8	18.6	17.4	16.3	15.3	14.4	12.8	10.3	8.56	7.33
	7	26.3	25.3	24.2	23.0	21.7	20.5	19.4	18.3	16.3	13.3	11.1	9.55
	8	30.5	29.6	28.5	27.3	26.0	24.8	23.6	22.4	20.2	16.7	14.0	12.1
	9	34.6	33.8	32.8	31.6	30.4	29.2	27.9	26.7	24.3	20.3	17.2	14.8
	10	38.8	38.0	37.0	35.9	34.7	33.5	32.2	31.0	28.5	24.1	20.6	17.9
	11	42.9	42.1	41.2	40.2	39.1	37.9	36.7	35.4	32.8	28.1	24.3	21.2
	12	47.0	46.3	45.4	44.5	43.4	42.2	41.0	39.8	37.2	32.3	28.0	24.6
160	2	5.95	5.32	4.80	4.31	3.96	3.60	3.30	3.08	2.66	2.10	1.71	1.44
	3	10.1	9.25	8.49	7.76	7.07	6.56	6.06	5.62	4.93	3.91	3.20	2.73
	4	14.4	13.6	12.7	11.8	11.0	10.3	9.55	8.97	7.92	6.35	5.24	4.48
	5	18.7	17.9	17.0	16.1	15.2	14.3	13.5	12.7	11.3	9.20	7.66	6.57
	6	22.9	22.2	21.4	20.5	19.5	18.6	17.7	16.8	15.2	12.5	10.5	9.07
	7	27.0	26.4	25.6	24.8	23.9	23.0	22.0	21.1	19.3	16.2	13.8	11.9
	8	31.1	30.6	29.9	29.1	28.3	27.3	26.4	25.4	23.6	20.1	17.3	15.0
	9	35.2	34.7	34.1	33.4	32.5	31.7	30.8	29.8	27.9	24.2	21.1	18.5
	10	39.3	38.8	38.2	37.6	36.8	36.0	35.1	34.2	32.3	28.5	25.1	22.1
	11	43.4	42.9	42.4	41.8	41.1	40.3	39.5	38.6	36.7	32.8	29.2	26.0
	12	47.4	47.0	46.5	45.9	45.3	44.5	43.7	42.9	41.1	37.3	33.4	30.0

* See p. 3—24 for more details regarding these tables.

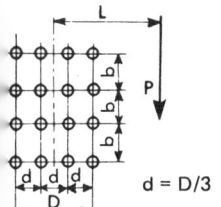

d = D/3

ECCENTRIC LOADS ON BOLT GROUPS

Coefficients C*

Table 3-21

D = 480 mm												Number of Bolts in Each Row	Pitch b mm
Moment Arm, L, Millimetres													
75	100	125	150	175	200	225	250	300	400	500	600		
2.91	2.69	2.51	2.33	2.18	2.04	1.90	1.79	1.58	1.26	1.05	0.89	1	
6.00	5.56	5.17	4.79	4.49	4.18	3.93	3.71	3.27	2.67	2.21	1.89	2	
9.32	8.62	7.99	7.48	6.96	6.54	6.17	5.78	5.15	4.18	3.50	2.99	3	
12.8	11.9	11.1	10.3	9.72	9.08	8.58	8.12	7.20	5.92	4.98	4.26	4	
16.6	15.5	14.5	13.5	12.7	11.9	11.2	10.6	9.54	7.80	6.57	5.67	5	
20.5	19.2	18.1	16.9	15.9	15.0	14.2	13.4	12.0	9.95	8.41	7.21	6	80
24.6	23.1	21.8	20.6	19.4	18.2	17.3	16.4	14.8	12.2	10.4	8.95	7	
28.7	27.3	25.8	24.3	23.0	21.7	20.6	19.6	17.7	14.8	12.6	10.9	8	
32.9	31.4	29.8	28.3	26.8	25.4	24.1	23.0	20.8	17.5	14.9	12.9	9	
37.0	35.6	34.0	32.4	30.8	29.3	27.9	26.6	24.1	20.3	17.4	15.2	10	
41.2	39.8	38.2	36.6	34.9	33.3	31.8	30.4	27.6	23.3	20.1	17.5	11	
45.4	44.0	42.4	40.8	39.1	37.4	35.8	34.2	31.4	26.6	22.9	20.0	12	
6.05	5.59	5.21	4.83	4.52	4.21	3.97	3.71	3.30	2.67	2.24	1.91	2	
9.41	8.70	8.10	7.59	7.07	6.65	6.22	5.88	5.26	4.27	3.58	3.05	3	
13.1	12.1	11.3	10.6	9.95	9.31	8.80	8.26	7.41	6.10	5.09	4.39	4	
16.9	15.9	14.8	13.8	13.0	12.2	11.6	11.0	9.80	8.10	6.84	5.90	5	
20.9	19.7	18.6	17.4	16.4	15.5	14.6	13.9	12.5	10.3	8.74	7.56	6	90
25.1	23.8	22.5	21.2	20.1	19.0	17.9	17.0	15.4	12.8	10.9	9.45	7	
29.2	27.9	26.5	25.1	23.8	22.6	21.5	20.4	18.5	15.5	13.2	11.5	8	
33.4	32.1	30.7	29.2	27.8	26.5	25.2	24.0	21.8	18.4	15.7	13.7	9	
37.6	36.3	34.9	33.4	32.0	30.6	29.1	27.8	25.4	21.4	18.5	16.1	10	
41.7	40.5	39.1	37.7	36.1	34.6	33.2	31.8	29.2	24.7	21.3	18.6	11	
45.9	44.7	43.4	41.9	40.4	38.9	37.4	35.9	33.0	28.2	24.4	21.4	12	
6.09	5.64	5.21	4.87	4.56	4.25	4.00	3.74	3.33	2.70	2.26	1.93	2	
9.53	8.83	8.22	7.65	7.19	6.77	6.33	5.99	5.36	4.36	3.66	3.12	3	
13.3	12.4	11.6	10.8	10.1	9.54	8.96	8.49	7.61	6.23	5.25	4.54	4	
17.3	16.2	15.1	14.3	13.3	12.6	11.9	11.3	10.1	8.41	7.11	6.09	5	
21.3	20.2	19.0	17.9	16.9	16.0	15.2	14.3	12.9	10.8	9.14	7.92	6	100
25.5	24.3	23.1	21.8	20.7	19.7	18.6	17.6	16.0	13.4	11.4	9.89	7	
29.6	28.5	27.2	25.9	24.7	23.5	22.3	21.3	19.3	16.2	13.9	12.1	8	
33.8	32.7	31.4	30.1	28.8	27.5	26.2	25.0	22.9	19.3	16.6	14.5	9	
38.0	36.9	35.6	34.3	33.0	31.6	30.2	29.0	26.7	22.6	19.5	17.1	10	
42.1	41.1	39.9	38.6	37.2	35.8	34.5	33.1	30.5	26.1	22.6	19.8	11	
46.3	45.2	44.1	42.8	41.5	40.1	38.7	37.3	34.6	29.8	25.9	22.7	12	
6.19	5.74	5.30	4.95	4.64	4.33	4.08	3.82	3.41	2.77	2.32	1.98	2	
9.79	9.06	8.43	7.89	7.43	6.95	6.57	6.17	5.53	4.55	3.83	3.27	3	
13.7	12.8	12.0	11.3	10.6	9.95	9.43	8.88	7.99	6.62	5.59	4.80	4	
17.7	16.8	15.8	14.9	14.1	13.3	12.6	11.9	10.8	8.98	7.61	6.59	5	
21.9	20.9	19.9	18.9	17.9	16.9	16.1	15.3	13.9	11.6	9.91	8.60	6	120
26.1	25.1	24.1	23.0	21.9	20.9	19.9	18.9	17.3	14.6	12.5	10.8	7	
30.3	29.3	28.3	27.2	26.0	24.9	23.9	22.8	20.9	17.8	15.3	13.3	8	
34.4	33.5	32.5	31.4	30.3	29.2	28.0	26.9	24.8	21.2	18.3	16.0	9	
38.5	37.7	36.8	35.7	34.6	33.4	32.3	31.1	28.8	24.9	21.6	19.0	10	
42.7	41.9	41.0	40.0	38.9	37.7	36.5	35.3	32.9	28.7	25.1	22.1	11	
46.8	46.0	45.2	44.2	43.1	42.0	40.8	39.6	37.3	32.7	28.7	25.5	12	
6.38	5.92	5.51	5.12	4.80	4.52	4.23	4.00	3.58	2.92	2.46	2.10	2	
10.2	9.54	8.94	8.39	7.88	7.41	7.02	6.62	5.96	4.93	4.16	3.60	3	
14.3	13.6	12.9	12.1	11.5	10.9	10.3	9.77	8.84	7.38	6.27	5.43	4	
18.5	17.8	17.0	16.2	15.4	14.6	13.9	13.3	12.1	10.1	8.71	7.57	5	
22.7	22.0	21.2	20.4	19.5	18.7	17.9	17.1	15.7	13.3	11.5	10.0	6	160
26.8	26.2	25.4	24.7	23.8	22.9	22.0	21.2	19.6	16.8	14.5	12.8	7	
31.0	30.4	29.7	28.9	28.1	27.2	26.4	25.4	23.7	20.6	17.9	15.8	8	
35.1	34.5	33.9	33.1	32.3	31.5	30.6	29.7	27.9	24.5	21.6	19.1	9	
39.2	38.7	38.1	37.4	36.6	35.8	34.9	34.1	32.2	28.6	25.4	22.7	10	
43.2	42.8	42.2	41.6	40.8	40.1	39.3	38.4	36.6	32.9	29.4	26.4	11	
47.3	46.9	46.3	45.7	45.1	44.3	43.5	42.7	40.9	37.2	33.6	30.3	12	

* See p. 3—24 for more details regarding these tables.

ECCENTRIC LOAD ON BOLT GROUPS SPECIAL CASE

High Strength Bolts

For connections of the type shown in Figure 3—2 where the bolts are subjected to both shear and tension due to the effect of the eccentric load, the following design method may be used when the fasteners are high strength bolts which have been tightened to the specified minimum initial tension.

Figure 3—2 (a) shows a bracket connected with bolts having an initial tension, T_o. Using an elastic analysis, and assuming that the connection material is rigid, the moment effect on the connection can be represented by a series of coupled forces whose neutral axis passes through the centroidal axis of the group, Figure 3—2 (b).

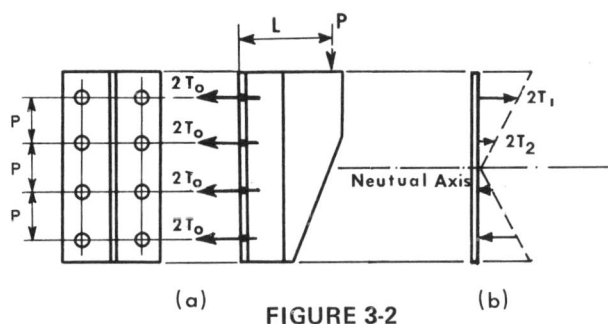

(a)   FIGURE 3-2   (b)

The fasteners in the top half of the connection are subject to applied shear and tension forces, and the connection should be proportioned so that the maximum bolt tension, T_1, due to the moment, PL, when combined with the shear on the bolt meets the requirements of CAN3-S16.1-M78 for bolts subject to combined shear and tension, clause 13.11.4 for bearing-type connections or clause 13.12.3 for slip-resistant connections.

Example 1

Given:

Check the adequacy of eight M20 A325M bolts (2 rows of 4 at 80 mm pitch) for the connection shown in Figure 3—2 for a factored load P of 300 kN at an eccentricity L of 150 mm. Assume the material thickness is adequate so that prying action on the bolts is not significant.

Solution:

Determine the maximum factored tension T_1 in one bolt by taking ΣM about the centre of the bolt group.

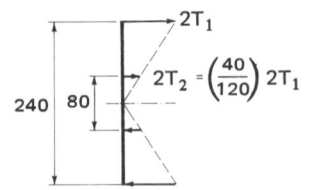

$$(2T_1 \times 240) + (2T_1 \times 40/120 \times 80) = 300 \times 150$$

$$480T_1 + 53.3T_1 = 300 \times 150$$

$T_1 = 84.4$ kN < 131 kN (Table 3—4)

Factored shear per bolt $= 300/8 = 37.5$ kN < 105 kN (Table 3—4)

Check combined shear and tension for $V_f/T_f = 37.5/84.4 = 0.44$

From Table 3—8, page 3—13, for bearing-type connections

Maximum $V_f = 51$ kN (by interpolation) > 37.5 kN — OK

Maximum $T_p = 115$ kN (by interpolation) > 84.4 — OK

Example 2

Given:

Determine the number of M20 A325M bolts required assuming the connection in Example 1 is to be designed as a slip-resistant connection for a specified load of 200 kN assuming clean mill scale faying surfaces.

Solution:

Try 10 bolts (2 rows of 5 at 80 mm pitch)
Taking Σ M about centre of bolt group gives

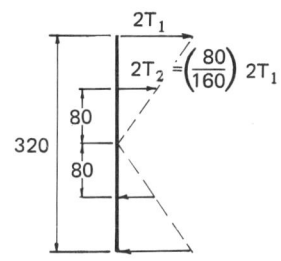

$$(2T_1 \times 320) + (T_1 \times 160) = 200 \times 150$$

$$640T_1 + 160T_1 = 200 \times 150$$

$$T_1 = 37.5 \text{ kN}$$

Similarly T_f = 300 $\times$ 150/800 = 56.3 kN < 131 kN (Table 3—4)

Specified shear per bolt = 200/10 = 20 kN < 40 kN (Table 3—11)

Check combined shear and tension for V/T = 20/37.5 = 0.53

From Table 3—12, page 3—17, for V/T of 0.60

Maximum V = 26.4 kN > 20 kN — OK

Minimum T = 44 kN > 37.5 kN — OK

WELD DATA

FACTORED RESISTANCE OF WELDS**

Type of Weld	Type of Load and Orientation	Factored Resistance
Complete joint penetration groove welds	Tension or compression parallel to axis of weld*	Same as for base metal
	Tension normal to effective throat	
	Compression normal to effective throat	
	Shear on effective throat	The smaller of (a) base metal $V_r = 0.66 \, \phi \, A_m \, F_y$ or (b) weld metal $V_r = 0.50 \, \phi \, A_w \, X_u$
Partial joint penetration groove welds	Tension or compression parallel to axis of weld*	Same as for base metal
	Compression normal to effective throat	Same as for base metal
	Tension other than parallel to axis of weld	The smaller of (a) base metal $V_r = 0.66 \, \phi \, A_m \, F_y$ or (b) weld metal $V_r = 0.50 \, \phi \, A_w \, X_u$
	Shear on effective throat	
Fillet Welds	Tension or compression parallel to axis of weld*	Same as for base metal
	Tension or compression other than parallel to axis of weld	The smaller of (a) base metal $V_r = 0.66 \, \phi \, A_m \, F_y$ or (b) weld metal $V_r = 0.50 \, \phi \, A_w \, X_u$
	Shear on effective throat	
Plug and slot welds	Shear on effective throat	

* No load transfer occurs.

X_u = ultimate strength as rated by the Electrode Classification number.

** Factored resistance of welds based upon Clause 13.13.1, CAN3-S16.1-M78. More detailed information on the factored resistance of welds is currently (1980) being prepared for inclusion in CSA W59 by the CSA Technical Committee on Welding of Bridges, Buildings and Machinery.

See CAN3-S16.1-M78, Clause 20.9 for the capacity of welds in combination, and Clause 20.10 for welds in combination with other fasteners.

ELECTRODE CLASSIFICATION[1] AND UNIT FACTORED WELD RESISTANCE[2], $\phi = 0.90$

Table 3-22

	WELD METAL				BASE METAL			
Proposed Metric Electrode Classification Number	Imperial Electrode Classification Number	Unit Factored Resistance On Weld Metal (MPa)			Specified Minimum Tensile Strength of Base Metal F_u (MPa)	Base Metal Specification and Grade CSA G40.21-M or ASTM	F_y (MPa)	Unit Factored Resistance on Base Metal $0.66\phi F_y$
		Shear on Effective Throat, A_w $0.50\phi X_u$	Shear per Millimetre of Fillet Weld Size $0.50\phi X_u/\sqrt{2}$					
E410XX	E60XX	184	130		410 400	260W, 260WT A36	260 250	154 149
E480XX	E70XX	216	153		450[3] 480 480 415 450 435 460 485	300W, 300WT 350W, 350WT 350R, 350A 380W, 380WT A572 Gr 42 A572 Gr 50 A441 F_y = 42 A441 F_y = 46 A441 F_y = 50	300 350 380 290 345 290 315 345	178 208 226 172 205 172 187 205
E550XX	E80XX	248	175		520	400W, 400WT 400A, 400AT	400	238
E620XX	E90XX	279	197		590	480W, 480WT 480A, 480AT	480	285
E690XX	E100XX	310	220					
E760XX	E110XX	342	242		800	700Q, 700QT	700	416
E830XX	E120XX	374	264					

1. For complete information concerning electrode classification and strength matching of base metals in Imperial Units, refer to CSA W59.
2. Factored weld resistance (kN) = Tabulated unit resistances x (A_w or A_m)/10^3.
3. F_u = 410 for 300W HSS.

WELD DATA

Table 3-23 — FACTORED SHEAR RESISTANCE ON EFFECTIVE THROAT PER MILLIMETRE OF WELD LENGTH (kN)

Electrode Classification	Unit Shear Resist. (MPa)	Effective Throat Thickness (mm).												
		5	6	7	8	10	12	16	20	25	30	35	40	50
E 410 XX	184	.920	1.10	1.29	1.47	1.84	2.21	2.94	3.68	4.60	5.52	6.44	7.36	9.20
E 480 XX	216	1.08	1.30	1.51	1.73	2.16	2.59	3.46	4.32	5.40	6.48	7.56	8.64	10.8
E 550 XX	248	1.24	1.49	1.74	1.98	2.48	2.98	3.97	4.96	6.20	7.44	8.68	9.92	12.4
E 620 XX	279	1.40	1.67	1.95	2.23	2.79	3.35	4.46	5.58	6.98	8.37	9.76	11.2	14.0
E 690 XX	310	1.55	1.86	2.17	2.48	3.10	3.72	4.96	6.20	7.75	9.30	10.8	11.4	15.5
E 760 XX	342	1.71	2.05	2.39	2.74	3.42	4.10	5.47	6.84	8.55	10.3	12.0	13.7	17.1
E 830 XX	374	1.87	2.24	2.62	2.99	3.74	4.49	5.98	7.48	9.35	11.2	13.1	15.0	18.7

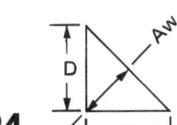

$A_W = D/\sqrt{2}$

Table 3-24 — FACTORED SHEAR RESISTANCE* OF FILLET WELDS PER MILLIMETRE OF WELD LENGTH, kN

Metric Size Fillet Welds				Fillet Weld Size, D		Imperial Size Fillet Welds			
Electrode Classification						Electrode Classification			
E410XX	E480XX	E550XX	E620XX	mm	inches	E410XX	E480XX	E550XX	E620XX
.650	.765	.875	.985	5	3/16	.619	.729	.833	.938
.780	.918	1.05	1.18	6	1/4	.826	.972	1.11	1.25
1.04	1.22	1.40	1.58	8	5/16	1.03	1.21	1.39	1.56
1.30	1.53	1.75	1.97	10	3/8	1.24	1.46	1.67	1.88
1.56	1.84	2.10	2.36	12	7/16	1.44	1.70	1.94	2.19
1.82	2.14	2.45	2.76	14	1/2	1.65	1.94	2.22	2.50
2.08	2.45	2.80	3.15	16	5/8	2.06	2.43	2.78	3.13
2.34	2.75	3.15	3.55	18	3/4	2.48	2.91	3.33	3.75
2.60	3.06	3.50	3.94	20					
184	216	248	279	Unit Factored Shear Resistance on Effective Throat (MPa)					
130	153	175	197	Unit Factored Shear Resistance per millimetre of fillet weld size (MPa)					

*Tabulated resistances for both metric and Imperial size fillet welds are based on X_u for the proposed metric electrode classification.

ECCENTRIC LOADS ON WELD GROUPS

When the line of action of a load on a weld group does not pass through the centre of gravity of the weld group, the connection is eccentrically loaded. The traditional method of analysis of these weld groups has been elastic. Work reported in Reference 2 showed that the margins of safety for eccentrically loaded weld groups analysed elastically were both high and variable. Reference 2 suggested a method of analysis based upon the load-deformation characteristics of the weld and the instantaneous centre of rotation analogy similar to that for eccentrically loaded bolt groups. For this method of analysis the weld group is considered to be divided into a discrete number of finite weld elements. The resistance of the weld group to the external eccentric load is provided by the combined resistances of the weld elements.

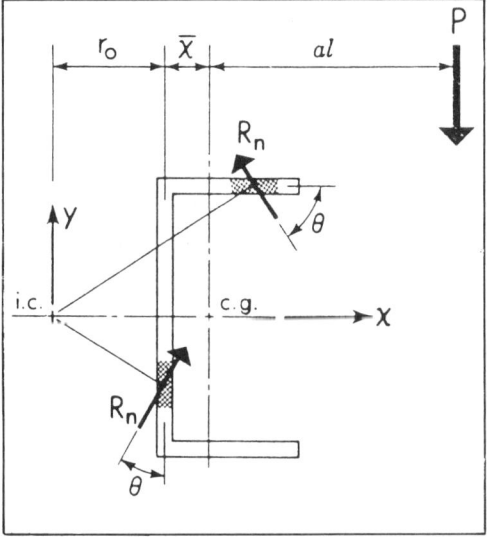

The resistance of each weld element can then be assumed to act on a line perpendicular to the radius, that radius being from the instantaneous centre of rotation to the centroid of the weld element, and can be expressed as follows:

$$R_n = R_{ULT} (1 - e^{-\mu\Delta})^\lambda \quad \text{(Reference 2)}$$

where

R_{ULT}, μ, Δ and λ will depend on the angle θ, the angle between the orientation of the weld and the resistance, R_n, and have been determined from test specimens. (For definition of symbols see page 3—24 but applied to a weld element).

The ultimate load is obtained when the ultimate strength and deformation, Δ, of some weld element is reached. The resistance of the remaining weld elements is then computed from the above expression in which Δ is assumed to vary linearly from the instantaneous centre.

The correct location of the instantaneous centre is assured when the connection is in equilibrium, that is, when the three equations of statics, $\Sigma F_x = 0$, $\Sigma F_y = 0$ and $\Sigma M = 0$ are simultaneously satisfied.

References:

1. Crawford, S. F. and Kulak, G. L., "Eccentrically Loaded Bolted Connections", Journal of the Structural Division, ASCE, Vol. 97, No. ST3, March, 1971.

2. Butler, L. J., Pal, S., and Kulak, G. L., "Eccentrically Loaded Welded Connections", Journal of the Structural Division, ASCE, Vol. 98, No. ST5, May, 1972.

Tables

1. General

The values listed in Tables 3—25 to 3—31 inclusive were computed using the instantaneous centre of rotation method outlined above in the following manner.

For the various values of 'a' the eccentricity parameter, a weld length and corresponding eccentricity were selected for the appropriate weld configuration. The ultimate capacity was then computed based on the weld length and eccentricity for ¼-inch (6.35 mm) weld size and E70XX (E480XX) electrode. Reference 2 gives, for the ¼-inch

(6.35 mm) weld, 1 inch (25.4 mm) long, made using an E60XX (E410XX) electrode, the following empirical equation for R_{ULT}, μ, λ and $\triangle_{max}$:

$$R_{ULT} = \frac{10 + \theta}{0.92 + 0.0603\theta}$$

$$\mu \quad = 75e^{0.0114\theta}$$

$$\lambda \quad = 0.4e^{0.0146\theta}$$

$$\triangle_{max} = 0.225\,(\theta + 5)^{-0.47}$$

where θ is the angle (degrees) between the resultant force and the axis of the weld.

R_{ULT} was modified by the ratio of the electrode strengths because E60XX (E410XX) and E70XX (E480XX) have nearly the same specified ultimate elongations.

The ultimate capacities were reduced for a base weld leg size of 1 mm by division and then multiplied by the product of 0.50 ϕ (ϕ = 0.90) to provide a nominal margin of safety of 3.33 (α_L = 1.5). The tabulated coefficient C is this reduced capacity divided by the weld length, l, in millimetres.

Values of the coefficient C above the horizontal line in each table are based on the resistance of the weld metal given in Table 5 of CAN3-S16.1-M78 for the weld group concentrically loaded.

2. Use of Tables

The coefficients listed in Tables 3—25 to 3—31 inclusive are based on the use of E480XX (E70XX) electrodes. For E410XX (E60XX) electrodes use 0.85 of the tabulated values.

(a) To determine the capacity of the eccentrically loaded weld group, P, in kilonewtons, multiply the coefficient C by the number of millimetres of weld leg size, D, and the length, l, of the vertical leg of the weld, in millimetres.

(b) To determine the number of millimetres of weld leg required divide the factored load, P, in kilonewtons, by the appropriate coefficient C, and the length, l, of the vertical leg in millimetres.

Values of C above the solid line are governed by the factored resistance of the weld group considered to be loaded concentrically.

3. Other Weld Configurations

For situations not covered by the tables of "Eccentric Loads on Weld Groups", the method of analysis in which the vector sum of the factored longitudinal and transverse shear loads does not exceed the factored resistances of the weld is recommended as being more convenient to use as it can readily be computed.

Example

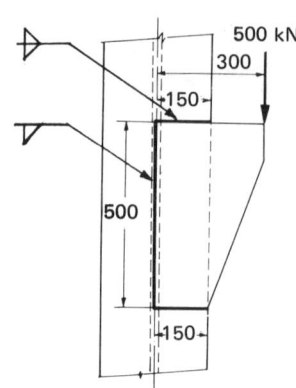

Given:

A column bracket supports a factored load of 500 kN. The width of the bracket is 300 mm. Welds are made using E480XX electrodes. For the weld configuration shown, find the required weld size. Steel is G40.21-M 300W.

Solution:

Referring to Table 3—26

$$D = \frac{P}{Cl}$$

= number of millimetres of fillet weld leg size

$k = 150/500 = 0.3$

From the bottom line of Table 3—26, for $k = 0.3$ $x = 0.056$.

Referring to the figure in Table 3—26, $al + xl = 300$

For $l = 500$, $500\,a + (0.056 \times 500) = 300$, $a = 0.544$

For $a = 0.544$ and $k = 0.3$, C = 0.18 by interpolation

Therefore D = $\dfrac{500}{0.18 \text{ x } 500}$ = 5.5, say 6 mm.

Use 6 mm fillet welds made with E480XX electrodes.

Notes:

1. The final choice of the fillet weld size to be used in an actual connection will also be dependent upon the minimum and maximum sizes required by (a) the physical thickness of the parts joined and (b) the requirements of CSA Standard W59.

2. The strength of an actual connection will also be dependent upon the resistances of the connected parts.

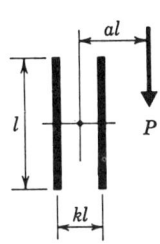

P = Factored eccentric load in kilonewtons.
l = Length of each weld in millimetres.
D = Number of millimetres in fillet weld size.
C = Coefficients tabulated below.

$$P = CDl$$

Required Minimum $C = \dfrac{P}{Dl}$

Required Minimum $D = \dfrac{P}{Cl}$

Required Minimum $l = \dfrac{P}{CD}$

a	k																
---	0.0	0.1	0.2	0.3	0.4	0.5	0.6	0.7	0.8	0.9	1.0	1.2	1.4	1.6	1.8	2.0
0.2	.305	.305	.305	.305	.305	.305	.305	.305	.305	.305	.305	.305	.305	.305	.305	.305
0.3	.276	.276	.278	.281	.284	.287	.289	.291	.293	.295	.296	.298	.300	.301	.302	.303
0.4	.229	.230	.234	.240	.245	.250	.255	.259	.263	.266	.268	.273	.277	.280	.282	.284
0.5	.192	.194	.200	.207	.214	.220	.226	.232	.237	.241	.245	.251	.256	.261	.264	.267
0.6	.165	.167	.173	.181	.188	.196	.203	.209	.214	.219	.224	.232	.238	.243	.248	.252
0.7	.144	.146	.151	.160	.168	.176	.183	.190	.196	.201	.206	.215	.222	.228	.233	.238
0.8	.127	.129	.135	.143	.151	.159	.167	.174	.180	.186	.191	.200	.208	.214	.220	.225
0.9	.114	.116	.121	.129	.137	.145	.153	.160	.166	.172	.177	.187	.195	.202	.209	.214
1.0	.103	.105	.110	.118	.126	.133	.141	.148	.154	.160	.166	.176	.184	.191	.198	.204
1.2	.086	.088	.093	.100	.107	.115	.122	.128	.135	.141	.146	.156	.165	.173	.179	.186
1.4	.074	.076	.080	.086	.093	.100	.107	.113	.119	.125	.131	.140	.149	.157	.164	.170
1.6	.065	.067	.071	.076	.083	.089	.095	.101	.107	.113	.118	.128	.136	.144	.151	.157
1.8	.058	.059	.063	.068	.074	.080	.086	.092	.097	.102	.107	.117	.125	.133	.140	.146
2.0	.052	.053	.057	.062	.067	.073	.078	.084	.089	.094	.099	.108	.116	.123	.130	.136
2.2	.048	.049	.052	.056	.061	.066	.072	.077	.082	.087	.091	.100	.108	.115	.122	.128
2.4	.044	.045	.048	.052	.056	.061	.066	.071	.076	.080	.085	.093	.101	.108	.114	.120
2.6	.040	.041	.044	.048	.052	.057	.061	.066	.071	.075	.079	.087	.094	.101	.108	.113
2.8	.037	.038	.041	.044	.048	.053	.057	.062	.066	.070	.074	.082	.089	.095	.102	.107
3.0	.035	.036	.038	.041	.045	.049	.054	.058	.062	.066	.070	.077	.084	.090	.096	.102

*Coefficients in table are for E480XX electrodes.
The effect of eccentricity has been neglected for cases above the solid horizontal line.

Coefficients C*

Table 3-26

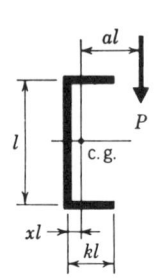

P = Factored eccentric load in kilonewtons.
l = Length of weld parallel to load
$\quad\quad P$ in millimetres.
D = Number of millimetres in fillet weld size.
C = Coefficients tabulated below.
xl = Distance from vertical weld to
$\quad\quad$ center of gravity of weld group.

$P = CDl$

Required Minimum $C = \dfrac{P}{Dl}$

Required Minimum $D = \dfrac{P}{Cl}$

Required Minimum $l = \dfrac{P}{CD}$

a	\multicolumn{16}{c	}{k}
	0.0	0.1	0.2	0.3	0.4	0.5	0.6	0.7	0.8	0.9	1.0	1.2	1.4	1.6	1.8	2.0
0.2	.153	.183	.214	.244	.275	.305	.336	.366	.397	.428	.458	.519	.580	.641	.702	.763
0.3	.138	.180	.214	.244	.275	.305	.336	.366	.397	.428	.458	.519	.580	.641	.702	.763
0.4	.114	.152	.188	.221	.254	.286	.320	.353	.387	.422	.455	.519	.580	.641	.702	.763
0.5	.096	.129	.161	.192	.222	.252	.282	.313	.345	.376	.409	.474	.544	.615	.687	.761
0.6	.082	.111	.140	.169	.196	.223	.251	.280	.308	.338	.368	.431	.496	.563	.632	.704
0.7	.072	.097	.122	.149	.174	.199	.225	.251	.278	.306	.334	.393	.455	.519	.586	.654
0.8	.063	.085	.109	.133	.156	.179	.203	.227	.252	.278	.305	.360	.419	.480	.545	.610
0.9	.057	.077	.098	.119	.141	.163	.184	.207	.231	.255	.280	.333	.388	.447	.508	.572
1.0	.051	.069	.088	.108	.129	.149	.169	.190	.212	.235	.259	.308	.360	.417	.476	.537
1.2	.043	.058	.074	.091	.109	.126	.144	.163	.182	.203	.223	.268	.317	.368	.422	.479
1.4	.037	.050	.064	.079	.094	.110	.126	.142	.159	.177	.196	.238	.282	.329	.378	.430
1.6	.033	.044	.056	.069	.083	.097	.111	.126	.141	.158	.176	.213	.253	.296	.342	.391
1.8	.029	.039	.050	.062	.074	.087	.100	.113	.127	.142	.159	.192	.230	.269	.312	.356
2.0	.026	.035	.045	.055	.067	.078	.090	.102	.115	.130	.144	.176	.210	.247	.286	.328
2.2	.024	.032	.041	.050	.061	.072	.082	.093	.106	.119	.132	.162	.193	.228	.264	.303
2.4	.022	.029	.037	.046	.056	.066	.076	.086	.098	.110	.122	.150	.179	.211	.246	.282
2.6	.020	.027	.035	.043	.052	.061	.070	.080	.091	.102	.113	.139	.167	.197	.229	.263
2.8	.019	.025	.032	.040	.048	.057	.065	.074	.085	.095	.106	.130	.156	.184	.215	.247
3.0	.017	.023	.030	.037	.045	.053	.061	.070	.079	.089	.099	.122	.147	.173	.202	.232
x	0	.008	.029	.056	.089	.125	.164	.204	.246	.289	.333	.424	.516	.610	.704	.800

*Coefficients in table are for E480XX electrodes.
The effect of eccentricity has been neglected for cases above the solid line.

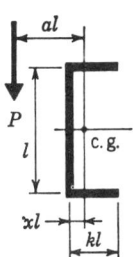

P = Factored eccentric load in kilonewtons.
l = Length of weld parallel to load P in millimetres.
D = Number of millimetres in fillet weld size.
C = Coefficients tabulated below.
xl = Distance from vertical weld to center of gravity of weld group.

$P = CDl$

Required Minimum $C = \dfrac{P}{Dl}$

Required Minimum $D = \dfrac{P}{Cl}$

Required Minimum $l = \dfrac{P}{CD}$

a	\multicolumn{16}{c}{k}															
	0.0	0.1	0.2	0.3	0.4	0.5	0.6	0.7	0.8	0.9	1.0	1.2	1.4	1.6	1.8	2.0
0.2	.153	.183	.214	.244	.275	.305	.336	.366	.397	.428	.458	.519	.580	.641	.702	.763
0.3	.138	.180	.214	.244	.275	.305	.336	.366	.397	.428	.458	.519	.580	.641	.702	.763
0.4	.114	.152	.189	.226	.263	.297	.331	.365	.397	.428	.458	.519	.580	.641	.702	.763
0.5	.096	.128	.161	.195	.229	.264	.296	.328	.360	.392	.424	.488	.555	.622	.691	.761
0.6	.082	.110	.138	.166	.199	.231	.264	.295	.325	.356	.387	.449	.513	.578	.644	.711
0.7	.072	.095	.118	.147	.177	.207	.237	.266	.296	.326	.355	.415	.475	.537	.601	.666
0.8	.063	.084	.105	.131	.157	.186	.215	.244	.272	.299	.327	.384	.443	.502	.563	.626
0.9	.057	.075	.095	.117	.143	.169	.195	.222	.249	.276	.303	.357	.412	.470	.529	.589
1.0	.051	.067	.086	.106	.130	.154	.179	.205	.231	.256	.281	.333	.387	.441	.497	.556
1.2	.043	.056	.072	.090	.110	.131	.153	.176	.199	.223	.246	.293	.341	.392	.444	.498
1.4	.037	.048	.062	.078	.094	.114	.133	.153	.175	.196	.217	.260	.305	.351	.399	.449
1.6	.033	.042	.055	.069	.083	.100	.117	.136	.155	.174	.194	.234	.274	.318	.362	.409
1.8	.029	.038	.048	.061	.074	.089	.105	.122	.138	.157	.175	.211	.250	.289	.331	.374
2.0	.026	.034	.044	.055	.067	.080	.095	.110	.125	.142	.159	.193	.229	.266	.304	.345
2.2	.024	.031	.040	.050	.061	.073	.086	.100	.114	.129	.144	.178	.210	.245	.282	.320
2.4	.022	.029	.036	.046	.056	.067	.079	.091	.105	.119	.133	.163	.195	.228	.262	.297
2.6	.020	.026	.034	.042	.052	.062	.073	.085	.097	.109	.123	.151	.182	.212	.245	.278
2.8	.019	.025	.031	.039	.048	.058	.068	.079	.090	.101	.114	.140	.169	.199	.229	.261
3.0	.017	.023	.029	.037	.045	.054	.064	.073	.084	.095	.107	.131	.158	.187	.215	.246
x	0	.008	.029	.056	.089	.125	.164	.204	.246	.289	.333	.424	.516	.610	.704	.800

*Coefficients in table are for E480XX electrodes.
The effect of eccentricity has been neglected for cases above the solid horizontal line.

ECCENTRIC LOADS ON WELD GROUPS

Coefficients C*

Table 3-28

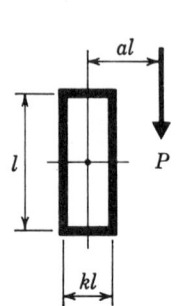

P = Factored eccentric load in kilonewtons.
l = Length of longer welds in millimetres.
D = Number of millimetres in fillet weld size.
C = Coefficients tabulated below.
Note: When load P is perpendicular to longer side l use table on facing page.

$$P = CDl$$

Required Minimum $C = \dfrac{P}{Dl}$

Required Minimum $D = \dfrac{P}{Cl}$

Required Minimum $l = \dfrac{P}{CD}$

a	k										
	0.0	0.1	0.2	0.3	0.4	0.5	0.6	0.7	0.8	0.9	1.0
0.2	.305	.336	.366	.397	.428	.458	.489	.519	.550	.580	.611
0.3	.276	.318	.360	.397	.428	.458	.489	.519	.550	.580	.611
0.4	.229	.267	.307	.346	.383	.417	.451	.486	.520	.555	.590
0.5	.192	.226	.263	.300	.337	.370	.403	.436	.469	.503	.536
0.6	.165	.194	.228	.262	.297	.330	.362	.394	.425	.457	.490
0.7	.144	.170	.200	.232	.265	.297	.327	.357	.388	.418	.449
0.8	.127	.150	.178	.208	.238	.269	.297	.326	.355	.384	.414
0.9	.114	.135	.159	.187	.216	.245	.272	.299	.327	.355	.383
1.0	.103	.122	.145	.170	.197	.224	.250	.276	.302	.329	.357
1.2	.086	.102	.122	.144	.167	.191	.216	.239	.264	.288	.313
1.4	.074	.088	.105	.124	.145	.167	.190	.211	.233	.255	.278
1.6	.065	.077	.092	.109	.128	.148	.169	.188	.208	.229	.250
1.8	.058	.069	.082	.098	.115	.133	.152	.170	.188	.208	.227
2.0	.052	.062	.074	.088	.104	.120	.137	.155	.172	.190	.207
2.2	.048	.056	.067	.081	.095	.110	.125	.142	.158	.174	.191
2.4	.044	.051	.062	.074	.087	.101	.116	.131	.146	.161	.177
2.6	.040	.047	.057	.069	.081	.093	.107	.122	.136	.150	.165
2.8	.037	.044	.053	.064	.075	.087	.100	.114	.127	.140	.154
3.0	.035	.041	.049	.060	.070	.081	.094	.106	.119	.132	.145

*Coefficients in table are for E480XX electrodes.
The effect of eccentricity has been neglected for cases above the solid horizontal line.

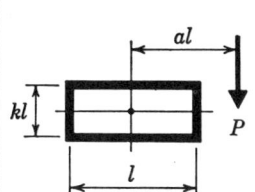

P = Factored eccentric load in kilonewtons.
l = Length of longer welds in millimetres.
D = Number of millimetres in fillet weld size.
C = Coefficients tabulated below.
Note: When load P is parallel to longer side l use table on facing page.

$$P = CDl$$

Required Minimum $C = \dfrac{P}{Dl}$

Required Minimum $D = \dfrac{P}{Cl}$

Required Minimum $l = \dfrac{P}{CD}$

a	k										
	0.0	0.1	0.2	0.3	0.4	0.5	0.6	0.7	0.8	0.9	1.0
0.2	.278	.309	.349	.388	.428	.458	.489	.519	.550	.580	.611
0.3	.230	.258	.297	.335	.375	.417	.463	.508	.550	.580	.611
0.4	.194	.220	.256	.291	.330	.367	.410	.453	.499	.543	.590
0.5	.168	.191	.223	.256	.293	.329	.366	.406	.449	.492	.536
0.6	.147	.168	.198	.228	.263	.296	.332	.367	.407	.448	.490
0.7	.130	.149	.177	.205	.237	.268	.302	.336	.371	.409	.449
0.8	.117	.134	.160	.186	.216	.245	.276	.308	.343	.376	.414
0.9	.106	.122	.145	.170	.197	.225	.255	.284	.317	.349	.383
1.0	.096	.111	.133	.156	.182	.207	.236	.264	.294	.324	.357
1.2	.082	.095	.114	.133	.157	.180	.205	.230	.257	.283	.313
1.4	.071	.083	.099	.117	.138	.158	.181	.203	.228	.252	.278
1.6	.063	.073	.088	.104	.123	.141	.162	.182	.204	.226	.250
1.8	.056	.065	.079	.093	.110	.127	.146	.165	.185	.205	.227
2.0	.051	.059	.072	.085	.100	.116	.133	.150	.169	.187	.207
2.2	.047	.054	.065	.077	.092	.106	.122	.138	.155	.173	.191
2.4	.043	.050	.060	.071	.085	.098	.113	.127	.144	.160	.177
2.6	.040	.046	.056	.066	.079	.091	.105	.118	.134	.149	.165
2.8	.037	.043	.052	.062	.073	.085	.098	.111	.125	.139	.154
3.0	.034	.040	.049	.058	.069	.079	.092	.104	.117	.130	.145

*Coefficients in table are for E480XX electrodes.
The effect of eccentricity has been neglected for cases above the solid horizontal line.

ECCENTRIC LOADS ON WELD GROUPS

Coefficients C*

Table 3-30

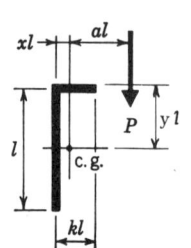

P = Factored eccentric load in kilonewtons.
l = Length of weld parallel to load P in millimetres.
D = Number of millimetres in fillet weld size.
C = Coefficients tabulated below.
xl = Distance from vertical weld to center of gravity of weld group.

$$P = CDl$$

Required Minimum $C = \dfrac{P}{Dl}$

Required Minimum $D = \dfrac{P}{Cl}$

Required Minimum $l = \dfrac{P}{CD}$

a	\multicolumn{16}{c}{k}
	0.0	0.1	0.2	0.3	0.4	0.5	0.6	0.7	0.8	0.9	1.0	1.2	1.4	1.6	1.8	2.0
0.2	.153	.168	.183	.199	.214	.229	.244	.260	.275	.290	.305	.336	.366	.397	.428	.458
0.3	.138	.156	.175	.192	.208	.223	.238	.254	.270	.287	.304	.336	.366	.397	.428	.458
0.4	.114	.130	.147	.162	.177	.192	.206	.220	.235	.250	.266	.299	.335	.373	.411	.451
0.5	.096	.110	.124	.137	.151	.166	.179	.192	.205	.220	.234	.266	.300	.336	.373	.412
0.6	.082	.094	.107	.118	.130	.143	.157	.169	.181	.195	.209	.239	.271	.305	.341	.378
0.7	.072	.082	.093	.103	.114	.126	.138	.150	.162	.174	.188	.216	.246	.279	.313	.349
0.8	.063	.073	.082	.092	.101	.112	.123	.135	.146	.158	.170	.197	.226	.257	.290	.324
0.9	.057	.065	.074	.082	.091	.101	.111	.123	.133	.144	.155	.180	.208	.238	.269	.302
1.0	.051	.059	.067	.074	.082	.091	.101	.112	.122	.132	.143	.166	.193	.221	.251	.283
1.2	.043	.050	.056	.062	.069	.077	.085	.095	.104	.113	.122	.144	.168	.194	.221	.250
1.4	.037	.043	.048	.054	.060	.067	.074	.082	.090	.098	.107	.127	.148	.172	.197	.224
1.6	.033	.037	.042	.047	.053	.058	.065	.072	.080	.087	.095	.113	.133	.154	.177	.202
1.8	.029	.033	.038	.042	.047	.052	.058	.065	.072	.079	.086	.102	.120	.140	.161	.184
2.0	.026	.030	.034	.038	.042	.047	.052	.058	.065	.071	.078	.093	.109	.127	.147	.168
2.2	.024	.027	.031	.035	.038	.043	.048	.053	.059	.065	.071	.085	.100	.117	.136	.155
2.4	.022	.025	.028	.032	.035	.039	.044	.049	.055	.060	.066	.079	.093	.108	.126	.144
2.6	.020	.023	.026	.029	.033	.036	.041	.045	.051	.056	.061	.073	.086	.101	.117	.134
2.8	.019	.021	.024	.027	.030	.034	.038	.042	.047	.052	.057	.068	.081	.094	.109	.126
3.0	.017	.020	.023	.025	.028	.032	.035	.039	.044	.049	.053	.064	.075	.088	.103	.118
x	0	.005	.017	.035	.057	.083	.112	.144	.178	.213	.250	.327	.408	.492	.579	.667
y	.500	.455	.417	.385	.357	.333	.312	.294	.278	.263	.250	.227	.208	.192	.179	.167

*Coefficients in table are for E480XX electrodes.
The effect of eccentricity has been neglected for cases above the solid horizontal line.

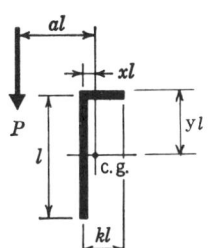

P = Factored eccentric load in kilonewtons.
l = Length of weld parallel to load P in millimetres.
D = Number of millimetres in fillet weld size.
C = Coefficients tabulated below.
xl = Distance from vertical weld to center of gravity of weld group.

$$P = CDl$$

Required Minimum $C = \dfrac{P}{Dl}$

Required Minimum $D = \dfrac{P}{Cl}$

Required Minimum $l = \dfrac{P}{CD}$

a	k 0.0	0.1	0.2	0.3	0.4	0.5	0.6	0.7	0.8	0.9	1.0	1.2	1.4	1.6	1.8	2.0
0.2	.153	.168	.183	.199	.214	.229	.244	.260	.275	.290	.305	.336	.366	.397	.428	.458
0.3	.138	.156	.174	.189	.205	.219	.234	.250	.265	.282	.300	.336	.366	.397	.428	.458
0.4	.114	.130	.146	.159	.173	.188	.202	.217	.233	.249	.266	.303	.338	.372	.407	.443
0.5	.096	.110	.122	.135	.149	.162	.176	.191	.206	.221	.237	.273	.310	.343	.377	.413
0.6	.082	.094	.105	.117	.129	.142	.154	.169	.183	.198	.213	.248	.284	.318	.351	.386
0.7	.072	.082	.092	.102	.114	.125	.138	.151	.164	.179	.193	.226	.260	.295	.327	.360
0.8	.063	.072	.081	.091	.101	.112	.124	.136	.149	.162	.176	.207	.240	.275	.305	.338
0.9	.057	.064	.073	.082	.091	.102	.112	.123	.135	.148	.161	.191	.222	.255	.286	.318
1.0	.051	.058	.066	.074	.082	.092	.102	.113	.124	.136	.149	.176	.207	.238	.269	.300
1.2	.043	.049	.055	.062	.070	.078	.087	.096	.106	.117	.128	.153	.180	.209	.239	.268
1.4	.037	.042	.048	.054	.060	.067	.075	.083	.092	.102	.112	.134	.159	.186	.215	.242
1.6	.033	.037	.042	.047	.053	.059	.066	.073	.082	.090	.099	.120	.142	.167	.193	.220
1.8	.029	.033	.037	.042	.047	.053	.059	.066	.073	.081	.089	.108	.129	.151	.176	.201
2.0	.026	.030	.034	.038	.042	.048	.053	.059	.066	.073	.081	.098	.117	.138	.161	.185
2.2	.024	.027	.031	.034	.039	.043	.048	.054	.060	.067	.074	.089	.107	.127	.148	.170
2.4	.022	.025	.028	.031	.035	.040	.044	.050	.055	.062	.068	.082	.099	.117	.137	.157
2.6	.020	.023	.026	.029	.033	.037	.041	.046	.051	.057	.063	.076	.092	.109	.127	.146
2.8	.019	.021	.024	.027	.030	.034	.038	.043	.048	.053	.059	.071	.086	.101	.118	.136
3.0	.017	.020	.022	.025	.028	.032	.036	.040	.044	.049	.055	.067	.080	.095	.110	.127
x	0	.005	.017	.035	.057	.083	.112	.144	.178	.213	.250	.327	.408	.492	.579	.667
y	.500	.455	.417	.385	.357	.333	.312	.294	.278	.263	.250	.227	.208	.192	.179	.167

*Coefficients in table are for E480XX electrodes.
The effect of eccentricity has been neglected for cases above the solid horizontal line.

NOTES

ECCENTRIC LOADS ON WELD GROUPS
SHEAR AND MOMENT

For the case of the eccentrically loaded fillet weld group shown below in Figure 3—3, an analysis similar to that for the in-plane eccentricity is used but modified to account for the bearing of the plate at ultimate load. The magnitude and location of the horizontal force, H_B, due to plate bearing, is derived assuming a triangular stress block at ultimate load. (See Figure 3—4). According to Reference 1, the triangular stress block assumption provides a better prediction of the ultimate load than either a rectangular or parabolic distribution. The vertical force, V_B, below the neutral axis is assumed as the shear resistance of that portion of the weld below the neutral axis. This method of analysis accounts for the load-deformation characteristics of the weld.

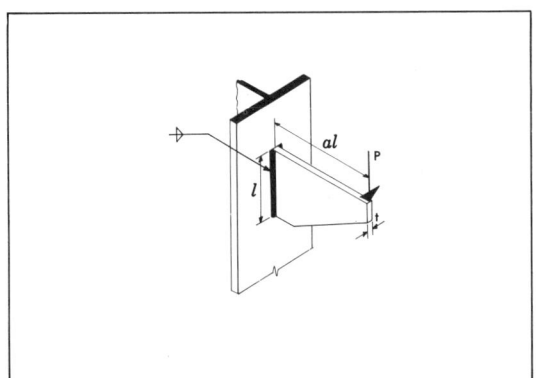

Figure 3-3

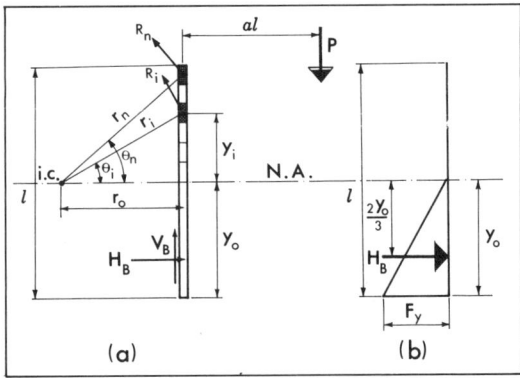

Figure 3-4

Table

Table 3—32 has been computed based upon the use of E480XX electrodes and $F_y = 300$ MPa following the method outlined in Reference 1. The coefficient C' (P/l) is tabulated for various plate thicknesses, t, and fillet weld sizes. For joints using lower strength materials the value of C' may be multiplied by $F_y/300$.

The tabulated values are conservative when used with plate material in excess of 300 MPa yield. The maximum value of C' is determined by shear in the plate and is accounted for in the tabulated values.

References:

1. Dawe, J. L. and Kulak, G. L., "Welded Connections Under Combined Shear and Moment", Proc. of ASCE J. of Struct. Div. Vol. 100, ST4, April 1974.

Example

Given:

A 12 mm plate carrying a 180 kN factored load is welded to a column with a pair of fillet welds 250 mm long. Find the fillet weld size required if the 180 kN load acts at a 130 mm eccentricity.

Solution:

l = 250 mm
al = 130 mm, therefore a = 130/250 = 0.52

Therefore, C' required = P/l = 180/250 = 0.72

Try 6 mm fillet weld

From Table 3—32 for t = 12 mm and 6 mm weld size:

C' = 0.754 for a = 0.50 and 0.629 for a = 0.60

Therefore for a = 0.52, C' = 0.73 (by interpolation) > 0.72 — OK

The minimum weld size based upon the thickness of the materials joined and the resistance of the connected parts must also be checked.

ECCENTRIC LOADS ON WELD GROUPS
Coefficients C′*
Table 3-32

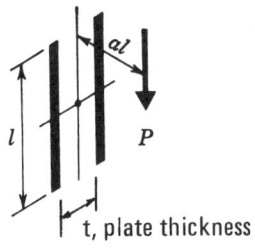

P = Factored eccentric load (kN)

l = Length of fillet welds parallel to load P (mm)

C′ = Coefficients tabulated below

P = C′ l

Required minimum C′ = P/l

Required minimum l = P/C′

Plate Thickness	8 mm	10 mm		12 mm			16 mm		
Weld Size	5	5	6	5	6	8	6	8	10
a 0.2	1.30	1.47	1.60	1.55	1.76	2.00	1.90	2.34	2.60
0.3	0.889	1.04	1.10	1.16	1.24	1.36	1.47	1.66	1.78
0.4	0.671	0.784	0.828	0.885	0.941	1.02	1.13	1.25	1.34
0.5	0.537	0.630	0.665	0.710	0.754	0.818	0.911	1.01	1.07
0.6	0.448	0.526	0.555	0.594	0.629	0.683	0.762	0.839	0.895
0.7	0.385	0.450	0.475	0.509	0.540	0.586	0.653	0.720	0.767
0.8	0.336	0.394	0.416	0.446	0.473	0.512	0.573	0.631	0.673
0.9	0.298	0.350	0.369	0.396	0.420	0.455	0.509	0.560	0.598
1.0	0.269	0.316	0.332	0.357	0.379	0.410	0.458	0.506	0.537
1.2	0.223	0.263	0.276	0.297	0.316	0.342	0.382	0.421	0.448
1.4	0.191	0.225	0.238	0.255	0.270	0.292	0.327	0.360	0.384
1.6	0.168	0.197	0.207	0.224	0.236	0.256	0.286	0.315	0.336
1.8	0.150	0.175	0.184	0.198	0.210	0.228	0.255	0.280	0.299
2.0	0.134	0.157	0.166	0.178	0.188	0.205	0.229	0.251	0.269
2.2	0.122	0.143	0.151	0.162	0.172	0.186	0.208	0.229	0.244
2.4	0.111	0.132	0.137	0.149	0.158	0.170	0.191	0.210	0.224
2.6	0.103	0.121	0.127	0.136	0.145	0.157	0.176	0.194	0.206
2.8	0.096	0.113	0.118	0.127	0.135	0.146	0.162	0.180	0.192
3.0	0.089	0.105	0.111	0.119	0.126	0.137	0.152	0.168	0.179

Plate Thickness	20 mm			25 mm				40 mm			
Weld Size	8	10	12	8	10	12	14	10	12	14	16
a 0.2	2.50	2.93	3.21	2.60	3.13	3.56	3.89	3.35	3.94	4.50	5.01
0.3	1.89	2.07	2.20	2.10	2.37	2.55	2.69	2.85	3.23	3.54	3.79
0.4	1.45	1.57	1.66	1.65	1.81	1.93	2.03	2.31	2.55	2.74	2.90
0.5	1.17	1.26	1.33	1.33	1.46	1.55	1.63	1.89	2.07	2.21	2.33
0.6	0.974	1.05	1.11	1.12	1.22	1.29	1.36	1.59	1.74	1.85	1.95
0.7	0.836	0.900	0.949	0.959	1.04	1.11	1.16	1.37	1.49	1.59	1.67
0.8	0.732	0.789	0.833	0.840	0.916	0.973	1.02	1.20	1.31	1.39	1.46
0.9	0.651	0.701	0.739	0.747	0.813	0.865	0.906	1.07	1.16	1.24	1.30
1.0	0.586	0.632	0.664	0.673	0.733	0.779	0.815	0.965	1.05	1.11	1.17
1.2	0.488	0.526	0.554	0.562	0.610	0.649	0.679	0.806	0.873	0.930	0.977
1.4	0.418	0.451	0.475	0.481	0.523	0.557	0.582	0.690	0.749	0.797	0.836
1.6	0.367	0.394	0.415	0.421	0.458	0.487	0.510	0.604	0.655	0.696	0.733
1.8	0.326	0.351	0.369	0.373	0.407	0.432	0.452	0.537	0.581	0.620	0.652
2.0	0.293	0.316	0.333	0.336	0.366	0.390	0.408	0.484	0.528	0.558	0.586
2.2	0.266	0.287	0.302	0.306	0.333	0.353	0.370	0.440	0.476	0.507	0.533
2.4	0.244	0.263	0.277	0.281	0.305	0.324	0.339	0.403	0.437	0.465	0.489
2.6	0.226	0.242	0.256	0.259	0.282	0.300	0.313	0.371	0.404	0.429	0.451
2.8	0.209	0.225	0.237	0.240	0.261	0.278	0.291	0.345	0.374	0.399	0.419
3.0	0.195	0.210	0.221	0.224	0.244	0.260	0.272	0.322	0.349	0.372	0.390

*Coefficients in table are for E480XX electrodes and plate with F_y = 300 MPa.

FRAMED BEAM SHEAR CONNECTIONS

General

This section of Part 3 contains information on four common types of beam shear connections traditionally considered standard in the industry. Included are double angle connections, simple end plate connections, single angle connections and Tee-connections.

These types of connections are generally designed for strength requirements only, under the effects of factored loads, and the capacities of welds and of bolts in bearing-type connections are based on their factored resistances. These capacities are to be used with factored loads.

Bolt capacities for slip-resistant joints have also been included, when designing shear connections which are subject to repeated loads, for double angle and end plate connections based on clean mill scale faying surfaces, $\mu = 0.59$, and are to be used with specified loads only.

Tables of bolt and weld capacities are based on M20 and M22 A325M bolts and 3/4 and 7/8-inch diameter A325 bolts for bolted connections, and on E480XX electrodes for welded joints, and assume the use of detail material with a specified minimum yield strength, F_y, of 300 MPa.

Although based on specific arrangements of bolts and welds the tables are general in nature, and are intended to facilitate the design of all types of shear connections and not to preclude the use of other types of connections. It is anticipated that these tables will be used by steel fabricators in the preparation of their drawing office and shop standards, to assist design authorities in the checking of fabricator standards, and in the teaching of structural steel design and detailing at educational institutions.

The standard connections of any individual fabricator may differ from those shown in the tables, especially with regard to length and size of angles and other detail material, and of gauge and pitch of bolts, and will depend on the particular fabrication methods employed and on the fabricator's usual source of material.

Minimum Material Thickness

Associated with the tables listing capacities of welds and capacities of bolts in bearing-type connections, is information concerning the minimum required thickness of supporting and supported material to develop the full connector capacities. These minimum thicknesses have been developed for three different values of minimum specified material yield strength (F_y = 250, 300 and 350 MPa) and were determined in the following manner.

For welded connections, for each weld size and for each value of F_y the two equations for V_r (Table 5, CAN3-S16.1-M78), namely, $V_r = 0.66 \phi A_m F_y$ for the base metal or $V_r = 0.5 \phi A_w X_u$ for the weld metal with $X_u = 480$ MPa were equated to the factored shear resistance of the web of the supported beam, $V_r = \phi A_w F_s$ with $F_s = 0.66 F_y$, and solved for the web material thickness, t.

For bolts in bearing-type connections, the minimum material thickness was derived by equating the bearing capacity of the material to the shear capacity of the bolts and assumes that supported beams are not coped. For webs of beams (both supporting and supported) and for webs and flanges of columns (supporting) the maximum factored bearing resistance has been assumed, namely $B_r = \phi t n 3d F_u$ (Clause 13.10 (c)) while for framing angles, end plates and Tees, an end distance, e, equal to 1.5 bolt diameters has been assumed in computing the factored bearing resistance $B_r = \phi t n e F_u$. The factored bearing resistance of the angles, end plates and Tees, is thus one-half the factored bearing resistance for the webs or flanges. Bolt shear values were either double or single shear as appropriate, thus for bearing type connections, the following conditions arise for the tabulated values of minimum thickness.

(a) For double angle connections the minimum thickness is that required for the web of the supported beam, for the connection angle, and for the supporting material when beams frame from two sides. One-half the value listed is required for the thickness of supporting material when the beams frame from one side only.

(b) For end plate connections, the minimum thickness is that required for the supporting material when beams frame in from one side only. Double the value listed is required for the end plate and also for the supporting material when beams frame from two sides.

(c) For single angle connections the minimum thickness is that required for the web of the supported beam and for the supporting material when beams frame from one side only. Double the value listed is required for the connection angle and for the supporting material when beams frame from two sides.

(d) For Tee connections the minimum thickness is that required for the web of the supported beam, for the flange of the Tee and for the supporting material when beams frame from two sides. Double the value listed is required for the web of the Tee and one-half the value listed for the supporting material when beams frame from one side.

DOUBLE ANGLE BEAM CONNECTIONS

Tables 3—33 and 3—34 on pages 3—58 and 3—59 list, respectively, capacities of bolted and welded double angle beam connections. At the bottom of each table are values for minimum material thickness required to develop the connector capacities listed in the corresponding columns. For material thickness less than those listed, the corresponding connector capacities must be reduced by the ratio of the thickness of material supplied to the thickness of material listed. Any combination of welded or bolted legs can be selected from the tables.

Bolt capacities are based on concentric loading as tests have shown that eccentricity does not influence the ultimate strength of the bolts in connections using only one line of bolts in the web framing leg. Weld capacities include the effect of eccentricity for connection angles up to 310 mm in length. For longer connection angles the weld capacity is not reduced by the effect of eccentricity.

The connection angle length, L, has been based on a bolt pitch of 80 mm assuming an end distance of 35 mm. For connections angles with both legs welded the angle lengths can be adjusted and capacities interpolated in accordance with the length used. Suggested minimum and maximum depths of supported beams appropriate to each length of connection angle have been included. The suggested maximum depth assumes a connection length not less than half the depth of the beam to provide some measure of stiffness and stability, and it should be recognized that these depths may not always be appropriate for a particular structure.

Table 3—33 for bolted connections lists bolt capacities for both bearing-type and slip-resistant connections for three sizes of angle (width of leg and gauge dimension) and includes values for 2 to 13 bolts per vertical line based on a bolt pitch of 80 mm. For web framing legs, bolt capacities are based on the "double shear" condition and for outstanding legs on the "single shear" condition. This two vertical lines of bolts in the outstanding legs (one line in each angle leg) have the same capacity as one vertical line in the web framing leg. When beams are connected to both sides of the supporting material, the total bolt capacity in the outstanding legs is double that listed, provided the thickness of the supporting material is equal to or greater than that listed for the web of the supported beam.

For connection angles, the minimum required thickness to develop the bolt capacities (based on an assumed end distance of 1.5 bolt diameters) is the same as that listed for the web of the supported beam. This thickness will also provide adequate shear capacity for the angles. To ensure connection flexibility the angle thickness selected should not be greater than necessary, with a minimum thickness of 6 mm for practical reasons. When connection angles are less than 10 mm thick, bolt threads may intercept a shear plane, in which case the bolt capacity must be reduced to 70% of the tabulated values. (See clause 22.1.4 and clause 13.11.2 of CAN3-S16.1-M78).

Table 3—34 for welded connections lists weld capacities for the weld configurations shown for both web framing legs with welds and outstanding legs with welds. Values are tabulated for four sizes of fillet welds and are based on the length and size (angle width W) of connection angles listed. The weld capacities for the outstanding leg assumes an angle thickness equal to the weld plus 1 mm in determining the capacity under eccentric load.

Design of bearing-type connections for types and sizes of bolts other than those shown in Table 3—33 will be facilitated by the tables of resistances on pages 3—7 to 3—11 inclusive and for slip-resistant connections to the tables on page 3—15.

Supported Beams with Copes.

Tests conducted at the Universities of Toronto and Texas have indicated the importance of bolt spacing in double angle beam end connections when the supported beam has the top flange coped, with the coped web subjected to high bearing stresses, termed "Block Shear" in Reference (1). It may be necessary in some instances, to increase the bolt pitch and/or the edge distance for bolts in the beam web. Tests cited in Reference (2) have shown that capacities of single row connections computed by assuming shear along the 'block shear line' are conservative, however, with two rows of bolts in the web framing leg, the effects of eccentricity should be taken into account in determining the capacity of connections where the top flange of the supported beam is coped.

References

1. Birkemoe, P. C. and Gilmor, M. I., "Behaviour of Bearing Critical Double Angle Beam Connections", Eng. J. AISC, Fourth Quarter, 1978.
2. Yura, J. A., Birkemoe, P. E. and Ricles, J. M., "Beam Web Shear Connections — An Experimental Study", Beam-to-Column Building Connections: State of the Art, ASCE, Preprint 80-179, April, 1980.

Example 1

Bolted to beam web, bearing-type, welded to column flange.

Given:

W530×92 beam connected to flange of W250×73 column

Reaction due to factored loads = 715 kN.

Beam web thickness = 10.2 mm, Column flange thickness = 14.2 mm.

G40.21-M 300W Material, M20 A325M bolts, E480XX electrodes.

Solution:

Web framing legs — bolted (Table 3—33)

Four bolts per vertical line provide a capacity of 840 kN.

Web thickness required for F_y = 300 (F_u = 450 MPa) steel
= 11.7 x 715/840 = 10.0 mm < 10.2 mm — OK

Minimum angle length required = 310 mm.

Angle thickness required is same as web of supported beam = 10 mm.

Threads will be excluded from shear plane, no reduction in bolt capacity.

Connection capacity = 840 x 10.2/11.7 = 732 kN

Outstanding legs — welded (Table 3—34)

With L = 310 mm, W = 75 mm or 90 mm,

8 mm fillet welds provide a capacity of 754 kN > 715 kN — OK

10 mm thick angle required for bolting is also good for 8 mm fillet welds.

Use:

75 x 75 x 10 connection angles, 310 mm long, four M20 A325M bolts in web framing leg and 8 mm fillet welds on outstanding legs.

Example 2

Welded to beam web, bolted to column flange, bearing-type.

Given:

Same as example 1

Solution:

Web framing legs — welded (Table 3—34)

6 mm fillet welds provide a capacity of 806 kN with angle length L = 310 mm, W = 75 mm

or, 5 mm fillet welds provide a capacity of 794 kN with angle length L = 390 mm, W = 75 mm

Web thickness required for 6 mm fillet welds, L = 310 mm
= 10.3 x 715/806 = 9.1 mm < 10.2 mm — OK

Outstanding legs — bolted (Table 3—33)

Try 10 mm angle thickness (Threads excluded from shear plane).

For L = 310 mm, W = 75 mm or 90 mm, four bolts per vertical line, bearing capacity = 840 x 10/11.7 = 718 kN > 715 kN — OK

or, Try 8 mm angle thickness (threads intercept shear plane).

For L = 390 mm, W = 75 mm or 90 mm, five bolts per vertical line, bolt capacity = 0.70 x 1050 = 735 kN > 715 kN — OK

bearing capacity = 1050 x 8/11.7 = 718 kN > 715 kN — OK

Required thickness of supporting material, beams framing from one side, is one-half thickness of connection angles, therefore column flange thickness of 14.2 mm is good for either solution.

Use:

90 x 75 x 10 connection angles, 310 mm long, 90 mm outstanding legs, g = 130 mm with eight M20 A325M bolts (2 rows of 4) and 6 mm fillet welds.

or, 75 x 75 x 8 connection angles, 390 mm long, g = 100 mm with ten M20 A325M bolts (2 rows of 5) and 5 mm fillet welds.

Choice of angle size will depend on fabricators preferred standard dimensions for hole making in column flange and detail material.

Example 3

Bolted to beam web and bolted to both sides of supporting member — supported beams not coped — bearing-type.

Given:

W530×92 beam, Factored reaction 715 kN framing to both sides of web of WWF800×154 girder, web thickness 10.0 mm.
G40.21-M 300W material, M20 A325M bolts.

Solution:

Web framing legs — same as example 1

Outstanding legs — bolted to both sides of supporting member (Table 3—33).

Total reaction on girder web = 2 x 715 = 1430 kN

For beams connected to both sides of supporting member, bolt capacities are double those listed in table, and required web thickness of supporting member is the same as that given for web thickness of supported beam.

For angle L = 310 mm, W = 75 mm or 90 mm, web thickness of 10 mm, four M20 A325M bolts per vertical line, bearing capacity of web
= 2 x 840 x 10/11.7 = 1435 kN > 1430 kN — OK

Use:

90 x 90 x 10 connection angles, 310 mm long, four M20 A325M bolts per vertical line in both leg framing and outstanding legs.

BOLTED DOUBLE ANGLE[1] BEAM CONNECTIONS
Table 3-33

M20, M22 A325M Bolts
3/4, 7/8 A325 Bolts

BOLT CAPACITY — EITHER LEG WITH BOLTS

WEB FRAMING LEG   OUTSTANDING LEGS

Angle Width and Gauge		
W	g	g_1
100	140	65
90	130	60
75	100	45

Nominal depth of supported beam (mm)		Conn. Angle Length L (mm)	Bolts per Vertical Line	BEARING-TYPE CONNECTION[2] Factored Load Resistance (kN)				SLIP-RESISTANT CONNECTION[4] Specified Load Resistance (kN)			
				Bolt Size				Bolt Size			
min.	max.			3/4	M20	M22	7/8	3/4	M20	M22	7/8
				W = 90 mm		W = 100 mm		W = 90 mm		W = 100 mm	
200	310	150	2	378	420	508	516	145	160	193	197
310	460	230	3	568	630	762	774	217	240	290	296
380	610	310	4	757	840	1020	1030	290	320	386	394
460	760	390	5	946	1050	1270	1290	362	400	483	493
530	920	470	6	1140	1260	1520	1550	434	480	580	592
610	1100	550	7	1320	1470	1780	1810	507	560	676	690
690	1200	630	8	1510	1680	2030	2060	579	640	773	789
800		710	9	1700	1890	2290	2320	652	720	869	887
900		790	10	1890	2100	2540	2580	724	800	966	986
920		870	11	2080	2310	2790	2840	796	880	1060	1080
1100		950	12	2270	2520	3050	3100	869	960	1160	1180
1200		1030	13	2460	2730	3300	3350	941	1040	1260	1280
				W = 75 mm		W = 90 mm		W = 75 mm		W = 90 mm	
200	310	150	2	378	420	508	516	145	160	193	197
310	460	230	3	568	630	762	774	217	240	290	296
380	610	310	4	757	840	1020	1030	290	320	386	394
460	760	390	5	946	1050	1270	1290	362	400	483	493
530	920	470	6	1140	1260	1520	1550	434	480	580	592
610	1100	550	7	1320	1470	1780	1810	507	560	676	690
690	1200	630	8	1510	1680	2030	2060	579	640	773	789
800		710	9	1700	1890	2290	2320	652	720	869	887
900		790	10	1890	2100	2540	2580	724	800	966	986
920		870	11	2080	2310	2790	2840	796	880	1060	1080
1100		950	12	2270	2520	3050	3100	869	960	1160	1180
1200		1030	13	2460	2730	3300	3350	941	1040	1260	1280

Specified Minimum Yield Strength of Material (MPa)	Minimum Required Web Thickness of Supported Beam[3] (mm)			
F_y = 250 (F_u = 400 MPa)	12.4	13.1	14.4	14.5
F_y = 300 (F_u = 450 MPa)	11.0	11.7	12.8	12.9
F_y = 350 (F_u = 480 MPa)	10.3	10.9	12.0	12.1

1. Connection angles are assumed to be material with F_y = 300 MPa.
2. When threads intercept a shear plane, use 70% of the values tabulated for bearing-type connections.
3. For connection angles, and for supporting material with beams framing from both sides, minimum required thickness is equal to tabulated values for web thickness of supported beam, and for supporting material with beams framing from one side is one-half the tabulated values.
4. Tabulated values for slip resistant connections assume clean mill scale with μ = 0.59.

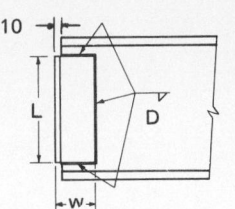

WEB FRAMING LEG WITH WELDS

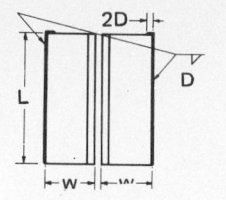

OUTSTANDING LEG WITH WELDS

WELDED DOUBLE ANGLE BEAM CONNECTIONS [a]
Table 3-34

E480XX
Fillet Welds

WELD CAPACITY Factored Load Resistance (kN)				WELD CAPACITY Factored Load Resistance (kN)				Conn. Angle Length L (mm)	Nominal Depth of Supported Beam (mm)	
Fillet Size D (mm)				Fillet Size D (mm)						
5	6	8	10	5	6	8	10		min.	max.
Angle Width W = 75 mm				Angle Width W = 90 mm						
394	473	631	789	135	157	202	246	150	200	310
550	660	880	1100	303	356	460	563	230	310	460
672	806	1080	1340	473	568	754	933	310	380	610
794	953	1270	1590	596	715	953	1190	390	460	760
916	1100	1470	1830	718	861	1150	1440	470	530	920
1040	1250	1660	2080	840	1010	1340	1680	550	610	1100
1160	1390	1860	2320	962	1150	1540	1920	630	690	1200
1280	1540	2050	2560	1080	1300	1740	2170	710	800	
1400	1690	2250	2810	1210	1450	1930	2410	790	900	
1530	1830	2440	3050	1330	1600	2130	2660	870	920	
1650	1980	2640	3300	1450	1740	2320	2900	950	1100	
1770	2130	2830	3540	1570	1890	2520	3150	1030	1200	
Angle Width W = 65 mm				Angle Width W = 75 mm						
382	459	612	765	146	170	218	265	150	200	310
519	623	831	1040	322	380	491	602	230	310	460
641	770	1030	1280	473	568	758	947	310	380	610
764	916	1220	1530	596	715	953	1190	390	460	760
886	1060	1420	1770	718	861	1150	1440	470	530	920
1010	1210	1610	2020	840	1010	1340	1680	550	610	1100
1130	1360	1810	2260	962	1150	1540	1920	630	690	1200
1250	1500	2000	2500	1080	1300	1740	2170	710	800	
1370	1650	2200	2750	1210	1450	1930	2410	790	900	
1500	1800	2390	2990	1330	1600	2130	2660	870	920	
1620	1940	2590	3240	1450	1740	2320	2900	950	1100	
1740	2090	2780	3480	1570	1890	2520	3150	1030	1200	
Minimum Required Web Thickness of Supported Beam (mm)				Minimum Thickness of Supporting Material with Beam Attached One Side [b]				Specified Minimum Yield Strength of Material (MPa)		
10.0	12.0	16.0	20.0	5.0	6.0	8.0	10.0	$F_y = 250$ (MPa)		
8.6	10.3	13.8	17.2	4.3	5.2	6.9	8.6	$F_y = 300$ (MPa)		
7.4	8.8	11.8	14.7	3.7	4.4	5.9	7.4	$F_y = 350$ (MPa)		

a. Connection angles are assumed to be material with $F_y = 300$ MPa.
b. For supporting material with beams framing from both sides, use double the tabulated value.

END PLATE CONNECTIONS

End plate connections with the connection plate welded to the supported beam and bolted to the supporting member have become increasingly popular due to their economy and ease of fabrication, and to their satisfactory performance. Continuing research has demonstrated that end plates are suitable for both simple beam shear connections and for moment connections (see page 3—72) when suitably proportioned.

The tighter tolerances required for fabrication of beams with end plates present no problems when beams are saw cut to length, and the use of simple jigging procedures makes it possible to locate and support end plates with a high degree of precision during fabrication and welding.

Research conducted to date on simple beam end plate shear connections indicates that their strength and flexibility compare favourably with double angle shear connections for similar material thickness, depth of connection and arrangement of bolts (gauge and pitch). It is suggested for practical reasons that the minimum thickness of end plates for simple beam connections be 6 mm, and that the maximum thickness be limited to 10 mm for adequate flexibility.

The gauge dimension, g, should preferably be between 100 mm and 150 mm for plates up to 10 mm thickness, but may be as low as 80 mm for minimum thickness plates and plates with F_y not greater than 300 MPa.

Table 3—36 lists the capacities of bolts and welds for typical end plate connections with from 2 to 8 bolts per vertical line, and the minimum thickness of supporting and supported material to develop the full capacity of the bolts and welds respectively. Also included in the table are reduction factors for calculating the effective bolt capacity in bearing-type connections, based on the bearing capacity of the end plate for end plate thicknesses of 6, 7, 8 and 10 mm, assuming an end distance of 1.5 bolt diameters.

Bolt capacities for slip-resistant joints are also included for those situations where bearing-type connections are not suitable.

Example

Given:

W410×60 beam, framing into web of WWF700×141 girder.

Factored reaction 325 kN.

Beam web thickness = 7.7 mm, girder web thickness = 9.0 mm

G40.21-M 300W steel, M20 A325M bolts, E480XX electrodes.

Solution:

Assume 7 mm thick end plate, effective bolt capacity for 3 bolts per vertical line = 630 × 0.60 = 378 kN > 325 kN — OK

For 230 mm long end plate, weld capacity for 5 mm fillet welds made with E480XX electrodes = 350 kN > 325 kN — OK

Minimum length of end plate required for 7.7 mm web thickness (300W steel) = 230 × 8.6/7.7 = 257 mm. Use 260 mm

Therefore weld capacity = 350 × 260/230 = 396 kN

Required web thickness of girder with beams framing from both sides is double that listed in the table

= 2 × 5.8 × 325/630 = 6.0 mm < 9.0 mm — OK

Use:

160 × 7 mm end plate, 260 mm long connected to web of supported beam with 5 mm E480XX fillet welds, with six M20 A325M bolts (2 rows of 3 at 100 mm gauge) with increased end distance and/or increased pitch.

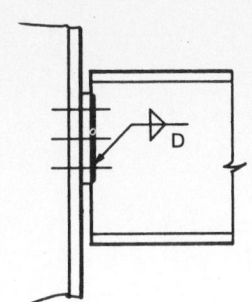

END PLATE BEAM CONNECTIONS
Table 3-36

M20, M22, A325M Bolts
3/4, 7/8, A325 Bolts
E480XX Fillet Welds

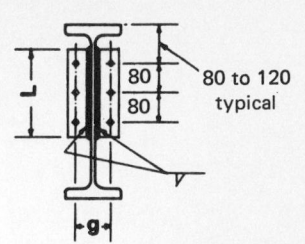

80 to 120 typical

Bolts per Vertical Line	BEARING-TYPE CONNECTION Factored Load Resistance [1] (kN) Bolt Size				WELD CAPACITY Factored Load Resistance (kN) Fillet Size D (mm)			Connection Plate Length (mm)
	3/4	M20	M22	7/8	5	6	8	
2	378	420	508	516	228	276	366	150
3	568	630	762	774	350	423	561	230
4	757	840	1020	1030	471	570	756	310
5	946	1050	1270	1290	593	718	952	390
6	1140	1260	1520	1550	714	865	1150	470
7	1320	1470	1780	1810	836	1010	1340	550
8	1510	1680	2030	2060	958	1160	1540	630

Material F_u (MPa)	Minimum Required Thickness of Supporting Material with Beams Framing From One Side [2] (mm)				Minimum Required Web Thickness of Supported Beam (mm)			Material F_y (MPa)
400	6.2	6.6	7.2	7.3	10.0	12.0	16.0	250
450	5.5	5.8	6.4	6.4	8.6	10.3	13.8	300
480	5.2	5.5	6.0	6.0	7.4	8.8	11.8	350

End Plate Thickness (mm)	Reduction Factors For Bolt Capacities To Develop Bearing Resistance of End Plates (F_y = 300 MPa)			
6	0.55	0.52	0.47	0.47
7	0.64	0.60	0.55	0.55
8	0.70	0.69	0.63	0.63
10	0.91	0.86	0.78	0.78

Bolts per Vertical Line	Slip-Resistant Connection Specified Load Resistance [3] (kN) Bolt Size			
	3/4	M20	M22	7/8
2	145	160	193	197
3	217	240	290	296
4	290	320	386	394
5	362	400	483	493
6	434	480	580	592
7	507	560	676	690
8	579	640	773	789

1. When threads intercept a shear plane, use 70% of the values tabulated for bearing connections.

2. Minimum required thickness of supporting material with beams framing from both sides is double that listed.

3. Tabulated values for slip-resistant connections assume clean mill scale with μ = 0.59.

SINGLE ANGLE BEAM CONNECTIONS

For some building applications, single angle connections provide satisfactory alternatives to double angle or end plate connections, and are particularly suitable for those cases where limited access prevents the erection of beams with double angle or end plate connections, and where speed of erection is a primary consideration.

Although the connection angle may be either bolted or welded to the supporting and supported members, usual practice involves shop fillet welding to the supporting member and field bolting to the web of the supported beam. However, for slip-resistant connections, it is recommended that the connection angle be bolted to the supporting member.

Tests carried out at the University of British Columbia (Lipson 1968, 1977, 1980) using 4 × 3 × 3/8 inch angles with the 4-inch leg bolted to the beam web with 3/4 inch diameter A325 bolts and the 3-inch leg welded to the supporting member with 1/4-inch E70XX fillet welds, demonstrated that welded-bolted single angle connections with from 2 to 12 bolts per vertical line possess adequate rotational capacity, and that in those connections loaded to ultimate capacity (2 to 8 bolts per vertical line) the failure occurred in the bolts when the weld pattern included welding along the heel and ends of the connection angle. The tests also demonstrated that the use of horizontal slotted holes in the connection angle reduced the moment at the bolts without affecting the ultimate capacity of the connection.

Table 3—37 has been prepared, based on this research, and assumes the use of 100 × 75 × 10 connection angles with the 75 mm leg welded to the supporting member and the 100 mm leg bolted to the supported web. The bolt capacities are given for M20 and M22 A325M bolts and 3/4 and 7/8 inch A325M bolts based on their factored shear resistance for the appropriate number of bolts, and the weld capacities have been established by assuming that a connection with 1/4-inch fillet welds has the same shear capacity as the 3/4-inch A 325 bolts and then pro-rating for the three sizes of fillet welds shown in the table (i.e. weld capacity = V_r (3/4-inch bolts) × D/6.35, where D is the fillet weld size in mm).

References

1. Lipson, S. L. "Single-Angle and Single-Plate Beam Framing Connections" Proceedings, Canadian Structural Engineering Conference, Toronto, Ontario, Canada, Feb., 1968, pp. 141-162.

2. _____ , "Single-Angle Welded-Bolted Connections", Struct. Division Journal ASCE, March 1977.

3. _____ , "Single-Angle Welded-Bolted Beam Connections", Canadian Journal of Civil Engineering, Volume 7, Number 2, June 1980.

Example

Single Angle welded-bolted beam connection (Table 3—37)

Given:

W410×60 beam, Factored reaction 325 kN.

Beam web thickness 7.7 mm, 100 × 75 × 10 connection angle.

G40.21-M 300W material, M20 A325M bolts, E480XX electrodes.

Solution:

Although the beam web is less than 10 mm thick, threads will not intercept the shear plane if bolts are properly installed, i.e. with the bolt head or with the nut and washer on the web side. With threads excluded from the shear plane, bolt capacity with four M20 A325M bolts = 420 kN > 325 kN — OK

Web thickness required = $5.8 \times 325/420 = 4.5$ mm < 7.7 mm — OK

Angle thickness required = $2 \times 4.5 = 9.0 < 10$ mm — OK

Angle length required for 4 bolts is 310 mm, and weld capacity using 6 mm E480XX fillet welds is 357 kN > 325 kN — OK

Use:

$100 \times 75 \times 10$ connection angle, 310 mm long, 75 mm leg welded to supporting member with 6 mm E480XX fillet welds, 100 mm leg bolted to web of supported beam with four M20 A325M bolts.

If threads are allowed to intercept the shear plane, bolt capacity with five M20 A325M bolts = $0.70 \times 525 = 368$ kN > 325 kN — OK

Web thickness required = $5.8 \times 325/525 = 3.6$ mm < 7.7 mm — OK

Angle thickness required = $2 \times 3.6 = 7.2$ mm < 10.0 mm — OK

5 mm E480XX fillet welds provides a capacity of 372 kN on an angle length of 390 mm > 325 kN — OK

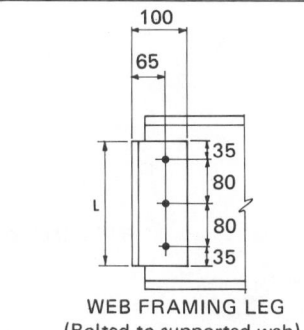

WEB FRAMING LEG
(Bolted to supported web)

SINGLE ANGLE BEAM CONNECTIONS
Table 3-37

**M20, M22 A325M Bolts
3/4, 7/8 A325 Bolts
E480XX Fillet Welds**

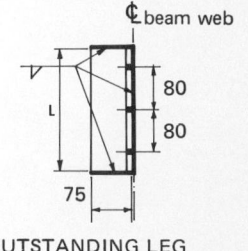

OUTSTANDING LEG
(Welded to supported Material)

Bolts per Vertical Line	BEARING-TYPE CONNECTION Factored Load Resistance (kN)[1]				WELD CAPACITY Factored Load Resistance (kN)			Connection Angle Length L (mm)
	Bolt Size				Fillet Size D (mm)			
	3/4	M20	M22	7/8	5	6	8	
2	189	210	254	258	149	179	238	150
3	284	315	381	387	224	268	358	230
4	378	420	508	516	298	357	476	310
5	473	525	635	645	372	447	596	390
6	568	630	762	774	447	537	716	470
7	662	735	889	903	521	626	834	550
8	756	840	1020	1030	595	714	952	630

Material F_u (MPa)	Minimum Required Web Thickness of Supported Beam[2] (mm)				Minimum Required Thickness of Supporting Material With Beams Framing From One Side (mm)			Material F_y (MPa)
400	6.2	6.6	7.2	7.3	5.0	6.0	8.0	250
450	5.5	5.8	6.4	6.4	4.3	5.2	6.9	300
480	5.2	5.5	6.0	6.0	3.7	4.4	5.9	350

1. When threads intercept a shear plane, use 70% of the values tabulated.
2. For connection angles minimum required thickness is double the tabulated values.

TEE-TYPE BEAM CONNECTIONS

Tee-type beam connections combine some of the characteristics of single angle connections with the web-framing leg bolted in single shear, and of double-angle connections with the outstanding legs welded to the supporting member.

Their main advantage is speed and ease of erection as the connection can be completed at the time the beam is erected. They are also commonly used where hole making in the supported member is undesirable, such as for connections to HSS columns, and to avoid having to cope the bottom flange of the supported beam for erection purposes.

Fabrication costs are generally higher than other types of simple beam connections due to the relatively higher costs to fabricate the Tee-sections.

Table 3–38 lists bolt and weld capacities for web-framing and outstanding legs respectively. The bolt capacities are the same as those listed in Table 3–37 for the web-framing legs of single angle connections, and the weld capacities are the same as those listed in Table 3–34 for the outstanding legs of welded double angle connections.

Example

Tee-Type welded-bolted beam connections (Table 3–38)

Given:

W410×60 beam, Factored reaction 325 kN.

Column — HSS 254.0×254.0×11.13

Beam web thickness 7.7 mm

G40.21-M 300W material, M20 A325M bolts, E480XX electrodes.

Solution:

Try Tee cut from W200×59 beam, web thickness = 9.1 mm.

Since the beam web and the Tee web are less than 10 mm thick, assume threads intercept the shear plane.

Five bolts per vertical line provide a capacity of 0.7×525 = 367 kN.

Beam web thickness required for F_y = 300 MPa
= 5.8×367/525 = 4.1 mm < 7.7 mm — OK

Tee web thickness required = 2×4.1 = 8.2 mm < 9.1 mm — OK

Length of Tee required for 5 bolts is 390 mm, and weld capacity for 5 mm fillet welds is 596 kN > 325 kN — OK

Use:

Tee cut from W200×59, 390 mm long, five M20 A325M bolts connecting webs of beam and Tee and 5 mm E480XX fillet welds to supporting material.

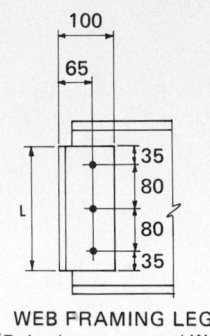

WEB FRAMING LEG
(Bolted to supported Web

TEE-TYPE BEAM CONNECTIONS
Table 3-38

M20, M22 A325M Bolts
3/4, 7/8 A325 Bolts
E480XX Fillet Welds

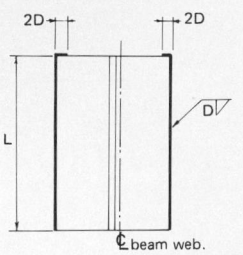

OUTSTANDING LEG
(Welded to supporting Material)

Bolts per Vertical Line	BEARING-TYPE CONNECTIONS Factored Load Resistance (kN)[1]				WELD CAPACITY Factored Load Resistance (kN)			Connection Angle Length L (mm)
	Bolt Size				Fillet Size D (mm)			
	3/4	M20	M22	7/8	5	6	8	
2	189	210	254	258	135	157	202	150
3	284	315	381	387	303	356	460	230
4	378	420	508	516	473	568	754	310
5	473	525	635	645	596	715	953	390
6	568	630	762	774	718	861	1150	470
7	662	735	889	903	840	1010	1340	550
8	756	840	1020	1030	962	1150	1540	630

Material F_u (MPa)	Minimum Required Web Thickness of Supported Beam[2] (mm)				Minimum Required Thickness of Supporting Material With Beams Framing from One Side (mm)			Material F_y (MPa)
400	6.2	6.6	7.2	7.3	5.0	6.0	8.0	250
450	5.5	5.8	6.4	6.4	4.3	5.2	6.9	300
480	5.2	5.5	6.0	6.0	3.7	4.4	5.9	350

1. When threads intercept a shear plane, use 70% of the values tabulated.
2. Minimum required thickness of Tee-web is double the tabulated values.

SEATED BEAM SHEAR CONNECTIONS

General

This section of the Handbook deals with the unstiffened angle seat, and the Tee-type stiffened seat. All seated beam connections are designed for simple shear only. Eccentricities produced by these connections are generally larger than for framed beam shear connections which may influence the design of the supporting members.

Seated beam shear connections are used in both industrial and commercial construction and their use can be attributed to simple shop fabrication with greater length tolerance for the beam than most other connections, together with ease and speed of erection. Although most commonly used as a beam-to-column detail, seated connections may be used for beam or truss to girder connections, but the girder web must be checked for adequate local resistance.

The unstiffened angle seat consists of a relatively heavy angle either shop welded or bolted to the face of the column flange, with the beam bolted or welded to the seat in the field. The same shop welded detail can be used on the column web, however, restricted welding access may be a problem.

Capacities of unstiffened angle seats are limited by the angle thickness, and stiffened angle seats may be used to extend the capacities of unstiffened angle seats for relatively thin angles. Stiffened seats such as Tee-stubs or those built up from plate can be designed to resist larger loads. Stiffened seats designed for heavy loads are generally referred to as brackets rather than seats and are not treated in this Handbook.

A seated beam connection must be stabilized with a flexible clip angle that is attached either to the top flange of the beam, or near the top of the beam web. The clip angle thickness should be great enough to allow welding to the beam and column, but small enough not to inhibit rotation of the beam.

Welds or bolts can be used to connect the clip angle to the beam and supporting member, and when welds are used, the fillet welds should be located along the toes of the angle.

UNSTIFFENED ANGLE SEAT CONNECTIONS

General

Table 3—39 lists capacities for two lengths of unstiffened angle seats assuming beams and seat angles of G40.21-M 300W material (F_y = 300 MPa) and welds made with E480XX electrodes. Bolt capacities are given for M20, M22 A325M bolts and 3/4, 7/8 inch A325 bolts.

Seat angle outstanding leg capacities have been developed using the plastic section modulus, Z_x, and the full length, L, of the unstiffened seat. Capacities listed will be conservative for seat angles or beams of steel with a specified minimum yield strength, F_y, greater than 300 MPa.

Although the gap between the end of the beam and the face of the supporting member, a, is nominally 10 mm, the tabulated values are based on 20 mm to allow for fabrication and erection length tolerances.

Referring to the drawing, outstanding leg capacities have been determined by satisfying two conditions simultaneously, namely, the possibility of crippling of the beam web, and the minimum thickness of the seat angle required.

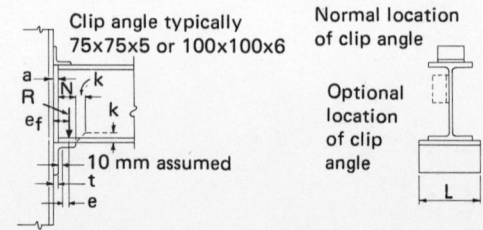

The applicable equations are:

Web crippling, $B_r = 1.25 \, \phi \, w \, (N + k) \, F_y / 1\,000$ (CAN3-S16.1-M78, Cl 15.8)

Angle thickness, $B_r = \phi \, F_y \, Lt^2 / 4e \times 1\,000$

where

B_r = Factored reaction (kN)

N = Required length of bearing (mm)

E_f = Effective eccentricity = $N/2 + a$ (mm)

e = $e_f - t - 10$ (mm)

F_y = Specified minimum yield strength of beam for web crippling and specified minimum yield strength of angle for angle thickness (MPa)

a = 20 mm for design, 10 mm for detailing (mm)

L = Length of angle seat (mm)

k = Beam k value (mm)

w = Beam web thickness (mm)

The vertical leg weld capacities have been calculated using the instantaneous shear centre model with an out of plane eccentricity, e_f, and assume the angle is equivalent to a bearing thickness of 25 mm. The vertical leg bolt capacities have been calculated using an elastic model and $e_f = 60$ mm for the reaction.

The tables have been developed assuming $k = 3w$. This assumption is conservative for the commonly used beam sections, though, it might give slightly unconservative results for a limited number of beam sections.

Exact Solution for Angle Thickness

For a given beam size and end reaction an exact solution for the required angle thickness of an unstiffened seat may be arrived at by combining the equations governing web crippling and angle thickness.

It can be shown that:

Angle thickness $t = \dfrac{-\beta + \sqrt{\beta^2 - 4 \, \alpha \, \gamma}}{2\alpha}$

where

α = $0.625\phi^2 \, F_{ya} \, F_{yb} \, w \, L$

β = $2.5\phi \, w \, F_{yb} \, B_r$

γ = $B_r^2 - \beta(k/2 - 10)$

F_{ya} = Yield strength of angle

F_{yb} = Yield strength of beam

Required Length of Bearing, $N = 2B_r^2 / \beta - k$

This procedure generally results in a smaller thickness of angle than Table 3—39 since the actual k of the beam is used instead of the value $k = 3w$ assumed in deriving Table 3—39.

Example

Given:

W530×82 beam, Factored reaction 220 kN

Beam web thickness 9.5 mm (10 mm nominal), flange width = 209 mm
G40.21-M 300W steel.

Solution:

(a) *Unstiffened angle seat outstanding leg*

Assuming beam will be welded to angle seat, select seat length greater than beam flange width.

Enter Table 3—39 with L = 230 mm (> 209 mm)

By interpolating for beam web thickness of 9.5 mm, an angle thickness of 16 mm provides an outstanding leg capacity of (249 + 226) / 2 = 238 kN > 220 kN — OK

If beam is bolted to angle seat, then seat length less than flange width can be used.

For L = 180 mm and beam web thickness of 9.5 mm, capacity provided for 16 mm angle thickness is (209 + 232) / 2 = 221 kN — OK

(b) *Vertical leg connection*

For welded connection, two 8 mm fillet welds on a vertical leg length of 150 mm provide a capacity of 247 kN > 220 kN.

For bolted connection, four M20 A325M bolts (threads excluded) provide a capacity of 302 kN. 150 mm leg required to provide adequate bolt clearance with 16 mm leg and M20 bolts.

For welded connection use 150×100×16 angle × 230 mm long with 150 mm leg vertical connected to supporting member with 8 mm E480XX fillet welds each side of vertical leg.

For bolted connection use 150×100×16 angle × 180 mm long with 150 mm leg vertical connected to supporting member with four M20 A325M bolts.

(c) *Stiffened Angle Seat*

If, for inventory reasons, 16 mm angles are not readily available, the fabricator might elect to use a thinner angle stiffened with a welded plate stiffener located under the beam web. A minimum 150 mm vertical leg would be required for welding or bolting to the supporting member, and the stiffener design and welding would depend on the size of angle used.

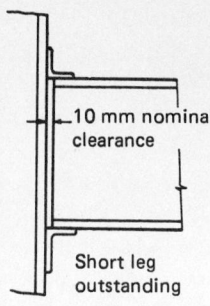

10 mm nominal clearance

Short leg outstanding

SEATED BEAM SHEAR CONNECTIONS
Table 3-39

UNSTIFFENED ANGLE
**M20, M22 A325M Bolts
3/4, 7/8 A325 Bolts
E480XX Fillet Welds
G40.21-M 300W Steel**

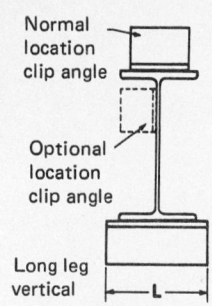

Normal location clip angle

Optional location clip angle

Long leg vertical — L

OUTSTANDING LEG CAPACITY (Factored Load Resistance (kN))										
Angle Length (mm)	L = 180					L = 230				
Angle Thickness (mm)	8	10	13	16	20	8	10	13	16	20
Beam Web Thickness (mm) 5	61	78	103	128	160	68	86	114	141	160
6	72	91	119	147	184	79	100	130	161	192
7	84	105	135	166	208	92	114	148	182	226
8	97	120	153	187	232	105	130	166	203	252
9		136	173	209	257		146	186	226	278
10		154	193	232	284		165	207	249	306
11			216	257	312			230	275	335
12			240	283	342			254	301	365

VERTICAL LEG WELD CAPACITY (kN)

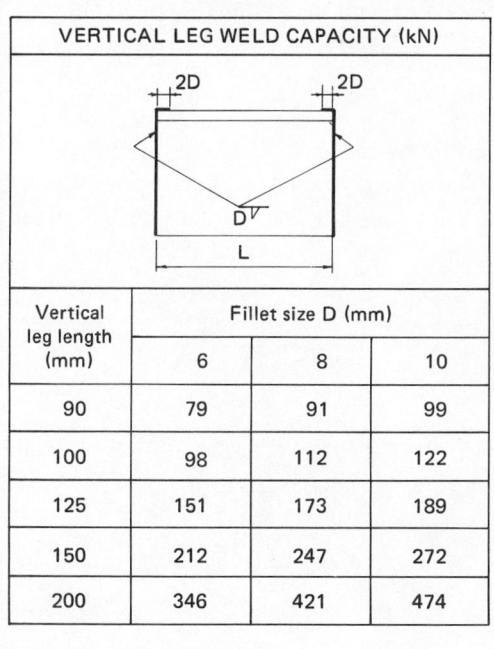

2D   2D

D

L

Vertical leg length (mm)	Fillet size D (mm)		
	6	8	10
90	79	91	99
100	98	112	122
125	151	173	189
150	212	247	272
200	346	421	474

VERTICAL LEG BOLT CAPACITY (kN)

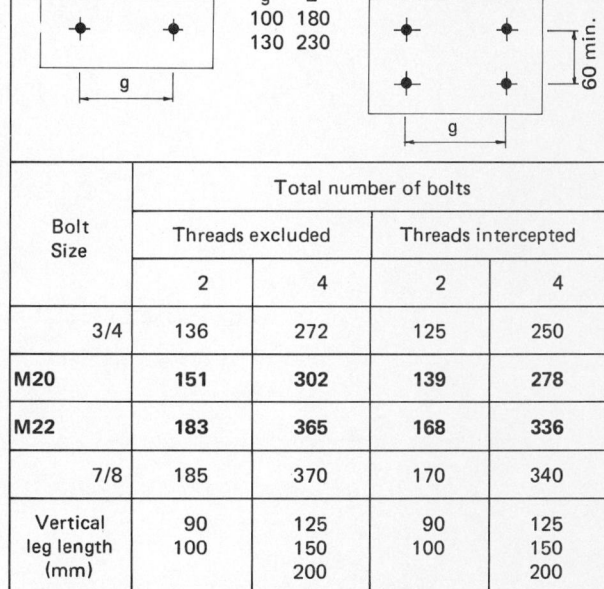

L

g   L
100 180
130 230

g

L

60 min.

g

	Total number of bolts			
Bolt Size	Threads excluded		Threads intercepted	
	2	4	2	4
3/4	136	272	125	250
M20	**151**	**302**	**139**	**278**
M22	**183**	**365**	**168**	**336**
7/8	185	370	170	340
Vertical leg length (mm)	90 100	125 150 200	90 100	125 150 200

ANGLE SIZES	
Leg Lengths (mm x mm)	Thickness Range (mm)
90 x 90	8, 10, 13
100 x 90	8, 10, 13
100 x 100	8, 10, 13, 16
125 x 90	8, 10, 13, 16
150 x 100	10, 13, 16
200 x 100 — Not Available from Canadian Mills.	10, 13, 16, 20

STIFFENED SEATED BEAM CONNECTIONS

Table 3—40 lists factored resistances of stiffened seats for the "T"-shaped weld configuration shown. Capacities are based on the use of E480XX electrodes, steel with a specified minimum yield strength F_y = 300 MPa, and a minimum stiffener thickness, t, equal to 1.7 times the fillet weld leg size to ensure that the shear resistance of the stiffener is not exceeded. Factored resistances tabulated are computed using the theory outlined on page 3—38 for "Eccentric Loads on Weld Groups — Shear and Moment", modified for the "T"-shaped weld configuration, with the length of the horizontal weld connecting the seat plate to the support equal to 0.4 times the length of the vertical weld connecting the stiffener plate to the support.

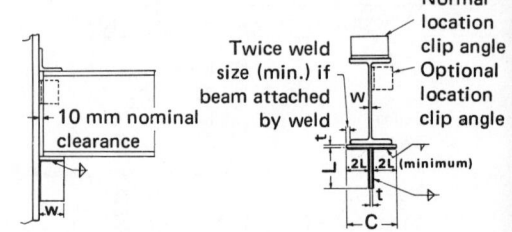

Stiffened seats must be proportioned so that the thickness "t" of the stiffener is not less than the web thickness "w" of the supported beam. Also, when the beam has a higher specified yield strength than the stiffener, the relationship, $t \times F_y$ (stiffener) = $w \times F_y$ (beam) shall be satisfied.

When the stiffener is fitted to bear against the seat, the amount of weld connecting the seat plate to the stiffener shall be equal to or greater than the capacity of the horizontal weld connecting the seat plate to the supporting member. Welds or bolts may be used to connect the supported beam to the seat and for attachment of the clip angle required to stabilize the beam.

When stiffened seats are in line on opposite sides of a column web, the size of the vertical fillet welds (for E480XX electrodes) shall not exceed $F_y/515$ times the thickness of the column web, so as not to exceed the shear resistance of the column web. As an alternative to limiting the weld size a longer seat may be used to reduce the shear stresses in the column web.

Example

Given:

W530×82 beam, factored resistance 450 kN

Web thickness = 9.5 mm, flange width = 209 mm, k distance = 29 mm

Connected to web of W310×118 column, web thickness = 11.9 mm

Design stiffened welded seat assuming beams connected to both sides of column web.

G40.21-M 300W steel, E480XX electrodes

Solution

(a) *Vertical stiffener*

Required length of bearing, N = ($B_r/1.25 \phi$ w F_y) — k   (cl 15.8 (b), S16.1-M78)

= (450×1 000/ 1.25×0.9×9.5×300) — 29 = 111 mm

For 10 mm clearance, minimum stiffener width = 111 + 10 = 121 mm

Try 125 mm stiffener width

For stiffeners both sides of column web, maximum effective weld size so that shear resistance of column web is not exceeded,

= 11.9×300/515 = 6.93 mm

Minimum stiffener thickness for shear = 1.7×6.93 = 11.9 mm

Try 12 mm stiffener with 6 mm fillet welds

From Table 3—40 with w = 125 mm, 6 mm fillet welds and L = 275 mm, capacity provided = 449 kN — OK

Check b/t = 125/12 = 10.4 < $200/\sqrt{F_y}$ = 11.6 — OK

Use 12×125 stiffener × 275 mm long welded to column web with 6 mm fillet welds, each side of stiffener.

(b) *Horizontal Seat Plate*

Try 12 mm plate and 6 mm fillet welds (same as vertical stiffener)

Minimum length of weld required to attach seat plate to column web = 2×0.2L = 0.4×275 = 110 mm

Minimum length of seat plate for horizontal welds

= 110 + (2×6) + 12 = 134 mm

Minimum length of seat plate assuming beam bolted to seat

= beam flange width = 209 min

Minimum length of seat plate assuming beam welded to seat

= 209 + 2 (2×6) = 233 mm

Use 12×125 seat plate × 210 mm long welded to support with 6 mm fillet welds on underside of seat and bolted to bottom flange of beam with two M20 A325M bolts

(c) *Weld between stiffener and seat plate*

Minimum length of weld required = 110 mm for 6 mm fillets

Length available = 2×125 = 250 mm

STIFFENED SEATED BEAM CONNECTIONS
Table 3-40
E480XX Electrodes

10 mm nominal clearance

Twice weld size (min.) if beam attached by weld

Normal location clip angle
Optional location clip angle

Seat Width W (mm)	Fillet Size* D (mm)	FACTORED RESISTANCE OF WELDS (kN)										
		Length of Stiffener L (mm)										
		150	175	200	225	250	275	300	325	350	400	450
100 e_f = 60	6	161	220	286	361	444	500	545	591	636	727	818
	8	212	288	378	480	590	666	727	788	848	969	1090
	10	260	356	468	593	731	833	909	985	1060	1210	1360
	12	307	422	556	704	869	1000	1090	1180	1270	1450	1640
125 e_f = 72.5	6	133	182	239	301	372	449	533	591	636	727	818
	8	175	240	316	397	490	594	707	788	848	969	1090
	10	215	297	388	493	611	738	878	985	1060	1210	1360
	12	254	351	461	586	727	879	1050	1180	1270	1450	1640
150 e_f = 85	6	114	155	203	258	320	385	458	537	621	727	818
	8	149	205	269	342	421	509	607	710	820	969	1090
	10	183	252	332	422	521	631	752	880	1020	1210	1360
	12	217	299	395	501	621	755	900	1050	1220	1450	1640
200 e_f = 110	6	88	120	158	200	247	299	357	417	484	632	796
	8	115	158	208	264	327	397	473	553	642	838	1060
	10	142	195	256	327	406	492	585	687	798	1040	1310
	12	168	231	305	389	483	585	697	820	950	1240	1570

*Minimum plate thickness, t = 1.7D.   Material F_y = 300 MPa

MOMENT CONNECTIONS

General

Continuous construction, as permitted by CAN3-S16.1-M78, requires moment resisting beam-to-column connections. Continuous construction also requires "rigid" connections that will maintain, virtually unchanged, the original angles between intersecting members at specified load.

Rigid moment connections can be provided by using welds, bolts or combinations of welds and bolts. Numerous configurations and details are possible, and Figure 3—5 illustrates four types common in current practice:

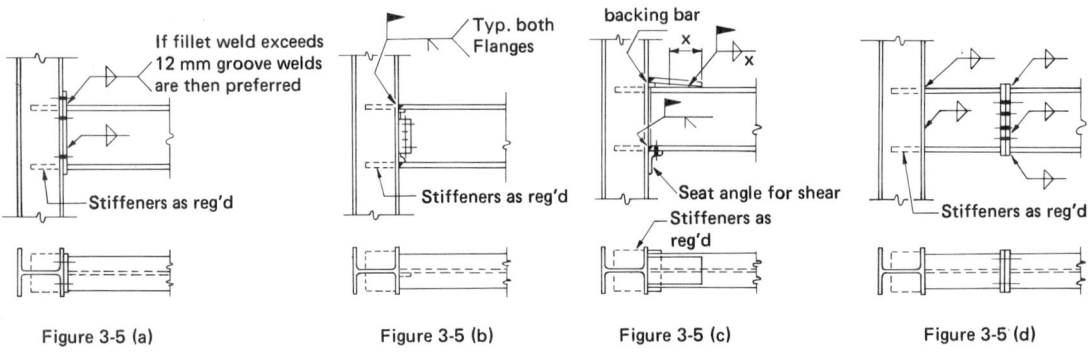

Figure 3-5 (a)   Figure 3-5 (b)   Figure 3-5 (c)   Figure 3-5 (d)

Figure 3—5 (a) illustrates a heavy plate shop fillet welded to the end of the beam and field bolted to the column. The end plate distributes the flange forces over a greater length of column web than does a fully welded joint, but the effects of prying action must be considered.

Figure 3—5 (b) illustrates beam flanges field welded directly to the column with groove welds. Shear capacity is developed by a seat angle, web framing angle or plate, or by welding the beam web directly to the column. Backing bars and run off tabs for the welds may be required.

Figure 3—5 (c) illustrates the use of moment plates shop welded to the column with groove welds and fillet-welded or bolted to the flanges of the beam. In place of a bottom plate, the bottom flange of the beam may be welded with a groove weld directly to the column, as shown in the sketch, using a seat angle as an erection seat and backing bar. Shear capacity is provided by the seat angle, or by other methods described above.

Figure 3—5 (d) illustrates the use of short beam sections shop welded to the column and bolted to the beam in the field using end plate type connections. The field connection may also be designed as a bolted or welded joint, the details being dependent on the forces to be transmitted at the joint.

In designing moment connections it is important to ensure that the connection provided will have adequate strength and stiffness, combined with sufficient rotation capacity to permit inelastic deformations to occur, as assumed or inherent in the analysis and design procedure used to proportion the structural frame. Since moment connections are highly restrained, careful design is necessary to accommodate possible stress concentrations resulting from welding. In particular, it is important to provide details with adequate ductility when framing into the weak axis of a column.

In order to ensure that the connection provided is consistent with the design assumptions used in proportioning the members of the structure, it is important that the designer provide the fabricator with complete information regarding moments and shears to be developed by the connection.

Column Stiffeners

The resistance of a column section to local deformation is important where rigid connections are required. When relatively small beams are connected to heavy columns, the columns may be sufficiently sturdy to provide the degree of fixity assumed in the design of beams. With large beams, however, the columns will usually have to be strengthened locally by means of stiffeners, doubler plates or both.

Column stiffeners are provided adjacent to the tension flanges of connecting beams in order to minimize curling of the column flanges and resultant overstressing of the central portion of the weld connecting the beam flange (or moment plate) to the column. Adjacent to the compression flanges of connecting beams, column stiffeners are provided to prevent buckling of the column web. Horizontal plate stiffeners are the most common among the various types of stiffeners that can be used. When the depths of the beams framing into opposite flanges of the column differ, inclined stiffeners or two horizontal plate stiffeners (one opposite the flange of each beam) may be used. For connections in which the shear generated in the column web exceeds its shear capacity, "doubler" plates or inclined plate stiffeners are used to increase locally the column web shear capacity.

Clause 20.3 of CAN3-S16.1-M78 specifies the requirements for stiffeners on the web of H-type columns when beams are rigidly framed to the column flange.

References

The following references contain more detailed information on the design of moment connections. Several of these references refer to allowable stress rules and must be interpreted for limit states applications. References 6 to 10 are most recent and many of the recommendations contained in these references have been adopted by CAN3-S16.1-M78.

1. "Structural Steel Design" — Tall et al — The Ronald Press Company.
2. "Design of Welded Structures" — Omer W. Blodgett — The James F. Lincoln Arc Welding Foundation.
3. "Welded Interior Beam-to-Column Connections" Graham, Sherbourne and Khabbaz — The American Institute of Steel Construction.
4. "Welded Structural Design" — Canadian Welding Bureau.
5. "Commentary on Plastic Design in Steel" — American Society of Civil Engineers.
6. "Behavior and Design of Steel Beam-to-Column Moment Connections" — Haung, Chen and Beedle — Welding Research Council Bulletin — October 1973.
7. "Test of a Fully-Welded Beam-to-Column Connection" — Regee, Haung and Chen — Welding Research Council Bulletin — October 1973.
8. "Recent Results on Connection Research at Lehigh" — Chen, Haung and Beedle — Regional Conference on Tall Buildings — Bangkok, January 1974, Pgs. 799-813.
9. "A Fresh Look at Bolted End Plate Behavior and Design" — N. Krishnamurthy — American Institute of Steel Construction Engineering Journal — Vol. 15, No. 2, 1978.
10. "A Limit State Design Method for the Tension Region of Bolted Beam-Column Connections" J. A. Packer, BE, MSc — The Structural Engineer October 1977/ No. 10/Volume 5.

Examples

Note: In the following examples, the solution chosen in each case is intended to illustrate only one of several satisfactory solutions that could be used. In any given situation, the design will be influenced by the individual fabricator's experience, fabrication methods and erection procedures.

Example 1

Given

Design an interior beam-to-column connection for the following forces and moments due to factored loads, assuming the unit specified dead and live loads are 3.8 kPa and 4.8 kPa respectively.

Factored beam moments = 320 kN·m, 240 kN·m

Factored beam shears = 130 kN, 110 kN

Beams = W410×60 framing into column flanges

Column = W310×86

Steel = CSA G40.21-M 300W, Use E480XX electrodes for welds.

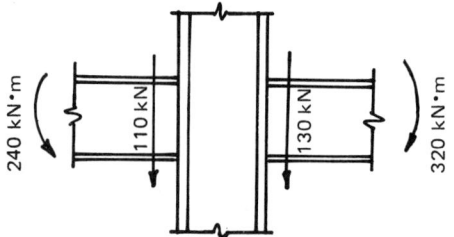

W310×86 Column	W410×60 Beam
t_c = 16.3 mm	t = 12.8 mm
w_c = 9.1 mm	w = 7.7 mm
k_c = 33 mm	d = 407 mm
b = 254 mm	b = 178 mm
d = 310 mm	
k_1 = 20 mm	
T = 244 mm	

Solution:

(a) Web Connection

The design of the connection for the beam web to the column flange need only account for the vertical shear, neglecting eccentricity.

Two alternatives are shown to illustrate a field bolted and a field welded condition.

(i) *Alternate 1* — Single plate field welded to beam web, shop welded to column flange, holes for erection bolts.

Beam web shear capacity per millimetre of beam depth = $\phi \, F_s \, w$

From Table on page 5 — 9, ϕF_s = 178, h/w < 60, unstiffened web.

Therefore $\phi \, F_s \, w$ = 178×7.7 = 1 370 N/mm

Maximum single fillet weld to develop this capacity = 1370/153 = 8.95 mm

(Table 3—23, unit factored weld resistance E480XX = 153 MPa)

Since only factored shear need be carried, try 5 mm fillet on 6 mm plate

Required weld length = 130/0.765 = 170 mm (Table 3—24)

Use 230 mm length of plate (same as that shown in Tables 3—33, 3—34 for a nominal beam depth of 410 mm)

Check plate for factored capacity (Clause 13.4.4, S16.1-M78)

= 0.9×6×230×0.5×300/1 000 = 186 kN > 130 kN — OK

Use 6X75X230 mm plate with 5 mm E480XX fillet welds.

(ii) *Alternate 2* — Single plate field bolted to beam web, M20 A325M bolts bearing-type, shop welded to column flange.

From Table 3—4, Factored shear resistance, single shear, threads intercepted for M20 A325M bolts = 73.5 kN

Therefore 2 bolts = 2×73.5 = 147 kN > 130 kN — OK

Check factored bearing resistance on beam web, w = 7.7 mm

From Table 3—6, bearing on 300W steel = 73.9 kN per bolt for end distance = 35 mm and t = 7 mm

For 2 bolts = 2×73.9 = 148 kN > 130 kN — OK

Try 7 mm plate, 230 mm long, 2 bolts at 160 mm pitch and check plate thickness for shear.

= 130×1 000/ (0.9×0.66×300×230) = 3.2 mm < 7 mm — OK

Use 7×80×230 plate and two M20 A325M bolts

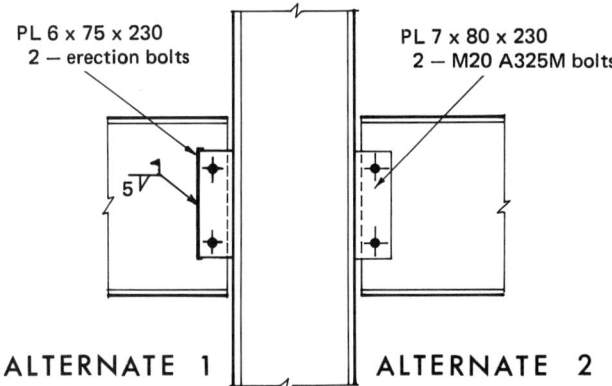

PL 6 x 75 x 230
2 — erection bolts

PL 7 x 80 x 230
2 — M20 A325M bolts

Alternate 2 replaces the two erection bolts with permanent high strength bolts and eliminates vertical field welding.

ALTERNATE 1   ALTERNATE 2

(b) Flange Connection

Two alternatives are shown to illustrate field bolted and field welded conditions.

(1) *Alternate 1* — Top and bottom flange plates shop welded to column, field bolted to beam flange with A325M bolts in slip-resistant connection.

The number of bolts required is determined on the basis of specified loads and all other strength checks are based on factored loads and factored resistances.

Determine the specified load moment using Figure 3—1 on page 3—4

Ratio D/L = 3.8/4.8 = 0.79 giving $(L + D) / (\alpha_L L + \alpha_D D)$ = 0.72

Therefore specified load moment = 0.72×320 = 230 kN·m

Flange force due to specified loads = 230×1 000/407 = 565 kN

From Table 3—11, assuming M22 A325M bolts, clean mill scale faying surfaces, number of bolts required.

= 565/48.3 = 11.7   Use 12 bolts (2 rows of 6)

Assuming 80 mm pitch, 40 mm end distance, 130 mm clear to column flange, plate length required = (5×80) + 40 + 130 = 570 mm

Flange force due to factored loads = 320×1 000/407 = 786 kN

Net area of plate required = 786×1 000/270 = 2 910 mm²
(Table 3—47, ϕ = 0.9, $A_n/A_g \geqslant 0.67$)

Calculate minimum gross width 'b' of plate so that A_n/A_g = 0.67

Net plate width = b — 2×(22 + 2) = (b — 48) mm

Therefore (b — 48) / b = 0.67 giving b = 145 mm (minimum)

Try 170 mm plate width, thickness required = 2 910 / (170 − 48) = 23.9 mm

Use 25 mm plate (first preference thickness)

Check ultimate strength

V_r = 12×127 = 1 524 kN > 786 kN   (Table 3—4, M22 A325M bolts threads excluded)

B_r for 25 mm plate is not a problem (Table 3—6)

(ii) *Alternate 2* − Moment plate field welded to column flange and top flange of beam, bottom flange of beam groove welded directly to column flange.

As in alternate 1, the moment plate is designed to transmit the beam flange force under factored loads = 786 kN.

Plate area required (gross) = 786×1 000/ (0.9×300) = 2 910 mm²

Select plate width narrower than beam flange width to permit downhand welding.

Try 150 mm plate, approx. max. weld size = [178 − (150 + 4)] / 2 = 12 mm

Plate thickness required = 2 910 / 150 = 19.4 mm

Use 20 mm plate (first preference thickness)

From Table 3—24, for E480XX electrode, 12 mm fillet weld = 1.84 kN/mm

Weld length required = 786 / 1.84 = 427 mm − Use 430 mm

End weld length = 150 mm, therefore length each side = (430 − 150) / 2 = 140 mm

It is generally recommended that an unwelded length of plate equal to at least 1.2 times the plate width be provided.

Therefore minimum plate length = 140 + (1.2×150) = 320 mm

Use 20×150×320 plate welded to column flange with full penetration groove weld and welded to top flange of beam with 12 mm fillet welds.

A possible third alternative would be to field weld the top and bottom flanges of the beam directly to the column flange with full penetration groove welds using backing bars welded to the column flange.

(c) Column Shear Capacity

The column will be subject to a shear force due to the unbalanced moment. CAN3-S16.1-M78 Clause 20.3 requires column webs to be stiffened if this shear exceeds

V_r = 0.55 ϕ w d F_y

   = 0.55×0.9×9.1×310×300 / 1 000 = 419 kN

Shear force = (320 − 240)×1 000 / 407 = 197 kN < 419 kN

Thus no reinforcing of the web is required for shear.

(d) Column Web Stiffeners

Check design of column web stiffeners to CAN3-S16.1-M78 Clause 20.3.

Cl. 20.3(a), B_r = 0.9×9.1×(12.8 + 5×33)×300 / 1 000 = 437 kN < 786 kN

Therefore stiffeners are required opposite bottom flange for capacity of 786−437 = 349 kN

Cl. 20.3(b), T_r = 0.9×7×16.3²×300 / 1 000 = 502 kN < 786 kN

Stiffeners are also required opposite top flange for capacity of 786 − 502 = 284 kN

Total stiffener area required at bottom flange = 349×1 000 / 0.9×300 = 1 290 mm²

Maximum b/t ratio (class 1 section) = 145 / $\sqrt{300}$ = 8.37

Try 90 mm individual stiffener width (beam flange = 178 mm wide).

Minimum t = 90 / 8.37 = 10.8 mm, Try 12 mm

Effective stiffener width to clear column k distance = 178 / 2 − 22 = 67 mm

Effective stiffener area = 2×67×12 = 1 610 mm² > 1 290 mm²—OK

Use two stiffeners 12×90 each side of column web opposite bottom flange.

Use same stiffeners opposite top flange.

(e) Stiffener Welds

Welds connecting stiffeners to column flange must be sufficient to develop force in stiffener of 349 kN

For double fillet welds at stiffener ends (length 67 mm) weld resistance required = 349 / 2×67 = 2.60 kN/mm.

From Table 3—24, 10 mm E480XX fillet welds = 2×1.53 = 3.06 kN/mm OK

Welds connecting stiffeners to column web must transfer shear forces due to unbalanced beam moment = 197 / 2 = 98.5 kN per side.

Approximate weld length available = T = 244 mm, assume 230 mm

Weld resistance required = 98.5 / 230 = 0.43 kN/mm

Use single 5 mm fillet weld on each stiffener = 0.77 kN/mm (Table 3-24)

Example 2

Given:

Design an exterior beam-to-column connection for an elastically designed frame, in which the column size is the same as example 1 and the beam is a W460×74 having a factored end moment of 320 kN·m and a factored reaction of 130 kN.

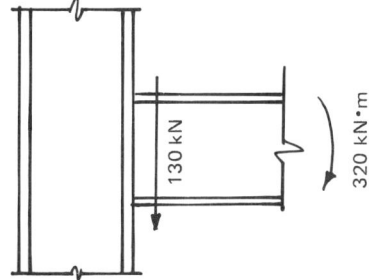

W310×86 column	W460×74 beam
See example 1 for dimensions	t = 14.5 mm
	w = 9.0 mm
	d = 457 mm
	b = 190 mm

Solution

This example is basically an extension of Example 1 and the solutions given are only intended to provide information on other possibilities.

(a) Web Connection

Use on unstiffened angle seat to carry the beam shear and to support the beam during erection.

From Table 3—39 for a beam web of 9 mm and a seat length of 230 mm, a 10 mm thick angle will provide an outstanding leg capacity of 146 kN > 130 kN. Also a vertical leg of 125 mm with 6 mm fillet welds provides a vertical leg capacity of 151 kN > 130 kN.

Use 125×90×10 angle × 230 mm long with 125 mm leg vertical, welded to column flange with 6 mm E480XX fillet welds.

(b) Flange Connection

Assume field welded connection with full penetration groove welds connecting top and bottom flanges of the beam directly to the column flange. (suggested alternate 3 in Example 1). The seat angle would serve as the backing bar for the bottom flange weld.

(c) Column Shear Capacity

Shear force = 320×1 000/457 = 700 kN

Diagonal stiffeners will be used to carry excess shear over shear capacity of column web = 419 kN (see Example 1)

Therefore horizontal component of stiffener force = 700—419 = 281 kN

If θ is angle between stiffener and horizontal plane then

$\cos \theta = 310/\sqrt{310^2 + 457^2} = 0.561$

Force in stiffener = 281/cos θ = 281/0.561 = 501 kN

Total stiffener area required = 501×1 000/0.9×300 = 1 860 mm²

For 90 mm wide stiffener, effective width = 67 mm (see Example 1)

Stiffener thickness required = 1 860/2×67 = 13.9 mm. Try 14 mm

Maximum b/t = 15, $(260/\sqrt{F_y}$ for web stiffeners)

b/t supplied = 90/14 = 6.4—OK

Use one 14×90 diagonal stiffener each side of column web.

(d) Horizontal Column Web Stiffeners

B_r = 0.9×9.1×(14.5 + 5×33)×300/1 000 = 441 kN < 700 kN

Stiffeners required at bottom flange for 700—441 = 259 kN

T_r = 0.9×7×16.3²×300/1 000 = 502 kN < 700 kN

Stiffeners required at top flange for 700—502 = 198 kN

Stiffener area required at bottom flange = 259×1 000/0.9×300 = 959 mm²

Use two 12X90 stiffeners (see Example 1)

(e) Stiffener Welds

Diagonal Stiffeners.

Welds connecting stiffeners to column flanges must be sufficient to develop force in stiffener of 501 kN.

For double fillet welds at stiffener ends (length 67 mm) weld resistance required = 501/2×67 = 3.74 kN/mm

From Table 3—24, 12 mm E480XX fillet welds = 2×1.84 = 3.68 kN/mm

Use 12 mm E480XX fillet welds top and bottom at each end of stiffener and a nominal 5 mm weld between stiffener and column web.

Horizontal Stiffeners

End weld must develop force in stiffener = 259 kN

Weld resistance required = 259×1 000/2×67 = 1.93 kN/mm

Double 8 mm fillets = 2×1.22 = 2.44 kN/mm (Table 3—24)

Welds connecting horizontal stiffeners to column web are required to transfer only a portion of the total horizontal shear force to the column web as the rest is transferred directly through the flange connection. Although the actual shear distribution is not known, a conservative approach is to design these welds to transfer the total design force in the stiffener. For an approximate weld length of 230 mm (see Example 1) weld resistance required is

$$259/2 \times 230 = 0.563 \text{ kN/mm}$$

Use single 5 mm E480XX fillet weld on each stiffener = 0.77 kN/mm.

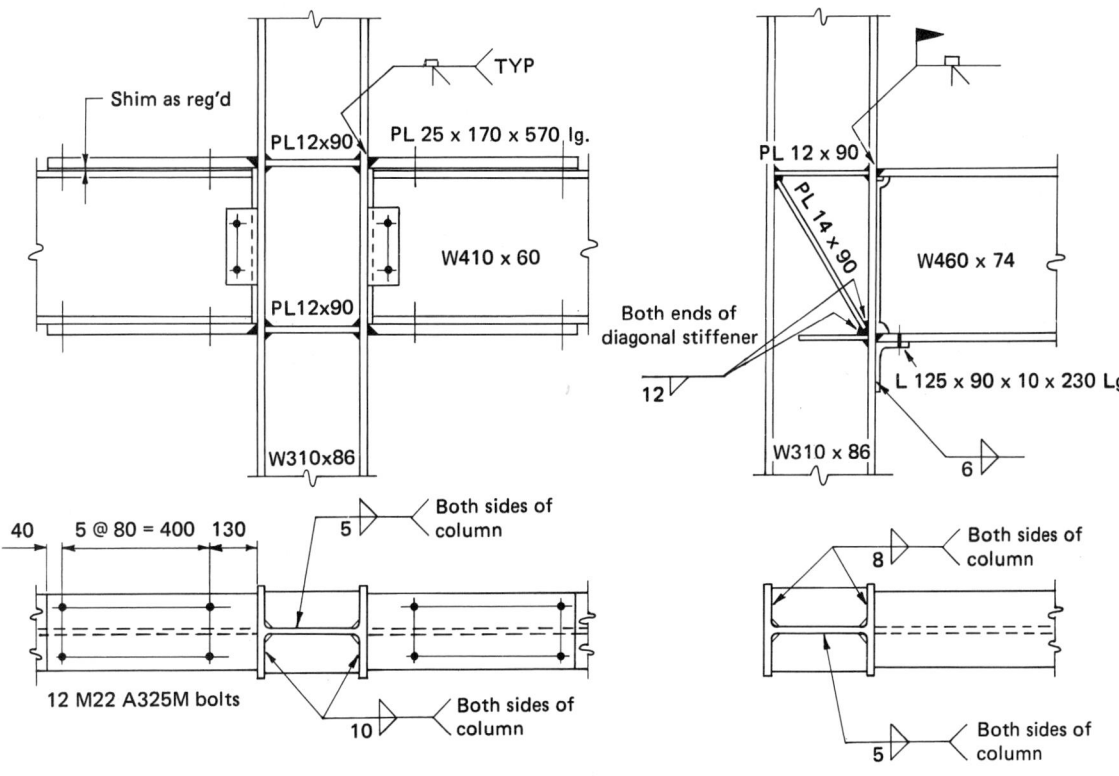

shop welded, field bolted.
web connection Alternate 2 .
flange connection Alternate 1.

Example 1

both shop and field welded.

Example 2

HOLLOW STRUCTURAL SECTION CONNECTIONS

General

The use of hollow structural sections as columns and truss components is becoming quite common. HSS members may be selected for various reasons including, aesthetics and/or weight reduction for compression members. This section of the Handbook (pages 3—80 to 3—88) shows sketches of some of the more commonly used details, and includes information on weld details appropriate to HSS connections. Details include:

Beam to HSS column connections	Figure 3—6, page 3—82
Truss to column and girder joints	Figure 3—7, page 3—83
HSS Truss joints	Figure 3—8, page 3—84
Connections for moment and shear	Figure 3—9, page 3—85
Other truss configurations	Figure 3—10, page 3—86

The beam and truss-to-column connections as shown in Figures 3—6 and 3—7 are simple shear connections designed in a conventional manner; however, for the Tee connection sufficient rotation of the joint must be allowed. Fang and White, in their article "Simple Framing Connections For Square Structural Tubing", published in the American Society of Civil Engineers, Structural Division Journal, April 1966, suggest a minimum width-to-thickness ratio for the Tee flange of 10, where the width is the full flange width.

Many of the design recommendations for connections have resulted from research sponsored by the International Committee for the Study and Development of Tubular Structures (CIDECT). Further information on joint design is contained in the Steel Company of Canada's publication, "Hollow Structural Sections Design Manual for Connections". Two other common references are: "Design of Welded Structures" by Blodgett, and the American Welding Society, D1.1, Section 10, "Design of New Tubular Structures". For end flattened round web members some guidance is available in a report entitled, "An Experimental Investigation of Flattened-end Tubular Truss Joints" by Morris, Frovich and Thiensiripipat, University of Manitoba, 1974.

Truss Joints

Since one of the prime applications of HSS members is in architecturally exposed areas, careful attention must be given to aesthetics of the joint design in addition to cost and fabrication techniques. The following points should be kept in mind when using HSS:

(1) Gap joints are usually the most economical joint type. Lap joints require additional profiling of web members and extra welding. Stiffened joints are usually the most expensive.

(2) If fatigue is a design consideration, careful attention should be paid to the joint details. It is suggested that lap joints with a lap of 50% be used for trusses subjected to fatigue loading.

(3) Joint efficiency increases as the width of the truss web members approaches the width of the HSS chord and is a maximum when web width equals the chord width. However, welding costs increase when welds are placed on the corner radii of the chord, therefore to obtain optimum strength and economy, the web width should be as wide as possible, but not greater than the width of the chord, minus at least twice the corner radius.

(4) Joint efficiency can also be improved by selecting chord members with a greater wall thickness. Sometimes a smaller size chord of thicker material will have about the same mass per meter as a larger, thinner wall HSS, but will not require joint stiffening or the more expensive lap joints.

(5) Profiling of round members is generally required when they are joined to other members, and if aesthetics allow, the web members to have the ends flattened instead of profiled, cost savings may be achieved.

(6) Secondary moments and stresses due to eccentricity "e" (See Figure 3—8) may be neglected provided the intersection of the centre lines of the web members lies within the middle 2/3 of the chord depth.

For HSS supplied with a 350 MPa minimum yield E480XX electrodes are normally used. Table 3—41 on page 3—87 gives the fillet weld size necessary to develop the strength of the parent material in either shear or tension, and is based on 350 MPa parent material and E480XX electrodes.

In HSS connections the individual members are usually welded all around. Table 3—42 on page 3—88 gives the length of welds for web members connected to chord members at various angles (θ).

FIGURE 3-6

BEAM TO HSS COLUMN CONNECTIONS

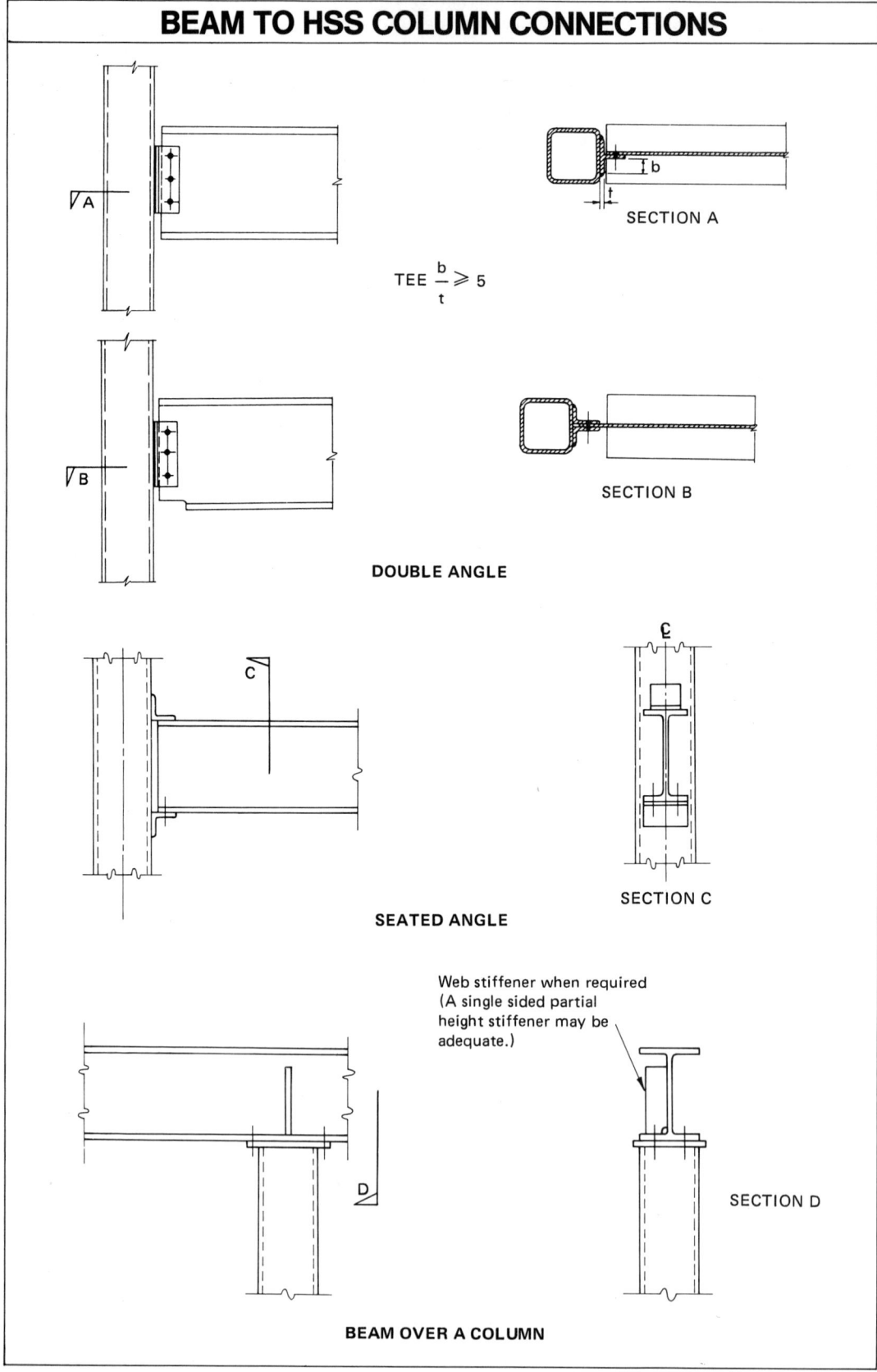

$$\text{TEE } \frac{b}{t} \geqslant 5$$

SECTION A

SECTION B

DOUBLE ANGLE

SEATED ANGLE

SECTION C

Web stiffener when required
(A single sided partial
height stiffener may be
adequate.)

SECTION D

BEAM OVER A COLUMN

FIGURE 3-7

TRUSS TO COLUMN AND GIRDER JOINTS

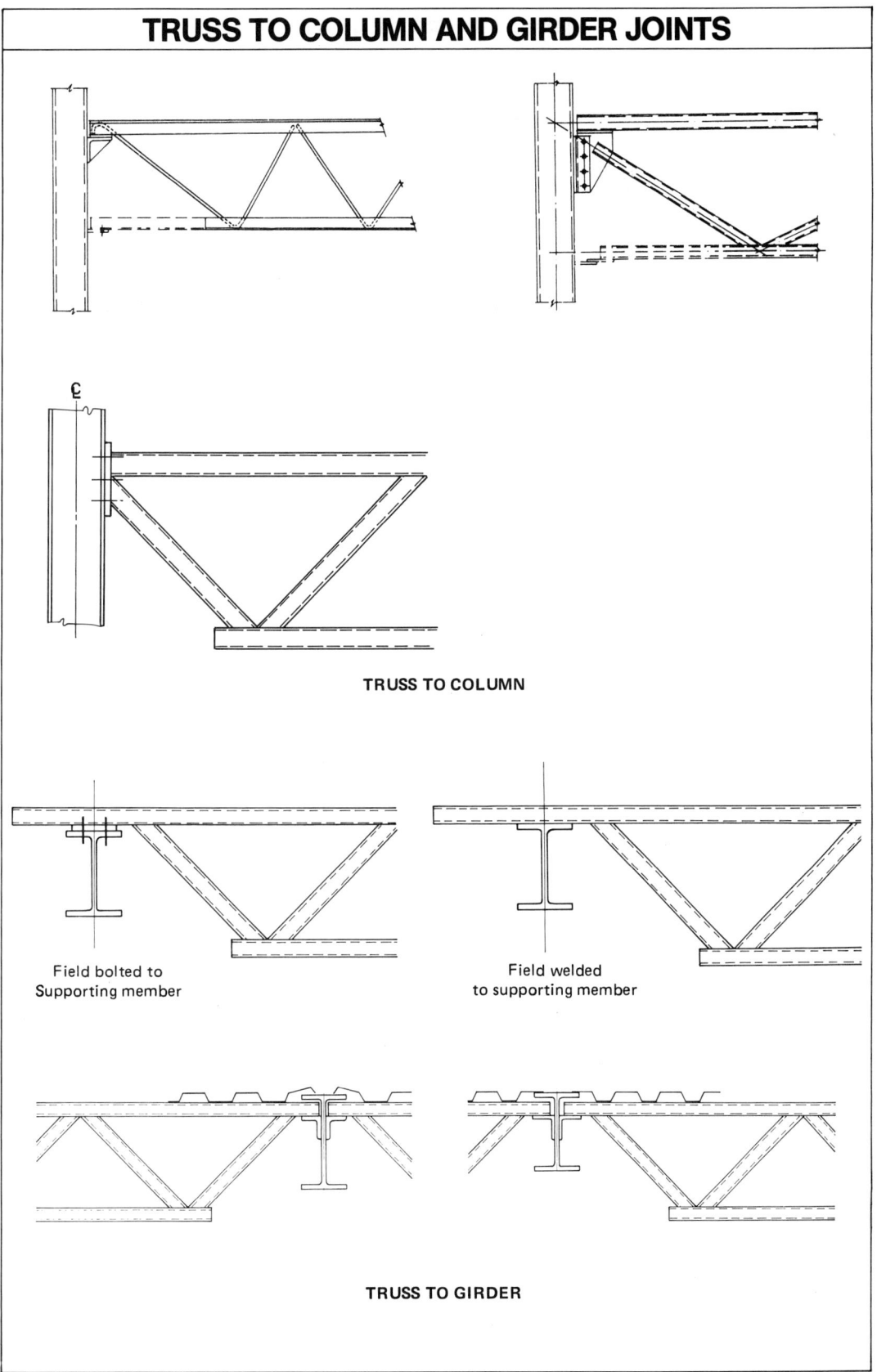

TRUSS TO COLUMN

Field bolted to
Supporting member

Field welded
to supporting member

TRUSS TO GIRDER

FIGURE 3-8
HSS TRUSS JOINTS

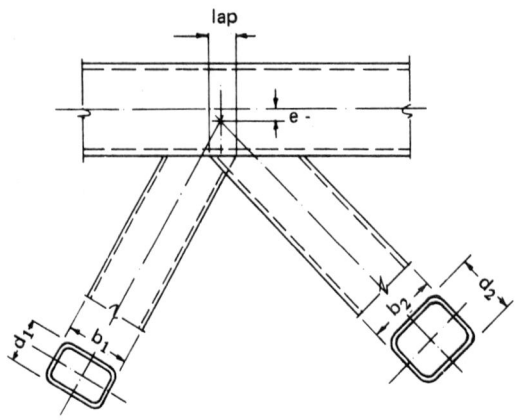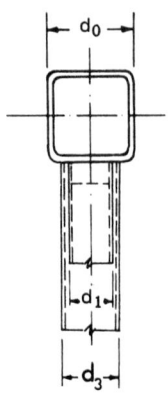

(a) LAP JOINT

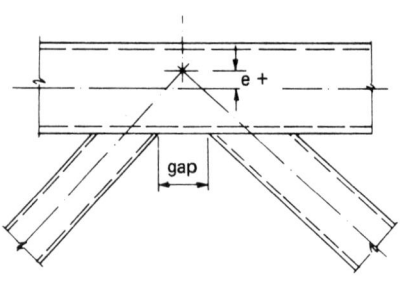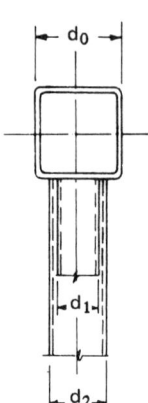

(b) GAP JOINT

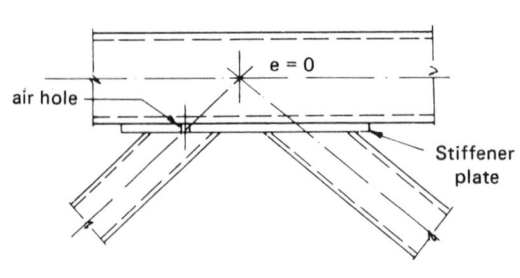

(c) STIFFENED GAP JOINT

FIGURE 3-9

CONNECTIONS FOR MOMENT AND SHEAR

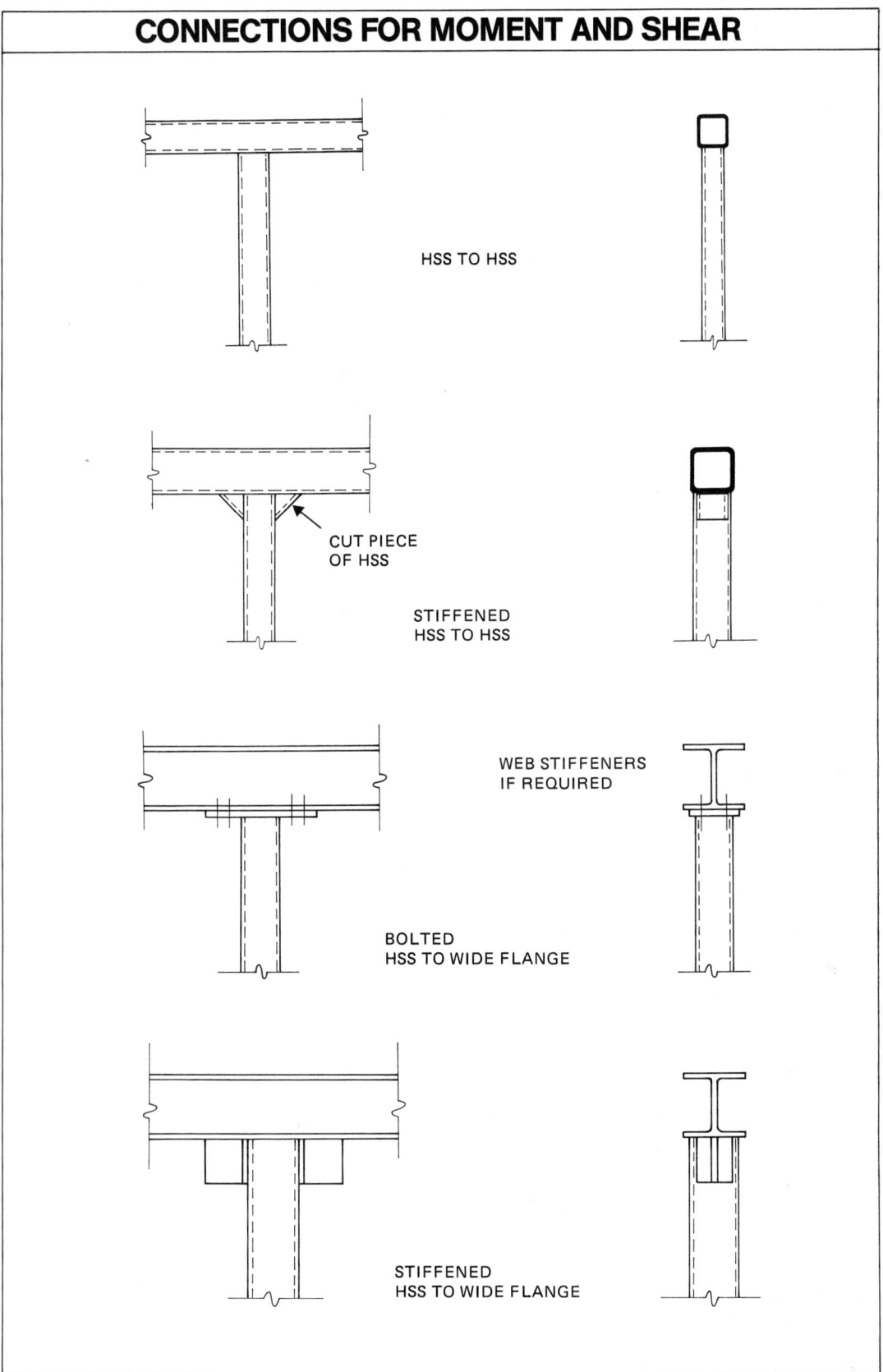

HSS TO HSS

CUT PIECE
OF HSS

STIFFENED
HSS TO HSS

WEB STIFFENERS
IF REQUIRED

BOLTED
HSS TO WIDE FLANGE

STIFFENED
HSS TO WIDE FLANGE

FIGURE 3-10

OTHER TRUSS CONFIGURATIONS

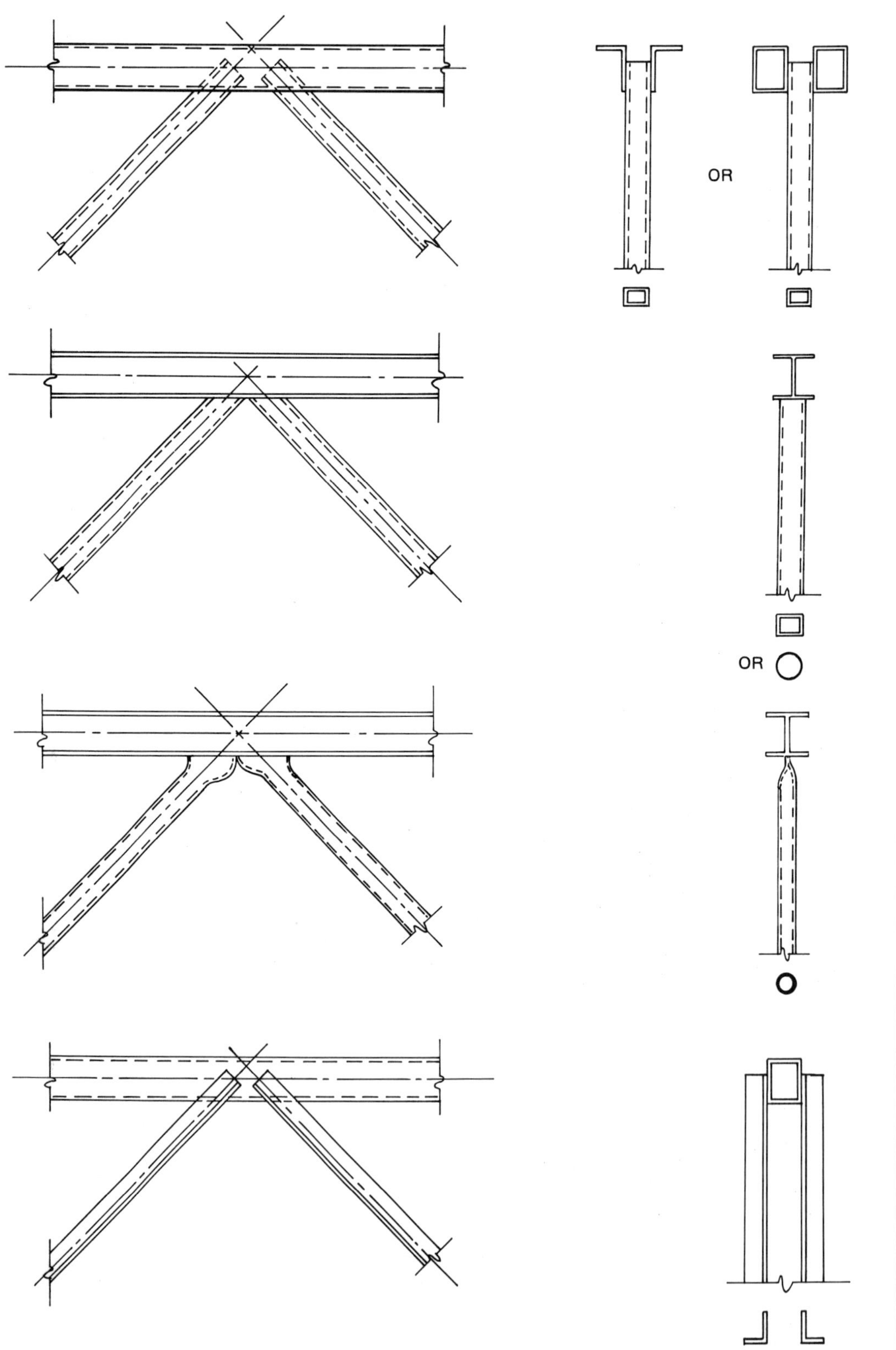

FIGURE 3-11

WELDING DETAILS FOR HOLLOW STRUCTURAL SECTIONS

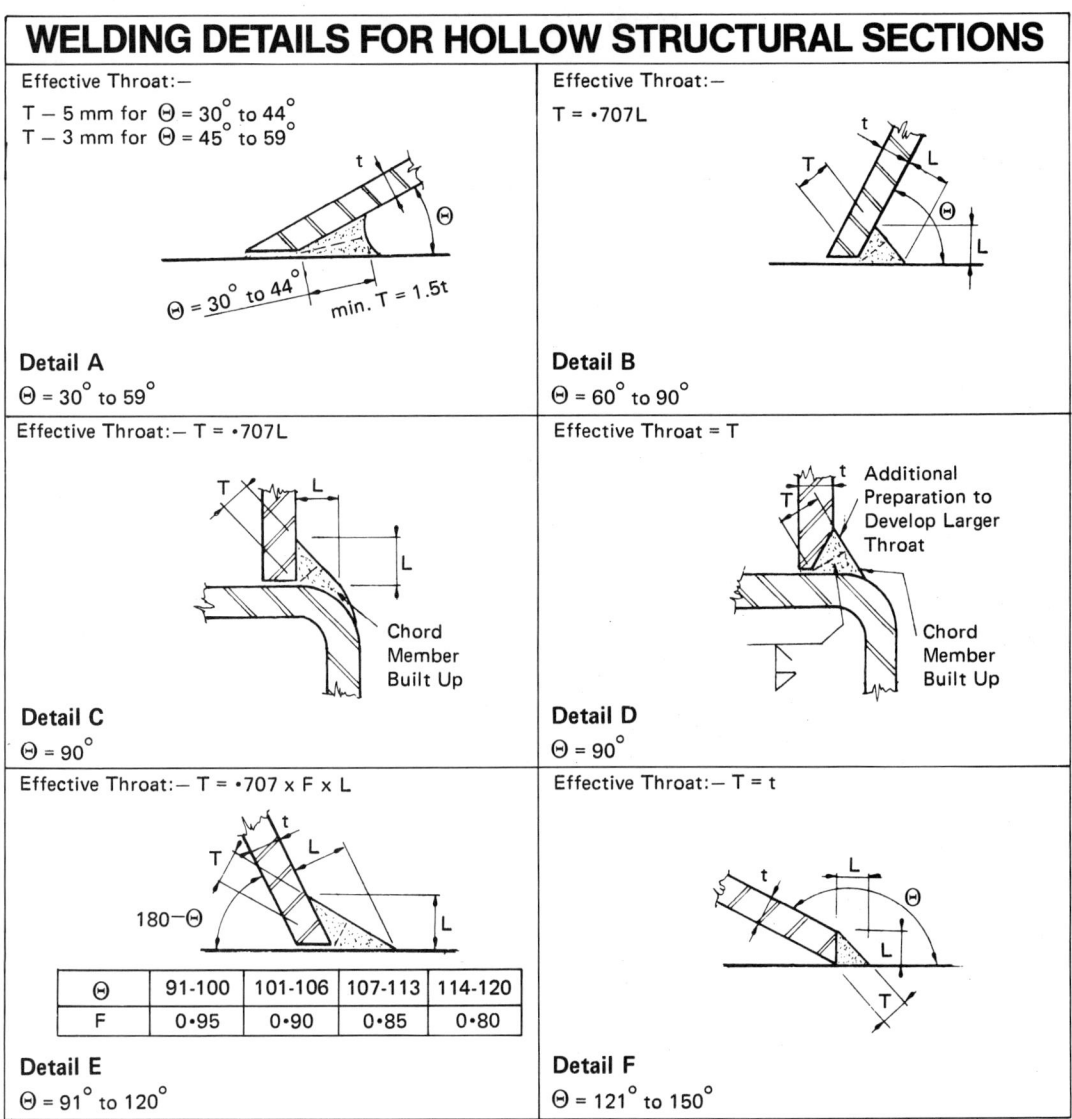

Detail A
$\Theta = 30°$ to $59°$

Effective Throat:—
T − 5 mm for $\Theta = 30°$ to $44°$
T − 3 mm for $\Theta = 45°$ to $59°$

$\Theta = 30°$ to $44°$ min. T = 1.5t

Detail B
$\Theta = 60°$ to $90°$

Effective Throat:—
T = •707L

Detail C
$\Theta = 90°$

Effective Throat:— T = •707L

Chord Member Built Up

Detail D
$\Theta = 90°$

Effective Throat = T

Additional Preparation to Develop Larger Throat

Chord Member Built Up

Detail E
$\Theta = 91°$ to $120°$

Effective Throat:— T = •707 x F x L

180−Θ

Θ	91-100	101-106	107-113	114-120
F	0•95	0•90	0•85	0•80

Detail F
$\Theta = 121°$ to $150°$

Effective Throat:— T = t

HSS CONNECTIONS
Fillet Size to Develop Wall Strength
Table 3-41

E480XX Fillet Welds $F_y = 350$ MPa

Wall Thickness (mm)	Fillet Leg Size (mm)	
	Wall in Shear	Wall in Tension
3.81	6	8
4.78	8	10
6.35	10	14
7.95	12	18
9.53	14	20
11.13	16	24
12.70	18	26

LENGTH OF WELD IN MILLIMETRES
HSS Web Members
Table 3-42

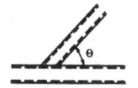

HSS Size b x d (mm)	Angle θ (Degrees)								
	30	35	40	45	50	55	60	65	70
25.4 x 25.4	152	139	130	123	117	113	109	107	105
31.8 x 31.8	191	174	163	154	147	141	137	134	131
38.1 x 38.1	229	209	195	184	176	169	164	160	157
50.8 x 50.8	305	279	260	245	234	226	219	214	210
63.5 x 63.5	381	348	325	307	293	282	274	267	262
76.2 x 76.2	457	418	389	368	351	338	328	321	315
88.9 x 88.9	533	488	454	429	410	395	383	374	367
101.6 x 101.6	610	557	519	491	468	451	438	427	419
127.0 x 127.0	762	697	649	613	586	564	547	534	524
152.4 x 152.4	914	836	779	736	703	677	657	641	629
177.8 x 177.8	1 070	976	909	858	820	790	766	748	734
203.2 x 203.2	1 220	1 110	1 040	981	937	903	876	855	839
254.0 x 254.0	1 520	1 390	1 300	1 230	1 170	1 130	1 090	1 070	1 050
304.8 x 304.8	1 830	1 670	1 560	1 470	1 410	1 350	1 310	1 280	1 260
50.8 x 25.4	254	228	209	194	183	175	168	163	159
25.4 x 50.8	203	190	181	173	168	164	160	158	156
76.2 x 50.8	406	367	339	317	301	288	278	270	264
50.8 x 76.2	356	330	310	296	285	276	270	265	261
101.6 x 50.8	508	456	418	389	367	350	336	326	318
50.8 x 101.6	406	380	361	347	336	327	321	315	311
88.9 x 63.5	483	437	404	378	359	344	332	323	316
63.5 x 88.9	432	399	375	357	344	333	324	318	313
101.6 x 76.2	559	507	469	440	418	400	387	377	369
76.2 x 101.6	508	469	440	419	402	389	379	371	365
127.0 x 50.8	610	544	497	461	433	412	395	382	372
50.8 x 127.0	457	431	412	398	387	378	371	366	362
127.0 x 63.5	635	570	522	486	459	437	420	407	397
63.5 x 127.0	508	475	452	434	420	409	401	394	389
127.0 x 76.2	660	595	548	512	484	462	446	433	423
76.2 x 127.0	559	520	491	470	453	440	430	422	416
152.4 x 101.6	813	735	677	634	601	575	555	540	528
101.6 x 152.4	711	659	621	592	570	553	539	529	521
177.8 x 127.0	965	874	807	757	718	688	665	646	632
127.0 x 177.8	864	798	751	715	687	666	649	636	626
203.2 x 101.6	1 020	912	835	778	734	699	672	652	636
101.6 x 203.2	813	761	723	694	672	654	641	631	623
203.2 x 152.4	1 120	1 010	937	880	835	801	774	753	737
152.4 x 203.2	1 020	938	881	837	804	778	758	743	731
215.9 x 50.8	965	854	773	712	665	629	600	578	561
50.8 x 215.9	635	609	590	575	564	556	549	544	540
254.0 x 152.4	1 320	1 190	1 100	1 020	968	925	891	865	845
152.4 x 254.0	1 120	1 040	982	939	906	880	860	844	832
304.8 x 203.2	1 630	1 470	1 350	1 270	1 200	1 150	1 110	1 080	1 060
203.2 x 304.8	1 420	1 320	1 240	1 180	1 140	1 110	1 080	1 060	1 040

TENSION MEMBERS

General

Members subject to axial tension (i.e. when the resultant tensile load on the member is co-incident with the longitudinal centroidal axis of the member) can be proportioned assuming a uniform stress distribution, and the factored tensile resistance shall be calculated on the basis of net area (Clause 12.1).

Net Area of Tension Members

Tables 3—43, 3—44 and 3—45 on the following pages are intended to simplify the calculation of net area according to the requirements of Clause 12.3.

Dimensions of Holes for Net Area

Table 3—43 on page 3—91 lists the specified hole diameter for various bolt sizes according to Clause 22.3.2, and the diameter of holes for calculating net area according to Clause 12.3.2.

Reduction of Area for Holes

Table 3—44 on page 3—91 lists values for the reduction of area for holes of different diameter in material of various thicknesses.

Net Width of Parts with Staggered Holes

Table 3—45 on page 3—92 lists values of $s^2/4g$ required to calculate the net width of any diagonal or zig-zag line of holes according to the requirements of Clause 12.3.3 for various pitches from 25 mm to 240 mm and for various gauges from 25 mm to 320 mm. Values of $s^2/4g$ for pitches and gauges between those listed can be interpolated.

Axial Tension

Table 3—46 on page 3—93 lists values of F_y, F_u, and Ratio F_y/F_u for the various structural quality steels covered by CSA G40.21-M for use in evaluating the requirements of Clause 12.3.4 and Clause 13.2.

Table 3—47 on page 3—93 lists values of Unit Factored Tensile Resistance, T_r/A_n, for different ratios of A_n/A_g according to the requirements of Clause 13.2.

Example

Given:

The hole pattern shown occurs at a bolted splice in a built-up tension member consisting of two C310×45 sections. Determine the net area of the member if the fasteners are M22 A325M bolts, and the factored tensile resistance of the member for material conforming to G40.21-M grades 300W, 350W and 480W steel.

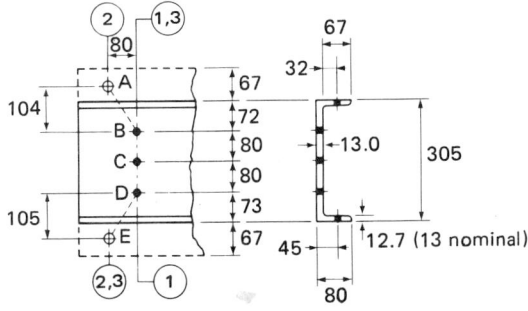

Solution:

(a) Gross area

Gross Area $2 - C310 \times 45 = A_g = 2 \times 5\ 690 = 11\ 380\ \text{mm}^2$

Gross width $= 305 + 2(80 - 13) = 439\ \text{mm}$ (Cl. 12.3.5, S16.1-M78)

(b) Deduction for net section

From Table 3—43, hole diameter for net area for M22 bolt $= 26\ \text{mm}$

Section 1—1

less 3 holes $= 3 \times 26 = -78\ \text{mm}$

Section 2—2

less 5 holes $= 5 \times 26 \qquad\qquad = -130$

plus $s^2/4g$ for AB $(s = 80, g = 104) = \quad +16$ (Table 3—45)*

plus $s^2/4g$ for DE $(s = 80, g = 105) = \quad \underline{+16}$

$\qquad\qquad\qquad\qquad\qquad\qquad\quad -98\ \text{mm (governs)}$

Section 3—3

less 4 holes $= 4 \times 26 \qquad\qquad = -104$

plus $s^2/4g$ for DE $(s = 80, g = 105) = + \quad \underline{16}$

$\qquad\qquad\qquad\qquad\qquad\qquad\quad -88\ \text{mm}$

*Values of $s^2/4g$ are obtained from Table 3—45 for $s = 80$ and interpolating by inspection for $g = 104$ and 105.

Net width $= 439 - 98 = 341\ \text{mm}$

Net area $= 2 \times 341 \times 13 = 8\ 870\ \text{mm}^2$

Ratio $A_n/A_g = 8\ 870\ /\ 11\ 380 = 0.78$

(c) Check A_n/A_g and Axial Tension (Cl. 12.3.4, Cl. 13.2, S16.1-M78)

For 300W steel

maximum $A_n/A_g = 0.85 > 0.78$ (Table 3—46)

also $A_n/A_g = 0.78$ is greater than $F_y/F_u = 0.67$

From Table 3—47, $T_r/A_n = 270\ \text{MPa}$ for $A_n/A_g = F_y/F_u = 0.67$

Therefore $T_r = 270 \times 8\ 870/1\ 000 = 2\ 390\ \text{kN}$

For 350W steel

maximum $A_n/A_g = 0.90 > 0.78$ (Table 3—46)

also $A_n/A_g = 0.78$ is equal to $F_y/F_u = 0.78$

From Table 3—47, $T_r/A_n = 315\ \text{MPa}$ for $A_n/A_g = F_y/F_u = 0.78$

Therefore $T_r = 315 \times 8\ 870/1\ 000 = 2\ 790\ \text{kN}$

For 480W steel

maximum $A_n/A_g = 0.90 > 0.78$ (Table 3—46)

also $A_n/A_g = 0.78$ is less than $F_y/F_u = 0.81$

From Table 3—47, $T_r/A_n = 398 + 0.6\ (425 - 398) = 414\ \text{MPa}$

Therefore $T_r = 414 \times 8\ 870/1\ 000 = 3\ 670\ \text{kN}$

Table 3-43
DIMENSIONS OF HOLES FOR NET AREA

Bolt Size		Specified Hole Diameter Clause 22.3.2		Diameter for Net Area Clause 12.3.2	
Metric	Imperial	Nominal Size (mm)	Oversize (mm)	Nominal Size (mm)	Oversize (mm)
M16		18	20	20	22
	3/4	22*	–	24	–
M20		22*	24	24	26
M22		24*	26	26	28
	7/8	24*	–	26	–
M24		27*	30	29	32
	1	27*	–	29	–
M27		29	35	31	37
M30		32	38	34	40
M36		38	42	40	44

* For nominal diameter of hole, see Clause 22.3.2(d).

Table 3-44
REDUCTION OF AREA FOR HOLES*

Material Thickness (mm)	Diameter of Hole (mm)											
	20	22	24	26	28	29	31	32	34	37	40	44
5	100	110	120	130	140	145	155	160	170	185	200	220
6	120	132	144	156	168	174	186	192	204	222	240	264
7	140	154	168	182	196	203	217	224	238	259	280	308
8	160	176	192	208	224	232	248	256	272	296	320	352
9	180	198	216	234	252	261	279	288	306	333	360	396
10	200	220	240	260	280	290	310	320	340	370	400	440
11	220	242	264	286	308	319	341	352	374	407	440	484
12	240	264	288	312	336	348	372	384	408	444	480	528
13	260	286	312	338	364	377	403	416	442	481	520	572
14	280	308	336	364	392	406	434	448	476	518	560	616
16	320	352	384	416	448	464	496	512	544	592	640	704
18	360	396	432	468	504	522	558	576	612	666	720	792
20	400	440	480	520	560	580	620	640	680	740	800	880
22	440	484	528	572	616	638	682	704	748	814	880	968
25	500	550	600	650	700	725	775	800	850	925	1 000	1 100
28	560	616	672	728	784	812	868	896	952	1 040	1 120	1 230
30	600	660	720	780	840	870	930	960	1 020	1 110	1 200	1 320
32	640	704	768	832	896	928	992	1 020	1 090	1 180	1 280	1 410
35	700	770	840	910	980	1 020	1 080	1 120	1 190	1 300	1 400	1 540
38	760	836	912	988	1 060	1 100	1 180	1 220	1 290	1 410	1 520	1 670
40	800	880	960	1 040	1 120	1 160	1 240	1 280	1 360	1 480	1 600	1 760
45	900	990	1 080	1 170	1 260	1 300	1 400	1 440	1 530	1 660	1 800	1 980
50	1 000	1 100	1 200	1 300	1 400	1 450	1 550	1 600	1 700	1 850	2 000	2 200
55	1 100	1 210	1 320	1 430	1 540	1 600	1 700	1 760	1 870	2 040	2 200	2 420
60	1 200	1 320	1 440	1 560	1 680	1 740	1 860	1 920	2 040	2 220	2 400	2 640
70	1 400	1 540	1 680	1 820	1 960	2 030	2 170	2 240	2 380	2 590	2 800	3 080
80	1 600	1 760	1 920	2 080	2 240	2 320	2 480	2 560	2 720	2 960	3 200	3 520
90	1 800	1 980	2 160	2 340	2 520	2 610	2 790	2 880	3 060	3 330	3 600	3 960
100	2 000	2 200	2 400	2 600	2 800	2 900	3 100	3 200	3 400	3 700	4 000	4 400

*Area (mm²) = Diameter of hole (mm) times material thickness (mm).

NET WIDTH OF TENSION MEMBERS
With Staggered Holes

Table 3-45
$s^2/4g$

Pitch "s" (mm)	Gauge "g" (mm)															
	25	30	35	40	45	50	60	70	80	100	120	160	200	240	280	320
25					3	3	3	2	2	2	1	1	1	1	1	0
30				6	5	4	4	3	3	2	2	1	1	1	1	1
35			9	8	7	6	5	5	4	3	3	2	2	1	1	1
40		13	11	10	9	8	7	6	5	4	3	2	2	2	1	1
45	20	17	14	13	11	10	8	7	6	5	4	3	3	2	2	2
50	25	21	18	16	14	12	10	9	8	6	4	4	3	3	2	2
55	30	25	22	19	17	15	13	11	9	8	6	5	4	3	3	2
60	36	30	26	22	20	18	15	13	11	9	7	6	4	4	3	3
65	42	35	30	26	23	21	18	15	13	11	9	7	5	4	4	3
70	49	41	35	31	27	24	20	17	15	12	10	8	6	5	4	4
75		47	40	35	31	28	23	20	18	14	12	9	7	6	5	4
80			46	40	36	32	27	23	20	16	13	10	8	7	6	5
90				51	45	40	34	29	25	20	17	13	10	8	7	6
100						50	42	36	31	25	21	16	12	10	9	8
110							50	43	38	30	25	19	15	13	11	9
120									45	36	30	22	18	15	13	11
130										42	35	26	21	18	15	13
140										49	41	31	24	20	17	15
150											47	35	28	23	20	18
160												40	32	27	23	20
170												45	36	30	26	23
180												51	40	34	29	25
190													45	38	32	28
200													50	42	36	31
210														46	39	34
220														50	43	38
230															47	41
240																45

Table 3-46

Material Specification and Grade	F_y (MPa)	F_u (MPa)	F_y/F_u	Assumed Maximum Ratio A_n/A_g (Cl. 12.3.4)	$0.85 \phi F_u$ (MPa) (Cl. 13.2(a)(ii))
230G	230	380	0.61	0.85	291
260W, 260WT	260	410	0.63	0.85	314
300 W (for HSS only)	300	410	0.73	0.85	314
300W, 300WT	300	450	0.67	0.85	344
350W	350	450	0.78	0.90	344
350G, 350WT, 350R, 350A, 350AT	350	480	0.73	0.85	367
380W, 380WT (HSS)	380	480	0.79	0.90	367
400W, 400WT, 400A, 400AT	400	520	0.77	0.90	398
400G	400	550	0.73	0.85	421
480W, 480WT, 480A, 480AT	480	590	0.81	0.90	451
700Q, 700QT	700	800	0.88	0.95	612

UNIT FACTORED TENSILE RESISTANCES T_r/A_n (MPa)

Table 3-47 — $\phi = 0.90$

Material Specification & Grade	Ratio A_n/A_g									Ratio A_n/A_g Equal to F_y/F_u
	0.3	0.4	0.5	0.6	0.65	0.70	0.75	0.80	0.85	
230G	103	137	171	205						207
260W, 260WT	111	148	185	221						234
300W (for HSS only)	111	148	185	221	239	258				270
300W, 300WT	122	162	203	243	263					270
350W	122	162	203	243	263	284	304			315
350G, 350WT, 350R, 350A, 350AT	130	173	216	259	281	302				315
380W, 380WT (HSS)	130	173	216	259	281	302	324			342
400W, 400WT, 400A, 400AT	140	187	234	281	304	328	351			360
400G	149	198	248	297	322	347				360
480W, 480WT, 480A, 480AT	159	212	266	319	345	372	398	425		432
700Q, 700QT	216	288	360	432	468	504	540	576	612	630

Values to the right of the heavy line are governed by $A_n/A_g \geqslant F_y/F_u$. See Clause 13.2(a) CAN3-S16.1-M78.

PART FOUR
COMPRESSION MEMBERS

General Information . . . . 4—3

Limits on Width-Thickness Ratios. . . . . 4—5

Unit Factored Compressive Resistances for Compression Members. . . . . 4—8

Stability Effects . . . . 4—14

Effective Lengths of Compression Members . . . . 4—22

Bending Factors for Beam-Columns . . . . 4—27

ω — Equivalent Uniform Bending Coefficients . . . . 4—30

C_e/A — Euler Buckling Load per Unit Area. . . . . 4—31

Amplification Factors, U. . . . . 4—32

Factored Axial Compressive Resistances of Columns . . . . 4—33

    WWF and W Shapes — CSA G40.21-M 300W steel. . . . . 4—36

    HSS — Class C — CSA G40.21-M 350W steel. . . . . 4—48

    HSS — Class H — CSA G40.21-M 350W steel. . . . . 4—72

Design of Beam-Columns. . . . . 4—96

Columns Subject to Biaxial Bending . . . . 4—108

Factored Moment Resistances of Columns . . . . 4—117

Double Angle Struts . . . . 4—122

Column Base Plates. . . . . 4—144

Anchor Bolts. . . . . 4—149

GENERAL INFORMATION

Limits on Width-Thickness Ratios

See page 4—5.

Unit Factored Compressive Resistances for Compression Members, C_r/A

See page 4—8.

Stability Effects

Pages 4—14 to 4—19 describe the two methods given in Clause 8 of CAN3-S16.1-M78 to account for the stability effects and three methods of computing the $P\Delta$ effects. Pages 4—20 and 4—21 are reprints of Appendix J of CAN3-S16.1-M78.

Effective Lengths of Compression Members

Pages 4—22 to 4—25 inclusive are reprints of Appendices B and C of CAN3-S16.1-M78. Table 4—5 on page 4—26 is based on a similar table in "Beam-Column Tables for Structural Shapes", published by Bethlehem Steel Corporation.

Bending Factors for Beam-Columns

See page 4—27.

ω — Equivalent Uniform Bending Coefficients

Table 4—7, page 4—30, lists values of ω for various ratios, M_{f_1}/M_{f_2}, of factored end bending moments applied to beam-columns. The values of ω are computed in accordance with the requirements of Clause 13.8.4, CAN3-S16.1-M78. See the Design of Beam-Columns, page 4—96, for more information.

C_e/A — Euler Buckling Load per Unit Area

Table 4—8, page 4—31, lists values of C_e/A for KL/r ratios varying from 1 to 200. The values of C_e/A have been computed in accordance with the definition in Clause 3.2, CAN3-S16.1-M78.

Amplification Factors

Table 4—9, page 4—32, has been prepared to facilitate the design of beam-columns in accordance with the requirements of Clause 13.8, CAN3-S16.1-M78. Values of the amplification factor corresponding to various combinations of C_f/C_e are listed.

Factored Axial Compressive Resistances of Columns

See page 4—33.

Design of Beam-Columns

See page 4—96.

Columns Subject to Biaxial Bending

Appendix F of CAN3-S16.1-M78 is reprinted on pages 4—109 to 4—111. Pages 4—112 to 4—115 contain design aids and examples.

Factored Moment Resistances of Columns

See page 4—117.

Double Angle Struts

The tables of factored axial compressive resistances for double angle struts, page 4—122 to 4—142 inclusive, are based on the requirements of Clause 13.3.1, CAN3-S16.1-M78.

Slender angles are included as the factored axial compressive resistance of these sections is computed based on the requirements of Clause 13.3.3, CAN3-S16.1-M78.

Factored axial compressive resistances with respect to various effective lengths, in millimetres, relative to both the X—X and Y—Y axis, and the U—U and V—V axis for starred angles, are listed for angles made for CSA G40.21-M 300W. F_y for G40.21-M 300W steel angles is 300 MPa for angles not exceeding 20 mm in thickness, and is 290 MPa for angles thicker than 20 mm.

The factored axial compressive resistances pertaining to effective lengths based on the Y—Y axis have been computed for angles spaced 10 mm back-to-back. To obtain factored compressive resistances for different spacing for classes 1, 2 and 3 angle struts, multiply the actual effective length.

by the ratio $\dfrac{r_y}{r_y'}$,

where

    r_y =   value listed at the bottom of the tables, for angles 10 mm back-to-back

    $r_y' = r_y$ listed in tables p. 6—72 to 6—77 inclusive of this Handbook for actual distance back-to-back.

Using the modified effective length, the factored axial compressive resistance value can be selected directly from the tables.

The value r_z tabulated by itself and as part of the following ratios, r_z/r_x, r_z/r_y, r_z/r_u, and r_z/r_v, which appear with the properties of double angle struts, is the radius of gyration for a single angle about the Z—Z axis of that single angle. The r values for all other axes are those for the double angle strut. See Part 6 of this Handbook for a more comprehensive list of angle properties.

The expressions in Clause 13.3.1, defining the axial load, and hence the resistance tables for double angle struts, are based on column strength for rolled W shapes. Double angles struts should be checked as to whether torsional-flexural buckling is critical.

Current research (1980) indicates that starred angles require two equally spaced points of interconnection (i.e. at third-points).

Column Base Plates

See page 4—144.

Anchor Bolts

See page 4—149.

LIMITS ON WIDTH-THICKNESS RATIOS

Table 4—1, on page 4—6, is taken from Clause 11 of CAN3-S16.1-M78 and for various elements in compression lists the width-thickness ratios for Class 1,2, and 3 sections.

Table 4—2 and the graph, Figure 4—1, on page 4—7, can be used to verify a section's Class. Table 4—2 lists the particular width-thickness ratio limit for various yield strengths for each general value given in Table 4—1 on page 4—6.

For webs in combined flexural and axial compression the graph of the reduction factor, $R, (R = 1 - X \frac{C_f}{C_y})$, Figure 4—1, for various C_f/C_y ratios may be used to determine R for any C_f/C_y ratio. Multiply that R by the appropriate value from Table 4—2 to determine the h/w limit.

Example

Given:

Find the h/w limit for a Class 2 column section whose C_f/C_y ratio is 0.70, F_y = 300 MPa, subject to combined flexural and axial compression.

Solution:

From the graph at the bottom of page 4—7, for C_f/C_y = 0.7 proceed up to the line labelled $1 - 0.43 \, C_f/C_y$ as required by Table 4—1 for a Class 2 beam-column when $C_f/C_y > 0.15$. Read the value of R from the scale at the left, R = 0.70.

For F_y = 300 MPa and a general value of $1180/\sqrt{F_y}$ as determined from Table 4—1, find the value of 68.1 in Table 4—2.

Therefore h/w $\leqslant$ 68.1 X 0.7
$\leqslant$ 47.7

Table 4-1
WIDTH-THICKNESS RATIOS: COMPRESSION ELEMENTS

Description of Element	Section Classification		
	Class 1 Plastic Design	Class 2 Compact	Class 3 Non-compact
Legs of angles and elements supported along one edge, except as noted	—	—	$\dfrac{b}{t} < \dfrac{200}{\sqrt{F_y}}$
Angles in continuous contact with other elements; plate girder stiffeners	—	—	$\dfrac{b}{t} < \dfrac{260}{\sqrt{F_y}}$
Stems of T sections	$\dfrac{b}{t} < \dfrac{145^*}{\sqrt{F_y}}$	$\dfrac{b}{t} < \dfrac{170^*}{\sqrt{F_y}}$	$\dfrac{b}{t} < \dfrac{340}{\sqrt{F_y}}$
Flanges of I or T sections; plates projecting from compression elements; outstanding legs of pairs of angles in continuous contact §	$\dfrac{b}{t} < \dfrac{145}{\sqrt{F_y}}$	$\dfrac{b}{t} < \dfrac{170}{\sqrt{F_y}}$	$\dfrac{b}{t} < \dfrac{260}{\sqrt{F_y}}$
Flanges of channels	—	—	$\dfrac{b}{t} < \dfrac{260}{\sqrt{F_y}}$
Flanges of rectangular hollow structural sections	$\dfrac{b}{t} < \dfrac{420}{\sqrt{F_y}}$	$\dfrac{b}{t} < \dfrac{525}{\sqrt{F_y}}$	$\dfrac{b}{t} < \dfrac{670}{\sqrt{F_y}}$
Flanges of box sections, flange cover plates and diaphragm plates, between lines of fasteners or welds	$\dfrac{b}{t} < \dfrac{525}{\sqrt{F_y}}$	$\dfrac{b}{t} < \dfrac{525}{\sqrt{F_y}}$	$\dfrac{b}{t} < \dfrac{670}{\sqrt{F_y}}$
Perforated cover plates	—	—	$\dfrac{b}{t} < \dfrac{840}{\sqrt{F_y}}$
Webs in axial compression	$\dfrac{h}{w} < \dfrac{670}{\sqrt{F_y}}$	$\dfrac{h}{w} < \dfrac{670}{\sqrt{F_y}}$	$\dfrac{h}{w} < \dfrac{670}{\sqrt{F_y}}$
Webs in flexural compression	$\dfrac{h}{w} < \dfrac{1\,100}{\sqrt{F_y}}$	$\dfrac{h}{w} < \dfrac{1\,370}{\sqrt{F_y}}$	$\dfrac{h}{w} < \dfrac{1\,810}{\sqrt{F_y}}$
Webs in combined flexural and axial compression	$\dfrac{h}{w} < \dfrac{1\,100}{\sqrt{F_y}}\left(1 - 1.40\dfrac{C_f}{C_y}\right)†$	when $\dfrac{C_f}{C_y} < 0.15$, $\dfrac{h}{w} < \dfrac{1\,370}{\sqrt{F_y}}\left(1 - 1.28\dfrac{C_f}{C_y}\right)†$; when $\dfrac{C_f}{C_y} > 0.15$, $\dfrac{h}{w} < \dfrac{1\,180}{\sqrt{F_y}}\left(1 - 0.43\dfrac{C_f}{C_y}\right)†$	when $\dfrac{C_f}{C_y} < 0.15$, $\dfrac{h}{w} < \dfrac{1.810}{\sqrt{F_y}}\left(1 - 1.69\dfrac{C_f}{C_y}\right)†$; when $\dfrac{C_f}{C_y} > 0.15$, $\dfrac{h}{w} < \dfrac{1\,470}{\sqrt{F_y}}\left(1 - 0.54\dfrac{C_f}{C_y}\right)†$
Circular hollow sections	$\dfrac{D}{t} < \dfrac{13\,000}{F_y}$	$\dfrac{D}{t} < \dfrac{18\,000}{F_y}$	$\dfrac{D}{t} < \dfrac{23\,000}{F_y}$

*See clause 11.1.3 of CAN3-S16.1-M78, page 1-30.

† $\dfrac{h}{w}$ need not be less than $\dfrac{670}{\sqrt{F_y}}$

§ Can be considered as Class 1 or Class 2 sections if angles are continuously connected by adequate mechanical fasteners or welds and there is an axis of symmetry in the plane of loading.

For Class 4 sections see Clause 11 of CAN3-S16.1-M78.

TABLE OF WIDTH-THICKNESS LIMITS
Table 4-2

General Value	F_y (MPa)									
	248	280	290	300	320	330	350	380	400	480
$145/\sqrt{F_y}$	9.2	8.7	8.5	8.4	8.1	8.0	7.8	7.4	7.2	6.6
$170/\sqrt{F_y}$	10.8	10.2	10.0	9.8	9.5	9.4	9.1	8.7	8.5	7.8
$200/\sqrt{F_y}$	12.7	12.0	11.7	11.5	11.2	11.0	10.7	10.2	10.0	9.1
$260/\sqrt{F_y}$	16.5	15.5	15.3	15.0	14.5	14.3	13.9	13.3	13.0	11.9
$340/\sqrt{F_y}$	21.6	20.3	20.0	19.6	19.0	18.7	18.2	17.4	17.0	15.5
$420/\sqrt{F_y}$	26.7	25.1	24.7	24.2	23.5	23.1	22.4	21.5	21.0	19.2
$525/\sqrt{F_y}$	33.3	31.4	30.8	30.3	29.3	28.9	28.1	26.9	26.2	24.0
$670/\sqrt{F_y}$	42.5	40.0	39.3	38.7	37.4	36.9	35.8	34.4	33.5	30.6
$840/\sqrt{F_y}$	53.3	50.2	49.3	48.5	47.0	46.2	44.9	43.1	42.0	38.3
$1100/\sqrt{F_y}$	69.8	65.7	64.6	63.5	61.5	60.6	58.8	56.4	55.0	50.2
$1180/\sqrt{F_y}$	74.9	70.5	69.3	68.1	66.0	65.0	63.1	60.5	59.0	53.8
$1370/\sqrt{F_y}$	87.0	81.9	80.4	79.1	76.6	75.4	73.2	70.3	68.5	62.5
$1470/\sqrt{F_y}$	93.3	87.8	86.3	84.9	82.2	80.9	78.6	75.4	73.5	67.1
$1810/\sqrt{F_y}$	115	108	106	104	101	99.6	96.7	92.8	90.5	82.6
$13\,000/F_y$	52.4	46.4	44.8	43.3	40.6	39.4	37.1	34.2	32.5	27.1
$18\,000/F_y$	72.6	64.3	62.1	60.0	56.2	54.5	51.4	47.4	45.0	37.5
$23\,000/F_y$	92.7	82.1	79.3	76.7	71.9	69.7	65.7	60.5	57.5	47.9

FIGURE 4-1
PLOT OF REDUCTION FACTOR R FOR WEBS OF BEAM-COLUMNS

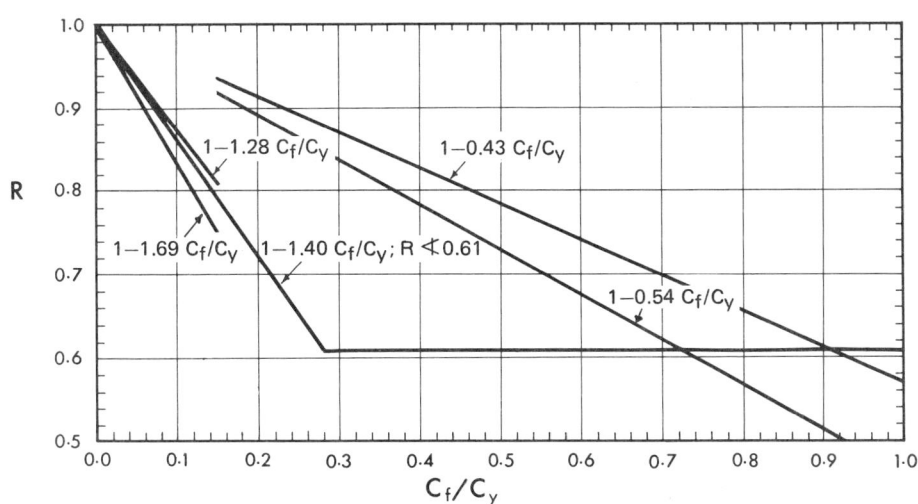

UNIT FACTORED COMPRESSIVE RESISTANCES FOR COMPRESSION MEMBERS, C_r/A

General

Table 4—3 on pages 4—9 to 4—12 lists the unit factored compressive resistance, C_r/A, in MPa, for compression members for steel with specified minimum yield points varying from 248 MPa to 700 MPa. The values for $F_y = 300$ are printed in bold faced type. The unit factored compressive resistances have been calculated in accordance with the requirements of Clause 13.3.1, CSA Standard CAN3-S16.1-M78 "Steel Structures for Buildings — Limit States Design", for values of KL/r from 1 to 200.

Table 4—4 on page 4—13 lists the unit factored compressive resistance, C_r/A, for compression members consisting of hollow structural sections manufactured according to CSA Standard G40.20-M, Class H for steel with a specified minimum yield point of 350 MPa. The unit factored compressive resistances have been calculated in accordance with the requirements of Clause 13.3.2 of CAN3-S16.1-78 for values of KL/r from 1 to 200.

Use

To obtain the factored compressive resistance, C_r, for doubly symmetric Class 1, 2 or 3 sections multiply the unit factored compressive resistance, C_r/A, for the appropriate F_y and KL/r ratio, by the cross-sectional area, A, of the column section.

Examples

1. Given:

   Find the factored compressive resistance of a W250×131 column of ASTM A36 steel ($F_y = 248$ MPa) for a KL/r ratio of 89.

Solution:

   From page 6—50 for W250×131, A = 16 700 mm². From Table 4—3, page 4—10, with KL/r = 89 and $F_y = 248$ MPa, $C_r/A = 137$ MPa.

   Therefore $C_r = 137$ MPa × 16 700 mm² = 2 290 × 10³ N = 2 290 kN

2. Given:

   Find the factored compressive resistance of an HSS 254.0 × 152.4 × 11.13 — Class H column for $F_y = 350$ MPa and KL/r = 89.

Solution:

   From page 6—88 for HSS 254.0 × 152.4 × 11.13, A = 8 230 mm²
   From Table 4—4, page 4—13, with KL/r = 89 and $F_y = 350$ MPa, $C_r/A = 195$ MPa.

   Therefore $C_r = 195$ MPa × 8 230 mm² = 1 600 × 10³ N = 1 600 kN

Notes:

1. Tables of C_r, factored axial compressive resistance, for columns in CSA G40.21-M grade 300W steels are given on pages 4—36 to 4—46.

2. Tables of C_r for HSS Class C columns in G40.21-M grade 350W steel are given on pages 4—48 to 4—71.

3. Tables of C_r for HSS Class H columns in G40.21-M grade 350W steel are given on pages 4—72 to 4—95.

4. For columns not manufactured in Canada, see Part 2, CISC Commentary, for more information on compressive resistance.

UNIT FACTORED COMPRESSIVE RESISTANCES, C$_r$/A (MPa)* FOR COMPRESSION MEMBERS
Ø = 0.90

$$\frac{KL}{r} = 1 \text{ to } 50$$

Table 4-3

$\frac{KL}{r}$	F$_y$ (MPa)									
	248	260	280	290	300	350	380	400	480	700
1	223	234	252	261	270	315	342	360	432	630
2	223	234	252	261	270	315	342	360	432	630
3	223	234	252	261	270	315	342	360	432	630
4	223	234	252	261	270	315	342	360	432	630
5	223	234	252	261	270	315	342	360	432	630
6	223	234	252	261	270	315	342	360	432	630
7	223	234	252	261	270	315	342	360	432	630
8	223	234	252	261	270	315	342	360	432	630
9	223	234	252	261	270	315	342	360	432	626
10	223	234	252	261	270	315	342	360	431	623
11	223	234	252	261	270	315	342	359	429	620
12	223	234	252	261	270	314	340	358	427	616
13	223	234	252	260	269	313	339	356	425	613
14	223	233	251	260	268	312	338	355	423	609
15	222	233	250	259	267	311	336	353	421	605
16	221	232	249	258	266	309	335	352	419	601
17	221	231	248	257	265	308	333	350	417	597
18	220	230	247	256	264	307	332	349	415	593
19	219	229	246	255	263	305	330	347	413	589
20	218	229	246	254	262	304	329	345	411	584
21	218	228	245	253	261	303	327	344	408	580
22	217	227	244	252	260	301	326	342	406	575
23	216	226	243	251	259	300	324	340	403	571
24	215	225	242	250	258	299	323	338	401	566
25	214	224	241	249	257	297	321	337	399	561
26	214	223	240	248	256	296	319	335	396	556
27	213	223	239	247	255	294	317	333	393	551
28	212	222	238	246	253	293	316	331	391	546
29	211	221	237	244	252	291	314	329	388	541
30	210	220	235	243	251	289	312	327	385	536
31	209	219	234	242	250	288	310	325	383	530
32	208	218	233	241	249	286	308	323	380	525
33	208	217	232	240	247	285	306	321	377	519
34	207	216	231	239	246	283	304	319	374	513
35	206	215	230	237	245	281	303	317	371	507
36	205	214	229	236	243	279	301	314	368	501
37	204	213	228	235	242	278	298	312	365	495
38	203	212	226	234	241	276	296	310	362	489
39	202	211	225	232	239	274	294	308	359	483
40	201	210	224	231	238	272	292	305	355	477
41	200	208	223	230	237	270	290	303	352	470
42	199	207	221	228	235	269	288	301	349	464
43	198	206	220	227	234	267	286	298	345	457
44	197	205	219	226	232	265	283	296	342	451
45	196	204	217	224	231	263	281	293	339	444
46	195	203	216	223	229	261	279	291	335	437
47	194	202	215	221	228	259	277	288	332	430
48	192	200	213	220	226	257	274	286	328	423
49	191	199	212	218	225	255	272	283	324	416
50	190	198	211	217	223	253	270	280	321	408

*Calculated in accordance with Clause 13.3.1 of CAN3-S16.1-M78.
 For Class H hollow structural sections, see Table 4-4, page 4-13.

$$\frac{KL}{r} = 51 \text{ to } 100$$

Table 4-3

$\frac{KL}{r}$	F_y (MPa)									
	248	260	280	290	300	350	380	400	480	700
51	189	197	209	215	**221**	251	267	278	317	401
52	188	195	208	214	**220**	248	265	275	313	393
53	187	194	206	212	**218**	246	262	272	309	386
54	186	193	205	211	**217**	244	260	269	306	377
55	184	192	203	209	**215**	242	257	267	302	368
56	183	190	202	208	**213**	240	254	264	298	359
57	182	189	200	206	**212**	237	252	261	294	351
58	181	188	199	204	**210**	235	249	258	290	343
59	180	186	197	203	**208**	233	247	255	286	335
60	178	185	196	201	**206**	231	244	252	282	328
61	177	184	194	199	**205**	228	241	249	277	320
62	176	182	193	198	**203**	226	238	246	273	313
63	174	181	191	196	**201**	223	236	243	269	307
64	173	179	190	194	**199**	221	233	240	265	300
65	172	178	188	193	**197**	219	230	237	260	294
66	171	177	186	191	**195**	216	227	234	254	288
67	169	175	185	189	**194**	214	224	231	249	282
68	168	174	183	187	**192**	211	221	227	245	276
69	167	172	181	186	**190**	209	218	224	240	271
70	165	171	179	184	**188**	206	215	221	235	266
71	164	169	178	182	**186**	203	212	217	231	260
72	162	168	176	180	**184**	201	209	213	227	255
73	161	166	174	178	**182**	198	206	209	222	251
74	160	165	173	176	**180**	195	202	206	218	246
75	158	163	171	174	**178**	193	199	202	214	241
76	157	161	169	172	**176**	190	195	198	211	237
77	155	160	167	170	**174**	186	192	195	207	232
78	154	158	165	168	**172**	183	188	192	203	228
79	152	157	163	167	**169**	180	185	188	200	224
80	151	155	162	165	**167**	177	182	185	196	220
81	149	153	160	163	**165**	174	179	182	193	216
82	148	152	158	160	**163**	171	176	179	190	213
83	146	150	156	158	**160**	169	173	176	187	209
84	145	148	154	156	**158**	166	171	173	184	205
85	143	147	152	154	**155**	163	168	171	181	202
86	142	145	149	151	**153**	161	165	168	178	198
87	140	143	147	149	**151**	158	163	165	175	195
88	138	141	145	147	**148**	156	160	163	172	192
89	137	139	143	144	**146**	154	158	160	170	189
90	135	137	141	142	**144**	151	155	158	167	186
91	133	135	139	140	**142**	149	153	155	164	183
92	131	133	137	138	**140**	147	151	153	162	180
93	129	131	135	136	**138**	145	148	151	159	177
94	127	129	133	134	**136**	143	146	149	157	174
95	126	128	131	132	**134**	141	144	146	155	171
96	124	126	129	130	**132**	139	142	144	152	168
97	122	124	127	129	**130**	137	140	142	150	166
98	121	122	125	127	**128**	135	138	140	148	163
99	119	121	124	125	**126**	133	136	138	146	161
100	117	119	122	123	**125**	131	134	136	144	158

*Calculated in accordance with Clause 13.3.1. of CAN3-S16.1-M78.
 For Class H hollow structural sections, see Table 4-4, page 4-13.

UNIT FACTORED COMPRESSIVE RESISTANCES, C$_r$/A (MPa)* FOR COMPRESSION MEMBERS

$\dfrac{KL}{r}$ = 101 to 150

$\emptyset$ = 0.90

Table 4-3

$\dfrac{KL}{r}$	F$_y$ (MPa)									
	248	260	280	290	300	350	380	400	480	700
101	116	118	120	122	**123**	129	132	134	142	156
102	114	116	119	120	**121**	127	131	133	140	154
103	113	114	117	119	**120**	126	129	131	138	151
104	111	113	116	117	**118**	124	127	129	136	149
105	110	112	114	115	**117**	122	125	127	134	147
106	108	110	113	114	**115**	121	124	126	132	145
107	107	109	111	113	**114**	119	122	124	130	142
108	106	107	110	111	**112**	118	120	122	128	139
109	104	106	108	110	**111**	116	119	121	127	137
110	103	105	107	108	**109**	115	117	119	125	134
111	102	103	106	107	**108**	113	116	117	123	132
112	101	102	104	106	**107**	112	114	116	122	130
113	99.4	101	103	104	**105**	110	113	114	120	128
114	98.2	99.7	102	103	**104**	109	111	113	118	126
115	97.0	98.5	101	102	**103**	108	110	112	117	123
116	95.9	97.3	99.5	101	**102**	106	109	110	115	121
117	94.8	96.1	98.3	99.4	**100**	105	107	109	114	119
118	93.7	95.0	97.2	98.2	**99.2**	104	106	107	112	118
119	92.6	93.9	96.0	97.0	**98.0**	102	105	106	111	116
120	91.5	92.8	94.9	95.9	**96.8**	101	103	105	110	114
121	90.4	91.8	93.8	94.8	**95.7**	99.9	102	104	108	112
122	89.4	90.7	92.7	93.7	**94.6**	98.7	101	102	107	110
123	88.4	89.7	91.6	92.6	**93.5**	97.6	99.7	101	106	109
124	87.4	88.7	90.6	91.5	**92.4**	96.4	98.5	99.8	104	107
125	86.4	87.7	89.6	90.5	**91.4**	95.3	97.3	98.6	103	105
126	85.5	86.7	88.6	89.5	**90.3**	94.2	96.2	97.4	102	104
127	84.5	85.7	87.6	88.4	**89.3**	93.1	95.1	96.3	100	102
128	83.6	84.8	86.6	87.5	**88.3**	92.0	93.9	95.1	99.1	101
129	82.7	83.8	85.6	86.5	**87.3**	91.0	92.9	94.0	97.5	99.3
130	81.8	82.9	84.7	85.5	**86.3**	89.9	91.8	92.9	96.1	97.9
131	80.9	82.0	83.8	84.6	**85.4**	88.9	90.7	91.8	94.7	96.5
132	80.0	81.1	82.8	83.6	**84.4**	87.9	89.7	90.8	93.3	95.1
133	79.2	80.3	81.9	82.7	**83.5**	86.9	88.6	89.7	92.0	93.7
134	78.3	79.4	81.1	81.8	**82.6**	85.9	87.6	88.7	90.7	92.4
135	77.5	78.6	80.2	81.0	**81.7**	85.0	86.6	87.7	89.4	91.2
136	76.7	77.7	79.3	80.1	**80.8**	84.0	85.7	86.7	88.1	89.9
137	75.9	76.9	78.5	79.2	**79.9**	83.1	84.7	85.7	86.9	88.7
138	75.1	76.1	77.7	78.4	**79.1**	82.2	83.8	84.7	85.7	87.5
139	74.3	75.3	76.8	77.6	**78.2**	81.3	82.8	83.8	84.5	86.3
140	73.6	74.5	76.0	76.7	**77.4**	80.4	81.9	82.8	83.4	85.2
141	72.8	73.8	75.2	75.9	**76.6**	79.5	81.0	81.6	82.3	84.0
142	72.1	73.0	74.5	75.1	**75.8**	78.7	80.1	80.5	81.2	82.9
143	71.3	72.3	73.7	74.4	**75.0**	77.8	79.2	79.4	80.1	81.9
144	70.6	71.5	72.9	73.6	**74.2**	77.0	78.4	78.4	79.0	80.8
145	69.9	70.8	72.2	72.8	**73.4**	76.1	77.2	77.3	78.0	79.8
146	69.2	70.1	71.4	72.1	**72.7**	75.3	76.2	76.3	77.0	78.8
147	68.5	69.4	70.7	71.3	**71.9**	74.5	75.2	75.3	76.0	77.8
148	67.9	68.7	70.0	70.6	**71.2**	73.7	74.2	74.4	75.0	76.8
149	67.2	68.0	69.3	69.9	**70.5**	73.0	73.3	73.4	74.1	75.8
150	66.5	67.3	68.6	69.2	**69.8**	72.2	72.3	72.5	73.1	74.9

*Calculated in accordance with Clause 13.3.1. of CAN3-S16.1-M78.
For Class H hollow structural sections, see Table 4-4, page 4-13.

UNIT FACTORED COMPRESSIVE RESISTANCES, C_r/A (MPa)* FOR COMPRESSION MEMBERS
$\varnothing = 0.90$

$\dfrac{KL}{r}$	F_y (MPa)									
	248	260	280	290	**300**	350	380	400	480	700
151	65.9	66.7	67.9	68.5	**69.1**	71.2	71.4	71.6	72.2	74.0
152	65.2	66.0	67.2	67.8	**68.4**	70.3	70.5	70.7	71.3	73.1
153	64.6	65.4	66.6	67.1	**67.7**	69.4	69.6	69.8	70.4	72.2
154	64.0	64.7	65.9	66.5	**67.0**	68.5	68.8	68.9	69.6	71.4
155	63.4	64.1	65.3	65.8	**66.3**	67.7	67.9	68.1	68.7	70.5
156	62.8	63.5	64.6	65.2	**65.7**	66.9	67.1	67.3	67.9	69.7
157	62.2	62.9	64.0	64.5	**65.0**	66.0	66.3	66.4	67.1	68.9
158	61.6	62.3	63.4	63.9	**64.4**	65.2	65.5	65.7	66.3	68.1
159	61.0	61.7	62.8	63.3	**63.7**	64.5	64.7	64.9	65.5	67.3
160	60.4	61.1	62.2	62.7	**63.1**	63.7	63.9	64.1	64.7	66.5
161	59.8	60.5	61.6	62.1	**62.5**	62.9	63.2	63.3	64.0	65.8
162	59.3	60.0	61.0	61.5	**61.9**	62.2	62.4	62.6	63.3	65.0
163	58.7	59.4	60.4	60.9	**61.1**	61.5	61.7	61.9	62.5	64.3
164	58.2	58.8	59.8	60.3	**60.4**	60.8	61.0	61.2	61.8	63.6
165	57.7	58.3	59.3	59.7	**59.7**	60.1	60.3	60.5	61.1	62.9
166	57.1	57.8	58.7	58.9	**59.0**	59.4	59.6	59.8	60.4	62.2
167	56.6	57.2	58.1	58.2	**58.3**	58.7	58.9	59.1	59.8	61.5
168	56.1	56.7	57.5	57.6	**57.6**	58.0	58.3	58.4	59.1	60.9
169	55.6	56.2	56.8	56.9	**57.0**	57.4	57.6	57.8	58.4	60.2
170	55.1	55.7	56.2	56.3	**56.3**	56.7	57.0	57.2	57.8	59.6
171	54.6	55.1	55.5	55.6	**55.7**	56.1	56.4	56.5	57.2	59.0
172	54.1	54.6	54.9	55.0	**55.1**	55.5	55.7	55.9	56.6	58.3
173	53.6	54.1	54.3	54.4	**54.5**	54.9	55.1	55.3	55.9	57.7
174	53.1	53.7	53.7	53.8	**53.9**	54.3	54.5	54.7	55.3	57.1
175	52.6	53.0	53.1	53.2	**53.3**	53.7	54.0	54.1	54.8	56.5
176	52.2	52.4	52.6	52.6	**52.7**	53.1	53.4	53.5	54.2	56.0
177	51.7	51.8	52.0	52.1	**52.2**	52.6	52.8	53.0	53.6	55.4
178	51.3	51.3	51.4	51.5	**51.6**	52.0	52.3	52.4	53.1	54.8
179	50.6	50.7	50.9	51.0	**51.1**	51.5	51.7	51.9	52.5	54.3
180	50.1	50.2	50.4	50.4	**50.5**	50.9	51.2	51.3	52.0	53.8
181	49.6	49.7	49.8	49.9	**50.0**	50.4	50.6	50.8	51.4	53.2
182	49.0	49.1	49.3	49.4	**49.5**	49.9	50.1	50.3	50.9	52.7
183	48.5	48.6	48.8	48.9	**49.0**	49.4	49.6	49.8	50.4	52.2
184	48.0	48.1	48.3	48.4	**48.4**	48.9	49.1	49.3	49.9	51.7
185	47.5	47.6	47.8	47.9	**48.0**	48.4	48.6	48.8	49.4	51.2
186	47.0	47.1	47.3	47.4	**47.5**	47.9	48.1	48.3	48.9	50.7
187	46.6	46.7	46.8	46.9	**47.0**	47.4	47.6	47.8	48.4	50.2
188	46.1	46.2	46.3	46.4	**46.5**	46.9	47.2	47.3	48.0	49.8
189	45.6	45.7	45.9	46.0	**46.0**	46.5	46.7	46.9	47.5	49.3
190	45.2	45.3	45.4	45.5	**45.6**	46.0	46.2	46.4	47.0	48.8
191	44.7	44.8	45.0	45.1	**45.1**	45.5	45.8	45.9	46.6	48.4
192	44.3	44.4	44.5	44.6	**44.7**	45.1	45.3	45.5	46.2	48.2
193	43.8	43.9	44.1	44.2	**44.3**	44.7	44.9	45.1	45.7	47.7
194	43.4	43.5	43.7	43.7	**43.8**	44.2	44.5	44.6	45.3	47.2
195	43.0	43.1	43.2	43.3	**43.4**	43.8	44.1	44.2	44.9	46.7
196	42.6	42.7	42.8	42.9	**43.0**	43.4	43.6	43.8	44.4	46.2
197	42.2	42.3	42.4	42.5	**42.6**	43.0	43.2	43.4	44.0	45.8
198	41.8	41.8	42.0	42.1	**42.2**	42.6	42.8	43.0	43.6	45.3
199	41.4	41.4	41.6	41.7	**41.8**	42.2	42.4	42.6	43.2	44.9
200	41.0	41.1	41.2	41.3	**41.4**	41.8	42.0	42.2	42.8	44.4

*Calculated in accordance with Clause 13.3.1. of CAN3-S16.1-M78.
For Class H hollow structural sections, see Table 4-4, page 4-13.

UNIT FACTORED COMPRESSIVE RESISTANCES, C_r/A (MPa)* FOR CLASS H HOLLOW STRUCTURAL SECTIONS
$\emptyset = 0.90$

$\frac{KL}{r}$	$\frac{C_r}{A}$ (MPa)	$\frac{KL}{r}$	$\frac{C_r}{A}$ (MPa)	$\frac{KL}{r}$	$\frac{C_r}{A}$ (MPa)	$\frac{KL}{r}$	$\frac{C_r}{A}$ (MPa)	$\frac{KL}{r}$	$\frac{C_r}{A}$ (MPa)
1	315	41	298	81	219	121	113	161	67.1
2	315	42	297	82	216	122	112	162	66.3
3	315	43	296	83	213	123	110	163	65.5
4	315	44	295	84	210	124	109	164	64.7
5	315	45	293	85	207	125	107	165	64.0
6	315	46	292	86	204	126	106	166	63.3
7	315	47	291	87	201	127	104	167	62.5
8	315	48	289	88	198	128	103	168	61.8
9	315	49	288	89	195	129	102	169	61.1
10	315	50	286	90	192	130	100	170	60.4
11	315	51	285	91	188	131	99.0	171	59.8
12	315	52	283	92	184	132	97.7	172	59.1
13	315	53	281	93	181	133	96.5	173	58.4
14	315	54	280	94	177	134	95.3	174	57.8
15	315	55	278	95	174	135	94.1	175	57.2
16	315	56	276	96	170	136	93.0	176	56.5
17	315	57	274	97	167	137	91.7	177	55.9
18	314	58	273	98	164	138	90.4	178	55.3
19	314	59	271	99	161	139	89.1	179	54.7
20	314	60	269	100	158	140	87.9	180	54.2
21	314	61	267	101	156	141	86.7	181	53.6
22	313	62	265	102	153	142	85.5	182	53.0
23	313	63	263	103	150	143	84.4	183	52.5
24	312	64	261	104	148	144	83.2	184	51.9
25	312	65	259	105	145	145	82.1	185	51.4
26	311	66	256	106	143	146	81.0	186	50.9
27	311	67	254	107	140	147	80.0	187	50.4
28	310	68	252	108	138	148	78.9	188	49.9
29	309	69	250	109	136	149	77.9	189	49.4
30	309	70	247	110	134	150	76.9	190	48.9
31	308	71	245	111	132	151	75.9	191	48.4
32	307	72	242	112	130	152	75.0	192	47.9
33	306	73	240	113	128	153	74.0	193	47.4
34	306	74	237	114	126	154	73.1	194	47.0
35	305	75	235	115	124	155	72.2	195	46.5
36	304	76	232	116	122	156	71.3	196	46.1
37	303	77	230	117	120	157	70.4	197	45.6
38	302	78	227	118	118	158	69.6	198	45.2
39	301	79	224	119	117	159	68.7	199	44.8
40	300	80	222	120	115	160	67.9	200	44.4

*Calculated in accordance with Clause 13.3.2 of CAN3-S16.1-M78. For Class C hollow structural sections, use Table 4–3, pages 4–9 to 4–12.

STABILITY EFFECTS

General

Clause 8.6 of CSA Standard CAN3-S16.1-M78 stipulates that the sway effects produced by the vertical loads acting on the structure in its displaced configuration be accounted for either directly in the analysis for forces and moments (PΔ analysis) or approximately by the use of effective length factors greater than 1.0 — with certain restrictions.

The effective length factor (K) permitted is then dependent upon the method chosen for including the sway effects and is given in Clauses 9.3.2 and 9.3.3 of CAN3-S16.1-M78.

PΔ Method of Analysis

(i) Iterative Method

Appendix J, Guide to Calculation of Stability Effects, of CAN3-S16.1-M78, pages 4—20 to 4—21, describes an iterative procedure whereby artificial storey shears are computed and added to the primary horizontal loads in computing the moments and forces in the structure. This method accounts directly for the sway effects, the stiffness and the actual deflected shape of the lateral load resisting system.

Since, for hand computation and preliminary analysis the iterative method can become onerous, several one-step PΔ methods of analysis can be found in the literature.

(ii) One-step, Maximum Deflection Method

In this method, the PΔ artificial storey shears are computed assuming that sway deflections will be limited to a known value. Thus the PΔ effects will be estimated based upon a maximum deflection. The designer can then control the deflections by the appropriate selection of member stiffness.

(iii) Modified Iterative Method

This method replaces the expression for V_i' given in step 3 of Appendix J with the following:

$$V_i' = \cfrac{1}{\cfrac{1}{\dfrac{\Sigma P_i(\Delta_{i+1} - \Delta_i)}{h_i}} - \cfrac{1}{\Sigma V_i}}$$

where ΣV_i = the total first order shear at storey i

and where the remaining terms are as defined in Appendix J.

By using the expression for V_i' given above, convergence in one cycle is reported by Beaulieu and Picard (Ref. 5).

Regardless of which of the above PΔ methods is used, the term ΣP_i is taken as the sum of the column loads causing the PΔ shear which is carried by the lateral load system under consideration. The deflections are those due to the application of either the lateral loads used for the strength design when the load combinations involve lateral loads, or the maximum out-of-plumbs when only vertical loads are being considered.

Effective Length Factor (K) Method

Clause 8.6.3 of CAN3-S16.1-M78 permits the use of effective length factors greater than 1.0 for the design of columns as an approximate method by which to account for the sway effects but limits this method to moment resisting frames analysed elastically. Appendix B, Effective Lengths of Compression Members in Frames, and Appendix C, Criteria for Estimating Effective Column Lengths in Continuous Frames of CAN3-

S16.1-M78 are found on pages 4—22 to 4—25. In addition, trial values of K_x and K_y are found in Table 4—5 on page 4—26.

Effective length factors are used in the design of the columns in frames for which the $P\Delta$ effects are computed but they are then equal to or less than 1.0, and can be estimated with the aid of Table 4—5 on page 4—26.

References

Additional information on stability effects can be obtained from the following references:

1. Adams, P. F., "Design of Steel Beam-Columns", Canadian Steel Construction Council — 1974.

2. Adams, P. F., Krentz, H. A., Kulak, G. L., "Limit States Design in Structural Steel — SI Units", CISC, 1979.

3. "Guide to Stability Design Criteria for Metal Structures, (3rd edition)" — Structural Stability Research Council — John Wiley & Sons — 1976.

4. Wood, B. R., Beaulieu, D., Adams, P. F., "Further Aspects of Design by P-Delta Method" — Proceedings ASCE Journal of the Structural Division, Vol. 102, No. ST3, March, 1976.

5. Beaulieu, D., Picard, A., "Le Calcul et la Distribution des Efforts dan les Batiments", Canadian Structural Engineering Conference, 1980, CSCC.

6. Part 2 of this book.

Example.

1. **Given:**

   For the three-storey, three-bay structure shown below, the roof and floor systems are relatively rigid diaphragms and hence the stability for the entire building is provided by the exterior rigid frames. Determine the preliminary design loads for columns 1C2 and 2C2 with sway effects included in the analysis. Use Appendix J, CAN3-S16.1-M78, assuming the load combination of dead + full wind governs the design of the rigid frame column, 1C2.

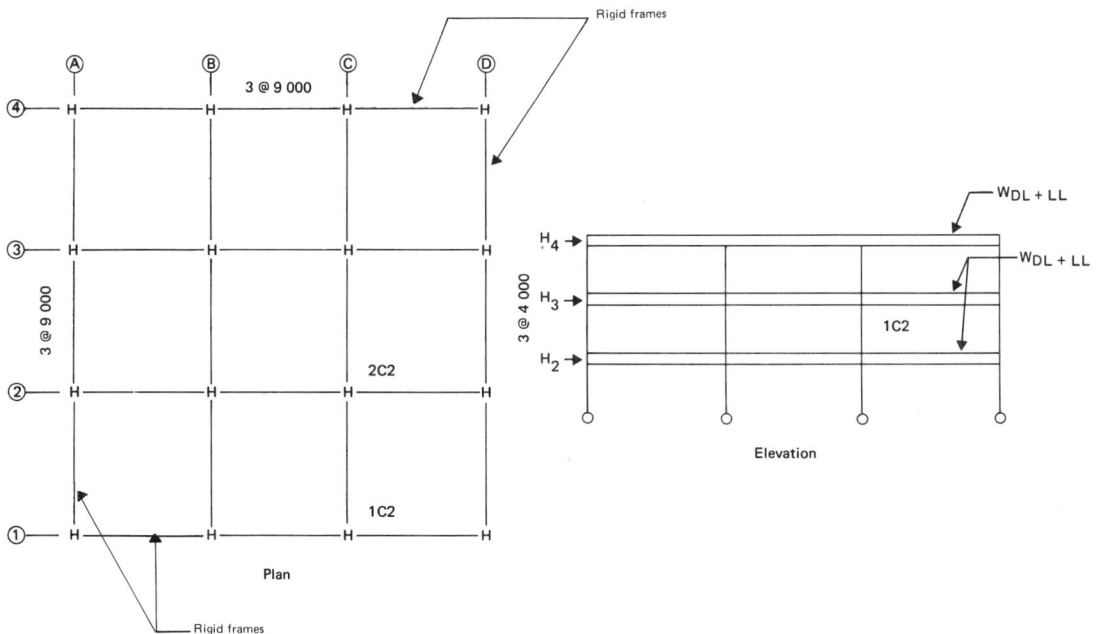

Gravity loads (kPa)

	DL	LL
roof	1.10	1.50
floor	4.30	2.40

Spandrel wall load = 7.5 kN/m

Wind loads: 1/10 year wind, q_{10} = 0.36 kPa; 1/30 year wind, q_{30} = 0.43 kPa

Solution:

Factored 1/30 wind loads are taken as

H_4 = 43.4 kN; H_3 = H_2 = 83.6 kN

a) *Deflections*

The deflections due to the factored 1/30 wind plus dead load combination are 26 mm, 21 mm and 14 mm for Δ_4, Δ_3 and Δ_2 respectively and where determined from an elastic first order frame analysis based upon assumed member stiffnesses.

b) *Gravity loads*

Since four of the interior columns "lean" (for stability) upon each rigid frame, the gravity loads used in the PΔ analysis must include the loads supported by these interior columns in addition to the gravity loads supported directly by the columns of the rigid frame.

Tributary area = 13.5 m $\times$ 27.0 m = 365 m^2; one-half perimeter = 27 + 27 = 54 m

Therefore, for the third storey, ΣP_3 = 1.25 (365 $\times$ 1.1 + 54.0 $\times$ 7.5) = 1 010 kN, for second storey, ΣP_2 = ΣP_3 + 1.25 (365 $\times$ 4.3 + 54 $\times$ 7.5) = ΣP_3 + 2 465
= 3 470 kN.

for first storey, ΣP_1 = ΣP_2 + 2 465 = 5 940 kN

c) *PΔ analysis*

Using the first order deflections due to the factored 1/30 year wind, the PΔ shears, V$'$, artificial forces H$'$ and the PΔ forces, H + H$'$, are computed and tabulated below.

e.g. $V'_2 = \dfrac{\Sigma P_2 \ (\Delta_{f_3} - \Delta_{f_2})}{h}$ (from Appendix J, CAN3-S16.1-M78)

Therefore $V'_2 = \dfrac{3\ 470\ (21 - 14)}{4\ 000} = 6.07$ kN

$H'_3 = V'_2 - V'_3 = 6.07 - 1.26 = 4.81$ kN

The trial frame is sufficiently stiff that covergence is achieved in 2 cycles.

Iteration	Floor Level	Factored Wind Load, H (kN)	Sum of Column Factored Axial Load ΣP (kN)	Deflection Δ_f (mm)	PΔ Shear V' (kN)	PΔ Force H' (kN)	H + H' (kN)
	4	43.4		26		1.26	44.7
			1010		1.26		
	3	83.6		21		4.81	88.4
			3470		6.07		
	2	83.6		14		14.72	98.3
			5940		20.79		
	1						
	4			28		1.26	44.7
					1.26		
First	3			23		4.81	88.4
					6.07		
	2			16		17.69	101.3
					23.76		
	1						
	4			28			
Second	3			24			
	2			16			
	1						

d) *Preliminary Design Parameters*

i) Interior Column, 2C2

Tributary area = $9 \times 9 = 81$ m^2

Live load reduction factor = $0.3 + \sqrt{9.8/81}$ (See Part 4, NBCC, 1980)

$$= 0.648$$

Total factored axial load, $C_f = 81 \times [1.25 (1.1 + 4.3)$

$$+ 1.5 (1.5 + 2.4 \times 0.648)] = 918 \text{ kN}$$

Since column has simple connections, assume $K_x = K_y = 1.0$

ii) Rigid frame column, 1C2

Using the forces determined from PΔ analysis, after convergence, the design moments for the beams and columns can be determined from an elastic frame analysis.

For column, 1C2, they are taken as:

$C_f = 450$ kN, $M_{f_1} = - 47.3$ kN·m, $M_{f_2} = - 163$ kN·m

$\omega = 0.48$ (Table 4—7, page 4—30, double curvature)

Since PΔ forces are included in M_{f_1} and M_{f_2}, K may be less than or equal to 1.0.

Use $K_x = 0.90$ and $K_y = 1.0$ for trial values.

2. Given:

Same as example 1, except that the maximum deflection is used to estimate the PΔ forces. The deflection limit for specified lateral load is h/500.

Solution:

Deflection under specified wind load, $h/500 = \Delta_s$.

Since the wind load used to compute the deflection under specified loads is the 1/10 year wind, the deflection must be increased to that due to the 1/30 year wind before computing the $P\Delta$ effect.

Therefore, lateral deflection under factored loads,

$$\Delta_f = \Delta_s \times \alpha_Q \times \frac{q\,30}{q\,10}\,(\alpha_Q = 1.5 - \text{Clause } 7.2.3 - \text{S16.1-M78})$$

$$= \Delta_s \times 1.5 \times \frac{0.43}{0.36}$$

$$= 1.79\,\Delta_s$$

The following table summarizes the $P\Delta$ forces.

Floor Level	Factored Wind Load, H (kN)	Sum of Column Factored Axial Loads ΣP (kN)	Deflection Δ_f (mm)	$P\Delta$ Shear V' (kN)	$P\Delta$ Force H' (kN)	H + H' (kN)
4	43.4		43		3.54	46.9
		1010		3.54		
3	83.6		29		9.47	93.1
		3470		13.01		
2	83.6		14		7.78	91.4
		5940		20.79		
1						

In this example the $P\Delta$ forces are over-estimated for Levels 4 and 3 and under-estimated for Level 2 when compared to the more accurate Iterative Method results.

Preliminary Design Parameters

i) Interior Column, 2C2
   Same as in example 1

ii) Rigid frame column 1C2
   For above $P\Delta$ analysis and frame analysis

   $C_f = 450$ kN; $M_{f_1} = -52.9$ kN·m, $M_{f_2} = -167$ kN·m

   $\omega = 0.47$ (Table 4—7, page 4—30, double curvature)

3. Given:

Same as example 1, except use the modified iteration method to determine $P\Delta$ forces.

e.g.
$$V_2' = \cfrac{1}{\cfrac{1}{\cfrac{\Sigma P_2\,(\Delta_{f_3} - \Delta_{f_2})}{h}} - \cfrac{1}{\Sigma V_2}}$$

$\Sigma V_2 = H_4 + H_3 = 48.4 + 83.6 = 127$ kN

Therefore,

$$V_2' = \cfrac{1}{\cfrac{1}{\cfrac{3470\,(21-14)}{4000}} - \cfrac{1}{127}} = 6.37 \text{ kN}$$

Floor Level	Factored Wind Load, H (kN)	Sum of Column Factored Axial Loads ΣP (kN)	Deflection Δ_f (mm)	PΔ Shear V' (kN)	PΔ Force H' (kN)	H + H' (kN)	Sum of 1st Order Shear ΣV (kN)
4	43.4		26		1.30	44.7	
		1 010		1.30			43.4
3	83.6		21		5.07	88.7	
		3 470		6.37			127.0
2	83.6		14		16.70	100.3	
		5 940		23.07			210.6
1							

Since the PΔ forces computed above are similar to those determined in example 1, the factored loads and moments for design will be similar to those of example 1. (See page 4–17).

4. **Given:**

For the moment resisting frame of example 1, determine the preliminary design parameters for column 1C2 using the effective length factor method for dead plus wind loads.

Solution:

From an elastic analysis for the rigid frame, for factored dead plus wind load combination, the following forces and moments were obtained:

C_f = 450 kN, M_{f_1} = $-$ 49.2 kN·m, M_{f_2} = $-$ 152 kN·m

ω = 0.85 (Clause 13.8.4(ii), CAN3-S16.1-M78)

Use Table 4–5, page 4–26, to select trial values of K_x and K_y .

K_x = 2.25; K_y = 1.80 (case E)

The use of the K factor for this example is an approximate method of accounting for the PΔ effects and does not account for the additional PΔ effect of the interior columns which "lean" on the rigid frame.

For a method of selecting an appropriate steel shape for the beam-columns, see Beam-Columns, page 4–96 to 4–107.

Guide to Calculation of Stability Effects*

J1.   **General**

J1.1   This Appendix gives one approach to the calculation of the additional bending moments and forces generated by the vertical loads acting through the deflected shape of the structure. By this approach the above moments and forces are incorporated into the results of the analysis of the structure; alternatively a second order analysis, which formulates equilibrium on the deformed structure, may be used to include the stability effects.

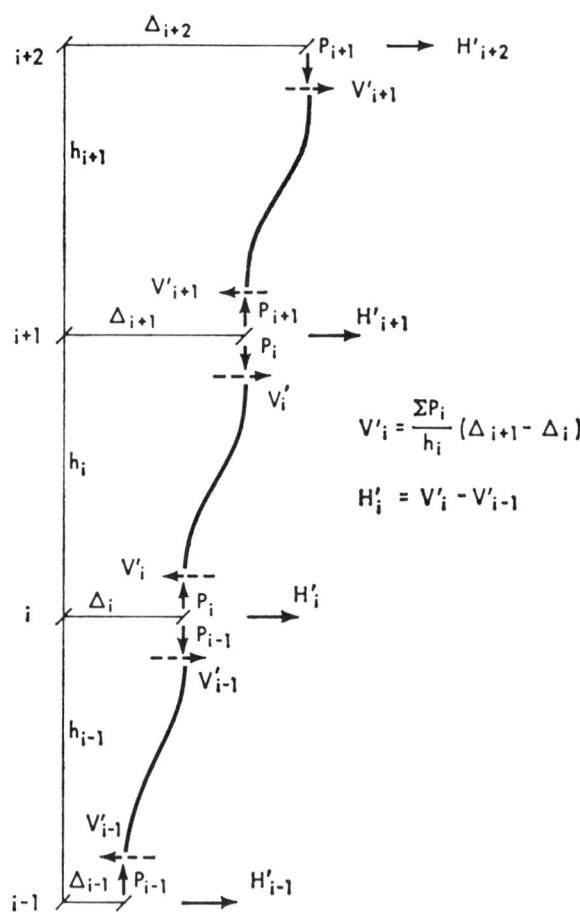

$$V'_i = \frac{\Sigma P_i}{h_i}(\Delta_{i+1} - \Delta_i)$$

$$H'_i = V'_i - V'_{i-1}$$

Figure J1
Sway Forces Due to Vertical Loads

J2. **Combined Loading Case**

J2.1 Step 1 — Apply the factored load combination to the structure (see Clause 7.2.2).

Step 2 — Compute the lateral deflections at each floor level (Δ_i) by first order elastic analysis.

Step 3 — Compute the artificial storey shears V'_i due to the sway forces.

where

$$V'_i \quad = \frac{\Sigma P_i}{h_i}\left(\Delta_{i+1} - \Delta_i\right)$$

$\quad\quad\quad$ = artificial shear in storey i due to the sway forces

$\Sigma P_i \quad$ = sum of the column axial loads in storey i

$h_i \quad$ = height of storey i

Δ_{i+1}, Δ_i = displacements of level i + 1 and i, respectively

Step 4 — Compute the artificial lateral loads H'
$$H'_i = V'_{i-1} - V'_i$$

Step 5 — Repeat Step 1 applying the artificial lateral loads H'_i in addition to the factored load combination.

Step 6 — Repeat Steps 2 through 5 until satisfactory convergence is achieved. Lack of convergence within 5 cycles may indicate an excessively flexible structure.

J3. **Vertical Loads Only**

J3.1 Since vertical loads do not normally produce significant sway deflections of the structure the initial sway forces are computed on the basis of the sway displacements in each storey equal to the erection tolerance permitted by Clause 28.7.1. Using these deflections the calculations are commenced at Step 3 of the procedure described in Clause J2.1.

Effective Lengths of Compression Members in Frames*

B1. The slenderness ratio of a compression member is defined as the ratio of the effective length to the applicable radius of gyration. The effective length KL may be thought of as the actual unbraced length L multiplied by a factor K such that the product KL is equal to the length of a pin-ended compression member of equal capacity to the actual member. The effective length factor K of a column of finite unbraced length is therefore dependent upon the conditions of restraint afforded to the column at its braced locations and theoretically may vary from 0.5 to infinity. In practical building applications, K would be somewhat greater than 0.5 in the most favourable situation and in all probability would not exceed 5 in the most unfavourable situation.

B2. A variation in K between 0.65 and 2.0 would apply to the majority of cases likely to be encountered in actual structures.

B3. When proportioning columns on the basis of effective lengths the designer is presented with two basic situations which have a pronounced effect upon the strength of axially loaded columns.

(a) For structures in which the sway effects have been included in the analysis to determine the design moments and forces the effective length factor is determined from the degree of rotational restraint afforded at the ends of the unbraced length and K will be equal to or less than 1.0. In Appendix C this case is identified as the side-sway prevented case;

(b) For structures in which the sway effects have not been included in the analysis to determine the design moments and forces the effective length factor is determined from the degree of rotational and translational restraint afforded at the ends of the unbraced length and K will be equal to or greater than 1.0. In Appendix C this case is identified as the side-sway permitted case.

B4. Figure B1 illustrates six idealized cases in which joint rotation and translation are either fully realized or non-existent.

B5. Figure B2 shows diagrammatically for a frame with columns pinned at their bases the difference in effective column length when the sway effect is and is not included in the analysis to determine the design moments and forces. In the former case, the effect of the loads acting at the displacement Δ_b has been included in the analysis and the effective length, K_aL is based on the sway prevented condition ($K_aL \leq L$) which accounts only for the effect of the displacement Δ_a on column stability. In the latter case, the effective length K_bL is based on the sway permitted condition ($K_bL > L$) in an attempt to include the influence of the displacement Δ_b on column stability.

B6. The use of the sway permitted case is approximate only as the moments and forces due to the sway effects are not taken into account in the design of the girders. In frames that depend on means other than frame action to achieve stability, such as bracing, the bracing shall be designed to resist the combined effects of the superimposed loads plus the loads due to the sway effects.

Appendix B of CAN3–S16.1–M78

B7. In Figure B2 the column bases are shown to be pinned and G_L would theoretically be infinity. In practical situations, however, the restraining effect of the normal flat-ended column base detail exerts a beneficial influence on the true effective length of the column, even where the footing is designed only for vertical load. Thus in most cases G_L can be taken as 10 (or less where justified) in the computation of K.

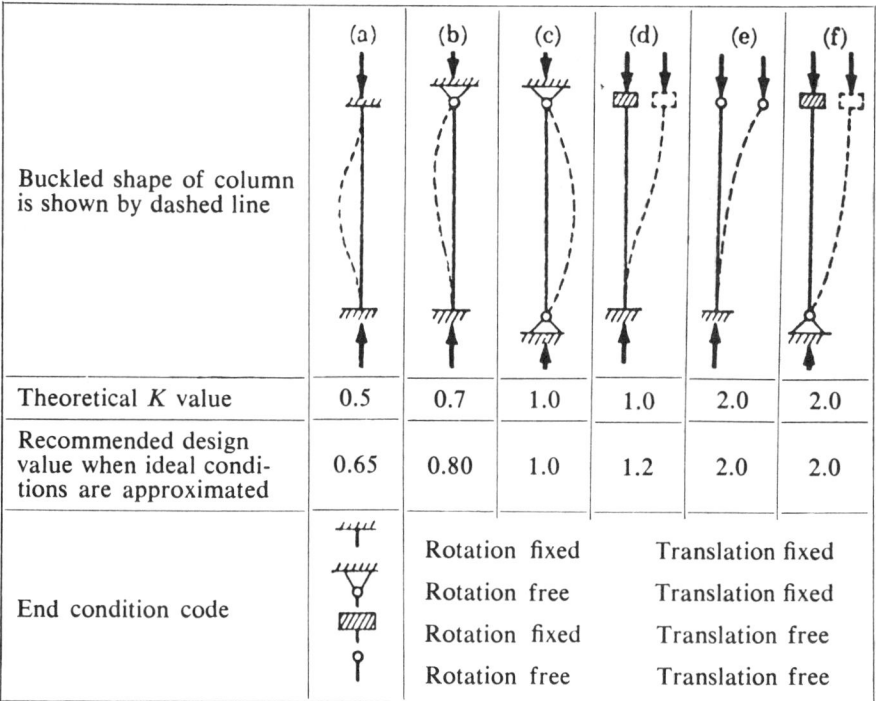

	(a)	(b)	(c)	(d)	(e)	(f)
Buckled shape of column is shown by dashed line						
Theoretical K value	0.5	0.7	1.0	1.0	2.0	2.0
Recommended design value when ideal conditions are approximated	0.65	0.80	1.0	1.2	2.0	2.0
End condition code		Rotation fixed		Translation fixed		
		Rotation free		Translation fixed		
		Rotation fixed		Translation free		
		Rotation free		Translation free		

Figure B1

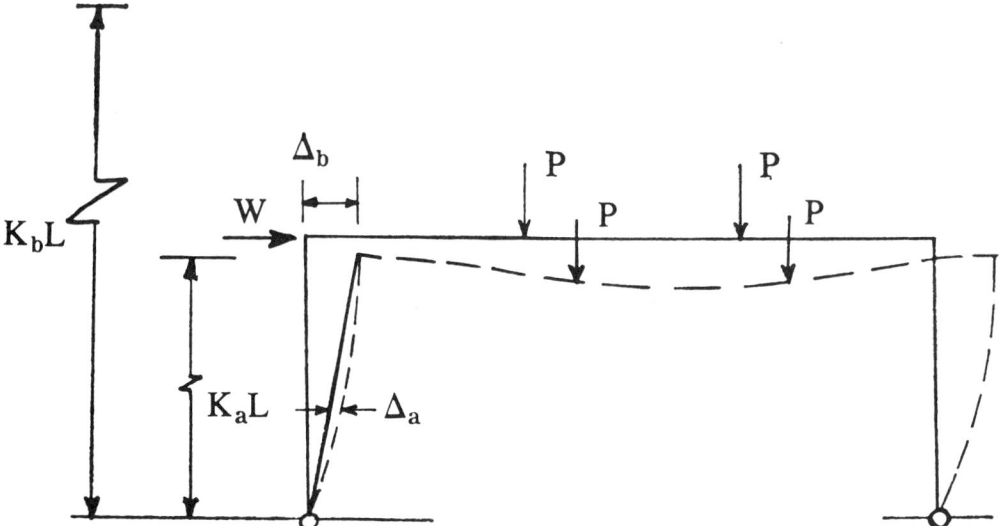

Criteria for Estimating Effective Column Lengths* in Continuous Frames

C1. Two cases influencing the design of columns in continuous frames are considered:

(a) Sway effects included in the analysis — side-sway prevented;

(b) Sway effects not included in the analysis — side-sway permitted.

C2. Figure C1 is a nomograph applicable to cases in which the equivalent I/L of adjacent girders which are rigidly attached to the columns are known, and is based on the assumption that all columns in the portion of the framework considered reach their individual critical loads simultaneously.

In the usual building frame not all columns would be loaded so as to simultaneously reach their buckling loads, and thus some conservatism is introduced in the interest of simplification.

C3. The equations upon which these nomographs are based are:

(a) Side-sway prevented:

$$\frac{G_U G_L}{4}(\pi/K)^2 + \left(\frac{G_U + G_L}{2}\right)\left(1 - \frac{\pi/K}{\tan \pi/K}\right) + 2\frac{\tan \pi/2K}{\pi/K} = 1$$

(b) Side-sway permitted:

$$\frac{G_U G_L(\pi/K)^2 - 36}{6(G_U + G_L)} = \frac{\pi/K}{\tan \pi/K}$$

C4. Subscripts U and L refer to the joints at the two ends of the column section being considered. G is defined as

$$G = \frac{\Sigma I_c/L_c}{\Sigma I_g/L_g}$$

in which Σ indicates a summation for all members rigidly connected to that joint and lying in the plane in which buckling of the column is being considered, I_c is the moment of inertia and L_c the unsupported length of a column section, and I_g is the moment of inertia and L_g the unsupported length of a girder or other restraining member. I_c and I_g are taken about axes perpendicular to the plane of buckling being considered.

C5. For column ends supported by, but not rigidly connected to, a footing or foundation, "G" may be taken as 10 for practical designs. If the column end is rigidly attached to a properly designed footing, "G" may be taken as 1.0. Smaller values may be used if justified by analysis.

C6. Refinements in girder I_g/L_g may be made when conditions at the far end of any particular girder are known definitely or when a conservative estimate can be made. For the case with no side-sway, multiply girder stiffnesses by the following factors:

1.5 for far end of girder hinged;
2.0 for far end of girder fixed against rotation;
(i.e., rigidly attached to a support which is itself relatively rigid).

C7. For the case with side-sway permitted, multiply girder stiffnesses by 0.5 for far end of girder hinged.

C8. Having determined G_U and G_L for a column section, the effective length factor K is determined by constructing a straight line between the appropriate points on the scales for G_U and G_L.

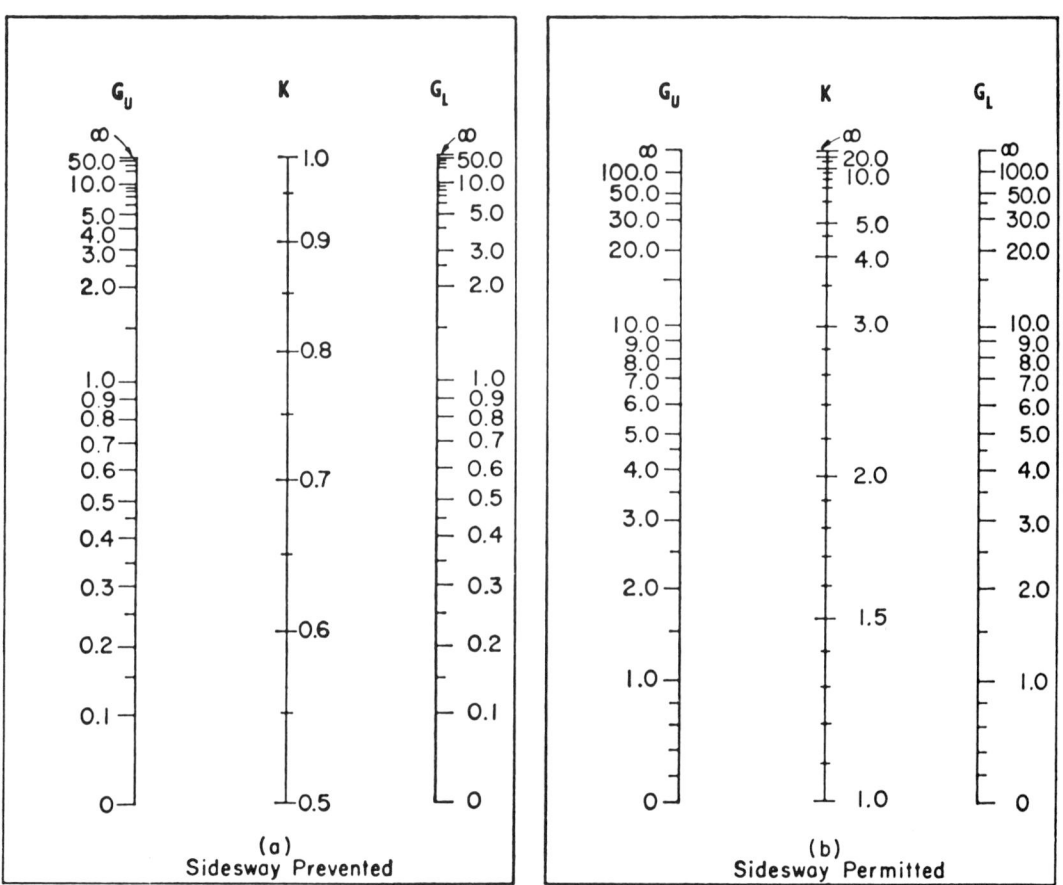

Figure C1
Alignment Chart for Effective Length
of Columns in Continuous Frames

TRIAL VALUES OF K_X and K_Y
Table 4-5

Case	PΔ Effects Included	Beam-to-Column Connections		Single Storey Frame		Multi-Storey Frame		Bottom Storey of Multi-Storey	
		Top of Column	Bottom of Column	G_L	K_X and K_Y	K_X	K_Y	K_X	K_Y
A	YES	Flexible	Flexible		1.00	1.00	1.00	1.00	1.00
B	YES	Flexible	Rigid	1.00	0.87	0.95	0.95	0.87	0.87
C	YES	Rigid	Flexible	10.0	0.80	0.95	0.95	0.90	0.90
D	YES	Rigid	Rigid	1.00	0.75	0.90	0.90	0.80	0.80
E	NO	Rigid	Rigid	1.00	1.25	2.25	1.80	1.60	1.60
F	NO	Rigid	Flexible	10.0	1.80			2.50	2.00

Cases A to D inclusive are applicable to frames for which the elastic analysis to determine forces and moments include the sway effects or for frames in which the sway effects, as well as the lateral loads, are resisted by bracing or shear walls (Clause 9.3.2, CAN3-S16.1-M78).

Cases E and F are applicable to moment resisting frames for which the elastic analysis to determine forces and moments does not include the sway effects. Thus the values of $K > 1.00$ provide an approximate means of accounting for the sway effects (Clause 9.3.3, CAN3-S16.1-M78).

Table 4—5 has been provided to assist designers to estimate the effective lengths of columns and beam-columns. It is intended primarily to serve as a guide in obtaining trial sections, the properties of which can be used in a column analysis procedure to verify the suitability of the trial sections, or to indicate whether or not lighter or heavier sections are required.

Pages 4—22 to 4—25 inclusive provide more detailed information on effective lengths of compression members and a more precise method of determining effective lengths.

BENDING FACTORS FOR BEAM-COLUMNS

The initial selection of a suitable steel section subject to axial load and moment can be simplified by replacing the applied axial load and bending moments with an equivalent axial load. This procedure is discussed in more detail on page 4—96.

To simulate the effect of the bending moments, the applied moment (larger of the two end moments for columns with unequal end moments) can be multiplied by a "bending factor" which is determined for each structural steel shape from the properties of that shape. Table 4—6 lists approximate bending factors for each nominal size group of WWF columns, W shapes and hollow structural sections. This approximate bending factor is sufficiently accurate for an initial shape selection.

The bending factors are computed as follows:

$B_x = 10^3 A/Z_x$ for Class 1 and Class 2 sections

   $= 10^3 A/S_x$ for Class 3 and Class 4 sections

$B_y = 10^3 A/Z_y$ for Class 1 and Class 2 sections

   $= 10^3 A/S_y$ for Class 3 and Class 4 sections

where

   A = total cross sectional area of the structural shape

   S = elastic section modulus, about the X—X or Y—Y axis, as appropriate

   Z = plastic section modulus, about the X—X or Y—Y axis, as appropriate

As a result, the bending factors are in m^{-1} units, and multiplying a bending moment in kilonewton metres by a bending factor from Table 4—6 results in an equivalent axial load in kilonewtons.

For Class 1 and 2 WWF and W shapes two values of B_x and B_y are tabulated. The values tabulated under the sub-heading "stability" are the base value of B_x and B_y computed as described above for use when dealing with the equation in Clause 13.8.2(c) of CAN3-S16.1-M78. The values tabulated under the sub-heading "strength" are 0.85 of B_x for stability and 0.60 of B_y for stability and are useful when dealing with the equation in Clause 13.8.2(b) of CAN3-S16.1-M78.

In cases where the factored moment resistance must be reduced when the unsupported length of compression flange exceeds L_u, the bending factors may be used to estimate the size of column required (which usually will require revision) or the bending factors can be increased to compensate for the reduction in M_r.

Nominal Size	B_x (m^{-1}) Class 1 & Class 2 Sections Strength	Stability	Class 3 & Class 4 Sections	B_y (m^{-1}) Class 1 & Class 2 Sections Strength	Stability	Class 3 & Class 4 Sections
WWF550	3.79	4.46	5.05	5.36	8.93	13.6
WWF500	4.14	4.88	5.47	5.98	9.97	15.1
WWF450	4.59	5.40	6.04	6.57	11.0	16.6
WWF400	5.21	6.13	6.93	7.37	12.3	18.6
WWF350	6.04	7.10	8.12	8.36	13.9	21.1
920 x 420	2.37	2.79	3.15	8.86	14.8	22.8
920 x 305	2.52	2.97	3.42	14.3	23.9	37.7
840 x 400	2.54	2.99	3.39	9.35	15.6	24.1
840 x 290	2.73	3.21	3.70	15.0	25.1	39.3
760 x 380	2.79	3.28	3.69	9.62	16.0	24.7
760 x 265	3.04	3.57	4.12	16.6	27.7	43.5
690 x 355	3.10	3.65	4.10	10.3	17.1	26.4
690 x 255	3.32	3.91	4.47	16.7	27.9	43.5
610 x 325	3.48	4.09	4.61	11.2	18.6	28.6
610 x 230	3.72	4.38	5.00	18.3	30.5	47.5
530 x 315	3.91	4.60	5.18	11.2	18.7	28.7
530 x 210	4.21	4.95	5.65	19.5	32.4	50.6
460 x 285	4.54	5.34	5.99	12.2	20.4	31.3
460 x 190	4.87	5.73	6.52	21.0	35.0	54.4
410 x 260	5.02	5.91	6.63	12.9	21.5	32.9
410 x 180	5.41	6.37	7.21	21.8	36.4	56.3
410 x 140	5.73	6.74	7.74	31.9	53.1	83.3
360 x 430	4.56	5.36	6.81	6.50	10.8	16.7
360 x 405	5.01	5.90	7.08	7.03	11.7	18.0
360 x 395	5.38	6.33	7.23	7.47	12.4	18.9
360 x 370	5.60	6.58	7.29	8.19	13.6	20.7
360 x 255	5.82	6.85	7.67	12.8	21.3	32.6
360 x 205	6.02	7.09	7.90	17.0	28.3	43.4
360 x 170	6.16	7.25	8.15	22.5	37.4	57.6
310 x 330	5.73	6.74	8.22	8.86	14.8	22.7
310 x 310	6.34	7.46	8.48	9.78	16.3	24.9
310 x 255	6.64	7.82	8.65	12.5	20.8	31.6
310 x 200	6.83	8.04	8.96	16.4	27.3	41.9
310 x 165	6.81	8.02	8.96	21.7	36.1	55.4
250 x 255	7.77	9.14	10.4	11.7	19.5	29.6
250 x 200	8.23	9.69	10.8	15.9	26.5	40.3
250 x 145	8.19	9.64	10.8	24.2	40.4	62.1
200 x 200	9.74	11.5	12.9	14.8	24.6	37.5
200 x 165	10.2	12.0	13.4	19.4	32.3	49.2
150 x 150	13.3	15.6	17.5	21.0	35.0	53.3
130 x 125	16.2	19.1	21.6	24.0	40.0	61.1
100 x 100	20.4	24.0	27.8	31.0	51.6	79.4

Size	B_x (m^{-1})		B_y (m^{-1})	
	Class 1 & Class 2 Sections	Class 3 & Class 4 Sections	Class 1 & Class 2 Sections	Class 3 & Class 4 Sections
304.8 x 203.2	9.81	11.9	13.0	14.9
254 x 152.4	12.2	15.1	17.3	20.1
203.2 x 152.4	14.7	17.9	17.9	20.9
203.2 x 101.6	15.9	20.4	26.0	30.5
177.8 x 127	17.1	21.1	21.6	25.5
152.4 x 101.6	20.3	25.4	27.0	32.1
127 x 76.2	25.1	32.0	36.1	43.2
127 x 63.5	26.1	34.1	42.9	51.8
127 x 50.8	27.1	36.2	53.0	64.3
101.6 x 76.2	30.3	38.0	37.1	44.9
101.6 x 50.8	32.4	42.0	53.1	63.6
88.9 x 63.5	34.8	43.5	44.0	52.8
76.2 x 50.8	42.3	54.7	56.4	69.8
50.8 x 25.4	66.1	87.1	109	133
304.8 x 304.8	9.10	10.6	9.10	10.6
254 x 254	11.0	12.9	11.0	12.9
203.2 x 203.2	13.9	16.6	13.9	16.6
177.8 x 177.8	16.0	19.0	16.0	19.0
152.4 x 152.4	18.9	22.7	18.9	22.7
127 x 127	22.8	27.6	22.8	27.6
101.6 x 101.6	28.8	35.2	28.8	35.2
88.9 x 88.9	33.1	40.6	33.1	40.6
76.2 x 76.2	38.4	46.9	38.4	46.9
63.5 x 63.5	46.2	56.5	46.2	56.5
50.8 x 50.8	58.8	73.1	58.8	73.1
38.1 x 38.1	79.7	100	79.7	100
31.8 x 31.8	96.3	122	96.3	122
25.4 x 25.4	126	165	126	165

VALUES OF ω *
Table 4-7

Single Curvature				Double Curvature			
$\dfrac{M_{f_1}}{M_{f_2}}$	ω	$\dfrac{M_{f_1}}{M_{f_2}}$	ω	$\dfrac{M_{f_1}}{M_{f_2}}$	ω	$\dfrac{M_{f_1}}{M_{f_2}}$	ω
1.00	1.00	0.50	0.80	0.00	0.60	0.55	0.40
0.95	0.98	0.45	0.78	0.05	0.58	0.60	0.40
0.90	0.96	0.40	0.76	0.10	0.56	0.65	0.40
0.85	0.94	0.35	0.74	0.15	0.54	0.70	0.40
0.80	0.92	0.30	0.72	0.20	0.52	0.75	0.40
0.75	0.90	0.25	0.70	0.25	0.50	0.80	0.40
0.70	0.88	0.20	0.68	0.30	0.48	0.85	0.40
0.65	0.86	0.15	0.66	0.35	0.46	0.90	0.40
0.60	0.84	0.10	0.64	0.40	0.44	0.95	0.40
0.55	0.82	0.05	0.62	0.45	0.42	1.00	0.40
		0.00	0.60	0.50	0.40		

*See Clause 13.8.4, CAN3-S16.1-M78.

The value of ω is used to modify the bending term in the beam-column interaction equation to account for various end moment and loading conditions of the columns.

For columns of a frame not subject to transverse loads between supports and where the analysis to determine the forces and moments in the members includes sway effects, use the values of ω shown in Table 4—7. For columns of frames where the analysis does not include the sway effects, $\omega = 0.85$ for members bent in double curvature or subject to moment at one end and 1.0 for members bent in single curvature due to moments at both ends.

For members subject to distributed loads or a series of point loads between supports, $\omega = 1.0$ and for members subject to a concentrated load or moment between supports, $\omega = 0.85$.

The values of ω given in Table 4—7 are derived from

$$\omega = 0.6 + 0.4 \, (M_{f_1}/M_{f_2})$$

for members bent in single curvature, and

$$\omega = 0.6 - 0.4 \, (M_{f_1}/M_{f_2})$$

for members bent in double curvature, but not less than 0.4 where

M_{f_1} = the smaller factored end moment

M_{f_2} = the larger factored end moment

C$_e$/A EULER BUCKLING LOAD
PER UNIT OF AREA, MPa

Table 4-8

$\dfrac{KL}{r}$	$\dfrac{C_e}{A}$ (MPa)	$\dfrac{KL}{r}$	$\dfrac{C_e}{A}$ (MPa)	$\dfrac{KL}{r}$	$\dfrac{C_e}{A}$ (MPa)	$\dfrac{KL}{r}$	$\dfrac{C_e}{A}$ (MPa)	$\dfrac{KL}{r}$	$\dfrac{C_e}{A}$ (MPa)
1	1 970 000	41	1 172	81	300	121	135	161	76.0
2	492 500	42	1 117	82	293	122	132	162	75.1
3	218 889	43	1 065	83	286	123	130	163	74.1
4	123 125	44	1 018	84	279	124	128	164	73.2
5	78 800	45	973	85	273	125	126	165	72.4
6	54 722	46	931	86	266	126	124	166	71.5
7	40 204	47	892	87	260	127	122	167	70.6
8	30 781	48	855	88	254	128	120	168	69.8
9	24 321	49	820	89	249	129	118	169	69.0
10	19 700	50	788	90	243	130	117	170	68.2
11	16 281	51	757	91	238	131	115	171	67.4
12	13 681	52	729	92	233	132	113	172	66.6
13	11 657	53	701	93	228	133	111	173	65.8
14	10 051	54	676	94	223	134	110	174	65.1
15	8 756	55	651	95	218	135	108	175	64.3
16	7 695	56	628	96	214	136	107	176	63.6
17	6 817	57	606	97	209	137	105	177	62.9
18	6 080	58	586	98	205	138	103	178	62.2
19	5 457	59	566	99	201	139	102	179	61.5
20	4 925	60	547	100	197	140	101	180	60.8
21	4 467	61	529	101	193	141	99.1	181	60.1
22	4 070	62	512	102	189	142	97.7	182	59.5
23	3 724	63	496	103	186	143	96.3	183	58.8
24	3 420	64	481	104	182	144	95.0	184	58.2
25	3 152	65	466	105	179	145	93.7	185	57.6
26	2 914	66	452	106	175	146	92.4	186	56.9
27	2 702	67	439	107	172	147	91.2	187	56.3
28	2 513	68	426	108	169	148	89.9	188	55.7
29	2 342	69	414	109	166	149	88.7	189	55.1
30	2 189	70	402	110	163	150	87.6	190	54.6
31	2 050	71	391	111	160	151	86.4	191	54.0
32	1 924	72	380	112	157	152	85.3	192	53.4
33	1 809	73	370	113	154	153	84.2	193	52.9
34	1 704	74	360	114	152	154	83.1	194	52.3
35	1 608	75	350	115	149	155	82.0	195	51.8
36	1 520	76	341	116	146	156	81.0	196	51.3
37	1 439	77	332	117	144	157	79.9	197	50.8
38	1 364	78	324	118	141	158	78.9	198	50.2
39	1 295	79	316	119	139	159	77.9	199	49.7
40	1 231	80	308	120	137	160	77.0	200	49.3

To obtain C_e, in kilonewtons, multiply the tabular value by the cross sectional area, A_x, in square millimetres, and divide by 1 000.

AMPLIFICATION FACTORS*$U = \dfrac{1}{1 - \dfrac{C_f}{C_e}}$

Table 4-9

$\dfrac{C_f}{C_e}$	U	$\dfrac{C_f}{C_e}$	U	$\dfrac{C_f}{C_e}$	U	$\dfrac{C_f}{C_e}$	U
.01	1.01	.26	1.35	.51	2.04	.76	4.17
.02	1.02	.27	1.37	.52	2.08	.77	4.35
.03	1.03	.28	1.39	.53	2.13	.78	4.55
.04	1.04	.29	1.41	.54	2.17	.79	4.76
.05	1.05	.30	1.43	.55	2.22	.80	5.00
.06	1.06	.31	1.45	.56	2.27	.81	5.26
.07	1.08	.32	1.47	.57	2.33	.82	5.56
.08	1.09	.33	1.49	.58	2.38	.83	5.88
.09	1.10	.34	1.52	.59	2.44	.84	6.25
.10	1.11	.35	1.54	.60	2.50	.85	6.67
.11	1.12	.36	1.56	.61	2.56	.86	7.14
.12	1.14	.37	1.59	.62	2.63	.87	7.69
.13	1.15	.38	1.61	.63	2.70	.88	8.33
.14	1.16	.39	1.64	.64	2.78	.89	9.09
.15	1.18	.40	1.67	.65	2.86	.90	10.0
.16	1.19	.41	1.69	.66	2.94	.91	11.1
.17	1.20	.42	1.72	.67	3.03	.92	12.5
.18	1.22	.43	1.75	.68	3.13	.93	14.3
.19	1.23	.44	1.79	.69	3.23	.94	16.7
.20	1.25	.45	1.82	.70	3.33	.95	20.0
.21	1.27	.46	1.85	.71	3.45	.96	25.0
.22	1.28	.47	1.89	.72	3.57	.97	33.3
.23	1.30	.48	1.92	.73	3.70	.98	50.0
.24	1.32	.49	1.96	.74	3.85	.99	100.0
.25	1.33	.50	2.00	.75	4.00		

*See Clause 13.8, CAN3-S16.1-M78.

FACTORED AXIAL COMPRESSIVE RESISTANCES OF COLUMNS

Tables

The tables on pages 4—36 to 4—71 inclusive list the factored axial compressive resistances, C_r, in kilonewtons, for WWF, W and M100×19 shapes and HSS produced to the requirements of CSA Standard G40.20-M, Class C.

The factored axial compressive resistances have been computed, for effective lengths with respect to the least radius of gyration varying from 0 mm to a maximum of 12 000 mm, in accordance with the requirements of Clauses 13.3.1 and 13.3.3, CAN3-S16.1M78, "Steel Structures for Buildings — Limit States Design".

The tables on pages 4—72 to 4—95 inclusive list the factored axial compressive resistances, C_r, in kilonewtons, for HSS produced to the requirements of CSA Standard G40.20-M, Class H, in accordance with the requirements of Clauses 13.3.2 and 13.3.3, CAN3-S16.1-M78.

The factored axial compressive resistances for Class 4 sections have been computed in accordance with the requirements of Clause 13.3.3 of CAN3-S16.1-78 and are so identified in the tables.

At the top of each table is listed the applicable steel grade. The metric designation of each shape is given at the top of the columns while the equivalent Imperial size and mass are listed at the bottom of the tables. Information on the properties of each section plus design data has been included at the bottom of the tables. The following are included:

Area	=	Total cross-sectional area, square millimetres.
Z_x	=	Plastic section modulus for bending about X—X axis, $10^3 \, mm^3$
S_x	=	Elastic section modulus for bending about X—X axis, $10^3 \, mm^3$
r_x	=	Radius of gyration about the strong, X—X, axis, millimetres.
Z_y	=	Plastic section modulus for bending about Y—Y axis, $10^3 \, mm^3$
S_y	=	Elastic section modulus for bending about Y—Y axis, $10^3 \, mm^3$
r_y	=	Radius of gyration about the weak, Y—Y, axis, millimetres.
r_x/r_y	=	Ratio of radius of gyration of X—X axis to that for Y—Y axis.
M_{rx}	=	Factored moment resistance for bending about the X—X axis, computed considering $L < L_u$, using the Class of the section considering bending about the X—X axis only and the value of F_y shown, for Class 1 and 2 section, $\phi \, Z_x F_y \times 10^{-6}$; for Class 3 sections, $\phi \, S_x F_y \times 10^{-6}$ and for Class 4 sections Clause 13.5(c) of S16.1—M78, kilonewton metres.
M_{ry}	=	Factored moment resistance for bending about the Y—Y axis computed using the Class of the section considering bending about the Y—Y axis only and the value of F_y shown, for Class 1 and 2 section, $\phi \, Z_y F_y \times 10^{-6}$; for Class 3 sections, $\phi \, S_y F_y \times 10^{-6}$; and for class 4 sections, Clause 13.5(c) of S16.1-M78, kilonewton metres.

For sections which have identical X—X and Y—Y axis properties one value of the above quantities is shown without subscripted headings.

For the tables containing WWF, W and M shapes the following additional constants are tabulated:

J	=	St. Venant torsional constant, $10^3 \, mm^4$
C_w	=	Warping torsional constant, $10^9 \, mm^6$
L_u	=	Maximum unsupported length of compression flange for which no reduction in M_r is required, millimetres.
F_y	=	Specified minimum yield strength of the section, megapascals.

Three sets of tables are provided.

Set 1 — CSA G40.21-M grade 300W
  — WWF and W shapes plus M100×19
  — only shapes available from Canadian mills are included.

Set 2 — HSS conforming to CSA G40.20-M, Class C
  — CSA G40.21-M grade 350W.

Set 3 — HSS conforming to CSA G40.20-M, Class H
  — CSA G40.21-M grade 350W.

In each set of tables, structural sections which are either Class 3 or 4, in the grade of steel for which the loads have been computed, are identified. In Set 1, those welded sections in which the flange-to-web welds do not develop the entire web strengths are identified.

Design of Axially Loaded Columns

The design of axially loaded columns (columns theoretically not subjected to combined bending and compression) involves the determination of the governing effective length and the selection of a section with the required resistance at that effective length. Factored axial compressive resistance tables for columns enable a designer to select a suitable section directly, without following a trial-and-error procedure.

Since the factored axial compressive resistances, C_r, listed in the tables supplied have been computed on the basis of the least radius of gyration (r_y) for each section, the tables apply directly only to columns unbraced about the Y—Y axis. In certain cases, however, it is necessary to investigate the capacity of a column with reference to both the X—X axis and the Y—Y axis, or with reference only to the X—X axis. The ratio r_x/r_y included in the table of properties at the bottom of each resistance table provides a convenient means of investigating the strength of a column with respect to the X—X axis.

In general, a column having an effective length $K_x L_x$ with respect to the X—X axis will be able to carry a factored load equal to the tabulated factored axial compressive resistance based upon the effective length $K_y L_y$ with respect to the Y—Y axis if

$$K_x L_x \leqslant K_y L_y (r_x/r_y)$$

Examples

1. Given:

A W310 column is required to carry a factored axial load of 3 600 kN. The effective length $K_y L_y$ along the weak axis is 4 500 mm. The effective length $K_x L_x$ along the strong axis is 7 600 mm. Use CSA G40.21-M 300W steel.

Solution:

With $K_y L_y$ = 4 500, the lightest W310 section with sufficient factored axial compressive resistance is W310×143. C_r = 3 850 kN; r_x/r_y = 1.75.

$K_x L_x$ = 7 600 mm

$K_y L_y (r_x/r_y)$ = 4 500 × 1.75
            = 7 875 mm > 7 600 — O.K.

The W310×143 has a factored compressive resistance of 3 850 kN with an effective length of $K_x L_x$ = 7 875 mm, and hence the section is adequate. Use W310×143.

2. **Given:**

   Same as example 1, except $K_x L_x = 9\ 500$ mm

Solution:

   $K_y L_y = 4\ 500$ mm

   $K_x L_x = 9\ 500$ mm

   Equivalent $K_y L_y$, for $K_x L_x$ of 9 500 mm $= K_x L_x/(r_x/r_y)$.

   Assuming that a heavy W310 section will be adequate, $r_x/r_y = 1.75$.

   Equivalent $K_y L_y = 9\ 500/1.75$

   $\qquad\qquad\qquad = 5\ 430 > 4\ 500$ mm

   Therefore $K_x L_x$ governs, and the effective $K_y L_y$ is 5 430 mm.

   With $K_y L_y = 5\ 430$ mm, a W310×158 is the lightest W310 that has a factored axial compressive resistance greater than the factored axial load of 3 600 kN (C_r for 5 500 mm = 3 790 kN; $r_x/r_y = 1.76$)

   Use W310×158

Other steel grades

   For columns of steels other than G40.21-M 300W for WWF and W shapes, or G40.21-M 350W for HSS, see example 1, page 4—8, for a method of determining the factored axial compressive resistance of the section. For steel grades with higher specified minimum yield points, these tables are conservative.

WWF COLUMNS
Factored Axial Compressive
Resistances, C$_r$, in kN

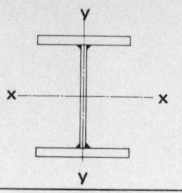

Designation		WWF550			WWF550		WWF500		
Mass (kg/m)		**721	**620	503	420	†217*	**651	**561	456
	0	24 000	20 600	16 800	14 500	6 290	21 700	18 700	15 200
	2 000	23 800	20 500	16 700	14 400	6 240	21 400	18 500	15 100
	2 250	23 700	20 400	16 600	14 300	6 200	21 200	18 400	15 000
	2 500	23 500	20 300	16 500	14 200	6 160	21 100	18 300	14 900
	2 750	23 300	20 200	16 400	14 100	6 120	20 900	18 100	14 700
	3 000	23 200	20 000	16 300	14 000	6 080	20 700	18 000	14 600
	3 250	23 000	19 900	16 200	13 900	6 040	20 500	17 800	14 500
	3 500	22 800	19 800	16 100	13 800	5 990	20 300	17 700	14 400
	3 750	22 600	19 600	15 900	13 700	5 940	20 100	17 500	14 300
	4 000	22 400	19 500	15 800	13 600	5 900	19 900	17 400	14 200
	4 250	22 200	19 300	15 700	13 500	5 850	19 700	17 200	14 000
	4 500	22 000	19 200	15 600	13 400	5 800	19 500	17 100	13 900
	4 750	21 800	19 000	15 400	13 300	5 740	19 300	16 900	13 800
	5 000	21 600	18 800	15 300	13 100	5 690	19 100	16 700	13 600
	5 250	21 400	18 700	15 200	13 000	5 640	18 900	16 600	13 500
	5 500	21 200	18 500	15 000	12 900	5 580	18 600	16 400	13 400
	6 000	20 700	18 100	14 800	12 600	5 470	18 200	16 000	13 100
	6 500	20 200	17 700	14 500	12 400	5 340	17 600	15 600	12 800
	7 000	19 700	17 400	14 100	12 100	5 220	17 100	15 200	12 400
	7 500	19 200	17 000	13 800	11 800	5 090	16 600	14 800	12 100
	8 000	18 600	16 500	13 500	11 500	4 950	16 000	14 300	11 700
	8 500	18 000	16 100	13 100	11 100	4 810	15 400	13 900	11 400
	9 000	17 500	15 600	12 800	10 800	4 660	14 800	13 400	11 000
	9 500	16 800	15 200	12 400	10 500	4 510	14 100	12 900	10 600
	10 000	16 200	14 700	12 000	10 100	4 350	13 400	12 400	10 200
	10 500	15 500	14 200	11 600	9 750	4 190	12 700	11 800	9 770
	11 000	14 900	13 700	11 200	9 380	4 020	11 900	11 300	9 330
	11 500	14 100	13 100	10 800	8 990	3 850	11 200	10 600	8 820
	12 000	13 300	12 600	10 400	8 550	3 640	10 600	10 100	8 340

(Left column label, read vertically: Effective length (KL) in millimetres with respect to least radius of gyration)

PROPERTIES AND DESIGN DATA

Area (mm^2)	92 000	79 100	64 200	53 600	27 700	83 000	71 600	58 200
Z$_x$ (10^{3}mm^3)	19 000	17 600	14 800	12 400	6 580	15 400	14 300	12 100
S$_x$ (10^{3}mm^3)	16 000	15 200	13 100	11 100	6 090	12 800	12 300	10 600
r$_x$ (mm)	218	230	237	239	246	196	207	214
Z$_y$ (10^{3}mm^3)	9 470	9 180	7 610	6 100	3 040	7 850	7 590	6 290
S$_y$ (10^{3}mm^3)	6 080	6 050	5 040	4 030	2 020	5 030	5 000	4 170
r$_y$ (mm)	135	145	147	144	142	123	132	134
r$_x$/r$_y$	1.61	1.59	1.61	1.66	1.73	1.59	1.57	1.60
M$_{rx}$ (kN•m) (L<L$_u$)	4 960	4 590	3 860	3 350	1 640	4 020	3 730	3 160
M$_{ry}$ (kN•m)	2 470	2 400	1 990	1 650	545	2 050	1 980	1 640
J(10^{3}mm^4)	110 000	83 100	47 000	24 700	3 160	99 400	75 400	42 700
C$_w$ (10^{9}mm^6)	100 000	99 900	86 700	72 100	39 000	60 800	60 500	52 700
L$_u$ (mm)	14 900	14 200	12 400	10 500	9 120	14 900	14 100	12 000
F$_y$ (MPa)	290	290	290	300	300	290	290	290

IMPERIAL SIZE AND MASS

Mass (lb./ft.)	484	416	338	282	146	437	377	306
Nominal Depth and Width (in.)	22 x 22			22 x 22		20 x 20		

* Resistance for this column calculated according to CAN3-S16.1-M78 Clause 13.3.3.
† Class 3 in bending.
** Welding does not fully develop web strenth for this section.

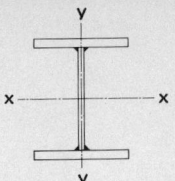

Designation		WWF500						
Mass (kg/m)		381	343	306	276	†254	†223	†197*
Effective length (KL) in millimetres with respect to least radius of gyration	0	13 100	11 800	10 500	9 500	8 720	7 690	6 050
	2 000	13 000	11 700	10 400	9 390	8 610	7 600	5 980
	2 250	12 900	11 600	10 300	9 330	8 550	7 540	5 940
	2 500	12 800	11 500	10 200	9 260	8 480	7 490	5 890
	2 750	12 700	11 400	10 200	9 190	8 420	7 430	5 850
	3 000	12 600	11 300	10 100	9 110	8 350	7 370	5 800
	3 250	12 500	11 200	9 990	9 040	8 280	7 300	5 750
	3 500	12 400	11 100	9 910	8 960	8 200	7 240	5 700
	3 750	12 300	11 000	9 810	8 880	8 130	7 170	5 650
	4 000	12 200	10 900	9 720	8 790	8 050	7 100	5 600
	4 250	12 100	10 800	9 620	8 710	7 970	7 030	5 540
	4 500	11 900	10 700	9 520	8 620	7 890	6 960	5 490
	4 750	11 800	10 600	9 420	8 530	7 800	6 880	5 430
	5 000	11 700	10 500	9 320	8 440	7 720	6 810	5 370
	5 250	11 600	10 400	9 210	8 340	7 630	6 730	5 310
	5 500	11 400	10 300	9 100	8 240	7 530	6 650	5 250
	6 000	11 200	10 000	8 870	8 040	7 340	6 480	5 120
	6 500	10 900	9 740	8 630	7 830	7 140	6 300	4 980
	7 000	10 600	9 470	8 370	7 610	6 940	6 120	4 840
	7 500	10 300	9 180	8 110	7 380	6 720	5 930	4 700
	8 000	9 930	8 880	7 840	7 140	6 490	5 730	4 540
	8 500	9 600	8 570	7 550	6 880	6 250	5 520	4 380
	9 000	9 250	8 240	7 260	6 620	6 010	5 300	4 220
	9 500	8 880	7 910	6 950	6 350	5 760	5 080	4 040
	10 000	8 510	7 560	6 630	6 070	5 490	4 850	3 870
	10 500	8 120	7 200	6 280	5 790	5 200	4 590	3 690
	11 000	7 670	6 770	5 910	5 440	4 890	4 320	3 460
	11 500	7 230	6 380	5 570	5 130	4 610	4 070	3 270
	12 000	6 830	6 030	5 260	4 840	4 350	3 840	3 080

PROPERTIES AND DESIGN DATA

	381	343	306	276	†254	†223	†197*
Area (mm²)	48 600	43 800	39 000	35 200	32 300	28 500	25 200
Z_x (10^3mm³)	10 100	9 100	8 060	7 420	6 780	6 010	5 410
S_x (10^3mm³)	9 010	8 140	7 240	6 740	6 160	5 500	4 990
r_x (mm)	215	216	215	218	218	219	223
Z_y (10^3mm³)	5 040	4 420	3 800	3 530	3 160	2 770	2 510
S_y (10^3mm³)	3 330	2 920	2 500	2 330	2 080	1 830	1 670
r_y (mm)	131	129	127	129	127	127	129
r_x/r_y	1.64	1.67	1.69	1.69	1.72	1.72	1.73
M_{rx} (kN•m) (L<L_u)	2 730	2 460	2 180	2 000	1 660	1 480	1 350
M_{ry} (kN•m)	1 360	1 190	1 030	953	562	494	451
J(10^3mm⁴)	22 500	15 400	10 200	7 920	5 820	3 970	2 870
C_w (10^9mm⁶)	44 100	39 400	34 500	32 500	29 400	26 200	24 000
L_u (mm)	10 000	9 330	8 750	8 620	8 830	8 550	8 420
F_y (MPa)	300	300	300	300	300	300	300

IMPERIAL SIZE AND MASS

Mass (lb./ft.)	256	230	205	185	170	150	132
Nominal Depth and Width (in.)				20 x 20			

† Class 3 in bending.
* Resistance for this column calculated according to CAN3-S16.1-M78 Clause 13.3.3.

WWF COLUMNS
Factored Axial Compressive Resistances, C_r, in kN

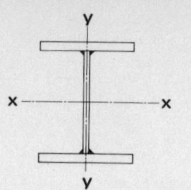

Designation		WWF450		WWF450						
Mass (kg/m)		**503	409	342	308	274	248	228	†201	†177
	0	16 700	13 600	11 800	10 600	9 450	8 530	7 830	6 910	6 100
	2 000	16 500	13 400	11 600	10 400	9 270	8 380	7 680	6 780	5 990
	2 250	16 300	13 300	11 500	10 300	9 190	8 310	7 620	6 720	5 940
	2 500	16 200	13 200	11 400	10 200	9 110	8 240	7 550	6 660	5 890
	2 750	16 100	13 100	11 300	10 200	9 030	8 170	7 480	6 600	5 840
	3 000	15 900	13 000	11 200	10 100	8 940	8 090	7 410	6 540	5 780
	3 250	15 800	12 900	11 100	9 960	8 850	8 010	7 330	6 470	5 730
	3 500	15 600	12 800	11 000	9 860	8 760	7 930	7 260	6 410	5 670
	3 750	15 500	12 600	10 900	9 750	8 660	7 840	7 180	6 340	5 610
	4 000	15 300	12 500	10 700	9 650	8 560	7 760	7 090	6 260	5 550
	4 250	15 200	12 400	10 600	9 530	8 460	7 670	7 010	6 190	5 480
	4 500	15 000	12 200	10 500	9 420	8 350	7 570	6 920	6 110	5 420
	4 750	14 800	12 100	10 400	9 300	8 250	7 480	6 830	6 030	5 350
	5 000	14 600	12 000	10 200	9 180	8 140	7 380	6 740	5 950	5 280
	5 250	14 400	11 800	10 100	9 050	8 020	7 280	6 650	5 870	5 210
	5 500	14 300	11 700	9 950	8 920	7 900	7 180	6 550	5 780	5 130
	6 000	13 900	11 400	9 670	8 660	7 660	6 960	6 350	5 600	4 980
	6 500	13 500	11 000	9 360	8 380	7 400	6 740	6 130	5 410	4 820
	7 000	13 000	10 700	9 050	8 080	7 130	6 500	5 910	5 220	4 650
	7 500	12 600	10 300	8 720	7 780	6 850	6 250	5 680	5 010	4 470
	8 000	12 100	9 950	8 370	7 460	6 560	6 000	5 430	4 800	4 290
	8 500	11 600	9 560	8 010	7 120	6 250	5 730	5 180	4 570	4 100
	9 000	11 100	9 160	7 640	6 780	5 940	5 450	4 920	4 340	3 900
	9 500	10 600	8 740	7 250	6 410	5 580	5 160	4 620	4 080	3 690
	10 000	9 990	8 320	6 800	5 990	5 210	4 820	4 320	3 810	3 440
	10 500	9 360	7 800	6 370	5 610	4 880	4 510	4 040	3 570	3 230
	11 000	8 800	7 330	5 980	5 270	4 580	4 240	3 800	3 350	3 030
	11 500	8 290	6 900	5 630	4 960	4 320	3 990	3 580	3 160	2 850
	12 000	7 820	6 520	5 320	4 680	4 070	3 760	3 370	2 980	2 690

Left axis label: Effective length (KL) in millimetres with respect to least radius of gyration

PROPERTIES AND DESIGN DATA

	**503	409	342	308	274	248	228	201	177
Area (mm²)	64 100	52 200	43 600	39 300	35 000	31 600	29 000	25 600	22 600
Z_x (10^3mm³)	11 400	9 640	8 100	7 290	6 470	5 960	5 450	4 840	4 360
S_x (10^3mm³)	9 620	8 380	7 150	6 480	5 770	5 380	4 920	4 400	4 000
r_x (mm)	184	190	192	193	193	196	196	197	200
Z_y (10^3mm³)	6 150	5 100	4 090	3 580	3 080	2 860	2 560	2 250	2 040
S_y (10^3mm³)	4 050	3 380	2 700	2 360	2 030	1 890	1 690	1 490	1 350
r_y (mm)	119	121	118	116	114	116	114	114	116
r_x/r_y	1.55	1.57	1.63	1.66	1.69	1.69	1.72	1.73	1.72
M_{rx} (kN•m) (L<L_u)	2 980	2 520	2 190	1 970	1 750	1 610	1 470	1 190	1 080
M_{ry} (kN•m)	1 610	1 330	1 100	967	832	772	691	402	364
J (10^3mm⁴)	67 800	38 400	20 200	13 900	9 140	7 120	5 230	3 570	2 580
C_w (10^9mm⁶)	34 700	30 400	25 500	22 900	20 100	18 900	17 200	15 300	14 000
L_u (mm)	14 100	11 900	9 620	8 860	8 190	8 020	7 700	7 900	7 730
F_y (MPa)	290	290	300	300	300	300	300	300	300

IMPERIAL SIZE AND MASS

Mass (lb./ft.)	337	275	229	207	184	166	152	134	119
Nominal Depth and Width (in.)	18 x 18		18 x 18						

† Class 3 in bending.
** Welding does not fully develop web strength for this section.

G40.21-M 300W
$\phi = 0.90$

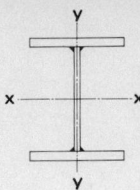

Designation		WWF400		WWF400						
Mass (kg/m)		**444	362	303	273	243	220	202	178	†157
Effective length (KL) in millimetres with respect to least radius of gyration	0	14 800	12 100	10 400	9 400	8 370	7 560	6 940	6 130	5 430
	2 000	14 400	11 800	10 200	9 160	8 150	7 360	6 750	5 960	5 290
	2 250	14 300	11 700	10 100	9 070	8 070	7 290	6 690	5 910	5 230
	2 500	14 200	11 600	9 970	8 980	7 980	7 220	6 620	5 850	5 180
	2 750	14 000	11 500	9 870	8 880	7 900	7 140	6 550	5 780	5 130
	3 000	13 900	11 400	9 760	8 790	7 810	7 060	6 470	5 720	5 070
	3 250	13 700	11 200	9 650	8 680	7 710	6 980	6 390	5 650	5 010
	3 500	13 600	11 100	9 530	8 580	7 620	6 890	6 310	5 580	4 950
	3 750	13 400	11 000	9 410	8 470	7 510	6 800	6 230	5 500	4 880
	4 000	13 200	10 800	9 290	8 360	7 410	6 710	6 140	5 430	4 820
	4 250	13 100	10 700	9 160	8 240	7 300	6 610	6 060	5 350	4 750
	4 500	12 900	10 600	9 030	8 120	7 190	6 520	5 960	5 270	4 680
	4 750	12 700	10 400	8 890	7 990	7 080	6 410	5 870	5 180	4 600
	5 000	12 500	10 300	8 750	7 870	6 960	6 310	5 770	5 100	4 530
	5 250	12 300	10 100	8 610	7 740	6 840	6 200	5 670	5 010	4 450
	5 500	12 100	9 960	8 460	7 600	6 720	6 090	5 570	4 920	4 370
	6 000	11 700	9 630	8 160	7 320	6 460	5 860	5 360	4 730	4 210
	6 500	11 300	9 280	7 830	7 020	6 190	5 620	5 130	4 530	4 030
	7 000	10 800	8 910	7 490	6 710	5 900	5 370	4 890	4 320	3 850
	7 500	10 300	8 530	7 140	6 390	5 600	5 100	4 650	4 100	3 660
	8 000	9 820	8 140	6 770	6 050	5 290	4 820	4 390	3 870	3 460
	8 500	9 290	7 720	6 380	5 690	4 940	4 520	4 100	3 620	3 250
	9 000	8 700	7 280	5 930	5 280	4 580	4 190	3 800	3 350	3 010
	9 500	8 100	6 780	5 510	4 910	4 260	3 900	3 530	3 120	2 800
	10 000	7 560	6 330	5 150	4 580	3 970	3 640	3 290	2 910	2 610
	10 500	7 080	5 920	4 820	4 290	3 720	3 400	3 080	2 720	2 440
	11 000	6 640	5 560	4 520	4 020	3 490	3 190	2 890	2 550	2 290
	11 500	6 250	5 230	4 250	3 780	3 280	3 000	2 720	2 400	2 150
	12 000	5 890	4 930	4 000	3 560	3 090	2 830	2 560	2 260	2 030

PROPERTIES AND DESIGN DATA

Area (mm²)		56 600	46 200	38 600	34 800	31 000	28 000	25 700	22 700	20 100
Z_x (10^3mm³)		8 770	7 480	6 300	5 680	5 050	4 660	4 260	3 790	3 420
S_x (10^3mm³)		7 300	6 410	5 500	5 000	4 470	4 170	3 830	3 430	3 120
r_x (mm)		161	166	169	170	170	173	173	174	176
Z_y (10^3mm³)		4 870	4 030	3 230	2 840	2 440	2 260	2 020	1 780	1 610
S_y (10^3mm³)		3 200	2 670	2 130	1 870	1 600	1 490	1 330	1 170	1 070
r_y (mm)		106	108	105	104	102	103	102	102	103
r_x/r_y		1.52	1.54	1.61	1.63	1.67	1.68	1.70	1.71	1.71
M_{rx} (kN•m) ($L < L_u$)		2 290	1 950	1 700	1 530	1 360	1 260	1 150	1 020	842
M_{ry} (kN•m)		1 270	1 050	872	767	659	610	545	481	289
J(10^3mm⁴)		60 100	34 100	17 900	12 300	8 110	6 320	4 640	3 170	2 290
C_w (10^9mm⁶)		18 500	16 300	13 800	12 400	11 000	10 300	9 380	8 390	7 700
L_u (mm)		14 300	11 800	9 310	8 440	7 690	7 470	7 120	6 830	7 070
F_y (MPa)		290	290	300	300	300	300	300	300	300

IMPERIAL SIZE AND MASS

Mass (lb./ft.)		298	243	203	183	163	147	135	119	105
Nominal Depth and Width (in.)		16 x 16		16 x 16						

† Class 3 in bending.
** Welding does not fully develop web strength for this section.

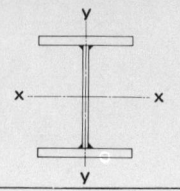
Designation		WWF350		WWF350						
Mass (kg/m)		**385	315	263	238	212	192	176	155	137
Effective length (KL) in millimetres with respect to least radius of gyration	0	12 800	10 500	9 070	8 180	7 290	6 590	6 050	5 350	4 720
	2 000	12 400	10 200	8 760	7 880	7 010	6 350	5 820	5 140	4 550
	2 250	12 300	10 100	8 660	7 790	6 930	6 270	5 750	5 080	4 500
	2 500	12 100	9 940	8 550	7 700	6 840	6 200	5 680	5 020	4 440
	2 750	12 000	9 820	8 440	7 600	6 750	6 110	5 600	4 950	4 380
	3 000	11 800	9 690	8 330	7 490	6 660	6 030	5 520	4 880	4 320
	3 250	11 700	9 570	8 210	7 380	6 560	5 940	5 440	4 810	4 260
	3 500	11 500	9 430	8 090	7 270	6 450	5 850	5 360	4 730	4 200
	3 750	11 300	9 290	7 970	7 160	6 350	5 760	5 270	4 650	4 130
	4 000	11 200	9 150	7 840	7 030	6 240	5 660	5 180	4 570	4 060
	4 250	11 000	9 000	7 700	6 910	6 120	5 560	5 080	4 490	3 980
	4 500	10 800	8 850	7 560	6 780	6 000	5 450	4 980	4 400	3 910
	4 750	10 600	8 690	7 420	6 650	5 880	5 350	4 880	4 310	3 830
	5 000	10 400	8 530	7 270	6 510	5 750	5 230	4 780	4 220	3 750
	5 250	10 200	8 360	7 110	6 370	5 620	5 120	4 670	4 120	3 670
	5 500	9 970	8 190	6 960	6 220	5 490	5 000	4 560	4 020	3 580
	6 000	9 530	7 830	6 630	5 920	5 210	4 750	4 330	3 820	3 410
	6 500	9 060	7 460	6 280	5 590	4 920	4 490	4 090	3 600	3 220
	7 000	8 570	7 060	5 920	5 260	4 610	4 220	3 830	3 370	3 020
	7 500	8 060	6 640	5 540	4 890	4 250	3 920	3 540	3 110	2 810
	8 000	7 470	6 180	5 080	4 490	3 900	3 600	3 250	2 850	2 580
	8 500	6 890	5 700	4 690	4 130	3 600	3 310	2 990	2 630	2 370
	9 000	6 380	5 280	4 340	3 830	3 330	3 070	2 770	2 430	2 200
	9 500	5 930	4 910	4 030	3 550	3 090	2 850	2 570	2 260	2 040
	10 000	5 530	4 570	3 760	3 310	2 880	2 650	2 390	2 100	1 900
	10 500	5 170	4 270	3 510	3 090	2 690	2 480	2 240	1 960	1 770
	11 000	4 840	4 010	3 290	2 890	2 510	2 320	2 090	1 840	1 660
	11 500	4 550	3 760	3 080	2 720	2 360	2 180	1 960	1 720	1 560
	12 000	4 280	3 540	2 900	2 550	2 220	2 050	1 850	1 620	1 470

PROPERTIES AND DESIGN DATA

Area (mm²)		49 100	40 200	33 600	30 300	27 000	24 400	22 400	19 800	17 500
Z_x (10³mm³)		6 510	5 580	4 730	4 280	3 810	3 520	3 220	2 870	2 590
S_x (10³mm³)		5 300	4 710	4 070	3 720	3 330	3 120	2 870	2 580	2 350
r_x (mm)		137	143	146	146	147	150	150	151	153
Z_y (10³mm³)		3 730	3 090	2 480	2 170	1 870	1 740	1 550	1 360	1 240
S_y (10³mm³)		2 450	2 040	1 630	1 430	1 230	1 140	1 020	899	817
r_y (mm)		93.5	94.2	92.3	90.8	89.2	90.5	89.4	89.0	90.4
r_x/r_y		1.47	1.52	1.58	1.61	1.65	1.66	1.68	1.70	1.69
M_{rx} (kN•m) (L<L_u)		1 700	1 460	1 280	1 160	1 030	950	869	775	699
M_{ry} (kN•m)		974	806	670	586	505	470	418	367	335
$J(10³mm⁴)$		52 500	29 800	15 700	10 800	7 070	5 520	4 060	2 760	2 000
C_W (10⁹mm⁶)		9 030	8 040	6 870	6 210	5 490	5 190	4 720	4 230	3 890
L_u (mm)		14 600	11 900	9 130	8 130	7 270	6 980	6 580	6 230	6 070
F_y (MPa)		290	290	300	300	300	300	300	300	300

IMPERIAL SIZE AND MASS

Mass (lb./ft.)		258	211	177	159	142	128	118	104	92
Nominal Depth and Width (in.)		14 x 14				14 x 14				

** Welding does not fully develop web strength for this section.

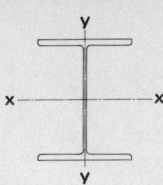

Designation		W360			W310				
Mass (kg/m)		79	72	64*	283	253	226	202	179
Effective length (KL) in millimetres with respect to least radius of gyration	0	2 730	2 460	2 200	9 400	8 400	7 540	6 730	5 950
	2 000	2 390	2 150	1 920	8 990	8 030	7 200	6 420	5 670
	2 250	2 320	2 080	1 860	8 870	7 920	7 100	6 330	5 590
	2 500	2 230	2 010	1 790	8 750	7 810	7 000	6 240	5 510
	2 750	2 150	1 930	1 720	8 620	7 700	6 890	6 150	5 420
	3 000	2 060	1 850	1 640	8 490	7 570	6 780	6 050	5 330
	3 250	1 960	1 760	1 570	8 350	7 450	6 670	5 940	5 240
	3 500	1 870	1 670	1 480	8 200	7 310	6 550	5 830	5 140
	3 750	1 760	1 580	1 400	8 050	7 180	6 420	5 720	5 040
	4 000	1 650	1 470	1 300	7 900	7 030	6 290	5 600	4 930
	4 250	1 520	1 360	1 200	7 730	6 890	6 160	5 480	4 830
	4 500	1 410	1 260	1 110	7 570	6 730	6 020	5 350	4 710
	4 750	1 310	1 170	1 030	7 390	6 580	5 870	5 220	4 600
	5 000	1 220	1 090	963	7 210	6 410	5 730	5 090	4 470
	5 250	1 140	1 020	900	7 030	6 240	5 570	4 950	4 350
	5 500	1 070	955	844	6 840	6 070	5 410	4 810	4 220
	6 000	948	845	746	6 440	5 710	5 080	4 510	3 950
	6 500	844	752	660	6 020	5 330	4 730	4 190	3 670
	7 000	756	674	569	5 560	4 890	4 330	3 820	3 340
	7 500	681	606	496	5 070	4 460	3 950	3 490	3 050
	8 000	612	544	436	4 650	4 090	3 620	3 200	2 790
	8 500	545	484	386	4 280	3 770	3 330	2 940	2 570
	9 000	489	434	344	3 960	3 480	3 080	2 720	2 370
	9 500	441	392	309	3 670	3 230	2 860	2 520	2 200
	10 000				3 410	3 000	2 660	2 340	2 040
	10 500				3 190	2 800	2 480	2 180	1 910
	11 000				2 980	2 620	2 320	2 040	1 780
	11 500				2 790	2 450	2 170	1 910	1 670
	12 000				2 620	2 300	2 030	1 790	1 560

PROPERTIES AND DESIGN DATA

Area (mm²)	10 100	9 110	8 140	36 000	32 200	28 900	25 800	22 800
Z_x (10^3 mm³)	1 430	1 280	1 140	5 100	4 490	3 980	3 510	3 050
S_x (10^3 mm³)	1 280	1 150	1 030	4 310	3 830	3 420	3 050	2 680
r_x (mm)	150	149	148	148	146	144	142	140
Z_y (10^3 mm³)	362	322	284	2 340	2 060	1 830	1 610	1 400
S_y (10^3 mm³)	236	210	186	1 530	1 350	1 190	1 050	919
r_y (mm)	48.9	48.5	48.1	82.7	81.7	80.9	80.2	79.5
r_x/r_y	3.07	3.07	3.08	1.79	1.79	1.78	1.77	1.76
M_{rx} (kN•m) (L<L_u)	386	346	308	1 330	1 170	1 040	916	796
M_{ry} (kN•m)	97.7	86.9	76.7	611	538	478	420	365
J (10^3 mm⁴)	814	603	438	20 400	14 800	10 800	7 740	5 380
C_w (10^9 mm⁶)	687	600	524	6 330	5 370	4 620	3 960	3 340
L_u (mm)	3 270	3 190	3 110	9 110	8 370	7 730	7 170	6 660
F_y (MPa)	300	300	300	290	290	290	290	290

IMPERIAL SIZE AND MASS

Mass (lb./ft.)	53	48	43	190	170	152	136	120
Nominal Depth and Width (in.)		14 x 8				12 x 12		

* Resistance for this column calculated according to CAN3-S16.1-M78 Clause 13.3.3.

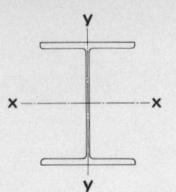
Designation		W310						W310	
Mass (kg/m)		158	143	129	118	107	97[†]	86	79
Effective length (KL) in millimetres with respect to least radius of gyration	0	5 430	4 910	4 450	4 050	3 670	3 320	2 970	2 730
	2 000	5 160	4 670	4 230	3 840	3 480	3 150	2 740	2 510
	2 250	5 080	4 600	4 160	3 780	3 430	3 100	2 690	2 460
	2 500	5 000	4 530	4 100	3 720	3 380	3 050	2 630	2 410
	2 750	4 920	4 460	4 030	3 660	3 320	3 000	2 570	2 350
	3 000	4 840	4 380	3 960	3 600	3 260	2 940	2 500	2 290
	3 250	4 750	4 300	3 890	3 530	3 200	2 890	2 430	2 230
	3 500	4 660	4 220	3 810	3 460	3 130	2 830	2 360	2 160
	3 750	4 560	4 130	3 730	3 380	3 070	2 770	2 290	2 090
	4 000	4 460	4 040	3 640	3 310	3 000	2 710	2 210	2 020
	4 250	4 360	3 940	3 560	3 230	2 920	2 640	2 130	1 940
	4 500	4 250	3 850	3 470	3 150	2 850	2 570	2 050	1 870
	4 750	4 140	3 750	3 370	3 060	2 770	2 500	1 960	1 780
	5 000	4 030	3 640	3 280	2 970	2 690	2 430	1 870	1 700
	5 250	3 910	3 530	3 180	2 880	2 610	2 350	1 780	1 610
	5 500	3 790	3 420	3 080	2 790	2 520	2 270	1 670	1 510
	6 000	3 530	3 190	2 860	2 590	2 340	2 110	1 490	1 340
	6 500	3 250	2 940	2 620	2 370	2 140	1 930	1 330	1 200
	7 000	2 950	2 660	2 370	2 150	1 940	1 750	1 200	1 090
	7 500	2 690	2 430	2 160	1 960	1 770	1 590	1 090	987
	8 000	2 460	2 220	1 980	1 790	1 620	1 460	996	900
	8 500	2 260	2 050	1 820	1 650	1 490	1 340	912	824
	9 000	2 090	1 890	1 680	1 520	1 370	1 240	838	757
	9 500	1 940	1 750	1 560	1 410	1 270	1 140	772	697
	10 000	1 800	1 630	1 450	1 310	1 180	1 060	714	644
	10 500	1 680	1 520	1 350	1 220	1 100	990	656	589
	11 000	1 570	1 410	1 260	1 140	1 030	924	600	539
	11 500	1 460	1 320	1 180	1 060	961	864	551	495
	12 000	1 370	1 240	1 100	997	900	809	508	457

PROPERTIES AND DESIGN DATA

	158	143	129	118	107	97	86	79
Area (mm²)	20 100	18 200	16 500	15 000	13 600	12 300	11 000	10 100
Z_x (10³mm³)	2 670	2 420	2 160	1 950	1 770	1 590	1 420	1 280
S_x (10³mm³)	2 360	2 150	1 940	1 750	1 590	1 440	1 280	1 160
r_x (mm)	139	138	137	135	135	134	135	132
Z_y (10³mm³)	1 220	1 110	991	893	806	725	533	478
S_y (10³mm³)	805	729	652	588	531	478	351	314
r_y (mm)	78.9	78.8	77.8	77.5	77.3	77.0	63.6	62.9
r_x/r_y	1.76	1.75	1.76	1.74	1.75	1.74	2.12	2.10
M_{rx} (kN•m) (L<L_u)	721	653	583	526	478	389	383	346
M_{ry} (kN•m)	329	300	268	241	218	129	144	129
J(10³mm⁴)	3 780	2 870	2 130	1 600	1 220	912	877	657
C_w (10⁹mm⁶)	2 840	2 540	2 220	1 970	1 760	1 560	961	847
L_u (mm)	6 080	5 820	5 580	5 390	5 220	5 410	4 250	4 140
F_y (MPa)	300	300	300	300	300	300	300	300

IMPERIAL SIZE AND MASS

Mass (lb./ft.)	106	96	87	79	72	65	58	53
Nominal Depth and Width (in.)	12 x 12						12 X 10	

† Class 3 in bending.

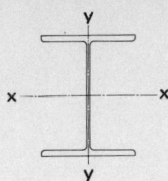
Designation		W310			W250				
Mass (kg/m)		74	67	60	167	149	131	115	101
Effective length (KL) in millimetres with respect to least radius of gyration	0	2 560	2 300	2 050	5 750	5 130	4 510	3 940	3 480
	2 000	2 260	2 020	1 800	5 360	4 780	4 190	3 660	3 230
	2 250	2 190	1 960	1 740	5 270	4 690	4 120	3 590	3 170
	2 500	2 110	1 890	1 680	5 170	4 600	4 030	3 520	3 100
	2 750	2 030	1 820	1 620	5 060	4 500	3 950	3 440	3 030
	3 000	1 950	1 740	1 550	4 940	4 400	3 860	3 360	2 960
	3 250	1 870	1 660	1 480	4 830	4 290	3 760	3 280	2 890
	3 500	1 770	1 580	1 410	4 700	4 180	3 660	3 190	2 810
	3 750	1 680	1 490	1 330	4 580	4 060	3 560	3 100	2 730
	4 000	1 580	1 410	1 250	4 440	3 940	3 450	3 000	2 640
	4 250	1 460	1 300	1 150	4 300	3 820	3 340	2 900	2 550
	4 500	1 350	1 200	1 070	4 160	3 690	3 220	2 800	2 460
	4 750	1 260	1 120	991	4 010	3 550	3 100	2 690	2 360
	5 000	1 170	1 040	924	3 850	3 410	2 970	2 580	2 260
	5 250	1 100	974	864	3 690	3 260	2 840	2 470	2 160
	5 500	1 030	913	810	3 530	3 110	2 710	2 340	2 040
	6 000	911	808	716	3 150	2 770	2 410	2 090	1 820
	6 500	812	720	638	2 830	2 490	2 160	1 870	1 630
	7 000	728	645	572	2 560	2 250	1 950	1 690	1 470
	7 500	656	581	515	2 330	2 050	1 780	1 540	1 340
	8 000	593	524	464	2 130	1 870	1 620	1 400	1 220
	8 500	529	467	413	1 950	1 710	1 490	1 290	1 120
	9 000	474	419	370	1 800	1 580	1 370	1 180	1 030
	9 500	428	378	334	1 660	1 460	1 260	1 090	949
	10 000				1 530	1 350	1 170	1 010	878
	10 500				1 420	1 250	1 080	937	814
	11 000				1 320	1 160	1 000	862	746
	11 500				1 220	1 060	918	792	685
	12 000				1 120	980	847	730	632

PROPERTIES AND DESIGN DATA

	W310 74	W310 67	W310 60	W250 167	W250 149	W250 131	W250 115	W250 101
Area (mm^2)	9 490	8 510	7 590	21 300	19 000	16 700	14 600	12 900
Z_x (10^3mm^3)	1 190	1 060	941	2 430	2 130	1 850	1 600	1 400
S_x (10^3mm^3)	1 060	949	849	2 080	1 840	1 610	1 410	1 240
r_x (mm)	132	131	130	119	117	115	114	113
Z_y (10^3mm^3)	350	310	275	1 140	1 000	870	753	656
S_y (10^3mm^3)	229	203	180	746	656	571	495	432
r_y (mm)	49.7	49.3	49.1	68.1	67.4	66.8	66.3	65.6
r_x/r_y	2.66	2.66	2.65	1.75	1.74	1.72	1.72	1.72
M_{rx} (kN•m) ($L<L_u$)	321	286	254	656	575	499	432	378
M_{ry} (kN•m)	94.5	83.7	74.2	308	270	235	203	177
J (10^3mm^4)	745	545	397	6 310	4 510	3 120	2 130	1 490
C_w (10^9mm^6)	505	439	384	1 630	1 390	1 160	976	829
L_u (mm)	3 380	3 280	3 200	6 670	6 160	5 680	5 270	4 950
F_y (MPa)	300	300	300	300	300	300	300	300

IMPERIAL SIZE AND MASS

	W310 74	W310 67	W310 60	W250 167	W250 149	W250 131	W250 115	W250 101
Mass (lb./ft.)	50	45	40	112	100	88	77	68
Nominal Depth and Width (in.)		12 x 8				10 x 10		

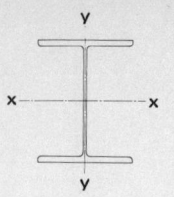
Designation		W250			W250		
Mass (kg/m)		89	80	73	67	58	49
Effective length (KL) in millimetres with respect to least radius of gyration	0	3 080	2 750	2 510	2 310	2 000	1 690
	2 000	2 850	2 550	2 320	2 040	1 770	1 480
	2 250	2 800	2 500	2 270	1 980	1 720	1 440
	2 500	2 740	2 450	2 230	1 920	1 660	1 390
	2 750	2 680	2 390	2 180	1 850	1 600	1 330
	3 000	2 610	2 340	2 120	1 780	1 540	1 280
	3 250	2 550	2 280	2 070	1 710	1 470	1 220
	3 500	2 470	2 210	2 010	1 630	1 400	1 160
	3 750	2 400	2 150	1 950	1 550	1 330	1 100
	4 000	2 320	2 080	1 880	1 460	1 250	1 030
	4 250	2 240	2 000	1 820	1 360	1 160	950
	4 500	2 160	1 930	1 750	1 260	1 080	880
	4 750	2 080	1 850	1 680	1 170	1 000	818
	5 000	1 990	1 770	1 610	1 100	933	763
	5 250	1 900	1 690	1 530	1 030	873	713
	5 500	1 790	1 590	1 440	962	819	669
	6 000	1 590	1 420	1 280	852	725	592
	6 500	1 430	1 270	1 150	760	646	527
	7 000	1 290	1 150	1 040	682	580	472
	7 500	1 170	1 040	944	615	522	425
	8 000	1 070	953	861	557	473	383
	8 500	980	873	789	500	423	341
	9 000	901	803	725	449	379	306
	9 500	831	740	669	405	342	276
	10 000	769	684	618	367	311	
	10 500	712	634	572			
	11 000	652	580	523			
	11 500	599	532	480			
	12 000	552	491	443			

PROPERTIES AND DESIGN DATA

Area (mm²)	11 400	10 200	9 280	8 550	7 420	6 250
Z_x (10^3mm³)	1 230	1 090	985	901	770	633
S_x (10^3mm³)	1 100	982	891	806	693	572
r_x (mm)	112	111	110	110	108	106
Z_y (10^3mm³)	574	513	463	332	283	228
S_y (10^3mm³)	378	338	306	218	186	150
r_y (mm)	65.2	65.0	64.7	51.0	50.3	49.2
r_x/r_y	1.72	1.71	1.70	2.16	2.15	2.15
M_{rx} (kN•m) (L<L_u)	332	294	266	243	208	171
M_{ry} (kN•m)	155	139	125	89.6	76.4	61.6
J(10^3mm⁴)	1 040	757	575	625	409	241
C_w (10^9mm⁶)	713	623	553	324	268	211
L_u (mm)	4 690	4 520	4 390	3 570	3 410	3 240
F_y (MPa)	300	300	300	300	300	300

IMPERIAL SIZE AND MASS

Mass (lb./ft.)	60	54	49	45	39	33
Nominal Depth and Width (in.)		10 x 10			10 x 8	

G40.21-M 300W
∅ = 0.90

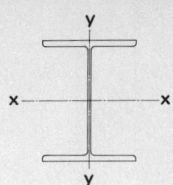

W COLUMNS
Factored Axial Compressive Resistances, C_r, in kN

Designation		W200						W200	
Mass (kg/m)		100	86	71	59	52	46	42	36
Effective length (KL) in millimetres with respect to least radius of gyration	0	3 430	3 000	2 460	2 040	1 800	1 580	1 430	1 240
	2 000	3 070	2 680	2 190	1 810	1 600	1 400	1 200	1 030
	2 250	2 990	2 610	2 130	1 760	1 550	1 360	1 140	983
	2 500	2 900	2 530	2 070	1 710	1 500	1 320	1 090	935
	2 750	2 810	2 450	2 000	1 650	1 450	1 270	1 030	883
	3 000	2 710	2 360	1 930	1 590	1 400	1 220	967	828
	3 250	2 610	2 270	1 850	1 520	1 340	1 170	901	770
	3 500	2 500	2 170	1 780	1 460	1 280	1 120	825	703
	3 750	2 390	2 070	1 690	1 390	1 220	1 060	753	641
	4 000	2 270	1 970	1 610	1 310	1 150	1 000	690	587
	4 250	2 150	1 860	1 520	1 230	1 080	937	635	540
	4 500	2 010	1 730	1 410	1 140	1 000	868	587	499
	4 750	1 870	1 610	1 310	1 060	932	807	544	463
	5 000	1 750	1 510	1 220	992	870	753	506	430
	5 250	1 630	1 410	1 150	929	814	705	472	401
	5 500	1 530	1 320	1 070	871	763	661	441	375
	6 000	1 360	1 170	953	772	676	585	387	329
	6 500	1 210	1 050	851	689	603	522	343	291
	7 000	1 090	941	764	618	542	469	299	254
	7 500	987	850	690	558	489	423	263	222
	8 000	895	771	626	506	443	383	232	197
	8 500	815	702	570	457	400	344		
	9 000	735	631	511	410	359	309		
	9 500	663	569	461	370	323	278		
	10 000	601	516	418	336	294	253		
	10 500	548	471	381					
	11 000								
	11 500								
	12 000								

PROPERTIES AND DESIGN DATA

	100	86	71	59	52	46	42	36
Area (mm²)	12 700	11 100	9 110	7 560	6 660	5 860	5 310	4 580
Z_x (10³mm³)	1 150	981	803	653	570	496	446	380
S_x (10³mm³)	989	853	709	582	512	448	399	342
r_x (mm)	94.3	92.4	91.7	89.9	89.0	88.1	87.8	86.7
Z_y (10³mm³)	533	458	375	303	266	230	165	141
S_y (10³mm³)	349	300	246	199	175	151	108	92.6
r_y (mm)	53.7	53.2	52.8	51.9	51.7	51.1	41.2	40.8
r_x/r_y	1.76	1.74	1.74	1.73	1.72	1.72	2.13	2.12
M_{rx} (kN•m) (L < L_u)	310	265	217	176	154	134	120	103
M_{ry} (kN•m)	144	124	101	81.8	71.8	62.1	44.5	38.1
J (10³mm⁴)	2 090	1 400	818	465	324	221	223	146
C_w (10⁹mm⁶)	386	318	250	196	167	141	84.0	69.6
L_u (mm)	5 020	4 620	4 150	3 780	3 620	3 460	2 850	2 730
F_y (MPa)	300	300	300	300	300	300	300	300

IMPERIAL SIZE AND MASS

Mass (lb./ft.)	67	58	48	40	35	31	28	24
Nominal Depth and Width (in.)	8 x 8						8 x 6½	

4-45

W and M COLUMNS
Factored Axial Compressive Resistances, C_r, in kN

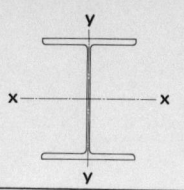

Designation	W200		W150			M100
Mass (kg/m)	31	27	37	30	22†	19
0	1 080	915	1 280	1 020	769	664
2 000	807	674	1 040	832	616	390
2 250	749	622	991	790	582	333
2 500	685	566	937	746	546	289
2 750	612	502	878	698	508	253
3 000	545	446	816	648	468	223
3 250	489	400	746	590	421	199
3 500	441	361	676	534	381	178
3 750	401	328	616	487	347	160
4 000	365	299	564	446	317	143
4 250	335	273	519	410	291	127
4 500	308	251	479	378	269	114
4 750	284	231	444	350	249	103
5 000	262	213	412	325	231	
5 250	241	195	384	303	214	
5 500	221	178	358	282	200	
6 000	187	151	314	247	174	
6 500			273	214	149	
7 000			237	186	130	
7 500			208	163		
8 000						
8 500						
9 000						
9 500						
10 000						
10 500						
11 000						
11 500						
12 000						

Effective length (KL) in millimetres with respect to least radius of gyration

PROPERTIES AND DESIGN DATA

Area (mm²)	4 000	3 390	4 730	3 790	2 850	2 460
Z_x (10³mm³)	335	279	310	244	176	99.8
S_x (10³mm³)	299	249	274	219	159	86.4
r_x (mm)	88.6	87.2	68.5	67.4	65.2	42.3
Z_y (10³mm³)	93.8	76.1	140	111	77.6	44.8
S_y (10³mm³)	61.1	49.6	91.8	72.6	50.9	28.1
r_y (mm)	32.0	31.2	38.7	38.3	36.8	23.9
r_x/r_y	2.77	2.79	1.77	1.76	1.77	1.77
M_{rx} (kN•m) (L<L_u)	90.4	75.3	83.7	65.9	42.9	26.9
M_{ry} (kN•m)	25.3	20.5	37.8	30.0	13.7	12.1
J(10³mm⁴)	119	71.3	193	101	41.8	78.5
C_w (10⁹mm⁶)	40.9	32.5	40.0	30.3	20.4	3.02
L_u (mm)	2 150	2 050	2 910	2 680	2 590	2 210
F_y (MPa)	300	300	300	300	300	300

IMPERIAL SIZE AND MASS

Mass (lb./ft.)	21	18	25	20	15	13
Nominal Depth and Width (in.)	8 x 5¼		6 x 6			M4 x 4

† Class 3 in bending.

FACTORED AXIAL COMPRESSIVE RESISTANCES
Hollow Structural Sections

Class C

For rectangular hollow sections, see page 4—48.
For square hollow sections, see page 4—56.
For round hollow sections, see page 4—64.

Class H

For rectangular hollow sections, see page 4—72.
For square hollow sections, see page 4—80.
For round hollow sections, see page 4—88.

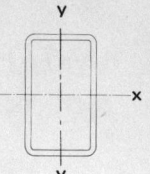

Size (mm)		304.8 x 203.2					254.0 x 152.4		
Thickness (mm)		12.7	11.13	9.53	††7.95	6.35‡	12.7	11.13	9.53
Mass (kg/m)		93.0	82.4	71.3	60.1	48.6	72.7	64.6	56.1
Effective length (KL) in millimetres with respect to least radius of gyration	0	3 720	3 310	2 860	2 410	1 830	2 920	2 590	2 250
	1 000	3 700	3 300	2 850	2 410	1 820	2 860	2 540	2 210
	1 250	3 660	3 260	2 820	2 380	1 800	2 810	2 500	2 170
	1 500	3 610	3 220	2 790	2 350	1 780	2 750	2 450	2 130
	1 750	3 560	3 170	2 750	2 320	1 760	2 690	2 400	2 090
	2 000	3 510	3 130	2 710	2 290	1 730	2 630	2 340	2 040
	2 250	3 460	3 080	2 670	2 250	1 710	2 570	2 290	1 990
	2 500	3 400	3 030	2 630	2 220	1 680	2 500	2 230	1 940
	2 750	3 340	2 980	2 580	2 180	1 650	2 420	2 160	1 880
	3 000	3 280	2 920	2 540	2 140	1 630	2 340	2 090	1 830
	3 250	3 210	2 870	2 490	2 100	1 590	2 260	2 020	1 770
	3 500	3 140	2 810	2 440	2 060	1 560	2 170	1 950	1 700
	3 750	3 070	2 740	2 380	2 010	1 530	2 080	1 870	1 640
	4 000	3 000	2 680	2 330	1 970	1 500	1 990	1 790	1 570
	4 250	2 920	2 610	2 270	1 920	1 460	1 890	1 700	1 490
	4 500	2 840	2 540	2 210	1 870	1 420	1 790	1 610	1 420
	4 750	2 760	2 470	2 150	1 820	1 380	1 670	1 510	1 330
	5 000	2 680	2 390	2 090	1 770	1 350	1 560	1 410	1 250
	5 250	2 590	2 320	2 020	1 710	1 300	1 460	1 320	1 170
	5 500	2 500	2 240	1 950	1 660	1 260	1 370	1 240	1 100
	5 750	2 410	2 160	1 880	1 600	1 220	1 290	1 170	1 030
	6 000	2 310	2 070	1 810	1 540	1 170	1 220	1 100	973
	6 500	2 090	1 880	1 650	1 410	1 080	1 090	986	871
	7 000	1 890	1 700	1 490	1 270	976	980	888	784
	7 500	1 720	1 550	1 360	1 160	889	887	803	710
	8 000	1 580	1 420	1 250	1 060	814	806	730	645
	8 500	1 450	1 310	1 150	977	749	735	666	589
	9 000	1 340	1 200	1 060	902	691	672	610	539
	9 500	1 240	1 120	979	835	640	606	552	490
	10 000	1 150	1 040	909	776	595	549	500	444
	10 500	1 070	964	846	722	554	500	456	405

PROPERTIES AND DESIGN DATA

	12.7	11.13	9.53	††7.95	6.35‡	12.7	11.13	9.53
Area (mm²)	11 800	10 500	9 090	7 660	6 190	9 260	8 230	7 150
Z_x (10³mm³)	1 190	1 060	925	787	640	746	671	589
S_x (10³mm³)	964	867	762	652	535	592	537	475
r_x (mm)	111	112	113	114	115	90.1	91.0	91.9
Z_y (10³mm³)	896	802	701	596	486	522	470	413
S_y (10³mm³)	769	693	611	524	431	441	401	357
r_y (mm)	81.2	81.9	82.7	83.4	84.1	60.2	61.0	61.7
r_x/r_y	1.37	1.37	1.37	1.37	1.36	1.50	1.49	1.49
M_{rx} (kN•m)	375	334	291	248	202	235	211	186
M_{ry} (kN•m)	282	253	221	165	123	164	148	130

IMPERIAL SIZE AND MASS

	12.7	11.13	9.53	††7.95	6.35‡	12.7	11.13	9.53
Mass (lb./ft.)	62.5	55.4	47.9	40.4	32.6	48.9	43.4	37.7
Thickness (in.)	.500	.438	.375	.313	.250	.500	.438	.375
Size (in.)	12 x 8					10 x 6		

†† Class 3 in bending about Y-Y axis.
‡ Class 4 in bending about Y-Y axis and resistance for this column calculated according to CAN3-S16.1-M78 Clause 13.3.3.

Size (mm)	254.0 x 152.4		203.2 x 152.4					
Thickness (mm)	7.95	††6.35	12.7	11.13	9.53	7.95	6.35	4.78‡
Mass (kg/m)	47.5	38.4	62.6	55.7	48.5	41.1	33.4	25.5

Effective length (KL) in millimetres with respect to least radius of gyration	0	1 910	1 540	2 510	2 240	1 950	1 650	1 340	1 020
	1 000	1 870	1 520	2 450	2 190	1 910	1 620	1 310	1 000
	1 250	1 840	1 490	2 410	2 150	1 870	1 590	1 290	988
	1 500	1 810	1 460	2 360	2 110	1 840	1 560	1 270	970
	1 750	1 770	1 440	2 310	2 060	1 800	1 530	1 240	950
	2 000	1 730	1 400	2 250	2 010	1 760	1 490	1 210	929
	2 250	1 690	1 370	2 190	1 960	1 710	1 450	1 180	907
	2 500	1 650	1 340	2 130	1 900	1 660	1 420	1 150	884
	2 750	1 600	1 300	2 060	1 850	1 610	1 370	1 120	859
	3 000	1 550	1 260	1 990	1 790	1 560	1 330	1 080	833
	3 250	1 500	1 220	1 920	1 720	1 510	1 280	1 050	806
	3 500	1 450	1 180	1 840	1 650	1 450	1 240	1 010	777
	3 750	1 390	1 140	1 760	1 580	1 390	1 190	970	747
	4 000	1 340	1 090	1 670	1 510	1 330	1 130	928	716
	4 250	1 280	1 040	1 590	1 430	1 260	1 080	885	683
	4 500	1 210	992	1 490	1 350	1 190	1 020	840	649
	4 750	1 150	942	1 380	1 260	1 110	956	789	613
	5 000	1 070	880	1 290	1 170	1 040	893	737	572
	5 250	1 000	824	1 210	1 100	971	837	691	536
	5 500	942	774	1 140	1 030	912	785	649	504
	5 750	886	729	1 070	970	858	739	610	474
	6 000	836	688	1 010	915	809	697	576	447
	6 500	748	616	900	818	724	624	515	400
	7 000	674	555	809	735	651	561	464	361
	7 500	611	503	732	665	589	508	420	326
	8 000	555	451	664	604	535	462	382	291
	8 500	507	400	605	550	488	421	348	258
	9 000	465	357	547	500	446	385	319	230
	9 500	424	320	493	451	402	348	290	206
	10 000	384	289	448	409	364	316	262	186
	10 500	350	262	408	373	332	288	239	169

PROPERTIES AND DESIGN DATA

Area (mm²)	6 050	4 900	7 970	7 100	6 180	5 240	4 250	3 250
Z_x (10^3 mm³)	503	411	528	476	419	360	295	228
S_x (10^3 mm³)	409	338	423	385	343	297	246	192
r_x (mm)	92.7	93.6	73.4	74.2	75.1	75.9	76.7	77.5
Z_y (10^3 mm³)	353	290	432	390	344	295	243	188
S_y (10^3 mm³)	309	256	358	327	292	254	211	165
r_y (mm)	62.4	63.1	58.5	59.3	60.0	60.7	61.5	62.2
r_x/r_y	1.49	1.48	1.25	1.25	1.25	1.25	1.25	1.25
M_{rx} (kN•m)	158	129	166	150	132	113	92.9	71.8
M_{ry} (kN•m)	111	80.6	136	123	108	92.9	76.5	50.8

IMPERIAL SIZE AND MASS

Mass (lb./ft.)	31.9	25.8	42.1	37.5	32.6	27.6	22.4	17.1
Thickness (in.)	.313	.250	.500	.438	.375	.313	.250	.188
Size (in.)	10 x 6		8 x 6					

†† Class 3 in bending about Y-Y axis.
‡ Class 4 in bending about Y-Y axis and resistance for this column calculated according to CAN3-S16.1-M78 Clause 13.3.3.

RECTANGULAR HOLLOW SECTIONS
Factored Axial Compressive
Resistances, C$_r$, in kN

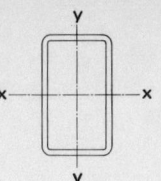

G40.21-M 350W

ϕ = 0.90

Size (mm)	203.2 x 101.6						177.8 x 127.0#		
Thickness (mm)	12.7	11.13	9.53	7.95	6.35	4.78 ‡	12.7	11.13	9.53
Mass (kg/m)	52.4	46.9	40.9	34.8	28.3	21.7	52.4	46.9	40.9

Effective length (KL) in millimetres with respect to least radius of gyration

	12.7	11.13	9.53	7.95	6.35	4.78	12.7	11.13	9.53
0	2 100	1 880	1 640	1 400	1 140	869	2 100	1 880	1 640
1 000	1 980	1 770	1 550	1 320	1 080	826	2 020	1 810	1 580
1 250	1 910	1 710	1 500	1 280	1 050	802	1 970	1 770	1 550
1 500	1 840	1 650	1 450	1 230	1 010	775	1 920	1 720	1 510
1 750	1 760	1 580	1 390	1 190	972	747	1 860	1 670	1 460
2 000	1 670	1 510	1 320	1 130	930	715	1 800	1 610	1 420
2 250	1 580	1 420	1 250	1 080	885	682	1 730	1 560	1 370
2 500	1 480	1 340	1 180	1 010	836	646	1 660	1 490	1 310
2 750	1 370	1 240	1 100	949	785	607	1 580	1 430	1 260
3 000	1 250	1 150	1 020	880	730	567	1 500	1 360	1 200
3 250	1 120	1 030	920	800	669	523	1 420	1 280	1 130
3 500	1 020	932	833	725	606	474	1 330	1 200	1 070
3 750	927	848	758	660	552	432	1 230	1 120	995
4 000	847	776	694	604	506	395	1 120	1 020	914
4 250	778	713	638	556	465	364	1 040	944	842
4 500	718	658	589	513	429	336	959	874	780
4 750	664	609	545	475	398	311	890	811	724
5 000	615	565	506	441	369	289	829	756	675
5 250	572	525	470	410	344	269	774	706	630
5 500	533	490	439	383	321	246	724	661	590
5 750	498	457	410	358	300	225	679	620	554
6 000	461	426	384	335	281	207	638	583	521
6 500	396	366	330	290	245	176	567	518	463
7 000	344	318	286	252	213	152	506	462	414
7 500	302	279	251	221	187	132	447	411	370
8 000			223	196	165	116	395	363	327
8 500						103	352	324	291
9 000							316	290	261
9 500							286	262	236
10 000									
10 500									

PROPERTIES AND DESIGN DATA

	12.7	11.13	9.53	7.95	6.35	4.78	12.7	11.13	9.53
Area (mm^2)	6 680	5 970	5 210	4 430	3 610	2 760	6 680	5 970	5 210
Z$_x$ (10^{3}mm^3)	405	367	325	281	232	180	377	342	303
S$_x$ (10^{3}mm^3)	307	282	253	221	185	145	297	272	244
r$_x$ (mm)	68.4	69.3	70.3	71.2	72.2	73.1	62.8	63.7	64.6
Z$_y$ (10^{3}mm^3)	246	224	199	172	143	111	298	270	240
S$_y$ (10^{3}mm^3)	201	186	168	148	125	99.0	243	224	202
r$_y$ (mm)	39.1	39.8	40.5	41.2	42.0	42.7	48.1	48.8	49.6
r$_x$/r$_y$	1.75	1.74	1.73	1.73	1.72	1.71	1.31	1.30	1.30
M$_{rx}$ (kN•m)	128	116	102	88.5	73.1	56.7	119	108	95.4
M$_{ry}$ (kN•m)	77.5	70.6	62.7	54.2	45.0	30.5	93.9	85.0	75.6

IMPERIAL SIZE AND MASS

	12.7	11.13	9.53	7.95	6.35	4.78	12.7	11.13	9.53
Mass (lb./ft.)	35.2	31.5	27.5	23.4	19.0	14.6	35.2	31.5	27.5
Thickness (in.)	.500	.438	.375	.313	.250	.188	.500	.438	.375
Size (in.)	8 x 4						7 x 5		

‡ Class 4 in bending about Y-Y axis and resistance for this column calculated according to CAN3-S16.1-M78 Clause 13.3.3.
# Check manufacturer for current availability.

RECTANGULAR HOLLOW SECTIONS
Factored Axial Compressive Resistances, C_r, in kN

Size (mm)	177.8 x 127.0 #			152.4 x 101.6				
Thickness (mm)	7.95	6.35	††4.78	11.13	9.53	7.95	6.35	4.78
Mass (kg/m)	34.8	28.3	21.7	38.0	33.3	28.4	23.2	17.9

Effective length (KL) in millimetres with respect to least radius of gyration

KL								
0	1 400	1 140	869	1 520	1 340	1 140	932	718
1 000	1 350	1 100	842	1 430	1 260	1 080	881	680
1 250	1 320	1 080	823	1 380	1 210	1 040	853	659
1 500	1 280	1 050	803	1 330	1 170	1 000	822	636
1 750	1 250	1 020	782	1 270	1 120	959	789	611
2 000	1 210	989	759	1 200	1 060	914	752	583
2 250	1 170	955	734	1 130	1 000	865	713	554
2 500	1 120	920	707	1 060	938	812	671	523
2 750	1 070	883	679	976	870	756	627	489
3 000	1 030	843	650	885	794	697	579	454
3 250	972	801	618	796	714	626	524	413
3 500	917	757	586	720	646	567	475	374
3 750	859	711	551	655	588	516	432	341
4 000	792	659	513	599	538	472	396	312
4 250	730	607	473	550	494	434	364	287
4 500	676	562	438	507	456	400	336	265
4 750	628	523	407	468	421	370	311	245
5 000	585	487	379	434	391	344	288	228
5 250	547	455	355	403	363	320	268	212
5 500	512	427	332	376	338	298	250	198
5 750	481	401	312	350	316	278	234	185
6 000	452	377	294	323	293	260	219	173
6 500	402	335	262	277	251	223	188	150
7 000	359	300	234	241	218	194	164	130
7 500	323	270	211	211	192	170	144	114
8 000	285	240	188				127	101
8 500	254	214	168					
9 000	228	192	150					
9 500	206	173	136					
10 000	187	157	123					
10 500								

PROPERTIES AND DESIGN DATA

Area (mm²)	4 430	3 610	2 760	4 840	4 240	3 620	2 960	2 280
Z_x (10^3 mm³)	261	216	167	230	205	178	148	116
S_x (10^3 mm³)	213	178	140	179	162	143	121	95.6
r_x (mm)	65.4	66.2	67.1	53.1	54.0	54.8	55.7	56.5
Z_y (10^3 mm³)	207	171	133	172	154	134	112	87.8
S_y (10^3 mm³)	177	148	117	140	128	113	96.1	76.6
r_y (mm)	50.3	51.1	51.8	38.4	39.1	39.9	40.6	41.3
r_x/r_y	1.30	1.30	1.29	1.38	1.38	1.38	1.37	1.37
M_{rx} (kN•m)	82.2	68.0	52.6	72.4	64.6	56.1	46.6	36.5
M_{ry} (kN•m)	65.2	53.9	36.9	54.2	48.5	42.2	35.3	27.7

IMPERIAL SIZE AND MASS

Mass (lb./ft.)	23.4	19.0	14.6	25.5	22.4	19.1	15.6	12.0
Thickness (in.)	.313	.250	.188	.438	.375	.313	.250	.188
Size (in.)	7 x 5			6 x 4				

†† Class 3 in bending about Y-Y axis.
# Check manufacturer for current availability.

RECTANGULAR HOLLOW SECTIONS
Factored Axial Compressive Resistances, C_r, in kN

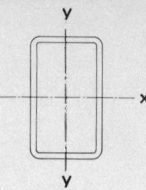

G40.21-M 350W

$\phi = 0.90$

Size (mm)		127.0 x 76.2				127.0 x 63.5			
Thickness (mm)		9.53	7.95	6.35	4.78	9.53	7.95	6.35	4.78
Mass (kg/m)		25.7	22.1	18.2	14.1	23.8	20.5	16.9	13.1
	0	1 030	888	731	564	954	822	677	526
	1 000	922	798	659	511	813	706	586	459
	1 250	870	755	625	485	748	653	544	428
	1 500	812	706	587	457	675	593	497	393
	1 750	747	653	545	426	593	526	444	354
	2 000	676	595	499	392	500	448	383	310
	2 250	594	530	449	354	426	382	327	265
	2 500	516	461	391	311	368	330	283	230
	2 750	453	405	344	274	322	289	248	201
	3 000	402	359	305	243	283	255	219	178
	3 250	359	321	273	217	251	226	194	158
	3 500	322	289	246	196	224	202	174	142
	3 750	291	261	222	177	197	180	156	127
	4 000	264	237	202	161	174	159	138	114
	4 250	240	216	184	147	155	141	123	101
	4 500	216	196	168	135	140	127	110	91
	4 750	195	176	152	122		115	100	82
	5 000	176	160	138	111			91	75
	5 250	161	146	125	101				
	5 500	147	134	115	93				
	5 750		123	106	85				
	6 000			98	79				
	6 500								
	7 000								
	7 500								
	8 000								
	8 500								
	9 000								
	9 500								
	10 000								
	10 500								

Effective length (KL) in millimetres with respect to least radius of gyration

PROPERTIES AND DESIGN DATA

	127.0 x 76.2				127.0 x 63.5			
Area (mm²)	3 280	2 820	2 320	1 790	3 030	2 610	2 150	1 670
Z_x (10^3 mm³)	126	111	93.3	73.8	112	98.9	83.6	66.3
S_x (10^3 mm³)	96.4	86.4	74.0	59.5	83.2	75.1	64.8	52.4
r_x (mm)	43.2	44.1	45.1	45.9	41.7	42.7	43.7	44.6
Z_y (10^3 mm³)	87.5	77.2	65.2	51.7	67.4	60.0	51.0	40.7
S_y (10^3 mm³)	70.5	63.8	55.1	44.7	53.6	49.1	42.9	35.2
r_y (mm)	28.6	29.4	30.1	30.8	23.7	24.4	25.1	25.9
r_x/r_y	1.51	1.50	1.50	1.49	1.76	1.75	1.74	1.73
M_{rx} (kN•m)	39.7	35.0	29.4	23.2	35.3	31.2	26.3	20.9
M_{ry} (kN•m)	27.6	24.3	20.5	16.3	21.2	18.9	16.1	12.8

IMPERIAL SIZE AND MASS

Mass (lb./ft.)	17.3	14.9	12.2	9.45	16.0	13.8	11.4	8.81
Thickness (in.)	.375	.313	.250	.188	.375	.313	.250	.188
Size (in.)		5 x 3				5 x 2½		

Size (mm)		127.0 x 50.8				101.6 x 76.2			
Thickness (mm)		9.53	7.95	6.35	4.78	9.53	7.95	6.35	4.78
Mass (kg/m)		21.9	18.9	15.6	12.2	21.9	18.9	15.6	12.2
	0	879	759	627	488	879	759	627	488
	1 000	683	600	503	397	779	677	563	440
	1 250	594	528	447	356	732	639	532	417
	1 500	489	444	384	309	680	595	498	392
	1 750	397	361	313	255	622	548	460	363
	2 000	330	300	261	213	559	495	419	332
	2 250	279	254	221	181	485	435	372	299
	2 500	239	218	190	155	420	377	324	260
	2 750	206	189	164	135	369	332	284	229
	3 000	175	162	144	118	327	294	252	203
	3 250	150	139	123	102	292	262	225	181
	3 500	131	121	107	89	262	236	203	163
	3 750		106	94	78	236	213	183	148
	4 000				69	214	193	166	134
	4 250					193	176	151	122
	4 500					173	157	137	112
	4 750					156	142	124	101
	5 000					141	129	112	91
	5 250					129	117	102	83
	5 500					118	108	94	76
	5 750							86	70
	6 000								
	6 500								
	7 000								
	7 500								
	8 000								
	8 500								
	9 000								
	9 500								
	10 000								
	10 500								

Effective length (KL) in millimetres with respect to least radius of gyration

PROPERTIES AND DESIGN DATA

	127.0 x 50.8				101.6 x 76.2			
Area (mm^2)	2 790	2 410	1 990	1 550	2 790	2 410	1 990	1 550
Z_x (10^3mm^3)	97.7	86.9	73.8	58.9	87.6	77.7	65.9	52.5
S_x (10^3mm^3)	70.0	63.8	55.5	45.3	67.2	61.0	52.8	43.0
r_x (mm)	39.9	41.0	42.1	43.1	35.0	35.8	36.7	37.5
Z_y (10^3mm^3)	48.9	44.0	37.9	30.5	71.3	63.5	54.0	43.1
S_y (10^3mm^3)	37.8	35.3	31.4	26.2	56.3	51.4	44.8	36.6
r_y (mm)	18.6	19.3	20.0	20.7	27.7	28.5	29.3	30.0
r_x/r_y	2.15	2.13	2.10	2.08	1.26	1.26	1.25	1.25
M_{rx} (kN•m)	30.8	27.4	23.2	18.6	27.6	24.5	20.8	16.5
M_{ry} (kN•m)	15.4	13.9	11.9	9.61	22.5	20.0	17.0	13.6

IMPERIAL SIZE AND MASS

	127.0 x 50.8				101.6 x 76.2			
Mass (lb./ft.)	14.7	12.7	10.5	8.17	14.7	12.7	10.5	8.17
Thickness (in.)	.375	.313	.250	.188	.375	.313	.250	.188
Size (in.)		5 x 2				4 x 3		

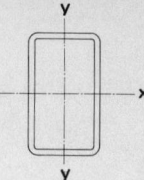

RECTANGULAR HOLLOW SECTIONS
Factored Axial Compressive
Resistances, C_r, in kN

G40.21-M 350W

$\phi = 0.90$

Size (mm)	101.6 x 50.8					88.9 x 63.5		
Thickness (mm)	7.95	6.35	4.78	3.81	3.18	7.95	6.35	4.78
Mass (kg/m)	15.8	13.1	10.3	8.37	7.09	15.8	13.1	10.3
0	633	526	413	337	284	633	526	413
1 000	494	417	333	274	233	536	450	356
1 250	432	369	297	246	209	492	415	330
1 500	358	312	256	213	183	442	375	301
1 750	290	254	210	176	152	387	331	268
2 000	241	211	175	147	126	324	280	230
2 250	204	179	148	125	107	276	239	196
2 500	175	153	128	107	92	239	207	170
2 750	151	133	111	93	80	208	181	148
3 000	129	115	97	82	70	183	159	131
3 250	110	98	83	71	61	162	141	116
3 500	96	85	72	61	53	144	126	104
3 750	84	75	64	54	47	127	111	93
4 000			56	48	41	112	98	82
4 250						100	88	73
4 500						90	79	66
4 750							71	59
5 000								
5 250								
5 500								
5 750								
6 000								
6 500								
7 000								
7 500								
8 000								
8 500								
9 000								
9 500								
10 000								
10 500								

Effective length (KL) in millimetres with respect to least radius of gyration

PROPERTIES AND DESIGN DATA

Area (mm²)	2 010	1 670	1 310	1 070	903	2 010	1 670	1 310
Z_x (10^3 mm³)	58.8	50.6	40.8	33.9	29.0	54.9	47.1	38.0
S_x (10^3 mm³)	43.5	38.4	31.8	26.8	23.1	42.1	37.1	30.6
r_x (mm)	33.2	34.2	35.1	35.7	36.1	30.5	31.4	32.3
Z_y (10^3 mm³)	35.4	30.7	24.9	20.8	17.9	43.2	37.2	30.1
S_y (10^3 mm³)	27.9	25.1	21.1	18.0	15.6	34.3	30.4	25.3
r_y (mm)	18.8	19.5	20.3	20.7	21.0	23.3	24.0	24.8
r_x/r_y	1.77	1.75	1.73	1.73	1.72	1.31	1.31	1.30
M_{rx} (kN•m)	18.5	15.9	12.9	10.7	9.13	17.3	14.8	12.0
M_{ry} (kN•m)	11.2	9.67	7.84	6.55	5.64	13.6	11.7	9.48

IMPERIAL SIZE AND MASS

Mass (lb./ft.)	10.6	8.81	6.89	5.62	4.76	10.6	8.81	6.89
Thickness (in.)	.313	.250	.188	.150	.125	.313	.250	.188
Size (in.)	4 x 2					3½ x 2½		

RECTANGULAR HOLLOW SECTIONS
Factored Axial Compressive
Resistances, C_r, in kN

Size (mm)	88.9 x 63.5		76.2 x 50.8				50.8 x 25.4	
Thickness (mm)	3.81	3.18	7.95	6.35	4.78	3.81	3.18	2.54
Mass (kg/m)	8.37	7.09	12.6	10.6	8.35	6.85	3.28	2.71
0	337	284	504	425	334	275	132	109
1 000	292	247	385	332	266	220	53	46
1 250	271	230	332	290	235	196	38	33
1 500	248	211	269	240	199	168	29	25
1 750	222	189	218	195	162	137	21	19
2 000	192	164	181	162	135	114		15
2 250	164	140	152	137	114	97		
2 500	142	122	130	117	98	83		
2 750	124	106	111	101	85	72		
3 000	109	94	94	86	73	63		
3 250	97	84	81	74	63	54		
3 500	87	75	70	65	55	47		
3 750	78	67		57	48	41		
4 000	69	60						
4 250	62	53						
4 500	55	48						
4 750	50	43						
5 000	45	39						
5 250								
5 500								
5 750								
6 000								
6 500								
7 000								
7 500								
8 000								
8 500								
9 000								
9 500								
10 000								
10 500								

Effective length (KL) in millimetres with respect to least radius of gyration

PROPERTIES AND DESIGN DATA

Area (mm²)	1 070	903	1 600	1 350	1 060	872	418	345
Z_x (10^3 mm³)	31.5	27.0	35.9	31.4	25.7	21.6	6.33	5.35
S_x (10^3 mm³)	25.8	22.3	26.6	24.1	20.3	17.3	4.81	4.15
r_x (mm)	32.8	33.1	25.1	26.1	27.0	27.5	17.1	17.5
Z_y (10^3 mm³)	25.0	21.4	26.7	23.5	19.3	16.3	3.84	3.27
S_y (10^3 mm³)	21.4	18.5	20.5	18.8	16.0	13.8	3.14	2.75
r_y (mm)	25.2	25.5	18.0	18.8	19.6	20.0	9.77	10.1
r_x/r_y	1.30	1.30	1.39	1.39	1.38	1.37	1.75	1.74
M_{rx} (kN•m)	9.92	8.50	11.3	9.89	8.10	6.80	1.99	1.69
M_{ry} (kN•m)	7.87	6.74	8.41	7.40	6.08	5.13	1.21	1.03

IMPERIAL SIZE AND MASS

Mass (lb./ft.)	5.62	4.76	8.46	7.11	5.61	4.60	2.21	1.82
Thickness (in.)	.150	.125	.313	.250	.188	.150	.125	.100
Size (in.)	3½ x 2½		3 x 2				2 x 1	

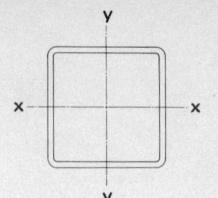
Size (mm)		304.8 x 304.8					254.0 x 254.0		
Thickness (mm)		12.70	11.13	9.53	††7.95	‡6.35	12.70	11.13	9.53
Mass (kg/m)		113	100	86.5	72.8	58.7	93.0	82.4	71.3
	0	4 540	4 030	3 460	2 920	2 110	3 720	3 310	2 860
	1 000	4 540	4 030	3 460	2 920	2 110	3 720	3 310	2 860
	1 250	4 540	4 030	3 460	2 920	2 100	3 700	3 290	2 850
	1 500	4 510	4 010	3 450	2 910	2 100	3 660	3 260	2 820
	1 750	4 470	3 980	3 420	2 890	2 090	3 620	3 220	2 790
	2 000	4 440	3 950	3 390	2 860	2 070	3 580	3 190	2 760
	2 250	4 400	3 910	3 360	2 840	2 050	3 540	3 150	2 730
	2 500	4 360	3 880	3 330	2 810	2 030	3 490	3 110	2 700
	2 750	4 310	3 840	3 300	2 790	2 010	3 450	3 070	2 660
	3 000	4 270	3 800	3 270	2 760	1 990	3 400	3 030	2 630
	3 250	4 220	3 760	3 230	2 730	1 970	3 350	2 990	2 590
	3 500	4 180	3 720	3 200	2 700	1 950	3 300	2 940	2 550
	3 750	4 130	3 670	3 160	2 670	1 930	3 250	2 900	2 510
	4 000	4 080	3 630	3 120	2 640	1 910	3 190	2 850	2 470
	4 250	4 020	3 580	3 090	2 610	1 880	3 130	2 800	2 430
	4 500	3 970	3 540	3 040	2 570	1 860	3 080	2 740	2 380
	4 750	3 910	3 490	3 000	2 540	1 840	3 010	2 690	2 340
	5 000	3 860	3 440	2 960	2 500	1 810	2 950	2 640	2 290
	5 250	3 800	3 390	2 920	2 470	1 780	2 890	2 580	2 240
	5 500	3 740	3 330	2 870	2 430	1 760	2 820	2 520	2 190
	5 750	3 680	3 280	2 830	2 390	1 730	2 750	2 460	2 140
	6 000	3 610	3 220	2 780	2 350	1 700	2 680	2 400	2 080
	6 500	3 480	3 110	2 680	2 270	1 640	2 530	2 270	1 970
	7 000	3 340	2 990	2 580	2 190	1 580	2 380	2 130	1 860
	7 500	3 200	2 860	2 470	2 100	1 510	2 210	1 980	1 730
	8 000	3 050	2 730	2 360	2 000	1 450	2 020	1 820	1 590
	8 500	2 890	2 590	2 240	1 910	1 380	1 870	1 680	1 470
	9 000	2 720	2 440	2 120	1 800	1 300	1 730	1 550	1 360
	9 500	2 530	2 280	1 980	1 690	1 220	1 600	1 440	1 260
	10 000	2 360	2 120	1 850	1 570	1 140	1 490	1 340	1 180
	10 500	2 210	1 990	1 730	1 470	1 070	1 400	1 260	1 100

Left axis label: Effective length (KL) in millimetres with respect to least radius of gyration

PROPERTIES AND DESIGN DATA

Area (mm²)		14 400	12 800	11 000	9 280	7 480	11 800	10 500	9 090
Z (10³mm³)		1 560	1 390	1 210	1 030	833	1 060	945	825
S (10³mm³)		1 330	1 190	1 040	886	723	888	799	703
r (mm)		118	119	120	121	121	97.6	98.4	99.1
M_r (kN•m)		491	438	381	279	207	334	298	260

IMPERIAL SIZE AND MASS

Mass (lb./ft.)		76.1	67.3	58.1	48.9	39.4	62.5	55.4	47.9
Thickness (in.)		.500	.438	.375	.313	.250	.500	.438	.375
Size (in.)		12 x 12					10 x 10		

†† Class 3 in bending.
‡ Class 4 in bending and resistance for this column calculated according to CAN3-S16.1-M78 Clause 13.3.3.

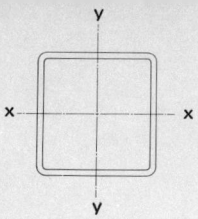

SQUARE HOLLOW SECTIONS
Factored Axial Compressive
Resistances, C_r, in kN

Size (mm)	254.0 x 254.0		203.2 x 203.2				
Thickness (mm)	7.95	‡6.35	12.70	11.13	9.53	7.95	6.35
Mass (kg/m)	60.1	48.6	72.7	64.6	56.1	47.5	38.4
0	2 410	1 950	2 920	2 590	2 250	1 910	1 540
1 000	2 410	1 940	2 900	2 580	2 240	1 900	1 540
1 250	2 400	1 930	2 860	2 540	2 210	1 870	1 520
1 500	2 380	1 920	2 820	2 510	2 180	1 850	1 500
1 750	2 350	1 900	2 780	2 470	2 150	1 820	1 480
2 000	2 330	1 880	2 740	2 440	2 120	1 800	1 460
2 250	2 300	1 860	2 690	2 400	2 080	1 770	1 430
2 500	2 280	1 840	2 640	2 350	2 050	1 740	1 410
2 750	2 250	1 820	2 590	2 310	2 010	1 700	1 380
3 000	2 220	1 790	2 540	2 260	1 970	1 670	1 360
3 250	2 190	1 770	2 480	2 210	1 930	1 640	1 330
3 500	2 150	1 740	2 420	2 160	1 880	1 600	1 300
3 750	2 120	1 720	2 360	2 110	1 840	1 560	1 270
4 000	2 090	1 690	2 300	2 050	1 790	1 520	1 240
4 250	2 050	1 660	2 230	2 000	1 740	1 480	1 200
4 500	2 010	1 630	2 170	1 940	1 690	1 440	1 170
4 750	1 970	1 600	2 090	1 870	1 640	1 400	1 140
5 000	1 930	1 570	2 020	1 810	1 580	1 350	1 100
5 250	1 890	1 540	1 950	1 740	1 530	1 300	1 060
5 500	1 850	1 500	1 870	1 680	1 470	1 250	1 020
5 750	1 810	1 470	1 790	1 610	1 410	1 200	984
6 000	1 760	1 440	1 690	1 530	1 340	1 150	943
6 500	1 670	1 360	1 520	1 370	1 210	1 040	849
7 000	1 580	1 290	1 380	1 240	1 090	938	769
7 500	1 470	1 210	1 250	1 130	995	854	700
8 000	1 360	1 110	1 150	1 030	910	781	641
8 500	1 250	1 030	1 050	949	836	718	589
9 000	1 160	949	969	874	771	662	543
9 500	1 070	882	896	809	713	612	502
10 000	1 000	822	831	750	661	568	466
10 500	936	768	772	697	615	528	434

Effective length (KL) in millimetres with respect to least radius of gyration

PROPERTIES AND DESIGN DATA

Area (mm²)	7 660	6 190	9 260	8 230	7 150	6 050	4 900
Z (10³mm³)	702	571	650	584	513	438	359
S (10³mm³)	602	494	538	488	432	373	308
r (mm)	99.9	101	76.8	77.6	78.4	79.2	79.9
M_r (kN•m)	221	156	205	184	162	138	113

IMPERIAL SIZE AND MASS

Mass (lb./ft.)	40.4	32.6	48.9	43.4	37.7	31.9	25.8
Thickness (in.)	.313	.250	.500	.438	.375	.313	.250
Size (in.)	10 x 10		8 x 8				

‡ Class 4 in bending and resistance for this column calculated according to CAN3-S16.1-M78 Clause 13.3.3.

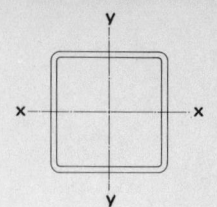

Size (mm)		177.8 x 177.8						152.4 x 152.4		
Thickness (mm)		12.70	11.13	9.53	7.95	6.35	††4.78	12.70	11.13	9.53
Mass (kg/m)		62.6	55.7	48.5	41.1	33.4	25.5	52.4	46.9	40.9
	0	2 510	2 240	1 950	1 650	1 340	1 020	2 100	1 880	1 640
	1 000	2 470	2 210	1 920	1 630	1 320	1 010	2 050	1 830	1 600
	1 250	2 440	2 170	1 890	1 610	1 300	998	2 010	1 800	1 570
	1 500	2 400	2 140	1 860	1 580	1 280	982	1 970	1 760	1 540
	1 750	2 350	2 100	1 830	1 550	1 260	966	1 920	1 720	1 500
	2 000	2 310	2 060	1 790	1 520	1 240	949	1 870	1 680	1 470
	2 250	2 260	2 010	1 760	1 490	1 210	930	1 820	1 630	1 430
	2 500	2 200	1 970	1 720	1 460	1 190	911	1 760	1 580	1 390
	2 750	2 150	1 920	1 680	1 430	1 160	890	1 700	1 530	1 340
	3 000	2 090	1 870	1 630	1 390	1 130	869	1 640	1 470	1 290
	3 250	2 030	1 820	1 590	1 350	1 100	846	1 570	1 410	1 240
	3 500	1 970	1 760	1 540	1 310	1 070	823	1 500	1 350	1 190
	3 750	1 900	1 700	1 490	1 270	1 040	798	1 430	1 290	1 140
	4 000	1 830	1 640	1 440	1 230	1 000	772	1 350	1 220	1 080
	4 250	1 760	1 580	1 390	1 190	969	746	1 270	1 150	1 020
	4 500	1 690	1 520	1 330	1 140	932	718	1 180	1 070	953
	4 750	1 610	1 450	1 280	1 090	894	690	1 090	997	887
	5 000	1 530	1 380	1 220	1 040	855	660	1 020	931	828
	5 250	1 430	1 300	1 150	989	815	629	956	871	775
	5 500	1 350	1 220	1 080	930	766	593	897	817	727
	5 750	1 270	1 150	1 020	876	722	559	843	769	684
	6 000	1 200	1 090	960	827	682	528	794	724	645
	6 500	1 070	973	861	742	611	474	709	647	576
	7 000	970	878	777	670	552	428	637	581	517
	7 500	879	797	705	608	501	389	574	524	467
	8 000	801	726	643	555	457	355	521	475	424
	8 500	733	665	589	508	419	325	471	433	386
	9 000	673	611	541	467	385	299	422	387	347
	9 500	620	562	498	430	355	276	381	349	313
	10 000	570	519	460	398	328	255	345	317	284
	10 500	519	473	421	365	303	236	315	289	259

Effective length (KL) in millimetres with respect to least radius of gyration

PROPERTIES AND DESIGN DATA										
Area (mm²)		7 970	7 100	6 180	5 240	4 250	3 250	6 680	5 970	5 210
Z (10³mm³)		484	436	385	330	271	209	341	310	275
S (10³mm³)		396	361	322	279	231	181	275	253	227
r (mm)		66.4	67.2	68.0	68.8	69.6	70.3	56.0	56.8	57.6
M_r (kN•m)		152	137	121	104	85.4	††57.0	107	97.6	86.6

IMPERIAL SIZE AND MASS										
Mass (lb./ft.)		42.1	37.5	32.6	27.6	22.4	17.1	35.2	31.5	27.5
Thickness (in.)		.500	.438	.375	.313	.250	.188	.500	.438	.375
Size (in.)		7 x 7						6 x 6		

†† Class 3 in bending.

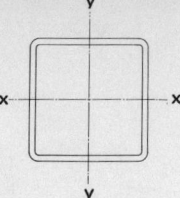

SQUARE HOLLOW SECTIONS
Factored Axial Compressive
Resistances, C_r, in kN

Size (mm)		152.4 x 152.4			127.0 x 127.0				
Thickness (mm)		7.95	6.35	4.78	11.13	9.53	7.95	6.35	4.78
Mass (kg/m)		34.8	28.3	21.7	38.0	33.3	28.4	23.2	17.9
	0	1 400	1 140	869	1 520	1 340	1 140	932	718
	1 000	1 360	1 110	851	1 460	1 280	1 100	898	693
	1 250	1 340	1 090	836	1 420	1 250	1 070	877	677
	1 500	1 310	1 070	820	1 380	1 220	1 040	853	659
	1 750	1 280	1 050	802	1 340	1 180	1 010	828	640
	2 000	1 250	1 020	784	1 290	1 140	974	801	619
	2 250	1 220	996	764	1 240	1 090	938	771	598
	2 500	1 180	968	743	1 180	1 040	899	740	574
	2 750	1 150	938	720	1 120	995	857	707	549
	3 000	1 110	907	697	1 060	942	813	672	523
	3 250	1 070	874	672	996	886	767	635	495
	3 500	1 020	840	646	928	827	718	596	466
	3 750	977	804	619	846	758	662	554	436
	4 000	930	766	591	776	696	608	508	400
	4 250	880	727	562	715	641	560	468	369
	4 500	825	685	532	661	593	518	433	341
	4 750	768	637	495	613	550	481	402	317
	5 000	717	595	462	571	512	448	375	295
	5 250	671	557	433	533	478	418	350	276
	5 500	630	523	406	498	447	391	328	258
	5 750	593	492	382	467	420	367	307	242
	6 000	559	464	361	439	394	345	289	228
	6 500	499	415	322	389	350	306	257	203
	7 000	449	373	290	345	312	273	229	181
	7 500	406	337	262	302	274	241	204	162
	8 000	368	306	238	267	242	213	180	143
	8 500	335	279	217	238	216	190	160	127
	9 000	303	254	198	214	194	171	144	114
	9 500	273	229	179			154	130	103
	10 000	248	207	162					
	10 500	226	189	148					

Effective length (KL) in millimetres with respect to least radius of gyration

PROPERTIES AND DESIGN DATA

Area (mm^2)		4 430	3 610	2 760	4 840	4 240	3 620	2 960	2 280
Z (10^3mm^3)		237	195	152	205	183	159	132	103
S (10^3mm^3)		198	166	130	164	149	132	111	88.1
r (mm)		58.4	59.2	59.9	46.4	47.2	48.0	48.8	49.6
M_r (kN•m)		74.7	61.4	47.9	64.6	57.6	50.1	41.6	32.4

IMPERIAL SIZE AND MASS

Mass (lb./ft.)		23.4	19.0	14.6	25.5	22.4	19.1	15.6	12.0
Thickness (in.)		.313	.250	.188	.438	.375	.313	.250	.188
Size (in.)		6 x 6			5 x 5				

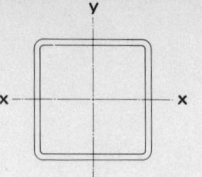
Size (mm)	101.6 x 101.6				88.9 x 88.9			
Thickness (mm)	9.53	7.95	6.35	4.78	9.53	7.95	6.35	4.78
Mass (kg/m)	25.7	22.1	18.2	14.1	21.9	18.9	15.6	12.2
0	1 030	888	731	564	879	759	627	488
1 000	964	831	686	530	800	694	576	450
1 250	928	801	662	513	762	662	550	431
1 500	889	768	636	493	719	627	522	410
1 750	845	732	607	472	673	588	491	387
2 000	798	693	576	448	621	546	458	362
2 250	747	651	542	423	566	500	421	334
2 500	693	606	506	397	502	448	382	305
2 750	635	558	468	368	442	395	337	271
3 000	567	502	424	337	392	351	299	241
3 250	509	451	381	302	351	314	268	216
3 500	460	407	345	274	317	283	242	195
3 750	418	371	314	249	287	257	220	177
4 000	382	339	287	228	261	234	200	161
4 250	351	311	264	209	238	214	183	148
4 500	323	286	243	193	218	196	168	136
4 750	298	265	224	179	200	180	155	125
5 000	276	245	208	166	182	164	142	115
5 250	256	228	193	154	165	150	130	106
5 500	238	212	180	143	151	137	119	97
5 750	219	196	168	134	139	126	109	89
6 000	202	181	155	124	128	116	101	82
6 500	173	155	133	107			87	70
7 000	151	135	115	93				
7 500		118	101	81				
8 000								
8 500								
9 000								
9 500								
10 000								
10 500								

Effective length (KL) in millimetres with respect to least radius of gyration

PROPERTIES AND DESIGN DATA

Area (mm^2)	3 280	2 820	2 320	1 790	2 790	2 410	1 990	1 550
Z (10^3mm^3)	110	96.6	81.3	64.3	80.2	71.2	60.5	48.2
S (10^3mm^3)	87.4	78.4	67.3	54.2	62.7	57.0	49.5	40.3
r (mm)	36.8	37.6	38.4	39.2	31.6	32.4	33.2	34.0
M_r (kN•m)	34.6	30.4	25.6	20.3	25.3	22.4	19.1	15.2

IMPERIAL SIZE AND MASS

Mass (lb./ft.)	17.3	14.9	12.2	9.45	14.7	12.7	10.5	8.17
Thickness (in.)	.375	.313	.250	.188	.375	.313	.250	.188
Size (in.)	4 x 4				3½ x 3½			

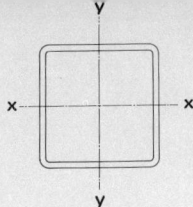

SQUARE HOLLOW SECTIONS
Factored Axial Compressive Resistances, C_r, in kN

Size (mm)		76.2 x 76.2			63.5 x 63.5			
Thickness (mm)		7.95	6.35	4.78	6.35	4.78	3.81	3.18
Mass (kg/m)		15.8	13.1	10.3	10.6	8.35	6.85	5.82
Effective length (KL) in millimetres with respect to least radius of gyration	0	633	526	413	425	334	275	233
	1 000	559	468	369	358	284	235	200
	1 250	524	440	348	327	261	217	185
	1 500	486	409	325	292	235	196	168
	1 750	443	375	300	253	207	174	149
	2 000	395	338	272	211	174	147	127
	2 250	341	294	240	180	148	125	108
	2 500	296	255	208	155	128	109	94
	2 750	259	224	183	136	112	95	82
	3 000	229	199	162	119	99	84	72
	3 250	205	177	145	106	87	74	64
	3 500	183	159	130	93	78	66	57
	3 750	165	144	118	82	68	59	51
	4 000	150	130	107	72	60	52	45
	4 250	134	118	97	64	54	46	40
	4 500	120	105	87	58	48	41	36
	4 750	108	95	79			37	33
	5 000	98	86	71				
	5 250	90	79	65				
	5 500		72	60				
	5 750			55				
	6 000							
	6 500							
	7 000							
	7 500							
	8 000							
	8 500							
	9 000							
	9 500							
	10 000							
	10 500							

PROPERTIES AND DESIGN DATA

	76.2 x 76.2			63.5 x 63.5			
Area (mm²)	2 010	1 670	1 310	1 350	1 060	872	741
Z (10^3mm³)	49.7	42.7	34.4	28.0	22.9	19.2	16.5
S (10^3mm³)	39.0	34.4	28.5	22.1	18.7	15.9	13.9
r (mm)	27.2	28.0	28.8	22.8	23.6	24.1	24.4
M_r (kN•m)	15.7	13.5	10.8	8.82	7.21	6.05	5.20

IMPERIAL SIZE AND MASS

Mass (lb./ft.)	10.6	8.81	6.89	7.11	5.61	4.60	3.91
Thickness (in.)	.313	.250	.188	.250	.188	.150	.125
Size (in.)		3 x 3			2½ x 2½		

SQUARE HOLLOW SECTIONS
Factored Axial Compressive Resistances, C_r, in kN

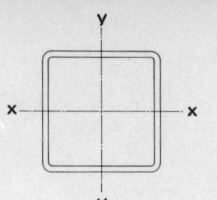

G40.21-M 350W

$\phi = 0.90$

Size (mm)	50.8 x 50.8					38.1 x 38.1			
Thickness (mm)	6.35	4.78	3.81	3.18	2.79	4.78	3.81	3.18	2.54
Mass (kg/m)	8.05	6.45	5.33	4.55	4.05	4.54	3.81	3.28	2.71
Effective length (KL) in millimetres with respect to least radius of gyration									
0	324	259	214	183	163	182	153	132	109
1 000	245	200	167	144	129	110	96	85	71
1 250	209	173	146	127	113	82	72	64	54
1 500	168	142	122	106	96	63	56	50	42
1 750	136	115	99	86	78	50	45	40	34
2 000	113	96	82	72	65	41	37	33	28
2 250	95	81	69	61	55	33	29	26	23
2 500	81	69	59	52	47	27	24	22	19
2 750	69	60	51	45	41			18	16
3 000	58	50	44	39	35				
3 250	50	43	38	33	30				
3 500	43	38	33	29	26				
3 750			29	25	23				
4 000									
4 250									
4 500									
4 750									
5 000									
5 250									
5 500									
5 750									
6 000									
6 500									
7 000									
7 500									
8 000									
8 500									
9 000									
9 500									
10 000									
10 500									

PROPERTIES AND DESIGN DATA

Area (mm^2)	1 030	821	679	580	516	578	485	418	345
Z (10^3mm^3)	16.3	13.8	11.7	10.2	9.15	6.91	6.04	5.34	4.51
S (10^3mm^3)	12.5	10.9	9.54	8.42	7.64	5.27	4.77	4.31	3.71
r (mm)	17.6	18.4	18.9	19.2	19.4	13.2	13.7	14.0	14.3
M_r (kN•m)	5.13	4.35	3.69	3.21	2.88	2.18	1.90	1.68	1.42

IMPERIAL SIZE AND MASS

Mass (lb./ft.)	5.41	4.33	3.58	3.06	2.72	3.05	2.56	2.21	1.82
Thickness (in.)	.250	.188	.150	.125	.110	.188	.150	.125	.100
Size (in.)	2 x 2					1½ x 1½			

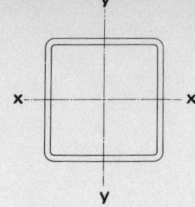

SQUARE HOLLOW SECTIONS
Factored Axial Compressive
Resistances, C_r, in kN

Size (mm)	31.8 x 31.8			25.4 x 25.4	
Thickness (mm)	3.81	3.18	2.54	3.18	2.54
Mass (kg/m)	3.06	2.65	2.20	2.01	1.69
0	123	106	89	81	68
1 000	59	53	46	28	25
1 250	43	39	34	20	18
1 500	33	30	26	14	13
1 750	25	23	20	11	10
2 000	20	18	16		
2 250		14	13		
2 500					
2 750					
3 000					
3 250					
3 500					
3 750					
4 000					
4 250					
4 500					
4 750					
5 000					
5 250					
5 500					
5 750					
6 000					
6 500					
7 000					
7 500					
8 000					
8 500					
9 000					
9 500					
10 000					
10 500					

Effective length (KL) in millimetres with respect to least radius of gyration

PROPERTIES AND DESIGN DATA

Area (mm^2)	389	338	281	257	216
Z (10^3 mm^3)	3.92	3.51	3.01	2.05	1.79
S (10^3 mm^3)	3.01	2.77	2.44	1.56	1.41
r (mm)	11.1	11.4	11.7	8.79	9.12
M$_r$ (kN•m)	1.23	1.11	0.948	0.646	0.564

IMPERIAL SIZE AND MASS

Mass (lb./ft.)	2.05	1.78	1.48	1.35	1.14
Thickness (in.)	.150	.125	.100	.125	.100
Size (in.)	1¼ x 1¼			1 x 1	

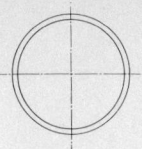
Size (mm)		406.4 OD					355.6 OD		
Thickness (mm)		12.7	11.13	9.53	7.95	6.35	12.7	11.13	9.53
Mass (kg/m)		123	108	93.3	78.1	62.6	107	94.6	81.3
	0	4 950	4 350	3 750	3 130	2 510	4 320	3 780	3 280
	1 000	4 950	4 350	3 750	3 130	2 510	4 320	3 780	3 280
	1 250	4 950	4 350	3 750	3 130	2 510	4 320	3 780	3 280
	1 500	4 950	4 350	3 750	3 130	2 510	4 300	3 760	3 260
	1 750	4 920	4 330	3 730	3 120	2 500	4 260	3 740	3 240
	2 000	4 890	4 300	3 710	3 100	2 490	4 230	3 710	3 210
	2 250	4 850	4 270	3 680	3 080	2 470	4 190	3 670	3 180
	2 500	4 820	4 240	3 650	3 060	2 450	4 150	3 640	3 160
	2 750	4 780	4 200	3 620	3 030	2 430	4 110	3 610	3 130
	3 000	4 740	4 170	3 600	3 010	2 410	4 070	3 570	3 100
	3 250	4 700	4 140	3 570	2 980	2 390	4 030	3 540	3 060
	3 500	4 660	4 100	3 540	2 960	2 370	3 990	3 500	3 030
	3 750	4 620	4 060	3 500	2 930	2 350	3 940	3 460	3 000
	4 000	4 570	4 030	3 470	2 910	2 330	3 900	3 420	2 960
	4 250	4 530	3 990	3 440	2 880	2 310	3 850	3 380	2 930
	4 500	4 480	3 950	3 400	2 850	2 290	3 800	3 330	2 890
	4 750	4 440	3 910	3 370	2 820	2 260	3 750	3 290	2 850
	5 000	4 390	3 860	3 330	2 790	2 240	3 700	3 250	2 810
	5 250	4 340	3 820	3 290	2 760	2 210	3 640	3 200	2 770
	5 500	4 290	3 780	3 260	2 730	2 190	3 590	3 150	2 730
	5 750	4 240	3 730	3 220	2 690	2 160	3 530	3 100	2 690
	6 000	4 180	3 680	3 180	2 660	2 130	3 470	3 050	2 650
	6 500	4 070	3 590	3 090	2 590	2 080	3 350	2 950	2 560
	7 000	3 950	3 490	3 010	2 520	2 020	3 230	2 840	2 460
	7 500	3 830	3 380	2 920	2 450	1 960	3 090	2 720	2 360
	8 000	3 710	3 270	2 820	2 370	1 900	2 960	2 610	2 260
	8 500	3 580	3 160	2 720	2 290	1 830	2 810	2 480	2 150
	9 000	3 440	3 040	2 620	2 200	1 770	2 660	2 350	2 040
	9 500	3 300	2 920	2 520	2 120	1 700	2 490	2 200	1 910
	10 000	3 150	2 790	2 410	2 030	1 620	2 330	2 060	1 780
	10 500	3 000	2 660	2 290	1 930	1 550	2 180	1 930	1 670

Effective length (KL) in millimetres with respect to least radius of gyration

PROPERTIES AND DESIGN DATA

Area (mm^2)		15 700	13 800	11 900	9 950	7 980	13 700	12 000	10 400
Z (10^3mm^3)		1 970	1 740	1 500	1 260	1 020	1 490	1 320	1 140
S (10^3mm^3)		1 500	1 330	1 150	972	786	1 130	1 010	873
r (mm)		139	140	140	141	141	121	122	122
M$_r$ (kN•m)		621	548	472	397	248	469	416	359

IMPERIAL SIZE AND MASS

Mass (lb./ft.)		82.9	72.9	62.7	52.5	42.1	72.2	63.5	54.7
Thickness (in.)		.500	.438	.375	.313	.250	.500	.438	.375
Size (in.)				16 OD				14 OD	

Size (mm)	355.6 OD		323.9 OD				
Thickness (mm)	7.95	6.35	12.7	11.13	9.53	7.95	6.35
Mass (kg/m)	68.2	54.7	97.5	85.9	73.9	61.9	49.7
0	2 730	2 200	3 910	3 430	2 960	2 490	1 990
1 000	2 730	2 200	3 910	3 430	2 960	2 490	1 990
1 250	2 730	2 200	3 900	3 430	2 960	2 490	1 990
1 500	2 720	2 190	3 870	3 400	2 940	2 470	1 980
1 750	2 700	2 170	3 840	3 370	2 910	2 440	1 960
2 000	2 680	2 150	3 800	3 340	2 890	2 420	1 940
2 250	2 660	2 140	3 760	3 310	2 860	2 400	1 920
2 500	2 640	2 120	3 720	3 280	2 830	2 370	1 900
2 750	2 610	2 100	3 680	3 240	2 800	2 350	1 880
3 000	2 590	2 080	3 640	3 210	2 770	2 320	1 860
3 250	2 560	2 060	3 600	3 170	2 730	2 300	1 840
3 500	2 530	2 030	3 550	3 130	2 700	2 270	1 820
3 750	2 510	2 010	3 510	3 090	2 670	2 240	1 800
4 000	2 480	1 990	3 460	3 050	2 630	2 210	1 770
4 250	2 450	1 970	3 410	3 000	2 590	2 180	1 750
4 500	2 420	1 940	3 360	2 960	2 550	2 150	1 720
4 750	2 390	1 920	3 300	2 910	2 510	2 110	1 700
5 000	2 350	1 890	3 250	2 860	2 470	2 080	1 670
5 250	2 320	1 860	3 190	2 810	2 430	2 040	1 640
5 500	2 290	1 840	3 130	2 760	2 390	2 010	1 610
5 750	2 250	1 810	3 070	2 710	2 340	1 970	1 580
6 000	2 220	1 780	3 010	2 660	2 300	1 930	1 550
6 500	2 140	1 720	2 890	2 550	2 200	1 850	1 490
7 000	2 060	1 660	2 750	2 430	2 100	1 770	1 420
7 500	1 980	1 590	2 610	2 310	2 000	1 690	1 350
8 000	1 900	1 520	2 470	2 190	1 890	1 600	1 280
8 500	1 810	1 450	2 300	2 050	1 770	1 500	1 200
9 000	1 720	1 380	2 130	1 900	1 640	1 390	1 120
9 500	1 610	1 290	1 980	1 770	1 520	1 290	1 040
10 000	1 510	1 210	1 850	1 650	1 420	1 210	968
10 500	1 410	1 130	1 730	1 540	1 330	1 130	906

Effective length (KL) in millimetres with respect to least radius of gyration

PROPERTIES AND DESIGN DATA

Area (mm^2)	8 680	6 970	12 400	10 900	9 410	7 890	6 330
Z (10^{3}mm^3)	961	775	1 230	1 090	942	794	640
S (10^{3}mm^3)	738	598	930	827	719	608	493
r (mm)	123	123	110	111	111	112	112
M$_r$ (kN•m)	303	188	387	343	297	250	202

IMPERIAL SIZE AND MASS

Mass (lb./ft.)	45.8	36.8	65.5	57.7	49.6	41.6	33.4
Thickness (in.)	.313	.250	.500	.438	.375	.313	.250
Size (in.)	14 OD		12.75 OD				

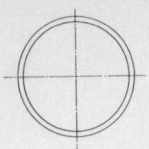
Size (mm)		273.1 OD					219.1 OD		
Thickness (mm)		12.7	11.13	9.53	7.95	6.35	12.7	11.13	9.53
Mass (kg/m)		81.6	71.9	61.9	52.0	41.8	64.6	57.1	49.3
Effective length (KL) in millimetres with respect to least radius of gyration	0	3 280	2 890	2 490	2 090	1 680	2 590	2 290	1 980
	1 000	3 280	2 890	2 490	2 090	1 680	2 570	2 270	1 960
	1 250	3 250	2 860	2 470	2 070	1 660	2 530	2 240	1 930
	1 500	3 210	2 830	2 440	2 050	1 650	2 500	2 210	1 910
	1 750	3 180	2 800	2 410	2 030	1 630	2 460	2 170	1 880
	2 000	3 140	2 770	2 380	2 000	1 610	2 420	2 140	1 840
	2 250	3 100	2 730	2 350	1 980	1 590	2 370	2 100	1 810
	2 500	3 060	2 690	2 320	1 950	1 570	2 330	2 060	1 780
	2 750	3 010	2 660	2 290	1 920	1 550	2 280	2 010	1 740
	3 000	2 970	2 620	2 260	1 890	1 520	2 230	1 970	1 700
	3 250	2 920	2 570	2 220	1 870	1 500	2 170	1 920	1 660
	3 500	2 870	2 530	2 180	1 830	1 480	2 120	1 870	1 620
	3 750	2 820	2 490	2 140	1 800	1 450	2 060	1 820	1 580
	4 000	2 770	2 440	2 110	1 770	1 420	2 000	1 770	1 530
	4 250	2 710	2 390	2 060	1 740	1 400	1 930	1 710	1 480
	4 500	2 650	2 340	2 020	1 700	1 370	1 870	1 660	1 440
	4 750	2 590	2 290	1 980	1 660	1 340	1 800	1 600	1 390
	5 000	2 530	2 240	1 930	1 630	1 310	1 730	1 540	1 330
	5 250	2 470	2 180	1 890	1 590	1 280	1 660	1 470	1 280
	5 500	2 410	2 130	1 840	1 550	1 250	1 580	1 410	1 220
	5 750	2 340	2 070	1 790	1 510	1 210	1 490	1 330	1 160
	6 000	2 270	2 010	1 740	1 460	1 180	1 410	1 260	1 100
	6 500	2 130	1 880	1 630	1 380	1 110	1 270	1 130	984
	7 000	1 980	1 750	1 520	1 280	1 040	1 140	1 020	890
	7 500	1 800	1 600	1 390	1 170	950	1 040	927	809
	8 000	1 650	1 470	1 270	1 080	872	950	847	739
	8 500	1 520	1 350	1 170	992	803	871	777	678
	9 000	1 410	1 250	1 080	918	743	802	715	624
	9 500	1 310	1 160	1 010	852	690	740	661	577
	10 000	1 220	1 080	936	793	642	685	612	534
	10 500	1 130	1 010	874	740	599	636	568	496

PROPERTIES AND DESIGN DATA

	273.1 OD					219.1 OD		
Area (mm^2)	10 400	9 160	7 890	6 620	5 320	8 230	7 270	6 270
Z (10^3mm^3)	862	764	662	559	452	542	482	419
S (10^3mm^3)	646	577	502	427	347	402	360	315
r (mm)	92.2	92.7	93.2	93.8	94.3	73.1	73.6	74.2
M$_r$ (kN•m)	272	241	209	176	142	171	152	132

IMPERIAL SIZE AND MASS

Mass (lb./ft.)	54.8	48.3	41.6	34.9	28.1	43.4	38.4	33.1
Thickness (in.)	.500	.438	.375	.313	.250	.500	.438	.375
Size (in.)	10.75 OD					8.625 OD		

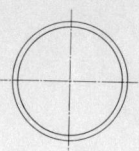

ROUND HOLLOW SECTIONS
Factored Axial Compressive Resistances, C_r, in kN

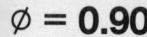

Size (mm)	219.1 OD			168.3 OD			
Thickness (mm)	7.95	6.35	4.78	9.53	7.95	6.35	4.78
Mass (kg/m)	41.4	33.3	25.3	37.3	31.4	25.4	19.3
0	1 660	1 340	1 010	1 500	1 260	1 020	775
1 000	1 650	1 330	1 010	1 460	1 230	993	757
1 250	1 630	1 310	994	1 430	1 210	974	743
1 500	1 600	1 290	980	1 400	1 180	954	727
1 750	1 580	1 270	966	1 370	1 150	932	711
2 000	1 550	1 250	950	1 330	1 120	909	693
2 250	1 520	1 230	934	1 290	1 090	884	675
2 500	1 500	1 210	916	1 250	1 060	857	655
2 750	1 470	1 180	898	1 210	1 020	829	634
3 000	1 430	1 160	879	1 170	987	800	612
3 250	1 400	1 130	859	1 120	948	769	588
3 500	1 370	1 100	839	1 070	907	736	564
3 750	1 330	1 070	817	1 020	864	702	538
4 000	1 290	1 040	795	964	819	667	512
4 250	1 250	1 010	771	907	773	630	484
4 500	1 210	980	747	841	718	587	452
4 750	1 170	947	722	782	668	546	421
5 000	1 130	912	696	730	624	510	393
5 250	1 080	876	669	683	584	477	368
5 500	1 040	839	642	641	548	448	345
5 750	983	800	613	603	515	421	324
6 000	929	756	579	568	485	397	306
6 500	835	679	520	507	433	354	273
7 000	755	614	470	455	389	318	246
7 500	686	558	428	411	351	287	222
8 000	627	510	391	372	319	261	201
8 500	575	468	359	337	290	237	183
9 000	530	431	331	302	260	213	165
9 500	490	399	306	272	234	192	149
10 000	453	369	283	247	212	174	135
10 500	421	343	263	225	194	159	123

Effective length (KL) in millimetres with respect to least radius of gyration

PROPERTIES AND DESIGN DATA

	219.1 OD			168.3 OD			
Area (mm^2)	5 270	4 240	3 220	4 750	4 000	3 230	2 460
Z (10^3mm^3)	355	288	220	241	205	167	128
S (10^3mm^3)	269	219	169	179	153	126	97.6
r (mm)	74.7	75.3	75.8	56.2	56.8	57.3	57.8
M$_r$ (kN•m)	112	90.7	69.3	75.9	64.6	52.6	40.3

IMPERIAL SIZE AND MASS

	219.1 OD			168.3 OD			
Mass (lb./ft.)	27.8	22.4	17.0	25.1	21.1	17.0	13.0
Thickness (in.)	.313	.250	.188	.375	.313	.250	.188
Size (in.)	8.625 OD			6.625 OD			

ROUND HOLLOW SECTIONS
Factored Axial Compressive Resistances, C_r, in kN

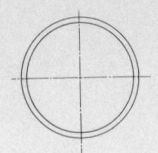

G40.21-M 350W

$\phi = 0.90$

Size (mm)	141.3 OD				114.3 OD		
Thickness (mm)	9.53	7.95	6.35	4.78	7.95	6.35	4.78
Mass (kg/m)	31.0	26.1	21.1	16.1	20.9	16.9	12.9
Effective length (KL) in millimetres with respect to least radius of gyration							
0	1 240	1 050	847	646	838	677	517
1 000	1 190	1 010	815	621	784	635	485
1 250	1 160	982	795	606	756	613	469
1 500	1 130	954	773	590	725	588	451
1 750	1 090	924	749	572	692	562	431
2 000	1 050	892	723	553	655	533	409
2 250	1 010	857	696	532	615	501	386
2 500	968	820	667	510	573	468	361
2 750	921	781	635	487	527	432	334
3 000	871	740	603	462	475	391	304
3 250	818	696	568	436	427	351	273
3 500	762	649	531	409	386	317	247
3 750	697	596	489	378	351	289	225
4 000	639	546	449	347	321	264	206
4 250	589	503	414	320	294	242	189
4 500	544	466	383	296	271	223	174
4 750	505	432	355	275	251	206	161
5 000	470	402	331	256	232	191	149
5 250	439	376	309	239	216	178	139
5 500	411	351	289	224	201	166	129
5 750	385	330	271	210	186	154	121
6 000	361	310	255	197	171	142	111
6 500	320	275	226	175	147	122	96
7 000	286	245	202	156	128	106	83
7 500	250	215	178	138	112	93	73
8 000	221	190	157	122			
8 500	197	169	140	109			
9 000	177	152	126	98			
9 500			114	88			
10 000							
10 500							
PROPERTIES AND DESIGN DATA							
Area (mm^2)	3 950	3 330	2 690	2 050	2 660	2 150	~ 1 640
Z (10^3 mm^3)	166	142	116	89.1	90.1	74.1	57.4
S (10^3 mm^3)	122	105	86.9	67.7	66.1	55.1	43.2
r (mm)	46.7	47.2	47.8	48.3	37.7	38.2	38.8
M_r (kN•m)	52.3	44.7	36.5	28.1	28.4	23.3	18.1
IMPERIAL SIZE AND MASS							
Mass (lb./ft.)	20.8	17.6	14.2	10.8	14.0	11.4	8.68
Thickness (in.)	.375	.313	.250	.188	.313	.250	.188
Size (in.)	5.562 OD				4.5 OD		

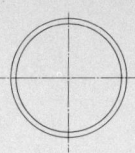
Size (mm)		101.6 OD				88.9 OD			
Thickness (mm)		7.95	6.35	4.78	3.81	7.95	6.35	4.78	3.81
Mass (kg/m)		18.4	14.9	11.4	9.19	15.9	12.9	9.92	8.00
	0	737	598	457	369	636	520	397	321
	500	726	590	451	364	621	508	388	315
	750	703	572	437	353	597	489	374	303
	1 000	677	551	422	341	569	466	357	290
	1 250	647	528	404	327	537	441	339	275
	1 500	614	502	385	311	501	413	317	258
	1 750	578	473	363	294	462	381	294	240
	2 000	538	442	340	276	419	347	269	219
	2 250	495	408	315	256	370	309	241	197
	2 500	449	371	288	234	321	268	210	172
	2 750	396	329	256	209	282	236	184	151
	3 000	352	293	228	186	250	209	163	134
	3 250	316	263	205	167	223	187	146	120
	3 500	285	237	185	151	201	168	131	108
	3 750	258	215	168	137	181	152	119	98
	4 000	235	196	153	125	164	138	108	89
	4 250	215	179	140	114	150	126	98	81
	4 500	198	165	129	105	135	114	90	74
	4 750	182	152	119	97	121	102	81	67
	5 000	167	140	110	90	110	93	73	60
	5 250	152	128	101	82	100	85	67	55
	5 500	139	117	92	75	92	78	61	50
	5 750	128	108	84	69	85	71	56	46
	6 000	118	99	78	64				43
	6 500	102	85	67	55				
	7 000								
	7 500								
	8 000								
	8 500								
	9 000								
	9 500								

Effective length (KL) in millimetres with respect to least radius of gyration

PROPERTIES AND DESIGN DATA									
Area (mm²)		2 340	1 900	1 450	1 170	2 020	1 650	1 260	1 020
Z (10^3 mm³)		69.9	57.7	44.8	36.5	52.3	43.4	33.9	27.6
S (10^3 mm³)		50.8	42.6	33.6	27.6	37.6	31.7	25.2	20.8
r (mm)		33.2	33.8	34.3	34.6	28.8	29.3	29.8	30.1
M_r (kN•m)		22.0	18.2	14.1	11.5	16.5	13.7	10.7	8.69

IMPERIAL SIZE AND MASS									
Mass (lb./ft.)		12.3	10.0	7.67	6.17	10.7	8.69	6.66	5.37
Thickness (in.)		.313	.250	.188	.150	.313	.250	.188	.150
Size (in.)		4 OD				3.5 OD			

ROUND HOLLOW SECTIONS
Factored Axial Compressive Resistances, C_r, in kN

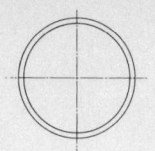

G40.21-M 350W

$\phi = 0.90$

Size (mm)		73.0 OD				60.3 OD			
Thickness (mm)		6.35	4.78	3.81	3.18	6.35	4.78	3.81	3.18
Mass (kg/m)		10.4	8.04	6.50	5.48	8.45	6.54	5.31	4.48
Effective length (KL) in millimetres with respect to least radius of gyration	0	419	321	261	220	340	263	213	180
	500	402	309	251	212	319	247	201	170
	750	381	294	239	202	296	230	187	158
	1 000	357	275	224	189	268	209	171	145
	1 250	328	254	207	175	236	185	152	129
	1 500	296	230	189	160	198	158	130	111
	1 750	260	204	167	142	161	128	106	91
	2 000	219	173	143	122	134	107	89	76
	2 250	187	148	122	104	113	91	75	64
	2 500	162	128	105	90	97	78	64	55
	2 750	141	112	92	79	84	67	56	48
	3 000	124	98	81	69	72	58	49	42
	3 250	110	87	72	62	62	50	42	36
	3 500	98	78	65	55	54	44	36	31
	3 750	87	69	57	49	47	38	32	27
	4 000	77	61	51	43				24
	4 250	68	54	45	39				
	4 500	61	49	41	35				
	4 750		44	37	31				
	5 000								
	5 250								
	5 500								
	5 750								
	6 000								
	6 500								
	7 000								
	7 500								
	8 000								
	8 500								
	9 000								
	9 500								

PROPERTIES AND DESIGN DATA

Area (mm²)		1 330	1 020	828	698	1 080	834	676	571
Z (10^3mm³)		28.3	22.3	18.3	15.5	18.6	14.8	12.2	10.4
S (10^3mm³)		20.4	16.4	13.6	11.7	13.2	10.7	8.99	7.74
r (mm)		23.7	24.2	24.5	24.7	19.2	19.7	20.0	20.2
M_r (kN•m)		8.91	7.02	5.76	4.88	5.86	4.66	3.84	3.28

IMPERIAL SIZE AND MASS

Mass (lb./ft.)		7.01	5.40	4.37	3.68	5.68	4.40	3.57	3.01
Thickness (in.)		.250	.188	.150	.125	.250	.188	.150	.125
Size (in.)		2.875 OD				2.375 OD			

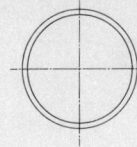
Size (mm)		48.3 OD				42.2 OD		33.4 OD		26.7 OD	
Thickness (mm)		4.78	3.81	3.18	2.79	3.18	2.54	3.18	2.54	3.18	2.54
Mass (kg/m)		5.13	4.18	3.54	3.13	3.06	2.48	2.37	1.93	1.84	1.51
Effective length (KL) in millimetres with respect to least radius of gyration	0	206	168	142	126	123	100	95	77	74	61
	500	187	153	130	115	109	89	78	64	54	45
	750	167	137	117	104	95	78	62	51	36	30
	1 000	144	119	101	90	78	64	43	36	24	20
	1 250	115	96	83	74	58	49	32	27	17	15
	1 500	90	75	65	58	45	38	24	20	12	10
	1 750	72	60	52	46	36	30	18	16		
	2 000	59	50	43	38	30	25	14	12		
	2 250	50	42	36	32	24	20				
	2 500	41	35	30	27	20	17				
	2 750	34	29	25	22	16	14				
	3 000	29	25	21	19						
	3 250										
	3 500										
	3 750										
	4 000										
	4 250										
	4 500										
	4 750										
	5 000										
	5 250										
	5 500										
	5 750										
	6 000										
	6 500										
	7 000										
	7 500										
	8 000										
	8 500										
	9 000										
	9 500										

PROPERTIES AND DESIGN DATA

Area (mm^2)		654	533	451	399	390	316	302	246	235	193
Z (10^{3}mm^3)		9.09	7.56	6.48	5.79	4.85	4.00	2.91	2.42	1.77	1.49
S (10^{3}mm^3)		6.48	5.50	4.77	4.29	3.54	2.96	2.09	1.77	1.24	1.07
r (mm)		15.5	15.8	16.0	16.1	13.8	14.1	10.7	10.9	8.39	8.59
M_r (kN•m)		2.86	2.38	2.04	1.82	1.53	1.26	0.917	0.762	0.558	0.469

IMPERIAL SIZE AND MASS

Mass (lb./ft.)		3.45	2.81	2.38	2.10	2.06	1.67	1.59	1.30	1.24	1.02
Thickness (in.)		.188	.150	.125	.110	.125	.100	.125	.100	.125	.100
Size (in.)		1.9 OD				1.66 OD		1.315 OD		1.05 OD	

RECTANGULAR HOLLOW SECTIONS
Factored Axial Compressive Resistances, C_r, in kN

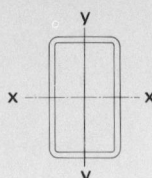

G40.21-M 350W
CLASS H
$\phi = 0.90$

Size (mm)	304.8 x 203.2					254.0 x 152.4		
Thickness (mm)	12.7	11.13	9.53	††7.95	6.35‡	12.7	11.13	9.53
Mass (kg/m)	93.0	82.4	71.3	60.1	48.6	72.7	64.6	56.1

Effective length (KL) in millimetres with respect to least radius of gyration		304.8 x 203.2					254.0 x 152.4		
	0	3 720	3 310	2 860	2 410	1 830	2 920	2 590	2 250
	1 000	3 720	3 310	2 860	2 410	1 820	2 910	2 590	2 250
	1 250	3 720	3 310	2 860	2 410	1 810	2 900	2 580	2 240
	1 500	3 710	3 300	2 860	2 410	1 800	2 890	2 570	2 230
	1 750	3 700	3 290	2 850	2 400	1 790	2 870	2 550	2 220
	2 000	3 680	3 280	2 840	2 390	1 780	2 840	2 520	2 190
	2 250	3 660	3 260	2 820	2 380	1 760	2 800	2 490	2 170
	2 500	3 640	3 240	2 810	2 370	1 750	2 760	2 460	2 140
	2 750	3 610	3 210	2 780	2 350	1 730	2 710	2 410	2 100
	3 000	3 570	3 180	2 760	2 330	1 710	2 650	2 370	2 060
	3 250	3 530	3 150	2 730	2 300	1 690	2 590	2 310	2 020
	3 500	3 490	3 110	2 700	2 280	1 670	2 520	2 250	1 970
	3 750	3 440	3 070	2 660	2 250	1 650	2 450	2 190	1 910
	4 000	3 390	3 020	2 620	2 220	1 620	2 360	2 120	1 850
	4 250	3 330	2 970	2 580	2 180	1 600	2 280	2 040	1 790
	4 500	3 270	2 920	2 540	2 140	1 570	2 180	1 960	1 720
	4 750	3 210	2 860	2 490	2 100	1 540	2 080	1 870	1 640
	5 000	3 130	2 800	2 430	2 060	1 510	1 970	1 780	1 560
	5 250	3 060	2 730	2 380	2 010	1 470	1 860	1 680	1 480
	5 500	2 980	2 660	2 320	1 960	1 440	1 730	1 570	1 390
	5 750	2 890	2 590	2 260	1 910	1 400	1 590	1 450	1 290
	6 000	2 810	2 510	2 190	1 860	1 360	1 480	1 340	1 190
	6 500	2 610	2 350	2 050	1 740	1 280	1 280	1 160	1 030
	7 000	2 400	2 160	1 890	1 610	1 200	1 120	1 020	905
	7 500	2 160	1 950	1 720	1 470	1 100	998	907	803
	8 000	1 920	1 730	1 530	1 310	1 000	895	813	720
	8 500	1 720	1 560	1 370	1 170	897	801	730	648
	9 000	1 560	1 410	1 240	1 060	800	717	653	580
	9 500	1 420	1 280	1 130	963	718	646	589	523
	10 000	1 300	1 170	1 030	881	648	585	533	474
	10 500	1 190	1 080	948	811	588	533	486	431

PROPERTIES AND DESIGN DATA

	304.8 x 203.2					254.0 x 152.4		
Area (mm²)	11 800	10 500	9 090	7 660	6 190	9 260	8 230	7 150
Z_x (10^3 mm³)	1 190	1 060	925	787	640	746	671	589
S_x (10^3 mm³)	964	867	762	652	535	592	537	475
r_x (mm)	111	112	113	114	115	90.1	91.0	91.9
Z_y (10^3 mm³)	896	802	701	596	486	522	470	413
S_y (10^3 mm³)	769	693	611	524	431	441	401	357
r_y (mm)	81.2	81.9	82.7	83.4	84.1	60.2	61.0	61.7
r_x/r_y	1.37	1.37	1.37	1.37	1.36	1.50	1.49	1.49
M_{rx} (kN•m)	375	334	291	248	202	235	211	186
M_{ry} (kN•m)	282	253	221	165	123	164	148	130

IMPERIAL SIZE AND MASS

Mass (lb./ft.)	62.5	55.4	47.9	40.4	32.6	48.9	43.4	37.7
Thickness (in.)	.500	.438	.375	.313	.250	.500	.438	.375
Size (in.)	12 x 8					10 x 6		

†† Class 3 in bending about Y-Y axis.

‡ Class 4 in bending about Y-Y axis and resistance for this column calculated according to CAN3-S16.1-M78 Clause 13.3.3.

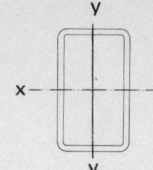

G40.21-M 350W
CLASS H
$\phi = 0.90$

RECTANGULAR HOLLOW SECTIONS
Factored Axial Compressive
Resistances, C_r, in kN

Size (mm)		254.0 x 152.4		203.2 x 152.4					
Thickness (mm)		7.95	††6.35	12.7	11.13	9.53	7.95	6.35	4.78‡
Mass (kg/m)		47.5	38.4	62.6	55.7	48.5	41.1	33.4	25.5
	0	1 910	1 540	2 510	2 240	1 950	1 650	1 340	1 020
	1 000	1 900	1 520	2 510	2 230	1 940	1 650	1 340	1 010
	1 250	1 900	1 510	2 500	2 230	1 940	1 640	1 330	1 000
	1 500	1 890	1 500	2 480	2 210	1 930	1 630	1 330	992
	1 750	1 880	1 480	2 460	2 190	1 910	1 620	1 320	981
	2 000	1 860	1 460	2 430	2 170	1 890	1 610	1 300	967
	2 250	1 840	1 440	2 400	2 140	1 870	1 590	1 290	952
	2 500	1 810	1 410	2 360	2 110	1 840	1 560	1 270	936
	2 750	1 780	1 390	2 320	2 070	1 810	1 540	1 250	917
	3 000	1 750	1 360	2 260	2 030	1 770	1 500	1 220	897
	3 250	1 710	1 330	2 210	1 980	1 730	1 470	1 200	875
	3 500	1 670	1 290	2 140	1 920	1 680	1 430	1 170	851
	3 750	1 620	1 250	2 080	1 860	1 630	1 390	1 130	826
	4 000	1 580	1 210	2 000	1 800	1 580	1 340	1 100	799
	4 250	1 520	1 170	1 920	1 730	1 520	1 300	1 060	770
	4 500	1 470	1 130	1 830	1 650	1 450	1 240	1 020	739
	4 750	1 400	1 080	1 740	1 570	1 380	1 190	974	706
	5 000	1 340	1 030	1 640	1 490	1 310	1 130	926	672
	5 250	1 270	975	1 540	1 400	1 230	1 060	876	636
	5 500	1 200	920	1 410	1 290	1 150	992	823	598
	5 750	1 110	862	1 300	1 190	1 060	915	760	558
	6 000	1 030	801	1 210	1 100	979	847	704	517
	6 500	891	684	1 050	955	849	734	610	441
	7 000	781	589	920	839	745	645	535	380
	7 500	693	513	818	746	662	573	475	331
	8 000	621	451	733	669	594	513	426	291
	8 500	561	400	652	596	531	460	383	258
	9 000	502	357	584	534	475	412	343	230
	9 500	452	320	526	481	428	371	309	206
	10 000	409	289	477	436	388	336	280	186
	10 500	373	262	434	397	353	306	255	169

(Left axis label: Effective length (KL) in millimetres with respect to least radius of gyration)

PROPERTIES AND DESIGN DATA

Area (mm²)		6 050	4 900	7 970	7 100	6 180	5 240	4 250	3 250
Z_x (10^3mm³)		503	411	528	476	419	360	295	228
S_x (10^3mm³)		409	338	423	385	343	297	246	192
r_x (mm)		92.7	93.6	73.4	74.2	75.1	75.9	76.7	77.5
Z_y (10^3mm³)		353	290	432	390	344	295	243	188
S_y (10^3mm³)		309	256	358	327	292	254	211	165
r_y (mm)		62.4	63.1	58.5	59.3	60.0	60.7	61.5	62.2
r_x/r_y		1.49	1.48	1.25	1.25	1.25	1.25	1.25	1.25
M_{rx} (kN•m)		158	129	166	150	132	113	92.9	71.8
M_{ry} (kN•m)		111	80.6	136	123	108	92.9	76.5	50.8

IMPERIAL SIZE AND MASS

Mass (lb./ft.)	31.9	25.8	42.1	37.5	32.6	27.6	22.4	17.1
Thickness (in.)	.313	.250	.500	.438	.375	.313	.250	.188
Size (in.)	10 x 6		8 x 6					

†† Class 3 in bending about Y-Y axis.
‡ Class 4 in bending about Y-Y axis and resistance for this column calculated according to CAN3-S16.1-M78 Clause 13.3.3.

RECTANGULAR HOLLOW SECTIONS
Factored Axial Compressive Resistances, C$_r$, in kN

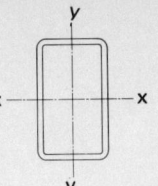

G40.21-M 350W
CLASS H
$\phi = 0.90$

Size (mm)	203.2 x 101.6						177.8 x 127.0 #		
Thickness (mm)	12.7	11.13	9.53	7.95	6.35	4.78‡	12.7	11.13	9.53
Mass (kg/m)	52.4	46.9	40.9	34.8	28.3	21.7	52.4	46.9	40.9
0	2 100	1 880	1 640	1 400	1 140	869	2 100	1 880	1 640
1 000	2 080	1 860	1 630	1 380	1 130	844	2 100	1 870	1 640
1 250	2 050	1 840	1 610	1 370	1 120	830	2 080	1 860	1 620
1 500	2 010	1 800	1 580	1 340	1 100	812	2 060	1 840	1 610
1 750	1 960	1 760	1 540	1 310	1 070	792	2 030	1 810	1 590
2 000	1 900	1 710	1 500	1 280	1 050	768	1 990	1 780	1 560
2 250	1 830	1 640	1 440	1 230	1 010	741	1 940	1 740	1 530
2 500	1 740	1 570	1 380	1 180	974	711	1 890	1 700	1 490
2 750	1 650	1 490	1 310	1 130	929	678	1 830	1 650	1 440
3 000	1 540	1 400	1 240	1 070	880	641	1 760	1 590	1 400
3 250	1 420	1 300	1 150	995	826	601	1 690	1 520	1 340
3 500	1 290	1 180	1 060	919	766	559	1 610	1 450	1 280
3 750	1 140	1 050	948	832	701	513	1 520	1 370	1 220
4 000	1 020	937	844	740	624	464	1 420	1 290	1 150
4 250	912	841	757	664	560	412	1 320	1 200	1 070
4 500	825	760	684	600	505	368	1 190	1 090	984
4 750	751	692	623	545	460	330	1 080	993	892
5 000	689	634	570	499	420	298	987	905	813
5 250	635	584	525	459	387	270	905	830	745
5 500	582	538	486	425	358	246	834	765	687
5 750	534	494	446	392	331	225	772	708	635
6 000	492	455	410	361	305	207	718	658	590
6 500	421	390	352	309	261	176	628	575	515
7 000	366	338	305	268	227	152	545	501	451
7 500	321	296	267	235	199	132	477	438	394
8 000			237	208	176	116	421	387	348
8 500						103	375	344	310
9 000							336	309	278
9 500							303	279	251
10 000									
10 500									

Effective length (KL) in millimetres with respect to least radius of gyration

PROPERTIES AND DESIGN DATA

	203.2 x 101.6						177.8 x 127.0		
Area (mm^2)	6 680	5 970	5 210	4 430	3 610	2 760	6 680	5 970	5 210
Z$_x$ (10^{3}mm^3)	405	367	325	281	232	180	377	342	303
S$_x$ (10^{3}mm^3)	307	282	253	221	185	145	297	272	244
r$_x$ (mm)	68.4	69.3	70.3	71.2	72.2	73.1	62.8	63.7	64.6
Z$_y$ (10^{3}mm^3)	246	224	199	172	143	111	298	270	240
S$_y$ (10^{3}mm^3)	201	186	168	148	125	99.0	243	224	202
r$_y$ (mm)	39.1	39.8	40.5	41.2	42.0	42.7	48.1	48.8	49.6
r$_x$/r$_y$	1.75	1.74	1.73	1.73	1.72	1.71	1.31	1.30	1.30
M$_{rx}$ (kN•m)	128	116	102	88.5	73.1	56.7	119	108	95.4
M$_{ry}$ (kN•m)	77.5	70.6	62.7	54.2	45.0	30.5	93.9	85.0	75.6

IMPERIAL SIZE AND MASS

	203.2 x 101.6						177.8 x 127.0		
Mass (lb./ft.)	35.2	31.5	27.5	23.4	19.0	14.6	35.2	31.5	27.5
Thickness (in.)	.500	.438	.375	.313	.250	.188	.500	.438	.375
Size (in.)	8 x 4						7 x 5		

‡ Class 4 in bending about Y-Y axis and resistance for this column calculated according to CAN3-S16. 1-M78 Clause 13.3.3.
\# Check manufacturer for current availability.

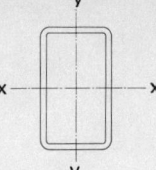

G40.21-M 350W
CLASS H
$\phi = 0.90$

RECTANGULAR HOLLOW SECTIONS
Factored Axial Compressive
Resistances, C_r, in kN

Size (mm)	177.8 x 127.0#			152.4 x 101.6				
Thickness (mm)	7.95	6.35	††4.78	11.13	9.53	7.95	6.35	4.78
Mass (kg/m)	34.8	28.3	21.7	38.0	33.3	28.4	23.2	17.9
0	1 400	1 140	869	1 520	1 340	1 140	932	718
1 000	1 390	1 130	867	1 510	1 320	1 130	924	712
1 250	1 380	1 130	862	1 480	1 300	1 110	912	704
1 500	1 370	1 120	854	1 450	1 280	1 090	896	692
1 750	1 350	1 100	844	1 420	1 250	1 070	876	677
2 000	1 330	1 080	831	1 370	1 210	1 040	850	658
2 250	1 300	1 060	815	1 310	1 160	997	821	636
2 500	1 270	1 040	797	1 250	1 110	954	786	610
2 750	1 230	1 010	776	1 180	1 040	904	747	581
3 000	1 190	979	753	1 100	977	849	704	549
3 250	1 150	944	727	1 010	902	787	656	513
3 500	1 100	905	698	907	820	720	603	474
3 750	1 050	863	666	800	724	641	541	430
4 000	988	817	632	712	645	571	481	383
4 250	925	768	596	640	579	512	432	343
4 500	858	715	556	579	524	463	390	310
4 750	778	653	511	528	477	422	355	282
5 000	709	595	466	484	437	386	325	258
5 250	650	545	427	446	403	356	299	237
5 500	598	501	393	407	369	328	277	220
5 750	554	464	363	373	339	301	254	203
6 000	514	431	337	344	312	277	234	187
6 500	449	375	294	295	267	237	201	160
7 000	394	331	259	256	232	206	174	139
7 500	345	290	227	225	204	181	153	121
8 000	304	256	201				135	107
8 500	271	227	178					
9 000	243	204	160					
9 500	219	184	144					
10 000	199	167	131					
10 500								

Effective length (KL) in millimetres with respect to least radius of gyration

PROPERTIES AND DESIGN DATA

Area (mm²)	4 430	3 610	2 760	4 840	4 240	3 620	2 960	2 280
Z_x (10^3 mm³)	261	216	167	230	205	178	148	116
S_x (10^3 mm³)	213	178	140	179	162	143	121	95.6
r_x (mm)	65.4	66.2	67.1	53.1	54.0	54.8	55.7	56.5
Z_y (10^3 mm³)	207	171	133	172	154	134	112	87.8
S_y (10^3 mm³)	177	148	117	140	128	113	96.1	76.6
r_y (mm)	50.3	51.1	51.8	38.4	39.1	39.9	40.6	41.3
r_x/r_y	1.30	1.30	1.29	1.38	1.38	1.38	1.37	1.37
M_{rx} (kN•m)	82.2	68.0	52.6	72.4	64.6	56.1	46.6	36.5
M_{ry} (kN•m)	65.2	53.9	36.9	54.2	48.5	42.2	35.3	27.7

IMPERIAL SIZE AND MASS

Mass (lb./ft.)	23.4	19.0	14.6	25.5	22.4	19.1	15.6	12.0
Thickness (in.)	.313	.250	.188	.438	.375	.313	.250	.188
Size (in.)	7 x 5			6 x 4				

†† Class 3 in bending about Y-Y axis.
# Check manufacturer for current availability.

RECTANGULAR HOLLOW SECTIONS
Factored Axial Compressive Resistances, C_r, in kN

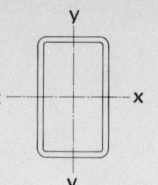

G40.21-M 350W
CLASS H
$\phi = 0.90$

Size (mm)	127.0 x 76.2				127.0 x 63.5			
Thickness (mm)	9.53	7.95	6.35	4.78	9.53	7.95	6.35	4.78
Mass (kg/m)	25.7	22.1	18.2	14.1	23.8	20.5	16.9	13.1
0	1 030	888	731	564	954	822	677	526
1 000	999	862	710	549	900	779	644	503
1 250	968	836	691	535	854	742	616	482
1 500	926	803	665	516	794	694	579	455
1 750	874	761	632	492	721	635	533	422
2 000	811	710	592	463	633	564	478	383
2 250	739	651	547	429	527	479	415	337
2 500	656	584	494	391	436	396	343	282
2 750	558	504	433	347	369	334	289	238
3 000	477	431	370	297	318	288	249	204
3 250	414	374	320	258	277	251	217	178
3 500	364	328	281	226	240	219	190	157
3 750	324	292	250	201	210	191	167	138
4 000	289	262	224	180	186	169	147	121
4 250	257	233	201	162	165	151	131	108
4 500	230	209	180	145	148	135	117	97
4 750	207	188	162	130		122	106	87
5 000	188	170	147	118			96	79
5 250	171	155	133	108				
5 500	157	142	122	98				
5 750		130	112	90				
6 000			104	83				
6 500								
7 000								
7 500								
8 000								
8 500								
9 000								
9 500								
10 000								
10 500								

Effective length (KL) in millimetres with respect to least radius of gyration

PROPERTIES AND DESIGN DATA

Area (mm²)	3 280	2 820	2 320	1 790	3 030	2 610	2 150	1 670
Z_x (10^3 mm³)	126	111	93.3	73.8	112	98.9	83.6	66.3
S_x (10^3 mm³)	96.4	86.4	74.0	59.5	83.2	75.1	64.8	52.4
r_x (mm)	43.2	44.1	45.1	45.9	41.7	42.7	43.7	44.6
Z_y (10^3 mm³)	87.5	77.2	65.2	51.7	67.4	60.0	51.0	40.7
S_y (10^3 mm³)	70.5	63.8	55.1	44.7	53.6	49.1	42.9	35.2
r_y (mm)	28.6	29.4	30.1	30.8	23.7	24.4	25.1	25.9
r_x/r_y	1.51	1.50	1.50	1.49	1.76	1.75	1.74	1.73
M_{rx} (kN•m)	39.7	35.0	29.4	23.2	35.3	31.2	26.3	20.9
M_{ry} (kN•m)	27.6	24.3	20.5	16.3	21.2	18.9	16.1	12.8

IMPERIAL SIZE AND MASS

Mass (lb./ft.)	17.3	14.9	12.2	9.45	16.0	13.8	11.4	8.81
Thickness (in.)	.375	.313	.250	.188	.375	.313	.250	.188
Size (in.)	5 x 3				5 x 2½			

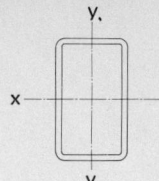
Size (mm)		127.0 x 50.8				101.6 x 76.2			
Thickness (mm)		9.53	7.95	6.35	4.78	9.53	7.95	6.35	4.78
Mass (kg/m)		21.9	18.9	15.6	12.2	21.9	18.9	15.6	12.2
Effective length (KL) in millimetres with respect to least radius of gyration	0	879	759	627	488	879	759	627	488
	1 000	782	683	570	448	847	734	608	475
	1 250	708	624	525	415	818	711	590	461
	1 500	613	549	468	374	780	680	566	444
	1 750	493	456	397	323	732	641	536	422
	2 000	388	358	315	261	675	595	500	395
	2 250	316	291	256	212	609	541	458	364
	2 500	265	243	213	176	532	480	410	329
	2 750	221	205	181	150	448	407	353	287
	3 000	187	173	153	127	383	348	302	245
	3 250	160	148	131	109	333	302	262	213
	3 500	139	129	114	95	293	266	230	187
	3 750		113	100	83	262	237	205	166
	4 000				73	231	211	184	149
	4 250					205	187	163	133
	4 500					184	168	146	119
	4 750					166	151	132	107
	5 000					150	137	119	97
	5 250					137	125	109	89
	5 500					125	114	100	81
	5 750							91	75
	6 000								
	6 500								
	7 000								
	7 500								
	8 000								
	8 500								
	9 000								
	9 500								
	10 000								
	10 500								

PROPERTIES AND DESIGN DATA

	127.0 x 50.8				101.6 x 76.2			
Area (mm^2)	2 790	2 410	1 990	1 550	2 790	2 410	1 990	1 550
Z_x (10^{3}mm^3)	97.7	86.9	73.8	58.9	87.6	77.7	65.9	52.5
S_x (10^{3}mm^3)	70.0	63.8	55.5	45.3	67.2	61.0	52.8	43.0
r_x (mm)	39.9	41.0	42.1	43.1	35.0	35.8	36.7	37.5
Z_y (10^{3}mm^3)	48.9	44.0	37.9	30.5	71.3	63.5	54.0	43.1
S_y (10^{3}mm^3)	37.8	35.3	31.4	26.2	56.3	51.4	44.8	36.6
r_y (mm)	18.6	19.3	20.0	20.7	27.7	28.5	29.3	30.0
r_x/r_y	2.15	2.13	2.10	2.08	1.26	1.26	1.25	1.25
M_{rx} (kN•m)	30.8	27.4	23.2	18.6	27.6	24.5	20.8	16.5
M_{ry} (kN•m)	15.4	13.9	11.9	9.61	22.5	20.0	17.0	13.6

IMPERIAL SIZE AND MASS

Mass (lb./ft.)	14.7	12.7	10.5	8.17	14.7	12.7	10.5	8.17
Thickness (in.)	.375	.313	.250	.188	.375	.313	.250	.188
Size (in.)	5 x 2				4 x 3			

RECTANGULAR HOLLOW SECTIONS
Factored Axial Compressive
Resistances, C$_r$, in kN

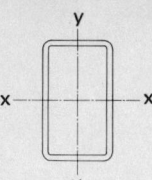

G40.21-M 350W
CLASS H
$\phi = 0.90$

Size (mm)	101.6 x 50.8					88.9 x 63.5		
Thickness (mm)	7.95	6.35	4.78	3.81	3.18	7.95	6.35	4.78
Mass (kg/m)	15.8	13.1	10.3	8.37	7.09	15.8	13.1	10.3
0	633	526	413	337	284	633	526	413
1 000	565	475	376	309	262	595	497	392
1 250	513	435	348	287	244	563	472	374
1 500	447	384	311	258	220	522	440	351
1 750	362	322	267	223	192	472	401	322
2 000	285	253	213	180	156	412	354	288
2 250	232	205	173	146	126	339	297	248
2 500	194	171	144	122	105	281	246	204
2 750	162	145	123	103	89	238	208	173
3 000	137	122	104	88	76	205	179	148
3 250	118	105	89	75	65	178	157	130
3 500	102	91	77	65	57	154	136	113
3 750	90	80	68	57	50	135	119	99
4 000			60	51	44	119	105	88
4 250						106	93	78
4 500						95	84	70
4 750							76	63
5 000								
5 250								
5 500								
5 750								
6 000								
6 500								
7 000								
7 500								
8 000								
8 500								
9 000								
9 500								
10 000								
10 500								

Effective length (KL) in millimetres with respect to least radius of gyration

PROPERTIES AND DESIGN DATA

Area (mm^2)	2 010	1 670	1 310	1 070	903	2 010	1 670	1 310
Z$_x$ (10^{3}mm^3)	58.8	50.6	40.8	33.9	29.0	54.9	47.1	38.0
S$_x$ (10^{3}mm^3)	43.5	38.4	31.8	26.8	23.1	42.1	37.1	30.6
r$_x$ (mm)	33.2	34.2	35.1	35.7	36.1	30.5	31.4	32.3
Z$_y$ (10^{3}mm^3)	35.4	30.7	24.9	20.8	17.9	43.2	37.2	30.1
S$_y$ (10^{3}mm^3)	27.9	25.1	21.1	18.0	15.6	34.3	30.4	25.3
r$_y$ (mm)	18.8	19.5	20.3	20.7	21.0	23.3	24.0	24.8
r$_x$/r$_y$	1.77	1.75	1.73	1.73	1.72	1.31	1.31	1.30
M$_{rx}$ (kN•m)	18.5	15.9	12.9	10.7	9.13	17.3	14.8	12.0
M$_{ry}$ (kN•m)	11.2	9.67	7.84	6.55	5.64	13.6	11.7	9.48

IMPERIAL SIZE AND MASS

Mass (lb./ft.)	10.6	8.81	6.89	5.62	4.76	10.6	8.81	6.89
Thickness (in.)	.313	.250	.188	.150	.125	.313	.250	.188
Size (in.)	4 x 2					3½ x 2½		

G40.21-M 350W
CLASS H
∅ = 0.90

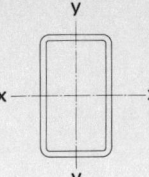

RECTANGULAR HOLLOW SECTIONS
Factored Axial Compressive Resistances, C_r, in kN

Size (mm)	88.9 x 63.5		76.2 x 50.8				50.8 x 25.4	
Thickness (mm)	3.81	3.18	7.95	6.35	4.78	3.81	3.18	2.54
Mass (kg/m)	8.37	7.09	12.6	10.6	8.35	6.85	3.28	2.71
0	337	284	504	425	334	275	132	109
1 000	321	271	443	379	302	250	63	56
1 250	307	260	398	345	277	230	43	38
1 500	289	245	339	300	245	205	31	27
1 750	266	226	267	243	206	174	23	20
2 000	239	204	210	191	162	138		16
2 250	208	178	171	156	131	112		
2 500	172	148	143	130	110	93		
2 750	145	125	119	109	93	79		
3 000	125	107	100	92	78	67		
3 250	109	94	86	79	67	57		
3 500	96	82	75	69	58	50		
3 750	84	72		60	51	44		
4 000	74	64						
4 250	66	57						
4 500	59	51						
4 750	53	46						
5 000	48	42						
5 250								
5 500								
5 750								
6 000								
6 500								
7 000								
7 500								
8 000								
8 500								
9 000								
9 500								
10 000								
10 500								

Effective length (KL) in millimetres with respect to least radius of gyration

PROPERTIES AND DESIGN DATA

Area (mm²)	1 070	903	1 600	1 350	1 060	872	418	345
Z_x (10³mm³)	31.5	27.0	35.9	31.4	25.7	21.6	6.33	5.35
S_x (10³mm³)	25.8	22.3	26.6	24.1	20.3	17.3	4.81	4.15
r_x (mm)	32.8	33.1	25.1	26.1	27.0	27.5	17.1	17.5
Z_y (10³mm³)	25.0	21.4	26.7	23.5	19.3	16.3	3.84	3.27
S_y (10³mm³)	21.4	18.5	20.5	18.8	16.0	13.8	3.14	2.75
r_y (mm)	25.2	25.5	18.0	18.8	19.6	20.0	9.77	10.1
r_x/r_y	1.30	1.30	1.39	1.39	1.38	1.37	1.75	1.74
M_{rx} (kN•m)	9.92	8.50	11.3	9.89	8.10	6.80	1.99	1.69
M_{ry} (kN•m)	7.87	6.74	8.41	7.40	6.08	5.13	1.21	1.03

IMPERIAL SIZE AND MASS

Mass (lb./ft.)	5.62	4.76	8.46	7.11	5.61	4.60	2.21	1.82
Thickness (in.)	.150	.125	.313	.250	.188	.150	.125	.100
Size (in.)	3½ x 2½		3 x 2				2 x 1	

SQUARE HOLLOW SECTIONS
Factored Axial Compressive Resistances, C_r, in kN

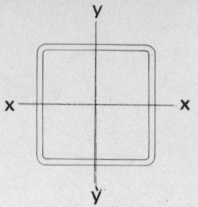

G40.21-M 350W
CLASS H
$\emptyset = 0.90$

Size (mm)	304.8 x 304.8					254.0 x 254.0		
Thickness (mm)	12.70	11.13	9.53	††7.95	‡6.35	12.70	11.13	9.53
Mass (kg/m)	113	100	86.5	72.8	58.7	93.0	82.4	71.3
0	4 540	4 030	3 460	2 920	2 110	3 720	3 310	2 860
1 000	4 540	4 030	3 460	2 920	2 110	3 720	3 310	2 860
1 250	4 540	4 030	3 460	2 920	2 100	3 720	3 310	2 860
1 500	4 540	4 030	3 470	2 920	2 100	3 720	3 310	2 860
1 750	4 530	4 030	3 460	2 920	2 090	3 710	3 300	2 860
2 000	4 530	4 030	3 460	2 920	2 080	3 700	3 290	2 850
2 250	4 520	4 020	3 460	2 920	2 080	3 690	3 280	2 840
2 500	4 510	4 010	3 450	2 910	2 070	3 680	3 270	2 830
2 750	4 500	4 000	3 440	2 900	2 060	3 660	3 260	2 820
3 000	4 490	3 990	3 430	2 890	2 050	3 640	3 240	2 800
3 250	4 470	3 970	3 420	2 880	2 040	3 610	3 220	2 790
3 500	4 450	3 960	3 400	2 870	2 030	3 590	3 190	2 770
3 750	4 430	3 940	3 390	2 860	2 020	3 550	3 170	2 740
4 000	4 400	3 920	3 370	2 840	2 000	3 520	3 140	2 720
4 250	4 370	3 890	3 350	2 830	1 990	3 480	3 100	2 690
4 500	4 340	3 860	3 320	2 810	1 970	3 440	3 070	2 660
4 750	4 310	3 840	3 300	2 790	1 960	3 400	3 030	2 630
5 000	4 270	3 800	3 270	2 770	1 940	3 350	2 990	2 600
5 250	4 230	3 770	3 250	2 740	1 920	3 300	2 950	2 560
5 500	4 190	3 730	3 210	2 720	1 900	3 250	2 900	2 520
5 750	4 150	3 700	3 180	2 690	1 880	3 200	2 850	2 480
6 000	4 100	3 650	3 150	2 660	1 860	3 140	2 800	2 430
6 500	4 000	3 570	3 070	2 600	1 820	3 010	2 690	2 340
7 000	3 890	3 470	2 990	2 530	1 780	2 870	2 570	2 230
7 500	3 770	3 360	2 900	2 460	1 730	2 720	2 430	2 120
8 000	3 630	3 250	2 800	2 380	1 670	2 550	2 290	2 000
8 500	3 490	3 120	2 700	2 290	1 620	2 370	2 130	1 860
9 000	3 340	2 990	2 580	2 190	1 560	2 160	1 950	1 710
9 500	3 170	2 840	2 460	2 090	1 490	1 960	1 770	1 550
10 000	3 000	2 690	2 330	1 990	1 420	1 790	1 620	1 420
10 500	2 810	2 530	2 200	1 870	1 350	1 640	1 480	1 300

Effective length (KL) in millimetres with respect to least radius of gyration

PROPERTIES AND DESIGN DATA

Area (mm^2)	14 400	12 800	11 000	9 280	7 480	11 800	10 500	9 090
Z (10^3mm^3)	1 560	1 390	1 210	1 030	833	1 060	945	825
S (10^3mm^3)	1 330	1 190	1 040	886	723	888	799	703
r (mm)	118	119	120	121	121	97.6	98.4	99.1
M$_r$ (kN•m)	491	438	381	279	207	334	298	260

IMPERIAL SIZE AND MASS

Mass (lb./ft.)	76.1	67.3	58.1	48.9	39.4	62.5	55.4	47.9
Thickness (in.)	.500	.438	.375	.313	.250	.500	.438	.375
Size (in.)	12 x 12					10 x 10		

†† Class 3 in bending
‡ Class 4 in bending and resistance for this column calculated according to CAN3-S16.1-M78 Clause 13.3.3.

G40.21-M 350W CLASS H $\phi = 0.90$

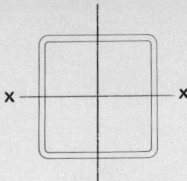

SQUARE HOLLOW SECTIONS
Factored Axial Compressive Resistances, C_r, in kN

Size (mm)	254.0 x 254.0		203.2 x 203.2				
Thickness (mm)	7.95	‡6.35	12.70	11.13	9.53	7.95	6.35
Mass (kg/m)	60.1	48.6	72.7	64.6	56.1	47.5	38.4
0	2 410	1 950	2 920	2 590	2 250	1 910	1 540
1 000	2 410	1 940	2 920	2 590	2 250	1 910	1 540
1 250	2 410	1 930	2 910	2 590	2 250	1 900	1 540
1 500	2 410	1 930	2 910	2 580	2 250	1 900	1 540
1 750	2 410	1 920	2 900	2 580	2 240	1 890	1 530
2 000	2 400	1 910	2 880	2 560	2 230	1 890	1 530
2 250	2 400	1 900	2 860	2 550	2 210	1 870	1 520
2 500	2 390	1 890	2 840	2 530	2 200	1 860	1 510
2 750	2 380	1 870	2 810	2 500	2 180	1 840	1 500
3 000	2 360	1 860	2 780	2 480	2 160	1 830	1 480
3 250	2 350	1 840	2 750	2 450	2 130	1 800	1 460
3 500	2 330	1 830	2 710	2 410	2 100	1 780	1 450
3 750	2 310	1 810	2 670	2 380	2 070	1 760	1 420
4 000	2 290	1 790	2 620	2 340	2 030	1 730	1 400
4 250	2 270	1 770	2 570	2 290	2 000	1 700	1 380
4 500	2 250	1 740	2 510	2 240	1 960	1 660	1 350
4 750	2 220	1 720	2 450	2 190	1 910	1 630	1 320
5 000	2 190	1 700	2 390	2 140	1 870	1 590	1 290
5 250	2 160	1 670	2 320	2 080	1 820	1 550	1 260
5 500	2 130	1 640	2 250	2 020	1 770	1 500	1 220
5 750	2 090	1 610	2 180	1 950	1 710	1 460	1 190
6 000	2 060	1 580	2 100	1 880	1 650	1 410	1 150
6 500	1 980	1 520	1 930	1 740	1 530	1 310	1 070
7 000	1 890	1 450	1 730	1 570	1 390	1 190	977
7 500	1 800	1 380	1 530	1 390	1 230	1 060	870
8 000	1 700	1 300	1 360	1 230	1 090	941	774
8 500	1 590	1 220	1 220	1 110	980	845	695
9 000	1 470	1 130	1 110	1 000	887	764	628
9 500	1 330	1 030	1 010	914	808	696	572
10 000	1 210	935	926	837	740	637	524
10 500	1 110	848	852	773	682	587	482

Effective length (KL) in millimetres with respect to least radius of gyration

PROPERTIES AND DESIGN DATA

Area (mm^2)	7 660	6 190	9 260	8 230	7 150	6 050	4 900
Z (10^{3}mm^3)	702	571	650	584	513	438	359
S (10^{3}mm^3)	602	494	538	488	432	373	308
r (mm)	99.9	101	76.8	77.6	78.4	79.2	79.9
M$_r$ (kN•m)	221	156	205	184	162	138	113

IMPERIAL SIZE AND MASS

Mass (lb./ft.)	40.4	32.6	48.9	43.4	37.7	31.9	25.8
Thickness (in.)	.313	.250	.500	.438	.375	.313	.250
Size (in.)	10 x 10		8 x 8				

‡ Class 4 in bending and resistance for this column calculated according to CAN3-S16.1-M78 Clause 13.3.3.

SQUARE HOLLOW SECTIONS
Factored Axial Compressive
Resistances, C_r, in kN

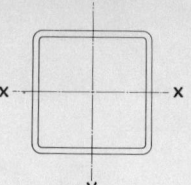

Size (mm)		177.8 x 177.8						152.4 x 152.4		
Thickness (mm)		12.70	11.13	9.53	7.95	6.35	††4.78	12.70	11.13	9.53
Mass (kg/m)		62.6	55.7	48.5	41.1	33.4	25.5	52.4	46.9	40.9
	0	2 510	2 240	1 950	1 650	1 340	1 020	2 100	1 880	1 640
	1 000	2 510	2 240	1 950	1 650	1 340	1 020	2 100	1 880	1 640
	1 250	2 500	2 230	1 940	1 650	1 340	1 020	2 090	1 870	1 630
	1 500	2 490	2 220	1 940	1 640	1 330	1 020	2 080	1 860	1 620
	1 750	2 480	2 210	1 920	1 630	1 320	1 010	2 060	1 840	1 610
	2 000	2 460	2 190	1 910	1 620	1 320	1 010	2 030	1 820	1 590
	2 250	2 440	2 170	1 890	1 610	1 300	998	2 000	1 790	1 570
	2 500	2 410	2 150	1 870	1 590	1 290	988	1 960	1 760	1 540
	2 750	2 370	2 120	1 850	1 570	1 280	977	1 920	1 720	1 510
	3 000	2 340	2 090	1 820	1 550	1 260	963	1 870	1 680	1 470
	3 250	2 290	2 050	1 790	1 520	1 240	948	1 820	1 640	1 440
	3 500	2 250	2 010	1 750	1 490	1 210	931	1 760	1 590	1 390
	3 750	2 190	1 960	1 720	1 460	1 190	913	1 700	1 530	1 350
	4 000	2 140	1 910	1 670	1 430	1 160	892	1 630	1 470	1 290
	4 250	2 080	1 860	1 630	1 390	1 130	871	1 550	1 410	1 240
	4 500	2 010	1 800	1 580	1 350	1 100	847	1 470	1 340	1 180
	4 750	1 940	1 740	1 530	1 310	1 070	822	1 390	1 260	1 120
	5 000	1 870	1 680	1 470	1 260	1 030	795	1 300	1 180	1 050
	5 250	1 790	1 610	1 420	1 210	994	766	1 190	1 090	976
	5 500	1 700	1 540	1 350	1 160	953	736	1 090	1 000	897
	5 750	1 610	1 460	1 290	1 110	910	704	1 010	925	828
	6 000	1 520	1 380	1 220	1 050	865	670	935	857	767
	6 500	1 310	1 190	1 060	920	762	593	813	745	666
	7 000	1 150	1 050	929	804	666	519	716	655	586
	7 500	1 020	925	822	712	589	459	637	583	521
	8 000	909	827	735	636	526	409	565	519	465
	8 500	820	746	662	573	474	369	502	461	414
	9 000	746	677	601	520	430	334	450	413	370
	9 500	672	612	545	473	392	305	405	372	334
	10 000	608	554	494	428	355	277	367	337	302
	10 500	553	505	449	390	323	252	335	307	276

Effective length (KL) in millimetres with respect to least radius of gyration

PROPERTIES AND DESIGN DATA

Area (mm²)		7 970	7 100	6 180	5 240	4 250	3 250	6 680	5 970	5 210
Z (10³mm³)		484	436	385	330	271	209	341	310	275
S (10³mm³)		396	361	322	279	231	181	275	253	227
r (mm)		66.4	67.2	68.0	68.8	69.6	70.3	56.0	56.8	57.6
M_r (kN•m)		152	137	121	104	85.4	57.0	107	97.6	86.6

IMPERIAL SIZE AND MASS

Mass (lb./ft.)		42.1	37.5	32.6	27.6	22.4	17.1	35.2	31.5	27.5
Thickness (in.)		.500	.438	.375	.313	.250	.188	.500	.438	.375
Size (in.)				7 x 7					6 x 6	

†† Class 3 in bending.

G40.21-M 350W
CLASS H
$\emptyset = 0.90$

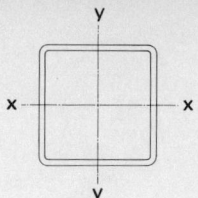

SQUARE HOLLOW SECTIONS
Factored Axial Compressive
Resistances, C_r, in kN

Size (mm)		152.4 x 152.4			127.0 x 127.0				
Thickness (mm)		7.95	6.35	4.78	11.13	9.53	7.95	6.35	4.78
Mass (kg/m)		34.8	28.3	21.7	38.0	33.3	28.4	23.2	17.9
Effective length (KL) in millimetres with respect to least radius of gyration	0	1 400	1 140	869	1 520	1 340	1 140	932	718
	1 000	1 390	1 140	869	1 520	1 330	1 140	929	716
	1 250	1 390	1 130	866	1 500	1 320	1 130	922	711
	1 500	1 380	1 130	861	1 490	1 300	1 110	912	704
	1 750	1 370	1 120	854	1 460	1 280	1 100	899	694
	2 000	1 350	1 100	845	1 430	1 260	1 080	883	682
	2 250	1 330	1 090	834	1 400	1 230	1 050	864	668
	2 500	1 310	1 070	821	1 350	1 190	1 020	841	651
	2 750	1 290	1 050	806	1 310	1 150	991	816	632
	3 000	1 260	1 030	790	1 250	1 110	955	787	611
	3 250	1 230	1 000	771	1 200	1 060	914	755	587
	3 500	1 190	976	750	1 130	1 010	869	720	561
	3 750	1 150	946	727	1 060	946	821	681	532
	4 000	1 110	913	703	986	882	768	640	501
	4 250	1 070	877	676	899	813	711	595	468
	4 500	1 020	839	648	810	732	644	543	431
	4 750	965	798	617	735	664	584	492	390
	5 000	910	754	584	671	606	533	449	356
	5 250	851	708	550	616	556	489	411	326
	5 500	782	653	510	568	512	451	379	300
	5 750	721	603	471	526	475	417	351	278
	6 000	668	558	436	490	441	388	326	258
	6 500	580	484	378	425	385	339	285	226
	7 000	510	425	332	368	333	294	248	197
	7 500	453	378	295	322	292	257	217	173
	8 000	406	339	265	285	258	227	192	152
	8 500	361	302	236	254	229	202	171	136
	9 000	323	270	212	227	206	181	153	122
	9 500	291	244	191			164	138	110
	10 000	264	221	173					
	10 500	240	201	157					

PROPERTIES AND DESIGN DATA

	152.4 x 152.4			127.0 x 127.0				
Area (mm²)	4 430	3 610	2 760	4 840	4 240	3 620	2 960	2 280
Z (10³mm³)	237	195	152	205	183	159	132	103
S (10³mm³)	198	166	130	164	149	132	111	88.1
r (mm)	58.4	59.2	59.9	46.4	47.2	48.0	48.8	49.6
M_r (kN•m)	74.7	61.4	47.9	64.6	57.6	50.1	41.6	32.4

IMPERIAL SIZE AND MASS

Mass (lb./ft.)	23.4	19.0	14.6	25.5	22.4	19.1	15.6	12.0
Thickness (in.)	.313	.250	.188	.438	.375	.313	.250	.188
Size (in.)	6 x 6			5 x 5				

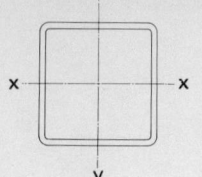

Size (mm)		101.6 x 101.6				88.9 x 88.9			
Thickness (mm)		9.53	7.95	6.35	4.78	9.53	7.95	6.35	4.78
Mass (kg/m)		25.7	22.1	18.2	14.1	21.9	18.9	15.6	12.2
	0	1 030	888	731	564	879	759	627	488
	1 000	1 020	877	722	558	858	743	614	479
	1 250	1 000	864	712	550	837	726	601	470
	1 500	980	845	697	540	809	703	583	457
	1 750	951	821	679	526	774	674	561	440
	2 000	915	793	656	509	731	639	534	420
	2 250	874	759	630	490	682	599	502	397
	2 500	827	720	599	467	625	553	466	370
	2 750	773	676	565	442	561	500	425	340
	3 000	713	627	526	413	485	439	379	306
	3 250	647	572	483	382	420	380	327	266
	3 500	569	508	435	347	368	333	287	233
	3 750	502	449	383	307	327	295	254	206
	4 000	448	400	342	273	293	264	227	184
	4 250	403	359	307	245	264	238	205	166
	4 500	365	325	278	222	237	215	186	151
	4 750	333	297	253	202	214	194	168	137
	5 000	306	272	232	185	194	175	152	124
	5 250	278	249	214	171	176	160	138	113
	5 500	254	228	195	157	161	146	126	103
	5 750	233	209	179	144	148	134	116	95
	6 000	215	192	165	132	137	124	107	87
	6 500	184	165	141	113			92	75
	7 000	160	143	123	98				
	7 500		126	108	86				
	8 000								
	8 500								
	9 000								
	9 500								
	10 000								
	10 500								

Effective length (KL) in millimetres with respect to least radius of gyration

PROPERTIES AND DESIGN DATA

Area (mm^2)		3 280	2 820	2 320	1 790	2 790	2 410	1 990	1 550
Z (10^{3}mm^3)		110	96.6	81.3	64.3	80.2	71.2	60.5	48.2
S (10^{3}mm^3)		87.4	78.4	67.3	54.2	62.7	57.0	49.5	40.3
r (mm)		36.8	37.6	38.4	39.2	31.6	32.4	33.2	34.0
M_r (kN•m)		34.6	30.4	25.6	20.3	25.3	22.4	19.1	15.2

IMPERIAL SIZE AND MASS

Mass (lb./ft.)		17.3	14.9	12.2	9.45	14.7	12.7	10.5	8.17
Thickness (in.)		.375	.313	.250	.188	.375	.313	.250	.188
Size (in.)		4 x 4				3½ x 3½			

G40.21-M 350W CLASS H
$\phi = 0.90$

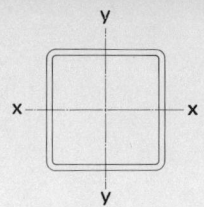

SQUARE HOLLOW SECTIONS
Factored Axial Compressive Resistances, C_r, in kN

Size (mm)	76.2 x 76.2			63.5 x 63.5			
Thickness (mm)	7.95	6.35	4.78	6.35	4.78	3.81	3.18
Mass (kg/m)	15.8	13.1	10.3	10.6	8.35	6.85	5.82
0	633	526	413	425	334	275	233
1 000	609	508	399	398	315	260	221
1 250	587	491	387	376	298	247	211
1 500	558	468	371	347	277	230	197
1 750	522	440	350	311	251	210	180
2 000	480	407	326	269	220	186	160
2 250	430	368	297	219	183	156	136
2 500	371	324	264	181	151	129	112
2 750	312	273	225	154	128	109	95
3 000	267	234	193	133	110	94	82
3 250	233	203	167	115	96	82	71
3 500	205	179	147	99	83	71	62
3 750	182	159	131	87	73	62	54
4 000	161	141	117	77	64	55	48
4 250	143	126	104	68	57	49	43
4 500	128	112	93	61	51	44	38
4 750	115	101	84			40	35
5 000	105	92	76				
5 250	95	84	69				
5 500		77	63				
5 750			58				
6 000							
6 500							
7 000							
7 500							
8 000							
8 500							
9 000							
9 500							
10 000							
10 500							

Effective length (KL) in millimetres with respect to least radius of gyration

PROPERTIES AND DESIGN DATA

Area (mm^2)	2 010	1 670	1 310	1 350	1 060	872	741
Z (10^3mm^3)	49.7	42.7	34.4	28.0	22.9	19.2	16.5
S (10^3mm^3)	39.0	34.4	28.5	22.1	18.7	15.9	13.9
r (mm)	27.2	28.0	28.8	22.8	23.6	24.1	24.4
M_r (kN•m)	15.7	13.5	10.8	8.82	7.21	6.05	5.20

IMPERIAL SIZE AND MASS

Mass (lb./ft.)	10.6	8.81	6.89	7.11	5.61	4.60	3.91
Thickness (in.)	.313	.250	.188	.250	.188	.150	.125
Size (in.)	3 x 3			2½ x 2½			

SQUARE HOLLOW SECTIONS
Factored Axial Compressive
Resistances, C_r, in kN

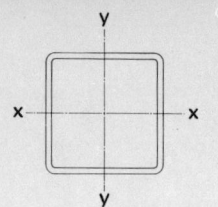

G40.21-M 350W
CLASS H
$\phi = 0.90$

Size (mm)		50.8 x 50.8					38.1 x 38.1			
Thickness (mm)		6.35	4.78	3.81	3.18	2.79	4.78	3.81	3.18	2.54
Mass (kg/m)		8.05	6.45	5.33	4.55	4.05	4.54	3.81	3.28	2.71
	0	324	259	214	183	163	182	153	132	109
	1 000	283	229	191	164	146	135	116	102	85
	1 250	252	207	174	150	134	101	91	81	69
	1 500	213	178	152	131	118	73	65	59	50
	1 750	165	142	124	109	99	56	50	45	38
	2 000	130	112	97	85	77	44	39	35	30
	2 250	106	91	79	69	63	35	31	28	24
	2 500	88	76	66	58	53	28	26	23	20
	2 750	73	64	55	49	44			19	16
	3 000	62	54	47	41	37				
	3 250	53	46	40	35	32				
	3 500	46	40	35	31	28				
	3 750			31	27	24				
	4 000									
	4 250									
	4 500									
	4 750									
	5 000									
	5 250									
	5 500									
	5 750									
	6 000									
	6 500									
	7 000									
	7 500									
	8 000									
	8 500									
	9 000									
	9 500									
	10 000									
	10 500									

Effective length (KL) in millimetres with respect to least radius of gyration

PROPERTIES AND DESIGN DATA

Area (mm^2)		1 030	821	679	580	516	578	485	418	345
Z (10^{3}mm^3)		16.3	13.8	11.7	10.2	9.15	6.91	6.04	5.34	4.51
S (10^{3}mm^3)		12.5	10.9	9.54	8.42	7.64	5.27	4.77	4.31	3.71
r (mm)		17.6	18.4	18.9	19.2	19.4	13.2	13.7	14.0	14.3
M$_r$ (kN•m)		5.13	4.35	3.69	3.21	2.88	2.18	1.90	1.68	1.42

IMPERIAL SIZE AND MASS

Mass (lb./ft.)		5.41	4.33	3.58	3.06	2.72	3.05	2.56	2.21	1.82
Thickness (in.)		.250	.188	.150	.125	.110	.188	.150	.125	.100
Size (in.)		2 x 2					1½ x 1½			

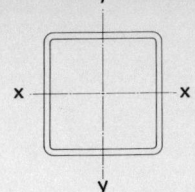

SQUARE HOLLOW SECTIONS
Factored Axial Compressive Resistances, C_r, in kN

Size (mm)	31.8 x 31.8			25.4 x 25.4	
Thickness (mm)	3.81	3.18	2.54	3.18	2.54
Mass (kg/m)	3.06	2.65	2.20	2.01	1.69
0	123	106	89	81	68
1 000	75	67	58	32	29
1 250	50	45	40	22	20
1 500	37	33	29	15	14
1 750	27	25	22	11	10
2 000	21	19	17		
2 250		15	13		
2 500					
2 750					
3 000					
3 250					
3 500					
3 750					
4 000					
4 250					
4 500					
4 750					
5 000					
5 250					
5 500					
5 750					
6 000					
6 500					
7 000					
7 500					
8 000					
8 500					
9 000					
9 500					
10 000					
10 500					

Effective length (KL) in millimetres with respect to least radius of gyration

PROPERTIES AND DESIGN DATA

Area (mm^2)	389	338	281	257	216
Z (10^3mm^3)	3.92	3.51	3.01	2.05	1.79
S (10^3mm^3)	3.01	2.77	2.44	1.56	1.41
r (mm)	11.1	11.4	11.7	8.79	9.12
M_r (kN•m)	1.23	1.11	0.948	0.646	0.564

IMPERIAL SIZE AND MASS

Mass (lb./ft.)	2.05	1.78	1.48	1.35	1.14
Thickness (in.)	.150	.125	.100	.125	.100
Size (in.)	1¼ x 1¼			1 x 1	

ROUND HOLLOW SECTIONS
Factored Axial Compressive
Resistances, C_r, in kN

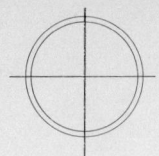

Size (mm)		406.4 OD					355.6 OD		
Thickness (mm)		12.7	11.13	9.53	7.95	6.35	12.7	11.13	9.53
Mass (kg/m)		123	108	93.3	78.1	62.6	107	94.6	81.3
	0	4 950	4 350	3 750	3 130	2 510	4 320	3 780	3 280
	1 000	4 950	4 350	3 750	3 130	2 510	4 320	3 780	3 280
	1 250	4 950	4 350	3 750	3 130	2 510	4 320	3 780	3 280
	1 500	4 950	4 350	3 750	3 130	2 510	4 320	3 780	3 280
	1 750	4 950	4 350	3 750	3 130	2 510	4 310	3 780	3 280
	2 000	4 950	4 350	3 750	3 130	2 510	4 310	3 780	3 270
	2 250	4 940	4 340	3 750	3 130	2 510	4 310	3 770	3 270
	2 500	4 940	4 340	3 740	3 130	2 510	4 300	3 760	3 260
	2 750	4 930	4 330	3 740	3 120	2 510	4 290	3 760	3 250
	3 000	4 920	4 320	3 730	3 120	2 500	4 270	3 740	3 250
	3 250	4 910	4 320	3 720	3 110	2 500	4 260	3 730	3 230
	3 500	4 890	4 300	3 710	3 100	2 490	4 240	3 720	3 220
	3 750	4 880	4 290	3 700	3 090	2 480	4 220	3 700	3 210
	4 000	4 860	4 270	3 690	3 080	2 470	4 200	3 680	3 190
	4 250	4 840	4 260	3 670	3 070	2 460	4 170	3 660	3 170
	4 500	4 820	4 240	3 650	3 060	2 450	4 140	3 630	3 150
	4 750	4 790	4 220	3 640	3 040	2 440	4 110	3 610	3 130
	5 000	4 770	4 190	3 620	3 030	2 430	4 080	3 580	3 100
	5 250	4 740	4 170	3 600	3 010	2 410	4 050	3 550	3 080
	5 500	4 710	4 140	3 570	2 990	2 400	4 010	3 520	3 050
	5 750	4 680	4 120	3 550	2 970	2 380	3 970	3 490	3 020
	6 000	4 640	4 090	3 520	2 950	2 370	3 930	3 450	2 990
	6 500	4 570	4 020	3 470	2 900	2 330	3 840	3 370	2 920
	7 000	4 480	3 950	3 410	2 850	2 290	3 740	3 280	2 850
	7 500	4 390	3 870	3 340	2 800	2 240	3 630	3 190	2 760
	8 000	4 290	3 780	3 260	2 740	2 190	3 510	3 090	2 680
	8 500	4 180	3 690	3 180	2 670	2 140	3 380	2 980	2 580
	9 000	4 070	3 590	3 090	2 600	2 080	3 240	2 860	2 480
	9 500	3 940	3 480	3 000	2 520	2 020	3 090	2 730	2 370
	10 000	3 810	3 360	2 900	2 440	1 960	2 930	2 590	2 250
	10 500	3 670	3 240	2 800	2 350	1 890	2 770	2 450	2 120

Left margin label: Effective length (KL) in millimetres with respect to least radius of gyration

PROPERTIES AND DESIGN DATA

	12.7	11.13	9.53	7.95	6.35	12.7	11.13	9.53
Area (mm^2)	15 700	13 800	11 900	9 950	7 980	13 700	12 000	10 400
Z (10^3mm^3)	1 970	1 740	1 500	1 260	1 020	1 490	1 320	1 140
S (10^3mm^3)	1 500	1 330	1 150	972	786	1 130	1 010	873
r (mm)	139	140	140	141	141	121	122	122
M_r (kN•m)	621	548	472	397	248	469	416	359

IMPERIAL SIZE AND MASS

Mass (lb./ft.)	82.9	72.9	62.7	52.5	42.1	72.2	63.5	54.7
Thickness (in.)	.500	.438	.375	.313	.250	.500	.438	.375
Size (in.)			16 OD				14 OD	

G40.21-M 350W
CLASS H
$\phi = 0.90$

ROUND HOLLOW SECTIONS
Factored Axial Compressive
Resistances, C_r, in kN

Size (mm)		355.6 OD		323.9 OD				
Thickness (mm)		7.95	6.35	12.7	11.13	9.53	7.95	6.35
Mass (kg/m)		68.2	54.7	97.5	85.9	73.9	61.9	49.7
	0	2 730	2 200	3 910	3 430	2 960	2 490	1 990
	1 000	2 730	2 200	3 910	3 430	2 960	2 490	1 990
	1 250	2 730	2 200	3 910	3 430	2 960	2 490	1 990
	1 500	2 730	2 200	3 910	3 430	2 960	2 490	1 990
	1 750	2 730	2 200	3 900	3 430	2 960	2 480	1 990
	2 000	2 730	2 190	3 900	3 430	2 960	2 480	1 990
	2 250	2 730	2 190	3 890	3 420	2 950	2 480	1 990
	2 500	2 720	2 190	3 880	3 410	2 950	2 470	1 980
	2 750	2 720	2 180	3 870	3 400	2 940	2 460	1 980
	3 000	2 710	2 180	3 850	3 390	2 920	2 450	1 970
	3 250	2 700	2 170	3 830	3 370	2 910	2 440	1 960
	3 500	2 690	2 160	3 810	3 350	2 890	2 430	1 950
	3 750	2 680	2 150	3 790	3 330	2 880	2 410	1 940
	4 000	2 660	2 140	3 760	3 310	2 860	2 400	1 920
	4 250	2 650	2 130	3 730	3 290	2 840	2 380	1 910
	4 500	2 630	2 110	3 700	3 260	2 810	2 360	1 890
	4 750	2 610	2 100	3 670	3 230	2 790	2 340	1 880
	5 000	2 590	2 080	3 630	3 200	2 760	2 320	1 860
	5 250	2 570	2 070	3 590	3 160	2 730	2 290	1 840
	5 500	2 550	2 050	3 550	3 130	2 700	2 270	1 820
	5 750	2 530	2 030	3 500	3 090	2 670	2 240	1 800
	6 000	2 500	2 010	3 460	3 050	2 630	2 210	1 780
	6 500	2 440	1 960	3 350	2 960	2 560	2 150	1 720
	7 000	2 380	1 910	3 240	2 860	2 470	2 080	1 670
	7 500	2 320	1 860	3 120	2 760	2 380	2 010	1 610
	8 000	2 240	1 800	2 980	2 640	2 280	1 920	1 540
	8 500	2 160	1 740	2 840	2 520	2 170	1 840	1 470
	9 000	2 080	1 670	2 680	2 380	2 060	1 740	1 400
	9 500	1 990	1 600	2 520	2 240	1 930	1 640	1 320
	10 000	1 890	1 520	2 330	2 090	1 800	1 530	1 230
	10 500	1 790	1 440	2 140	1 910	1 650	1 400	1 130

Effective length (KL) in millimetres with respect to least radius of gyration

PROPERTIES AND DESIGN DATA

Area (mm²)		8 680	6 970	12 400	10 900	9 410	7 890	6 330
Z (10³mm³)		961	775	1 230	1 090	942	794	640
S (10³mm³)		738	598	930	827	719	608	493
r (mm)		123	123	110	111	111	112	112
M_r (kN•m)		303	188	387	343	297	250	202

IMPERIAL SIZE AND MASS

Mass (lb./ft.)		45.8	36.8	65.5	57.7	49.6	41.6	33.4
Thickness (in.)		.313	.250	.500	.438	.375	.313	.250
Size (in.)		14 OD		12.75 OD				

ROUND HOLLOW SECTIONS
Factored Axial Compressive Resistances, C_r, in kN

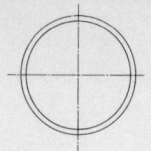

Size (mm)		273.1 OD					219.1 OD		
Thickness (mm)		12.7	11.13	9.53	7.95	6.35	12.7	11.13	9.53
Mass (kg/m)		81.6	71.9	61.9	52.0	41.8	64.6	57.1	49.3
	0	3 280	2 890	2 490	2 090	1 680	2 590	2 290	1 980
	1 000	3 280	2 890	2 490	2 090	1 680	2 590	2 290	1 980
	1 250	3 280	2 890	2 490	2 090	1 680	2 590	2 290	1 970
	1 500	3 270	2 880	2 480	2 080	1 670	2 580	2 280	1 970
	1 750	3 270	2 880	2 480	2 080	1 670	2 570	2 270	1 960
	2 000	3 260	2 870	2 470	2 070	1 670	2 560	2 260	1 950
	2 250	3 250	2 860	2 460	2 070	1 660	2 540	2 240	1 930
	2 500	3 230	2 850	2 450	2 060	1 650	2 510	2 220	1 920
	2 750	3 210	2 830	2 440	2 050	1 650	2 490	2 200	1 900
	3 000	3 190	2 810	2 420	2 030	1 640	2 460	2 170	1 870
	3 250	3 170	2 790	2 400	2 020	1 620	2 420	2 140	1 850
	3 500	3 140	2 770	2 380	2 000	1 610	2 380	2 110	1 820
	3 750	3 110	2 740	2 360	1 980	1 590	2 340	2 070	1 790
	4 000	3 070	2 710	2 340	1 960	1 580	2 290	2 030	1 750
	4 250	3 040	2 680	2 310	1 940	1 560	2 240	1 990	1 720
	4 500	3 000	2 640	2 280	1 910	1 540	2 190	1 940	1 680
	4 750	2 950	2 600	2 250	1 890	1 520	2 130	1 890	1 630
	5 000	2 900	2 560	2 210	1 860	1 500	2 070	1 830	1 590
	5 250	2 860	2 520	2 170	1 830	1 470	2 000	1 770	1 540
	5 500	2 800	2 470	2 140	1 800	1 450	1 930	1 710	1 490
	5 750	2 750	2 420	2 090	1 760	1 420	1 850	1 650	1 430
	6 000	2 690	2 370	2 050	1 730	1 390	1 780	1 580	1 370
	6 500	2 560	2 260	1 960	1 650	1 330	1 610	1 430	1 250
	7 000	2 420	2 140	1 850	1 560	1 260	1 410	1 260	1 100
	7 500	2 270	2 010	1 740	1 470	1 190	1 240	1 110	974
	8 000	2 100	1 860	1 620	1 370	1 110	1 110	992	868
	8 500	1 910	1 700	1 480	1 250	1 020	998	892	781
	9 000	1 720	1 530	1 330	1 130	917	905	809	707
	9 500	1 560	1 390	1 210	1 020	831	826	738	645
	10 000	1 430	1 270	1 100	935	759	757	677	592
	10 500	1 310	1 160	1 010	858	696	688	616	540

Effective length (KL) in millimetres with respect to least radius of gyration

PROPERTIES AND DESIGN DATA

Area (mm^2)		10 400	9 160	7 890	6 620	5 320	8 230	7 270	6 270
Z (10^3mm^3)		862	764	662	559	452	542	482	419
S (10^3mm^3)		646	577	502	427	347	402	360	315
r (mm)		92.2	92.7	93.2	93.8	94.3	73.1	73.6	74.2
M_r (kN•m)		272	241	209	176	142	171	152	132

IMPERIAL SIZE AND MASS

Mass (lb./ft.)		54.8	48.3	41.6	34.9	28.1	43.4	38.4	33.1
Thickness (in.)		.500	.438	.375	.313	.250	.500	.438	.375
Size (in.)		10.75 OD					8.625 OD		

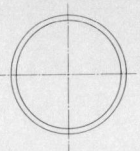

ROUND HOLLOW SECTIONS
Factored Axial Compressive
Resistances, C_r, in kN

Size (mm)		219.1 OD			168.3 OD			
Thickness (mm)		7.95	6.35	4.78	9.53	7.95	6.35	4.78
Mass (kg/m)		41.4	33.3	25.3	37.3	31.4	25.4	19.3
Effective length (KL) in millimetres with respect to least radius of gyration	0	1 660	1 340	1 010	1 500	1 260	1 020	775
	1 000	1 660	1 340	1 010	1 490	1 260	1 020	774
	1 250	1 660	1 330	1 010	1 490	1 250	1 010	771
	1 500	1 650	1 330	1 010	1 480	1 240	1 010	766
	1 750	1 650	1 330	1 010	1 460	1 230	996	759
	2 000	1 640	1 320	1 000	1 440	1 220	984	750
	2 250	1 630	1 310	995	1 420	1 200	970	740
	2 500	1 610	1 300	987	1 400	1 180	953	727
	2 750	1 600	1 290	977	1 370	1 150	934	713
	3 000	1 580	1 270	966	1 330	1 130	912	697
	3 250	1 560	1 250	953	1 300	1 100	888	679
	3 500	1 530	1 240	940	1 260	1 060	861	658
	3 750	1 510	1 210	924	1 210	1 030	832	637
	4 000	1 480	1 190	907	1 160	985	800	613
	4 250	1 450	1 170	889	1 110	942	766	587
	4 500	1 410	1 140	869	1 050	895	729	560
	4 750	1 380	1 110	848	991	845	689	530
	5 000	1 340	1 080	826	927	792	647	499
	5 250	1 300	1 050	802	851	731	599	464
	5 500	1 260	1 020	776	782	671	551	426
	5 750	1 210	981	749	722	620	508	393
	6 000	1 160	943	721	669	574	471	364
	6 500	1 060	862	660	582	499	409	316
	7 000	939	766	589	512	439	360	278
	7 500	829	676	520	456	391	320	247
	8 000	739	603	463	404	348	285	221
	8 500	664	542	416	359	309	254	197
	9 000	601	490	377	322	277	227	176
	9 500	548	447	343	290	249	205	159
	10 000	503	410	315	263	226	186	144
	10 500	460	376	289	240	206	169	131
PROPERTIES AND DESIGN DATA								
Area (mm^2)		5 270	4 240	3 220	4 750	4 000	3 230	2 460
Z (10^3mm^3)		355	288	220	241	205	167	128
S (10^3mm^3)		269	219	169	179	153	126	97.6
r (mm)		74.7	75.3	75.8	56.2	56.8	57.3	57.8
M_r (kN•m)		112	90.7	69.3	75.9	64.6	52.6	40.3
IMPERIAL SIZE AND MASS								
Mass (lb./ft.)		27.8	22.4	17.0	25.1	21.1	17.0	13.0
Thickness (in.)		.313	.250	.188	.375	.313	.250	.188
Size (in.)		8.625 OD			6.625 OD			

ROUND HOLLOW SECTIONS
Factored Axial Compressive Resistances, C_r, in kN

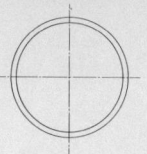

Size (mm)	141.3 OD				114.3 OD		
Thickness (mm)	9.53	7.95	6.35	4.78	7.95	6.35	4.78
Mass (kg/m)	31.0	26.1	21.1	16.1	20.9	16.9	12.9
0	1 240	1 050	847	646	838	677	517
1 000	1 240	1 040	844	643	827	669	511
1 250	1 230	1 040	837	638	815	659	504
1 500	1 210	1 020	828	631	797	646	494
1 750	1 190	1 010	815	622	775	628	481
2 000	1 170	988	800	611	748	607	465
2 250	1 140	965	781	597	717	582	447
2 500	1 110	937	760	581	680	554	426
2 750	1 070	906	736	563	639	521	402
3 000	1 030	871	708	542	593	485	375
3 250	980	832	678	520	542	445	346
3 500	929	789	644	495	482	399	313
3 750	872	743	607	467	425	352	276
4 000	811	693	568	438	379	314	246
4 250	742	638	525	406	341	282	221
4 500	669	575	475	369	308	255	200
4 750	607	521	431	335	281	232	182
5 000	554	476	393	305	258	213	167
5 250	508	437	361	280	236	196	154
5 500	469	402	332	258	216	179	141
5 750	434	373	308	239	198	164	129
6 000	404	347	286	222	182	151	119
6 500	351	302	250	194	156	130	102
7 000	304	262	217	168	136	113	88
7 500	266	229	190	147	119	99	78
8 000	235	202	167	130			
8 500	209	180	149	116			
9 000	188	162	134	104			
9 500			121	94			
10 000							
10 500							

Effective length (KL) in millimetres with respect to least radius of gyration

PROPERTIES AND DESIGN DATA							
Area (mm^2)	3 950	3 330	2 690	2 050	2 660	2 150	1 640
Z (10^3 mm^3)	166	142	116	89.1	90.1	74.1	57.4
S (10^3 mm^3)	122	105	86.9	67.7	66.1	55.1	43.2
r (mm)	46.7	47.2	47.8	48.3	37.7	38.2	38.8
M_r (kN•m)	52.3	44.7	36.5	28.1	28.4	23.3	18.1

IMPERIAL SIZE AND MASS							
Mass (lb./ft.)	20.8	17.6	14.2	10.8	14.0	11.4	8.68
Thickness (in.)	.375	.313	.250	.188	.313	.250	.188
Size (in.)	5.562 OD				4.5 OD		

G40.21-M 350W
CLASS H
$\phi = 0.90$

ROUND HOLLOW SECTIONS
Factored Axial Compressive Resistances, C_r, in kN

Size (mm)		101.6 OD				88.9 OD			
Thickness (mm)		7.95	6.35	4.78	3.81	7.95	6.35	4.78	3.81
Mass (kg/m)		18.4	14.9	11.4	9.19	15.9	12.9	9.92	8.00
	0	737	598	457	369	636	520	397	321
	500	737	598	457	369	635	519	396	321
	750	732	595	454	367	629	514	393	318
	1 000	722	587	449	362	616	504	385	312
	1 250	707	575	440	355	597	489	375	304
	1 500	686	559	428	346	571	469	360	292
	1 750	660	538	413	334	540	444	342	278
	2 000	628	514	394	319	502	415	320	260
	2 250	591	485	373	302	458	380	294	240
	2 500	548	451	348	283	408	340	265	217
	2 750	500	414	321	261	348	293	231	190
	3 000	445	372	290	236	297	250	197	163
	3 250	385	323	253	207	258	217	171	141
	3 500	337	283	221	182	227	191	150	124
	3 750	299	250	196	161	202	170	133	110
	4 000	267	224	175	143	180	152	120	99
	4 250	241	202	158	129	160	135	107	88
	4 500	219	183	143	117	144	121	96	79
	4 750	197	166	130	107	129	109	86	71
	5 000	179	150	118	97	117	99	78	64
	5 250	162	137	107	88	107	90	71	59
	5 500	149	125	98	80	98	83	65	54
	5 750	136	115	90	74	90	76	60	49
	6 000	126	106	83	68				46
	6 500	108	91	71	58				
	7 000								
	7 500								
	8 000								
	8 500								
	9 000								
	9 500								

Effective length (KL) in millimetres with respect to least radius of gyration

PROPERTIES AND DESIGN DATA

Area (mm²)	2 340	1 900	1 450	1 170	2 020	1 650	1 260	1 020
Z (10³ mm³)	69.9	57.7	44.8	36.5	52.3	43.4	33.9	27.6
S (10³ mm³)	50.8	42.6	33.6	27.6	37.6	31.7	25.2	20.8
r (mm)	33.2	33.8	34.3	34.6	28.8	29.3	29.8	30.1
M_r (kN•m)	22.0	18.2	14.1	11.5	16.5	13.7	10.7	8.69

IMPERIAL SIZE AND MASS

Mass (lb./ft.)	12.3	10.0	7.67	6.17	10.7	8.69	6.66	5.37
Thickness (in.)	.313	.250	.188	.150	.313	.250	.188	.150
Size (in.)		4 OD				3.5 OD		

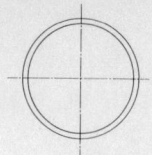
Size (mm)		73.0 OD				60.3 OD		
Thickness (mm)	6.35	4.78	3.81	3.18	6.35	4.78	3.81	3.18
Mass (kg/m)	10.4	8.04	6.50	5.48	8.45	6.54	5.31	4.48
0	419	321	261	220	340	263	213	180
500	417	320	260	219	336	260	211	178
750	409	314	255	215	325	252	204	173
1 000	395	304	247	209	306	238	193	164
1 250	375	289	236	199	279	218	178	151
1 500	349	270	221	187	245	193	159	135
1 750	316	246	202	171	202	163	135	116
2 000	278	218	180	153	159	129	107	92
2 250	231	184	153	131	129	104	87	75
2 500	191	152	126	108	108	87	72	62
2 750	162	129	107	91	91	74	62	53
3 000	139	111	92	79	77	62	52	45
3 250	122	97	80	69	66	53	45	38
3 500	105	84	70	60	57	46	39	33
3 750	92	74	61	52	50	41	34	29
4 000	81	65	54	46				26
4 250	73	58	48	41				
4 500	65	52	43	37				
4 750		47	39	33				
5 000								
5 250								
5 500								
5 750								
6 000								
6 500								
7 000								
7 500								
8 000								
8 500								
9 000								
9 500								

Effective length (KL) in millimetres with respect to least radius of gyration

PROPERTIES AND DESIGN DATA

Area (mm^2)	1 330	1 020	828	698	1 080	834	676	571
Z (10^{3}mm^3)	28.3	22.3	18.3	15.5	18.6	14.8	12.2	10.4
S (10^{3}mm^3)	20.4	16.4	13.6	11.7	13.2	10.7	8.99	7.74
r (mm)	23.7	24.2	24.5	24.7	19.2	19.7	20.0	20.2
M$_r$ (kN•m)	8.91	7.02	5.76	4.88	5.86	4.66	3.84	3.28

IMPERIAL SIZE AND MASS

Mass (lb./ft.)	7.01	5.40	4.37	3.68	5.68	4.40	3.57	3.01
Thickness (in.)	.250	.188	.150	.125	.250	.188	.150	.125
Size (in.)		2.875 OD				2.375 OD		

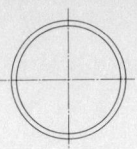
Size (mm)	48.3 OD				42.2 OD		33.4 OD		26.7 OD	
Thickness (mm)	4.78	3.81	3.18	2.79	3.18	2.54	3.18	2.54	3.18	2.54
Mass (kg/m)	5.13	4.18	3.54	3.13	3.06	2.48	2.37	1.93	1.84	1.51
Effective length (KL) in millimetres with respect to least radius of gyration										
0	206	168	142	126	123	100	95	77	74	61
500	201	164	139	123	118	96	88	72	63	53
750	189	155	131	116	109	89	75	62	46	39
1 000	170	140	119	106	94	77	54	46	27	23
1 250	144	119	102	91	74	62	36	31	18	16
1 500	110	93	80	72	53	45	26	22	13	11
1 750	84	70	61	54	41	34	20	17		
2 000	66	56	48	43	32	27	15	13		
2 250	54	45	39	35	26	22				
2 500	44	37	32	29	21	18				
2 750	36	31	27	24	17	15				
3 000	31	26	23	20						
3 250										
3 500										
3 750										
4 000										
4 250										
4 500										
4 750										
5 000										
5 250										
5 500										
5 750										
6 000										
6 500										
7 000										
7 500										
8 000										
8 500										
9 000										
9 500										

PROPERTIES AND DESIGN DATA

Area (mm^2)	654	533	451	399	390	316	302	246	235	193
Z (10^{3}mm^3)	9.09	7.56	6.48	5.79	4.85	4.00	2.91	2.42	1.77	1.49
S (10^{3}mm^3)	6.48	5.50	4.77	4.29	3.54	2.96	2.09	1.77	1.24	1.07
r (mm)	15.5	15.8	16.0	16.1	13.8	14.1	10.7	10.9	8.39	8.59
M_r (kN•m)	2.86	2.38	2.04	1.82	1.53	1.26	0.917	0.762	0.558	0.469

IMPERIAL SIZE AND MASS

Mass (lb./ft.)	3.45	2.81	2.38	2.10	2.06	1.67	1.59	1.30	1.24	1.02
Thickness (in.)	1.88	.150	.125	.110	.125	.100	.125	.100	.125	.100
Size (in.)	1.9 OD				1.66 OD		1.315 OD		1.05 OD	

DESIGN OF BEAM-COLUMNS

General

For members which are subject to both axial compression and bending (usually referred to as beam-columns), Clause 13.8 of CAN3-S16.1-M78, "Steel Structures for Buildings — Limit States Design" and Appendix F of that Standard are applicable.

Which particular subclause of Clause 13.8 is used depends upon the Class of section and the type of section, i.e. W, HSS or other. If a more detailed design of Class 1 and 2 sections is required than that given in Clause 13.8 then Appendix F is appropriate. (See page 4—108)

The following decision table has been reprinted from Appendix F of CAN3-S16.1-M78 to aid the designer in the selection of the appropriate design equations for beam-columns. References in the table are to the Clauses and subclause of CAN3-S16.1-M78 and its Appendix F.

BEAM-COLUMNS WITH BIAXIAL ECCENTRICITY
DECISION TABLE FOR DESIGN EQUATIONS

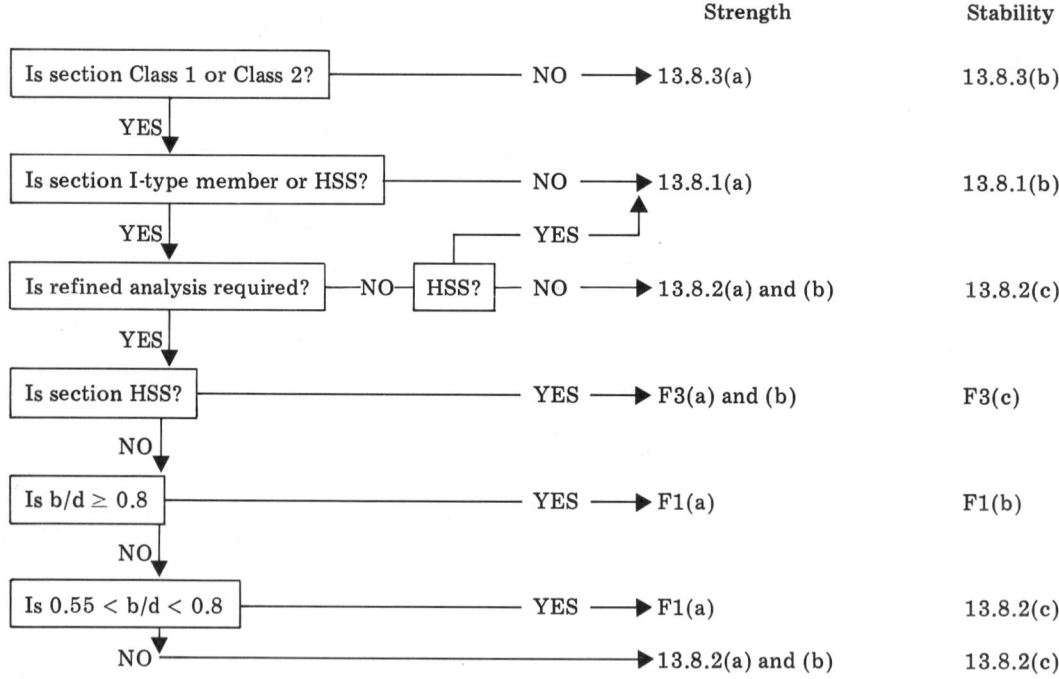

For Class 1 and Class 2 sections of I-shaped members the following equations apply when using Clause 13.8.2 of CAN3-S16.1-M78.

$$(1)\ \frac{M_{fx}}{M_{rx}} + \frac{M_{fy}}{M_{ry}} \leqslant 1.0$$

$$(2)\ \frac{C_f}{C_r} + \frac{0.85\,M_{fx}}{M_{rx}} + \frac{0.60\,M_{fy}}{M_{ry}} \leqslant 1.0$$

$$(3)\ \frac{C_f}{C_r} + \frac{\omega_x M_{fx}}{M_{rx}\left(1 - \dfrac{C_f}{C_{ex}}\right)} + \frac{\omega_y M_{fy}}{M_{ry}\left(1 - \dfrac{C_f}{C_{ey}}\right)} \leqslant 1.0$$

where

M_{fx}, M_{fy} = factored bending moment at the point under consideration when used with (1) and (2) above; the maximum computed factored bending moment occurring either at or between braced points when used with (3).

M_{rx} = factored moment resistance, for the X—X axis and is equal to $\phi\, Z_x F_y$ when used with (1) and (2) and is reduced according to Clause 13.6(a) of CAN3-S16.1-M78 depending upon the unbraced length of (3). In determining M_u according to Clause 13.6(a)(ii), ω should always be taken as 1.0, when used with (3).

M_{ry} = factored moment resistance for the Y—Y axis and is equal to $\phi\, Z_y F_y$.

C_f = factored axial load

C_r = factored axial compressive resistance of the member and is equal to $\phi\, A_x F_y$ for (2) and is determined according to Clause 13.3 of CAN3-S16.1-M78 for (3).

C_{ex}, C_{ey} = Euler buckling load equal to $1\,970\,000\ A/(KL/r)^2$ where KL/r is the slenderness ratio in the plane of bending.

ω_x, ω_y = Coefficient used to determine equivalent uniform bending effect. The equivalent uniform bending effect can be considered to be that derived from an imaginary uniform bending moment which approximates that effect due to the actual design moments.

For Class 3 and Class 4 sections.

$$(4)\ \frac{C_f}{C_r} + \frac{M_{fx}}{M_{rx}} + \frac{M_{fy}}{M_{ry}} \leqslant 1.0$$

$$(5)\ \frac{C_f}{C_r} + \frac{\omega_x M_{fx}}{M_{rx}\left(1 - \dfrac{C_f}{C_{ex}}\right)} + \frac{\omega_y M_{fy}}{M_{ry}\left(1 - \dfrac{C_f}{C_{ey}}\right)} \leqslant 1.0$$

where

C_f = factored axial load.

C_{ex}, C_{ey} = Euler buckling load.

C_r = factored axial compressive resistance of the member and is equal to $\phi\, A_x F_y$ for (4) and is determined according to Clause 13.3 for (5).

M_{fx} and M_{fy} = factored bending moments at the point under consideration when used with (4) and the maximum computed factored bending moment occurring either at or between braced points when used with (5).

M_{rx} = factored bending resistance for bending about the X—X axis. For Class 3 sections M_{rx} is equal to $\phi\, S_x F_y$ for (4) and is computed according to Clause 13.6(b) for (5). For Class 4 sections M_{rx} is computed according to Clause 13.5(c) for (4) and Clause 13.6(b) for (5). In determining M_u according to Clause 13.6(b)(ii), ω should always be taken as 1.0, when used with (5).

M_{ry} = factored bending resistance for bending about the Y—Y axis. For Class 3 sections M_{ry} is equal to $\phi\, S_y F_y$ for (4) and (5). For Class 4 sections M_{ry} is computed according to Clause 13.5.3.

ω_x, ω_y = same as for Class 1 and Class 2.

Expressions (1), (2) and (4) are strength requirements; expressions (3) and (5) are stability requirements. Either requirement may govern the design of a beam-column. Often one requirement will govern for one loading condition while the other requirement governs for a different loading condition.

The value of ω (ω_x or ω_y) depends upon the magnitude of the end moments, the presence or absence of transverse loads, and whether or not the sway effects (P$\triangle$ effects) have been included in the analysis which determined the forces and moments for the frame in which the beam-column is an integral part. The value of ω may be determined by analysis, or the following values may be used:

(a) for members not subject to transverse loads between supports.

    (i) For members of frames analysed in accordance with Clause 8.6.2 (sway effects included), $\omega = 0.6 + 0.4\,(M_{f_1}/M_{f_2})$ for members bent in single curvature, and $\omega = 0.6 - 0.4\,(M_{f_1}/M_{f_2})$, but not less than 0.4, for members bent in double curvature. (See Table 4—7);

    (ii) For members of frames analysed in accordance with Clause 8.6.3 (sway effects not included), $\omega = 0.85$ for members bent in double curvature or subject to a moment at one end only, or $\omega = 1.0$ for members bent in single curvature due to moments at both ends.

(b) for members subject to a distributed load or a series of point loads between supports, $\omega = 1.0$.

(c) for members subject to a concentrated load or moment between supports, the member may be considered to be divided into two segments at the point of load (or moment) application. Each segment is then treated as a member which depends on its own flexural stiffness to prevent sidesway in the plane of bending considered and $\omega = 0.85$. In computing the slenderness ratio KL/r, for use in (3) and (5), the total length of the members shall be used.

It is important to remember that, because the factored axial compressive resistance, C_r, in (3) and (5) is that if only compressive loads were present, it is always the value associated with the maximum effective slenderness ratio regardless of the axis about which bending occurs. C_e, on the other hand, is always computed from the slenderness ratio in the plane of bending.

References

Additional information on beam-columns can be obtained from the following references:

1. Part 2 of this book.

2. Adams, P. F., Krentz, H. A., Kulak, G. L., "Limit States Design in Structural Steel — SI Units", CISC, 1979.

3. Adams, P. F., "Design of Steel Beam-Columns", CSCC, 1974.

4. "Guide to Stability Design Criteria for Metal Structures", B. Johnston, Editor, Structural Stability Research Council (formerly Column Research Council) 3rd Edition, John Wiley, 1976.

5. "Column Selection Program 3 Users Manual", CISC, 1977.

The material provided in this Handbook should help the designer minimize the design time required when computers are not available. Designers with access to computers equipped with a FORTRAN compiler and medium size real or virtual memory should become familiar with the CISC-CSCC Column Selection Program 3. Other programmable devices can substantially reduce the designer's time required to select a suitable beam-column. Contact your nearest CISC office for more information.

Design

The selection of a suitable steel section to use as a beam-column is a trial-and-error procedure. A trial section must be selected and then its suitability checked in accordance with the appropriate equations (1) to (5) or those of Appendix F, CAN3-S16.1-M78 when, for a Class 1 or Class 2 section, a refined analysis of beam-column behaviour is desired. The procedure is then repeated if the initial choice was not suitable.

With the introduction of CAN3-S16.1-M78 "Steel Structures for Buildings — Limit States Design", the beam-column interaction equations have been formulated in terms of factored loads and member resistances. This simplifies checking the suitability of a trial selection since many of the terms are tabulated in various tables of this Handbook.

The following terms are a result of the analysis for forces and moments:

C_f = factored axial load,

M_{fx}, M_{fy} = factored bending moments.

The following terms can be determined from tables in this Handbook:

C_r = factored axial compressive resistance,

         = $\phi\, AF_y$ where A is tabulated or,

         = value in tables of factored axial compressive resistances of columns for the appropriate effective length, page 4—36*.

M_{rx} = factored moment resistance for X—X axis bending,

         = tabulated value with properties in tables of factored axial compressive resistances of columns when the unsupported length of compression flange, L, $< L_u$, page 4—36*, or,

         = tabulated in factored moment resistances for columns table under the appropriate heading for length of compression flange which is unsupported, or may be interpolated from these values, page 4—117*.

M_{ry} = factored moment resistance for Y—Y axis bending

         = tabulated value with properties in Column tables, page 4—36*.

ω_x, ω_y = equivalent uniform bending factor

         = tabulated in Table 4—7, page 4—30.

U   = $1/(1 - \dfrac{C_f}{C_e})$ = amplification factor

         = tabulated in Table 4—9, page 4—32, are values of U for various C_f/C_e ratios

C_e = Euler buckling load

         = tabulated as C_e/A for KL/r ratios from 1 to 200 in Table 4—8, page 4—31.

Trial Selection by Equivalent-Loads Method

Any convenient method can be used to choose a trial section. One method used here is that of equivalent-loads. Basically this method involves converting applied loads and

*First page of the series of like tables.

bending moments into two equivalent total axial loads, one computed from a "strength" requirement and the other from a "stability" requirement. The trial section, chosen from the tables of factored axial compressive resistances of columns, pages 4—36 to 4—95 inclusive, for the larger equivalent load is then checked using the appropriate expressions (1) to (5). This method is applicable only to prismatic members designed using expressions (1) to (5).

Beam-Columns Without Transverse Loads Between Brace Points

Strength Requirements

(6) $C_f' = C_f + M_{f_2} B$

C_f' = equivalent total factored axial load for strength (kilonewtons)

C_f = applied factored axial load (kilonewtons)

M_{f_2} = larger applied factored end moment (kilonewton metres)

B = appropriate bending factor (m^{-1}) chosen from Table 4—6.

Stability Requirements

(7) $C_f'' = C_f + (\omega\, M_{f_2})\left(B\dfrac{C_{rL}}{C_{ro}}\right)U$

C_f'' = equivalent total factored axial load for stability (kilonewtons)

ω = equivalent uniform bending factor

C_{rL} = factored axial compressive resistance at the actual effective length for the trial section chosen (kilonewtons)

C_{ro} = factored axial compressive resistance at an effective length of zero millimetres for the trial section chosen (kilonewtons)

U = an amplification factor, equal to $1/\left(1 - \dfrac{C_f}{C_e}\right)$ as listed in

Table 4—9 for various combinations of C_f/C_e in the plane of bending.

C_f, M_{f_2} and B are the same as for equation (6).

Multiplying the larger end moment, M_{f_2}, by the value of ω approximates the magnitude of a uniform moment along the unbraced length which has the same effect on the beam-column as the applied end moments, as far as stability requirements are concerned.

The expression C_{rL}/C_{ro} in equation (7) modifies the factor B to account for the difference between the capacity of the beam-column along the unbraced length and that at a brace location. If equation (7) is used with moments at the brace location, $C_{rL} = C_{ro}$ and the expression C_{rL}/C_{ro} can be deleted from equation (7).

The other refinement which equation (7) provides, as compared to equation (6), is the introduction of the amplification factor, U. This factor takes into account the increasing importance of the "secondary moment" introduced by the applied load as the curvature of the column under load increases. Accordingly, U increases rapidly as the length of the column (and hence the effective slenderness ratio in the plane of bending increases) and as the applied axial load increases.

When bending about two axes is involved, the second term of equation (6) and of equation (7) should be evaluated twice, using the values appropriate to each axis.

Equation (6) and (7) are accurate if the unbraced length of the compression flange of the beam-column $\leqslant L_u$. Values of L_u are listed in the tables of factored compressive resistances of columns. If L_u is exceeded, equations (6) and (7) still can be used to obtain a trial section, but the trial section may not be adequate when checked for compliance with Clause 13.8 of CAN3-S16.1-M78.

Although equation (7) looks cumbersome, it is easily used since all the unknowns in the equation can be picked directly from tables.

However equation (7) can be simplified, with a possible reduction in accuracy by assuming that the ratio $C_{rL}/C_{ro} = 0.70$. This is an average value for 300 MPa yield steel columns with KL/r from 40 to 80.

Beam-Columns With Transverse Loads Between Brace Points

For beam-columns subject to transverse loading between the brace locations, equation (6) satisfies the strength requirement if the larger end moment is greater than the maximum bending moment along the unbraced length.

The stability requirement is satisfied by a modified form of equation (7) identified as equation (7a). If the maximum bending moment along the unbraced length is greater than the larger end moment, equation (7a) will satisfy both the strength and stability requirements for the beam-column.

$$(7a)\ C_f'' = C_f + M_{f_2}' \left(B \frac{C_{rL}}{C_{ro}} \right) U$$

M_{f_2}' = the greater of the maximum bending moment along the unbraced length; or the larger end moment.

The other symbols are the same as for equation (7)

Suggested Design Procedure

Before the actual selection of a suitable steel section for a beam-column commences the designer must determine the significance of the sway effects and if they are significant the method of accounting for these sway effects in the design. This will then determine the forces, moments and values of the quantities in the beam-column equations such as ω and KL.

A. *Trial Section Selection*

1. Estimate effective length factors K_x and K_y, see Table 4—5.

2. Choose a nominal size group (WWF500, W310, etc.) from which the trial section will be chosen and select the appropriate bending factor or factors from Table 4—6.

3. Using equation (6), compute equivalent axial load for strength, C_f'.

4. Using C_f' select an initial trial section from the tables of factored axial compressive resistances of columns. C_f' must be $\leqslant C_r$ in the tables at effective length of zero millimetres.

5. Using equation (7), compute equivalent axial load for stability, C_f''. The value of ω can be chosen from Table 4—7 and the value of B will be the same value used to establish C_f'. The values of C_{rL} and C_{ro} will be those listed in the table of factored axial compressive resistances of columns for the initial trial section chosen in step 4. The value of U will be selected from Table 4—9, using the properties of the initial trial section chosen in step 4. Alternately an assumed value of C_{rL}/C_{ro} can be chosen such as 0.70. If the column is subject to transverse loads use equation (7a) for this step.

6. Using the factored axial compressive resistance tables verify that the initial trial section is adequate for C_f'' at the appropriate effective length, or choose a new trial section to satisfy C_f'' at the appropriate KL.

7. Using properties of the trial section, check estimate of effective length factors K_x and K_y, with the aid of Figure C1, page 4—25. If the actual K values are rea-

sonably close to estimated values, proceed to part B. If differences are large, Part A should be repeated using revised K values.

B. *Suitability of the Trial Section*

1. Using the properties and resistances of the trial section, check its suitability in accordance with the requirements of Clause 13.8 of CSA Standard CAN3-S16.1-M78. Since most of the values used in these equations are tabulated this should be a quick computation.

2. If the trial section is unsuitable, choose a new trial section (which should be the next lighter or heavier section listed) and verify suitability.

Examples

1. **Given:**

Design a steel column for the tenth storey of a 20-storey building for the loading conditions shown. Moments are due to rigidly framed beams and gravity loading, and cause bending about X—X axis of the column. The PΔ effects have been included in the analysis. Beams framing to minor axis have flexible connections. Steel is G40.21-M 300W.

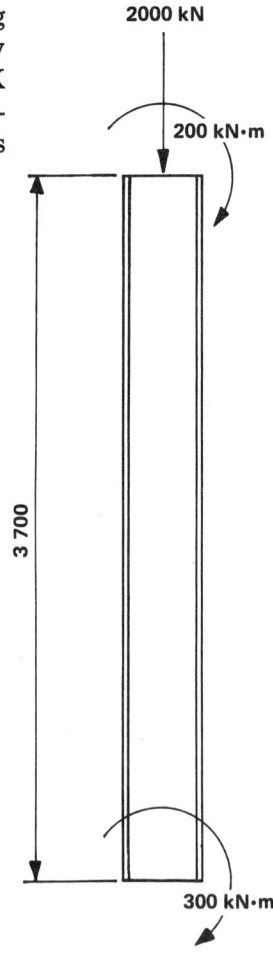

Solution:

$L = 3\ 700$ mm $\qquad M_{f_1} = 200$ kN·m

$C_f = 2\ 000$ kN $\qquad M_{f_2} = 300$ kN·m

A. From Table 4—5, $K_x = 0.90$ (case D)

$\qquad\qquad\qquad K_y = 1.00$ (case A)

$K_x L_x = 0.90 \times 3\ 700 = 3\ 330$ mm

$K_y L_y = 1.00 \times 3\ 700 = 3\ 700$ mm

Assume W310 Class 2 section

From Table 4—6 for 310×310 section, $B_x = 6.34$ m^{-1}

$C'_f = C_f + B_x M_{f_2} = 2\ 000 + 6.34\ (300) = 3\ 900$ kN

Select W310×118, page 4—42, Class 2 section in G40.21-M 300W

$A = 15\ 000$ mm^2 ; $r_x = 135$ mm, $r_y = 77.5$ mm;

$C_{ro} = 4\ 050$ kN (KL = 0);

$C_{rL} = 3\ 400$ kN (KL = 3 700 mm — by interpolation)

$M_{rx} = 526$ kN·m; $r_x/r_y = 1.74$

C_{ro} (for KL = 0) = 4 050 > 3 900 kN

$$C''_f = C_f + (\omega\ M_{f_2}) \left(B_x\ \frac{C_{rL}}{C_{ro}}\right) U$$

$M_{f_1}/M_{f_2} = 200/300 = 0.67$ (double curvature)

From Table 4—7, $\omega = 0.40$

$$\frac{K_x\ L_x}{r_x} = \frac{3\ 330}{135} = 25$$

From Table 4—8, $C_e/A = 3\ 152$ MPa

Then C_e = 3 152 MPa $\times$ 15 000 mm² = 47 300 $\times$ 10³ N

$$= 47\ 300 \text{ kN}$$

and C_f/C_e = 2 000/47 300 = 0.04

From Table 4—9, U = 1.04

From Table 4—6, B_x = 7.46 m⁻¹ (for stability)

$$C_f'' = 2\ 000 + 0.4 \times 300 \times (7.46 \times \frac{3\ 400}{4\ 050}) 1.04$$

$$= 2\ 000 + 782$$

$$= 2\ 780 < 3\ 400 \text{ kN} - \text{OK}$$

Use W310×118 as trial section.

Since the beam sizes are not known in this example (although they would be known in actual practice), we will assume:

G_{Ux} = 2.5 G_{Uy} = 10.0

G_{Lx} = 3.0 G_{Ly} = 12.0

(See page 4—24 for an explanation)

Using Figure C1, page 4—25, K_x = 0.88, K_y = 0.96.

These figures are close enough to the assumed figures to be considered satisfactory.

B. *(i) Strength check — W310×118*

$$\frac{C_f}{C_r} + 0.85 \frac{M_f}{M_r} \leqslant 1.0 \ \text{.........(expression (2))}$$

From Table of factored compressive resistances, page 4—42

C_{ro} = 4 050 kN

M_{rx} = 526 kN·m

h/w = (314 −2 $\times$ 18.7)/11.9 = 23.2

Since h/w for this section is less than the most severe h/w limit for a beam-column or column, the W310×118 will always be a Class 1 section in grade 300W steel. Therefore the value of M_{rx} from the tables may be used directly.

Therefore $\frac{2\ 000}{4\ 050} + 0.85 \frac{300}{526} = 0.979 < 1.00$

(ii) Stability check

$$\frac{C_f}{C_r} + \frac{\omega_x \ M_{fx} \ U}{M_{rx}} \leqslant 1.0 \ \text{.........(expression (3))}$$

ω_x = 0.40, U = 1.04 (from before)

$K_x L_x/(r_x/r_y)$ = 0.88 $\times$ 3 700/1.74 = 1 870 mm

$K_y L_y$ = 0.96 $\times$ 3 700 = 3 500 mm > 1 870 mm

Use 3 550 mm

Therefore

C_{rL} (KL = 3 550) = 3 440 kN, page 4—42 (by interpolation)

L = 3 700 mm < L_u = 5 390 mm

Therefore M_{rx} = 526 kN·m, page 4—42

$$\frac{C_f}{C_r} + \frac{\omega M_{fx} U_x}{M_{rx}} = \frac{2\,000}{3\,440} + \frac{0.4 \times 300 \times 1.04}{526}$$

$$= 0.819 < 1.00 - OK$$

Use W310×118 column section

Comments:

1. C_r could more accurately be determined by computing the KL/r values and entering the tables of Unit Factored Compressive Resistances for the larger $\frac{KL}{r}$ and multiplying that value by the column's area.

2. When $L > L_u$ the tables on pages 4—118, factored moments of resistances of columns will be more useful.

2. **Given:**

Same as example 1, except that the PΔ effects have not been included in the analysis for moments. Therefore the moments M_{f_1} and M_{f_2} are different from those used in example 1.

Solution:

L = 3 700 mm M_{f_1} = 180 kN·m
C_f = 2 000 kN M_{f_2} = 265 kN·m

A. From Table 4—5

K_x = 2.25 $K_x L_x$ = 2.25 × 3 700 = 8 330 mm
K_y = 1.00 $K_y L_y$ = 1.00 × 3 700 = 3 700 mm

From Table of factored axial compressive resistances for W310 sections, assume r_x/r_y = 1.75.

$K_x L_x/(r_x/r_y)$ = 8 330/1.75 = 4 760 > 3 700 mm

Use 4 800 mm for critical effective length with respect to the least radius of gyration. From example 1, a W310×118 is satisfactory for strength check.

C_{ro} = 4 050 kN; C_{rL} = 3 040 kN (for kL = 4 800 mm, by interpolation)

From Table 4—6 (stability) B = 7.46 m^{-1}

ω = 0.85 for double curvature, PΔ not included (Clause 13.8.4(a)(ii), CAN3-S16.1-M78)

$K_x L_x/r_x$ = 8 330/135 = 61.7   Use 62

From Table 4—8, C_e/A = 512 MPa (KL/r = 62)

Then C_e = 512 MPa × 15 000 mm² = 7 680 × 10³ N
= 7 680 kN

and C_f/C_e = 2 000/7 680 = 0.26

From Table 4—9, U = 1.35

$$C_f'' = 2\,000 + 0.85 \times 265 \times (7.46 \times \frac{3\,040}{4\,050}) \times 1.35$$

$$= 3\,700 \text{ kN}$$

C_{rL} for KL = 4 800 mm for W310×118 is 3 040 kN and less than 3 700 KN.

Therefore a larger section is required.

From factored axial compressive resistance table, page 4—42, for W310×143

C_{rL} = 3 720 > 3 700 kN (by interpolation for KL = 4 800 mm)

As in example 1, we will assume values of G in order to check the K factors estimated with the aid of Table 4—5.

Assume G_{Ux} = 4.0 $\qquad\qquad\qquad\qquad\qquad\qquad\qquad$ G_{Uy} = 15.0

$\qquad\quad G_{Lx}$ = 5.0 $\qquad\qquad\qquad\qquad\qquad\qquad\qquad\quad$ G_{Ly} = 18.0

Using Figure C1, page 4—25, K_x = 2.1 and K_y = 0.97.

Effective length factors are close enough to those assumed, so are satisfactory.

Use W310×143 section.

B. (i) *Strength check — W310×143*

$$\frac{C_f}{C_r} + 0.85\,\frac{M_f}{M_r} \leqslant 1.0 \ \text{.........(expression (2))}$$

From Table of factored compressive resistances, page 4—42, C_{ro} = 4 910 kN, M_{rx} = 653 kN·m.

Therefore

$$\frac{2\,000}{4\,910} + 0.85 \times \frac{265}{653} = 0.75 < 1.00 - \text{OK}$$

(ii) *Stability check*

$$\frac{C_f}{C_r} + \frac{\omega_x\,M_{fx}\,U}{M_{rx}} \leqslant 1.0 \ \text{.........(expression (3))}$$

ω_x = 0.85, U = 1.35 (as before)

C_{rL} = 3 720 KN (KL = 4 800 mm)

M_{rx} = 653 kN·m (since L = 3 700 mm < L_u = 5 820 mm), page 4—42

Therefore

$$\frac{2\,000}{3\,720} + \frac{0.85 \times 265 \times 1.35}{653} = 1.00 = 1.00 - \text{OK}$$

Use W310×143

3. **Given:**

Same as example 1, except that beams framing to Y—Y axis have rigid connections and induce moments of 100 kN·m at each end of the column. The direction of the moments is such that double curvature is induced in the column.

Solution:

$\quad$ L = 3 700 mm $\qquad\quad M_{fx_1}$ = 200 kN·m $\qquad M_{fy_1}$ = 100 kN·m

$\quad C_f$ = 2 000 kN $\qquad\quad M_{fx_2}$ = 300 kN·m $\qquad M_{fy_2}$ = 100 kN·m

A. From Table 4—5, K_x = 0.90 (case D)

$\qquad\qquad\qquad\qquad\quad K_y$ = 0.90 (case D)

$K_x L_x = K_y L_y$ = 0.90 × 3 700 mm = 3 330 mm

Assume W310 section, Class 2

For a Class 2, 310 × 310 W shape, from Table 4—6, page 4—28,

$B_x = 6.34$ and $B_y = 9.78$ for strength

$$C_f' = C_f + B_x M_{fx_2} + B_y M_{fy_2}$$
$$= 2\,000 + 6.34 \times 300 + 9.78 \times 100$$
$$= 4\,880 \text{ kN}$$

Select W310×143, page 4—42, Class 1 section in G40.21-M 300W.

$C_o = 4\,910$ kN $> 4\,880$ kN — OK

$A = 18\,200$ mm^2 $\qquad M_{rx} = 653$ kN·m

$r_x = 138$ mm $\qquad M_{ry} = 300$ kN·m

$r_y = 78.8$ mm

$C_{rL} = 4\,270$ kN (by interpolation for KL = 3 330 mm)

$$C_f'' = C_f + (\omega_x M_{fx_2}) \left(B_x \frac{C_{rLx}}{C_{ro}}\right) U_x + (\omega_y M_{fy_2}) \left(B_y \frac{C_{rLy}}{C_{ro}}\right) U_y$$

$M_{fx_1}/M_{fx_2} = 200/300 = 0.67$

$M_{fy_1}/M_{fy_2} = 100/100 = 1.00$

From Table 4—7, $\omega_x = 0.40$, $\omega_y = 0.40$

$K_x L_x/r_x = 3\,330/138 = 24$

$K_y L_y/r_y = 3\,330/78.8 = 42$

From Table 4—8, $(C_e/A)_x = 3\,420$ kN (KL = 24)

$\qquad\qquad\qquad (C_e/A)_y = 1\,117$ kN (KL = 42)

$C_{ex} = 3\,420$ kN $\times$ 18 200 mm^2 = 62 200 $\times$ 10^3 N

$\qquad\qquad\qquad\qquad\qquad = 62\,200$ kN

$C_{ey} = 1\,117$ kN $\times$ 18 200 mm^2 = 20 300 $\times$ 10^3 N

$\qquad\qquad\qquad\qquad\qquad = 20\,300$ kN

$C_f/C_{ex} = 2\,000/62\,200 = 0.03$

$C_f/C_{ey} = 2\,000/20\,300 = 0.10$

From Table 4—9, $U_x = 1.03$, $U_y = 1.11$

From Table 4—6, for stability $B_x = 7.46$ m^{-1},

$\qquad\qquad\qquad\qquad\qquad B_y = 16.3$ m^{-1}

$$C_f'' = 2\,000 + 0.40 \times 300 \times \left(7.46 \times \frac{4\,270}{4\,910}\right) 1.03$$

$$+ 0.40 \times 100 \times \left(16.3 \times \frac{4\,270}{4\,910}\right) 1.11$$

$$\doteq 3\,430 \text{ kN}$$

Since C_r for KL = 3 330 mm equals 4 270 kN > 3 430 kN, the W310×143 satisfies the stability requirement as well as the strength requirement.

Use W310×143 as trial section.

As in examples 1 and 2, K factors should be checked. It will be assumed that estimates of K are satisfactory.

B. (i) Strength check

$$\frac{C_f}{C_r} + \frac{0.85\,M_{fx}}{M_{rx}} + \frac{0.60\,M_{fy}}{M_{ry}} \leqslant 1.0 \quad \dots\dots\dots\dots\dots\dots\dots\dots\dots\dots\dots\dots\dots\dots\dots(2)$$

$$\frac{2\,000}{4\,910} + \frac{0.85 \times 300}{653} + \frac{0.60 \times 100}{300}$$

$$= 0.998 \leqslant 1.00 - \text{OK}$$

(ii) Stability check

$$\frac{C_f}{C_r} + \frac{\omega_x\,M_{fx}\,U_x}{M_{rx}} + \frac{\omega_y\,M_{fy}\,U_y}{M_{ry}} \leqslant 1.0 \quad \dots\dots\dots\dots\dots\dots\dots\dots\dots\dots\dots\dots(3)$$

Since $L < L_u$ (3 700 < 5 820 mm) Use full value of M_{rx} = 653 kN·m

Values of ω_x, ω_y, U_x, U_y as before as well as C_r for KL = 3 330

$$\frac{2\,000}{4\,270} + \frac{0.40 \times 300 \times 1.03}{653} + \frac{0.40 \times 100 \times 1.11}{300}$$

$$= 0.81 < 1.00 - \text{OK}$$

Use W310×143

Alternatively, this column could be designed in accordance with Appendix F, since it is a Class 1 section and the b/d ratio (309/323 = 0.96) is greater 0.80. See page 4—113 for more details.

Shear

Where beams with large end moments are connected to columns with thin webs, a check for shear in the column web may be necessary.

Columns Subject to Biaxial Bending*

The precise design of beam-columns to resist biaxial bending is extremely complex. More refined design expressions than those given in Clause 13 are available but these are shape dependent. Given below are design expressions for wide flange shapes within certain flange width/depth restrictions and square hollow structural sections.

To assist the designer in the rapid selection of the appropriate design equations, a decision table is also given.

F1. Class 1 and 2 wide flange shapes, in which the ratio of flange width/overall depth is not less than 0.8, may be proportioned so that:

(a) $$\left(\frac{M_{fx}}{M_{rcx}}\right)^{\zeta} + \left(\frac{M_{fy}}{M_{rcy}}\right)^{\zeta} \leq 1.0$$

(b) $$\left(\frac{\omega_x M_{fx}}{M_{ox}}\right)^{\eta} + \left(\frac{\omega_y M_{fy}}{M_{oy}}\right)^{\eta} \leq 1.0$$

Where M_{rcx}, M_{rcy} are the factored moment resistance of the section, reduced for the presence of axial load, and may be taken as:

$$M_{rcx} = 1.18 M_{rx}\left(1 - \frac{C_f}{C_y}\right) \leq M_{rx}$$

$$M_{rcy} = 1.19 M_{ry}\left[1 - \left(\frac{C_f}{C_y}\right)^2\right] \leq M_{ry}$$

Where M_{rx} and M_{ry} are defined in Clause 13.5(a)

M_{ox}, M_{oy} = maximum single curvature factored moment resistance of the column in the presence of the axial load but in the absence of the other orthogonal moment, which may be taken as:

$$M_{ox} = M_{rx}\left(1 - \frac{C_f}{C_r}\right)\left(1 - \frac{C_f}{C_{ex}}\right)$$

$$M_{oy} = M_{ry}\left(1 - \frac{C_f}{C_r}\right)\left(1 - \frac{C_f}{C_{ey}}\right)$$

$$\zeta = 1.6 - \frac{C_f/C_y}{2\ell n(C_f/C_y)}$$

$$\eta = 1.4 + \frac{C_f}{C_y}$$

where M_{rx} is defined in Clause 13.6(a), M_{ry} is defined in Clause 13.5(a) and C_r is defined in Clause 13.3.1.

Note: *For values of $C_f/C_y < 0.3$, the value of ζ may be taken equal to the value of η.*

F2. Class 1 and Class 2 wide flange shapes, in which the ratio of flange width/overall depth is not less than 0.55 may be proportioned so that:

(a) The requirements of the formula in F1(a) are satisfied;

(b) The requirements of Clause 13.8.2(c) are satisfied.

F3. Class 1 and Class 2 square hollow structural sections (rolled* or fabricated) may be proportioned so that:

(a) $\dfrac{M_{fx}}{M_{rx}} + 0.5\,\dfrac{M_{fy}}{M_{ry}} \le 1.0$

(b) $\dfrac{C_f}{C_r} + 0.85\left(\dfrac{M_{fx}}{M_{rx}} + 0.5\dfrac{M_{fy}}{M_{ry}}\right) \le 1.0$

where

M_{fx} = the numerically larger moment

M_{rx} and M_{ry} are defined in Clause 13.5(a)

$C_r = \phi A F_y$

Hot rolled or stress relieved such that residual stresses do not exceed $0.3F_y$.

(c) $\dfrac{C_f}{C_r} + v\left(\dfrac{\omega_x M_{fx}}{M_{rx}\left(1 - \dfrac{C_f}{C_{ex}}\right)} + \dfrac{\omega_y M_{fy}}{M_{ry}\left(1 - \dfrac{C_f}{C_{ey}}\right)}\right) \le 1.0$

where $v = \dfrac{\sqrt{(\omega_x M_{fx})^2 + (\omega_y M_{fy})^2}}{\omega_x M_{fx} + \omega_y M_{fy}}$

C_r is defined in Clause 13.3.1

M_{rx} is defined in Clause 13.6(a)

M_{ry} is defined in Clause 13.5(a)

Note: *Design of Class 1 and Class 2 sections in accordance with the above requirements takes advantage of the redistribution of stress after initiation of yielding, under the factored loads. Consideration should be given to this aspect of design if yielding under the specified loads would induce undesirable lateral deformations of a structure.*

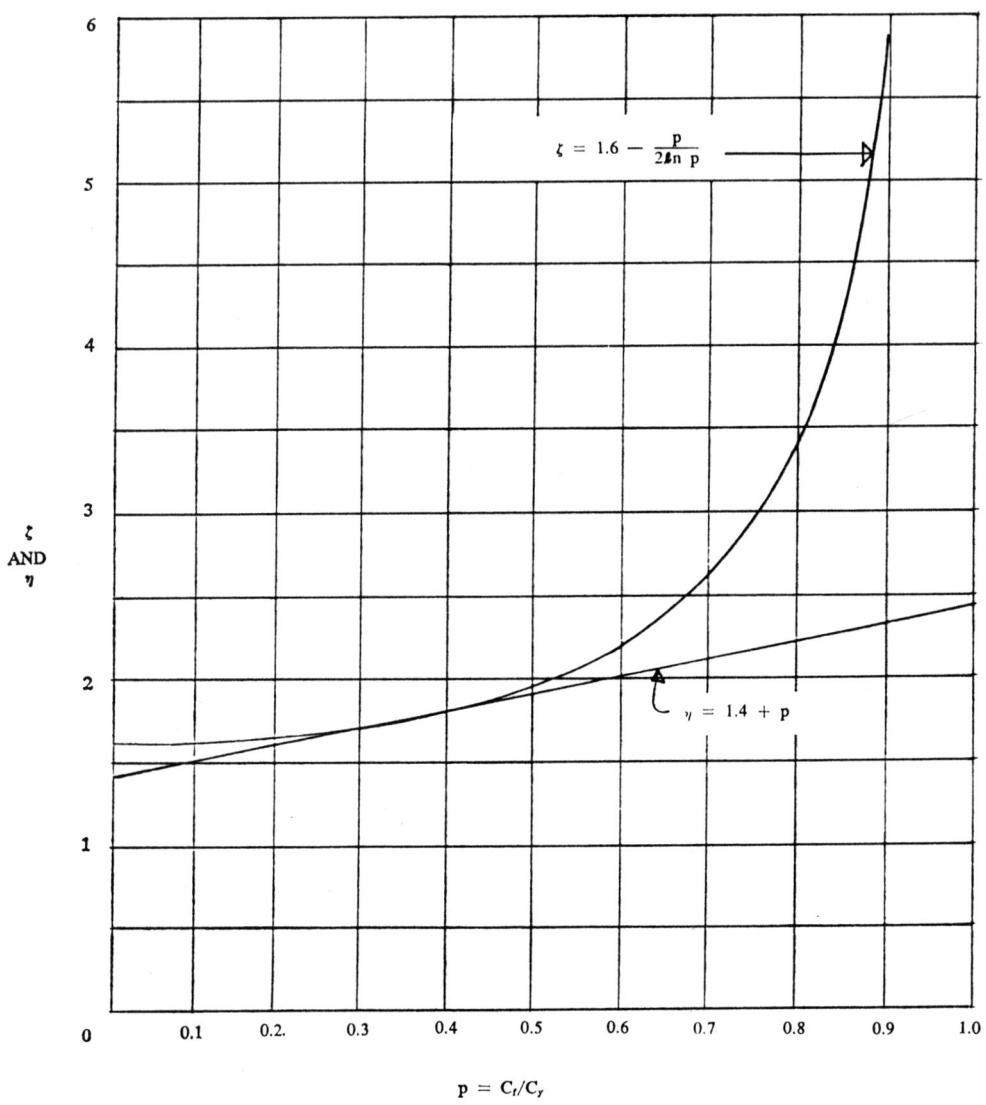

Figure F1
Plot of ζ and η Versus C_t/C_y

$$\left(\frac{M_x}{M_{ox}}\right)^\zeta + \left(\frac{M_y}{M_{oy}}\right)^\zeta = 1$$

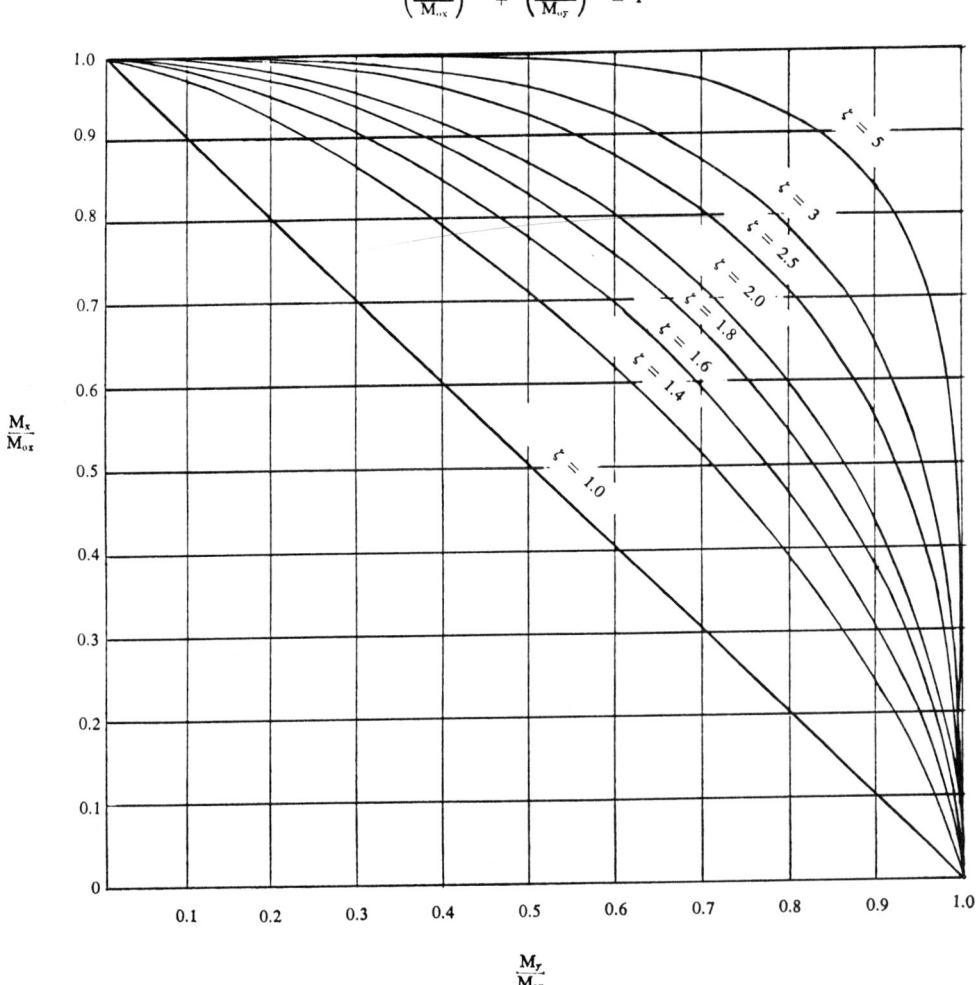

Figure F2
Plot of the Interaction Equation

REDUCED PLASTIC MOMENT RATIOS:

$\dfrac{M_{rc}}{M_r}$, FOR CLASS 1 and 2 SECTIONS DUE TO AXIAL LOAD

Table 4-10

	Axis X-X				$\dfrac{M_{rcx}}{M_{rx}} = 1.18\left(1 - \dfrac{C_f}{C_y}\right)$					
$\dfrac{C_f}{C_y}$	0.00	0.01	0.02	0.03	0.04	0.05	0.06	0.07	0.08	0.09
0.00	1.00	1.00	1.00	1.00	1.00	1.00	1.00	1.00	1.00	1.00
0.10	1.00	1.00	1.00	1.00	1.00	1.00	.991	.979	.968	.956
0.20	.944	.932	.920	.909	.897	.885	.873	.861	.850	.838
0.30	.826	.814	.802	.791	.779	.767	.755	.743	.732	.720
0.40	.708	.696	.684	.673	.661	.649	.637	.625	.614	.602
0.50	.590	.578	.566	.555	.543	.531	.519	.507	.496	.484
0.60	.472	.460	.448	.437	.425	.413	.401	.389	.378	.366
0.70	.354	.342	.330	.319	.307	.295	.283	.271	.260	.248
0.80	.235	.224	.212	.201	.189	.177	.165	.153	.142	.130
0.90	.118	.106	.094	.083	.071	.059	.047	.035	.024	.012

	Axis Y-Y				$\dfrac{M_{rcy}}{M_{ry}} = 1.19\left(1 - \left(\dfrac{C_f}{C_y}\right)^2\right)$					
$\dfrac{C_f}{C_y}$	0.00	0.01	0.02	0.03	0.04	0.05	0.06	0.07	0.08	0.09
0.00	1.00	1.00	1.00	1.00	1.00	1.00	1.00	1.00	1.00	1.00
0.10	1.00	1.00	1.00	1.00	1.00	1.00	1.00	1.00	1.00	1.00
0.20	1.00	1.00	1.00	1.00	1.00	1.00	1.00	1.00	1.00	1.00
0.30	1.00	1.00	1.00	1.00	1.00	1.00	1.00	1.00	1.00	1.00
0.40	1.00	.990	.980	.970	.960	.949	.938	.927	.916	.904
0.50	.893	.880	.868	.856	.843	.830	.817	.803	.790	.776
0.60	.762	.747	.733	.718	.703	.687	.672	.656	.640	.623
0.70	.607	.590	.573	.556	.538	.521	.503	.484	.466	.447
0.80	.428	.409	.390	.370	.350	.330	.310	.289	.268	.247
0.90	.226	.205	.183	.161	.139	.116	.093	.079	.047	.024

$\dfrac{C_f}{C_y}$ = Ratio of factored axial load, C_f, to axial compressive load at yield stress, C_y.

To obtain the factored moment resistance for a section reduced due to the presence of axial load, as required by Clause F1.(a) of Appendix F, S16.1-M78, M_{rcx} or M_{rcy}, determine the ratio C_f/C_y; enter Table 4—10 to obtain the reduced plastic moment ratio and then multiply that ratio by the appropriate factored moment resistance.

Tabulated values of moment resistance can be found:

1. For column sections in the tables of factored compressive resistances when $L < L_u$ or in the table of factored moment resistances for columns page 4—118 to 4—121.

2. For beam sections in the beam selection tables pages 5—98 to 5—109.

Example: On the use of Table 4—10:

Given:

A W310X143 column, 3 700 mm unsupported length, carries a factored axial load plus a bending moment. If the C_f/C_y ratio is 0.53 what is its reduced plastic moment, M_{rcx}, for design under the rules of Appendix F of CAN3-S16.1-M78.

Solution:

From page 4—42 $M_{rx} = M'_{rx} = 653$ kN·m

From Table 4—10   For $C_f/C_y = 0.53$ and axis X—X ratio = 0.555

$$M_{rcx} = 0.555 \times 653 = 362 \text{ kN·m}$$

Examples: For design of columns subject to biaxial bending.

1. **Given:**

Same as example 3 from page 4—105, except that the refined design equations of Appendix F of CAN3-S16.1-M78 will be used.

Solution:

$L = 3\ 700$ mm $M_{fx_1} = 200$ kN·m $M_{fy_1} = 100$ kN·m

$C_f = 2\ 000$ kN $M_{fx_2} = 300$ kN·m $M_{fy_2} = 100$ kN·m

Assume the section will have $b/d \geqslant 0.8$ and will be at least a Class 2 section. Try W310×118, from table of factored axial compressive resistances, 4—42.

$A_x = 15\ 000$ mm^2

$M_{rx} = 526$ kN·m

$M_{ry} = 241$ kN·m

$C_y = 300 \text{ MPa} \times 15\ 000 \text{ mm}^2 = 4\ 500 \times 10^3 \text{ N}$
$$= 4\ 500 \text{ kN}$$

$C_f/C_y = 2\ 000/4\ 500 = 0.44$

$$\zeta = 1.6 - \frac{C_f/C_y}{2\ell n\left(\dfrac{C_f}{C_y}\right)} = 1.6 - \frac{0.44}{2\ell n\ (0.44)} = 1.87 \text{ (See also Graph F1, page 4—110)}$$

$\eta = 1.4 + C_f/C_y = 1.84$ (See also Graph F2, page 4—111)

From Table 4—10, page 4—112, reduced plastic moment ratios are: X—X axis = 0.661 and Y—Y axis = 0.960.

Therefore $M_{rcx} = 526 \times 0.661 = 348$ kN·m
$$M_{rcy} = 241 \times 0.960 = 231 \text{ kN·m}$$

(i) Strength check

$$\left(\frac{M_{fx}}{M_{rcx}}\right)^{\zeta} + \left(\frac{M_{fy}}{M_{rcy}}\right)^{\zeta} = \left(\frac{300}{348}\right)^{1.87} + \left(\frac{100}{231}\right)^{1.87}$$

$$= 0.862^{1.87} + 0.433^{1.87} = 0.97 < 1.00 - \text{OK}$$

Or from Graph F2, p. 4—111, for the two moment ratios of 0.86 and 0.43 a ζ value of 1.8 is required $< 1.86 -$ OK.

(ii) Stability check

$\omega_x = 0.40$ and $\omega_y = 0.40$ (Table 4—7 p. 4—30)

$$M_{ox} = M_{rx}\left(1 - \frac{C_f}{C_r}\right)\left(1 - \frac{C_f}{C_{ex}}\right)$$

$$M_{oy} = M_{ry} \left(1 - \frac{C_f}{C_r}\right)\left(1 - \frac{C_f}{C_{ey}}\right)$$

From page 4—42, $K_y L_y = 3\ 330$ mm is critical. $C_{rL} = 3\ 500$ kN (by interpolation)

$K_x L_x / r_x = 3\ 330/135 = 24.7 \rightarrow C_{ex} = 3\ 152 \times 15\ 000/10^3 = 47\ 300$ kN

$K_y L_y / r_y = 3\ 330/77.5 = 43.0 \rightarrow C_{ey} = 1\ 065 \times 15\ 000/10^3 = 16\ 000$ kN

$C_f / C_{ex} = 2\ 000/47\ 300 = 0.042$

$C_f / C_{ey} = 2\ 000/16\ 000 = 0.125$

$C_f / C_r = 2\ 000/3\ 500 = 0.571$

$M_{ox} = 526\ (1 - 0.571)\ (1 - 0.042) = 216$

$M_{oy} = 241\ (1 - 0.571)\ (1 - 0.125) = 90.5$

$$\left(\frac{\omega_x M_{fx}}{M_{ox}}\right)^\eta + \left(\frac{\omega_y M_{fy}}{M_{oy}}\right)^\eta = \left(\frac{0.40 \times 300}{216}\right)^{1.84} + \left(\frac{0.40 \times 100}{90.5}\right)^{1.84}$$

$$= 0.556^{1.84} + 0.442^{1.84}$$

$$= 0.56 < 1.0 - \text{OK}$$

Or, by entering Graph F2, page 4—111, for the two moment ratios 0.56 and 0.44, η required is less than 1.0 and therefore section is OK.

2. **Given:**

Design a square HSS column suitable for the following factored loads.

$C_f = 1\ 700$ kN $L = 3\ 700$ mm

$M_{fx_1} = 200$ kN·m $M_{fy_1} = 100$ kN·m

$M_{fx_2} = 250$ kN·m $M_{fy_2} = 100$ kN·m

The moments include the PΔ effects and both the X—X and Y—Y axis moments induce double curvature in the column. G40.21-M 350W steel. Assume $K_x = K_y = 0.90$.

Solution:

Use a Class H, hollow structural section (See Appendix F Clause F3, CAN3-S16.1-M78)

Try HSS 304.8 × 304.8 × 11.13 — Class H

$A = 12\ 800$ mm²

$r = 119$ mm

$M_r = 438$ kN·m

$C_{ro} = \phi A F_y = 0.90 \times 12\ 800$ mm × 350 MPa

$\qquad\qquad = 4\ 030 \times 10^3$ N

$\qquad\qquad = 4\ 030$ kN

(i) *Strength check*

   (a) $\dfrac{M_{fx}}{M_{rx}} + 0.5 \dfrac{M_{fy}}{M_{ry}} = \dfrac{250}{438} + 0.5 \dfrac{100}{438}$

$\qquad\qquad\qquad = 0.68 < 1.0 - \text{OK}$

(b) $\dfrac{C_f}{C_{ro}} + 0.85\left(\dfrac{M_{fx}}{M_{rx}} + 0.5\,\dfrac{M_{fy}}{M_{ry}}\right) = \dfrac{1\,700}{4\,030} + 0.85\left(\dfrac{250}{438} + 0.5 \times \dfrac{100}{438}\right)$

$$= 1.00 = 1.0 - \text{OK}$$

(ii) Stability check

$M_{fx_1}/M_{fx_2} = 200/250 = 0.80$

$M_{fy_1}/M_{fy_2} = 100/100 = 1.00$

From Table 4—7, $\omega_x = 0.40$, $\omega_y = 0.40$

$KL/r = K_x L_x/r_x = K_y L_y/r_y = 0.9 \times 3\,700/119 = 28$

$C_{ex} = C_{ey} = 2\,513\ \text{MPa} \times \dfrac{12\,800}{1\,000}\ \text{mm}^2 = 32\,200\ \text{kN (Table 4—8, page 4—31)}$

$C_f/C_e = 1\,700/32\,200 = 0.05$

$C_{rL} = 3\,970$ (by inspection, for $KL = 3\,330$, page 4—80, since Class H)

$U = \dfrac{1}{1 - C_f/C_e} = 1.05$ (from Table 4—9, page 4—32)

$\nu = \dfrac{\sqrt{(\omega_x M_{fx})^2 + (\omega_y M_{fy})^2}}{\omega_x M_{fx} + \omega_y M_{fy}} = \dfrac{\sqrt{(0.40 \times 250)^2 + (0.40 \times 100)^2}}{0.40 \times 250 + 0.40 \times 100}$

$$= 0.769$$

$\dfrac{C_f}{C_r} + \nu\left(\dfrac{\omega_x M_{fx}}{M_{rx}\left(1 - \dfrac{C_f}{C_{ex}}\right)} + \dfrac{\omega_y M_{fy}}{M_{ry}\left(1 - \dfrac{C_f}{C_{ey}}\right)}\right) \leqslant 1.0$

or rewritten

$\dfrac{C_f}{C_{rL}} + \nu\left(\dfrac{\omega_x M_{fx}\ U_x}{M_{rx}} + \dfrac{\omega_y\ M_{fy}\ U_y}{M_{ry}}\right) \leqslant 1.0$

$= \dfrac{1\,700}{3\,970} + 0.769\left(\dfrac{0.40 \times 250 \times 1.05}{438} + \dfrac{0.40 \times 100 \times 1.05}{438}\right)$

$= 0.69 < 1.00 - \text{OK}$

Use HSS 304.8 × 304.8 × 11.13 — Class H section.

NOTES

FACTORED MOMENT RESISTANCES OF COLUMNS

The tables on pages 4—118 to 4—121 inclusive, list, for the WWF and W shapes normally used as columns: the factored moment resistance for strong axis bending, M_{rx}, in CSA G40.21-M 300W steel for cases where the unsupported length of compression flange, L, is less than L_u plus the factored moment resistance, M'_{rx}, where L is greater than L_u for values of L from 2.5 m to 18 m. The sections are ordered as in Part 6 of this book, that is, all of the sections of the same nominal dimensions are listed together.

The M_{rx} and M'_{rx} values are computed based on the Class of the section in bending about the X—X axis. For the W360×64, when used as a beam-column, the class of the section is dependent upon the ratio of the factored axial load to axial compressive load at yield stress, C_f/C_y. For G40.21-M grade 300W steel, the W360×64 becomes a Class 3 section when C_f/C_y exceeds 0.79 based upon the CAN3-S16.1-M78 limit for h/w of

$$\frac{1\,180}{\sqrt{F_y}}\left(1 - 0.43\,\frac{C_f}{C_y}\right)$$ and a Class 4 section when C_f/C_y exceeds 0.87 based upon the h/w

limit of $\dfrac{1\,470}{\sqrt{F_y}}\left(1 - 0.54\,\dfrac{C_f}{C_y}\right)$.

Thus the M_{rx} and M'_{rx} values listed must be reduced by multiplying by 0.90, the ratio of S_x/Z_x for the W360×64 section, when C_f/C_y exceeds 0.79.

Section	M$_{rx}$	M'$_{rx}$ For the Following Unsupported Lengths in Millimetres						
		2 500	3 000	3 500	4 000	4 500	5 000	5 500
WWF550X721	4 960	....	....	....	....	....	....	....
WWF550X620	4 590	....	....	....	....	....	....	....
WWF550X503	3 860	....	....	....	....	....	....	....
WWF550X420	3 350	....	....	....	....	....	....	....
*WWF550X217	1 640	....	....	....	....	....	....	....
WWF500X651	4 020	....	....	....	....	....	....	....
WWF500X561	3 730	....	....	....	....	....	....	....
WWF500X456	3 160	....	....	....	....	....	....	....
WWF500X381	2 730	....	....	....	....	....	....	....
WWF500X343	2 460	....	....	....	....	....	....	....
WWF500X306	2 180	....	....	....	....	....	....	....
WWF500X276	2 000	....	....	....	....	....	....	....
+WWF500X254	1 660	....	....	....	....	....	....	....
+WWF500X223	1 480	....	....	....	....	....	....	....
*WWF500X197	1 350	....	....	....	....	....	....	....
WWF450X503	2 980	....	....	....	....	....	....	....
WWF450X409	2 520	....	....	....	....	....	....	....
WWF450X342	2 190	....	....	....	....	....	....	....
WWF450X308	1 970	....	....	....	....	....	....	....
WWF450X274	1 750	....	....	....	....	....	....	....
WWF450X248	1 610	....	....	....	....	....	....	....
WWF450X228	1 470	....	....	....	....	....	....	....
+WWF450X201	1 190	....	....	....	....	....	....	....
+WWF450X177	1 080	....	....	....	....	....	....	....
WWF400X444	2 290	....	....	....	....	....	....	....
WWF400X362	1 950	....	....	....	....	....	....	....
WWF400X303	1 700	....	....	....	....	....	....	....
WWF400X273	1 530	....	....	....	....	....	....	....
WWF400X243	1 360	....	....	....	....	....	....	....
WWF400X220	1 260	....	....	....	....	....	....	....
WWF400X202	1 150	....	....	....	....	....	....	....
WWF400X178	1 020	....	....	....	....	....	....	....
+WWF400X157	842	...	...	...	...	...	...	...
WWF350X385	1 700	....	....	....	....	....	....	....
WWF350X315	1 460	....	....	....	....	....	....	....
WWF350X263	1 280	....	....	....	....	....	....	....
WWF350X238	1 160	....	....	....	....	....	....	....
WWF350X212	1 030	....	....	....	....	....	....	....
WWF350X192	950	...	...	...	...	...	....	....
WWF350X176	869	...	...	...	...	...	...	...
WWF350X155	775	...	...	...	...	...	...	...
WWF350X137	699	...	...	...	...	...	...	...
W360X79	386	...	...	379	364	348	331	315
W360X72	346	...	...	337	322	306	290	274
&W360X64	308	...	...	297	283	268	252	237

† Based on Class of section for X-X axis bending only, $\omega = 1.0$.
* Class 3 for flexure and Class 4 for axial compression.
+ Class 3 for flexure.
& Class 1 for flexure and Class 4 for axial compression.

Mass	M'_{rx} For the Following Unsupported Lengths in Millimetres								
	6 000	7 000	8 000	9 000	10 000	12 000	14 000	16 000	18 000
721	....	....	....	....	....	....	....	4 900	4 790
620	....	....	....	....	....	....	....	4 490	4 390
503	....	....	....	....	....	....	3 770	3 650	3 540
420	....	....	....	....	....	3 250	3 110	2 980	2 840
217	....	....	....	....	1 600	1 490	1 380	1 260	1 130
651	....	....	....	....	....	....	....	3 970	3 890
561	....	....	....	....	....	....	....	3 650	3 570
456	....	....	....	....	....	....	3 070	2 980	2 890
381	....	....	....	....	....	2 620	2 510	2 410	2 300
343	....	....	....	....	2 420	2 310	2 190	2 080	1 970
306	....	....	....	2 160	2 100	1 990	1 870	1 750	1 630
276	....	....	....	1 980	1 930	1 810	1 690	1 570	1 460
254	....	....	....	....	1 610	1 510	1 410	1 310	1 210
223	....	....	....	1 460	1 420	1 320	1 220	1 120	1 020
197	....	....	....	1 320	1 280	1 180	1 080	981	869
503	....	....	....	....	....	....	....	2 910	2 850
409	....	....	....	....	....	2 510	2 440	2 370	2 300
342	....	....	....	....	2 170	2 090	2 000	1 920	1 840
308	....	....	....	1 960	1 920	1 830	1 740	1 650	1 560
274	....	....	....	1 710	1 660	1 570	1 470	1 380	1 290
248	....	....	....	1 560	1 520	1 420	1 330	1 240	1 140
228	....	....	1 460	1 410	1 360	1 270	1 170	1 070	976
201	....	....	1 180	1 150	1 110	1 030	946	864	779
177	....	....	1 070	1 030	995	915	833	750	653
444	....	....	....	....	....	....	....	2 250	2 200
362	....	....	....	....	....	....	1 890	1 840	1 790
303	....	....	....	....	1 680	1 610	1 550	1 490	1 430
273	....	....	....	1 510	1 480	1 410	1 340	1 280	1 210
243	....	....	1 350	1 320	1 280	1 210	1 140	1 070	995
220	....	....	1 240	1 200	1 170	1 090	1 020	951	881
202	....	....	1 120	1 080	1 040	968	893	819	739
178	....	....	981	943	905	828	752	673	585
157	...	...	815	784	753	689	625	560	484
385	....	....	....	....	....	....	....	1 670	1 640
315	....	....	....	....	....	1 450	1 420	1 380	1 340
263	....	....	....	....	1 260	1 210	1 160	1 120	1 070
238	....	....	....	1 130	1 110	1 060	1 010	962	914
212	....	....	1 010	982	956	903	851	799	748
192	...	...	923	896	869	816	763	711	660
176	...	858	830	802	774	719	664	610	549
155	...	753	724	696	667	610	553	490	430
137	...	673	645	616	587	530	472	405	354
79	298	264	225	195	172	139	117	101	89.4
72	257	222	186	161	141	114	95.7	82.6	72.7
64	220	183	153	131	115	92.4	77.3	66.6	58.5

FACTORED MOMENT RESISTANCES†
OF COLUMNS, M_{rx} and M'_{rx} – kN·m

Section	M_{rx}	M'_{rx} For the Following Unsupported Lengths in Millimetres						
		2 500	3 000	3 500	4 000	4 500	5 000	5 500
W310X283	1 330	....	....	....	....	....	....	....
W310X253	1 170	....	....	....	....	....	....	....
W310X226	1 040	....	....	....	....	....	....	....
W310X202	916	...	...	...	...	...	...	...
W310X179	796	...	...	...	...	...	...	...
W310X158	721	...	...	...	...	...	...	...
W310X143	653	...	...	...	...	...	...	...
W310X129	583	...	...	...	...	...	...	...
W310X118	526	...	...	...	...	...	...	524
W310X107	478	...	...	...	...	...	...	472
+W310X97	389	...	...	...	...	...	...	387
W310X86	383	...	...	...	...	378	367	355
W310X79	346	...	...	...	...	338	327	316
W310X74	321	...	...	318	307	295	282	270
W310X67	286	...	...	281	270	258	246	234
W310X60	254	...	...	248	237	226	214	203
W250X167	656	...	...	...	...	...	...	...
W250X149	575	...	...	...	...	...	...	...
W250X131	499	...	...	...	...	...	...	...
W250X115	432	...	...	...	...	...	...	428
W250X101	378	...	...	...	...	...	377	369
W250X89	332	...	...	...	...	...	327	320
W250X80	294	...	...	...	...	...	287	280
W250X73	266	...	...	...	...	264	257	250
W250X67	243	...	...	...	237	229	221	213
W250X58	208	...	...	207	199	191	184	176
W250X49	171	...	...	167	160	153	146	138
W200X100	310	...	...	...	...	...	...	305
W200X86	265	...	...	...	...	...	261	256
W200X71	217	...	...	...	...	213	208	203
W200X59	176	...	...	...	174	169	164	159
W200X52	154	...	...	...	150	145	140	135
W200X46	134	...	...	...	129	124	119	114
W200X42	120	...	119	114	109	104	98.6	93.5
W200X36	103	...	100	95.3	90.4	85.5	80.5	75.5
W200X31	90.4	86.7	81.1	75.3	69.5	63.6	57.0	50.6
W200X27	75.3	70.8	65.4	59.7	54.0	47.5	41.2	36.4
W150X37	83.7	...	83.2	80.2	77.2	74.2	71.3	68.3
W150X30	65.9	...	64.1	61.2	58.3	55.4	52.5	49.7
+W150X22	42.9	...	41.2	39.0	36.8	34.5	32.2	29.9
M100X19	26.9	26.3	25.3	24.2	23.2	22.2	21.2	20.1

† Based on Class of section for X-X bending only, $\omega = 1.0$.
+ Class 3 for flexure.

Mass	M'$_{rx}$ For the Following Unsupported Lengths in Millimetres								
	6 000	7 000	8 000	9 000	10 000	12 000	14 000	16 000	18 000
283	....	....	....	....	1 310	1 260	1 220	1 170	1 120
253	....	....	....	1 160	1 130	1 090	1 040	997	951
226	....	....	1 030	1 010	987	941	896	851	807
202	...	...	897	874	851	807	762	718	674
179	...	788	766	744	721	678	634	591	548
158	...	699	675	652	628	582	536	490	436
143	649	626	602	578	555	509	463	412	363
129	573	550	527	504	481	435	390	336	296
118	513	490	467	444	421	375	324	279	245
107	461	438	415	393	370	324	272	234	205
97	379	361	342	324	305	268	226	194	169
86	344	320	297	273	248	200	167	144	127
79	305	282	258	235	207	166	139	119	105
74	258	233	206	179	159	129	109	94.6	83.5
67	222	198	169	147	129	105	88.5	76.6	67.5
60	191	166	139	120	106	85.3	71.7	61.9	54.5
167	...	651	634	618	601	569	537	505	473
149	...	561	545	529	513	482	450	419	388
131	494	478	462	447	431	400	369	338	302
115	420	405	389	374	358	328	297	262	232
101	361	346	330	315	300	270	236	205	181
89	312	296	281	266	250	220	186	161	142
80	272	257	242	227	212	179	151	130	115
73	242	227	212	198	183	149	126	108	95.5
67	205	189	174	157	139	114	96.5	83.8	74.1
58	168	153	137	119	105	85.7	72.4	62.8	55.4
49	130	115	97.2	84.0	74.1	60.0	50.5	43.6	38.5
100	300	289	279	269	258	238	217	194	172
86	251	240	230	220	210	190	169	147	130
71	198	188	178	168	158	137	117	101	89.9
59	154	144	134	124	114	93.4	79.3	69.0	61.0
52	131	121	111	101	89.7	73.4	62.2	54.0	47.8
46	109	99.8	90.1	78.6	69.6	56.7	48.0	41.6	36.7
42	88.4	77.7	66.7	58.4	52.1	42.8	36.4	31.6	28.0
36	70.6	59.2	50.6	44.2	39.3	32.2	27.3	23.7	21.0
31	45.6	38.0	32.7	28.7	25.6	21.0	17.9	15.6	13.8
27	32.6	27.1	23.1	20.2	18.0	14.7	12.5	10.9	9.6
37	65.4	59.7	53.3	47.0	42.1	34.8	29.7	25.9	23.0
30	46.8	40.4	34.8	30.6	27.3	22.5	19.1	16.7	14.8
22	27.3	22.6	19.3	16.8	15.0	12.3	10.4	9.0	8.0
19	19.1	16.8	14.7	13.0	11.7	9.8	8.4	7.3	6.5

DOUBLE ANGLE STRUTS
EQUAL LEG ANGLES

FACTORED AXIAL COMPRESSIVE RESISTANCES IN kN
LEGS 10 mm BACK TO BACK*

G40.21-M
300W
$\phi = 0.90$

Size (mm)			200 x 200						150 x 150			
Thickness (mm)			30	25	20	16†	13†	10†	20	16	13	10†
Mass (kg/m)			174	147	119	96.5	79.0	61.2	87.9	71.3	58.6	45.5
	X-X Axis	0	5 790	4 910	4 100	2 950	2 120	1 260	3 020	2 450	2 010	1 240
		500	5 790	4 910	4 100	2 950	2 120	1 260	3 020	2 450	2 010	1 240
		1 000	5 710	4 840	4 050	2 910	2 090	1 250	2 920	2 370	1 950	1 200
		1 500	5 530	4 680	3 920	2 820	2 030	1 210	2 770	2 250	1 850	1 140
		2 000	5 320	4 510	3 770	2 720	1 950	1 170	2 600	2 120	1 740	1 080
		2 500	5 080	4 310	3 600	2 600	1 870	1 120	2 410	1 970	1 620	1 000
		3 000	4 820	4 100	3 420	2 470	1 780	1 060	2 190	1 790	1 480	915
		3 500	4 540	3 860	3 220	2 330	1 680	1 000	1 950	1 600	1 320	820
		4 000	4 220	3 600	3 000	2 170	1 560	937	1 660	1 370	1 140	709
		4 500	3 890	3 310	2 760	2 000	1 440	866	1 420	1 170	973	605
		5 000	3 520	3 010	2 510	1 820	1 320	790	1 230	1 010	843	524
		5 500	3 100	2 660	2 210	1 610	1 170	702	1 070	888	737	459
		6 000	2 760	2 360	1 970	1 430	1 040	625	947	783	651	405
		6 500	2 470	2 120	1 760	1 280	929	560	841	696	579	360
		7 000	2 230	1 910	1 590	1 160	839	506	752	622	518	322
		7 500	2 020	1 730	1 440	1 050	761	459	669	557	465	290
		8 000	1 840	1 580	1 310	957	694	418	592	492	411	256
		8 500	1 690	1 450	1 200	875	635	383	527	439	366	228
		9 000	1 550	1 330	1 100	804	583	352	473	394	328	205
		9 500	1 420	1 220	1 020	740	537	324				
		10 000	1 310	1 130	936	683	496	299				
	Y-Y Axis	0	5 790	4 910	4 100	2 480	1 670	908	3 020	2 450	2 010	981
		500	5 790	4 910	4 100	2 480	1 660	907	3 020	2 450	2 010	980
		1 000	5 790	4 910	4 100	2 480	1 660	907	3 000	2 430	1 990	979
		1 500	5 710	4 830	4 030	2 470	1 660	906	2 910	2 360	1 940	976
		2 000	5 580	4 730	3 940	2 470	1 660	904	2 820	2 280	1 870	972
		2 500	5 450	4 610	3 840	2 460	1 650	902	2 710	2 200	1 800	967
		3 000	5 310	4 490	3 740	2 450	1 650	900	2 590	2 100	1 720	959
		3 500	5 150	4 350	3 620	2 430	1 640	896	2 470	1 990	1 630	947
		4 000	4 980	4 210	3 490	2 410	1 630	892	2 330	1 880	1 530	931
		4 500	4 800	4 050	3 360	2 380	1 610	887	2 170	1 750	1 430	878
		5 000	4 610	3 890	3 210	2 300	1 590	881	2 010	1 620	1 320	808
		5 500	4 410	3 710	3 060	2 190	1 570	873	1 840	1 470	1 200	730
		6 000	4 190	3 530	2 900	2 080	1 490	863	1 640	1 310	1 070	650
		6 500	3 960	3 330	2 730	1 950	1 400	828	1 470	1 180	956	584
		7 000	3 720	3 130	2 550	1 820	1 300	772	1 330	1 060	864	527
		7 500	3 460	2 900	2 340	1 670	1 190	704	1 210	967	785	479
		8 000	3 180	2 660	2 140	1 530	1 090	646	1 100	883	717	437
		8 500	2 930	2 450	1 980	1 410	1 010	595	1 010	809	657	401
		9 000	2 710	2 270	1 830	1 300	930	550	932	745	604	369
		9 500	2 520	2 110	1 700	1 210	863	511	860	687	558	340
		10 000	2 350	1 960	1 580	1 130	804	475	796	636	516	314

Effective length (KL) in millimetres with respect to indicated axis

PROPERTIES OF 2 ANGLES — 10 mm BACK TO BACK

	30	25	20	16†	13†	10†	20	16	13	10†
Area (mm²)	22 200	18 800	15 200	12 300	10 100	7 800	11 200	9 090	7 460	5 800
r_x (mm)	60.3	60.8	61.6	62.1	62.5	63.0	45.5	46.1	46.5	46.8
r_y (mm)	89.3	88.5	87.6	87.0	86.6	86.1	67.5	66.8	66.3	65.8
*r_z (mm)	39.0	39.1	39.3	39.5	39.7	39.9	29.3	29.4	29.6	29.8
*r_z/r_x	0.647	0.643	0.638	0.636	0.635	0.633	0.644	0.638	0.637	0.637
*r_z/r_y	0.437	0.442	0.449	0.454	0.458	0.463	0.434	0.440	0.446	0.453

IMPERIAL SIZE AND MASS

	30	25	20	16	13	10	20	16	13	10
Mass (lb./ft.)	117	98.8	80.0	64.8	53.1	41.1	59.1	47.9	39.4	30.6
Thickness (in.)	1.18	0.98	0.79	0.63	0.51	0.39	0.79	0.63	0.51	0.39
Size (in.)	7.87 x 7.87						5.91 x 5.91			

† Factored axial compressive resistances calculated in accordance with Clause 13.3.3 CAN3-S16.1-M78
* See p. 4-4 for more details regarding these tables.

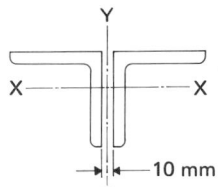

G40.21-M
300W
$\phi = 0.90$

←→ 10 mm

DOUBLE ANGLE STRUTS
Equal Leg Angles

FACTORED AXIAL COMPRESSIVE RESISTANCES IN kN
.*LEGS 10 mm BACK TO BACK

Size (mm)		125 x 125				100 x 100				
Thickness (mm)		16	13	10†	8†	16	13	10	8†	6†
Mass (kg/m)		58.8	48.4	37.7	30.4	46.2	38.2	29.8	24.1	18.3
X-X Axis	0	2 020	1 660	1 150	803	1 590	1 310	1 030	737	459
	500	2 010	1 660	1 140	799	1 570	1 290	1 010	727	452
	1 000	1 910	1 580	1 090	763	1 450	1 200	942	678	423
	1 500	1 790	1 470	1 020	715	1 310	1 090	855	616	385
	2 000	1 640	1 350	941	658	1 140	952	750	542	339
	2 500	1 470	1 210	846	593	939	789	627	455	286
	3 000	1 270	1 060	738	518	735	617	491	358	225
	3 500	1 040	871	612	431	594	499	397	289	182
	4 000	871	727	511	360	490	412	329	239	151
	4 500	739	617	434	306	411	346	276	201	127
	5 000	635	531	373	263	345	292	234	171	108
	5 500	552	461	324	229	287	243	195	143	90.4
	6 000	483	404	284	200		206	165	121	76.6
	6 500	417	350	247	175					
	7 000	362	304	215	152					
	7 500	318	267	188	133					
Y-Y Axis	0	2 020	1 660	963	623	1 590	1 310	1 030	613	345
	500	2 020	1 660	962	623	1 590	1 310	1 030	613	345
	1 000	1 980	1 630	960	621	1 540	1 270	989	611	344
	1 500	1 910	1 570	956	619	1 460	1 210	940	607	342
	2 000	1 830	1 500	950	616	1 380	1 130	883	599	339
	2 500	1 740	1 430	938	610	1 280	1 050	818	584	334
	3 000	1 640	1 340	920	602	1 170	959	744	532	326
	3 500	1 520	1 250	859	590	1 050	856	662	473	292
	4 000	1 400	1 140	786	546	905	736	566	403	248
	4 500	1 260	1 030	707	491	773	629	483	344	212
	5 000	1 110	900	616	427	669	544	418	297	183
	5 500	974	792	542	375	586	476	365	260	160
	6 000	865	703	481	333	517	420	322	229	141
	6 500	774	628	430	298	460	373	286	204	125
	7 000	697	566	387	268	411	334	256	182	112
	7 500	630	512	350	242	370	299	228	161	99.4
	8 000	573	465	318	220	327	264	202	142	87.8
	8 500	523	424	290	201	291	236	180	126	78.3
	9 000	479	388	265	183	261	211	161	113	
	9 500	434	351	238	165					
	10 000	393	318	216	150					

Effective length (KL) in millimetres with respect to indicated axis

PROPERTIES OF 2 ANGLES — 10 mm BACK TO BACK

	16	13	10†	8†	16	13	10	8†	6†
Area (mm²)	7 490	6 160	4 800	3 870	5 890	4 860	3 800	3 070	2 330
r_x (mm)	38.0	38.4	38.8	39.1	30.0	30.4	30.8	31.1	31.4
r_y (mm)	56.7	56.2	55.7	55.4	46.7	46.2	45.6	45.3	45.0
*r_z (mm)	24.4	24.5	24.7	24.8	19.5	19.5	19.7	19.8	19.9
*r_z/r_x	0.642	0.638	0.637	0.634	0.650	0.641	0.640	0.637	0.634
*r_z/r_y	0.430	0.436	0.443	0.448	0.418	0.422	0.432	0.437	0.442

IMPERIAL SIZE AND MASS

	16	13	10†	8†	16	13	10	8†	6†
Mass (lb./ft.)	39.5	32.5	25.3	20.4	31.0	25.7	20.0	16.2	12.3
Thickness (in.)	0.63	0.51	0.39	0.31	0.63	0.51	0.39	0.31	0.24
Size (in.)		4.92 x 4.92				3.94 x 3.94				

† Factored axial compressive resistances calculated in accordance with Clause 13.3.3 CAN3-S16.1-M78
* See p. 4-4 for more details regarding these tables.

DOUBLE ANGLE STRUTS
Equal Leg Angles

FACTORED AXIAL COMPRESSIVE RESISTANCES IN kN
LEGS 10 mm BACK TO BACK*

G40.21-M 300W
$\emptyset = 0.90$

Size (mm)		90 x 90				75 x 75				
Thickness (mm)		13	10	8	6†	13	10	8	6†	5†
Mass (kg/m)		34.1	26.7	21.6	16.4	28.0	22.0	17.8	13.6	11.4
X - X Axis	0	1 170	918	742	447	961	756	613	415	310
	500	1 150	898	727	439	925	729	591	401	300
	1 000	1 050	826	670	404	823	651	529	360	269
	1 500	932	733	596	361	689	548	447	305	229
	2 000	784	620	506	307	518	417	342	236	177
	2 500	607	483	396	242	382	308	253	174	131
	3 000	473	376	309	189	294	237	195	135	101
	3 500	380	303	249	152	233	189	155	107	80.6
	4 000	312	249	204	125	183	149	122	85.1	64.1
	4 500	258	206	170	104		119	97.9	68.0	51.2
	5 000	211	169	139	85.6					
	5 500			116	71.4					
Y - Y Axis	0	1 170	918	742	349	961	756	613	343	241
	500	1 170	918	742	349	956	751	608	343	241
	1 000	1 120	877	709	348	904	709	574	341	239
	1 500	1 060	827	668	345	840	658	532	336	237
	2 000	986	769	620	340	764	596	481	325	231
	2 500	901	701	565	332	675	524	422	284	211
	3 000	806	624	502	300	572	440	351	235	175
	3 500	696	535	429	255	465	358	285	191	142
	4 000	582	447	358	213	387	297	237	159	118
	4 500	496	381	305	181	328	252	201	134	99.6
	5 000	428	329	263	156	281	216	172	115	85.2
	5 500	373	286	229	136	244	187	149	99.4	73.7
	6 000	328	252	201	120	211	160	127	84.5	62.7
	6 500	291	223	178	106	181	138	109	72.3	53.8
	7 000	256	195	156	92.2	157	120	94.9		
	7 500	225	171	137	80.8					
	8 000	199	151	121	71.5					

Effective length (KL) in millimetres with respect to indicated axis

PROPERTIES OF 2 ANGLES – 10 mm BACK TO BACK

	13	10	8	6†	13	10	8	6†	5†
Area (mm²)	4 340	3 400	2 750	2 090	3 560	2 800	2 270	1 730	1 450
r_x (mm)	27.2	27.5	27.8	28.1	22.4	22.8	23.0	23.3	23.4
r_y (mm)	42.2	41.6	41.3	40.9	36.2	35.6	35.2	34.9	34.7
*r_z (mm)	17.6	17.6	17.7	17.9	14.6	14.6	14.7	14.8	14.9
*r_z/r_x	0.647	0.640	0.637	0.637	0.652	0.640	0.639	0.635	0.637
*r_z/r_y	0.417	0.423	0.429	0.438	0.403	0.410	0.418	0.424	0.429

IMPERIAL SIZE AND MASS

	13	10	8	6†	13	10	8	6†	5†
Mass (lb./ft.)	22	17.9	14.5	11.0	18.8	14.8	12.0	9.14	7.66
Thickness (in.)	0.51	0.39	0.31	0.24	0.51	0.39	0.31	0.24	0.20
Size (in.)	3.54 x 3.54				2.95 x 2.95				

† Factored axial compressive resistances calculated in accordance with Clause 13.3.3 CAN3-S16.1-M78
* See p. 4-4 for more details regarding these tables.

G40.21-M
300W
Ø = 0.90

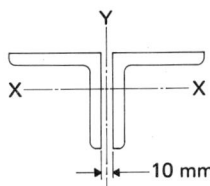

→ ←10 mm

DOUBLE ANGLE STRUTS
Equal Leg Angles

FACTORED AXIAL COMPRESSIVE RESISTANCES IN kN
*LEGS 10 mm BACK TO BACK

Size (mm)		65 x 65				55 x 55					
Thickness (mm)		10	8	6	5†	10	8	6	5	4†	3†
Mass (kg/m)		18.8	15.3	11.7	9.81	15.7	12.8	9.80	8.24	6.66	5.04

Effective length (KL) in millimetres with respect to indicated axis

X - X Axis

0		648	526	402	294	540	440	337	283	193	115
500		615	500	383	280	501	409	314	264	180	108
1 000		530	433	333	243	409	336	260	219	149	89.7
1 500		417	344	266	195	282	233	183	155	106	64.5
2 000		289	240	187	138	189	157	123	105	71.6	43.6
2 500		211	176	137	101	136	113	89.1	75.5	51.7	31.5
3 000		161	134	105	77.0	98.0	81.7	64.8	55.1	37.8	23.1
3 500		122	102	80.2	59.1						
4 000				62.2	45.8						

Y - Y Axis

0		648	526	402	239	540	440	337	283	153	81.3
500		640	519	397	238	529	430	330	277	152	81.0
1 000		598	485	370	236	487	395	302	254	151	80.4
1 500		545	441	336	232	433	350	267	224	146	78.9
2 000		482	389	295	214	367	296	224	187	126	75.0
2 500		407	327	246	179	287	229	172	143	96.3	57.0
3 000		323	258	194	140	224	179	134	112	75.0	44.4
3 500		261	209	157	113	180	144	108	89.5	60.2	35.6
4 000		216	173	129	93.6	148	118	88.4	73.4	49.3	29.1
4 500		182	145	109	78.6	123	97.4	72.6	60.1	40.3	23.7
5 000		155	123	92.4	66.5	100	79.7	59.4	49.2	32.9	19.4
5 500		130	103	76.9	55.4	83.9					
6 000		110	87.4	65.2	47.0						

PROPERTIES OF 2 ANGLES — 10 mm BACK TO BACK

	65 x 65				55 x 55					
Area (mm²)	2 400	1 950	1 490	1 250	2 000	1 630	1 250	1 050	848	642
r_x (mm)	19.5	19.8	20.1	20.2	16.4	16.6	16.9	17.0	17.1	17.3
r_y (mm)	31.7	31.3	30.9	30.7	27.7	27.3	26.9	26.7	26.5	26.3
*r_z (mm)	12.7	12.7	12.8	12.9	10.7	10.7	10.8	10.8	10.9	11.0
*r_z/r_x	0.651	0.641	0.637	0.639	0.652	0.645	0.639	0.635	0.637	0.636
*r_z/r_y	0.401	0.406	0.414	0.420	0.386	0.392	0.401	0.404	0.411	0.418

IMPERIAL SIZE AND MASS

	65 x 65				55 x 55					
Mass (lb./ft.)	12.6	10.3	7.86	6.59	10.5	8.60	6.59	5.54	4.48	3.39
Thickness (in.)	0.39	0.31	0.24	0.20	0.39	0.31	0.24	0.20	0.16	0.12
Size (in.)		2.56 x 2.56					2.17 x 2.17			

† Factored axial compressive resistances calculated in accordance with Clause 13.3.3 CAN3-S16.1-M78
* See p. 4-4 for more details regarding these tables.

DOUBLE ANGLE STRUTS
Equal Leg Angles

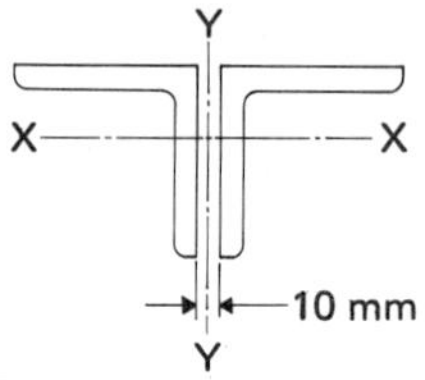

FACTORED AXIAL COMPRESSIVE RESISTANCES IN kN
LEGS 10 mm BACK TO BACK*

G40.21-M
300W
$\emptyset = 0.90$

Size (mm)		45 x 45					35 x 35			
Thickness (mm)		8	6	5	4	3†	6	5	4	3†
Mass (kg/m)		10.3	7.91	6.67	5.40	4.10	6.03	5.10	4.14	3.16
X-X Axis	0	354	273	229	186	112	207	175	143	100
	500	317	245	207	168	101	174	148	120	84.7
	1 000	234	183	155	127	76.6	102	87.8	72.2	51.3
	1 500	140	110	94.6	77.3	47.0	57.7	49.5	40.8	29.0
	2 000	92.1	72.6	62.5	51.1	31.1	34.8	30.0	24.8	17.4
	2 500	61.8	49.0	42.4	34.8	21.2				
Y-Y Axis	0	354	273	229	186	84.7	207	175	143	82.0
	500	342	263	221	179	84.3	196	166	135	81.5
	1 000	307	235	197	159	83.1	168	142	115	78.6
	1 500	261	198	166	134	79.5	131	109	87.6	60.8
	2 000	202	151	126	101	59.8	90.0	74.5	59.6	41.2
	2 500	149	112	92.9	74.2	44.1	65.6	54.3	43.4	30.0
	3 000	115	86.2	71.6	57.2	34.0	49.9	41.2	32.9	21.8
	3 500	91.8	68.5	56.8	45.4	26.9	37.5	30.8	24.5	16.2
	4 000	73.0	54.0	44.7	35.6	21.1				
	4 500	58.4	43.2	35.8						

Effective length (KL) in millimetres with respect to indicated axis

PROPERTIES OF 2 ANGLES — 10 mm BACK TO BACK

	8	6	5	4	3†	6	5	4	3†
Area (mm²)	1 310	1 010	850	688	522	768	650	528	402
r_x (mm)	13.4	13.6	13.8	13.9	14.0	10.5	10.6	10.7	10.8
r_y (mm)	23.4	22.9	22.7	22.5	22.3	19.1	18.8	18.6	18.4
*r_z (mm)	8.76	8.79	8.82	8.87	8.93	6.81	6.83	6.86	6.91
*r_z/r_x	0.654	0.646	0.639	0.638	0.638	0.649	0.644	0.641	0.640
*r_z/r_y	0.374	0.384	0.389	0.394	0.400	0.357	0.363	0.369	0.376

IMPERIAL SIZE AND MASS

	8	6	5	4	3†	6	5	4	3†
Mass (lb./ft.)	6.92	5.32	4.48	3.63	2.75	4.05	3.43	2.78	2.12
Thickness (in.)	0.31	0.24	0.20	0.16	0.12	0.24	0.20	0.16	0.12
Size (in.)	1.77 x 1.77					1.38 x 1.38			

† Factored axial compressive resistances calculated in accordance with Clause 13.3.3 CAN3-S16-1-M78
* See p. 4-4 for more details regarding these tables.

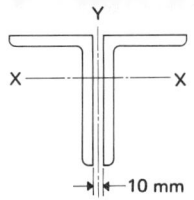

G40.21-M
300W
∅ = 0.90

←→ ‖←10 mm

DOUBLE ANGLE STRUTS
Unequal Leg Angles

FACTORED AXIAL COMPRESSIVE RESISTANCES IN kN
*LONG LEGS 10 mm BACK TO BACK

Size (mm)			150 x 100				125 x 90			
Thickness (mm)			16	13	10†	8†	16	13	10†	8†
Mass (kg/m)			58.8	48.4	37.7	30.4	50.0	41.2	32.2	26.0
Effective length (KL) in millimetres with respect to indicated axis	X-X Axis	0	2 020	1 660	1 030	678	1 720	1 420	984	687
		500	2 020	1 660	1 020	676	1 720	1 410	978	683
		1 000	1 960	1 610	996	657	1 630	1 350	936	654
		1 500	1 870	1 540	951	627	1 530	1 260	879	615
		2 000	1 760	1 450	898	593	1 410	1 160	812	568
		2 500	1 640	1 350	838	554	1 270	1 050	734	514
		3 000	1 500	1 240	771	510	1 110	921	645	453
		3 500	1 350	1 120	696	461	920	769	541	382
		4 000	1 170	977	612	406	768	642	452	319
		4 500	1 000	834	523	347	652	545	384	271
		5 000	869	723	453	300	561	469	331	233
		5 500	761	633	397	263	488	408	288	203
		6 000	672	559	351	233	427	358	252	178
		6 500	598	498	312	207	373	313	222	157
		7 000	535	446	280	186	324	272	192	136
		7 500	481	401	252	167	284	238	169	120
		8 000	428	358	225	150				106
		8 500	381	318	201	133				
		9 000	342	286	180	120				
		9 500		258	163	108				
	Y-Y Axis	0	2 020	1 660	865	539	1 720	1 420	859	568
		500	2 020	1 660	863	538	1 720	1 410	857	567
		1 000	1 930	1 590	857	535	1 630	1 340	850	562
		1 500	1 830	1 500	845	529	1 530	1 260	834	554
		2 000	1 700	1 390	824	519	1 410	1 160	799	539
		2 500	1 550	1 270	778	504	1 270	1 040	715	497
		3 000	1 380	1 130	689	452	1 110	906	620	429
		3 500	1 190	964	586	383	926	750	510	352
		4 000	995	805	490	320	773	626	426	294
		4 500	847	685	416	272	657	532	361	249
		5 000	731	591	359	234	565	457	310	214
		5 500	638	515	313	204	491	397	270	186
		6 000	561	453	275	179	431	348	235	163
		6 500	496	401	243	158	376	303	202	140
		7 000	436	351	212	138	327	263	175	122
		7 500	382	307	186	121	287	231	153	107
		8 000	338	272	164	107				

PROPERTIES OF 2 ANGLES — 10 mm BACK TO BACK									
Area (mm²)	7 490	6 160	4 800	3 870	6 370	5 250	4 100	3 310
r_x (mm)	47.4	47.8	48.3	48.5	39.0	39.4	39.8	40.1
r_y (mm)	41.9	41.4	40.9	40.6	39.2	38.7	38.1	37.8
*r_z (mm)	21.6	21.7	21.9	22.0	19.2	19.3	19.5	19.6
*r_z/r_x	0.456	0.454	0.453	0.454	0.492	0.490	0.490	0.489
*r_z/r_y	0.516	0.524	0.535	0.542	0.490	0.499	0.512	0.519

IMPERIAL SIZE AND MASS								
Mass (lb./ft.)	39.5	32.5	25.3	20.4	33.6	27.7	21.6	17.5
Thickness (in.)	0.63	0.51	0.39	0.31	0.63	0.51	0.39	0.31
Size (in.)		5.91 x 3.94				4.92 x 3.54		

† Factored axial compressive resistances calculated in accordance with Clause 13.3.3 CAN3-S16.1-M78
* See p. 4-4 for more details regarding these tables.

DOUBLE ANGLE STRUTS
Unequal Leg Angles

FACTORED AXIAL COMPRESSIVE RESISTANCES IN kN
LONG LEGS 10 mm BACK TO BACK*

G40.21-M
300W
$\emptyset = 0.90$

Size (mm)		125 x 75				100 x 90			
Thickness (mm)		13	10†	8†	6†	13	10	8†	6†
Mass (kg/m)		38.2	29.8	24.1	18.3	36.1	28.3	22.9	17.3
X-X Axis	0	1 310	912	534	358	1 240	972	699	435
	500	1 310	906	531	356	1 220	959	689	429
	1 000	1 250	868	524	341	1 140	894	644	401
	1 500	1 170	816	508	321	1 030	813	586	366
	2 000	1 080	754	465	297	906	715	517	323
	2 500	975	682	388	270	756	600	435	273
	3 000	856	601	304	238	592	472	343	216
	3 500	716	505	246	202	479	382	278	175
	4 000	598	422	203	169	396	316	230	145
	4 500	508	358	171	143	332	265	193	122
	5 000	438	309	144	124	281	226	165	103
	5 500	381	269	120	108	234	188	138	86.8
	6 000	334	236	102	94.5	199	159	117	73.5
	6 500	293	208		83.5				
	7 000	254	180		72.7				
	7 500	223	158		63.7				
	8 000				56.4				
Y-Y Axis	0	1 310	804	637	280	1 240	972	593	338
	500	1 300	801	634	279	1 240	971	592	338
	1 000	1 210	787	607	276	1 190	926	589	336
	1 500	1 100	756	571	270	1 120	871	582	333
	2 000	974	670	528	259	1 040	807	569	328
	2 500	822	561	479	214	942	732	524	319
	3 000	651	441	423	168	836	647	462	285
	3 500	527	357	357	135	713	547	389	239
	4 000	436	295	299	112	596	457	325	200
	4 500	367	248	254	93.8	507	388	276	170
	5 000	312	207	219	79.0	437	335	238	146
	5 500	262	173	190	65.9	381	292	207	127
	6 000	222	146	167	55.9	334	256	182	112
	6 500			148		296	226	160	98.0
	7 000			128		258	197	138	85.0
	7 500			112		226	172	121	74.6
	8 000			99.5		200	152	107	

Effective length (KL) in millimetres with respect to indicated axis

PROPERTIES OF 2 ANGLES — 10 mm BACK TO BACK

	125 x 75				100 x 90			
Area (mm²)	4 860	3 800	3 070	2 330	4 600	3 600	2 910	2 210
r_x (mm)	39.6	40.0	40.4	40.6	30.7	31.1	31.4	31.6
r_y (mm)	31.6	31.0	30.7	30.3	41.1	40.5	40.2	39.8
*r_z (mm)	16.2	16.3	16.4	16.6	18.4	18.5	18.6	18.7
*r_z/r_x	0.409	0.407	0.406	0.409	0.599	0.595	0.592	0.592
*r_z/r_y	0.513	0.526	0.534	0.548	0.448	0.457	0.463	0.470

IMPERIAL SIZE AND MASS

	125 x 75				100 x 90			
Mass (lb./ft.)	25.7	20.0	16.2	12.3	24.3	19.0	15.4	11.6
Thickness (in.)	0.51	0.39	0.31	0.24	0.51	0.39	0.31	0.24
Size (in.)	4.92 x 2.95				3.94 x 3.54			

† Factored axial compressive resistances calculated in accordance with Clause 13.3.3 CAN3-S16.1-M78
* See p. 4-4 for more details regarding these tables.

G40.21-M
300W
∅ = 0.90

← 10 mm

DOUBLE ANGLE STRUTS
Unequal Leg Angles

FACTORED AXIAL COMPRESSIVE RESISTANCES IN kN
*LONG LEGS 10 mm BACK TO BACK

Size (mm)		100 x 75				90 x 75				
Thickness (mm)		13	10	8†	6†	13	10	8	6†	5†
Mass (kg/m)		33.1	25.9	21.0	15.9	31.0	24.3	19.7	15.0	12.6
X-X Axis	0	1 140	891	641	399	1 070	837	678	409	293
	500	1 120	879	633	395	1 040	820	664	401	287
	1 000	1 050	821	592	369	961	756	613	371	266
	1 500	951	748	540	337	854	674	548	332	238
	2 000	836	660	477	299	724	573	468	285	204
	2 500	701	557	404	253	566	451	370	227	163
	3 000	552	440	321	202	442	352	289	177	127
	3 500	446	356	260	163	355	283	233	143	103
	4 000	369	295	215	135	292	233	192	117	84.5
	4 500	310	248	181	114	243	194	160	98.1	70.6
	5 000	264	211	154	96.9	198	159	131	80.9	58.3
	5 500	220	177	129	81.6	166	133	110	67.5	48.6
	6 000	186	150	110	69.2					
Y-Y Axis	0	1 140	891	557	321	1 070	837	678	333	225
	500	1 130	882	555	321	1 060	830	671	332	225
	1 000	1 060	828	548	318	997	781	631	329	223
	1 500	974	760	533	311	921	719	581	324	220
	2 000	872	678	485	300	830	646	520	312	214
	2 500	754	583	415	256	724	560	449	269	192
	3 000	612	470	333	205	597	458	365	218	155
	3 500	497	381	270	166	485	372	296	177	125
	4 000	412	316	224	138	403	309	246	146	104
	4 500	348	267	189	116	341	261	207	124	87.6
	5 000	297	228	161	98.8	292	223	177	105	74.8
	5 500	255	194	135	83.6	252	192	152	90.2	63.8
	6 000	216	164	114	70.8	214	163	129	76.4	54.0
	6 500	185	141	97.8		184	140	111	65.6	46.4

Effective length (KL) in millimetres with respect to indicated axis

PROPERTIES OF 2 ANGLES — 10 mm BACK TO BACK

	100 x 75				90 x 75				
Area (mm²)	4 210	3 300	2 670	2 030	3 950	3 100	2 510	1 910	1 600
r_x (mm)	31.1	31.5	31.8	32.0	27.7	28.0	28.3	28.6	28.7
r_y (mm)	33.6	33.1	32.7	32.4	34.6	34.0	33.6	33.3	33.1
*r_z (mm)	16.0	16.1	16.2	16.3	15.6	15.7	15.8	15.9	16.0
*r_z/r_x	0.514	0.511	0.509	0.509	0.563	0.561	0.558	0.556	0.557
*r_z/r_y	0.476	0.486	0.495	0.503	0.451	0.462	0.470	0.477	0.483

IMPERIAL SIZE AND MASS

	100 x 75				90 x 75				
Mass (lb./ft.)	22.2	17.4	14.1	10.7	20.8	16.3	13.2	10.1	8.47
Thickness (in.)	0.51	0.39	0.31	0.24	0.51	0.39	0.31	0.24	0.20
Size (in.)	3.94 x 2.95				3.54 x 2.95				

† Factored axial compressive resistances calculated in accordance with Clause 13.3.3 CAN3-S16.1-M78
* See p. 4-4 for more details regarding these tables.

DOUBLE ANGLE STRUTS
Unequal Leg Angles

FACTORED AXIAL COMPRESSIVE RESISTANCES IN kN
LONG LEGS 10 mm BACK TO BACK*

Size (mm)	90 x 65				80 x 60			
Thickness (mm)	10	8	6†	5†	10	8	6†	5†
Mass (kg/m)	22.8	18.5	14.0	11.8	20.4	16.6	12.6	10.6

Effective length (KL) in millimetres with respect to indicated axis

X-X Axis

KL	10	8	6†	5†	10	8	6†	5†
0	783	634	383	274	702	570	373	275
500	768	623	376	269	682	554	362	268
1 000	709	575	348	249	619	503	330	244
1 500	633	515	312	224	536	437	287	213
2 000	541	442	269	193	435	356	235	175
2 500	428	352	215	155	324	266	176	131
3 000	334	275	168	121	252	207	137	102
3 500	269	221	136	97.6	201	165	109	81.7
4 000	221	182	112	80.4	164	135	89.3	66.7
4 500	185	152	93.5	67.3	131	108	71.8	53.8
5 000	152	126	77.3	55.7		88.6	58.8	44.1
5 500	127	105	64.5	46.5				

Y-Y Axis

KL	10	8	6†	5†	10	8	6†	5†
0	783	634	318	217	702	570	317	223
500	769	623	317	216	687	557	316	222
1 000	712	576	312	213	632	511	310	219
1 500	640	516	302	208	562	453	294	211
2 000	552	443	265	189	476	381	246	181
2 500	444	353	210	149	371	295	189	138
3 000	347	276	164	116	289	230	147	108
3 500	280	222	132	93.8	233	185	118	86.4
4 000	231	183	109	77.2	191	152	97.0	70.8
4 500	193	153	91.0	64.4	159	125	79.6	57.9
5 000	160	126	74.8	52.8	130	102	65.1	47.4
5 500	134	105	62.4	44.1	108			

PROPERTIES OF 2 ANGLES — 10 mm BACK TO BACK

	10	8	6†	5†	10	8	6†	5†
Area (mm²)	2 900	2 350	1 790	1 500	2 600	2 110	1 610	1 350
r_x (mm)	28.3	28.6	28.9	29.0	25.0	25.2	25.4	25.6
r_y (mm)	29.1	28.7	28.4	28.2	27.6	27.2	26.8	26.6
*r_z (mm)	13.9	14.0	14.2	14.2	12.8	12.9	13.0	13.0
*r_z/r_x	0.491	0.490	0.491	0.490	0.512	0.512	0.512	0.508
*r_z/r_y	0.478	0.488	0.500	0.504	0.464	0.474	0.485	0.489

IMPERIAL SIZE AND MASS

	10	8	6†	5†	10	8	6†	5†
Mass (lb./ft.)	15.3	12.4	9.41	7.93	13.7	11.2	8.47	7.12
Thickness (in.)	0.39	0.31	0.24	0.20	0.39	0.31	0.24	0.20
Size (in.)	3.54 x 2.56				3.15 x 2.36			

† Factored axial compressive resistances calculated in accordance with Clause 13.3.3 CAN3-S16.1-M78
* See p.4-4 for more details regarding these tables.

G40.21-M 300W ∅ = 0.90

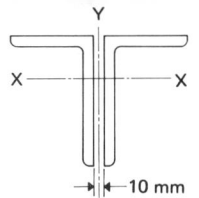

DOUBLE ANGLE STRUTS
Unequal Leg Angles

FACTORED AXIAL COMPRESSIVE RESISTANCE IN kN
*LONG LEGS 10 mm BACK TO BACK

Size (mm)		75 x 50			65 x 50			
Thickness (mm)		8	6†	5†	8	6	5†	4†
Mass (kg/m)		14.7	11.2	9.42	13.4	10.3	8.63	6.97

Effective length (KL) in millimetres with respect to indicated axis

X-X Axis

KL	8	6†	5†	8	6	5†	4†
0	505	343	257	462	354	258	179
500	488	332	249	440	337	247	171
1 000	439	299	224	383	295	216	150
1 500	375	256	193	307	238	174	121
2 000	293	202	153	216	169	124	87.1
2 500	217	149	113	158	124	91.2	63.9
3 000	168	115	87.5	121	94.9	69.8	49.0
3 500	134	92.0	69.7	92.9	73.2	54.0	38.0
4 000	107	73.8	56.1	72.1	56.8	41.9	29.5
4 500	85.4	59.0	44.8				

Y-Y Axis

KL	8	6†	5†	8	6	5†	4†
0	505	299	214	462	354	220	142
500	487	297	213	447	342	219	142
1 000	435	287	206	402	306	213	139
1 500	367	247	184	343	260	189	130
2 000	280	186	138	268	201	145	99.7
2 500	207	137	101	198	148	107	73.6
3 000	160	106	78.1	153	115	82.7	56.8
3 500	127	83.8	61.9	122	91.2	65.7	45.1
4 000	100	64.9	48.4	97.7	72.4	52.0	35.7
4 500	80.0			78.1	57.9	41.6	28.5

PROPERTIES OF 2 ANGLES — 10 mm BACK TO BACK

	8	6†	5†	8	6	5†	4†
Area (mm²)	1 870	1 430	1 200	1 710	1 310	1 100	888
r_x (mm)	23.7	23.9	24.1	20.2	20.5	20.6	20.8
r_y (mm)	22.9	22.5	22.3	23.7	23.3	23.1	23.0
*r_z (mm)	10.8	10.9	10.9	10.6	10.7	10.8	10.8
*r_z/r_x	0.456	0.456	0.452	0.525	0.522	0.524	0.519
*r_z/r_y	0.472	0.484	0.489	0.447	0.459	0.468	0.470

IMPERIAL SIZE AND MASS

	8	6†	5†	8	6	5†	4†
Mass (lb./ft.)	9.88	7.53	6.33	9.00	6.92	5.80	4.68
Thickness (in.)	0.31	0.24	0.20	0.31	0.24	0.20	0.16
Size (in.)	2.95 x 1.97			2.56 x 1.97			

† Factored axial compressive resistances calculated in accordance with Clause 13.3.3 CAN3-S16.1-M78

* See p. 4-4 for more details regarding these tables.

DOUBLE ANGLE STRUTS
Unequal Leg Angles

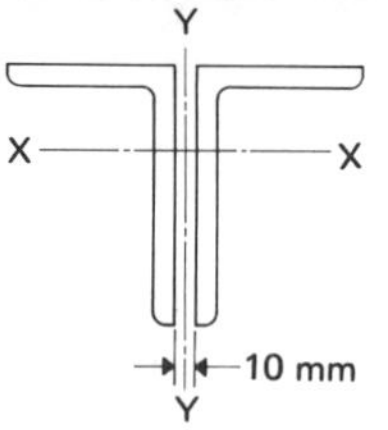

FACTORED AXIAL COMPRESSIVE RESISTANCES IN kN
LONG LEGS 10 mm BACK TO BACK*

G40.21-M
300W
∅ = 0.90

→| |←10 mm

Size (mm)		55 x 35				45 x 30			
Thickness (mm)		6	5	4†	3†	6	5	4	3†
Mass (kg/m)		7.91	6.67	5.40	4.10	6.50	5.49	4.46	3.39
X-X Axis	0	273	229	156	93.7	224	189	153	92.5
	500	255	215	146	87.9	202	171	139	84.1
	1 000	212	180	123	73.9	153	131	107	65.0
	1 500	153	131	89.5	54.5	94.0	81.0	66.4	40.8
	2 000	103	88.2	60.5	36.9	62.2	53.7	44.0	27.1
	2 500	74.6	63.8	43.8	26.7	42.5	36.9	30.3	18.8
	3 000	54.8	47.1	32.4	19.9				
	3 500			24.2	14.8				
Y-Y Axis	0	273	229	133	73.6	224	189	153	75.9
	500	255	214	131	72.7	206	174	141	74.7
	1 000	211	177	120	68.9	165	138	111	66.2
	1 500	150	125	83.5	48.9	109	90.5	72.2	42.4
	2 000	101	84.0	56.2	32.8	72.9	60.5	48.2	28.2
	2 500	73.3	60.6	40.5	23.6	52.1	43.1	34.1	19.8
	3 000	53.6	44.1	29.3	17.0	36.9	30.4	24.1	

Effective length (KL) in millimetres with respect to indicated axis

PROPERTIES OF 2 ANGLES — 10 mm BACK TO BACK

	55 x 35				45 x 30			
Area (mm²)	1 010	850	688	522	828	700	568	432
r_x (mm)	17.3	17.5	17.6	17.8	14.0	14.2	14.3	14.5
r_y (mm)	17.1	16.9	16.7	16.4	15.6	15.4	15.2	14.9
*r_z (mm)	7.55	7.59	7.65	7.72	6.44	6.47	6.51	6.57
*r_z/r_x	0.436	0.434	0.435	0.434	0.460	0.456	0.455	0.453
*r_z/r_y	0.442	0.449	0.458	0.471	0.413	0.420	0.428	0.441

IMPERIAL SIZE AND MASS

	55 x 35				45 x 30			
Mass (lb./ft.)	5.32	4.48	3.63	2.80	4.37	3.69	3.00	2.28
Thickness (in.)	0.24	0.20	0.16	0.12	0.24	0.20	0.16	0.12
Size (in.)	2.17 x 1.38				1.77 x 1.18			

† Factored axial compressive resistances calculated in accordance with Clause 13.3.3 CAN3-S16.1-M78
* See p. 4-4 for more details regarding these tables.

DOUBLE ANGLE STRUTS
Unequal Leg Angles
FACTORED AXIAL COMPRESSIVE RESISTANCES IN kN
*SHORT LEGS 10 mm BACK TO BACK

← 10 mm

Size (mm)		150 x 100				125 x 90			
Thickness (mm)		16	13	10†	8†	16	13	10†	8†
Mass (kg/m)		58.8	48.4	37.7	30.4	50.0	41.2	32.2	26.0

Effective length (KL) in millimetres with respect to indicated axis

X-X Axis

KL	16	13	10†	8†	16	13	10†	8†
0	2 020	1 660	1 030	678	1 720	1 420	984	687
500	1 980	1 630	1 010	666	1 670	1 380	960	671
1 000	1 830	1 510	934	617	1 520	1 260	878	614
1 500	1 630	1 350	839	555	1 330	1 100	772	541
2 000	1 400	1 160	722	480	1 090	913	642	451
2 500	1 100	926	580	388	821	691	490	345
3 000	863	723	453	303	638	537	381	269
3 500	695	583	366	245	511	431	306	216
4 000	572	480	301	202	417	352	250	177
4 500	477	401	252	169	337	286	204	145
5 000	392	331	209	140	276	234	167	118
5 500	327	276	174	117				

Y-Y Axis

KL	16	13	10†	8†	16	13	10†	8†
0	2 020	1 660	852	529	1 720	1 420	849	559
500	2 020	1 660	852	529	1 720	1 420	849	559
1 000	2 010	1 650	852	529	1 690	1 400	848	559
1 500	1 960	1 610	851	529	1 640	1 350	847	558
2 000	1 900	1 560	850	528	1 580	1 300	845	557
2 500	1 840	1 510	849	528	1 510	1 240	841	555
3 000	1 770	1 450	847	527	1 430	1 180	814	552
3 500	1 700	1 390	843	525	1 350	1 100	763	532
4 000	1 620	1 320	815	524	1 250	1 030	708	493
4 500	1 530	1 250	769	506	1 150	943	649	451
5 000	1 430	1 170	720	473	1 040	850	583	404
5 500	1 330	1 090	667	438	918	749	513	356
6 000	1 220	995	609	399	817	666	456	316
6 500	1 100	894	547	358	732	596	408	283
7 000	995	809	495	324	660	538	368	255
7 500	906	737	451	295	599	488	334	231
8 000	829	674	412	270	545	444	304	211
8 500	761	619	379	248	499	406	278	193
9 000	702	571	349	228	458	373	255	177
9 500	649	528	323	211	422	343	235	162
10 000	602	489	299	196	387	314	214	148

PROPERTIES OF 2 ANGLES – 10 mm BACK TO BACK

	16	13	10†	8†	16	13	10†	8†
Area (mm²)	7 490	6 160	4 800	3 870	6 370	5 250	4 100	3 310
r_x (mm)	28.3	28.7	29.0	29.3	25.6	26.0	26.4	26.6
r_y (mm)	73.3	72.7	72.2	71.8	61.2	60.7	60.1	59.8
*r_z (mm)	21.6	21.7	21.9	22.0	19.2	19.3	19.5	19.6
*r_z/r_x	0.763	0.756	0.755	0.751	0.750	0.742	0.739	0.737
*r_z/r_y	0.295	0.298	0.303	0.306	0.314	0.318	0.324	0.328

IMPERIAL SIZE AND MASS

	16	13	10†	8†	16	13	10†	8†
Mass (lb./ft.)	39.5	32.5	25.3	20.4	33.6	27.7	21.6	17.5
Thickness (in.)	0.63	0.51	0.39	0.31	0.63	0.51	0.39	0.31
Size (in.)	5.91 x 3.94				4.92 x 3.54			

† Factored axial compressive resistances calculated in accordance with Clause 13.3.3 CAN3-S16.1-M78
* See p. 4-4 for more details regarding these tables.

DOUBLE ANGLE STRUTS
Unequal Leg Angles
FACTORED AXIAL COMPRESSIVE RESISTANCES IN kN
SHORT LEGS 10 mm BACK TO BACK*

G40.21-M
300W
$\emptyset = 0.90$

Size (mm)			125 x 75				100 x 90		
Thickness (mm)		13	10†	8†	6†	13	10	8†	6†
Mass (kg/m)		38.2	29.8	24.1	18.3	36.1	28.3	22.9	17.3
X-X Axis	0	1 310	912	637	358	1 240	972	699	435
	500	1 250	873	611	343	1 210	950	684	426
	1 000	1 100	766	538	303	1 110	873	629	392
	1 500	889	625	441	249	983	773	558	349
	2 000	635	450	321	182	824	651	472	296
	2 500	466	331	236	134	634	504	367	232
	3 000	357	254	181	103	494	392	286	181
	3 500	277	198	142	81.1	397	315	230	146
	4 000	215	153	110	62.8	325	259	189	120
	4 500					267	214	157	99.8
	5 000					219	175	128	81.5
	5 500								68.0
Y-Y Axis	0	1 310	791	522	272	1 240	972	590	336
	500	1 310	791	522	272	1 240	972	590	335
	1 000	1 300	790	522	272	1 200	939	588	335
	1 500	1 260	790	522	272	1 150	895	585	333
	2 000	1 210	789	521	272	1 080	843	580	331
	2 500	1 160	787	520	272	1 010	783	561	327
	3 000	1 100	764	519	271	922	716	513	318
	3 500	1 040	720	502	271	829	642	459	283
	4 000	972	672	468	261	721	555	395	243
	4 500	899	620	431	241	616	474	338	208
	5 000	820	565	392	219	533	410	292	180
	5 500	728	500	346	193	467	359	256	157
	6 000	648	445	308	171	413	317	226	139
	6 500	581	399	276	154	367	282	201	123
	7 000	524	360	249	139	329	252	180	110
	7 500	476	326	226	126	295	227	161	98.7
	8 000	434	298	206	115	263	201	142	87.2
	8 500	397	272	189	105	234	179	127	77.7
	9 000	365	250	173	96.2	210	160	113	69.8
	9 500	336	230	159	88.6				
	10 000	311	213	147	81.5				

Effective length (KL) in millimetres with respect to indicated axis

PROPERTIES OF 2 ANGLES — 10 mm BACK TO BACK

	125 x 75				100 x 90			
Area (mm²)	4 860	3 800	3 070	2 330	4 600	3 600	2 910	2 210
r_x (mm)	20.7	21.0	21.3	21.5	26.9	27.2	27.5	27.8
r_y (mm)	63.0	62.4	62.0	61.6	47.4	46.8	46.5	46.1
*r_z (mm)	16.2	16.3	16.4	16.6	18.4	18.5	18.6	18.7
*r_z/r_x	0.783	0.776	0.770	0.772	0.684	0.680	0.676	0.673
*r_z/r_y	0.257	0.261	0.265	0.269	0.388	0.395	0.400	0.406

IMPERIAL SIZE AND MASS

	125 x 75				100 x 90			
Mass (lb./ft.)	25.7	20.0	16.2	12.3	24.3	19.0	15.4	11.6
Thickness (in.)	0.51	0.39	0.31	0.24	0.51	0.39	0.31	0.24
Size (in.)	4.92 x 2.95				3.94 x 3.54			

† Factored axial compressive resistances calculated in accordance with Clause 13.3.3 CAN3-S16-1-M78
* See p. 4-4 for more details regarding these tables.

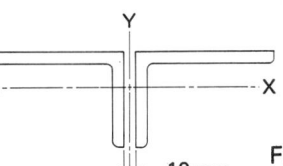

G40.21-M
300W
Ø = 0.90

DOUBLE ANGLE STRUTS
Unequal Leg Angles
FACTORED AXIAL COMPRESSIVE RESISTANCES IN kN
*SHORT LEGS 10 mm BACK TO BACK

Size (mm)			100 x 75				90 x 75				
Thickness (mm)			13	10	8†	6†	13	10	8	6†	5†
Mass (kg/m)			33.1	25.9	21.0	15.9	31.0	24.3	19.7	15.0	12.6
Effective length (KL) in millimetres with respect to indicated axis	X-X Axis	0	1 140	891	641	399	1 070	837	678	409	293
		500	1 090	856	616	385	1 020	805	653	394	282
		1 000	962	758	548	342	908	715	581	352	252
		1 500	792	629	457	286	753	597	487	297	213
		2 000	579	466	341	215	557	445	367	226	162
		2 500	426	343	251	159	410	328	271	166	120
		3 000	328	264	194	122	316	253	209	128	92.5
		3 500	258	209	153	96.9	250	200	166	102	73.5
		4 000	200	162	120	75.9	194	156	130	80.3	58.0
		4 500								64.3	46.4
	Y-Y Axis	0	1 140	891	550	316	1 070	837	678	330	222
		500	1 140	891	550	316	1 070	837	678	329	222
		1 000	1 100	864	549	315	1 020	803	650	329	222
		1 500	1 060	826	547	315	971	761	615	327	221
		2 000	999	781	544	314	909	711	574	324	220
		2 500	935	730	523	311	837	653	527	316	217
		3 000	863	672	481	299	755	588	473	284	203
		3 500	783	608	435	270	665	516	414	247	176
		4 000	696	538	383	237	561	433	347	206	147
		4 500	596	460	327	202	478	369	295	176	125
		5 000	517	398	283	175	413	319	255	152	108
		5 500	453	349	248	153	361	279	223	133	94.5
		6 000	401	309	219	136	318	245	196	117	83.2
		6 500	357	275	195	121	282	218	174	103	73.7
		7 000	320	246	175	108	252	194	154	91.5	65.2
		7 500	288	222	158	97.2	221	170	135	80.2	57.1
		8 000	261	199	141	86.9	196	150	120	70.9	50.5
		8 500	232	177	126	77.4	175	134	107	63.2	45.1
		9 000	208	159	113	69.4					
		9 500	188	144	102	62.7					

PROPERTIES OF 2 ANGLES — 10 mm BACK TO BACK

	100 x 75				90 x 75				
Area (mm²)	4 210	3 300	2 670	2 030	3 950	3 100	2 510	1 910	1 600
r_x (mm)	21.5	21.9	22.2	22.4	21.9	22.2	22.5	22.8	22.9
r_y (mm)	49.4	48.8	48.4	48.1	44.0	43.5	43.1	42.7	42.6
*r_z (mm)	16.0	16.1	16.2	16.3	15.6	15.7	15.8	15.9	16.0
*r_z/r_x	0.744	0.735	0.730	0.728	0.712	0.707	0.702	0.697	0.699
*r_z/r_y	0.324	0.330	0.335	0.339	0.355	0.361	0.367	0.372	0.376

IMPERIAL SIZE AND MASS

	100 x 75				90 x 75				
Mass (lb./ft.)	22.2	17.4	14.1	10.7	20.8	16.3	13.2	10.1	8.47
Thickness (in.)	0.51	0.39	0.31	0.24	0.51	0.39	0.31	0.24	0.20
Size (in.)	3.94 x 2.95				3.54 x 2.95				

† Factored axial compressive resistances calculated in accordance with Clause 13.3.3 CAN3-S16-1-M78
* See p. 4-4 for more details regarding these tables.

DOUBLE ANGLE STRUTS
Unequal Leg Angles

FACTORED AXIAL COMPRESSIVE RESISTANCE IN kN
SHORT LEGS 10 mm BACK TO BACK*

G40.21-M
300W
$\emptyset = 0.90$

Size (mm)		90 x 65				80 x 60			
Thickness (mm)		10	8	6†	5†	10	8	6†	5†
Mass (kg/m)		22.8	18.5	14.0	11.8	20.4	16.6	12.6	10.6
X-X Axis	0	783	634	383	274	702	570	373	275
	500	739	600	363	260	656	533	350	258
	1 000	631	514	312	224	546	446	294	217
	1 500	484	399	243	176	393	324	217	161
	2 000	330	273	167	122	265	219	147	109
	2 500	240	199	122	88.9	192	158	106	79.1
	3 000	182	151	93.0	67.7	141	117	79.0	59.0
	3 500	136	114	70.0	51.1			59.0	44.0
Y-Y Axis	0	783	634	313	212	702	570	313	219
	500	783	634	312	212	701	569	312	219
	1 000	754	610	312	212	668	542	312	218
	1 500	716	579	311	211	628	509	310	217
	2 000	671	542	310	210	581	470	306	216
	2 500	620	500	301	209	526	425	276	203
	3 000	562	453	272	194	464	373	242	178
	3 500	498	400	239	171	391	313	202	148
	4 000	423	339	202	144	327	261	169	124
	4 500	361	289	172	123	278	222	143	105
	5 000	312	250	149	106	239	191	123	90.4
	5 500	273	218	130	92.5	208	167	107	78.6
	6 000	240	192	115	81.5	183	146	94.1	68.9
	6 500	214	171	102	72.3	161	128	82.3	60.2
	7 000	191	152	90.7	64.5	140	111	71.5	52.2
	7 500	169	135	79.9	56.7	123	97.7	62.7	45.8
	8 000	149	119	70.7	50.2	109			
	8 500	133	106	63.0	44.7				

Effective length (KL) in millimetres with respect to indicated axis

PROPERTIES OF 2 ANGLES — 10 mm BACK TO BACK

	90 x 65				80 x 60			
Area (mm²)	2 900	2 350	1 790	1 500	2 600	2 110	1 610	1 350
r_x (mm)	18.7	19.0	19.2	19.4	17.3	17.5	17.8	17.9
r_y (mm)	44.9	44.5	44.1	43.9	40.2	39.8	39.4	39.2
*r_z (mm)	13.9	14.0	14.2	14.2	12.8	12.9	13.0	13.0
*r_z/r_x	0.743	0.737	0.740	0.732	0.740	0.737	0.730	0.726
*r_z/r_y	0.310	0.315	0.322	0.323	0.318	0.324	0.330	0.332

IMPERIAL SIZE AND MASS

	90 x 65				80 x 60			
Mass (lb./ft.)	15.3	12.4	9.41	7.93	13.7	11.2	8.47	7.12
Thickness (in.)	0.39	0.31	0.24	0.20	0.39	0.31	0.24	0.20
Size (in.)	3.54 x 2.56				3.15 x 2.36			

† Factored axial compressive resistances calculated in accordance with Clause 13.3.3 CAN3-S16-1-M78
* See p. 4-4 for more details regarding these tables.

G40.21-M 300W
$\emptyset = 0.90$

DOUBLE ANGLE STRUTS
Unequal Leg Angles
FACTORED AXIAL COMPRESSIVE RESISTANCES IN kN
*SHORT LEGS 10 mm BACK TO BACK

—10 mm

Size (mm)		75 x 50			65 x 50			
Thickness (mm)		8	6†	5†	8	6	5†	4†
Mass (kg/m)		14.7	11.2	9.42	13.4	10.3	8.63	6.97
X-X Axis	0	505	343	257	462	354	258	179
	500	457	312	234	420	322	236	163
	1 000	348	240	181	324	251	185	128
	1 500	214	150	113	204	159	118	82.5
	2 000	142	99.6	75.3	135	106	78.8	55.0
	2 500	97.2	68.8	52.2	93.8	73.7	55.3	38.7
Y-Y Axis	0	505	294	209	462	354	216	140
	500	503	294	209	457	350	216	140
	1 000	479	293	209	429	328	216	139
	1 500	448	292	208	394	301	214	138
	2 000	412	279	207	352	268	195	134
	2 500	370	250	186	303	230	167	115
	3 000	322	217	161	245	184	134	91.6
	3 500	266	179	133	198	150	108	74.2
	4 000	222	149	111	165	124	89.8	61.5
	4 500	189	126	93.9	139	104	75.6	51.8
	5 000	162	109	80.7	119	89.2	64.5	44.2
	5 500	141	94.4	70.1	101	75.8	54.7	37.4
	6 000	123	82.6	61.3	85.7	64.2	46.3	31.7
	6 500	107	71.5	53.0	73.7	55.2	39.8	
	7 000	93.1	62.1	46.0				
	7 500	81.7	54.5	40.4				

Effective length (KL) in millimetres with respect to indicated axis

PROPERTIES OF 2 ANGLES — 10 mm BACK TO BACK

	8	6†	5†	8	6	5†	4†
Area (mm²)	1 870	1 430	1 200	1 710	1 310	1 100	888
r_x (mm)	14.1	14.4	14.5	14.5	14.7	14.9	15.0
r_y (mm)	38.6	38.2	38.0	33.2	32.8	32.6	32.4
*r_z (mm)	10.8	10.9	10.9	10.6	10.7	10.8	10.8
*r_z/r_x	0.766	0.757	0.752	0.731	0.728	0.725	0.720
*r_z/r_y	0.280	0.285	0.287	0.319	0.326	0.331	0.333

IMPERIAL SIZE AND MASS

	8	6†	5†	8	6	5†	4†
Mass (lb./ft.)	9.88	7.53	6.33	9.00	6.92	5.80	4.68
Thickness (in.)	0.31	0.24	0.20	0.31	0.24	0.20	0.16
Size (in.)	2.95 x 1.97			2.56 x 1.97			

† Factored axial compressive resistances calculated in accordance with Clause 13.3.3 CAN3-S16.1-M78
* See p. 4-4 for more details regarding these tables.

DOUBLE ANGLE STRUTS
Unequal Leg Angles
FACTORED AXIAL COMPRESSIVE RESISTANCES IN kN
SHORT LEGS 10 mm BACK TO BACK*

**G40.21-M
300W
$\emptyset = 0.90$**

Size (mm)		55 x 35				45 x 30			
Thickness (mm)		6	5	4†	3†	6	5	4	3†
Mass (kg/m)		7.91	6.67	5.40	4.10	6.50	5.49	4.46	3.39
X-X Axis	0	273	229	156	93.7	224	189	153	92.5
	500	223	189	129	77.9	171	146	119	72.2
	1 000	122	104	72.2	44.5	80.4	69.3	57.4	35.3
	1 500	67.9	58.3	40.4	24.9	42.0	36.4	30.4	18.8
	2 000				14.9				
Y-Y Axis	0	273	229	129	70.5	224	189	153	73.2
	500	268	226	129	70.5	217	184	149	73.1
	1 000	249	209	129	70.4	197	166	135	72.9
	1 500	224	188	128	70.1	171	144	116	69.8
	2 000	195	163	110	65.8	139	116	93.6	55.8
	2 500	159	132	89.0	52.9	103	86.4	69.3	41.3
	3 000	124	103	69.6	41.3	80.2	67.0	53.8	32.0
	3 500	100	83.2	56.1	33.3	64.1	53.5	42.9	25.6
	4 000	82.8	68.6	46.3	27.5	52.3	43.6	34.9	20.7
	4 500	69.4	57.5	38.7	23.0	41.8	34.8	27.8	16.5
	5 000	58.0	47.9	32.2	19.0				
	5 500	48.3	39.9	26.8	15.9				

Effective length (KL) in millimetres with respect to indicated axis

PROPERTIES OF 2 ANGLES — 10 mm BACK TO BACK

	55 x 35				45 x 30			
Area (mm²)	1 010	850	688	522	828	700	568	432
r_x (mm)	9.76	9.89	10.0	10.2	8.35	8.46	8.59	8.71
r_y (mm)	29.7	29.4	29.2	29.0	25.0	24.8	24.6	24.4
*r_z (mm)	7.55	7.59	7.65	7.72	6.44	6.47	6.51	6.57
*r_z/r_x	0.774	0.767	0.765	0.757	0.771	0.765	0.758	0.754
*r_z/r_y	0.254	0.258	0.262	0.266	0.258	0.261	0.265	0.269

IMPERIAL SIZE AND MASS

	55 x 35				45 x 30			
Mass (lb./ft.)	5.32	4.48	3.63	2.80	4.37	3.69	3.00	2.28
Thickness (in.)	0.24	0.20	0.16	.012	0.24	0.20	0.16	0.12
Size (in.)	2.17 x 1.38				1.77 x 1.18			

† Factored axial compressive resistances calculated in accordance with Clause 13.3.3 CAN3-S16.1-M78
* See p. 4-4 for more details regarding these tables.

G40.21-M
300W
∅ = 0.90

DOUBLE ANGLE STRUTS
*STAR SHAPED

FACTORED AXIAL COMPRESSIVE RESISTANCES IN kN

Legs	16 mm apart			12 mm apart			12 mm apart	
Size (mm)	200 x 200			150 x 150			125 x 125	
Thickness (mm)	30	25	20	20	16	13	16	13
Mass (kg/m)	174	147	119	87.9	71.3	58.6	58.8	48.4

Effective length (KL) in millimetres with respect to indicated axis

U-U Axis

KL	30	25	20	20	16	13	16	13
0	5 790	4 910	4 100	3 020	2 450	2 010	2 020	1 660
500	5 790	4 910	4 100	3 020	2 450	2 010	2 020	1 660
1 000	5 790	4 910	4 100	3 020	2 450	2 000	2 000	1 640
1 500	5 760	4 870	4 060	2 950	2 390	1 960	1 940	1 590
2 000	5 660	4 780	3 990	2 870	2 320	1 900	1 880	1 540
2 500	5 550	4 690	3 910	2 780	2 250	1 840	1 800	1 480
3 000	5 440	4 590	3 820	2 690	2 170	1 770	1 720	1 410
3 500	5 310	4 490	3 720	2 580	2 080	1 700	1 630	1 330
4 000	5 180	4 370	3 620	2 470	1 990	1 620	1 530	1 250
4 500	5 040	4 250	3 510	2 350	1 890	1 530	1 430	1 160
5 000	4 890	4 120	3 390	2 220	1 780	1 440	1 310	1 060
5 500	4 740	3 980	3 270	2 080	1 660	1 340	1 190	949
6 000	4 570	3 840	3 140	1 940	1 540	1 240	1 060	844
6 500	4 390	3 680	3 000	1 770	1 400	1 120	948	757
7 000	4 210	3 520	2 850	1 610	1 260	1 010	857	684
7 500	4 020	3 360	2 700	1 460	1 150	921	778	621
8 000	3 820	3 180	2 540	1 340	1 050	843	710	567
8 500	3 610	3 000	2 360	1 230	968	774	651	519
9 000	3 370	2 780	2 190	1 140	894	714	599	477
9 500	3 140	2 590	2 030	1 050	827	661	552	440
10 000	2 930	2 420	1 900	979	768	613	511	406

V-V Axis

KL	30	25	20	20	16	13	16	13
0	5 790	4 910	4 100	3 020	2 450	2 010	2 020	1 660
500	5 790	4 910	4 100	3 020	2 450	2 010	2 020	1 660
1 000	5 780	4 890	4 090	2 970	2 410	1 980	1 960	1 610
1 500	5 640	4 780	4 000	2 860	2 330	1 910	1 870	1 540
2 000	5 490	4 660	3 890	2 740	2 230	1 830	1 760	1 450
2 500	5 320	4 520	3 780	2 610	2 120	1 750	1 640	1 360
3 000	5 140	4 370	3 650	2 460	2 000	1 650	1 510	1 250
3 500	4 940	4 200	3 510	2 290	1 870	1 540	1 360	1 130
4 000	4 720	4 020	3 350	2 110	1 730	1 430	1 190	993
4 500	4 490	3 830	3 190	1 910	1 570	1 300	1 020	848
5 000	4 240	3 620	3 020	1 680	1 390	1 150	881	735
5 500	3 970	3 400	2 830	1 480	1 220	1 010	772	644
6 000	3 690	3 160	2 630	1 310	1 090	901	682	569
6 500	3 370	2 900	2 410	1 170	972	807	607	507
7 000	3 050	2 630	2 180	1 060	875	727	544	454
7 500	2 780	2 400	1 990	957	793	659	489	409
8 000	2 550	2 190	1 820	871	721	599	437	366
8 500	2 340	2 020	1 680	795	659	548	389	326
9 000	2 160	1 860	1 550	728	603	502	349	293
9 500	2 000	1 730	1 430	662	552	461	315	264
10 000	1 860	1 600	1 330	600	500	417		

PROPERTIES OF 2 STARRED ANGLES

	30	25	20	20	16	13	16	13
Area (mm²)	22 200	18 800	15 200	11 200	9 090	7 460	7 490	6 160
r_u (mm)	105	103	100	77.6	75.8	74.4	65.7	64.3
r_v (mm)	75.8	76.8	77.7	57.3	58.1	58.6	47.9	48.4
*r_z (mm)	39.0	39.1	39.3	29.3	29.4	29.6	24.4	24.5
*r_z/r_u	0.371	0.380	0.393	0.378	0.388	0.398	0.371	0.381
*r_z/r_v	0.515	0.509	0.506	0.511	0.506	0.505	0.509	0.506

IMPERIAL SIZE AND MASS

	30	25	20	20	16	13	16	13
Mass (lb./ft.)	117	98.8	80.0	59.1	47.9	39.4	39.5	32.5
Thickness (in.)	1.18	0.98	0.79	0.79	0.63	0.51	0.63	0.51
Size (in.)	7.87 x 7.87			5.91 x 5.91			4.92 x 4.92	

* See page 4-4 for more details regarding these tables.
Research currently (1980) being conducted indicates that at least two equally spaced points of interconnection be used.
(1/3rd. points)

DOUBLE ANGLE STRUTS
STAR SHAPED*
FACTORED AXIAL COMPRESSIVE RESISTANCES IN kN

G40.21-M
300W
$\emptyset = 0.90$

Legs		10 mm apart			10 mm apart			8 mm apart		
Size (mm)		100 x 100			90 x 90			75 x 75		
Thickness (mm)		16	13	10	13	10	8	13	10	8
Mass (kg/m)		46.2	38.2	29.8	34.1	26.7	21.6	28.0	22.0	17.8
U-U Axis	0	1 590	1 310	1 030	1 170	918	742	961	756	613
	500	1 590	1 310	1 030	1 170	918	742	961	755	612
	1 000	1 550	1 280	999	1 140	888	717	918	720	582
	1 500	1 500	1 230	958	1 090	847	683	866	676	546
	2 000	1 430	1 170	911	1 030	799	643	804	625	503
	2 500	1 350	1 100	857	960	744	597	733	566	453
	3 000	1 260	1 030	796	884	682	546	652	499	396
	3 500	1 170	948	729	800	614	488	559	420	330
	4 000	1 060	858	656	707	535	422	467	351	276
	4 500	946	754	570	604	457	360	397	298	234
	5 000	822	655	495	524	395	312	343	257	201
	5 500	722	575	434	459	346	273	299	223	175
	6 000	641	510	385	406	306	241	263	196	154
	6 500	572	455	343	362	272	214	232	173	134
	7 000	515	409	308	324	244	191	204	150	116
	7 500	465	369	278	292	219	172	178	132	102
	8 000	422	335	252	262	195	152	158	116	
	8 500	385	305	227	233	174	135			
	9 000	348	273	204	209	156	122			
	9 500	314	247	184	189					
	10 000	285	224	167						
V-V Axis	0	1 590	1 310	1 030	1 170	918	742	961	756	613
	500	1 580	1 310	1 020	1 160	911	737	942	742	602
	1 000	1 500	1 240	973	1 090	859	696	869	686	557
	1 500	1 400	1 160	911	1 010	794	644	775	614	500
	2 000	1 280	1 070	838	906	716	583	660	527	431
	2 500	1 150	955	754	786	626	511	520	421	346
	3 000	991	828	657	644	518	426	406	329	270
	3 500	813	683	545	523	421	346	327	265	218
	4 000	678	569	455	434	350	288	269	218	180
	4 500	575	483	386	367	296	243	224	182	150
	5 000	494	415	332	313	253	208	184	151	124
	5 500	429	361	289	271	219	180	153	126	104
	6 000	375	316	253	229	186	154			
	6 500	323	273	220	197	160	132			
	7 000	280	237	191			115			
	7 500	246	208	168						

PROPERTIES OF 2 STARRED ANGLES

Area (mm²)		5 890	4 860	3 800	4 340	3 400	2 750	3 560	2 800	2 270
r_u (mm)		54.3	52.9	51.6	48.8	47.5	46.6	41.5	40.1	39.2
r_v (mm)		37.7	38.2	38.8	34.1	34.8	35.2	28.1	28.7	29.0
*r_z (mm)		19.5	19.5	19.7	17.6	17.6	17.7	14.6	14.6	14.7
*r_z/r_u		0.359	0.369	0.382	0.361	0.371	0.380	0.352	0.364	0.375
*r_z/r_v		0.517	0.510	0.508	0.516	0.506	0.503	0.520	0.509	0.507

IMPERIAL SIZE AND MASS

Mass (lb./ft.)		31.0	25.7	20.0	22.9	17.9	14.5	18.8	14.8	12.0
Thickness (in.)		0.63	0.51	0.39	0.51	0.39	0.31	0.51	0.39	0.31
Size (in.)		3.94 x 3.94			3.54 x 3.54			2.95 x 2.95		

Effective length (KL) in millimetres with respect to indicated axis

* See page 4-4 for more details regarding these tables.
Research currently (1980) being conducted indicates that at least two equally spaced points of interconnection be used. (1/3rd. points)

DOUBLE ANGLE STRUTS
*STAR SHAPED
FACTORED AXIAL COMPRESSIVE RESISTANCES IN kN

Legs		8 mm apart			8 mm apart			
Size (mm)		65 x 65			55 x 55			
Thickness (mm)		10	8	6	10	8	6	5
Mass (kg/m)		18.8	15.3	11.7	15.7	12.8	9.80	8.24
U-U Axis	0	648	526	402	540	440	337	283
	500	644	523	399	534	434	332	278
	1 000	609	493	376	499	405	309	257
	1 500	566	457	347	456	368	280	229
	2 000	514	413	312	404	324	244	196
	2 500	454	362	271	344	272	202	156
	3 000	384	302	223	274	215	158	122
	3 500	312	245	181	222	174	128	97.9
	4 000	260	204	150	184	144	106	80.6
	4 500	220	172	127	155	121	88.5	67.3
	5 000	189	148	109	132	103	74.6	55.3
	5 500	163	128	93.7	111	85.7	62.1	46.2
	6 000	141	109	79.5	94.0	72.6	52.7	
	6 500	121	93.8	68.3				
	7 000	105	81.6					
V-V Axis	0	648	526	402	540	440	337	283
	500	629	512	391	515	421	323	272
	1 000	569	464	356	450	369	284	240
	1 500	491	402	309	363	300	233	198
	2 000	395	326	252	258	216	169	145
	2 500	293	243	189	189	159	124	106
	3 000	227	189	147	145	122	95.2	81.7
	3 500	181	151	117	112	94.5	74.5	64.3
	4 000	147	123	95.8	86.7	73.3	57.7	49.8
	4 500	118	98.5	77.0				
	5 000			63.1				

Effective length (KL) in millimetres with respect to indicated axis

PROPERTIES OF 2 STARRED ANGLES

	10	8	6	10	8	6	5
Area (mm²)	2 400	1 950	1 490	2 000	1 630	1 250	1 050
r_u (mm)	36.1	35.2	34.3	32.1	31.2	30.3	28.4
r_v (mm)	24.6	25.0	25.3	20.5	20.9	21.2	21.5
*r_z (mm)	12.7	12.7	12.8	10.7	10.7	10.8	10.8
*r_z/r_u	0.352	0.361	0.373	0.333	0.343	0.356	0.380
*r_z/r_v	0.516	0.508	0.506	0.522	0.512	0.509	0.502

IMPERIAL SIZE AND MASS

	10	8	6	10	8	6	5
Mass (lb./ft.)	12.6	10.3	7.86	10.5	8.60	6.59	5.54
Thickness (in.)	0.39	0.31	0.24	0.39	0.31	0.24	0.20
Size (in.)	2.56 x 2.56			2.17 x 2.17			

* See page 4-4 for more details regarding these tables.
Research currently (1980) being conducted indicates that at least two equally spaced points of interconnection be used. (1/3rd. points)

DOUBLE ANGLE STRUTS
STAR SHAPED*
FACTORED AXIAL COMPRESSIVE RESISTANCES IN kN

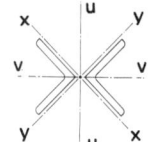

Legs		6 mm apart				6 mm apart		
Size (mm)		45 x 45				35 x 35		
Thickness (mm)		8	6	5	4	6	5	4
Mass (kg/m)		10.3	7.91	6.67	5.40	6.03	5.10	4.14

Effective length (KL) in millimetres with respect to indicated axis

U-U Axis

0		354	273	229	186	207	175	143
500		345	265	223	180	198	167	136
1 000		314	240	201	162	174	146	118
1 500		275	208	173	139	141	117	93.5
2 000		227	168	139	109	101	83.3	65.4
2 500		172	125	103	80.7	74.2	61.1	47.9
3 000		133	96.7	79.5	62.5	56.9	46.7	36.6
3 500		107	77.3	63.5	49.8	44.1	36.0	27.9
4 000		87.4	63.0	51.3	39.9	34.2	27.9	
4 500		70.8	50.2	41.0	31.9			
5 000		57.9						

V-V Axis

0		354	273	229	186	207	175	143
500		329	255	215	174	185	157	128
1 000		271	212	179	146	134	115	94.9
1 500		191	152	130	106	79.5	68.7	57.0
2 000		128	102	87.5	71.9	52.1	45.2	37.5
2 500		92.5	73.9	63.3	52.1	34.7	30.2	25.3
3 000		67.2	54.2	46.6	38.6			
3 500					28.8			

PROPERTIES OF 2 STARRED ANGLES

	8	6	5	4	6	5	4
Area (mm²)	1 310	1 010	850	688	768	650	528
r_u (mm)	25.9	24.8	24.4	23.9	20.8	20.4	19.9
r_v (mm)	16.8	17.2	17.4	17.6	13.1	13.3	13.5
*r_z (mm)	8.76	8.79	8.82	8.87	6.81	6.83	6.86
*r_z/r_u	0.338	0.354	0.361	0.371	0.327	0.335	0.345
*r_z/r_v	0.521	0.511	0.507	0.504	0.520	0.514	0.508

IMPERIAL SIZE AND MASS

	8	6	5	4	6	5	4
Mass (lb./ft.)	6.92	5.32	4.48	3.63	4.05	3.43	2.78
Thickness (in.)	0.31	0.24	0.20	0.16	0.24	0.20	0.16
Size (in.)	1.77 x 1.77				1.38 x 1.38		

*See page 4-4 for more details regarding these tables.
Research currently (1980) being conducted indicates that at least two equally spaced points of interconnection be used. (1/3rd. points)

NOTES

COLUMN BASE PLATES

Steel columns bearing upon concrete footings are generally fitted with steel base plates sufficient in area so as not to exceed the bearing resistance of the concrete. In general, the ends of such columns are milled or sawn to a plane surface so as to bear evenly upon the base plate. For columns where it is not necessary to transmit end moments, tension forces or shear forces into the footing, the assembly connecting the column to the base plate and thence to the footing need be strong enough only to hold the parts in line. Generally, two anchor bolts are sufficient for this purpose. In certain cases it may be more economical to omit milling or sawing the ends of lightly loaded columns and to design the connection between the base plate and the column for the total load acting upon the column.

The following method is recommended for designing base plates which are not subject to bending moments, shear forces and tension forces:

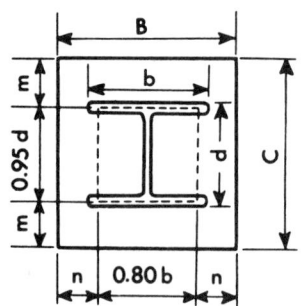

Let C_f = Total factored column load, kilonewtons;

A = B x C = Area of plate, square millimetres;

t_p = thickness of plate, millimetres;

F_y = specified minimum yield point of steel used for base plate, megapascals;

f'_c = specified 28-day strength of the concrete, megapascals;

ϕ = 0.90 for steel.

The following assumptions are made:

1. The factored column load C_f is uniformly distributed upon the base plate within an assumed rectangle whose dimensions are 0.95d and 0.80b. (See diagram):

2. The base plate exerts a uniform pressure upon the foundation.

3. The base plate projecting beyond the assumed dotted rectangle acts as a cantilever subject to the uniform pressure.

The base plate then may be designed as follows:

1. Determine the required area $A = C_f/B_r$ where B_r is the factored bearing resistance per unit of bearing area. For concrete B_r is assumed to be $0.85 \phi_c f'_c$ where ϕ_c = 0.63 in bearing. (ϕ_c has been adjusted from that given in CAN3-A23.3-M77 to account for the difference in load factors used in CAN3-A23.3-M77 and those used in CAN3-S16.1-M78.) Clause 8.15.3 of CSA CAN3-A23.3-M77 states when B_r may be increased.

2. Determine B and C so that the dimensions of m and n are approximately equal;

3. Determine m and n, for projections of the plate beyond the assumed dotted rectangle and solve for t_p, using the following formulae.

$$(1) \ldots t_p = \sqrt{\frac{2 \, C_f \, m^2}{BC \, \phi F_y}} \text{ or } \sqrt{\frac{2 \, C_f \, n^2}{BC \, \phi F_y}}, \text{ whichever is greater.}$$

These formulae were derived by equating the factored moment acting on that portion of the plate taken as a cantilever to the factored moment resistance of the plate ($M_r = \phi Z F_y$) and solving for the plate thickness, t_p.

In addition, in order to minimize deflection of the base plate, the thickness generally should be not less than approximately $1/5$ of the overhang m or n.

Examples

1. **Given:**

A W310×118 is subject to a factored axial load of 2 500 kN and is supported by a concrete foundation whose 28-day specified strength is 20 MPa. Design the base plate assuming that the specified minimum yield point of the steel is 300 MPa.

Solution:

For W310×118, b = 307 mm, d = 314 mm (page 6—49)

$$\text{Area of plate required} = \frac{2\ 500\ kN \times 10^3\ N/kN}{0.85 \times 0.63 \times 20\ MPa} = 233\ 000\ mm^2$$

Assume C = 500 mm

$$\text{Therefore, B required} = \frac{233\ 000}{500} = 466\ \text{Use 470 mm}$$

Calculate m and n

0.95d = 0.95 × 314 = 298 mm

$$\text{Therefore, m} = \frac{500 - 298}{2} = 101\ mm$$

0.80b = 0.80 × 307 = 246 mm

$$\text{Therefore, n} = \frac{470 - 246}{2} = 112\ mm$$

Use n for design

$$\text{Plate thickness, } t_p, \text{ required} = \sqrt{\frac{2 \times 2\ 500 \times 10^3 \times 112^2}{470 \times 500 \times 0.90 \times 300}}$$

$$= 31\ mm$$

$$\text{or, } t_p = \frac{n}{5} = \frac{112}{5} = 22\ mm < 31\ mm$$

Therefore use 35 mm, a first preference plate thickness.

Since the plate thickness of 35 mm is less than 40 mm, F_y = 300 MPa for G40.21-M grade 300W steel. For plates greater than 40 mm but less than or equal to 65 mm in thickness, F_y = 290 MPa and for plates greater than 65 mm in thickness, F_y = 280 MPa for G40.21-M 300W steel.

Therefore use PL 35 × 500 × 470 for base plate.

2. **Given:**

An HSS 203.2 × 203.2 × 9.53 supports a factored axial load of 1 550 kN.

Select a base plate assuming f'_c = 20 MPa and F_y = 300 MPa.

$$\text{Area required} = \frac{1\ 550 \times 10^3}{0.85 \times 0.63 \times 20} = 144\ 000\ mm$$

$$B = C = \sqrt{A} = \sqrt{144 \times 10^3} = 380\ mm$$

$$n = \frac{380 - (203 - 9)}{2} = 93\ mm$$

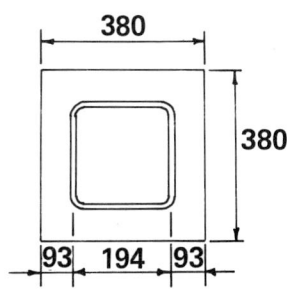

Therefore $t_p = \sqrt{\dfrac{2 \times 1\,550 \times 10^3 \times 93^2}{380 \times 380 \times 0.9 \times 300}} = 26.2$ mm

Use 30 mm, a first preference plate thickness.

Therefore use PL 30 × 380 × 380 for the base plate.

Design Chart

As an alternative to computing t_p, Figure 4–2, provides a means of selecting t_p knowing the length of cantilever, m or n, and the unit factored bearing resistance.

Example:

Given:

Same as example 1

Solution:

Unit factored bearing resistance = 0.85 × 0.63 × 20

= 10.7 MPa

From Figure 4–2 for 10.7 MPa and n = 112, select t_p = 35 mm.

For many of the heavier columns, single or double tier grillages may be found to be more economical than base plates bearing directly upon concrete.

Base plate assemblies which are subjected to applied bending moments, tension forces and shear forces must be proportioned to resist all such forces. In addition, the anchor bolts and connections will be required to resist calculated forces instead of being required only to hold the parts in alignment. The design of such base assemblies is more complex than that for a column subjected to axial load only and it is recommended that a suitable text relating to structural design be consulted.

Lightly Loaded Base Plates

With the use of the bearing resistance for concrete permitted by CAN3-A23.3-M77, the required area for the base plate is less than that required under the older allowable stress standards. By following the preceding design method the thickness of plate required will also be less than that required previously, since the cantilever lengths m and n have decreased. In the limit, as the base plate size approaches the column dimensions b and d, the thickness that would be required by the preceding method approaches zero. For the purpose of the discussion, a lightly loaded base plate is one wherein the required area is approximately equal to or less than the area bounded by the column dimensions b and d.

Several methods have been proposed in the literature to determine the plate thickness, t_p, in those cases. Two articles are as follows:

1. Design of Steel Bearing Plates, R. S. Fling, Engineering Journal, AISC, Vol. 7 No. 2, April 1970.

2. Preliminary Base Plate Selection, F. W. Stockwell, Jr. Engineering Journal, AISC, Vol. 12, No. 3, Third Quarter 1975.

The first paper uses yield line theory and derives an equation for plate thickness, t_p. Modified to suit limit states design procedures it is as follows:

$$(2) \ldots t_p = 0.43\, b\beta \sqrt{\frac{B_r}{\phi F_y\,(1 - \beta^2)}}$$

FIGURE 4-2
COLUMN BASE PLATE THICKNESS, tp

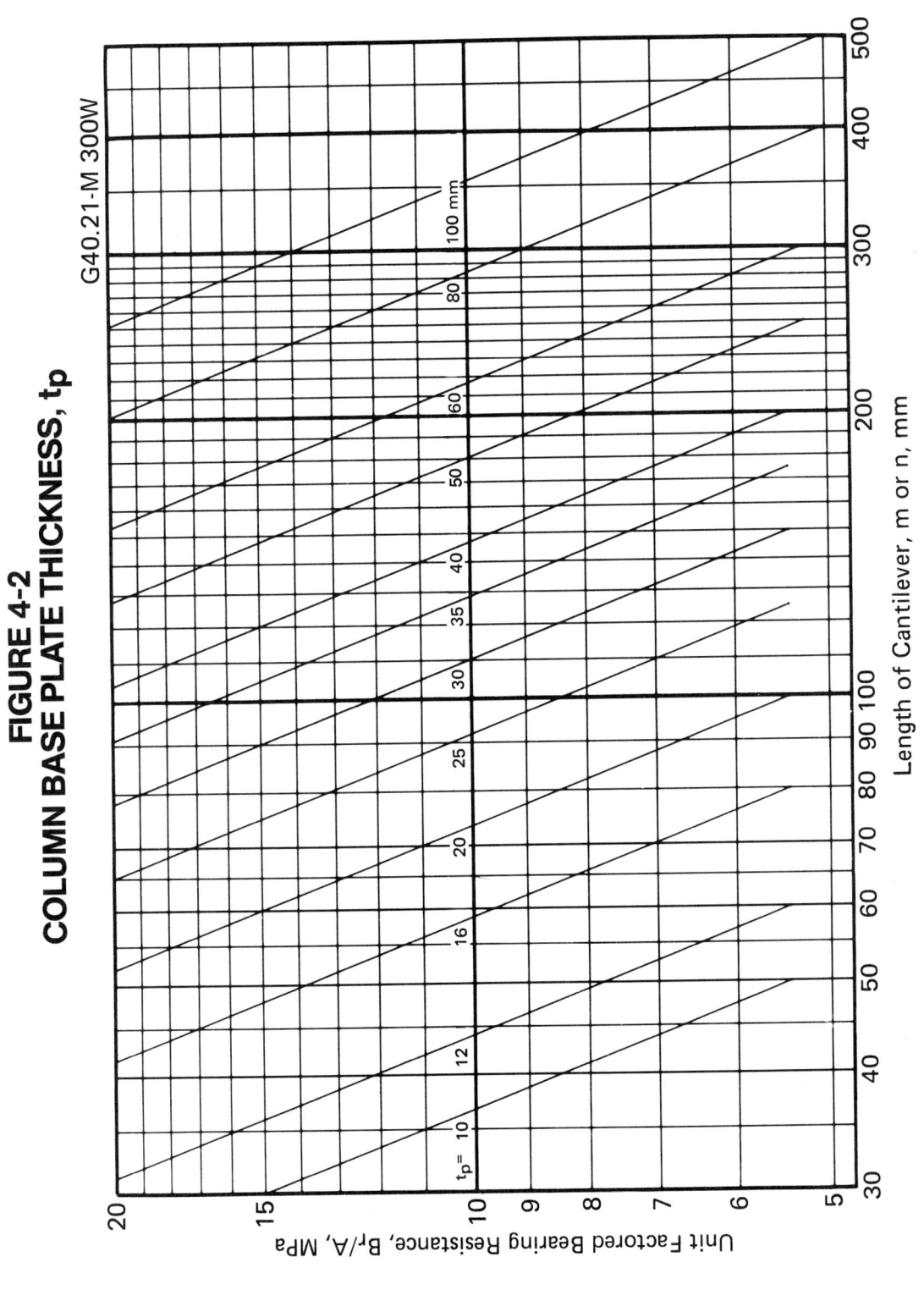

where

$$B_r = 0.85 \, \phi_c f_c' \quad (f_c' \text{ in MPa})$$

$$\beta = \sqrt{0.75 + \frac{1}{4\lambda^2}} - \frac{1}{2\lambda}$$

$\lambda = 2d/b$

b = column width, millimetres

d = column depth, millimetres

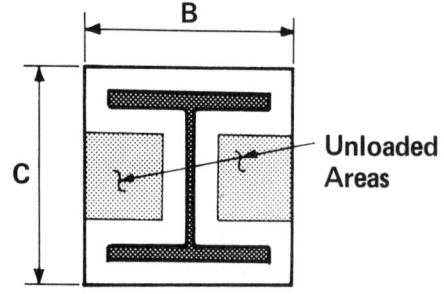

Unloaded Areas

The second paper assumes that only an H-shaped strip under a W column section will be loaded and the remainder of the plate would be unloaded.

The assumed width of the strip is purely a matter of engineering judgement. The thickness of plate would then be determined by equation (1) where m or n would equal one half of the width of the strip.

ANCHOR BOLTS

Theoretically, base plates for concentrically loaded columns do not require anchor bolts since neither end moments, nor horizontal forces are present. In practical situations, however, anchor bolts are provided to position the base of the column, to provide a means of levelling the base plate, and to take care of small end moments and horizontal forces which may occur.

In the case where anchor bolts are required to transfer end moments and horizontal forces due to lateral loads, crane loads, etc., the size and number can be determined from the applied loads and appropriate design methods. Although some of the following references are written in allowable stress design terms, they can be used in conjunction with CAN3-A23.3-M77 to develop equations in limit states design. Care should be taken to ensure that the correct performance factor for concrete is used, keeping in mind that the partial load factors for CAN3-A23.3-M77 and CAN3-S16.1-M78 are different but that the ratio of live load to dead load partial load factors is approximately equal.

1. John E. Lothers "Design in Structural Steel, Second Edition", Prentice-Hall Inc., 1965.
2. D. Nixon and P. F. Adams "Design of Light Industrial Buildings", Proceedings, Canadian Structural Engineering Conference, Toronto, 1978.
3. W. McGuire "Steel Structures", Prentice-Hall Inc., 1968.
4. L. Tall, Editor "Structural Steel Design, Second Edition", Ronald Press Co., 1964.
5. K.S.M. Structural Engineering Aspects of Headed Concrete Anchors and Deformed Bar Anchors in the Concrete Construction Industry, K.S.M. Welding Systems Division, Omark Industries, 1974.

Fabricators normally supply anchor bolts which they manufacture from round bar stock. The round bars are threaded at each end to receive washers and nuts. The material usually used for normal applications is produced to either ASTM A36 (F_y = 248 MPa) or CSA G40.21-M Grade 300W (F_y = 300 MPa). However, ASTM A36 round bar stock is more readily available and should be assumed in anchor bolt design unless it is known that G40.21-M will be used. For specialized applications, fastener suppliers or fabricators should be consulted.

When base plates are detailed to receive anchor bolts, holes should be sized to allow horizontal movement for alignment purposes. Although the actual anchor bolt hole sizes used will vary depending on fabricators shop and field practices, the following table can be used as a guide.

SUGGESTED ANCHOR BOLT HOLE* SIZES

Bolt Diameter	Suggested Hole Diameter
mm	mm
20	26
22	28
24	30
27	33
30	42
36	48
42	54
48	60
56	68
64	76

*Anchor bolt holes in base plates, which will receive anchor bolts which are grouted may be flame cut.

*Anchor bolt hole sizes will vary with individual fabricators depending on shop and field practices.

PART FIVE
FLEXURAL MEMBERS

General Information . . . .   5—3

Classes of Sections in Bending . . . .   5—5

Factored Ultimate Shear Stress in Girder Webs . . . .   5—8

Plate Girders . . . .   5—11

Composite Beams . . . .   5—18

Trial Selection Tables

130 mm Solid Slab . . . .   5—28
38 mm Deck + 65 mm Slab. . . . .   5—38
51 mm Deck + 65 mm Slab. . . . .   5—48
76 mm Deck + 65 mm Slab. . . . .   5—58
51 mm Deck + 85 mm Slab. . . . .   5—68
76 mm Deck + 85 mm Slab. . . . .   5—78

Deflection of Flexural Members . . . .   5—88

Factored Resistances of Beams . . . .   5—92

Beam Selection Tables . . . .   5—98

Beam Load Tables. . . . .   5—110

Beam Diagrams and Formulae. . . . .   5—132

Beam Bearing Plates . . . .   5—151

Beams with Web Holes . . . .   5—155

Guide for Floor Vibrations . . . .   5—169

GENERAL INFORMATION

Classes of Sections in Bending

Table 5—1, pages 5—5 to 5—7, lists the Class in bending of WWF, W and M shapes for ASTM A36 steel and for G40.21-M grades 300W and 350W steels. For these steel grades all S shapes are Class 1; all C and MC shapes are Class 3. The producer should be consulted as to the availability of any section in a steel grade other than 300W. To determine the Class of a section used as a beam-column for sections not listed in Table 5—1 or, for sections in steel grades other than those listed in Table 5—1, see "Limits on Width-Thickness Ratios", page 4—5.

Factored Ultimate Shear Stress in Girder Webs

The tables on pages 5—9 to 5—10 list the factored ultimate shear stress, ϕF_s, in a girder web for girders analysed elastically for steels with minimum specified yield points, F_y, of 248, 300 and 350 MPa. Aspect ratios (a/h) from 0.50 to 3.00 are covered for web slenderness ratios varying from a minimum of 50 (for F_y = 350) to a maximum of 320, (for F_y = 248). The factored ultimate shear stresses have been computed in accordance with the requirements of Clauses 13.4.1 of CAN3-S16.1-M78, "Steel Structures for Buildings — Limit States Design". The required gross area of intermediate stiffeners, as a percentage of web area (hw), is shown in italics below the factored ultimate shear stress and has been computed in accordance with the requirements of Clause 15.6.3 of CAN3-S16.1-M78.

Plate Girders

For design information and illustrative example, see page 5—11.

Composite Beams

Trial Selection Tables for composite beams consisting of either solid slab or cover slab with cellular steel deck (hollow composite construction) are given on pages 5—28 to 5—87. See page 5—18 for explanatory text.

Deflection of Flexural Members

For design chart, table, and illustrative examples, see page 5—88.

Beam Selection Tables

The factored moment resistances of beams are listed in descending order on pages 5—98 to 5—109 to facilitate the design of flexural members. For explanatory text, see page 5—92.

Beam Load Tables

The total uniformly distributed factored loads for laterally supported beam of spans to 22 000 mm are listed on pages 5—110 to 5—131. For explanatory text, see page 5—93.

Beam Diagrams and Formulae

Pages 5—132 to 5—150 contain diagrams and formulae to facilitate the design of flexural members in accordance with "elastic theory".

Beam Bearing Plates

For design information, design chart and illustrative example, see page 5—151.

Beams with Web Holes

For design information, design tables and illustrative example, see page 5—155.

Guide for Floor Vibration

Pages 5—169 to 5—175 inclusive are reprints of Appendix G of CAN3-S16.1-M78.

Table 5-1 — CLASSES OF SECTIONS IN BENDING†

Designation	Steel Grades # ASTM A36	CSA G40.21-M 300W	CSA G40.21-M 350W	Designation	Steel Grades # ASTM A36	CSA G40.21-M 300W	CSA G40.21-M 350W
WWF1200X487	2	2	2	WWF500X651	1	1	1
X403	2	2	3	X561	1	1	1
X364	2	2	2	X456	1	1	1
X302	2	2	2	X381	1	1	1
X263	2	2	2	X343	1	1	1
				X306	1	1	2
WWF1100X458	2	2	2	X276	1	2	2
X388	2	2	3	X254	2	3	3
X335	2	2	3	X223	3	3	3
X291	2	2	3	X197	3	3	3
X255	2	2	3				
X220	2	2	3	WWF450X503	1	1	1
				X409	1	1	1
WWF1000X447	1	2	2	X342	1	1	1
X377	1	2	2	X308	1	1	1
X324	1	2	2	X274	1	1	1
X280	1	2	2	X248	1	1	2
X244	1	2	3	X228	1	2	2
X200	1	2	2	X201	2	3	3
				X177	3	3	3
WWF900X417	2	2	3				
X347	2	2	3	WWF400X444	1	1	1
X293	2	2	3	X362	1	1	1
X249	2	2	3	X303	1	1	1
X213	2	2	3	X273	1	1	1
X192	2	2	3	X243	1	1	1
X169	2	2	3	X220	1	1	1
				X202	1	1	2
WWF800X332	2	2	2	X178	1	2	3
X279	2	2	3	X157	2	3	3
X235	2	2	3				
X198	2	2	3	WWF350X385	1	1	1
X164	2	2	3	X315	1	1	1
X154	2	2	3	X263	1	1	1
				X238	1	1	1
WWF700X222	2	2	2	X212	1	1	1
X203	2	2	2	X192	1	1	1
X185	2	2	3	X176	1	1	1
X164	2	2	2	X155	1	1	2
X151	2	2	2	X137	1	2	2
X141	2	2	3				
				W920X446*	1	1	1
WWF550X721	1	1	1	X417*	1	1	1
X620	1	1	1	X387*	1	1	1
X503	1	1	1	X365*	1	1	1
X420	1	1	1	X342*	1	1	1
X217	3	3	3				
				W920X313*	1	1	1
				X289*	1	1	1
				X271*	1	1	1
				X253*	1	1	1
				X238*	1	1	1
				X223*	1	1	1
				X201*	1	1	1

*Not available from Canadian mills.
† See Clause 11.1 and Table 1 of CAN3-S16.1-M78.
#Check with manufacturer for shape availability for grades other than 300W.
Note: For the grades of steel shown, S shapes are always Class 1. C and MC shapes are Class 3 for all grades.

CLASSES OF SECTIONS IN BENDING†   Table 5-1

| Designation | Steel Grades # | | | Designation | Steel Grades # | | |
| | ASTM | CSA G40.21-M | | | ASTM | CSA G40.21-M | |
	A36	300W	350W		A36	300W	350W
W840X359*	1	1	1	W460X177*	1	1	1
X329*	1	1	1	X158*	1	1	1
X299*	1	1	1	X144*	1	1	1
				X128*	1	1	1
W840X226*	1	1	1	X113*	1	1	2
X210*	1	1	1				
X193*	1	1	1	W460X106	1	1	1
X176*	1	1	2	X97	1	1	1
				X89	1	1	1
W760X314*	1	1	1	X82	1	1	1
X284*	1	1	1	X74	1	1	1
X257*	1	1	1	X67	1	1	1
				X61	1	2	2
W760X196*	1	1	1				
X185*	1	1	1	W460X68*	1	1	1
X173*	1	1	1	X60*	1	1	1
X161*	1	1	1	X52*	1	1	1
X147*	1	1	2				
				W410X149*		1	1
W690X265*	1	1	1	X132*	1	1	1
X240*	1	1	1	X114*	1	1	1
X217*	1	1	1	X100*	1	1	1
W690X170*	1	1	1	W410X85	1	1	1
X152*	1	1	1	X74	1	1	1
X140*	1	1	1	X67	1	1	1
X125*	1	1	2	X60	1	1	1
				X54	1	1	2
W610X241	1	1	1				
X217	1	1	1	W410X46	1	1	1
X195	1	1	1	X39	1	1	2
X174	1	1	1				
X155	1	2	2	W360X1086*	1	1	1
				X990*	1	1	1
W610X140	1	1	1	X900*	1	1	1
X125	1	1	1	X818*	1	1	1
X113	1	1	1	X744*	1	1	1
X101	1	1	1	X677*	1	1	1
W610X92*	1	1	1	W360X634*	1	1	1
X82*	1	1	1	X592*	1	1	1
				X551*	1	1	1
W530X219*	1	1	1	X509*	1	1	1
X196*	1	1	1	X463*	1	1	1
X182*	1	1	1	X421*	1	1	1
X165*	1	1	1	X382*	1	1	1
X150*	1	1	1	X347*	1	1	1
				X314*	1	1	1
W530X138	1	1	1	X287*	1	1	1
X123	1	1	1	X262*	1	1	1
X109	1	1	1	X237*	1	1	1
X101	1	1	1	X216*	1	1	1
X92	1	1	1				
X82	1	1	2	W360X196*	1	1	1
				X179*	1	1	2
W530X85*	1	1	1	X162*	1	2	2
X74*	1	1	1	X147*	2	2	3
X66*	1	1	1	X134*	2	3	3

* Not available from Canadian mills.
† See Clause 11.1 and Table 1 of CAN3-S16.1-M78.
# Check with manufacturer for shape availability for grades other than 300W.
Note: For the grades of steel shown, S shapes are always Class 1. C and MC shapes are Class 3 for all grades.

Table 5-1 — CLASSES OF SECTIONS IN BENDING†

Designation	ASTM A36	CSA G40.21-M 300W	350W	Designation	ASTM A36	CSA G40.21-M 300W	350W
W360X122*	1	1	1	W250X67	1	1	1
X110*	1	1	1	X58	1	1	1
X101*	1	1	1	X49	1	2	3
X91*	1	1	1				
				W250X45	1	1	1
W360X79	1	1	1	X39	1	1	1
X72	1	1	1	X33	1	1	2
X64	1	1	1				
				W250X28*	1	1	1
W360X57	1	1	1	X25*	1	1	1
X51	1	1	1	X22*	1	1	1
X45	1	2	2	X18*	2	2	3
W360X39	1	1	1	W200X100	1	1	1
X33	1	1	1	X86	1	1	1
				X71	1	1	1
W310X500*	1	1	1	X59	1	1	1
X454*	1	1	1	X52	1	1	2
X415*	1	1	1	X46	2	2	3
X375*	1	1	1				
X342*	1	1	1	W200X42	1	1	1
X313*	1	1	1	X36	1	1	2
W310X283	1	1	1	W200X31	1	1	1
X253	1	1	1	X27	1	1	2
X226	1	1	1				
X202	1	1	1	W200X22*	1	1	1
X179	1	1	1	X19*	1	1	2
X158	1	1	1	X15*	2	2	3
X143	1	1	1				
X129	1	1	1	W150X37	1	1	1
X118	1	1	2	X30	1	1	2
X107	1	2	2	X22	3	3	3
X97	2	3	3				
				W150X24*	1	1	1
W310X86	1	1	2	X18*	1	1	1
X79	1	2	2	X14*	1	2	3
W310X74	1	1	1	W130X28*	1	1	1
X67	1	1	1	X24*	1	1	1
X60	1	1	1				
				W100X19*	1	1	1
W310X52	1	1	1				
X45	1	1	1				
X39	1	2	2				
				M310X17.6*	1	2	2
W310X33*	1	1	1				
X28*	1	1	1	M250X13.4*	1	1	2
X24*	1	1	1				
X21*	1	2	2	M200X9.7*	1	1	1
W250X167	1	1	1	M150X29.8*	1	1	2
X149	1	1	1				
X131	1	1	1	M150X6.5*	1	1	1
X115	1	1	1				
X101	1	1	1	M130X28.1*	1	1	1
X89	1	1	1				
X80	1	1	2	M100X19	1	1	1
X73	1	2	2				

* Not available from Canadian mills.
† See Clause 11.1 and Table 1 of CAN3-S16.1-M78.
\# Check with manufacturer for shape availability for grades other than 300W.
Note: For the grades of steel shown, S shapes are always Class 1. C and MC shapes are Class 3 for all grades.

5-7

FACTORED ULTIMATE SHEAR STRESS (ϕF_S) (Elastic Analysis) in Girder Webs, MPa

$F_y = 248$ MPa
$\phi = 0.90$

Required Gross Area of Intermediate Stiffeners, as percent of Web Area ($\frac{h}{w}$) shown below Factored Ultimate Shear Stress (ϕF_s, MPa)*†

Web Slenderness Ratio $\frac{h}{w}$	Aspect Ratio $\frac{a}{h}$: Stiffener Spacing to Web Depth										No Intermediate Stiffeners
	0.50	0.67	0.75	1.00	1.25	1.50	1.75	2.00	2.50	3.00	
60									147	147 *0.77*	147
70								147 *1.06*	144 *0.89*	141 *0.77*	135
80				147 *1.46*	144 *1.37*	137 *1.26*	132 *1.15*	129 *1.06*	127 *0.89*	125 *0.77*	118
90			147 *1.50*	140 *1.46*	129 *1.37*	125 *1.26*	123 *1.15*	120 *1.06*	117 *0.89*	115 *0.83*	105
100			147 *1.50*	128 *1.46*	123 *1.37*	119 *1.39*	116 *1.95*	113 *2.19*	107 *2.26*	103 *2.13*	86.5
110		147 *1.49*	137 *1.50*	123 *1.46*	118 *2.52*	111 *3.33*	106 *3.61*	102 *3.64*	95.8 *3.42*	91.5 *3.10*	71.4
120	147 *1.38*	137 *1.49*	128 *1.50*	119 *2.77*	111 *4.30*	104 *4.81*	98.0 *4.88*	93.6 *4.75*	87.1 *4.30*	82.5 *3.83*	60.0
130	147 *1.38*	128 *1.49*	125 *1.50*	114 *4.53*	104 *5.69*	97.4 *5.96*	91.7 *5.86*	87.1 *5.61*	80.3 *4.99*	75.6 *4.40*	51.1
140	147 *1.38*	126 *1.49*	122 *2.09*	109 *5.92*	99.7 *6.80*	92.5 *6.88*	86.7 *6.64*	82.0 *6.29*	75.0 *5.53*	70.0 *4.86*	44.1
150	138 *1.38*	123 *1.74*	119 *3.76*	105 *7.05*	95.8 *7.68*	88.5 *7.62*	82.7 *7.27*	77.9 *6.84*	70.7 *5.97*	65.5 *5.22*	38.4
160	129 *1.38*	121 *3.32*	116 *5.12*	102 *7.97*	92.7 *8.41*	85.3 *8.22*	79.4 *7.79*	74.5 *7.29*	67.1 *6.33*		33.7
170	127 *1.38*	118 *4.64*	113 *6.25*	99.2 *8.73*	90.0 *9.02*	82.6 *8.72*	76.6 *8.21*	71.7 *7.66*			29.9
180	126 *1.38*	115 *5.74*	110 *7.19*	97.0 *9.37*	87.8 *9.52*	80.4 *9.14*	74.3 *8.57*	69.3 *7.97*			26.7
190	124 *1.68*	113 *6.68*	108 *7.99*	95.2 *9.91*	86.0 *9.95*	78.5 *9.49*	72.4 *8.88*				23.9
200	123 *2.87*	111 *7.48*	106 *8.67*	93.6 *10.4*	84.4 *10.3*	76.9 *9.79*					21.6
220	119 *4.77*	108 *8.76*	103 *9.77*	91.0 *11.1*	81.9 *10.9*						17.8
240	116 *6.21*	105 *9.73*	101 *10.6*	89.1 *11.7*							15.0
260	114 *7.34*	103 *10.5*	99.2 *11.3*								12.8
280	112 *8.23*	102 *11.1*	97.8 *11.8*								11.0
300	110 *8.95*	101 *11.6*	96.7 *12.2*								9.61
320	109 *9.54*										8.45

* Percentages shown are for gross area of a pair of intermediate stiffeners. For single stiffeners on one side of web only, multiply values by 1.8 for angle stiffener and 2.4 for plate stiffeners.
† For stiffeners whose F_y is not the same as the web, multiply gross area by ratio of F_y of web to F_y of stiffener.

FACTORED ULTIMATE SHEAR STRESS (ϕF_s)
(Elastic Analysis) in Girder Webs, MPa

Required Gross Area of Intermediate Stiffeners, as percent of Web Area (h w) shown below Factored Ultimate Shear Stress (ϕF_s, MPa)*†

Web Slenderness Ratio $\frac{h}{w}$	Aspect Ratio $\frac{a}{h}$: Stiffener Spacing to Web Depth										No Intermediate Stiffeners
	0.50	0.67	0.75	1.00	1.25	1.50	1.75	2.00	2.50	3.00	
50											178
60									178 *0.77*		174
70					178 *1.37*	172 *1.26*	166 *1.15*	163 *1.06*	158 *0.89*	155 *0.77*	149
80			178 *1.50*	173 *1.46*	159 *1.37*	153 *1.26*	150 *1.15*	148 *1.06*	144 *0.89*	141 *0.77*	130
90			178 *1.50*	155 *1.46*	149 *1.37*	145 *1.26*	141 *1.75*	138 *2.02*	131 *2.12*	127 *2.02*	106
100		178 *1.49*	166 *1.50*	149 *1.46*	143 *2.52*	135 *3.33*	128 *3.61*	123 *3.64*	116 *3.42*	111 *3.10*	86.5
110	178 *1.38*	164 *1.49*	154 *1.50*	144 *2.96*	133 *4.46*	124 *4.94*	118 *4.99*	112 *4.84*	104 *4.37*	98.9 *3.90*	71.4
120	178 *1.38*	154 *1.49*	151 *1.50*	136 *4.83*	125 *5.93*	116 *6.16*	110 *6.03*	104 *5.75*	95.8 *5.10*	89.9 *4.50*	60.0
130	175 *1.38*	151 *1.49*	147 *2.62*	130 *6.28*	119 *7.08*	110 *7.11*	103 *6.84*	97.6 *6.46*	89.0 *5.67*	83.0 *4.98*	51.1
140	163 *1.38*	148 *2.41*	142 *4.33*	125 *7.43*	114 *7.99*	105 *7.87*	98.3 *7.49*	92.5 *7.03*	83.7 *6.12*	77.4 *5.35*	44.1
150	155 *1.38*	144 *4.01*	138 *5.70*	122 *8.36*	110 *8.73*	102 *8.48*	94.3 *8.01*	88.3 *7.48*	79.3 *6.49*	72.9 *5.65*	38.4
160	153 *1.38*	140 *5.32*	134 *6.83*	118 *9.12*	107 *9.33*	98.3 *8.98*	91.0 *8.44*	85.0 *7.86*	75.8 *6.78*		33.7
170	151 *1.38*	137 *6.41*	131 *7.76*	116 *9.75*	105 *9.83*	95.6 *9.39*	88.2 *8.79*	82.1 *8.16*			29.9
180	149 *2.64*	134 *7.32*	129 *8.54*	114 *10.3*	102 *10.2*	93.4 *9.74*	85.9 *9.09*	79.8 *8.42*			26.7
190	146 *3.79*	132 *8.10*	127 *9.21*	112 *10.7*	101 *10.6*	91.5 *10.0*	84.0 *9.34*				23.9
200	144 *4.77*	130 *8.75*	125 *9.77*	110 *11.1*	99.0 *10.9*	89.9 *10.3*					21.6
220	140 *6.34*	127 *9.81*	122 *10.7*	108 *11.7*	96.5 *11.4*						17.8
240	137 *7.53*	125 *10.6*	120 *11.4*	106 *12.2*							15.0
260	134 *8.46*	123 *11.2*	118 *11.9*								12.8

* Percentages shown are for gross area of a pair of intermediate stiffeners. For single stiffeners on one side of web only, multiply values by 1.8 for angle stiffener and 2.4 for plate stiffeners.
† For stiffeners whose F_y is not the same as the web, multiply gross area by ratio of F_y of web to F_y of stiffener.

FACTORED ULTIMATE SHEAR STRESS (∅Fₛ) (Elastic Analysis) in Girder Webs, MPa

$F_y = 350$ MPa
$\varnothing = 0.90$

Required Gross Area of Intermediate Stiffeners, as percent of Web Area (h w) shown below Factored Ultimate Shear Stress (ϕF_s, MPa)*†

Web Slenderness Ratio $\frac{h}{w}$	Aspect Ratio $\frac{a}{h}$: Stiffener Spacing to Web Depth										No Intermediate Stiffeners
	0.50	0.67	0.75	1.00	1.25	1.50	1.75	2.00	2.50	3.00	
50										208 *0.77*	207
60							208 *1.15*	205 *1.06*	199 *0.89*	196 *0.77*	188
70				208 *1.46*	196 *1.37*	186 *1.26*	181 *1.15*	178 *1.06*	174 *0.89*	172 *0.77*	161
80			208 *1.50*	187 *1.46*	177 *1.37*	172 *1.26*	168 *1.15*	165 *1.29*	160 *1.54*	156 *1.54*	135
90		208 *1.49*	199 *1.50*	176 *1.46*	168 *1.86*	161 *2.79*	154 *3.15*	148 *3.24*	140 *3.09*	134 *2.83*	106
100	208 *1.38*	195 *1.49*	181 *1.50*	169 *2.53*	157 *4.11*	147 *4.66*	140 *4.74*	133 *4.63*	124 *4.21*	118 *3.75*	86.5
110	208 *1.38*	180 *1.49*	176 *1.50*	160 *4.63*	147 *5.78*	137 *6.03*	129 *5.92*	122 *5.66*	113 *5.03*	106 *4.44*	71.4
120	205 *1.38*	176 *1.49*	172 *2.55*	152 *6.23*	139 *7.04*	129 *7.08*	121 *6.82*	114 *6.44*	104 *5.65*	97.1 *4.96*	60.0
130	189 *1.38*	173 *2.48*	166 *4.39*	146 *7.48*	133 *8.03*	123 *7.90*	114 *7.51*	108 *7.05*	97.4 *6.14*	90.1 *5.36*	51.1
140	180 *1.38*	168 *4.18*	160 *5.85*	141 *8.46*	128 *8.81*	118 *8.54*	109 *8.07*	103 *7.53*	92.0 *6.52*	84.5 *5.69*	44.1
150	178 *1.38*	163 *5.56*	156 *7.03*	137 *9.26*	124 *9.44*	114 *9.07*	105 *8.51*	98.4 *7.92*	87.7 *6.84*	80.0 *5.94*	38.4
160	176 *1.69*	159 *6.68*	152 *8.00*	134 *9.91*	121 *9.95*	111 *9.49*	102 *8.88*	95.0 *8.24*	84.2 *7.09*		33.7
170	173 *3.08*	156 *7.62*	149 *8.80*	132 *10.5*	119 *10.4*	108 *9.85*	99.4 *9.18*	92.2 *8.51*			29.9
180	169 *4.24*	153 *8.40*	147 *9.47*	129 *10.9*	117 *10.7*	106 *10.1*	97.1 *9.43*	89.9 *8.73*			26.7
190	167 *5.22*	151 *9.06*	145 *10.0*	128 *11.3*	115 *11.0*	104 *10.4*	95.2 *9.65*				23.9
200	164 *6.06*	149 *9.63*	143 *10.5*	126 *11.6*	113 *11.3*	102 *10.6*					21.6
220	160 *7.41*	146 *10.5*	140 *11.3*	123 *12.1*	111 *11.7*						17.8

* Percentages shown are for gross area of a pair of intermediate stiffeners. For single stiffeners on one side of web only, multiply values by 1.8 for angle stiffener and 2.4 for plate stiffeners.
† For stiffeners whose F_y is not the same as the web, multiply gross area by ratio of F_y of web to F_y of stiffener.

PLATE GIRDERS

General

When the required capacity of a steel flexural member exceeds that which can be provided by the rolled or welded wide flange sections listed in this book, a plate girder usually will provide an economical solution to the problem. A plate girder is composed basically of a relatively thin web connecting two flanges. The flanges may consist of plates, shapes, tubes or combinations thereof. Transverse or longitudinal stiffeners (generally plates or small shapes) may be used to increase the strength of the web. Heavy concentrated loads and reactions usually are supported directly on bearing stiffeners.

Clause 15 of CSA Standard CAN3-S16.1-M78, "Steel Structures for Buildings — Limit States Design", contains requirements for the design of plate girders. Clause 15.1 specifies that girders shall be proportioned by the moment of inertia method, i.e., $M_r = \phi \dfrac{I}{c} F_y$. In order to obtain a trial section it is often convenient to use an approximate method. One method is to assume that the applied bending moment is resisted by the flanges alone, so that the required area of one flange, A_f, is given approximately by

$$A_f = \frac{M_f}{\phi F_y d_{eff}}$$

where M_f = bending moment in the girder under factored load, ϕ = the performance factor, 0.90, F_y = specified minimum yield stress and d_{eff} = an assumed effective girder depth. The moment of resistance of the trial section should be checked using the formula

$$M_r = \phi \frac{I}{c} F_y > M_f$$

where ϕ = the performance factor, 0.90, c = the distance from the neutral axis to the extreme fibre of a plate girder flange and I = the moment of inertia of the girder (gross or net, in accordance with Clause 15.1, CAN3-S16.1-M78. The moment of inertia, I, can be quickly computed with the aid of the formulae on page 7—45 and an electronic calculator.

Flanges

In a symmetrical plate girder the compression flange will govern the flange design. The compression flange may fail either by buckling or by yielding. Three possible buckling modes, and the clauses in CAN3-S16.1-M78 intended to minimize the possibility of these buckling failures are:

1. Local flange buckling   — Clause 11.2, Table 1
                               — $b/2t \leqslant 260/\sqrt{F_y}$
                               — Limits on Width-Thickness Ratios, page 4—5

2. Lateral buckling   — Clause 13.6

3. Vertical buckling   — Clause 13.4.3

$$- \frac{h}{w} \leqslant \frac{83\,000}{F_y}$$

where F_y = specified minimum yield point of compression flange steel, megapascals
     h = clear depth of web, between flanges, millimetres
     w = web thickness, millimetres
     b = flange width, millimetres
     t = flange thickness, millimetres

In addition, the portion of a slender girder web subject to compressive bending stress tends to deflect laterally. This lateral deflection causes a stress redistribution within the girder which results in an increase in the compression flange stress. This increase is insignificant for relatively thick webs, but when the web slenderness ratio (h/w) exceeds $1810/\sqrt{M_r/\phi S}$, Clause 15.3, CAN3-S16.1-M78 limits the factored moment resistance to M_r' as follows:

$$M_r' = M_r \left[1.0 - 0.0005 \frac{A_w}{A_f} \left(\frac{h}{w} - 1810 \Big/ \sqrt{M_r/\phi S}\right)\right]$$

where M_r' = reduced factored moment resistance

M_r = factored moment resistance determined by Clause 13.5 or 13.6 but not exceeding ϕM_y

S = elastic section modulus, I/c, cubic millimetres

ϕ = performance factor, 0.90

A_w = web area, square millimetres

A_f = compression flange area, square millimetres

and the other symbols are as previously defined.

In designing long girders, economy may be achieved by reducing the area of flange plates where the bending moment is substantially less than the maximum. Weight savings gained must be balanced against the costs of making the flange splices. Tapered or haunched girders are other alternatives which are sometimes used.

Webs

Plate girder webs are subjected to a complex combination of bending and shear stresses. The shear capacity of unstiffened plate girder webs decreases rapidly as the web slenderness ratio increases. The use of transverse web stiffeners increases the factored shear resistance of plate girder webs, with the increase depending on the spacing of the stiffeners (i.e., the aspect ratio, a/h, where a = stiffener spacing and h = clear web depth).

Clause 13.4.1 of CAN3-S16.1-M78 specifies the factored shear resistances for both stiffened and unstiffened girder webs, which have been proportioned elastically, for different values of web slenderness ratio. The tables on pages 5—8 to 5—10 inclusive list factored ultimate shear stresses, from which the factored shear resistance can be computed according to Clause 13.4.1, for plate girder webs tabulated for various combinations of web slenderness ratio, stiffener aspect ratio, and several different specified minimum yield points.

The formulas in Clause 13.4.1 take into consideration the post-buckling strength of transversely stiffened plate girder webs in establishing the factored shear resistance. In addition to shear resistance, the stability of thin webs subject to loads on the compression edge of the web plate (Clause 15.9, CAN3-S16.1-M78) and web crippling (Clause 15.8, CAN3-S16.1-M78) must be investigated.

Stiffeners

Bearing stiffeners, intermediate transverse stiffeners and longitudinal stiffeners are commonly used with thin web plate girders. Longitudinal stiffeners are often used in bridge construction but seldom in building construction. CSA Standard CAN3-S16.1-M78 provides detailed requirements only for bearing stiffeners (Clause 15.5) and intermediate transverse stiffeners (Clause 15.6). The tables on pages 5—8 to 5—10, from which the factored ultimate shear stress can be obtained, list also the required gross area of intermediate transverse stiffeners as a percentage of the web area.

Maximum spacing of transverse stiffeners, when required, must not exceed 3h for web slenderness ratios (h/w) up to 150. For h/w over 150, the maximum spacing (a_{max}) is established by the formula

$$a_{max} = \frac{67\,500h}{(h/w)^2}$$

At the end panels or at panels containing large openings, the smaller panel dimension, a or h, must not exceed $1150w/\sqrt{V_f/\phi A_w}$ where V_f is the largest shear in the panel.

In designing plate girders, thin-web girders with stiffeners should be compared with girders with thicker webs but no intermediate transverse stiffeners, to obtain the most economical solution. Framing angles at the ends of plate girders, provided they comprise a significant proportion of the girder depth ($\frac{2}{3}$ or more) can be considered to provide web stability at girder ends.

References

Additional information on plate girders can be obtained from the following references:

1. Part 2 of the book.
2. Beedle et al., "Structural Steel Design". The Ronald Press.
3. McGuire, "Steel Structures", Prentice Hall.
4. Adams, Krentz and Kulak, "Limit States Design in Structural Steel — SI Units", CISC.
5. Balser and Thurilmann, "Strength of Plate Girders in Bending", Proc. ASCE. J. Struc. Div., Vol. 87, No. ST6, Aug. 1961.
6. Basler, "Strength of Plate Girders in Shear", Proc. ASCE. J. Struc. Div., Vol. 87, No. ST7, Oct. 1961.
7. Basler, "Strength of Plate Girders Under Combined Bending and Shear", Proc. ASCE. J. Struc. Div., Vol. 87, Nos. ST7, Oct. 1961.

Example

Given:

Design a simply supported welded plate girder spanning 22 m and loaded as shown. The compression flange is laterally supported along the entire length of the member. The uniform load includes an estimate of 3.50 kN/m for the girder. Total depth is limited to 1800 mm. Use CSA G40.21-M 300W steel.

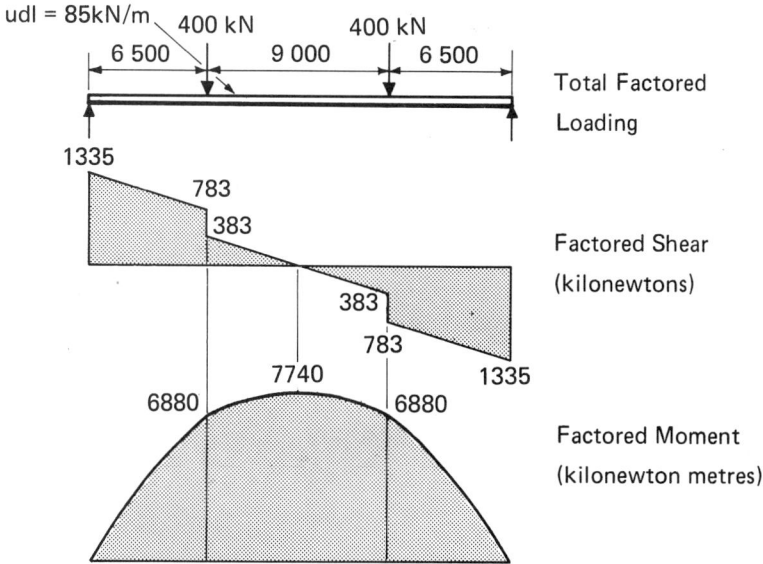

Solution:

Web — Preliminary

Assume clear depth, h = 1 750 mm

Maximum h/w permitted = 83 000/300 = 277 (Clause 13.4.3, CAN3-S16.1-M78)

Minimum w permitted = 1 750/277 = 6.3 mm

Maximum h/w permitted before the factored moment resistance is reduced

$$= 1\,810/\sqrt{M_r/\phi S} \quad \text{(Clause 15.3, CAN3-S16.1-M78)}$$

For $M_r = \phi SF_y - h/w = 1\,810/\sqrt{F_y} = 1\,810/\sqrt{300} = 105$

To keep reduction in M_r small, try h/w = 200

Try 8 X 1 750 web — h/w = 219 (8 mm is a first preference thickness)

Assume stiffened web with a/h ≃ 1.25

Factored ultimate shear stress in girder web = 1 335 X 10^3N/(1 750 X 8)
$$= 95.4 \text{ MPa} < 96.5 \text{ MPa}$$
$$\text{(table page 5—9)}$$

Flanges — Preliminary

Approximate flange area, $A_f = \dfrac{M_f}{\phi F_y d_{eff}}$

Assumed d_{eff} = 1 800 mm

Maximum ultimate stress = ϕF_y = 0.90 X 300 = 270 MPa

Assume ultimate stress 250 MPa (Allowing for reduction due to thin web)

Therefore, $A_f = \dfrac{7\,740 \text{ kN·m} \times 10^6}{250 \times 1\,800} = 17\,200 \text{ mm}^2$

Flange slenderness ratio, $\dfrac{b}{2t} \leqslant \dfrac{260}{\sqrt{F_y}}$ (Table 1, CAN3-S16.1-M78) = 15.0 (page 4—7)

For 25 X 680 flange plate
b/2t = 13.6 < 15 — OK
A_f = 680 X 25 = 17 000 mm²

Check — Preliminary Section

(a) Compute I of girder

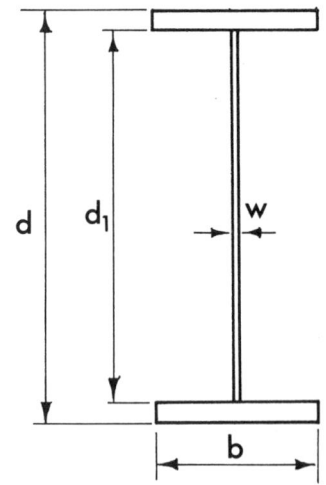

$$I = \frac{bd^3 - (b\text{-}w)\,d_1^3}{12}$$

$$I = \frac{680 \times 1\,800^3 - (680 - 8)\,1\,750^3}{12} = 30\,400 \times 10^6 \text{ mm}^4$$

S of girder = 30 400 X 10^6/900 = 33 800 X 10^3 mm³

Therefore, $M_r = \phi SF_y$ = 0.9 X 33 800 X 10^3 X 300 X 10^{-6} = 9 126 kN·m

A_w = 8 X 1 750 = 14 000 mm²; A_f = 17 000 mm²

The reduced moment resistance,

$$M'_r = M_r \left[1.0 - 0.0005 \frac{A_w}{A_f} \left(\frac{h}{w} - 1810/\sqrt{M_r/\phi S} \right) \right]$$

$$= 9\,126 \left[1.0 - 0.0005 \frac{14\,000}{17\,000} \left(219 - 1\,810/\sqrt{\frac{9126 \times 10^6}{0.9 \times 33\,800 \times 10^3}} \right) \right]$$

$$= 9\,126 \left[1.0 - 0.0005 \times 0.824 \, (219 - 105) \right]$$

$$= 8\,700 \text{ kN·m} > 7\,740 \text{ kN·m} - \text{OK}$$

(b) To check web stability, assume flange is restrained against rotation by virtue of a top slab or deck.

$$B_r \leqslant \phi \frac{115\,000}{(h/w)^2} \left[5.5 + \frac{4}{(a/h)^2} \right] A \quad \text{(Clause 15.9(a) CAN3-S16.1-M78)}$$

From the table on page 5—9, the maximum a/h ratio permitted for h/w = 219 is 1.25.

Three checks are required, the first for the portion of the girder web which is stiffened, the second for the unstiffened web area, the third under the concentrated load.

$$A = a \times w = a/h \times A_w = 1.25 \times 14\,000 = 17\,500 \text{ mm}^2$$

$$B_r \text{ (stiffened area)} = 0.9 \times \frac{115\,000}{219^2} \left[5.5 + \frac{4}{(1.25)^2} \right] 17\,500$$

$$= 304\,000 \text{ N}$$
$$= 304 \text{ kN}$$

$$B_r \text{ (unstiffened area)} = 0.9 \times \frac{115\,000}{219^2} \left[5.5 \right] 17\,500$$

$$= 208\,000 \text{ N} = 208 \text{ kN}$$

Load per panel length = 85 kN/m $\times 10^{-3} \times 1.25 \times 1\,750 = 186$ kN < 208 kN

Therefore, web stability does not govern the design in the case of the UDL.

At the concentrated load,

Load per panel   = 186 kN

Concentrated load = 400 kN

Total   = 586 kN

B_r (stiffened area) = 304 kN $<$ 586 kN, therefore stiffeners at cross beam locations are required.

Stiffener Spacing

Maximum stiffener spacing in end panel

$$= 1\,150 \, w/\sqrt{V_f/\phi A_w} \quad \text{(Clause 15.6.1, CAN3-S16.1-M78)}$$

$$= 1\,150 \times 8/\sqrt{1\,335 \times 10^3/(0.9 \times 8 \times 1\,750)}$$

$$= 894 \text{ mm, Use 800 mm}$$

At the first stiffener 800 mm from end of girder.

$$V_f = 1\,335 - \frac{85 \text{ kN/m}}{1\,000} \times 800 = 1\,270 \text{ kN}$$

From table on page 5—9, with h/w = 219, $\phi F_s \simeq 96.5$ MPa with a maximum permissible a/h = 1.25

Therefore V_r = 96.5 MPa × 8 × 1 750 = 1 351 × 10^3 N = 1 351 kN < 1 270 kN — OK

Therefore intermediate stiffeners can be spaced at a maximum distance a = 1.25 h, anywhere between the two end stiffeners, a = 1.25 × 1 750 = 2 180 mm.

With no stiffeners, maximum ϕF_s = 17.8 MPa (page 5—9) and maximum V_r = 17.8 × 8 × 1 750 = 249 × 10^3 N = 249 kN.

From the beam shear diagram, V_f = 249 kN occurs 8 070 mm from each end. Therefore the middle 5 860 mm of the girder (2 930 mm each side of the centre line) require no intermediate stiffeners. Stiffener spacing will be as shown below:

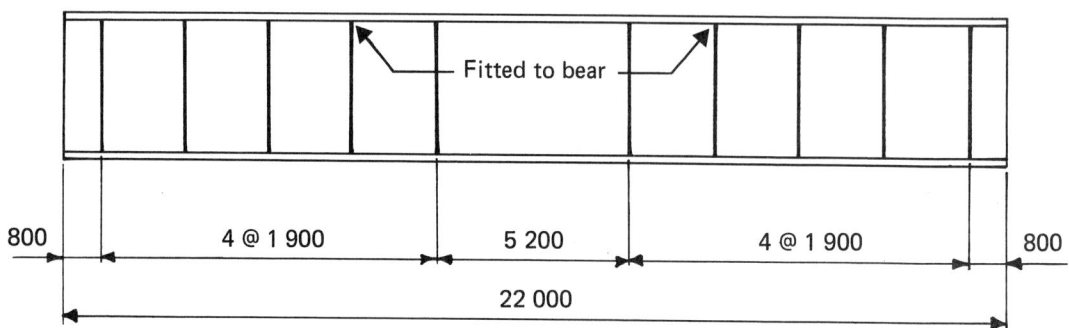

Stiffener Size

a) Intermediate stiffeners

The ends of the girder frame into columns, and the connection angles will serve as end stiffeners.

For the intermediate stiffeners, from the table on page 5—9, with h/w = 219 and actual a/h = 1 900/1 750 = 1.09, required total area of stiffener ≃ 11.7% of web area.

Assuming that the stiffeners will be used in pairs, required area of one stiffener = 0.5 × 0.117 × 8 × 1 750 = 819 mm².

Maximum b/t = $260/\sqrt{F_y}$ = 15.0 (See page 5—14)

Required I = $(h/50)^4$ = 1.5 × 10^6 mm⁴ (per pair of stiffeners)
              (Clause 15.6.3, CAN3-S16.1-M78)

Use stiffeners 8 × 110 — A = 880 mm² > 819 mm²; b/t = 13.8 < 15.0

            I (pair) = 7.1 × 10^6 mm⁴ > 1.5 × 10^6 mm⁴

b) Stiffeners at cross beam locations

Try two 8 × 110 stiffeners
Compute KL/r of stiffeners plus web (25 × w)
A = (2 × 8 × 110) + (25 × 8 × 8) = 3 360 mm²

I = 8 × 228^3/12 = 7.90 × 10^6 mm⁴

r = $\sqrt{7.90 \times 10^6/3\ 360}$ = 48.5 mm

KL/r = 0.75 × 1 750/48.5 = 27

C_r/A = 255 MPa (Table 4—3, page 4—9)

C_r = 255 × 3 360 = 857 × 10^3 N = 857 kN > 400 kN

Therefore use 8 × 110 fitted stiffeners at cross beam locations.

Combined Shear and Moment

Combined shear and moment in girder webs is governed by Clause 13.4.6 of CAN3-S16.1-M78. Worst effect is under the concentrated load; $V_f = 783$ kN, $M_f = 6\ 880$ kN·m. Check if h/w exceeds $502\sqrt{k_v/F_y}$ limit given in Clause 13.4.3.

For $a/h = 1.00$, $k_v = 9.34$ (Table 3, CAN3-S16.1-M78, page 1—37)

$$h/w = 502\sqrt{k_v/F_y} = 502\sqrt{9.34/300} = 88.6 < 219$$

Therefore Clause 13.4.6 is to be checked,

From page 5—9, for $a/h = 1.00$ and $h/w = 220$, $\phi F_s = 108$ MPa

$$\frac{V_f}{V_r} = \frac{783 \times 10^3 N}{8 \times 1\ 750 \times 108\ MPa} = 0.518 < 1.0 - OK$$

$$\frac{M_f}{M_r} = \frac{6\ 880}{8\ 700} = 0.790 < 1.00 - OK$$

$$0.727\frac{M_f}{M_r} + 0.455\frac{V_f}{V_r} = 0.727 \times 0.790 + 0.455 \times 0.518 = 0.81 < 1.00 - OK$$

Final Section

Use 25×680 flange plates.
Use $8 \times 1\ 750$ web plate.
Use 8×110 stiffeners spaced as shown on page 5—16.

Area of girder (minus stiffeners)
Flanges — $2 \times 25 \times 680 = 34\ 000$ mm²
Web — $8 \times 1\ 750 \qquad = 14\ 000$ mm²
$\overline{\qquad\qquad\qquad\text{Total} = 48\ 000 \text{ mm}^2}$

$$\text{Dead load of girder} = \frac{48\ 000 \times 7\ 850\ kg/m^3 \times 9.81}{10^6} = 3\ 700\ N/m = 3.70\ kN/m$$

Dead load assumed in design = 3.50 kN/m $\simeq$ 3.70 — OK

Since there is reserve moment capacity, the flange area could be reduced, if desired, to obtain a lighter girder. Alternatively, a thinner girder web with more stiffeners might be used.

Girder-to-Column Connections

The girder-to-column connections may consist of a pair of header angles, bolted or welded to the web plate and to the supporting column flange. When detailing these header angles it must be remembered that they must serve also as web stiffeners. The angles therefore must be almost equal in length to the clear depth of the web.

Note: A deep header connection of the type described above can develop an appreciable bending moment which may be detrimental to the behaviour of the column or the girder if not taken into account.

In the interests of simplicity, this moment has been neglected in the above example. However, the effects of this moment upon the members should be considered in practice. A method of assessing this moment is described in "Advanced Design in Structural Steel" by J. E. Lothers, Prentice Hall, 1960.

COMPOSITE BEAMS

General

A composite beam, in general, consists of a steel beam and concrete slab so inter-connected that both the steel beam and the slab act jointly to resist bending. In practice there are several combinations which effectively act as composite beams: a steel beam or girder with a concrete slab inter-connected with mechanical shear connectors, a steel beam or girder fully encased by the concrete in such a way that the encased beam and the concrete slab behave monolithically, or a steel beam or girder with a cellular steel deck and concrete cover slab inter-connected by mechanical shear connectors. Clause 17 of CAN3-S16.1-M78, "Steel Structures for Buildings — Limit States Design", contains requirements for composite beams.

Some of the advantages offered by composite construction are:

1. Reduction in weight of steel members required.
2. Reduction in depth of steel members required.
3. Reduction in deflections.
4. Ease of modification of electrical utilities when cellular steel deck is used.

The most common type of composite construction utilizes some form of mechanical shear connector welded to the top flange of the beam. In any economic analysis, the weight savings and other advantages of composite construction must be weighed against the added cost of these connectors.

Composite construction is most advantageous when heavy loads and long spans are involved. For this reason composite construction is widely used in bridge construction. With the reduction in the weight of the floor assembly when cellular steel deck is used, composite beams consisting of steel beams with cellular steel deck and concrete cover slab are frequently used in buildings.

The design of composite beams may be facilitated by the use of the CISC-CSICC Floor System Selection program and the RESST program. These programs carry out pre-liminary designs for various steel flooring systems including composite systems with vari-ous slab thicknesses and also include composite systems consisting of various cellular steel deck and cover slab combinations. An improved version of this program is available for use on the HP System 45 desk top computer. Programmable calculators can also be used very effectively in the design of composite beams. Programs for the HP-97 and 41C programmable pocket calculators are also available from the CISC head office. Further information on computer aided design may be obtained from the CISC.

Tables

The Composite Beam Trial Selection Tables, pages 5—28 to 5—87 are based on the use of CSA G40.21-M 300W steel and list composite beams using W shapes manufac-tured in Canada from 200 mm to 610 mm nominal depth. Tables are provided for the following:

a) 130 mm solid slab with a 28-day specified concrete strength, f'_c, of 20 MPa.

b) 38, 51 and 76 mm cellular steel deck and 65 mm concrete cover slabs with f'_c of 20 MPa.

c) 51 and 76 mm cellular steel deck and 85 mm concrete cover slab with f'_c of 25 MPa.

The shapes are listed in descending order of nominal depth and mass. In the tables the following properties and resistances are listed:

b = flange width of steel shape, millimetres

t = flange thickness of steel shape, millimetres

b_1 = Effective width of the concrete used in computing values of M_{rc}, Q_r, I_1 and S_{s_1} less than or equal to $b + 16t_s$ where t_s equals the overall slab thickness or overall cover slab plus cellular steel deck thickness. Refer to Clause 17.3.2 of CAN3-S16.1-M78, millimetres.

M_{rc} = Factored moment resistance of the composite beam for percentages of shear connection from 50 to 100 (Clause 17.4.3, CAN3-S16.1-M78), kilonewton metres.

$Q_{r100\%}$ = Required sum of all the factored resistances of the shear connectors between points of maximum and zero moment for 100 per cent shear connection; equal to either $\phi A_s F_y$ or $0.85\, \phi_c\, btf'_c$, (Clause 17.4.3, 17.4.5 and 17.4.6, CAN3-S16.1-M78), kilonewtons

I_1 = Moment of inertia of the composite section computed using a mass density of 2300 kg/m³ for $f'_c = 20$ MPa and a mass density of 1850 kg/m³ for $f'_c = 25$ MPa, 10^6 mm⁴.

S_{s_1} = Section modulus of the composite section related to the extreme fibre of the bottom flange of the steel beam based on the value of I_1, 10^3 mm³.

For the bare steel shape:

M_r = Factored moment resistance of the steel beam alone, kilonewton metres.

V_r = Factored shear resistance of the steel beam alone, kilonewtons.

L_u = Maximum unsupported length of compression flange of the steel beam alone for which no reduction in M_r is required, millimetres.

I_x = Moment of inertia about the X—X axis of the steel beam alone, 10^6 mm⁴.

S_x = Section modulus of the steel beam alone, 10^3 mm³.

Since the concrete slab and/or the cellular steel deck inhibit movement of the top flange, lateral buckling is not a consideration under composite action. During construction however certain beams or girders may have some length of unsupported compression flange greater than L_u. The moment resistance of these members can be found in the "Beam Selection Tables" on pages 5—98 to 5—109 for the appropriate unsupported length of compression flange.

The factored shear resistance, V_r, tabulated is computed according to Clause 13.4.1, CAN3-S16.1-M78 for the appropriate h/w ratio.

Shear Connectors

Clauses 17.4.5 and 17.4.6, CAN3-S16.1-M78 stipulate the requirements for total factored horizontal shear force that must be resisted by shear connectors.

For full (i.e. 100%) shear connection the total factored horizontal shear force, V_h, to be transferred between the point of maximum positive moment and the points of zero moment is either

= $\phi A_s F_y$ when the plastic neutral axis is in the slab, or

= $0.85\, \phi_c\, btf'_c$ when the plastic neutral axis is in the steel section

For partial shear connection the total factored horizontal shear force, V_h, is the sum of the factored resistances of all the shear connectors between points of maximum positive and zero moment. Clause 17.4.4, CAN3-S16.1-M78, limits the minimum amount of partial shear connection to 50 percent of $\phi A_s F_y$ or $0.85\, \phi_c\, btf'_c$ whichever is the lesser when computing flexural strength.

Generally, shear connectors may be evenly spaced in regions of positive or negative bending. However, where there is a concentrated load within a region of positive bending, the number of shear connectors and, hence, the shear connector spacing, is determined by Clause 17.4.8, CAN3-S16.1-M78.

The factored shear resistance, q_r, of end-welded studs for solid slabs where the stud height is at least 4 stud diameters and cellular steel deck with concrete cover slabs where the flute average width is at least twice the height of the cellular steel deck and the projection of the stud is at least 2 stud diameters above the top surface of the cellular steel deck are given in the Table 5—3 on page 5—21 and have been computed according to Clause 17.3.6(a) of CAN3-S16.1-M78.

Factored shear resistances of studs for selected cases of cellular steel deck with cover slab are given in the Table 5—2 on page 5—20 (Table 8, CAN3-S16.1-M78).

Deflections

A composite beam is stiffer than a similar non-composite beam, and deflections are reduced when composite construction is used. Due to creep of the concrete slab, the maximum deflection may increase over a period of time, especially if the full load is sustained. Deflection during construction, when the steel beam alone supports the loads, should be checked. Cambering or the use of temporary shoring will reduce the final total deflection.

If the steel beam is unshored during construction, Clause 17.6, CAN3-S16.1-M78 limits the sum of the stresses in the tension flange, due to the specified loads applied before the concrete strength reached $0.75\ f_c'$ plus the stresses at the same location due to the remaining specified loads considered to act on the composite section, to $0.90\ F_y$.

References

Additional information on composite beams can be obtained from the following references:

1. Adams, P. F., Krentz, H. A., and Kulak, G. L., "Limit States Design in Structural Steel — SI Units", CISC, 1979.

2. Beedle et al., "Structural Steel Design", Ronald Press. New York, 1964.

3. Robinson, H., "Composite Beam Incorporating Cellular Steel Decking", ASCE Proc. J. of Struct. Div. Vol. 95, ST3 March 1969.

4. Report of ASCE Task Committee on Composite Construction, "Composite Steel-Concrete Construction" ASCE Proc. J. of Struct. Div. Vol. 100, ST5, May 1974.

5. Kennedy, D.J.L. et al., "Limit States Design", Proc. of Canadian Structural Engineering Conference, 1976, Can. Steel Const. Council, Willowdale, 1976.

Table 5-2
Factored Shear Resistances of Studs
for Selected Cases of Cellular Steel Deck
and Cover Slabs

Height of Cellular Steel Deck (mm)	Flute Average Width, Minimum (mm)	Depth of Cover Slab (mm)	Stud Size d x h (mm x mm)	No. of Studs per Flute	Factored Shear Resistance* q_r (newtons)
40	50	65	14 x 75	1	19 200
40	50	65	20 x 75	1	40 000
				2	60 800 per pair
40	50	90	20 x 100	1	63 200
				2	90 400 per pair

*Factored shear resistances given in Table 5-2 are derived from test and reflect the influence of flute geometry and stiffness on the useful capacity of studs.

Table 5-3
Factored Shear Resistances of End Welded Headed Studs, q_r, kilonewtons
For Solid Slabs and for Cover Slabs with
Wide Flute Cellular Deck*

Stud Diameter		Mass Density of Concrete w_c	Factored Shear Resistance, q_r, in kilonewtons for various concrete strengths f'_c, MPa		
in.	mm	kg/m^3	20 MPa	25 MPa	30 MPa
	12	2300	29.5	34.8	40.0
		1850	25.0	29.6	33.9
1/2		2300	33.0	39.0	44.7
		1850	28.0	33.1	38.0
5/8		2300	51.6	61.0	69.9
		1850	43.8	51.8	59.4
	16	2300	52.4	61.9	71.0
		1850	44.5	52.6	60.3
3/4		2300	74.3	87.8	101
		1850	63.1	74.6	85.5
	20	2300	81.9	96.8	111
		1850	69.5	82.2	94.2
	22	2300	99.0	117	134
		1850	84.1	99.4	114
7/8		2300	101	119	137
		1850	85.9	101	116

*$q_r = 0.5 \, \phi_{sc} \, A_{sc} \sqrt{f'_c \, E_c} \leqslant 450 \, \phi_{sc} \, A_{sc}$

where $E_c = w_c^{1.5} \, 0.043 \, \sqrt{f'_c}$ and $\phi_{sc} = 0.80$

Examples

1. **Given:**

Select a simple span composite beam to span 12 m carrying a uniformly distributed specified load of 20 kN/m live load and 7 kN/m dead load. Beam spacing is 3 m. Live load deflection is limited to L/360. Use G40.21-M 300W steel, 76 mm cellular steel deck, 65 mm cover slab of 20 MPa concrete.

Solution

Effect of factored loads $= \alpha_D D + \alpha_L L = 1.25 \times 7 + 1.50 \times 20 = 38.8$ kN/m

Therefore, w_f

$$M_f = \frac{w_f L^2}{8} = \frac{38.8 \times 12^2}{8} = 698 \text{ kN} \cdot \text{m}$$

$$R = V_f = \frac{w_f L}{2} = \frac{38.8 \times 12}{2} = 233 \text{ kN}$$

To meet the deflection limit of L/360 use Figure 5—1 and Table 5—4, pages 5—90 to 5—91, to compute the minimum I required. See page 5—88 on Deflections for an explanation of this method.

Total specified live load, $W = 20 \times 12 = 240$ kN

$B_d = 1.0$ (standard case)

$I_{req'd} = W \times C_d \times B_d = 240 \times 3.4 \times 10^6 \times 1.0 = 816 \times 10^6 \text{ mm}^4$

Effective Width (Clause 17.3.2.1)

a) $0.25 \text{ L} = 0.25 \times 12 = 3 \text{ m} = 3\,000 \text{ mm}$

b) beam spacing $= 3 \text{ m} = 3\,000 \text{ mm}$

c) b + 16t — assume b = 200 mm

Therefore, $b + 16t = 200 + 16 \times (76 + 65) = 2\,460 \text{ mm} < 3\,000 \text{ mm}$

Therefore b + 16t rule governs.

Beam Selection

From composite beam selection tables for 76 mm cellular steel deck with 65 mm cover slab, page 5—60, the first suitable shape is a W460 $\times$ 82 with M_{rc} for 50 per cent shear connection = 736 kN·m; however, for the same mass the W530 $\times$ 82 can be selected.

Select W530 $\times$ 82 with 50 percent shear connection ($b_1 = 2\,470$ mm)

M_{rc} (50%) = 830 kN·m $>$ 698 kN·m — OK

V_r = 894 kN $>$ 233 kN — OK

I_1 = $1\,390 \times 10^6 \text{ mm}^4 > 816 \times 10^6 \text{ mm}^4$ — OK

Q_r (100%) = $1\,830$; $S_{s_1} = 2\,800 \times 10^3 \text{ mm}^3$; $M_r = 559$ kN·m; $L_u = 2\,860$ mm

Check Steel Beam Under Dead Load

As required by Clause 17.7, the steel section alone shall be capable of supporting all factored loads applied before concrete hardens. Assume this to be the total design dead load ($\alpha_D D$).

$$\alpha_D D = 1.25 \times 7 = 8.75 \text{ kN/m}$$

$$M_{fD} = \frac{8.75 \times 12^2}{8} = 157 \text{ kN·m} < M_r = 559 \text{ kN·m}$$

In this case the steel deck when fastened to the steel beam will provide sufficient lateral support to the compression flange of the beam during construction. Thus $M_r = 559$ kN·m may be used.

Check Unshored Beam Tension Flange (Clause 17.6)

Assume specified dead load (7 kN/m) is applied before concrete strength reaches $0.75f_c'$.

S of steel beam = $1\,810 \times 10^3 \text{ mm}^3$

Stress in tension flange due to specified dead load acting on steel beam alone,

$$f_1 = \frac{M_D}{S} = \frac{7 \times 12\,000^2}{8 \times 1\,810 \times 10^3} = 69.6 \text{ MPa}$$

Stress in tension flange due to specified live load acting on composite section,

$$f_2 = \frac{M_L}{S_{s_1}} = \frac{20 \times 12\,000^2}{8 \times 2\,800 \times 10^3} = 129 \text{ MPa}$$

$$0.9 \, F_y = 0.9 \times 300 = 270 \text{ MPa}$$

$$f_1 + f_2 = 69.6 + 129 = 199 \text{ MPa} < 270 \text{ MPa} - \text{OK}$$

Shear Connectors

$$Q_r \text{ (100\%)} = 1\,830 \text{ kN}$$

The 76 mm deck to be used will have a flute width of at least 152 mm (2 × 76). Therefore Table 5—3, page 5—21, may be used to determine, q_r, factored shear resistance of the studs.

Assume (a) mass density = $2\,300 \text{ kg/m}^3$

(b) 20 mm stud will be used.

Check beam flange thickness = 20/2.5 = 8 mm < 13.3 mm − OK
(Clause 17.3.5.5; CAN3-S16.1-M78)

$$q_r = 81.9 \text{ kN}$$

No. of studs required = 2 × Q_r (100%) × Percent connection/100/q_r
$$= 2 \times 1\,830 \times 50/100/81.9$$
$$= 22.3 \text{ use 24 studs.}$$

Since there are no concentrated loads, the studs can be spaced uniformly along the full length of the beam as permitted by the cellular deck flutes.

Example 2

2. **Given:**

Design a simple span composite truss to span 12 m carrying a 3 m wide office floor with a live load of 4.8 kPa and a partition load of 1.0 kPa. Floor slab consists of 76 mm deep wide rib profile deck with 65 mm of $2\,300 \text{ kg/m}^3$ and 20 MPa concrete cover slab. Truss overall depth = span /16 or 750 mm. Live load deflection is to be limited to span /360, and compute approximate shop camber.

Solution:

Compute Factored Loads

Dead load (concrete + deck + steel) = 2.60 kPa
Dead load (partitions)   = 1.00 kPa

Total specified dead load   = 3.60 kPa

Tributary floor area = 12 × 3 = 36 m²

Live load reduction factor (office) = $0.3 + \sqrt{9.8/A} = 0.822$

Reduced live load = 0.822 × 4.8 = 3.95 kPa

Total factored load = 1.25 × D + 1.5 × L
= 1.25 × 3.6 + 1.5 × 3.95 = 10.4 kPa

Factored mid span moment = $\dfrac{10.4 \times 3 \times 12^2}{8}$ = 562 kN·m

Compute Trial Bottom Chord Size

Step 1

Determine effective slab width:
least value of — span/4   = 3 000 mm
          — flange width + 16 thickness (slab & deck) = 2 332 mm
          — centres of truss   = 3 000 mm

Therefore effective slab width = 2 332 mm (Clause 17.3.2.1 — CAN3-S16.1-M78)

Step 2

Determine neutral axis position, a, neglecting top chord — (See Clause 17.4.2 of CAN3-S16.1-M78) — Assume HSS 101.6 × 76.2

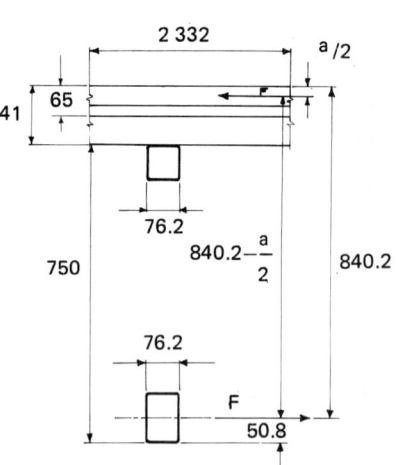

— Equating external and internal moments (Clause 17.4.3(a) — CAN3-S16.1-M78) (840.2 − a/2) × F = 562 × 1 000 . . . (1)

— Compute slab force F (kN).
F = 0.67 × 0.85 × a × 2 332 × 20/1 000
F = 26.56a . . . . (2)

— Equating (1) and (2) and solving for 'a'
(840.2 − a/2) 26.56a = 562 000
a² − 1 680.4a + 42 319 = 0

Therefore a = 25.6 mm

Step 3

Find bottom chord force, F = 26.56a = 680 kN

A req'd (a) for W shape, F_y = 300 MPa, A = $\dfrac{680 \times 10^3}{0.9 \times 300}$ = 2 519 mm²

(b) for HSS, F_y = 350 MPa, A = $\dfrac{680 \times 10^3}{0.9 \times 350}$ = 2 159 mm²

Try HSS 101.6 × 76.2 × 7.95, A = 2 410 mm²

Compute Trial Top Chord Size

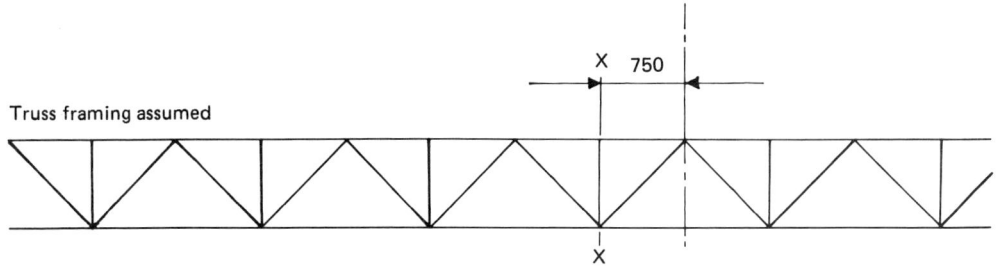

Truss framing assumed

Assume factored bending moment on steel truss under slab pouring @ XX = 260 kN·m; and assume factored local bending at top chord under slab pouring = 1.0 kN·m.

Therefore factored axial force = $\dfrac{260 \times 1\,000}{661.1}$ = 393 kN

Try HSS 76.2 × 76.2 × 6.35

$\dfrac{KL}{r} = \dfrac{0.9 \times 750}{28} = 24$; $A_s = 1\,670$ mm²

C_r/A (for Class C HSS F_y = 350) = 299 MPa (See Table 4–3)

C_r = 499 kN; t = 6.35

$\dfrac{b}{t} = \dfrac{h}{w} \simeq \dfrac{76.2 - 2 \times (2t)}{t} = 8.0$

Since b/t < 22.4 and h/w < 35.8, HSS 76.2 × 76.2 × 6.35 is Class 1.

M_r = 13.5 kN·m (see page 4–61)

Therefore interaction value = $\dfrac{C_f}{C_r} + \dfrac{M_f}{M_r} = \dfrac{393}{499} + \dfrac{1}{13.5} = 0.86 < 1$

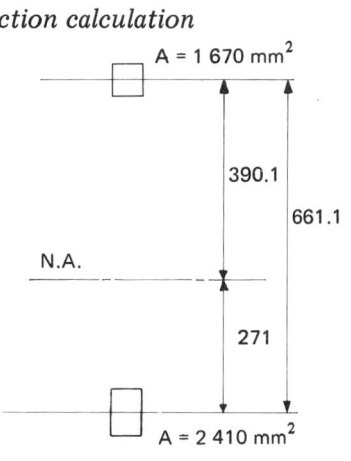

Note: top chord thickness is also governed by the requirement of shear stud welding. (Clause 17.3.5.5, CAN3-S16.1-M78.)

Estimate effective moment of inertia of steel truss for deflection calculation

Neutral axis of chords from C.G. of bottom chord
$1\,670 \times 661.1/(1\,670 + 2\,410) = 271$ mm

Moment of inertia of chords $(I_t + I_b)$ =
$(1.31 + 3.10) \times 10^6$ mm⁴

Therefore moment of inertia of truss

$\simeq 0.85 \times (2\,410 \times 271^2 + 1\,670 \times 390^2) + (I_t + I_b)$

(Note: Estimate 15% reduction to account for deflections contributed by web strain)

$\simeq (366 + 4.4) \times 10^6$ mm⁴

$\simeq 370 \times 10^6$ mm⁴

Compute camber (2.6 kPa)

Camber $\simeq \Delta$ under slab pour

$$= \frac{5}{384} \frac{WL^3}{EI} = \frac{5}{384} \times \frac{93.6 \times 12\,000^3 \times 10^3}{200\,000 \times 370 \times 10^6}$$

$$= 28.5 \text{ mm}$$

Therefore assume shop camber of 28 mm

Compute composite truss moment of inertia

$$E_{concrete} \simeq w_c^{1.5} \; 0.043 \sqrt{f'_c}$$

$$\simeq .2\,300^{1.5} \times 0.043 \times \sqrt{20}$$

$$\simeq 21\,200 \text{ MPa}$$

$E_{steel} \quad = 200\,000$ MPa

$n = E_{steel}/E_{concrete} = 9.43$

Transformed slab width $= \dfrac{2\,332}{9.43} = 247$ mm

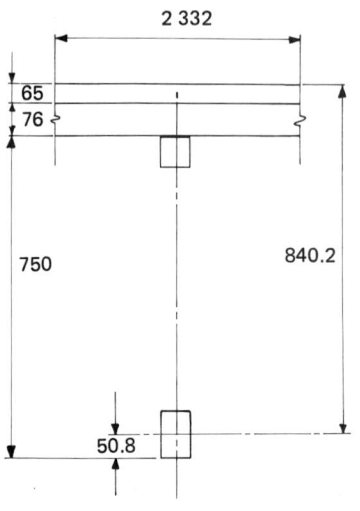

Material	Area (a) (mm²)	distance (d) to top (mm)	ad	ad²
Concrete	16 055	32.5	521 788	17 x 10⁶
Steel	2 410	840.2	2 024 882	1 701 x 10⁶
Total	18 465		2 546 670	1 718 x 10⁶

Neutral axis $= \dfrac{2\,546\,670}{18\,465} = 138$ mm

I about NA $= 1\,718 \times 10^6 - 18\,465 \times 138^2$

$$= 1\,370 \times 10^6 \text{ mm}^4$$

Assume I lost for web deflection due to strain

$\simeq 15\%$ of I of truss chords $(431 \times 10^6 \text{ mm}^4)$

$= 65 \times 10^6 \text{ mm}^4$

Therefore moment of inertia of composite truss

$\simeq (1\,370 - 65) \times 10^6 \simeq 1\,300 \times 10^6 \text{ mm}^4$

Compute LL Deflection (Live load = $3.95 \times 3 \times 12 = 142$ kN)

$$\Delta_{LL} = \frac{5}{384} \times \frac{WL^3}{EI} \times (1.15 \text{ for the deck} + 0.15 \text{ for creep}) \text{ (Clause 17.3.1.1)}$$

$$= \frac{5}{384} \times \frac{142 \times 12\,000^3 \times 10^3}{200\,000 \times 1\,300 \times 10^6} \times 1.30$$

$$= 16 \text{ mm} < 33 \text{ mm (L/360)}$$

Compute number of shear studs using 16mm diameter studs

Factored Q force to be developed by shear connectors = F = 680 kN

Using 16 mm studs in wide rib profile steel deck (rib width/deck height > 2) with concrete of density 2 300 kg/m³ and strength 20 MPa, factored shear resistance per stud = 52.4 kN (see table on page 5—21).

Therefore number of shear studs per half span $= \dfrac{680}{52.4} = 13$

Therefore use $26 - 16$ mm studs per truss.

Web Members

Web members consisting of angles welded to outside face of truss chords, HSS or other shapes, can be sized by traditional means.

Preliminary Truss

Therefore use an HSS $76.2 \times 76.2 \times 6.35$ for top chord and an HSS $101.6 \times 76.2 \times 7.95$ for the bottom chord for the preliminary truss design.

COMPOSITE BEAMS
Trial Selection Tables

G40.21-M 300W
20 MPa Concrete

130 mm Slab
$\varnothing = 0.90, \varnothing_c = 0.67, \varnothing_{sc} = 0.80$

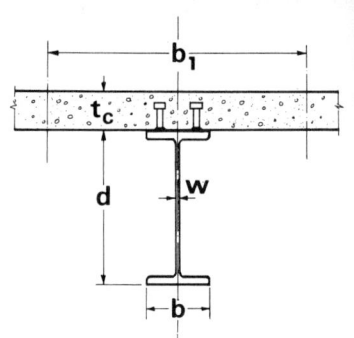

Steel Shape	b_1	Composite Beam									Steel Shape Data*	
		Factored Resistances							Properties			
		M_{rc} in kilonewton metres for various percentages of shear connection						Q_r† for 100%	I_1	S_{s_1}		
	mm	100%	90%	80%	70%	60%	50%	kN	10^6mm^4	10^3mm^3		
W610X241	2 410	2 810	2 800	2 780	2 750	2 710	2 640	3 570	4 540	8 790	M_r	2 070
W24X162	1 990	2 750	2 740	2 710	2 680	2 630	2 560	2 950	4 310	8 660	V_r	2 030
b = 329	1 570	2 680	2 660	2 620	2 580	2 530	2 480	2 320	4 040	8 500	L_u	5 200
t = 31.0	1 140	2 560	2 540	2 510	2 470	2 420	2 380	1 690	3 690	8 270	I_x	2 150
	720	2 410	2 390	2 360	2 330	2 300	2 270	1 070	3 260	7 940	S_x	6 780
W610X217	2 410	2 550	2 530	2 520	2 500	2 460	2 400	3 570	4 130	7 940	M_r	1 850
W24X146	1 990	2 490	2 480	2 460	2 430	2 390	2 330	2 950	3 930	7 830	V_r	1 850
b = 328	1 570	2 430	2 410	2 380	2 350	2 300	2 250	2 320	3 690	7 690	L_u	5 080
t = 27.7	1 140	2 330	2 300	2 270	2 240	2 200	2 150	1 690	3 370	7 480	I_x	1 910
	720	2 180	2 160	2 140	2 110	2 080	2 040	1 070	2 970	7 190	S_x	6 070
W610X195	2 410	2 290	2 290	2 270	2 250	2 220	2 170	3 570	3 740	7 110	M_r	1 640
W24X131	1 990	2 240	2 230	2 220	2 200	2 160	2 110	2 950	3 560	7 010	V_r	1 710
b = 327	1 560	2 190	2 170	2 150	2 120	2 080	2 020	2 310	3 340	6 890	L_u	4 940
t = 24.4	1 140	2 100	2 080	2 050	2 020	1 980	1 930	1 690	3 060	6 710	I_x	1 680
	720	1 970	1 940	1 920	1 890	1 860	1 830	1 070	2 700	6 450	S_x	5 400
W610X174	2 410	2 060	2 050	2 040	2 020	2 000	1 960	3 570	3 370	6 340	M_r	1 450
W24X117	1 980	2 010	2 000	1 990	1 970	1 940	1 900	2 930	3 210	6 250	V_r	1 540
b = 325	1 560	1 960	1 950	1 930	1 910	1 870	1 820	2 310	3 020	6 140	L_u	4 830
t = 21.6	1 140	1 890	1 870	1 840	1 810	1 780	1 740	1 690	2 770	5 990	I_x	1 470
	720	1 760	1 740	1 720	1 700	1 670	1 640	1 070	2 440	5 760	S_x	4 780
W610X155	2 400	1 850	1 840	1 830	1 810	1 790	1 760	3 550	3 030	5 640	M_r	1 280
W24X104	1 980	1 800	1 790	1 780	1 770	1 740	1 710	2 930	2 900	5 570	V_r	1 380
b = 324	1 560	1 750	1 740	1 730	1 710	1 680	1 640	2 310	2 730	5 480	L_u	4 740
t = 19.0	1 140	1 690	1 680	1 660	1 630	1 600	1 560	1 690	2 510	5 350	I_x	1 290
	720	1 580	1 560	1 540	1 520	1 490	1 460	1 070	2 210	5 140	S_x	4 220
W610X140	2 310	1 710	1 700	1 690	1 670	1 650	1 610	3 420	2 760	5 050	M_r	1 120
W24X94	1 910	1 660	1 650	1 640	1 620	1 600	1 550	2 830	2 640	4 980	V_r	1 440
b = 230	1 500	1 610	1 600	1 590	1 560	1 530	1 480	2 220	2 490	4 890	L_u	3 320
t = 22.2	1 100	1 540	1 530	1 500	1 470	1 440	1 400	1 630	2 290	4 770	I_x	1 120
	690	1 420	1 410	1 380	1 360	1 330	1 300	1 020	2 000	4 560	S_x	3 630
W610X125	2 310	1 530	1 530	1 520	1 500	1 480	1 450	3 420	2 490	4 500	M_r	991
W24X84	1 900	1 490	1 480	1 470	1 460	1 440	1 400	2 810	2 380	4 440	V_r	1 300
b = 229	1 500	1 440	1 440	1 430	1 410	1 380	1 340	2 220	2 250	4 370	L_u	3 250
t = 19.6	1 100	1 390	1 370	1 360	1 330	1 300	1 260	1 630	2 070	4 260	I_x	985
	690	1 280	1 270	1 250	1 220	1 200	1 170	1 020	1 820	4 090	S_x	3 220

† No. of studs/beam = 2 x Q_r x percent shear connection/100/q_r (per stud)

* Units — M_r — kN•m L_u — mm   b — mm
  V_r — kN I_x — 10^6mm^4 t — mm
                    S_x — 10^3mm^3

The Imperial designation for each steel beam is listed below the SI designation to assist designers involved with drawings using Imperial designations.

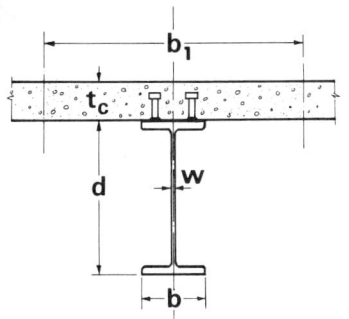

COMPOSITE BEAMS
Trial Selection Tables

G40.21-M 300W
20 MPa Concrete

130 mm Slab
$\phi = 0.90$, $\phi_c = 0.67$, $\phi_{sc} = 0.80$

Steel Shape	Composite Beam										Steel Shape Data*	
		Factored Resistances							Properties			
	b_1	M_{rc} in kilonewton metres for various percentages of shear connection						Q_r† for 100%	I_1	S_{s_1}		
	mm	100%	90%	80%	70%	60%	50%	kN	$10^6\,mm^4$	$10^3\,mm^3$		
W610X113	2 310	1 400	1 400	1 390	1 380	1 360	1 330	3 420	2 270	4 070	M_r	888
W24X76	1 900	1 360	1 360	1 350	1 330	1 320	1 280	2 810	2 180	4 020	V_r	1 210
b = 228	1 500	1 320	1 310	1 300	1 290	1 260	1 230	2 220	2 060	3 950	L_u	3 180
t = 17.3	1 100	1 270	1 260	1 240	1 220	1 190	1 150	1 630	1 900	3 860	I_x	875
	690	1 170	1 160	1 140	1 120	1 090	1 060	1 020	1 670	3 700	S_x	2 880
W610X101	2 310	1 280	1 280	1 270	1 260	1 240	1 210	3 420	2 050	3 650	M_r	783
W24X68	1 900	1 240	1 240	1 230	1 220	1 200	1 170	2 810	1 970	3 600	V_r	1 130
b = 228	1 500	1 200	1 190	1 180	1 170	1 150	1 120	2 220	1 870	3 540	L_u	3 110
t = 14.9	1 100	1 150	1 140	1 130	1 110	1 080	1 050	1 630	1 730	3 460	I_x	764
	690	1 060	1 050	1 030	1 010	985	957	1 020	1 520	3 320	S_x	2 530
W530X138	2 290	1 520	1 510	1 500	1 480	1 460	1 420	3 390	2 210	4 480	M_r	975
W21X93	1 890	1 470	1 460	1 450	1 440	1 410	1 370	2 800	2 110	4 420	V_r	1 440
b = 214	1 490	1 420	1 410	1 400	1 380	1 350	1 300	2 210	1 980	4 330	L_u	3 180
t = 23.6	1 090	1 360	1 340	1 320	1 300	1 270	1 230	1 610	1 820	4 220	I_x	861
	690	1 250	1 230	1 220	1 190	1 170	1 140	1 020	1 590	4 030	S_x	3 140
W530X123	2 290	1 370	1 370	1 350	1 340	1 320	1 290	3 390	2 000	4 020	M_r	867
W21X83	1 890	1 330	1 320	1 310	1 300	1 280	1 240	2 800	1 910	3 960	V_r	1 270
b = 212	1 490	1 280	1 270	1 260	1 250	1 220	1 180	2 210	1 800	3 890	L_u	3 100
t = 21.2	1 090	1 230	1 210	1 200	1 180	1 150	1 110	1 610	1 650	3 790	I_x	761
	690	1 130	1 120	1 100	1 080	1 060	1 030	1 020	1 450	3 630	S_x	2 800
W530X109	2 290	1 230	1 230	1 220	1 200	1 180	1 160	3 390	1 790	3 570	M_r	764
W21X73	1 890	1 190	1 180	1 180	1 160	1 150	1 120	2 800	1 720	3 520	V_r	1 110
b = 211	1 490	1 140	1 140	1 130	1 120	1 100	1 070	2 210	1 620	3 460	L_u	3 040
t = 18.8	1 090	1 100	1 090	1 080	1 060	1 030	1 000	1 610	1 500	3 380	I_x	667
	690	1 020	1 010	990	971	949	924	1 020	1 310	3 240	S_x	2 480
W530X101	2 290	1 160	1 150	1 140	1 130	1 110	1 090	3 390	1 680	3 330	M_r	707
W21X68	1 890	1 120	1 110	1 100	1 090	1 070	1 050	2 800	1 610	3 280	V_r	1 040
b = 210	1 490	1 070	1 070	1 060	1 050	1 030	1 000	2 210	1 530	3 230	L_u	2 990
t = 17.4	1 090	1 020	1 020	1 010	995	972	943	1 610	1 410	3 150	I_x	617
	690	956	944	929	911	890	866	1 020	1 240	3 020	S_x	2 300
W530X92	2 290	1 070	1 060	1 050	1 040	1 020	996	3 190	1 540	3 030	M_r	637
W21X62	1 890	1 030	1 030	1 020	1 010	992	971	2 800	1 480	2 990	V_r	969
b = 209	1 490	988	985	978	968	953	928	2 210	1 400	2 940	L_u	2 930
t = 15.6	1 090	943	940	932	918	897	870	1 610	1 300	2 870	I_x	552
	690	881	870	856	839	819	795	1 020	1 140	2 760	S_x	2 070

† No. of studs/beam = 2 x Q_r x percent shear connection/100/q_r (per stud)

* Units — M_r — kN•m L_u — mm   b — mm
$\quad\quad\quad$ V_r — kN I_x — $10^6\,mm^4$ t — mm
$\quad\quad\quad\quad\quad\quad$ S_x — $10^3\,mm^3$

The Imperial designation for each steel beam is listed below the SI designation to assist designers involved with drawings using Imperial designations.

COMPOSITE BEAMS
Trial Selection Tables

G40.21-M 300W
20 MPa Concrete

130 mm Slab
$\emptyset = 0.90$, $\emptyset_c = 0.67$, $\emptyset_{sc} = 0.80$

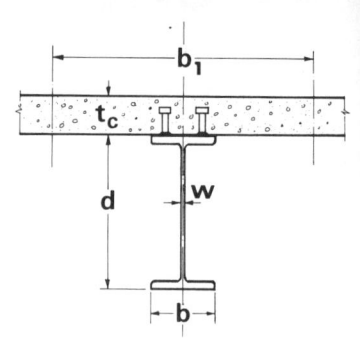

Steel Shape	b_1	M$_{rc}$ in kilonewton metres for various percentages of shear connection						Q_r† for 100%	I_1	S_{s_1}	Steel Shape Data*	
	mm	100%	90%	80%	70%	60%	50%	kN	10^6 mm^4	10^3 mm^3		
W530X82	2 290	963	955	943	928	908	885	2 830	1 380	2 690	M$_r$	559
W21X55	1 890	930	928	921	911	895	876	2 800	1 330	2 660	V$_r$	894
b = 209	1 490	890	887	881	872	859	838	2 210	1 260	2 620	L$_u$	2 860
t = 13.3	1 090	847	844	838	827	809	783	1 610	1 170	2 550	I$_x$	479
	690	791	782	769	753	734	711	1 020	1 030	2 460	S$_x$	1 810
W460X106	2 270	1 070	1 070	1 060	1 050	1 030	1 000	3 360	1 380	3 110	M$_r$	645
W18X71	1 880	1 030	1 030	1 020	1 010	988	966	2 780	1 320	3 060	V$_r$	1 050
b = 194	1 480	987	982	974	963	946	920	2 190	1 250	3 000	L$_u$	2 910
t = 20.6	1 080	939	934	925	910	889	862	1 600	1 140	2 920	I$_x$	488
	680	871	861	847	831	812	790	1 010	998	2 790	S$_x$	2 080
W460X97	2 270	992	989	981	967	948	923	3 320	1 270	2 850	M$_r$	589
W18X65	1 880	953	950	942	929	913	892	2 780	1 220	2 810	V$_r$	947
b = 193	1 480	910	906	899	888	874	852	2 190	1 160	2 760	L$_u$	2 870
t = 19.0	1 080	864	860	853	841	823	799	1 600	1 060	2 690	I$_x$	445
	680	805	796	784	770	752	731	1 010	931	2 570	S$_x$	1 910
W460X89	2 270	929	924	914	899	879	855	3 080	1 190	2 650	M$_r$	543
W18X60	1 870	892	889	882	870	854	834	2 770	1 140	2 610	V$_r$	866
b = 192	1 480	851	848	841	831	817	799	2 190	1 080	2 560	L$_u$	2 830
t = 17.7	1 080	806	803	797	787	772	749	1 600	999	2 500	I$_x$	410
	680	753	745	735	721	704	684	1 010	875	2 400	S$_x$	1 770
W460X82	2 270	858	850	839	823	804	781	2 810	1 090	2 420	M$_r$	494
W18X55	1 870	826	824	817	806	791	771	2 770	1 050	2 390	V$_r$	812
b = 191	1 480	786	783	777	768	755	738	2 190	998	2 350	L$_u$	2 770
t = 16.0	1 080	743	740	734	726	713	693	1 600	924	2 290	I$_x$	370
	680	694	687	678	666	650	631	1 010	812	2 200	S$_x$	1 610
W460X74	2 270	789	779	767	751	732	709	2 550	1 000	2 210	M$_r$	445
W18X50	1 870	762	757	749	737	722	703	2 550	965	2 180	V$_r$	733
b = 190	1 480	725	722	717	708	695	680	2 190	918	2 140	L$_u$	2 730
t = 14.5	1 080	683	680	675	668	657	639	1 600	852	2 090	I$_x$	333
	680	637	632	624	613	599	581	1 010	752	2 010	S$_x$	1 460
W460X67	2 270	730	720	707	691	672	651	2 340	923	2 030	M$_r$	405
W18X45	1 870	708	701	692	680	664	645	2 340	890	2 000	V$_r$	688
b = 190	1 480	674	672	667	658	646	631	2 190	848	1 960	L$_u$	2 660
t = 12.7	1 080	633	631	626	619	609	592	1 600	789	1 920	I$_x$	300
	680	589	585	578	567	552	535	1 010	698	1 840	S$_x$	1 320

† No. of studs/beam = 2 x Q$_r$ x percent shear connection/100/q$_r$ (per stud)

* Units — M$_r$ — kN•m   L$_u$ — mm   b — mm
          V$_r$ — kN   I$_x$ — 10^6 mm^4 t — mm
                      S$_x$ — 10^3 mm^3

The Imperial designation for each steel beam is listed below the SI designation to assist designers involved with drawings using Imperial designations.

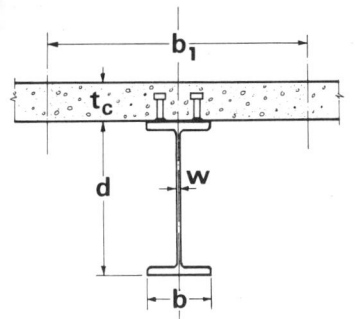

COMPOSITE BEAMS
Trial Selection Tables

G40.21-M 300W
20 MPa Concrete

130 mm Slab
$\varnothing = 0.90, \varnothing_C = 0.67, \varnothing_{SC} = 0.80$

Steel Shape		Composite Beam										Steel Shape Data*	
		Factored Resistances							Properties				
	b_1	M_{rc} in kilonewton metres for various percentages of shear connection						Q_r† for 100%	I_1	S_{s_1}			
	mm	100%	90%	80%	70%	60%	50%	kN	10^6 mm^4	10^3 mm^3		
W460X61	2 270	659	648	634	619	601	581	2 100	826	1 810	M_r	354
W18X41	1 870	641	633	623	610	594	576	2 100	797	1 780	V_r	650
b = 189	1 470	613	610	605	596	584	569	2 100	759	1 750	L_u	2 580
t = 10.8	1 080	574	572	568	561	552	537	1 600	709	1 710	I_x	259
	680	531	528	522	512	499	482	1 010	629	1 640	S_x	1 150
W410X85	2 260	822	815	804	788	769	745	2 920	959	2 330	M_r	467
W16X57	1 870	788	785	778	767	751	731	2 770	921	2 290	V_r	810
b = 181	1 470	747	743	737	727	714	697	2 180	871	2 250	L_u	2 730
t = 18.2	1 070	702	699	693	685	672	653	1 580	802	2 190	I_x	315
	680	653	648	639	628	613	595	1 010	704	2 100	S_x	1 510
W410X74	2 260	739	729	717	701	682	659	2 580	858	2 070	M_r	408
W16X50	1 860	711	707	699	687	672	652	2 580	824	2 040	V_r	714
b = 180	1 470	673	671	665	655	643	627	2 180	782	2 000	L_u	2 670
t = 16.0	1 070	630	628	622	615	605	588	1 580	723	1 950	I_x	275
	680	585	582	575	565	552	535	1 010	637	1 870	S_x	1 330
W410X67	2 260	673	663	649	633	615	594	2 320	781	1 870	M_r	367
W16X45	1 860	651	644	635	622	607	588	2 320	752	1 850	V_r	643
b = 179	1 470	617	615	610	601	590	574	2 180	715	1 810	L_u	2 610
t = 14.4	1 070	576	574	569	562	553	539	1 580	663	1 760	I_x	246
	680	533	530	525	517	505	490	1 010	586	1 700	S_x	1 200
W410X60	2 260	601	590	576	561	543	524	2 050	699	1 660	M_r	321
W16X40	1 860	584	576	565	552	537	519	2 050	674	1 640	V_r	558
b = 178	1 470	557	554	548	539	528	513	2 050	642	1 610	L_u	2 580
t = 12.8	1 070	518	516	512	506	497	485	1 580	598	1 570	I_x	216
	680	476	475	471	465	455	442	1 010	531	1 510	S_x	1 060
W410X54	2 260	544	532	519	504	487	469	1 840	626	1 490	M_r	283
W16X36	1 860	530	521	510	497	482	466	1 840	604	1 470	V_r	539
b = 177	1 470	509	504	496	487	475	460	1 840	577	1 440	L_u	2 480
t = 10.9	1 070	473	472	468	461	453	442	1 580	538	1 400	I_x	186
	680	432	431	428	422	413	400	1 010	479	1 350	S_x	924
W410X46	2 220	477	466	453	439	424	407	1 590	549	1 290	M_r	239
W16X31	1 830	467	457	446	434	420	404	1 590	530	1 270	V_r	503
b = 140	1 440	450	444	436	426	414	400	1 590	507	1 240	L_u	1 930
t = 11.2	1 050	421	420	417	411	402	392	1 550	474	1 210	I_x	156
	670	383	381	378	374	365	353	992	424	1 170	S_x	773

† No. of studs/beam = 2 x Q_r x percent shear connection/100/q_r (per stud)

* Units — M_r — kN•m L_u — mm   b — mm
  V_r — kN I_x — 10^6 mm^4 t — mm
   S_x — 10^3 mm^3

The Imperial designation for each steel beam is listed below the SI designation to assist designers involved with drawings using Imperial designations.

COMPOSITE BEAMS
Trial Selection Tables

G40.21-M 300W
20 MPa Concrete

130 mm Slab
$\emptyset = 0.90$, $\emptyset_c = 0.67$, $\emptyset_{sc} = 0.80$

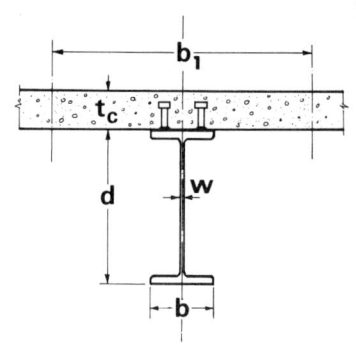

Steel Shape	b_1	Composite Beam									Steel Shape Data*	
		Factored Resistances							Properties			
		M_{rc} in kilonewton metres for various percentages of shear connection						$Q_r^†$ for 100%	I_1	S_{s_1}		
	mm	100%	90%	80%	70%	60%	50%	kN	10^6mm^4	10^3mm^3		
W410X39	2 220	408	397	385	373	359	344	1 350	468	1 090	M_r	197
W16X26	1 830	400	391	381	369	356	342	1 350	453	1 070	V_r	448
b = 140	1 440	389	381	373	363	352	340	1 350	434	1 050	L_u	1 860
t = 8.8	1 050	368	365	360	353	345	334	1 350	407	1 030	I_x	127
	670	332	331	329	325	318	308	992	367	988	S_x	634
W360X79	2 290	695	686	674	658	639	616	2 730	720	2 000	M_r	386
W14X53	1 890	664	661	654	643	628	608	2 730	690	1 960	V_r	593
b = 205	1 490	625	622	616	607	594	578	2 210	652	1 920	L_u	3 270
t = 16.8	1 090	582	579	574	567	557	544	1 610	602	1 870	I_x	227
	690	536	534	530	523	512	498	1 020	527	1 790	S_x	1 280
W360X72	2 280	634	624	611	595	576	554	2 460	652	1 800	M_r	346
W14X48	1 880	609	604	595	583	567	548	2 460	626	1 770	V_r	536
b = 204	1 480	573	570	565	556	544	529	2 190	593	1 740	L_u	3 190
t = 15.1	1 080	531	529	524	517	508	496	1 600	548	1 690	I_x	201
	690	487	485	482	476	467	455	1 020	482	1 620	S_x	1 150
W360X64	2 280	574	563	549	534	516	495	2 200	590	1 620	M_r	308
W14X43	1 880	554	547	537	524	509	490	2 200	567	1 600	V_r	476
b = 203	1 480	524	522	517	509	497	483	2 190	538	1 560	L_u	3 110
t = 13.5	1 080	484	482	477	471	462	450	1 600	498	1 520	I_x	178
	680	440	439	435	431	423	412	1 010	439	1 460	S_x	1 030
W360X57	2 250	528	517	503	488	471	452	1 950	553	1 460	M_r	273
W14X38	1 860	513	504	493	481	465	448	1 950	532	1 440	V_r	504
b = 172	1 460	488	484	478	469	457	442	1 950	506	1 410	L_u	2 550
t = 13.1	1 070	451	449	445	439	430	419	1 580	470	1 370	I_x	161
	680	410	408	405	400	392	381	1 010	417	1 320	S_x	897
W360X51	2 250	476	465	452	437	421	403	1 740	498	1 310	M_r	241
W14X34	1 860	464	455	444	431	417	400	1 740	480	1 290	V_r	455
b = 171	1 460	444	439	431	421	409	395	1 740	457	1 260	L_u	2 500
t = 11.6	1 070	412	411	407	401	392	381	1 580	426	1 230	I_x	141
	680	372	370	367	363	357	346	1 010	379	1 180	S_x	796
W360X45	2 250	427	415	403	389	374	358	1 550	445	1 160	M_r	210
W14X30	1 860	417	407	397	384	371	355	1 550	429	1 150	V_r	433
b = 171	1 460	401	395	387	377	365	352	1 550	409	1 120	L_u	2 430
t = 9.8	1 070	375	374	370	364	356	345	1 550	382	1 090	I_x	122
	680	336	335	332	328	322	313	1 010	342	1 050	S_x	691

† No. of studs/beam = 2 x Q_r x percent shear connection/100/q_r (per stud)

* Units — M_r — kN•m L_u — mm   b — mm
         V_r — kN I_x — 10^6mm^4 t — mm
                              S_x — 10^3mm^3

The Imperial designation for each steel beam is listed below the SI designation to assist designers involved with drawings using Imperial designations.

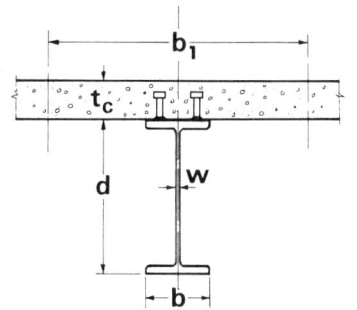

COMPOSITE BEAMS
Trial Selection Tables

G40.21-M 300W
20 MPa Concrete

130 mm Slab
$\phi = 0.90$, $\phi_c = 0.67$, $\phi_{sc} = 0.80$

Steel Shape		Composite Beam									Steel Shape Data*	
		Factored Resistances							Properties			
	b_1	M_{rc} in kilonewton metres for various percentages of shear connection						Q_r† for 100%	I_1	S_{s_1}		
	mm	100%	90%	80%	70%	60%	50%	kN	$10^6 mm^4$	$10^3 mm^3$		
W360X39	2 210	376	365	354	341	327	312	1 340	392	1 010	M_r	179
W14X26	1 820	369	359	349	337	324	311	1 340	379	995	V_r	409
b = 128	1 440	357	350	341	331	320	308	1 340	362	977	L_u	1 790
t = 10.7	1 050	337	333	328	321	313	303	1 340	338	950	I_x	102
	660	300	299	296	292	286	278	977	303	910	S_x	580
W360X33	2 210	318	308	297	286	274	261	1 130	331	847	M_r	146
W14X22	1 820	312	303	294	283	272	260	1 130	321	836	V_r	361
b = 127	1 430	304	297	288	279	269	258	1 130	307	821	L_u	1 720
t = 8.5	1 050	290	285	279	272	264	254	1 130	289	800	I_x	82.7
	660	260	259	257	253	248	241	977	260	766	S_x	474
W310X129	2 390	936	931	921	906	885	859	3 540	906	2 940	M_r	583
W12X87	1 970	891	886	877	863	846	824	2 920	861	2 890	V_r	742
b = 308	1 550	843	839	831	820	805	787	2 300	805	2 820	L_u	5 580
t = 20.6	1 130	794	790	784	775	764	748	1 670	732	2 730	I_x	308
	720	743	740	734	725	713	697	1 070	633	2 600	S_x	1 940
W310X118	2 390	865	861	852	838	818	793	3 540	829	2 680	M_r	526
W12X79	1 970	822	817	809	796	779	758	2 920	790	2 630	V_r	666
b = 307	1 550	776	772	764	754	740	722	2 300	739	2 570	L_u	5 390
t = 18.7	1 130	728	724	718	710	699	685	1 670	674	2 490	I_x	275
	720	678	676	671	663	652	638	1 070	583	2 380	S_x	1 750
W310X107	2 390	801	798	790	776	757	733	3 540	762	2 450	M_r	478
W12X72	1 970	759	755	748	735	719	698	2 920	727	2 400	V_r	604
b = 306	1 550	714	711	704	694	680	664	2 300	682	2 350	L_u	5 220
t = 17.0	1 130	668	664	659	651	641	628	1 670	623	2 280	I_x	248
	720	620	617	613	607	597	584	1 070	541	2 180	S_x	1 590
W310X97	2 390	741	736	726	711	692	668	3 320	698	2 230	M_r	389
W12X65	1 970	701	698	690	679	663	643	2 920	666	2 190	V_r	543
b = 305	1 550	657	654	648	638	625	609	2 300	627	2 140	L_u	5 410
t = 15.4	1 130	612	609	604	596	586	574	1 670	574	2 080	I_x	222
	720	565	563	559	554	546	534	1 070	499	1 980	S_x	1 440
W310X86	2 330	680	673	662	646	627	604	2 970	641	2 010	M_r	383
W12X58	1 930	646	644	637	626	611	591	2 860	613	1 970	V_r	503
b = 254	1 520	605	602	596	586	574	558	2 250	578	1 930	L_u	4 250
t = 16.3	1 110	561	558	553	545	536	524	1 640	530	1 870	I_x	199
	700	514	512	508	503	496	484	1 040	461	1 790	S_x	1 280

† No. of studs/beam = 2 x Q_r x percent shear connection/100/q_r (per stud)

* Units — M_r — kN•m L_u — mm b — mm
 V_r — kN I_x — $10^6 mm^4$ t — mm
  S_x — $10^3 mm^3$

The Imperial designation for each steel beam is listed below the SI designation to assist designers involved with drawings using Imperial designations.

COMPOSITE BEAMS
Trial Selection Tables

G40.21-M 300W
20 MPa Concrete

130 mm Slab
$\emptyset = 0.90$, $\emptyset_C = 0.67$, $\emptyset_{SC} = 0.80$

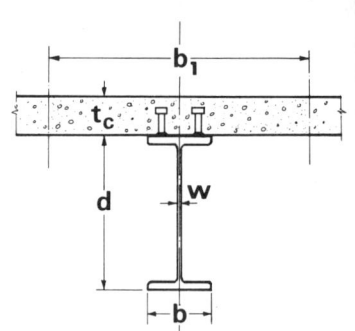

Steel Shape	b_1	Composite Beam										Steel Shape Data*	
		Factored Resistances								Properties			
		M_{rc} in kilonewton metres for various percentages of shear connection						Q_r† for 100%	I_1	S_{s_1}		
	mm	100%	90%	80%	70%	60%	50%	kN	10^6 mm^4	10^3 mm^3		
W310X79	2 330	632	623	610	594	575	553	2 730	587	1 840	M_r	346
W12X53	1 930	603	599	592	580	565	545	2 730	562	1 810	V_r	480
b = 254	1 520	563	560	555	546	533	518	2 250	530	1 770	L_u	4 140
t = 14.6	1 110	520	517	513	505	496	484	1 640	488	1 720	I_x	177
	700	474	472	469	464	457	446	1 040	425	1 640	S_x	1 160
W310X74	2 290	604	595	582	566	547	525	2 560	562	1 730	M_r	321
W12X50	1 890	578	573	565	553	537	518	2 560	538	1 700	V_r	519
b = 205	1 490	540	538	532	523	511	495	2 210	508	1 660	L_u	3 380
t = 16.3	1 090	498	495	491	483	474	462	1 610	468	1 610	I_x	165
	690	453	451	447	442	434	422	1 020	408	1 540	S_x	1 060
W310X67	2 280	549	538	524	509	490	469	2 300	507	1 560	M_r	286
W12X45	1 880	527	520	511	498	483	464	2 300	486	1 530	V_r	463
b = 204	1 480	494	492	487	479	467	452	2 190	459	1 500	L_u	3 280
t = 14.6	1 080	453	451	447	440	431	419	1 600	423	1 450	I_x	145
	690	411	409	405	401	394	384	1 020	372	1 390	S_x	949
W310X60	2 280	496	485	471	456	438	419	2 050	459	1 400	M_r	254
W12X40	1 880	479	471	460	447	432	414	2 050	440	1 380	V_r	405
b = 203	1 480	452	449	443	434	422	408	2 050	417	1 350	L_u	3 200
t = 13.1	1 080	413	412	408	401	392	381	1 600	386	1 310	I_x	129
	680	371	369	366	362	356	347	1 010	339	1 250	S_x	849
W310X52	2 250	456	445	432	417	400	382	1 800	434	1 260	M_r	226
W12X35	1 850	443	434	423	410	395	379	1 800	418	1 240	V_r	429
b = 167	1 460	422	417	410	400	388	374	1 800	397	1 210	L_u	2 570
t = 13.2	1 070	388	387	383	377	368	357	1 580	368	1 180	I_x	118
	670	346	345	342	337	332	323	992	324	1 130	S_x	747
W310X45	2 250	394	383	370	356	342	325	1 540	376	1 080	M_r	191
W12X30	1 850	384	375	364	352	338	323	1 540	362	1 070	V_r	368
b = 166	1 460	369	363	354	344	333	319	1 540	345	1 050	L_u	2 490
t = 11.2	1 070	343	342	338	332	323	313	1 540	321	1 020	I_x	99.2
	670	303	302	299	295	290	283	992	285	971	S_x	634
W310X39	2 250	345	335	323	310	297	282	1 330	331	945	M_r	165
W12X26	1 850	338	328	318	307	294	280	1 330	319	932	V_r	320
b = 165	1 460	327	319	311	301	290	278	1 330	305	915	L_u	2 440
t = 9.7	1 070	307	304	298	291	283	273	1 330	285	890	I_x	85.1
	670	271	269	267	263	258	251	992	254	851	S_x	549

† No. of studs/beam = 2 x Q_r x percent shear connection/100/q_r (per stud)

* Units — M_r — kN•m L_u — mm   b — mm
          V_r — kN I_x — 10^6 mm^4 t — mm
                              S_x — 10^3 mm^3

The Imperial designation for each steel beam is listed below the SI designation to assist designers involved with drawings using Imperial designations.

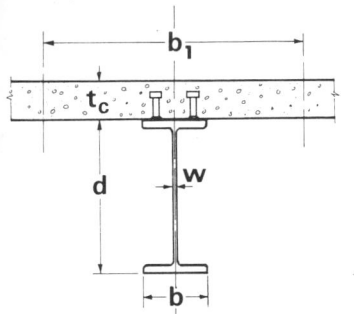

COMPOSITE BEAMS
Trial Selection Tables

G40.21-M 300W
20 MPa Concrete

130 mm Slab
$\emptyset = 0.90$, $\emptyset_c = 0.67$, $\emptyset_{sc} = 0.80$

Steel Shape	b_1	Composite Beam									Steel Shape Data*	
		Factored Resistances							Properties			
		M_{rc} in kilonewton metres for various percentages of shear connection						Q_r† for 100%	I_1	S_{s_1}		
	mm	100%	90%	80%	70%	60%	50%	kN	10^6 mm⁴	10^3 mm³		
W250X101	2 340	685	682	674	661	642	618	3 460	567	2 080	M_r	378
W10X68	1 930	644	641	633	621	605	584	2 860	539	2 040	V_r	560
b = 257	1 520	601	597	590	580	566	549	2 250	503	1 980	L_u	4 950
t = 19.6	1 110	554	551	545	537	527	514	1 640	457	1 910	I_x	164
	700	506	503	499	494	485	474	1 040	392	1 810	S_x	1 240
W250X89	2 340	623	616	605	590	571	547	3 080	508	1 850	M_r	332
W10X60	1 930	586	583	576	565	549	530	2 860	484	1 810	V_r	496
b = 256	1 520	544	541	535	525	512	496	2 250	453	1 770	L_u	4 690
t = 17.3	1 110	500	497	491	484	474	462	1 640	413	1 710	I_x	143
	700	452	450	447	441	435	425	1 040	355	1 620	S_x	1 100
W250X80	2 340	568	559	547	531	512	489	2 750	460	1 670	M_r	294
W10X54	1 930	538	535	527	516	501	482	2 750	438	1 630	V_r	429
b = 255	1 520	498	495	490	481	468	453	2 250	411	1 590	L_u	4 520
t = 15.6	1 110	455	452	448	440	431	419	1 640	376	1 540	I_x	126
	700	409	407	404	399	393	384	1 040	324	1 460	S_x	982
W250X73	2 330	524	514	501	485	466	445	2 510	421	1 520	M_r	266
W10X49	1 930	500	494	485	473	457	438	2 510	403	1 500	V_r	388
b = 254	1 520	463	461	456	447	435	420	2 250	378	1 460	L_u	4 390
t = 14.2	1 110	421	419	414	407	398	387	1 640	346	1 410	I_x	113
	700	376	375	371	367	361	353	1 040	300	1 340	S_x	891
W250X67	2 280	494	483	470	454	436	415	2 310	399	1 410	M_r	243
W10X45	1 880	472	466	456	444	428	410	2 310	381	1 390	V_r	408
b = 204	1 480	439	437	432	424	412	397	2 190	358	1 350	L_u	3 570
t = 15.7	1 080	398	396	392	385	376	364	1 600	328	1 310	I_x	104
	690	356	354	350	346	339	331	1 020	286	1 240	S_x	806
W250X58	2 280	436	424	411	395	378	359	2 000	348	1 230	M_r	208
W10X39	1 880	419	411	400	387	372	355	2 000	333	1 210	V_r	359
b = 203	1 480	394	390	384	375	363	348	2 000	314	1 180	L_u	3 410
t = 13.5	1 080	356	354	350	343	335	324	1 600	289	1 140	I_x	87.3
	680	313	312	309	304	298	291	1 010	252	1 080	S_x	693
W250X49	2 280	373	361	348	334	318	301	1 690	296	1 040	M_r	171
W10X33	1 880	361	352	341	328	314	298	1 690	284	1 020	V_r	326
b = 202	1 480	343	337	329	319	308	294	1 690	269	998	L_u	3 240
t = 11.0	1 080	312	311	307	302	293	283	1 600	248	967	I_x	70.6
	680	272	270	268	264	258	251	1 010	217	917	S_x	572

† No. of studs/beam = 2 x Q_r x percent shear connection/100/q_r (per stud)

* Units — M_r — kN•m L_u — mm   b — mm
  V_r — kN I_x — 10^6 mm⁴   t — mm
  S_x — 10^3 mm³

The Imperial designation for each steel beam is listed below the SI designation to assist designers involved with drawings using Imperial designations.

COMPOSITE BEAMS
Trial Selection Tables

G40.21-M 300W
20 MPa Concrete

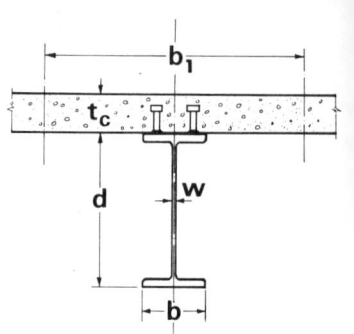

130 mm Slab
$\varnothing = 0.90$, $\varnothing_c = 0.67$, $\varnothing_{sc} = 0.80$

Steel Shape	b_1	\multicolumn{6}{c	}{M_{rc} in kilonewton metres for various percentages of shear connection}	Q_r† for 100%	I_1	S_{s_1}	Steel Shape Data*
	mm	100%	90%	80%	70%	60%	50%	kN	$10^6\,mm^4$	$10^3\,mm^3$	
W250X45	2 230	359	348	335	322	307	290	1 540	300	983	M_r 163
W10X30	1 840	349	340	329	317	303	288	1 540	288	967	V_r 360
b = 148	1 450	334	327	319	309	297	284	1 540	273	947	L_u 2 360
t = 13.0	1 060	307	306	302	296	288	277	1 540	253	917	I_x 71.1
	670	268	267	264	260	254	247	992	223	872	S_x 534
W250X39	2 230	312	301	289	277	263	249	1 330	261	851	M_r 139
W10X26	1 840	305	295	285	273	261	247	1 330	251	838	V_r 308
b = 147	1 450	293	286	278	268	257	244	1 330	239	821	L_u 2 280
t = 11.2	1 060	274	270	265	258	250	239	1 330	222	797	I_x 60.1
	670	238	237	234	230	225	218	992	196	759	S_x 459
W250X33	2 230	267	257	246	235	223	210	1 130	223	723	M_r 114
W10X22	1 840	261	252	243	232	221	209	1 130	215	712	V_r 280
b = 146	1 450	253	246	237	228	218	207	1 130	205	698	L_u 2 180
t = 9.1	1 060	239	234	228	221	213	203	1 130	191	679	I_x 48.9
	670	210	209	206	203	198	191	992	170	647	S_x 379
W200X100	2 290	613	610	602	588	569	545	3 390	449	1 850	M_r 310
W8X67	1 890	573	569	561	549	532	511	2 800	425	1 810	V_r 592
b = 210	1 490	529	525	518	507	494	476	2 210	395	1 750	L_u 5 020
t = 23.7	1 090	483	479	473	465	454	441	1 610	356	1 680	I_x 113
	690	433	431	426	421	412	402	1 020	302	1 580	S_x 989
W200X86	2 290	550	543	533	517	498	474	3 000	393	1 620	M_r 265
W8X58	1 890	514	512	505	493	478	458	2 800	372	1 590	V_r 514
b = 209	1 490	473	470	464	454	441	424	2 210	347	1 540	L_u 4 620
t = 20.6	1 090	429	426	420	413	403	390	1 610	314	1 480	I_x 94.7
	690	382	379	375	370	363	353	1 020	267	1 390	S_x 853
W200X71	2 290	469	459	446	430	411	390	2 460	331	1 350	M_r 217
W8X48	1 890	445	439	430	418	403	384	2 460	315	1 330	V_r 393
b = 206	1 490	409	407	401	392	380	365	2 210	294	1 290	L_u 4 150
t = 17.4	1 090	367	365	360	353	344	332	1 610	268	1 240	I_x 76.6
	690	323	321	317	312	306	298	1 020	229	1 170	S_x 709
W200X59	2 290	400	388	375	359	342	322	2 040	279	1 130	M_r 176
W8X40	1 890	383	375	364	351	336	318	2 040	266	1 110	V_r 341
b = 205	1 490	357	354	347	338	326	312	2 040	249	1 080	L_u 3 780
t = 14.2	1 090	318	317	312	306	297	286	1 610	228	1 040	I_x 61.1
	690	276	274	271	267	261	254	1 020	196	983	S_x 582

† No. of studs/beam = 2 x Q_r x percent shear connection/100/q_r (per stud)

* Units — M_r — kN•m L_u — mm   b — mm
              V_r — kN I_x — $10^6\,mm^4$ t — mm
                                  S_x — $10^3\,mm^3$

The Imperial designation for each steel beam is listed below the SI designation to assist designers involved with drawings using Imperial designations.

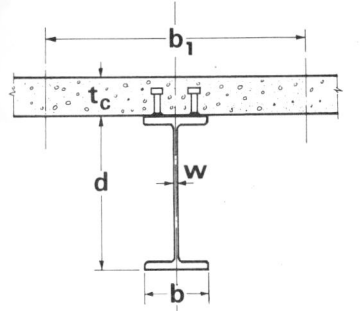

COMPOSITE BEAMS
Trial Selection Tables

G40.21-M 300W
20 MPa Concrete

130 mm Slab
$\emptyset = 0.90$, $\emptyset_C = 0.67$, $\emptyset_{SC} = 0.80$

Steel Shape		Composite Beam										Steel Shape Data*	
		Factored Resistances							Properties				
	b_1	M_{rc} in kilonewton metres for various percentages of shear connection						$Q_r{}^\dagger$ for 100%	I_1	S_{s_1}			
	mm	100%	90%	80%	70%	60%	50%	kN	10^6mm^4	10^3mm^3		
W200X52	2 280	357	345	332	317	301	283	1 800	248	1 000	M_r	154
W8X35	1 880	343	334	323	311	296	280	1 800	237	984	V_r	290
b = 204	1 480	323	318	310	301	289	274	1 800	222	960	L_u	3 620
t = 12.6	1 080	289	288	284	278	269	259	1 600	203	927	I_x	52.7
	690	249	247	245	240	235	227	1 020	177	875	S_x	512
W200X46	2 280	318	307	294	280	265	249	1 580	221	888	M_r	134
W8X31	1 880	308	298	287	275	261	246	1 580	211	873	V_r	260
b = 203	1 480	292	285	277	267	255	242	1 580	199	852	L_u	3 460
t = 11.0	1 080	265	263	260	254	246	235	1 580	183	824	I_x	45.5
	680	225	223	221	217	211	204	1 010	159	778	S_x	448
W200X42	2 250	293	282	270	257	243	227	1 430	205	810	M_r	120
W8X28	1 850	285	275	264	252	239	225	1 430	196	796	V_r	263
b = 166	1 460	272	265	256	246	235	222	1 430	185	778	L_u	2 850
t = 11.8	1 070	249	246	242	235	227	216	1 430	171	753	I_x	40.9
	670	210	209	207	203	197	190	992	149	711	S_x	399
W200X36	2 250	255	245	233	221	209	195	1 240	179	703	M_r	103
W8X24	1 850	249	239	229	218	206	193	1 240	171	691	V_r	222
b = 165	1 460	239	232	223	214	203	191	1 240	162	676	L_u	2 730
t = 10.2	1 070	222	218	212	205	197	187	1 240	150	655	I_x	34.4
	670	188	187	185	181	176	170	992	131	621	S_x	342
W200X31	2 210	231	221	211	200	188	176	1 080	167	627	M_r	90.4
W8X21	1 830	226	217	207	197	186	175	1 080	161	618	V_r	240
b = 134	1 440	218	211	203	194	184	173	1 080	153	605	L_u	2 150
t = 10.2	1 050	205	200	194	187	179	169	1 080	141	586	I_x	31.4
	660	177	176	174	170	165	159	977	124	557	S_x	299
W200X27	2 210	197	188	179	169	159	149	915	143	534	M_r	75.3
W8X18	1 830	194	185	177	168	158	148	915	138	527	V_r	214
b = 133	1 440	188	181	173	165	156	146	915	132	516	L_u	2 050
t = 8.4	1 050	179	173	167	160	153	144	915	123	502	I_x	25.8
	660	158	157	154	150	145	139	915	109	477	S_x	249

$\dagger$ No. of studs/beam = 2 x Q_r x percent shear connection/100/q_r (per stud)

* Units — M_r — kN•m L_u — mm   b — mm
          V_r — kN I_x — 10^6mm^4 t — mm
                   S_x — 10^3mm^3

The Imperial designation for each steel beam is listed below the SI designation to assist designers involved with drawings using Imperial designations.

COMPOSITE BEAMS
Trial Selection Tables

G40.21-M 300W
20 MPa Concrete

38 mm Deck with 65 mm Slab
$\emptyset = 0.90$, $\emptyset_c = 0.67$, $\emptyset_{sc} = 0.80$

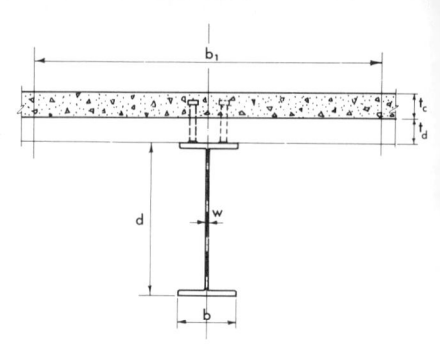

Steel Shape	Composite Beam											Steel Shape Data*	
		Factored Resistances							Properties				
	b_1	M_{rc} in kilonewton metres for various percentages of shear connection						Q_r† for 100%	I_1	S_{s_1}			
	mm	100%	90%	80%	70%	60%	50%	kN	10^6mm^4	10^3mm^3		
W610X241	1 980	2 520	2 490	2 460	2 420	2 380	2 330	1 470	3 580	8 200	M_r	2 070
W24X162	1 630	2 460	2 430	2 400	2 360	2 330	2 290	1 210	3 390	8 060	V_r	2 030
b = 329	1 290	2 390	2 360	2 330	2 310	2 270	2 240	955	3 190	7 890	L_u	5 200
t = 31.0	940	2 310	2 290	2 270	2 240	2 220	2 200	696	2 960	7 680	I_x	2 150
	590	2 220	2 210	2 190	2 180	2 160	2 150	437	2 690	7 420	S_x	6 780
W610X217	1 980	2 290	2 260	2 230	2 190	2 150	2 110	1 470	3 270	7 420	M_r	1 850
W24X146	1 630	2 230	2 200	2 170	2 140	2 100	2 060	1 210	3 100	7 290	V_r	1 850
b = 328	1 280	2 160	2 130	2 110	2 080	2 050	2 020	948	2 900	7 140	L_u	5 080
t = 27.7	940	2 080	2 060	2 040	2 020	2 000	1 970	696	2 690	6 950	I_x	1 910
	590	2 000	1 980	1 970	1 950	1 940	1 920	437	2 440	6 710	S_x	6 070
W610X195	1 980	2 060	2 040	2 010	1 970	1 930	1 890	1 470	2 970	6 650	M_r	1 640
W24X131	1 630	2 010	1 980	1 950	1 920	1 890	1 850	1 210	2 810	6 540	V_r	1 710
b = 327	1 280	1 940	1 920	1 890	1 860	1 840	1 810	948	2 630	6 410	L_u	4 940
t = 24.4	940	1 870	1 850	1 830	1 810	1 780	1 760	696	2 430	6 240	I_x	1 680
	590	1 790	1 770	1 760	1 740	1 730	1 710	437	2 190	6 010	S_x	5 400
W610X174	1 970	1 860	1 830	1 800	1 770	1 730	1 690	1 460	2 680	5 940	M_r	1 450
W24X117	1 630	1 800	1 780	1 750	1 720	1 690	1 650	1 210	2 540	5 840	V_r	1 540
b = 325	1 280	1 740	1 720	1 690	1 670	1 640	1 610	948	2 380	5 720	L_u	4 830
t = 21.6	940	1 670	1 650	1 630	1 610	1 590	1 570	696	2 190	5 570	I_x	1 470
	590	1 590	1 580	1 560	1 550	1 540	1 520	437	1 960	5 360	S_x	4 780
W610X155	1 970	1 670	1 640	1 620	1 590	1 550	1 520	1 460	2 430	5 300	M_r	1 280
W24X104	1 630	1 620	1 600	1 570	1 540	1 510	1 480	1 210	2 310	5 220	V_r	1 380
b = 324	1 280	1 560	1 540	1 520	1 490	1 470	1 440	948	2 150	5 110	L_u	4 740
t = 19.0	940	1 490	1 480	1 460	1 440	1 420	1 390	696	1 980	4 970	I_x	1 290
	590	1 420	1 400	1 390	1 380	1 360	1 350	437	1 770	4 780	S_x	4 220
W610X140	1 880	1 510	1 490	1 460	1 430	1 390	1 360	1 390	2 200	4 710	M_r	1 120
W24X94	1 550	1 460	1 440	1 410	1 380	1 350	1 320	1 150	2 080	4 630	V_r	1 440
b = 230	1 220	1 400	1 380	1 360	1 330	1 310	1 280	903	1 940	4 530	L_u	3 320
t = 22.2	890	1 330	1 320	1 300	1 280	1 260	1 230	659	1 780	4 390	I_x	1 120
	560	1 260	1 250	1 230	1 220	1 200	1 190	415	1 580	4 200	S_x	3 630
W610X125	1 880	1 360	1 340	1 320	1 290	1 260	1 220	1 390	2 000	4 210	M_r	991
W24X84	1 550	1 320	1 300	1 270	1 250	1 220	1 180	1 150	1 890	4 140	V_r	1 300
b = 229	1 220	1 260	1 240	1 220	1 200	1 170	1 140	903	1 770	4 050	L_u	3 250
t = 19.6	890	1 200	1 180	1 160	1 150	1 120	1 100	659	1 610	3 930	I_x	985
	560	1 130	1 110	1 100	1 090	1 070	1 060	415	1 430	3 760	S_x	3 220

† No. of studs/beam = 2 x Q_r x percent shear connection/100/q_r (per stud)
* Units — M_r — kN•m L_u — mm   b — mm
 V_r — kN I_x — 10^6mm^4 t — mm
    S_x — 10^3mm^3

The Imperial designation for each steel beam is listed below the SI designation to assist designers involved with drawings using Imperial designations.

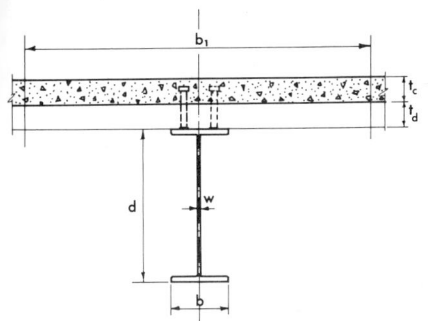

COMPOSITE BEAMS
Trial Selection Tables

G40.21-M 300W
20 MPa Concrete

38 mm Deck with 65 mm Slab
$\emptyset = 0.90$, $\emptyset_c = 0.67$, $\emptyset_{sc} = 0.80$

Steel Shape	b_1	M_{rc} in kilonewton metres for various percentages of shear connection						Q_r† for 100%	I_1	S_{s_1}	Steel Shape Data*	
		100%	90%	80%	70%	60%	50%	kN	10^6 mm^4	10^3 mm^3		
	mm											
W610X113	1 880	1 240	1 230	1 200	1 180	1 150	1 110	1 390	1 840	3 810	M_r	888
W24X76	1 550	1 200	1 180	1 160	1 140	1 110	1 080	1 150	1 740	3 750	V_r	1 210
b = 228	1 220	1 150	1 130	1 110	1 090	1 070	1 040	903	1 620	3 670	L_u	3 180
t = 17.3	890	1 090	1 070	1 060	1 040	1 020	999	659	1 480	3 560	I_x	875
	560	1 020	1 010	996	983	970	956	415	1 300	3 400	S_x	2 880
W610X101	1 880	1 130	1 110	1 090	1 070	1 040	1 010	1 390	1 670	3 420	M_r	783
W24X68	1 550	1 090	1 070	1 050	1 030	1 000	971	1 150	1 580	3 370	V_r	1 130
b = 228	1 220	1 040	1 030	1 010	984	960	933	903	1 470	3 290	L_u	3 110
t = 14.9	890	985	969	952	933	914	893	659	1 340	3 190	I_x	764
	560	915	903	891	878	865	851	415	1 180	3 040	S_x	2 530
W530X138	1 860	1 330	1 310	1 280	1 250	1 220	1 190	1 380	1 750	4 160	M_r	975
W21X93	1 540	1 280	1 260	1 240	1 210	1 180	1 150	1 140	1 650	4 090	V_r	1 440
b = 214	1 210	1 230	1 210	1 190	1 170	1 140	1 120	896	1 540	3 990	L_u	3 180
t = 23.6	880	1 170	1 150	1 130	1 120	1 100	1 080	652	1 400	3 860	I_x	861
	560	1 100	1 090	1 080	1 070	1 050	1 040	415	1 240	3 680	S_x	3 140
W530X123	1 860	1 200	1 180	1 160	1 140	1 110	1 070	1 380	1 590	3 740	M_r	867
W21X83	1 530	1 160	1 140	1 120	1 100	1 070	1 040	1 130	1 500	3 670	V_r	1 270
b = 212	1 210	1 110	1 090	1 070	1 050	1 030	1 010	896	1 400	3 590	L_u	3 100
t = 21.2	880	1 050	1 040	1 020	1 010	987	968	652	1 280	3 470	I_x	761
	560	989	978	967	955	942	929	415	1 130	3 320	S_x	2 800
W530X109	1 860	1 080	1 060	1 050	1 020	996	966	1 380	1 440	3 330	M_r	764
W21X73	1 530	1 040	1 030	1 010	986	961	934	1 130	1 360	3 280	V_r	1 110
b = 211	1 210	1 000	984	966	946	924	900	896	1 270	3 210	L_u	3 040
t = 18.8	880	946	931	916	900	882	864	652	1 160	3 100	I_x	667
	560	884	873	862	851	838	826	415	1 020	2 960	S_x	2 480
W530X101	1 860	1 010	998	982	961	935	906	1 380	1 360	3 110	M_r	707
W21X68	1 530	979	964	946	926	902	875	1 130	1 290	3 060	V_r	1 040
b = 210	1 210	938	923	906	887	866	843	896	1 200	2 990	L_u	2 990
t = 17.4	880	886	873	858	842	825	807	652	1 090	2 900	I_x	617
	560	826	816	805	794	782	769	415	960	2 770	S_x	2 300
W530X92	1 860	931	921	906	886	862	834	1 380	1 250	2 840	M_r	637
W21X62	1 530	903	889	873	853	830	804	1 130	1 190	2 790	V_r	969
b = 209	1 210	865	850	834	815	795	772	896	1 110	2 730	L_u	2 930
t = 15.6	880	815	802	787	772	755	737	652	1 010	2 650	I_x	552
	560	756	746	735	724	712	700	415	884	2 530	S_x	2 070

† No. of studs/beam = 2 x Q_r x percent shear connection/100/q_r (per stud)

* Units — M_r — kN•m L_u — mm   b — mm
        V_r — kN I_x — 10^6 mm^4 t — mm
                      S_x — 10^3 mm^3

The Imperial designation for each steel beam is listed below the SI designation to assist designers involved with drawings using Imperial designations.

COMPOSITE BEAMS
Trial Selection Tables

G40.21-M 300W
20 MPa Concrete

38 mm Deck with 65 mm Slab
$\emptyset = 0.90$, $\emptyset_c = 0.67$, $\emptyset_{sc} = 0.80$

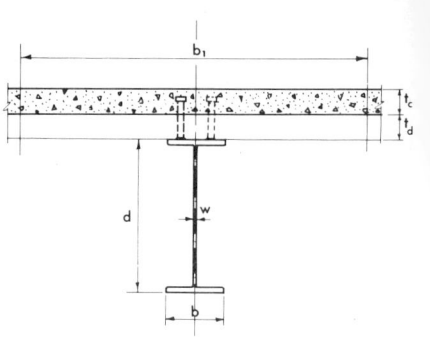

Steel Shape	b₁	Composite Beam									Steel Shape Data*	

Steel Shape	b_1	M_{rc} 100%	90%	80%	70%	60%	50%	Q_r for 100%	I_1	S_{s1}	Steel Shape Data*	
	mm	100%	90%	80%	70%	60%	50%	kN	$10^6\,mm^4$	$10^3\,mm^3$		
W530X82	1 860	836	828	815	798	776	749	1 380	1 130	2 520	M_r	559
W21X55	1 530	812	800	785	766	745	720	1 130	1 070	2 480	V_r	894
b = 209	1 210	777	764	748	731	711	689	896	1 000	2 430	L_u	2 860
t = 13.3	880	730	717	703	688	672	654	652	911	2 360	I_x	479
	560	673	663	653	642	630	618	415	796	2 250	S_x	1 810
W460X106	1 840	925	913	897	877	854	827	1 360	1 100	2 880	M_r	645
W18X71	1 520	895	881	864	845	824	800	1 130	1 040	2 830	V_r	1 050
b = 194	1 200	857	843	827	810	791	770	888	968	2 760	L_u	2 910
t = 20.6	870	808	796	783	768	753	737	644	876	2 670	I_x	488
	550	753	744	735	724	714	703	407	765	2 540	S_x	2 080
W460X97	1 840	851	842	829	812	791	766	1 360	1 020	2 650	M_r	589
W18X65	1 520	826	815	800	783	763	740	1 130	970	2 600	V_r	947
b = 193	1 200	792	780	765	749	731	711	888	904	2 540	L_u	2 870
t = 19.0	870	748	736	724	710	695	679	644	818	2 460	I_x	445
	550	695	686	677	667	657	646	407	713	2 340	S_x	1 910
W460X89	1 840	794	786	775	760	741	718	1 360	962	2 460	M_r	543
W18X60	1 520	772	762	749	733	714	692	1 130	912	2 420	V_r	866
b = 192	1 200	742	730	717	701	684	664	888	850	2 370	L_u	2 830
t = 17.7	870	700	689	676	663	649	633	644	771	2 300	I_x	410
	550	649	640	631	621	611	600	407	671	2 190	S_x	1 770
W460X82	1 840	732	724	715	702	685	663	1 360	890	2 250	M_r	494
W18X55	1 520	711	703	692	677	660	639	1 130	845	2 220	V_r	812
b = 191	1 200	684	674	662	647	631	612	888	789	2 170	L_u	2 770
t = 16.0	870	645	635	623	611	597	582	644	716	2 110	I_x	370
	550	597	588	580	570	560	550	407	622	2 010	S_x	1 610
W460X74	1 840	672	665	657	646	631	611	1 360	822	2 050	M_r	445
W18X50	1 520	652	646	636	624	607	588	1 130	781	2 020	V_r	733
b = 190	1 190	628	619	608	595	579	561	881	728	1 980	L_u	2 730
t = 14.5	870	593	584	573	561	547	533	644	663	1 920	I_x	333
	550	547	539	531	521	512	501	407	576	1 830	S_x	1 460
W460X67	1 840	623	616	608	598	584	564	1 360	761	1 880	M_r	405
W18X45	1 520	604	598	589	577	561	542	1 130	724	1 860	V_r	688
b = 190	1 190	581	572	561	548	533	515	881	676	1 820	L_u	2 660
t = 12.7	870	547	537	527	515	501	486	644	616	1 770	I_x	300
	550	501	493	484	475	465	454	407	535	1 680	S_x	1 320

† No. of studs/beam = 2 x Q_r x percent shear connection/100/q_r (per stud)

* Units — M_r — kN•m L_u — mm   b — mm
     V_r — kN I_x — $10^6\,mm^4$ t — mm
     S_x — $10^3\,mm^3$

The Imperial designation for each steel beam is listed below the SI designation to assist designers involved with drawings using Imperial designations.

COMPOSITE BEAMS
Trial Selection Tables

G40.21-M 300W
20 MPa Concrete

38 mm Deck with 65 mm Slab
$$\emptyset = 0.90, \; \emptyset_c = 0.67, \; \emptyset_{sc} = 0.80$$

Steel Shape	b_1	M_{rc} in kilonewton metres for various percentages of shear connection						$Q_r^\dagger$ for 100%	I_1	S_{s_1}	Steel Shape Data*	
	mm	100%	90%	80%	70%	60%	50%	kN	$10^6\,mm^4$	$10^3\,mm^3$		
W460X61	1 840	565	558	550	541	528	510	1 360	684	1 670	M_r	354
W18X41	1 520	546	540	533	522	507	488	1 130	652	1 650	V_r	650
b = 189	1 190	525	517	507	495	480	463	881	610	1 620	L_u	2 580
t = 10.8	870	493	484	474	462	449	435	644	557	1 570	I_x	259
	550	449	441	432	423	414	403	407	483	1 500	S_x	1 150
W410X85	1 830	691	683	674	661	645	624	1 350	772	2 150	M_r	467
W16X57	1 510	670	662	651	637	621	601	1 120	731	2 120	V_r	810
b = 181	1 190	644	634	622	609	593	576	881	681	2 070	L_u	2 730
t = 18.2	870	608	598	587	575	563	548	644	617	2 000	I_x	315
	550	562	554	546	537	528	518	407	535	1 900	S_x	1 510
W410X74	1 830	620	613	604	594	580	562	1 350	696	1 910	M_r	408
W16X50	1 510	600	594	585	573	559	540	1 120	661	1 880	V_r	714
b = 180	1 190	578	570	560	547	533	516	881	616	1 840	L_u	2 670
t = 16.0	870	546	537	527	516	503	490	644	560	1 790	I_x	275
	550	503	495	487	479	470	460	407	485	1 700	S_x	1 330
W410X67	1 830	567	560	552	542	531	514	1 350	639	1 730	M_r	367
W16X45	1 510	547	541	534	524	511	495	1 120	607	1 710	V_r	643
b = 179	1 190	527	521	512	501	487	472	881	568	1 670	L_u	2 610
t = 14.4	870	499	491	482	471	459	446	644	516	1 620	I_x	246
	550	458	451	444	436	427	418	407	447	1 550	S_x	1 200
W410X60	1 830	510	503	495	486	476	463	1 350	576	1 540	M_r	321
W16X40	1 510	491	485	478	471	460	446	1 120	549	1 520	V_r	558
b = 178	1 190	472	467	460	451	439	425	881	515	1 490	L_u	2 580
t = 12.8	870	448	442	434	424	413	401	644	469	1 450	I_x	216
	550	412	406	398	391	382	373	407	407	1 380	S_x	1 060
W410X54	1 830	465	458	451	442	433	421	1 350	518	1 370	M_r	283
W16X36	1 510	447	441	435	427	417	404	1 120	494	1 350	V_r	539
b = 177	1 190	428	423	417	408	397	383	881	464	1 330	L_u	2 480
t = 10.9	870	406	399	392	382	372	360	644	424	1 290	I_x	186
	550	371	364	357	350	342	333	407	368	1 230	S_x	924
W410X46	1 790	413	407	400	392	383	371	1 330	455	1 180	M_r	239
W16X31	1 480	396	391	385	378	369	356	1 100	436	1 170	V_r	503
b = 140	1 160	377	373	368	360	349	336	859	410	1 140	L_u	1 930
t = 11.2	850	357	351	344	336	325	314	629	375	1 110	I_x	156
	540	324	318	312	305	297	288	400	326	1 060	S_x	773

$\dagger$ No. of studs/beam = 2 x Q_r x percent shear connection/100/q_r (per stud)

* Units — M_r — kN•m L_u — mm   b — mm
  V_r — kN I_x — $10^6\,mm^4$ t — mm
  S_x — $10^3\,mm^3$

The Imperial designation for each steel beam is listed below the SI designation to assist designers involved with drawings using Imperial designations.

COMPOSITE BEAMS
Trial Selection Tables

G40.21-M 300W
20 MPa Concrete

38 mm Deck with 65 mm Slab
$\varnothing = 0.90$, $\varnothing_c = 0.67$, $\varnothing_{sc} = 0.80$

Steel Shape	b_1	M_{rc} in kilonewton metres for various percentages of shear connection						Q_r† for 100%	I_1	S_{s_1}	Steel Shape Data*	
	mm	100%	90%	80%	70%	60%	50%	kN	10^6 mm^4	10^3 mm^3		
W410X39	1 790	362	357	350	342	333	323	1 330	390	996	M_r	197
W16X26	1 480	346	341	335	328	320	310	1 100	375	984	V_r	448
b = 140	1 160	328	324	319	312	303	292	859	354	967	L_u	1 860
t = 8.8	850	309	305	298	291	281	270	629	326	943	I_x	127
	540	280	275	268	261	254	245	400	284	901	S_x	634
W360X79	1 850	571	564	555	545	535	520	1 370	577	1 830	M_r	386
W14X53	1 530	551	545	537	529	517	502	1 130	547	1 800	V_r	593
b = 205	1 200	530	524	517	507	495	481	888	508	1 760	L_u	3 270
t = 16.8	880	505	498	490	480	469	457	652	461	1 710	I_x	227
	560	468	462	455	448	440	431	415	399	1 630	S_x	1 280
W360X72	1 850	522	515	506	497	487	474	1 370	526	1 650	M_r	346
W14X48	1 530	502	496	489	481	471	458	1 130	499	1 630	V_r	536
b = 204	1 200	482	477	471	462	451	438	888	465	1 590	L_u	3 190
t = 15.1	880	459	453	446	437	427	415	652	423	1 550	I_x	201
	560	426	420	413	406	398	390	415	366	1 470	S_x	1 150
W360X64	1 850	475	468	460	451	441	430	1 370	478	1 480	M_r	308
W14X43	1 530	456	450	443	436	427	416	1 130	455	1 460	V_r	476
b = 203	1 200	436	431	426	419	409	397	888	425	1 430	L_u	3 110
t = 13.5	880	416	411	404	396	387	376	652	387	1 390	I_x	178
	560	385	380	374	367	359	351	415	335	1 330	S_x	1 030
W360X57	1 820	442	435	428	419	409	398	1 350	451	1 340	M_r	273
W14X38	1 500	423	418	411	404	395	383	1 110	429	1 320	V_r	504
b = 172	1 180	404	400	394	387	377	365	874	402	1 290	L_u	2 550
t = 13.1	860	384	378	371	363	354	343	637	366	1 250	I_x	161
	550	353	347	341	334	327	319	407	317	1 200	S_x	897
W360X51	1 820	403	397	390	381	372	361	1 350	407	1 190	M_r	241
W14X34	1 500	385	380	374	366	358	348	1 110	389	1 180	V_r	455
b = 171	1 180	367	362	357	351	342	331	874	365	1 160	L_u	2 500
t = 11.6	860	347	343	337	330	321	311	637	333	1 120	I_x	141
	550	320	315	309	302	295	287	407	289	1 070	S_x	796
W360X45	1 820	367	361	354	346	337	327	1 350	365	1 060	M_r	210
W14X30	1 500	350	344	338	331	324	314	1 110	350	1 050	V_r	433
b = 171	1 180	331	327	322	317	309	298	874	329	1 030	L_u	2 430
t = 9.8	860	313	309	303	297	288	278	637	301	999	I_x	122
	550	287	282	276	270	263	255	407	262	956	S_x	691

† No. of studs/beam = 2 x Q_r x percent shear connection/100/q_r (per stud)

* Units — M_r — kN•m L_u — mm   b — mm
 V_r — kN I_x — 10^6 mm^4 t — mm
                    S_x — 10^3 mm^3

The Imperial designation for each steel beam is listed below the SI designation to assist designers involved with drawings using Imperial designations.

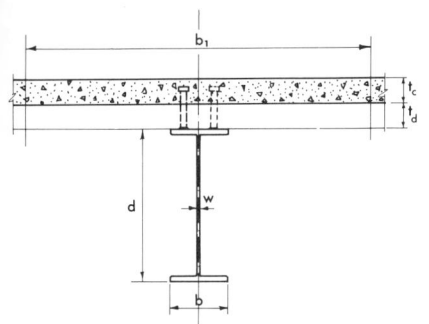

COMPOSITE BEAMS
Trial Selection Tables

G40.21-M 300W
20 MPa Concrete

38 mm Deck with 65 mm Slab
$\phi = 0.90$, $\phi_c = 0.67$, $\phi_{sc} = 0.80$

Steel Shape	b_1	M_{rc} in kilonewton metres for various percentages of shear connection						Q_r† for 100%	I_1	S_{s_1}	Steel Shape Data*	
	mm	100%	90%	80%	70%	60%	50%	kN	$10^6\,mm^4$	$10^3\,mm^3$		
W360X39	1 780	330	325	318	310	301	291	1 320	322	916	M_r	179
W14X26	1 470	314	309	303	296	288	279	1 090	309	904	V_r	409
b = 128	1 150	296	291	287	281	274	264	851	291	888	L_u	1 790
t = 10.7	840	277	274	269	262	254	245	622	267	864	I_x	102
	530	252	248	242	236	230	222	392	232	825	S_x	580
W360X33	1 780	281	275	269	261	253	244	1 130	274	766	M_r	146
W14X22	1 460	273	268	263	256	249	241	1 080	263	757	V_r	361
b = 127	1 150	256	252	247	242	236	228	851	250	745	L_u	1 720
t = 8.5	840	238	235	232	226	219	210	622	230	727	I_x	82.7
	530	217	213	208	202	196	189	392	201	695	S_x	474
W310X129	1 960	784	775	765	754	741	723	1 450	704	2 680	M_r	583
W12X87	1 610	760	753	745	733	719	703	1 190	661	2 630	V_r	742
b = 308	1 270	737	729	720	709	695	680	940	612	2 570	L_u	5 580
t = 20.6	930	706	698	689	679	668	656	689	553	2 480	I_x	308
	590	667	660	653	646	638	629	437	481	2 350	S_x	1 940
W310X118	1 960	718	709	700	690	678	662	1 450	648	2 450	M_r	526
W12X79	1 610	695	688	680	671	658	642	1 190	609	2 400	V_r	666
b = 307	1 270	673	666	658	648	635	621	940	564	2 340	L_u	5 390
t = 18.7	930	645	638	629	620	609	597	689	510	2 260	I_x	275
	590	608	601	594	587	579	570	437	442	2 150	S_x	1 750
W310X107	1 950	658	650	641	631	620	606	1 440	598	2 230	M_r	478
W12X72	1 610	636	630	622	614	602	588	1 190	564	2 190	V_r	604
b = 306	1 270	615	609	602	593	582	568	940	523	2 140	L_u	5 220
t = 17.0	930	590	584	576	567	557	545	689	473	2 070	I_x	248
	590	555	549	543	536	528	520	437	409	1 970	S_x	1 590
W310X97	1 950	603	595	586	576	565	553	1 440	550	2 030	M_r	389
W12X65	1 610	582	575	568	560	550	537	1 190	520	2 000	V_r	543
b = 305	1 270	561	555	549	541	531	519	940	483	1 950	L_u	5 410
t = 15.4	930	538	533	526	517	508	497	689	437	1 890	I_x	222
	590	506	501	494	488	480	472	437	377	1 800	S_x	1 440
W310X86	1 900	551	543	535	525	514	503	1 410	508	1 830	M_r	383
W12X58	1 570	530	524	517	509	500	488	1 160	480	1 800	V_r	503
b = 254	1 240	510	505	499	491	482	470	918	447	1 760	L_u	4 250
t = 16.3	900	488	482	476	468	459	448	666	403	1 700	I_x	199
	570	457	452	446	439	432	424	422	348	1 620	S_x	1 280

† No. of studs/beam = 2 x Q_r x percent shear connection/100/q_r (per stud)

* Units — M_r — kN•m L_u — mm b — mm
  V_r — kN I_x — $10^6\,mm^4$ t — mm
   S_x — $10^3\,mm^3$

The Imperial designation for each steel beam is listed below the SI designation to assist designers involved with drawings using Imperial designations.

COMPOSITE BEAMS
Trial Selection Tables

G40.21-M 300W
20 MPa Concrete

38 mm Deck with 65 mm Slab
$\emptyset = 0.90$, $\emptyset_c = 0.67$, $\emptyset_{sc} = 0.80$

Steel Shape	b_1	Composite Beam									Steel Shape Data*	
		Factored Resistances							Properties			
		M_{rc} in kilonewton metres for various percentages of shear connection						Q_r† for 100%	I_1	S_{s_1}		
	mm	100%	90%	80%	70%	60%	50%	kN	10^6mm^4	10^3mm^3		
W310X79	1 900	510	503	495	485	475	463	1 410	466	1 670	M_r	346
W12X53	1 570	490	484	477	469	460	449	1 160	442	1 640	V_r	480
b = 254	1 240	470	465	459	452	443	431	918	411	1 610	L_u	4 140
t = 14.6	900	448	443	437	429	420	410	666	371	1 560	I_x	177
	570	418	413	407	401	394	386	422	320	1 480	S_x	1 160
W310X74	1 850	487	480	472	462	452	440	1 370	446	1 570	M_r	321
W12X50	1 530	468	462	455	447	437	425	1 130	423	1 540	V_r	519
b = 205	1 200	447	442	436	428	418	406	888	393	1 510	L_u	3 380
t = 16.3	880	426	420	413	405	396	385	652	355	1 460	I_x	165
	560	394	389	383	377	369	362	415	306	1 390	S_x	1 060
W310X67	1 850	444	437	429	420	410	399	1 370	404	1 410	M_r	286
W12X45	1 530	425	419	413	405	396	385	1 130	384	1 390	V_r	463
b = 204	1 200	405	400	395	388	379	368	888	357	1 360	L_u	3 280
t = 14.6	880	385	380	374	367	358	348	652	324	1 320	I_x	145
	560	357	352	346	340	333	325	415	279	1 250	S_x	949
W310X60	1 850	405	398	391	382	372	361	1 370	368	1 270	M_r	254
W12X40	1 530	386	381	374	367	359	349	1 130	350	1 250	V_r	405
b = 203	1 200	367	362	357	351	344	334	888	327	1 220	L_u	3 200
t = 13.1	880	347	344	339	333	325	315	652	297	1 190	I_x	129
	560	323	318	313	307	301	293	415	256	1 130	S_x	849
W310X52	1 820	379	373	366	357	347	337	1 350	351	1 140	M_r	226
W12X35	1 500	361	356	349	342	334	325	1 110	334	1 120	V_r	429
b = 167	1 180	342	338	333	327	319	310	874	313	1 100	L_u	2 570
t = 13.2	860	323	319	314	308	300	291	637	285	1 070	I_x	118
	540	298	293	288	282	276	269	400	245	1 020	S_x	747
W310X45	1 810	335	329	322	314	305	294	1 340	305	976	M_r	191
W12X30	1 500	318	313	306	300	292	283	1 110	292	964	V_r	368
b = 166	1 180	300	295	290	285	278	270	874	275	947	L_u	2 490
t = 11.2	860	281	278	274	269	262	254	637	251	921	I_x	99.2
	540	259	255	251	245	240	233	400	216	879	S_x	634
W310X39	1 810	301	295	289	281	272	262	1 330	269	851	M_r	165
W12X26	1 500	285	280	274	267	260	252	1 110	259	841	V_r	320
b = 165	1 180	267	263	258	253	247	240	874	244	827	L_u	2 440
t = 9.7	860	249	246	242	238	232	225	637	224	807	I_x	85.1
	540	229	226	222	217	212	206	400	194	772	S_x	549

† No. of studs/beam = 2 x Q_r x percent shear connection/100/q_r (per stud)
* Units — M_r — kN•m L_u — mm   b — mm
         V_r — kN I_x — 10^6mm^4 t — mm
                   S_x — 10^3mm^3

The Imperial designation for each steel beam is listed below the SI designation to assist designers involved with drawings using Imperial designations.

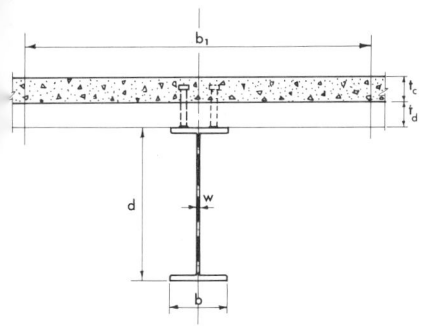

COMPOSITE BEAMS
Trial Selection Tables

G40.21-M 300W
20 MPa Concrete

38 mm Deck with 65 mm Slab
$$\emptyset = 0.90, \emptyset_C = 0.67, \emptyset_{SC} = 0.80$$

Steel Shape		Composite Beam										Steel Shape Data*	
		Factored Resistances							Properties				
	b_1	M_{rc} in kilonewton metres for various percentages of shear connection						Q_r† for 100%	I_1	S_{s_1}			
	mm	100%	90%	80%	70%	60%	50%	kN	$10^6 mm^4$	$10^3 mm^3$		
W250X101	1 910	544	536	527	517	506	493	1 410	436	1 860	M_r	378
W10X68	1 570	522	516	508	499	490	477	1 160	409	1 820	V_r	560
b = 257	1 240	501	495	489	481	471	460	918	378	1 780	L_u	4 950
t = 19.6	900	477	472	466	458	449	439	666	338	1 710	I_x	164
	570	447	442	437	431	424	417	422	289	1 610	S_x	1 240
W250X89	1 900	489	482	473	463	453	441	1 410	393	1 660	M_r	332
W10X60	1 570	469	462	455	447	438	427	1 160	370	1 630	V_r	496
b = 256	1 240	448	443	437	430	422	411	918	342	1 590	L_u	4 690
t = 17.3	900	426	422	416	409	401	391	666	307	1 530	I_x	143
	570	399	394	389	383	377	370	422	262	1 440	S_x	1 100
W250X80	1 900	445	438	430	420	410	398	1 410	357	1 490	M_r	294
W10X54	1 570	425	419	412	404	395	386	1 160	337	1 460	V_r	429
b = 255	1 240	405	400	394	388	381	371	918	312	1 430	L_u	4 520
t = 15.6	900	384	380	375	369	362	353	666	280	1 380	I_x	126
	570	359	355	350	345	339	333	422	239	1 310	S_x	982
W250X73	1 900	412	405	397	388	377	366	1 410	328	1 360	M_r	266
W10X49	1 570	392	386	380	372	363	354	1 160	311	1 340	V_r	388
b = 254	1 240	372	368	362	356	349	340	918	289	1 310	L_u	4 390
t = 14.2	900	352	348	344	338	332	323	666	259	1 260	I_x	113
	570	329	325	321	316	310	304	422	222	1 200	S_x	891
W250X67	1 850	389	382	374	365	355	344	1 370	311	1 260	M_r	243
W10X45	1 530	370	364	357	350	341	332	1 130	295	1 240	V_r	408
b = 204	1 200	350	345	340	334	327	318	888	273	1 210	L_u	3 570
t = 15.7	880	330	326	322	316	309	301	652	247	1 170	I_x	104
	560	307	303	298	293	287	281	415	211	1 110	S_x	806
W250X58	1 850	347	341	333	324	315	304	1 370	273	1 090	M_r	208
W10X39	1 530	329	323	317	309	301	292	1 130	259	1 070	V_r	359
b = 203	1 200	309	305	300	294	287	279	888	241	1 050	L_u	3 410
t = 13.5	880	290	287	283	278	271	264	652	218	1 020	I_x	87.3
	560	269	265	261	256	251	245	415	187	966	S_x	693
W250X49	1 850	305	298	291	283	274	263	1 370	233	918	M_r	171
W10X33	1 530	287	282	275	268	260	252	1 130	222	905	V_r	326
b = 202	1 200	268	264	259	253	247	240	888	208	887	L_u	3 240
t = 11.0	880	249	246	242	238	232	225	652	189	861	I_x	70.6
	560	230	226	223	218	213	207	415	162	819	S_x	572

† No. of studs/beam = 2 x Q_r x percent shear connection/100/q_r (per stud)

* Units — M_r — kN•m L_u — mm   b — mm

         V_r — kN I_x — $10^6 mm^4$ t — mm

                     S_x — $10^3 mm^3$

The Imperial designation for each steel beam is listed below the SI designation to assist designers involved with drawings using Imperial designations.

COMPOSITE BEAMS
Trial Selection Tables

G40.21-M 300W
20 MPa Concrete

38 mm Deck with 65 mm Slab
$\emptyset = 0.90$, $\emptyset_c = 0.67$, $\emptyset_{sc} = 0.80$

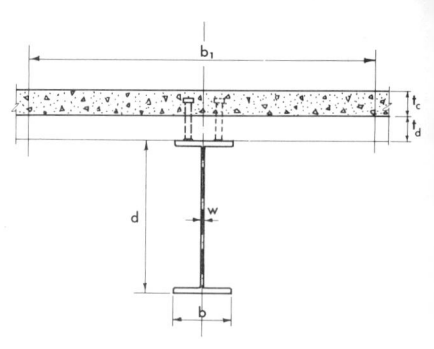

Steel Shape	b_1	Composite Beam									Steel Shape Data*	
		Factored Resistances							Properties			
		M_{rc} in kilonewton metres for various percentages of shear connection						Q_r† for 100%	I_1	S_{s1}		
	mm	100%	90%	80%	70%	60%	50%	kN	10^6mm^4	10^3mm^3		
W250X45	1 800	299	293	286	278	269	258	1 330	238	873	M_r	163
W10X30	1 480	281	276	270	263	255	247	1 100	226	860	V_r	360
b = 148	1 170	264	259	254	249	242	235	866	213	843	L_u	2 360
t = 13.0	850	245	241	237	233	227	219	629	193	818	I_x	71.1
	540	224	221	217	212	207	201	400	166	778	S_x	534
W250X39	1 800	268	262	255	248	239	229	1 330	208	754	M_r	139
W10X26	1 480	251	246	240	234	226	218	1 100	198	743	V_r	308
b = 147	1 170	234	230	225	219	213	207	866	187	730	L_u	2 280
t = 11.2	850	215	212	208	204	199	193	629	171	710	I_x	60.1
	540	197	194	190	186	181	176	400	147	677	S_x	459
W250X33	1 790	230	224	218	210	202	193	1 130	177	637	M_r	114
W10X22	1 480	222	218	212	206	199	191	1 100	170	629	V_r	280
b = 146	1 170	206	202	197	192	186	180	866	161	619	L_u	2 180
t = 9.1	850	188	185	182	178	173	167	629	148	602	I_x	48.9
	540	170	168	165	161	156	151	400	128	576	S_x	379
W200X100	1 860	471	463	454	443	432	419	1 380	336	1 620	M_r	310
W8X67	1 530	449	442	434	426	416	404	1 130	314	1 580	V_r	592
b = 210	1 210	427	422	415	408	398	387	896	288	1 530	L_u	5 020
t = 23.7	880	404	399	393	385	377	368	652	256	1 470	I_x	113
	560	375	371	366	360	354	348	415	216	1 370	S_x	989
W200X86	1 860	418	410	402	392	381	369	1 380	295	1 420	M_r	265
W8X58	1 530	397	391	383	375	366	355	1 130	277	1 390	V_r	514
b = 209	1 210	376	371	365	358	350	339	896	255	1 350	L_u	4 620
t = 20.6	880	354	350	344	338	330	321	652	226	1 290	I_x	94.7
	560	328	324	319	314	308	302	415	190	1 210	S_x	853
W200X71	1 850	357	350	342	332	322	311	1 370	250	1 180	M_r	217
W8X48	1 530	338	332	325	317	308	299	1 130	236	1 160	V_r	393
b = 206	1 210	318	313	307	301	294	286	896	218	1 130	L_u	4 150
t = 17.4	880	297	293	289	284	278	270	652	195	1 090	I_x	76.6
	560	275	272	268	263	258	252	415	164	1 020	S_x	709
W200X59	1 850	309	302	295	286	276	265	1 370	212	984	M_r	176
W8X40	1 530	290	285	278	271	263	254	1 130	200	967	V_r	341
b = 205	1 200	271	266	261	255	249	241	888	186	944	L_u	3 780
t = 14.2	880	252	248	244	240	234	227	652	167	911	I_x	61.1
	560	231	228	225	221	216	210	415	141	859	S_x	582

† No. of studs/beam = 2 x Q_r x percent shear connection/100/q_r (per stud)

* Units — M_r — kN•m L_u — mm   b — mm
  V_r — kN I_x — 10^6mm^4 t — mm
  S_x — 10^3mm^3

The Imperial designation for each steel beam is listed below the SI designation to assist designers involved with drawings using Imperial designations.

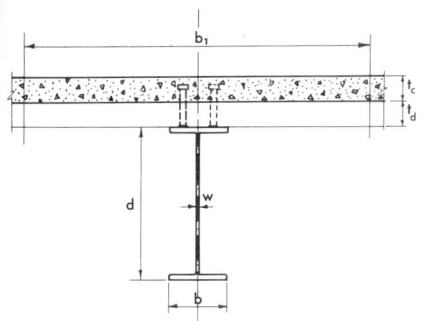

COMPOSITE BEAMS
Trial Selection Tables

G40.21-M 300W
20 MPa Concrete

38 mm Deck with 65 mm Slab
$\emptyset = 0.90$, $\emptyset_C = 0.67$, $\emptyset_{SC} = 0.80$

Steel Shape		Composite Beam										Steel Shape Data*	
		Factored Resistances								Properties			
	b_1	M_{rc} in kilonewton metres for various percentages of shear connection						Q_r† for 100%	I_1	S_{s_1}			
	mm	100%	90%	80%	70%	60%	50%	kN	$10^6 mm^4$	$10^3 mm^3$			
W200X52	1 850	281	275	267	259	250	239	1 370	189	871	M_r	154
W8X35	1 530	263	258	251	244	236	227	1 130	179	856	V_r	290
b = 204	1 200	244	240	235	229	222	215	888	167	837	L_u	3 620
t = 12.6	880	225	222	218	214	209	203	652	150	810	I_x	52.7
	560	206	203	200	197	192	187	415	128	766	S_x	512
W200X46	1 850	257	251	244	236	227	216	1 370	169	769	M_r	134
W8X31	1 530	240	234	228	221	214	205	1 130	161	758	V_r	260
b = 203	1 200	221	217	212	206	200	193	888	150	741	L_u	3 460
t = 11.0	880	203	199	196	191	187	181	652	136	719	I_x	45.5
	560	184	181	179	175	171	166	415	116	681	S_x	448
W200X42	1 810	241	236	229	221	212	202	1 340	157	700	M_r	120
W8X28	1 500	225	220	214	207	199	191	1 110	150	690	V_r	263
b = 166	1 180	207	203	198	192	186	179	874	140	675	L_u	2 850
t = 11.8	860	188	185	181	177	173	167	637	127	655	I_x	40.9
	540	169	167	164	161	157	152	400	108	620	S_x	399
W200X36	1 810	215	209	202	194	186	177	1 240	137	606	M_r	103
W8X24	1 500	202	198	192	185	178	170	1 110	131	597	V_r	222
b = 165	1 180	185	181	176	171	165	159	874	123	586	L_u	2 730
t = 10.2	860	167	164	161	157	152	147	637	112	569	I_x	34.4
	540	149	146	144	141	138	133	400	95.8	540	S_x	342
W200X31	1 780	196	190	184	176	168	160	1 080	129	542	M_r	90.4
W8X21	1 470	190	185	180	173	166	158	1 080	123	534	V_r	240
b = 134	1 160	174	170	165	160	154	148	859	116	524	L_u	2 150
t = 10.2	850	156	153	150	146	142	137	629	107	510	I_x	31.4
	530	138	136	133	130	127	122	392	91.5	485	S_x	299
W200X27	1 780	168	163	157	150	143	135	915	111	461	M_r	75.3
W8X18	1 470	164	159	154	148	141	134	915	106	454	V_r	214
b = 133	1 160	155	152	147	142	137	130	859	101	446	L_u	2 050
t = 8.4	850	139	136	132	129	124	120	629	92.9	435	I_x	25.8
	530	120	119	116	114	110	106	392	80.3	415	S_x	249

† No. of studs/beam = 2 x Q_r x percent shear connection/100/q_r (per stud)

* Units — M_r — kN•m L_u — mm   b — mm
              V_r — kN I_x — $10^6 mm^4$ t — mm
                            S_x — $10^3 mm^3$

The Imperial designation for each steel beam is listed below the SI designation to assist designers involved with drawings using Imperial designations.

COMPOSITE BEAMS
Trial Selection Tables

G40.21-M 300W
20 MPa Concrete

51 mm Deck with 65 mm Slab
$\varnothing = 0.90$, $\varnothing_c = 0.67$, $\varnothing_{sc} = 0.80$

Steel Shape	b_1	Composite Beam Factored Resistances M_{rc} in kilonewton metres for various percentages of shear connection						Q_r† for 100%	Properties I_1	S_{s_1}	Steel Shape Data*	
	mm	100%	90%	80%	70%	60%	50%	kN	10^6 mm^4	10^3 mm^3		
W610X241	2 190	2 580	2 550	2 510	2 460	2 420	2 370	1 620	3 780	8 420	M_r	2 070
W24X162	1 800	2 510	2 480	2 440	2 400	2 360	2 320	1 330	3 580	8 270	V_r	2 030
b = 329	1 420	2 430	2 400	2 370	2 340	2 300	2 270	1 050	3 350	8 080	L_u	5 200
t = 31.0	1 040	2 340	2 320	2 290	2 270	2 240	2 210	770	3 090	7 850	I_x	2 150
	660	2 250	2 230	2 210	2 200	2 180	2 160	489	2 790	7 560	S_x	6 780
W610X217	2 180	2 340	2 310	2 270	2 230	2 190	2 140	1 610	3 460	7 620	M_r	1 850
W24X146	1 800	2 270	2 240	2 210	2 170	2 130	2 090	1 330	3 270	7 490	V_r	1 850
b = 328	1 420	2 200	2 170	2 140	2 110	2 080	2 040	1 050	3 060	7 320	L_u	5 080
t = 27.7	1 040	2 110	2 090	2 070	2 040	2 020	1 990	770	2 810	7 110	I_x	1 910
	660	2 020	2 010	1 990	1 970	1 950	1 940	489	2 530	6 840	S_x	6 070
W610X195	2 180	2 110	2 090	2 050	2 010	1 970	1 920	1 610	3 140	6 840	M_r	1 640
W24X131	1 800	2 050	2 020	1 990	1 960	1 920	1 880	1 330	2 970	6 720	V_r	1 710
b = 327	1 420	1 980	1 950	1 930	1 900	1 860	1 830	1 050	2 780	6 580	L_u	4 940
t = 24.4	1 040	1 900	1 880	1 860	1 830	1 810	1 780	770	2 550	6 390	I_x	1 680
	650	1 810	1 790	1 780	1 760	1 740	1 730	481	2 270	6 120	S_x	5 400
W610X174	2 180	1 900	1 880	1 850	1 810	1 770	1 730	1 610	2 850	6 110	M_r	1 450
W24X117	1 800	1 850	1 820	1 790	1 760	1 720	1 680	1 330	2 690	6 010	V_r	1 540
b = 325	1 420	1 780	1 760	1 730	1 700	1 670	1 640	1 050	2 510	5 880	L_u	4 830
t = 21.6	1 040	1 700	1 680	1 660	1 640	1 610	1 590	770	2 300	5 710	I_x	1 470
	650	1 610	1 600	1 580	1 570	1 550	1 530	481	2 040	5 470	S_x	4 780
W610X155	2 180	1 710	1 690	1 660	1 630	1 590	1 550	1 610	2 590	5 460	M_r	1 280
W24X104	1 800	1 660	1 640	1 610	1 580	1 540	1 510	1 330	2 450	5 370	V_r	1 380
b = 324	1 420	1 600	1 580	1 550	1 520	1 490	1 460	1 050	2 280	5 250	L_u	4 740
t = 19.0	1 040	1 530	1 510	1 480	1 460	1 440	1 410	770	2 090	5 100	I_x	1 290
	650	1 440	1 420	1 410	1 390	1 380	1 360	481	1 840	4 880	S_x	4 220
W610X140	2 090	1 560	1 530	1 500	1 470	1 430	1 390	1 550	2 350	4 870	M_r	1 120
W24X94	1 720	1 500	1 480	1 450	1 420	1 380	1 350	1 270	2 220	4 780	V_r	1 440
b = 230	1 360	1 440	1 420	1 390	1 360	1 330	1 300	1 010	2 070	4 670	L_u	3 320
t = 22.2	990	1 360	1 340	1 320	1 300	1 280	1 250	733	1 880	4 520	I_x	1 120
	630	1 280	1 270	1 250	1 240	1 220	1 200	466	1 660	4 310	S_x	3 630
W610X125	2 090	1 400	1 380	1 360	1 330	1 290	1 250	1 550	2 140	4 350	M_r	991
W24X84	1 720	1 360	1 330	1 310	1 280	1 250	1 210	1 270	2 020	4 280	V_r	1 300
b = 229	1 360	1 300	1 280	1 250	1 230	1 200	1 170	1 010	1 880	4 180	L_u	3 250
t = 19.6	990	1 230	1 210	1 190	1 170	1 150	1 120	733	1 710	4 050	I_x	985
	630	1 150	1 130	1 120	1 100	1 090	1 070	466	1 500	3 860	S_x	3 220

† No. of studs/beam = 2 x Q$_r$ x percent shear connection/100/q$_r$ (per stud)

* Units —   M$_r$ — kN•m   L$_u$ — mm   b — mm
          V$_r$ — kN   I$_x$ — 10^6 mm^4 t — mm
                   S$_x$ — 10^3 mm^3

The Imperial designation for each steel beam is listed below the SI designation to assist designers involved with drawings using Imperial designations.

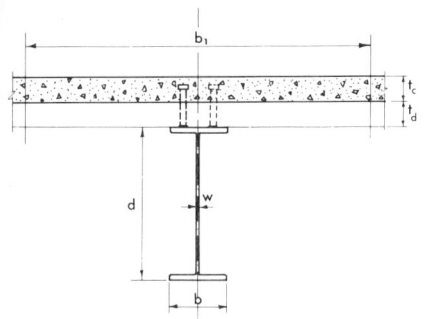

COMPOSITE BEAMS
Trial Selection Tables

G40.21-M 300W
20 MPa Concrete

51 mm Deck with 65 mm Slab
$\varnothing = 0.90$, $\varnothing_c = 0.67$, $\varnothing_{sc} = 0.80$

Steel Shape	b₁	Composite Beam Factored Resistances — M_{rc} in kilonewton metres for various percentages of shear connection						Q_r† for 100%	Properties I₁	S₁ₛ	Steel Shape Data*	
	mm	100%	90%	80%	70%	60%	50%	kN	10⁶mm⁴	10³mm³		
W610X113	2 080	1 280	1 270	1 240	1 210	1 180	1 140	1 540	1 960	3 940	M_r	888
W24X76	1 720	1 240	1 220	1 200	1 170	1 140	1 100	1 270	1 860	3 870	V_r	1 210
b = 228	1 350	1 190	1 170	1 140	1 120	1 090	1 060	999	1 730	3 790	L_u	3 180
t = 17.3	990	1 120	1 100	1 080	1 060	1 040	1 020	733	1 570	3 670	I_x	875
	630	1 040	1 030	1 010	1 000	984	968	466	1 380	3 500	S_x	2 880
W610X101	2 080	1 170	1 150	1 130	1 100	1 070	1 040	1 540	1 780	3 540	M_r	783
W24X68	1 720	1 130	1 110	1 090	1 060	1 030	997	1 270	1 690	3 480	V_r	1 130
b = 228	1 350	1 080	1 060	1 040	1 010	984	955	999	1 570	3 400	L_u	3 110
t = 14.9	990	1 010	996	977	956	934	911	733	1 430	3 290	I_x	764
	630	937	923	909	894	879	863	466	1 250	3 140	S_x	2 530
W530X138	2 070	1 370	1 350	1 320	1 290	1 260	1 220	1 530	1 880	4 310	M_r	975
W21X93	1 710	1 320	1 300	1 280	1 250	1 210	1 180	1 270	1 770	4 230	V_r	1 440
b = 214	1 350	1 270	1 240	1 220	1 200	1 170	1 140	999	1 640	4 130	L_u	3 180
t = 23.6	980	1 200	1 180	1 160	1 140	1 120	1 100	726	1 490	3 980	I_x	861
	620	1 120	1 110	1 090	1 080	1 060	1 050	459	1 300	3 780	S_x	3 140
W530X123	2 070	1 240	1 220	1 200	1 170	1 140	1 100	1 530	1 710	3 880	M_r	867
W21X83	1 710	1 200	1 180	1 160	1 130	1 100	1 070	1 270	1 620	3 810	V_r	1 270
b = 212	1 340	1 150	1 130	1 100	1 080	1 050	1 030	992	1 500	3 710	L_u	3 100
t = 21.2	980	1 080	1 060	1 050	1 030	1 010	984	726	1 360	3 590	I_x	761
	620	1 010	995	982	969	954	940	459	1 190	3 410	S_x	2 800
W530X109	2 070	1 120	1 100	1 080	1 060	1 030	995	1 530	1 550	3 460	M_r	764
W21X73	1 710	1 080	1 060	1 040	1 020	991	960	1 270	1 470	3 400	V_r	1 110
b = 211	1 340	1 030	1 010	994	972	947	921	992	1 360	3 320	L_u	3 040
t = 18.8	980	973	957	939	921	901	880	726	1 240	3 210	I_x	667
	620	902	890	877	864	850	836	459	1 080	3 050	S_x	2 480
W530X101	2 070	1 050	1 030	1 020	994	967	935	1 530	1 460	3 220	M_r	707
W21X68	1 700	1 010	998	978	956	929	900	1 260	1 380	3 170	V_r	1 040
b = 210	1 340	969	952	933	912	888	863	992	1 290	3 100	L_u	2 990
t = 17.4	980	913	897	881	863	843	822	726	1 170	3 000	I_x	617
	620	844	833	820	807	794	779	459	1 020	2 850	S_x	2 300
W530X92	2 070	965	954	939	919	893	862	1 530	1 350	2 940	M_r	637
W21X62	1 700	935	921	904	882	857	828	1 260	1 280	2 890	V_r	969
b = 209	1 340	894	879	861	840	817	792	992	1 190	2 830	L_u	2 930
t = 15.6	980	841	826	810	792	773	752	726	1 080	2 740	I_x	552
	620	774	762	750	737	724	710	459	938	2 610	S_x	2 070

† No. of studs/beam = 2 x Q_r x percent shear connection/100/q_r (per stud)

* Units — M_r — kN•m L_u — mm   b — mm
  V_r — kN I_x — 10⁶mm⁴   t — mm
  S_x — 10³mm³

The Imperial designation for each steel beam is listed below the SI designation to assist designers involved with drawings using Imperial designations.

COMPOSITE BEAMS
Trial Selection Tables

G40.21-M 300W
20 MPa Concrete

51 mm Deck with 65 mm Slab
$\emptyset = 0.90$, $\emptyset_c = 0.67$, $\emptyset_{sc} = 0.80$

Steel Shape	b_1	Factored Resistances M_{rc} in kilonewton metres for various percentages of shear connection						$Q_r^\dagger$ for 100%	Properties I_1	S_{s1}	Steel Shape Data*	
	mm	100%	90%	80%	70%	60%	50%	kN	$10^6\,mm^4$	$10^3\,mm^3$		
W530X82	2 070	869	859	846	828	805	776	1 530	1 210	2 620	M_r	559
W21X55	1 700	842	830	814	795	771	743	1 260	1 150	2 580	V_r	894
b = 209	1 340	805	791	774	755	733	708	992	1 080	2 520	L_u	2 860
t = 13.3	980	755	741	725	708	690	670	726	978	2 440	I_x	479
	620	691	679	668	655	642	628	459	847	2 320	S_x	1 810
W460X106	2 050	960	947	931	910	884	854	1 520	1 190	3 000	M_r	645
W18X71	1 690	928	913	895	874	850	823	1 250	1 120	2 950	V_r	1 050
b = 194	1 330	886	871	853	834	812	788	985	1 040	2 870	L_u	2 910
t = 20.6	970	833	819	804	788	770	752	718	943	2 770	I_x	488
	620	772	762	750	739	726	713	459	818	2 630	S_x	2 080
W460X97	2 050	885	874	861	842	820	792	1 520	1 110	2 760	M_r	589
W18X65	1 690	857	845	829	810	788	762	1 250	1 050	2 710	V_r	947
b = 193	1 330	820	806	791	772	752	729	985	974	2 650	L_u	2 870
t = 19.0	970	772	759	744	729	712	694	718	881	2 560	I_x	445
	610	712	702	691	680	668	655	452	760	2 420	S_x	1 910
W460X89	2 050	828	817	805	789	769	743	1 520	1 040	2 570	M_r	543
W18X60	1 690	801	791	777	760	739	714	1 250	986	2 520	V_r	866
b = 192	1 330	768	756	741	724	704	682	985	917	2 470	L_u	2 830
t = 17.7	970	723	710	697	682	665	648	718	831	2 390	I_x	410
	610	665	655	645	634	622	610	452	716	2 260	S_x	1 770
W460X82	2 050	764	754	743	729	711	687	1 520	964	2 350	M_r	494
W18X55	1 690	739	730	718	702	683	660	1 250	914	2 310	V_r	812
b = 191	1 330	709	698	685	669	651	630	985	852	2 260	L_u	2 770
t = 16.0	970	667	656	643	629	613	596	718	772	2 190	I_x	370
	610	612	603	593	582	571	559	452	666	2 080	S_x	1 610
W460X74	2 050	705	695	684	671	655	634	1 520	889	2 140	M_r	445
W18X50	1 690	679	671	661	648	630	609	1 250	845	2 110	V_r	733
b = 190	1 330	653	643	631	617	599	579	985	789	2 070	L_u	2 730
t = 14.5	970	615	604	592	579	563	547	718	717	2 000	I_x	333
	610	563	554	544	533	522	510	452	618	1 900	S_x	1 460
W460X67	2 050	655	646	635	623	608	587	1 520	823	1 960	M_r	405
W18X45	1 690	631	622	613	600	583	562	1 250	784	1 940	V_r	688
b = 190	1 330	605	596	584	570	553	533	985	733	1 900	L_u	2 660
t = 12.7	970	568	558	546	532	517	500	718	667	1 840	I_x	300
	610	516	507	497	487	476	464	452	575	1 750	S_x	1 320

† No. of studs/beam = 2 x Q_r x percent shear connection/100/q_r (per stud)
* Units — M_r — kN•m L_u — mm   b — mm
           V_r — kN I_x — $10^6\,mm^4$ t — mm
                       S_x — $10^3\,mm^3$

The Imperial designation for each steel beam is listed below the SI designation to assist designers involved with drawings using Imperial designations.

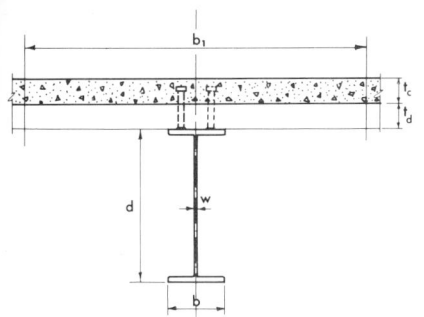

COMPOSITE BEAMS
Trial Selection Tables

G40.21-M 300W
20 MPa Concrete

51 mm Deck with 65 mm Slab
$\phi = 0.90$, $\phi_c = 0.67$, $\phi_{sc} = 0.80$

Steel Shape	Composite Beam								Properties		Steel Shape Data*	
		Factored Resistances										
	b_1	M_{rc} in kilonewton metres for various percentages of shear connection						Q_r† for 100%	I_1	S_{s_1}		
	mm	100%	90%	80%	70%	60%	50%	kN	10^6 mm^4	10^3 mm^3		
W460X61	2 050	597	587	577	565	552	532	1 520	741	1 750	M_r	354
W18X41	1 690	572	565	556	544	529	508	1 250	706	1 720	V_r	650
b = 189	1 330	548	540	529	516	500	481	985	662	1 690	L_u	2 580
t = 10.8	970	514	504	493	480	465	449	718	603	1 640	I_x	259
	610	464	455	446	435	424	412	452	520	1 560	S_x	1 150
W410X85	2 040	724	714	702	688	671	648	1 510	841	2 250	M_r	467
W16X57	1 680	698	689	677	662	644	622	1 240	796	2 210	V_r	810
b = 181	1 320	668	658	645	630	613	593	977	739	2 160	L_u	2 730
t = 18.2	970	629	618	606	593	578	562	718	669	2 090	I_x	315
	610	577	568	559	549	538	527	452	575	1 980	S_x	1 510
W410X74	2 040	653	643	632	619	604	584	1 510	758	2 000	M_r	408
W16X50	1 680	627	619	609	597	580	560	1 240	719	1 970	V_r	714
b = 180	1 320	601	592	581	567	551	533	977	670	1 930	L_u	2 670
t = 16.0	970	566	556	545	533	519	503	718	608	1 870	I_x	275
	610	517	509	500	490	480	469	452	522	1 770	S_x	1 330
W410X67	2 040	599	589	578	566	553	536	1 510	695	1 810	M_r	367
W16X45	1 680	574	566	556	546	532	514	1 240	661	1 780	V_r	643
b = 179	1 320	548	541	532	520	505	488	977	617	1 750	L_u	2 610
t = 14.4	970	518	509	499	487	474	459	718	561	1 700	I_x	246
	610	473	465	456	447	437	426	452	483	1 610	S_x	1 200
W410X60	2 030	540	531	521	509	497	482	1 500	626	1 610	M_r	321
W16X40	1 680	517	509	500	490	479	464	1 240	597	1 580	V_r	558
b = 178	1 320	492	486	478	469	456	440	977	560	1 550	L_u	2 580
t = 12.8	970	466	459	450	440	427	413	718	511	1 510	I_x	216
	610	426	418	410	402	392	382	452	440	1 440	S_x	1 060
W410X54	2 030	495	487	477	465	453	439	1 500	563	1 430	M_r	283
W16X36	1 680	473	465	456	447	436	421	1 240	538	1 410	V_r	539
b = 177	1 320	448	442	435	426	414	398	977	506	1 390	L_u	2 480
t = 10.9	970	423	416	408	398	386	372	718	462	1 350	I_x	186
	610	384	377	369	361	351	341	452	399	1 280	S_x	924
W410X46	2 000	444	436	426	415	403	390	1 480	496	1 240	M_r	239
W16X31	1 650	422	414	406	397	386	373	1 220	475	1 220	V_r	503
b = 140	1 300	398	392	385	377	366	352	962	448	1 200	L_u	1 930
t = 11.2	950	374	368	360	350	339	326	703	410	1 170	I_x	156
	600	338	331	323	315	306	296	444	355	1 110	S_x	773

† No. of studs/beam = 2 x Q_r x percent shear connection/100/q_r (per stud)

* Units — M_r — kN•m L_u — mm   b — mm

V_r — kN I_x — 10^6 mm^4 t — mm

S_x — 10^3 mm^3

The Imperial designation for each steel beam is listed below the SI designation to assist designers involved with drawings using Imperial designations.

COMPOSITE BEAMS
Trial Selection Tables

G40.21-M 300W
20 MPa Concrete

51 mm Deck with 65 mm Slab
$\emptyset = 0.90$, $\emptyset_c = 0.67$, $\emptyset_{sc} = 0.80$

Steel Shape	b_1	M_{rc} in kilonewton metres for various percentages of shear connection						Q_r† for 100%	I_1	S_{s_1}	Steel Shape Data*	
	mm	100%	90%	80%	70%	60%	50%	kN	$10^6 mm^4$	$10^3 mm^3$		
W410X39	2 000	385	377	368	358	346	334	1 350	425	1 040	M_r	197
W16X26	1 650	371	364	356	347	337	325	1 220	409	1 030	V_r	448
b = 140	1 300	348	342	336	329	319	306	962	387	1 010	L_u	1 860
t = 8.8	950	325	320	313	305	295	282	703	356	989	I_x	127
	600	293	287	280	272	263	253	444	310	945	S_x	634
W360X79	2 060	604	593	582	570	556	540	1 530	633	1 920	M_r	386
W14X53	1 700	578	569	560	549	537	520	1 260	599	1 890	V_r	593
b = 205	1 340	552	545	537	526	513	497	992	558	1 850	L_u	3 270
t = 16.8	980	523	516	506	496	483	470	726	504	1 790	I_x	227
	620	482	475	467	458	449	439	459	432	1 700	S_x	1 280
W360X72	2 060	554	544	533	521	508	493	1 530	577	1 740	M_r	346
W14X48	1 700	529	521	511	501	490	475	1 260	548	1 710	V_r	536
b = 204	1 340	504	497	489	480	468	453	992	511	1 670	L_u	3 190
t = 15.1	980	477	470	462	452	440	427	726	463	1 620	I_x	201
	620	439	432	425	416	407	398	459	397	1 540	S_x	1 150
W360X64	2 060	507	497	487	475	462	448	1 530	525	1 560	M_r	308
W14X43	1 700	482	474	465	456	445	432	1 260	499	1 540	V_r	476
b = 203	1 340	458	451	444	436	425	412	992	467	1 510	L_u	3 110
t = 13.5	980	432	427	419	411	400	388	726	424	1 460	I_x	178
	620	398	392	385	377	368	359	459	365	1 390	S_x	1 030
W360X57	2 030	473	464	454	443	430	416	1 500	494	1 400	M_r	273
W14X38	1 670	449	442	433	423	413	400	1 240	471	1 380	V_r	504
b = 172	1 320	425	419	412	404	393	380	977	442	1 360	L_u	2 550
t = 13.1	960	400	394	387	378	367	355	711	401	1 320	I_x	161
	610	366	359	352	345	336	327	452	346	1 250	S_x	897
W360X51	2 030	434	426	416	405	392	379	1 500	447	1 250	M_r	241
W14X34	1 670	411	404	395	386	375	364	1 240	427	1 240	V_r	455
b = 171	1 320	388	381	374	367	358	345	977	401	1 220	L_u	2 500
t = 11.6	960	363	358	352	343	334	322	711	366	1 180	I_x	141
	610	332	326	320	312	304	295	452	316	1 130	S_x	796
W360X45	2 030	398	389	380	369	357	344	1 500	401	1 110	M_r	210
W14X30	1 670	375	368	360	350	340	329	1 240	384	1 100	V_r	433
b = 171	1 320	352	346	339	332	323	312	977	362	1 080	L_u	2 430
t = 9.8	960	328	323	318	310	301	289	711	331	1 050	I_x	122
	610	299	293	287	280	272	263	452	287	1 000	S_x	691

† No. of studs/beam = 2 x Q_r x percent shear connection/100/q_r (per stud)

* Units — M_r — kN•m L_u — mm   b — mm
  V_r — kN I_x — $10^6 mm^4$ t — mm
  S_x — $10^3 mm^3$

The Imperial designation for each steel beam is listed below the SI designation to assist designers involved with drawings using Imperial designations.

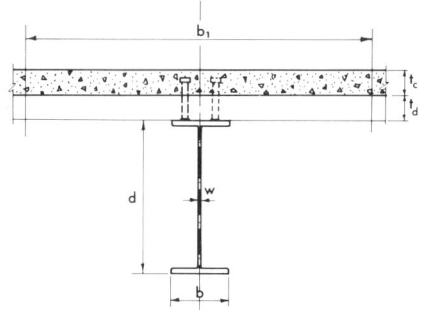

COMPOSITE BEAMS
Trial Selection Tables

G40.21-M 300W
20 MPa Concrete

51 mm Deck with 65 mm Slab
$\phi = 0.90$, $\phi_c = 0.67$, $\phi_{sc} = 0.80$

Steel Shape		Composite Beam									Steel Shape Data *	
		Factored Resistances							Properties			
	b_1	M_{rc} in kilonewton metres for various percentages of shear connection						Q_r † for 100%	I_1	S_{s_1}		
	mm	100%	90%	80%	70%	60%	50%	kN	10^6mm⁴	10^3mm³		
W360X39	1 980	353	345	336	326	314	302	1 340	353	963	M_r	179
W14X26	1 640	339	332	324	315	305	294	1 210	340	952	V_r	409
b = 128	1 290	316	310	304	296	288	277	955	321	935	L_u	1 790
t = 10.7	940	292	288	283	276	267	256	696	295	911	I_x	102
	600	265	260	254	247	239	231	444	256	870	S_x	580
W360X33	1 980	299	291	283	273	263	252	1 130	300	807	M_r	146
W14X22	1 640	293	286	279	270	261	251	1 130	289	797	V_r	361
b = 127	1 290	276	271	264	257	250	240	955	275	785	L_u	1 720
t = 8.5	940	253	249	244	238	231	221	696	254	766	I_x	82.7
	590	228	223	218	212	204	196	437	221	733	S_x	474
W310X129	2 160	817	806	793	779	764	744	1 600	774	2 820	M_r	583
W12X87	1 790	790	780	769	757	741	722	1 330	728	2 770	V_r	742
b = 308	1 410	761	752	742	729	714	697	1 040	671	2 700	L_u	5 580
t = 20.6	1 030	726	717	707	695	682	668	763	602	2 600	I_x	308
	650	681	673	665	656	647	637	481	517	2 450	S_x	1 940
W310X118	2 160	751	740	728	714	700	682	1 600	712	2 570	M_r	526
W12X79	1 780	723	714	704	692	678	661	1 320	670	2 530	V_r	666
b = 307	1 410	696	688	679	667	653	637	1 040	620	2 460	L_u	5 390
t = 18.7	1 030	664	656	646	635	623	609	763	556	2 370	I_x	275
	650	621	614	606	598	588	578	481	476	2 240	S_x	1 750
W310X107	2 160	692	681	669	656	641	625	1 600	659	2 350	M_r	478
W12X72	1 780	664	655	645	634	622	606	1 320	621	2 310	V_r	604
b = 306	1 410	637	630	622	612	599	584	1 040	575	2 250	L_u	5 220
t = 17.0	1 030	608	601	592	582	570	557	763	517	2 180	I_x	248
	650	568	562	554	546	537	528	481	442	2 060	S_x	1 590
W310X97	2 160	636	626	614	601	587	572	1 600	607	2 140	M_r	389
W12X65	1 780	609	600	591	580	568	554	1 320	573	2 100	V_r	543
b = 305	1 400	582	575	567	558	547	533	1 040	530	2 050	L_u	5 410
t = 15.4	1 030	555	549	541	532	521	509	763	478	1 990	I_x	222
	650	519	513	505	498	489	480	481	409	1 880	S_x	1 440
W310X86	2 110	584	573	562	549	536	521	1 560	560	1 930	M_r	383
W12X58	1 740	558	549	539	529	517	504	1 290	530	1 900	V_r	503
b = 254	1 370	531	524	516	508	497	484	1 010	491	1 850	L_u	4 250
t = 16.3	1 000	504	498	491	482	472	460	740	442	1 790	I_x	199
	630	469	463	457	449	441	432	466	378	1 700	S_x	1 280

† No. of studs/beam = 2 x Q_r x percent shear connection/100/q_r (per stud)

* Units — M_r — kN•m L_u — mm b — mm
  V_r — kN I_x — 10^6mm⁴ t — mm
  S_x — 10^3mm³

The Imperial designation for each steel beam is listed below the SI designation to assist designers involved with drawings using Imperial designations.

COMPOSITE BEAMS
Trial Selection Tables

G40.21-M 300W
20 MPa Concrete

51 mm Deck with 65 mm Slab
$\emptyset = 0.90$, $\emptyset_C = 0.67$, $\emptyset_{SC} = 0.80$

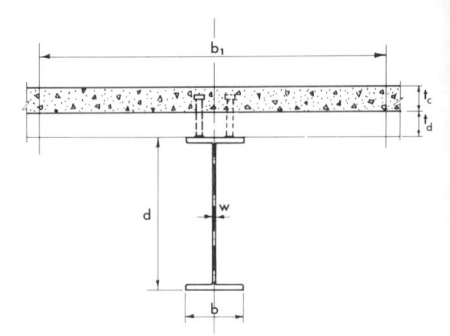

Steel Shape	b_1	Composite Beam									Steel Shape Data*	
		Factored Resistances							Properties			
		M_{rc} in kilonewton metres for various percentages of shear connection						Q_r† for 100%	I_1	S_{s_1}		
	mm	100%	90%	80%	70%	60%	50%	kN	$10^6\,mm^4$	$10^3\,mm^3$		
W310X79	2 110	543	533	522	509	496	481	1 560	516	1 760	M_r	346
W12X53	1 740	517	509	499	489	478	465	1 290	488	1 730	V_r	480
b = 254	1 370	491	484	477	469	458	445	1 010	453	1 700	L_u	4 140
t = 14.6	1 000	465	459	452	443	433	421	740	409	1 640	I_x	177
	630	431	425	418	411	402	393	466	348	1 550	S_x	1 160
W310X74	2 060	520	510	499	487	473	459	1 530	494	1 660	M_r	321
W12X50	1 700	495	486	477	467	455	441	1 260	467	1 630	V_r	519
b = 205	1 340	469	462	454	446	435	421	992	435	1 590	L_u	3 380
t = 16.3	980	442	436	429	420	409	397	726	392	1 540	I_x	165
	620	407	401	394	387	378	369	459	334	1 460	S_x	1 060
W310X67	2 060	476	467	456	444	431	417	1 530	448	1 490	M_r	286
W12X45	1 700	452	444	435	425	414	401	1 260	425	1 470	V_r	463
b = 204	1 340	427	420	413	405	395	382	992	396	1 430	L_u	3 280
t = 14.6	980	401	396	389	381	371	360	726	358	1 390	I_x	145
	620	369	363	357	350	342	333	459	306	1 320	S_x	949
W310X60	2 060	437	427	417	406	393	379	1 530	407	1 340	M_r	254
W12X40	1 700	413	405	396	386	376	364	1 260	388	1 320	V_r	405
b = 203	1 340	388	382	375	367	358	347	992	362	1 290	L_u	3 200
t = 13.1	980	363	358	353	346	337	326	726	329	1 250	I_x	129
	620	334	329	323	317	309	301	459	282	1 190	S_x	849
W310X52	2 020	410	401	391	380	368	354	1 500	387	1 200	M_r	226
W12X35	1 670	387	379	371	361	351	339	1 240	369	1 180	V_r	429
b = 167	1 310	363	356	349	342	333	322	970	346	1 160	L_u	2 570
t = 13.2	960	338	333	328	321	312	302	711	315	1 130	I_x	118
	610	310	305	299	293	285	277	452	271	1 070	S_x	747
W310X45	2 020	365	357	347	337	325	312	1 500	337	1 030	M_r	191
W12X30	1 670	343	336	328	319	308	297	1 240	323	1 020	V_r	368
b = 166	1 310	320	314	307	300	292	282	970	303	999	L_u	2 490
t = 11.2	960	296	291	286	281	273	264	711	278	973	I_x	99.2
	610	271	266	261	255	248	241	452	240	928	S_x	634
W310X39	2 020	323	315	305	295	284	272	1 330	297	898	M_r	165
W12X26	1 670	310	303	295	286	276	266	1 240	286	888	V_r	320
b = 165	1 310	287	281	275	268	260	251	970	270	873	L_u	2 440
t = 9.7	960	264	260	255	249	243	235	711	248	852	I_x	85.1
	610	240	237	232	227	220	213	452	216	815	S_x	549

† No. of studs/beam = 2 x Q_r x percent shear connection/100/q_r (per stud)

* Units — M_r — kN•m L_u — mm   b — mm
         V_r — kN I_x — $10^6\,mm^4$ t — mm
                 S_x — $10^3\,mm^3$

The Imperial designation for each steel beam is listed below the SI designation to assist designers involved with drawings using Imperial designations.

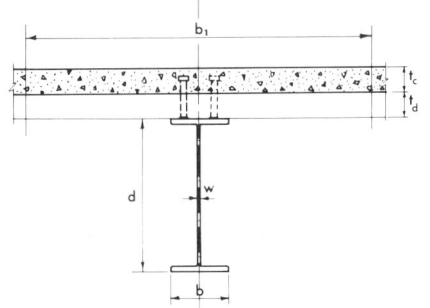

COMPOSITE BEAMS
Trial Selection Tables

G40.21-M 300W
20 MPa Concrete

51 mm Deck with 65 mm Slab
$\phi = 0.90$, $\phi_c = 0.67$, $\phi_{sc} = 0.80$

Steel Shape		Composite Beam										Steel Shape Data*	
		Factored Resistances							Properties				
	b_1	M_{rc} in kilonewton metres for various percentages of shear connection						Q_r† for 100%	I_1	S_{s_1}			
	mm	100%	90%	80%	70%	60%	50%	kN	10^6 mm⁴	10^3 mm³			
W250X101	2 110	577	566	554	541	527	511	1 560	487	1 980	M_r	378
W10X68	1 740	550	541	531	520	508	494	1 290	457	1 940	V_r	560
b = 257	1 370	522	515	507	498	487	474	1 010	421	1 890	L_u	4 950
t = 19.6	1 000	494	488	481	472	462	450	740	375	1 810	I_x	164
	630	459	454	447	440	432	424	466	316	1 700	S_x	1 240
W250X89	2 110	522	512	501	488	474	459	1 560	439	1 760	M_r	332
W10X60	1 740	496	487	478	467	456	443	1 290	414	1 730	V_r	496
b = 256	1 370	469	462	455	446	436	424	1 010	382	1 680	L_u	4 690
t = 17.3	1 000	442	437	430	422	413	402	740	341	1 620	I_x	143
	630	410	405	399	392	385	377	466	288	1 520	S_x	1 100
W250X80	2 110	478	468	457	444	431	416	1 560	399	1 580	M_r	294
W10X54	1 740	452	444	434	424	413	401	1 290	377	1 560	V_r	429
b = 255	1 370	426	419	412	404	395	384	1 010	349	1 520	L_u	4 520
t = 15.6	1 000	400	394	389	382	374	364	740	312	1 460	I_x	126
	630	371	366	360	354	347	340	466	264	1 380	S_x	982
W250X73	2 110	444	435	424	412	398	384	1 560	368	1 440	M_r	266
W10X49	1 740	419	411	402	392	381	369	1 290	348	1 420	V_r	388
b = 254	1 370	394	387	380	371	363	353	1 010	323	1 390	L_u	4 390
t = 14.2	1 000	367	362	357	351	343	334	740	290	1 340	I_x	113
	630	340	336	330	325	318	310	466	245	1 270	S_x	891
W250X67	2 060	421	412	401	389	376	362	1 530	349	1 340	M_r	243
W10X45	1 700	397	389	380	370	359	347	1 260	330	1 320	V_r	408
b = 204	1 340	372	365	358	350	341	331	992	307	1 290	L_u	3 570
t = 15.7	980	346	341	335	329	321	311	726	276	1 240	I_x	104
	620	318	313	308	302	295	288	459	234	1 170	S_x	806
W250X58	2 060	379	370	359	348	335	321	1 530	306	1 160	M_r	208
W10X39	1 700	355	347	339	329	318	307	1 260	291	1 140	V_r	359
b = 203	1 340	331	324	317	309	301	291	992	271	1 120	L_u	3 410
t = 13.5	980	306	301	295	290	282	273	726	245	1 080	I_x	87.3
	620	279	275	271	265	259	251	459	208	1 030	S_x	693
W250X49	2 060	336	327	317	306	294	281	1 530	262	979	M_r	171
W10X33	1 700	313	305	297	288	277	266	1 260	249	965	V_r	326
b = 202	1 340	289	283	276	269	260	251	992	234	946	L_u	3 240
t = 11.0	980	265	260	255	249	243	235	726	212	918	I_x	70.6
	620	240	236	232	226	220	214	459	181	871	S_x	572

† No. of studs/beam = 2 x Q_r x percent shear connection/100/q_r (per stud)

* Units — M_r — kN•m $\qquad$ L_u — mm $\qquad$ b — mm

$\qquad\quad$ V_r — kN $\qquad\qquad$ I_x — 10^6 mm⁴ $\qquad$ t — mm

$\qquad\qquad\qquad\qquad\quad$ S_x — 10^3 mm³

The Imperial designation for each steel beam is listed below the SI designation to assist designers involved with drawings using Imperial designations.

COMPOSITE BEAMS
Trial Selection Tables

G40.21-M 300W
20 MPa Concrete

51 mm Deck with 65 mm Slab
$\emptyset = 0.90$, $\emptyset_c = 0.67$, $\emptyset_{sc} = 0.80$

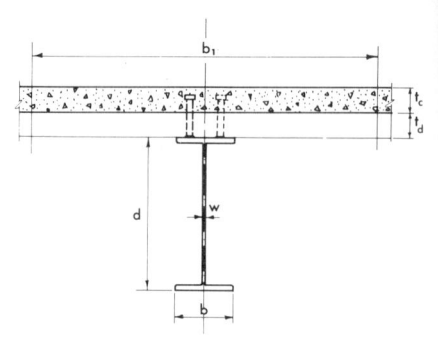

Steel Shape	b_1	\multicolumn{6}{c}{M_{rc} in kilonewton metres for various percentages of shear connection}					Q_r[†] for 100%	I_1	S_{s_1}	\multicolumn{2}{c}{Steel Shape Data*}
	mm	100%	90%	80%	70%	60%	50%	kN	$10^6\,mm^4$	$10^3\,mm^3$		
W250X45	2 000	329	321	311	300	288	275	1 480	265	928	M_r	163
W10X30	1 650	307	300	291	282	272	261	1 220	254	915	V_r	360
b = 148	1 300	284	278	271	263	255	246	962	238	897	L_u	2 360
t = 13.0	950	260	255	250	244	237	229	703	217	871	I_x	71.1
	600	234	231	226	221	214	207	444	185	827	S_x	534
W250X39	2 000	289	281	272	262	251	239	1 330	232	802	M_r	139
W10X26	1 650	276	269	261	252	243	232	1 220	222	791	V_r	308
b = 147	1 300	254	248	241	234	226	218	962	209	777	L_u	2 280
t = 11.2	950	230	226	221	216	210	202	703	192	756	I_x	60.1
	600	206	203	199	194	189	182	444	165	720	S_x	459
W250X33	2 000	248	240	232	222	212	202	1 130	198	679	M_r	114
W10X22	1 650	242	235	228	219	210	200	1 130	191	670	V_r	280
b = 146	1 300	225	220	214	207	199	191	962	181	659	L_u	2 180
t = 9.1	950	203	199	194	189	183	176	703	166	642	I_x	48.9
	600	179	177	173	169	163	157	444	144	614	S_x	379
W200X100	2 070	505	494	482	468	454	438	1 530	381	1 740	M_r	310
W8X67	1 700	477	468	457	446	434	420	1 260	356	1 700	V_r	592
b = 210	1 340	449	442	433	424	413	401	992	326	1 650	L_u	5 020
t = 23.7	980	421	415	408	399	390	379	726	288	1 570	I_x	113
	620	387	382	376	370	362	355	459	240	1 460	S_x	989
W200X86	2 070	451	441	429	416	402	387	1 530	336	1 520	M_r	265
W8X58	1 700	424	416	406	395	383	370	1 260	314	1 490	V_r	514
b = 209	1 340	398	391	383	374	364	352	992	289	1 450	L_u	4 620
t = 20.6	980	370	365	358	351	342	332	726	256	1 390	I_x	94.7
	620	339	334	329	323	316	309	459	213	1 290	S_x	853
W200X71	2 060	389	379	369	356	343	329	1 530	285	1 270	M_r	217
W8X48	1 700	364	356	347	337	325	313	1 260	269	1 250	V_r	393
b = 206	1 340	339	332	325	316	307	298	992	248	1 210	L_u	4 150
t = 17.4	980	313	308	302	296	289	280	726	221	1 170	I_x	76.6
	620	286	282	277	272	265	259	459	185	1 090	S_x	709
W200X59	2 060	340	331	321	310	297	283	1 530	241	1 060	M_r	176
W8X40	1 700	317	309	300	290	280	268	1 260	229	1 040	V_r	341
b = 205	1 340	292	286	279	271	262	253	992	212	1 020	L_u	3 780
t = 14.2	980	267	262	257	251	245	237	726	190	981	I_x	61.1
	620	241	238	234	229	223	217	459	160	922	S_x	582

† No. of studs/beam = 2 x Q_r x percent shear connection/100/q_r (per stud)

* Units — M_r — kN•m L_u — mm   b — mm
V_r — kN I_x — $10^6\,mm^4$ t — mm
S_x — $10^3\,mm^3$

The Imperial designation for each steel beam is listed below the SI designation to assist designers involved with drawings using Imperial designations.

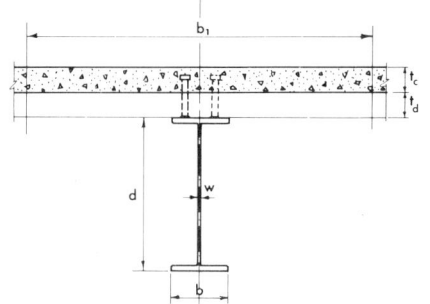

COMPOSITE BEAMS
Trial Selection Tables

G40.21-M 300W
20 MPa Concrete

51 mm Deck with 65 mm Slab
$\emptyset = 0.90$, $\emptyset_c = 0.67$, $\emptyset_{sc} = 0.80$

Steel Shape		Composite Beam										Steel Shape Data*	
		Factored Resistances							Properties				
	b_1	M_{rc} in kilonewton metres for various percentages of shear connection						$Q_r^†$ for 100%	I_1	S_{s_1}			
	mm	100%	90%	80%	70%	60%	50%	kN	10^6mm^4	10^3mm^3		
W200X52	2 060	312	303	294	282	270	256	1 530	215	937	M_r	154
W8X35	1 700	289	281	273	264	253	242	1 260	205	922	V_r	290
b = 204	1 340	265	259	252	244	236	227	992	191	902	L_u	3 620
t = 12.6	980	241	236	231	225	219	212	726	172	872	I_x	52.7
	620	215	212	209	204	199	193	459	145	823	S_x	512
W200X46	2 060	288	279	270	259	247	234	1 530	192	828	M_r	134
W8X31	1 700	265	258	250	241	230	219	1 260	183	815	V_r	260
b = 203	1 340	242	236	229	222	214	205	992	171	799	L_u	3 460
t = 11.0	980	218	213	208	203	197	190	726	155	774	I_x	45.5
	620	193	190	187	183	178	172	459	132	733	S_x	448
W200X42	2 020	269	260	251	240	229	216	1 430	179	754	M_r	120
W8X28	1 670	250	243	235	226	216	205	1 240	171	743	V_r	263
b = 166	1 310	227	221	214	207	199	190	970	160	727	L_u	2 850
t = 11.8	960	203	199	194	188	182	176	711	145	706	I_x	40.9
	610	179	176	173	169	164	159	452	124	669	S_x	399
W200X36	2 020	234	226	217	208	197	186	1 240	156	653	M_r	103
W8X24	1 670	228	221	213	204	194	184	1 240	149	644	V_r	222
b = 165	1 310	205	199	193	186	178	169	970	140	631	L_u	2 730
t = 10.2	960	182	178	173	168	162	155	711	128	613	I_x	34.4
	610	159	156	152	149	145	140	452	110	584	S_x	342
W200X31	1 990	213	205	197	188	178	168	1 080	146	583	M_r	90.4
W8X21	1 640	207	201	193	185	176	166	1 080	140	575	V_r	240
b = 134	1 290	193	188	181	175	167	159	955	133	564	L_u	2 150
t = 10.2	950	171	167	162	157	151	145	703	122	549	I_x	31.4
	600	148	145	142	138	134	128	444	105	523	S_x	299
W200X27	1 990	182	175	168	159	151	142	915	126	496	M_r	75.3
W8X18	1 640	178	172	165	158	149	141	915	121	489	V_r	214
b = 133	1 290	172	167	161	155	147	139	915	115	480	L_u	2 050
t = 8.4	940	153	148	144	139	133	127	696	106	468	I_x	25.8
	600	130	128	125	121	117	112	444	92.4	448	S_x	249

† No. of studs/beam = 2 x Q_r x percent shear connection/100/q_r (per stud)

* Units — M_r — kN•m L_u — mm   b — mm

           V_r — kN I_x — 10^6mm^4 t — mm

                              S_x — 10^3mm^3

The Imperial designation for each steel beam is listed below the SI designation to assist designers involved with drawings using Imperial designations.

COMPOSITE BEAMS
Trial Selection Tables

G40.21-M 300W
20 MPa Concrete

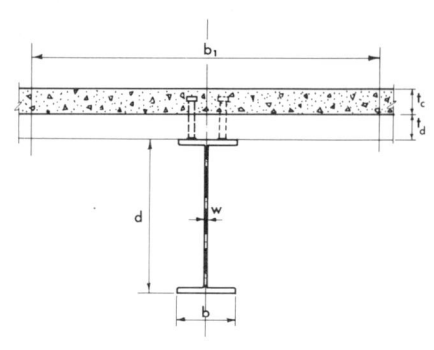

76 mm Deck with 65 mm Slab
$\emptyset = 0.90$, $\emptyset_C = 0.67$, $\emptyset_{SC} = 0.80$

Steel Shape	b_1	Composite Beam										Steel Shape Data*	
		Factored Resistances							Properties				
		M_{rc} in kilonewton metres for various percentages of shear connection						$Q_r^{\dagger}$ for 100%	I_1	S_{s1}		
	mm	100%	90%	80%	70%	60%	50%	kN	$10^6 mm^4$	$10^3 mm^3$		
W610X241	2 590	2 690	2 650	2 610	2 560	2 500	2 440	1 920	4 210	8 880	M_r	2 070
W24X162	2 130	2 610	2 570	2 530	2 480	2 430	2 380	1 580	3 960	8 700	V_r	2 030
b = 329	1 680	2 510	2 480	2 440	2 400	2 360	2 320	1 240	3 680	8 480	L_u	5 200
t = 31.0	1 230	2 410	2 380	2 350	2 320	2 290	2 250	911	3 360	8 200	I_x	2 150
	780	2 290	2 270	2 250	2 230	2 210	2 180	577	2 980	7 830	S_x	6 780
W610X217	2 580	2 450	2 410	2 370	2 320	2 270	2 210	1 910	3 850	8 050	M_r	1 850
W24X146	2 130	2 370	2 340	2 300	2 250	2 200	2 150	1 580	3 630	7 890	V_r	1 850
b = 328	1 680	2 280	2 250	2 210	2 180	2 140	2 090	1 240	3 370	7 700	L_u	5 080
t = 27.7	1 230	2 180	2 150	2 120	2 090	2 060	2 030	911	3 070	7 440	I_x	1 910
	780	2 070	2 050	2 030	2 010	1 980	1 960	577	2 720	7 100	S_x	6 070
W610X195	2 580	2 220	2 180	2 150	2 100	2 050	1 990	1 910	3 510	7 230	M_r	1 640
W24X131	2 130	2 150	2 110	2 080	2 030	1 990	1 940	1 580	3 310	7 100	V_r	1 710
b = 327	1 680	2 060	2 030	2 000	1 960	1 920	1 880	1 240	3 080	6 920	L_u	4 940
t = 24.4	1 230	1 960	1 940	1 910	1 880	1 850	1 820	911	2 800	6 700	I_x	1 680
	770	1 850	1 830	1 810	1 790	1 770	1 750	570	2 450	6 370	S_x	5 400
W610X174	2 580	2 000	1 970	1 940	1 890	1 850	1 790	1 910	3 190	6 470	M_r	1 450
W24X117	2 130	1 940	1 910	1 870	1 830	1 790	1 740	1 580	3 010	6 350	V_r	1 540
b = 325	1 680	1 860	1 830	1 800	1 760	1 720	1 680	1 240	2 790	6 200	L_u	4 830
t = 21.6	1 230	1 770	1 740	1 710	1 680	1 650	1 620	911	2 540	6 000	I_x	1 470
	770	1 660	1 640	1 620	1 600	1 580	1 560	570	2 220	5 700	S_x	4 780
W610X155	2 580	1 800	1 770	1 740	1 710	1 660	1 610	1 910	2 900	5 770	M_r	1 280
W24X104	2 130	1 740	1 720	1 690	1 650	1 610	1 560	1 580	2 740	5 680	V_r	1 380
b = 324	1 680	1 670	1 650	1 620	1 580	1 550	1 510	1 240	2 540	5 550	L_u	4 740
t = 19.0	1 230	1 590	1 560	1 540	1 510	1 480	1 450	911	2 310	5 370	I_x	1 290
	770	1 480	1 460	1 440	1 420	1 400	1 380	570	2 010	5 110	S_x	4 220
W610X140	2 490	1 650	1 620	1 590	1 550	1 510	1 460	1 840	2 650	5 170	M_r	1 120
W24X94	2 050	1 590	1 560	1 530	1 490	1 450	1 400	1 520	2 500	5 070	V_r	1 440
b = 230	1 620	1 520	1 490	1 460	1 420	1 390	1 350	1 200	2 320	4 950	L_u	3 320
t = 22.2	1 180	1 430	1 400	1 380	1 350	1 320	1 290	874	2 100	4 780	I_x	1 120
	750	1 320	1 310	1 290	1 270	1 250	1 230	555	1 820	4 530	S_x	3 630
W610X125	2 490	1 490	1 470	1 440	1 410	1 360	1 320	1 840	2 410	4 620	M_r	991
W24X84	2 050	1 440	1 410	1 380	1 350	1 310	1 270	1 520	2 280	4 540	V_r	1 300
b = 229	1 620	1 370	1 350	1 320	1 290	1 250	1 210	1 200	2 120	4 440	L_u	3 250
t = 19.6	1 180	1 290	1 270	1 240	1 210	1 190	1 160	874	1 910	4 290	I_x	985
	750	1 190	1 170	1 160	1 140	1 120	1 100	555	1 660	4 060	S_x	3 220

$\dagger$ No. of studs/beam = 2 x Q_r x percent shear connection/100/q_r (per stud)

* Units — M_r — kN•m L_u — mm   b — mm
          V_r — kN I_x — $10^6 mm^4$ t — mm
                                 S_x — $10^3 mm^3$

The Imperial designation for each steel beam is listed below the SI designation to assist designers involved with drawings using Imperial designations.

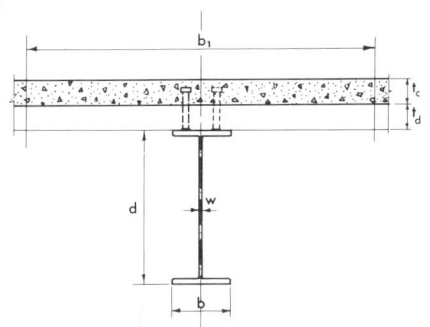

COMPOSITE BEAMS
Trial Selection Tables

G40.21-M 300W
20 MPa Concrete

76 mm Deck with 65 mm Slab
$\varnothing = 0.90$, $\varnothing_c = 0.67$, $\varnothing_{sc} = 0.80$

Steel Shape		Composite Beam										Steel Shape Data*	
		Factored Resistances							Properties				
	b_1	M_{rc} in kilonewton metres for various percentages of shear connection						$Q_r{}^\dagger$ for 100%	I_1	S_{s1}			
	mm	100%	90%	80%	70%	60%	50%	kN	10^6mm⁴	10^3mm³			
W610X113	2 480	1 360	1 350	1 320	1 290	1 250	1 210	1 840	2 210	4 190	M_r	888
W24X76	2 050	1 320	1 300	1 270	1 240	1 200	1 160	1 520	2 090	4 120	V_r	1 210
b = 228	1 610	1 260	1 230	1 210	1 180	1 140	1 110	1 190	1 950	4 020	L_u	3 180
t = 17.3	1 180	1 180	1 160	1 130	1 110	1 080	1 050	874	1 760	3 890	I_x	875
	750	1 080	1 070	1 050	1 030	1 010	991	555	1 520	3 690	S_x	2 880
W610X101	2 480	1 250	1 230	1 210	1 180	1 140	1 100	1 840	2 010	3 760	M_r	783
W24X68	2 050	1 200	1 180	1 160	1 130	1 090	1 050	1 520	1 910	3 700	V_r	1 130
b = 228	1 610	1 150	1 120	1 100	1 070	1 040	1 000	1 190	1 770	3 620	L_u	3 110
t = 14.9	1 180	1 070	1 050	1 030	1 000	974	945	874	1 610	3 500	I_x	764
	750	977	961	944	925	906	886	555	1 390	3 320	S_x	2 530
W530X138	2 470	1 460	1 440	1 410	1 370	1 330	1 280	1 830	2 140	4 620	M_r	975
W21X93	2 040	1 410	1 380	1 350	1 320	1 280	1 230	1 510	2 010	4 530	V_r	1 440
b = 214	1 610	1 340	1 310	1 280	1 250	1 220	1 180	1 190	1 860	4 410	L_u	3 180
t = 23.6	1 170	1 250	1 230	1 210	1 180	1 160	1 130	866	1 680	4 240	I_x	861
	740	1 160	1 140	1 130	1 110	1 090	1 070	548	1 440	4 000	S_x	3 140
W530X123	2 470	1 330	1 310	1 280	1 250	1 210	1 170	1 830	1 950	4 150	M_r	867
W21X83	2 040	1 280	1 260	1 230	1 200	1 160	1 120	1 510	1 840	4 070	V_r	1 270
b = 212	1 600	1 210	1 190	1 170	1 140	1 100	1 070	1 180	1 700	3 970	L_u	3 100
t = 21.2	1 170	1 140	1 120	1 090	1 070	1 040	1 020	866	1 540	3 830	I_x	761
	740	1 050	1 030	1 020	998	980	962	548	1 320	3 610	S_x	2 800
W530X109	2 470	1 190	1 180	1 160	1 130	1 090	1 050	1 830	1 770	3 700	M_r	764
W21X73	2 040	1 150	1 130	1 110	1 080	1 050	1 010	1 510	1 670	3 640	V_r	1 110
b = 211	1 600	1 100	1 080	1 050	1 030	996	963	1 180	1 550	3 550	L_u	3 040
t = 18.8	1 170	1 030	1 010	986	964	939	912	866	1 400	3 430	I_x	667
	740	941	926	910	893	876	858	548	1 200	3 240	S_x	2 480
W530X101	2 470	1 120	1 100	1 090	1 060	1 030	992	1 830	1 670	3 450	M_r	707
W21X68	2 030	1 080	1 060	1 040	1 020	986	950	1 500	1 580	3 390	V_r	1 040
b = 210	1 600	1 030	1 010	990	965	936	904	1 180	1 470	3 310	L_u	2 990
t = 17.4	1 170	966	947	927	905	881	855	866	1 330	3 200	I_x	617
	740	882	868	852	836	819	801	548	1 140	3 030	S_x	2 300
W530X92	2 470	1 040	1 020	1 000	983	954	918	1 830	1 540	3 150	M_r	637
W21X62	2 030	1 000	985	966	941	912	877	1 500	1 460	3 100	V_r	969
b = 209	1 600	955	937	916	892	864	833	1 180	1 360	3 030	L_u	2 930
t = 15.6	1 170	892	875	855	833	810	785	866	1 230	2 930	I_x	552
	740	811	797	782	766	749	731	548	1 050	2 780	S_x	2 070

† No. of studs/beam = 2 x Q_r x percent shear connection/100/q_r (per stud)

* Units — M_r — kN•m L_u — mm   b — mm
  V_r — kN I_x — 10^6mm⁴   t — mm
  S_x — 10^3mm³

The Imperial designation for each steel beam is listed below the SI designation to assist designers involved with drawings using Imperial designations.

COMPOSITE BEAMS
Trial Selection Tables

G40.21-M 300W
20 MPa Concrete

76 mm Deck with 65 mm Slab
$\phi = 0.90$, $\phi_c = 0.67$, $\phi_{sc} = 0.80$

Steel Shape	b_1	\multicolumn{6}{c}{M_{rc} in kilonewton metres for various percentages of shear connection}						$Q_r^\dagger$ for 100%	I_1	S_{s1}	Steel Shape Data*	
	mm	100%	90%	80%	70%	60%	50%	kN	$10^6 mm^4$	$10^3 mm^3$		
W530X82	2 470	942	926	908	889	863	830	1 830	1 390	2 800	M_r	559
W21X55	2 030	904	890	873	851	824	791	1 500	1 320	2 760	V_r	894
b = 209	1 600	863	847	828	805	779	749	1 180	1 230	2 700	L_u	2 860
t = 13.3	1 170	805	788	770	749	726	701	866	1 110	2 620	I_x	479
	740	727	713	699	683	667	649	548	957	2 480	S_x	1 810
W460X106	2 450	1 040	1 020	999	975	945	909	1 810	1 380	3 240	M_r	645
W18X71	2 020	995	979	958	933	904	870	1 500	1 300	3 180	V_r	1 050
b = 194	1 590	947	929	908	884	857	828	1 180	1 200	3 100	L_u	2 910
t = 20.6	1 160	884	867	848	828	806	782	859	1 080	2 990	I_x	488
	740	808	795	781	766	750	734	548	925	2 820	S_x	2 080
W460X97	2 450	960	943	924	903	877	845	1 810	1 280	2 970	M_r	589
W18X65	2 020	920	905	888	866	840	808	1 500	1 210	2 920	V_r	947
b = 193	1 590	877	862	843	821	796	768	1 180	1 120	2 860	L_u	2 870
t = 19.0	1 160	820	804	787	768	747	724	859	1 010	2 760	I_x	445
	730	746	734	720	706	691	675	540	863	2 600	S_x	1 910
W460X89	2 450	902	885	867	847	824	794	1 810	1 200	2 770	M_r	543
W18X60	2 020	863	848	833	813	789	759	1 500	1 140	2 720	V_r	866
b = 192	1 590	822	808	791	771	747	720	1 180	1 060	2 660	L_u	2 830
t = 17.7	1 160	770	755	738	720	699	677	859	956	2 570	I_x	410
	730	699	687	674	660	645	629	540	815	2 430	S_x	1 770
W460X82	2 450	838	822	804	785	763	736	1 810	1 110	2 530	M_r	494
W18X55	2 020	800	786	771	754	731	704	1 500	1 060	2 490	V_r	812
b = 191	1 590	761	749	733	714	692	667	1 180	985	2 440	L_u	2 770
t = 16.0	1 160	713	699	683	666	646	625	859	891	2 360	I_x	370
	730	646	634	622	608	594	578	540	760	2 230	S_x	1 610
W460X74	2 450	777	761	744	725	705	681	1 810	1 030	2 310	M_r	445
W18X50	2 020	740	726	712	696	676	651	1 500	977	2 280	V_r	733
b = 190	1 590	702	691	677	660	640	616	1 180	913	2 230	L_u	2 730
t = 14.5	1 160	658	646	631	615	596	575	859	828	2 160	I_x	333
	730	595	584	572	559	545	530	540	708	2 050	S_x	1 460
W460X67	2 450	727	712	695	677	657	633	1 810	951	2 120	M_r	405
W18X45	2 020	691	678	663	648	629	604	1 500	907	2 090	V_r	688
b = 190	1 590	653	642	630	613	593	569	1 180	849	2 050	L_u	2 660
t = 12.7	1 160	611	599	585	568	550	529	859	771	1 990	I_x	300
	730	549	538	525	512	498	483	540	660	1 890	S_x	1 320

† No. of studs/beam = 2 x Q_r x percent shear connection/100/q_r (per stud)
* Units — M_r — kN•m L_u — mm b — mm
   V_r — kN I_x — $10^6 mm^4$ t — mm
   S_x — $10^3 mm^3$

The Imperial designation for each steel beam is listed below the SI designation to assist designers involved with drawings using Imperial designations.

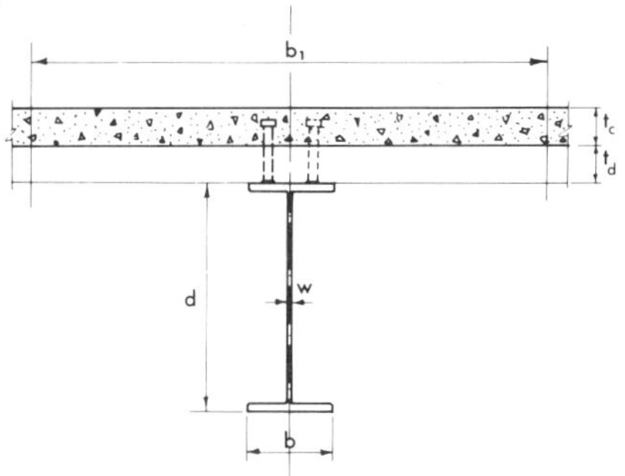

COMPOSITE BEAMS
Trial Selection Tables

G40.21-M 300W
20 MPa Concrete

76 mm Deck with 65 mm Slab
$\phi = 0.90$, $\phi_c = 0.67$, $\phi_{sc} = 0.80$

Steel Shape	Composite Beam										Steel Shape Data*	
		Factored Resistances							Properties			
	b_1	M_{rc} in kilonewton metres for various percentages of shear connection						Q_r† for 100%	I_1	S_{s1}		
	mm	100%	90%	80%	70%	60%	50%	kN	$10^6 mm^4$	$10^3 mm^3$		
W460X61	2 450	668	653	636	618	599	577	1 810	856	1 890	M_r	354
W18X41	2 020	632	619	605	590	572	549	1 500	818	1 860	V_r	650
b = 189	1 590	595	585	573	558	539	516	1 180	768	1 830	L_u	2 580
t = 10.8	1 160	555	544	530	515	497	477	859	700	1 780	I_x	259
	730	496	485	473	460	447	432	540	600	1 690	S_x	1 150
W410X85	2 440	798	781	763	744	722	696	1 810	982	2 450	M_r	467
W16X57	2 010	759	745	730	712	691	664	1 490	930	2 400	V_r	810
b = 181	1 580	719	707	692	674	653	629	1 170	864	2 350	L_u	2 730
t = 18.2	1 160	673	660	645	629	610	590	859	780	2 270	I_x	315
	730	609	598	586	574	560	546	540	662	2 140	S_x	1 510
W410X74	2 440	725	709	692	673	653	629	1 810	885	2 170	M_r	408
W16X50	2 010	688	674	659	643	625	601	1 490	841	2 140	V_r	714
b = 180	1 580	649	638	626	610	590	568	1 170	784	2 090	L_u	2 670
t = 16.0	1 160	608	596	583	567	550	530	859	710	2 030	I_x	275
	730	549	538	527	515	502	488	540	604	1 920	S_x	1 330
W410X67	2 440	671	655	638	620	600	578	1 810	811	1 970	M_r	367
W16X45	2 010	634	621	606	591	574	552	1 490	772	1 940	V_r	643
b = 179	1 580	596	585	574	560	542	521	1 170	722	1 900	L_u	2 610
t = 14.4	1 160	558	547	535	521	505	486	859	656	1 840	I_x	246
	730	503	493	482	471	458	444	540	560	1 750	S_x	1 200
W410X60	2 430	611	596	580	562	543	522	1 800	730	1 740	M_r	321
W16X40	2 010	576	564	550	534	518	500	1 490	698	1 720	V_r	558
b = 178	1 580	539	529	518	505	491	472	1 170	655	1 690	L_u	2 580
t = 12.8	1 160	502	494	484	471	456	439	859	598	1 640	I_x	216
	730	455	446	436	425	413	399	540	512	1 560	S_x	1 060
W410X54	2 430	566	551	535	518	499	478	1 800	657	1 560	M_r	283
W16X36	2 010	531	519	505	490	474	457	1 490	630	1 540	V_r	539
b = 177	1 580	495	485	474	462	448	430	1 170	593	1 510	L_u	2 480
t = 10.9	1 160	459	451	441	429	415	398	859	542	1 470	I_x	186
	730	413	404	394	383	371	359	540	466	1 400	S_x	924
W410X46	2 400	498	485	470	453	436	417	1 590	579	1 350	M_r	239
W16X31	1 980	479	467	454	440	424	407	1 470	556	1 330	V_r	503
b = 140	1 560	445	435	424	412	399	382	1 150	526	1 310	L_u	1 930
t = 11.2	1 140	408	401	392	381	367	351	844	482	1 270	I_x	156
	720	365	357	348	338	326	314	533	417	1 210	S_x	773

† No. of studs/beam = 2 x Q_r x percent shear connection/100/q_r (per stud)

* Units — M_r — kN•m; V_r — kN; L_u — mm; I_x — $10^6 mm^4$; S_x — $10^3 mm^3$; b — mm; t — mm

The Imperial designation for each steel beam is listed below the SI designation to assist designers involved with drawings using Imperial designations.

COMPOSITE BEAMS
Trial Selection Tables

G40.21-M 300W
20 MPa Concrete

76 mm Deck with 65 mm Slab
$\emptyset = 0.90$, $\emptyset_c = 0.67$, $\emptyset_{sc} = 0.80$

Steel Shape	b_1	Composite Beam									Steel Shape Data*	
		Factored Resistances							Properties			
		M_{rc} in kilonewton metres for various percentages of shear connection						$Q_r^\dagger$ for 100%	I_1	S_{s_1}		
	mm	100%	90%	80%	70%	60%	50%	kN	10^6 mm^4	10^3 mm^3		
W410X39	2 400	426	413	399	384	369	352	1 350	497	1 140	M_r	197
W16X26	1 980	419	407	395	381	366	351	1 350	478	1 130	V_r	448
b = 140	1 560	394	384	374	362	350	335	1 150	454	1 110	L_u	1 860
t = 8.8	1 140	359	351	343	334	321	306	844	419	1 080	I_x	127
	720	319	312	303	293	283	270	533	365	1 030	S_x	634
W360X79	2 460	677	661	643	624	603	581	1 820	749	2 100	M_r	386
W14X53	2 030	639	625	610	594	577	558	1 500	710	2 070	V_r	593
b = 205	1 600	600	589	577	564	548	529	1 180	661	2 030	L_u	3 270
t = 16.8	1 170	561	552	541	528	512	495	866	595	1 960	I_x	227
	740	511	502	492	481	469	457	548	505	1 850	S_x	1 280
W360X72	2 460	626	611	593	575	555	533	1 820	683	1 900	M_r	346
W14X48	2 030	589	576	562	546	529	511	1 500	649	1 870	V_r	536
b = 204	1 600	552	541	529	516	502	484	1 180	606	1 830	L_u	3 190
t = 15.1	1 170	513	505	495	483	469	452	866	548	1 780	I_x	201
	740	467	459	449	439	427	415	548	466	1 680	S_x	1 150
W360X64	2 460	578	563	546	528	509	487	1 820	621	1 710	M_r	308
W14X43	2 030	542	529	515	500	483	466	1 500	592	1 680	V_r	476
b = 203	1 600	505	495	483	471	458	442	1 180	554	1 650	L_u	3 110
t = 13.5	1 170	467	459	451	440	427	412	866	503	1 600	I_x	178
	740	425	417	409	399	388	376	548	429	1 520	S_x	1 030
W360X57	2 430	544	529	513	495	476	455	1 800	584	1 540	M_r	273
W14X38	2 000	508	496	482	467	451	433	1 480	558	1 520	V_r	504
b = 172	1 580	473	462	451	439	426	409	1 170	524	1 490	L_u	2 550
t = 13.1	1 150	435	427	418	407	394	379	851	476	1 450	I_x	161
	730	393	385	376	366	355	344	540	408	1 370	S_x	897
W360X51	2 430	500	486	470	453	434	414	1 740	528	1 370	M_r	241
W14X34	2 000	469	457	444	429	413	396	1 480	505	1 360	V_r	455
b = 171	1 580	434	424	413	401	389	374	1 170	476	1 330	L_u	2 500
t = 11.6	1 150	397	390	381	372	360	345	851	435	1 300	I_x	141
	730	358	351	343	333	323	311	540	374	1 230	S_x	796
W360X45	2 430	447	433	419	403	386	367	1 550	473	1 220	M_r	210
W14X30	2 000	433	421	408	393	378	361	1 480	454	1 210	V_r	433
b = 171	1 580	398	389	378	366	354	340	1 170	430	1 190	L_u	2 430
t = 9.8	1 150	362	355	347	338	326	313	851	394	1 150	I_x	122
	730	324	317	310	301	291	279	540	341	1 100	S_x	691

$\dagger$ No. of studs/beam = 2 x Q_r x percent shear connection/100/q_r (per stud)

* Units — M_r — kN•m L_u — mm   b — mm

           V_r — kN I_x — 10^6 mm^4 t — mm

                         S_x — 10^3 mm^3

The Imperial designation for each steel beam is listed below the SI designation to assist designers involved with drawings using Imperial designations.

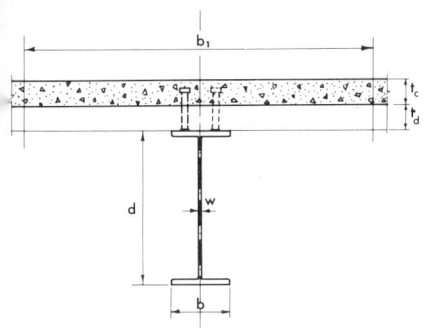

COMPOSITE BEAMS
Trial Selection Tables

G40.21-M 300W
20 MPa Concrete

76 mm Deck with 65 mm Slab
$\phi = 0.90$, $\phi_c = 0.67$, $\phi_{sc} = 0.80$

Steel Shape		Composite Beam								Properties		Steel Shape Data*	
		Factored Resistances											
	b_1	M_{rc} in kilonewton metres for various percentages of shear connection						Q_r† for 100%		I_1	S_{s_1}		
	mm	100%	90%	80%	70%	60%	50%	kN		$10^6 mm^4$	$10^3 mm^3$		
W360X39	2 380	394	381	367	353	337	321	1 340		418	1 060	M_r	179
W14X26	1 970	387	375	363	349	334	319	1 340		403	1 050	V_r	409
b = 128	1 550	362	352	342	330	318	304	1 150		382	1 030	L_u	1 790
t = 10.7	1 130	326	319	311	302	292	279	837		351	1 000	I_x	102
	720	290	283	276	267	258	247	533		306	959	S_x	580
W360X33	2 380	332	320	308	295	282	268	1 130		355	887	M_r	146
W14X22	1 970	327	316	305	293	280	266	1 130		343	877	V_r	361
b = 127	1 550	319	310	300	289	277	265	1 130		327	864	L_u	1 720
t = 8.5	1 130	287	280	272	264	254	243	837		303	844	I_x	82.7
	710	251	245	239	231	222	212	526		265	809	S_x	474
W310X129	2 560	894	876	857	836	813	789	1 900		924	3 110	M_r	583
W12X87	2 120	854	838	822	804	785	762	1 570		868	3 050	V_r	742
b = 308	1 670	811	799	786	770	751	730	1 240		797	2 960	L_u	5 580
t = 20.6	1 220	767	756	743	729	712	694	903		710	2 850	I_x	308
	770	711	701	691	679	667	654	570		597	2 660	S_x	1 940
W310X118	2 560	827	810	791	770	748	725	1 900		853	2 840	M_r	526
W12X79	2 110	787	772	756	739	720	699	1 560		801	2 780	V_r	666
b = 307	1 670	746	734	721	707	690	669	1 240		738	2 710	L_u	5 390
t = 18.7	1 220	704	694	682	668	652	635	903		658	2 610	I_x	275
	770	650	641	631	620	608	596	570		553	2 440	S_x	1 750
W310X107	2 560	767	750	731	711	690	667	1 900		790	2 590	M_r	478
W12X72	2 110	727	713	697	680	662	643	1 560		743	2 550	V_r	604
b = 306	1 670	687	676	663	650	634	615	1 240		687	2 480	L_u	5 220
t = 17.0	1 220	646	637	626	613	599	582	903		613	2 390	I_x	248
	770	597	588	579	568	557	544	570		516	2 250	S_x	1 590
W310X97	2 560	711	694	676	656	635	613	1 900		728	2 360	M_r	389
W12X65	2 110	672	657	642	626	608	589	1 560		686	2 320	V_r	543
b = 305	1 660	631	620	608	595	581	563	1 230		635	2 260	L_u	5 410
t = 15.4	1 220	592	583	574	562	549	533	903		569	2 180	I_x	222
	770	546	538	529	519	508	496	570		479	2 060	S_x	1 440
W310X86	2 510	657	641	623	604	583	561	1 860		672	2 130	M_r	383
W12X58	2 070	619	605	590	574	557	538	1 530		635	2 090	V_r	503
b = 254	1 630	580	569	557	544	530	514	1 210		589	2 040	L_u	4 250
t = 16.3	1 190	540	532	523	512	499	484	881		528	1 970	I_x	199
	750	496	489	480	470	460	448	555		445	1 860	S_x	1 280

† No. of studs/beam = 2 x Q_r x percent shear connection/100/q_r (per stud)

* Units — M_r — kN•m L_u — mm   b — mm
             V_r — kN I_x — $10^6 mm^4$ t — mm
                             S_x — $10^3 mm^3$

The Imperial designation for each steel beam is listed below the SI designation to assist designers involved with drawings using Imperial designations.

COMPOSITE BEAMS
Trial Selection Tables

G40.21-M 300W
20 MPa Concrete

76 mm Deck with 65 mm Slab
$\varnothing = 0.90$, $\varnothing_c = 0.67$, $\varnothing_{sc} = 0.80$

Steel Shape	b₁	Composite Beam										Steel Shape Data*	
		Factored Resistances							Properties				
		M_{rc} in kilonewton metres for various percentages of shear connection						$Q_r^{\dagger}$ for 100%	I_1	S_{s1}			
	mm	100%	90%	80%	70%	60%	50%	kN	$10^6\,mm^4$	$10^3\,mm^3$		
W310X79	2 510	616	600	583	564	543	521	1 860	619	1 950	M_r	346
W12X53	2 070	578	565	550	534	517	499	1 530	586	1 920	V_r	480
b = 254	1 630	540	529	517	504	491	475	1 210	545	1 870	L_u	4 140
t = 14.6	1 190	500	492	483	473	460	445	881	489	1 810	I_x	177
	750	457	450	441	432	421	410	555	413	1 710	S_x	1 160
W310X74	2 460	592	576	559	540	520	498	1 820	593	1 830	M_r	321
W12X50	2 030	555	542	527	511	494	476	1 500	563	1 800	V_r	519
b = 205	1 600	517	506	494	482	468	451	1 180	523	1 760	L_u	3 380
t = 16.3	1 170	478	470	461	449	436	421	866	471	1 700	I_x	165
	740	434	426	418	408	397	386	548	397	1 610	S_x	1 060
W310X67	2 460	548	533	516	498	478	456	1 820	538	1 650	M_r	286
W12X45	2 030	512	499	484	469	452	434	1 500	512	1 620	V_r	463
b = 204	1 600	474	464	452	440	426	411	1 180	477	1 590	L_u	3 280
t = 14.6	1 170	436	428	420	410	397	383	866	431	1 540	I_x	145
	740	395	388	380	370	360	349	548	365	1 450	S_x	949
W310X60	2 460	508	493	476	458	439	418	1 820	489	1 480	M_r	254
W12X40	2 030	472	459	445	430	414	397	1 500	467	1 460	V_r	405
b = 203	1 600	436	425	414	402	389	375	1 180	437	1 430	L_u	3 200
t = 13.1	1 170	398	390	382	373	362	349	866	396	1 390	I_x	129
	740	359	353	345	337	327	317	548	337	1 320	S_x	849
W310X52	2 420	480	465	450	432	413	393	1 790	464	1 330	M_r	226
W12X35	2 000	446	433	420	405	389	372	1 480	443	1 310	V_r	429
b = 167	1 570	409	399	388	376	363	350	1 160	416	1 290	L_u	2 570
t = 13.2	1 150	373	365	357	348	337	324	851	379	1 250	I_x	118
	730	335	328	321	313	303	293	540	324	1 190	S_x	747
W310X45	2 420	414	401	386	370	353	335	1 540	403	1 140	M_r	191
W12X30	2 000	401	389	376	362	346	329	1 480	387	1 120	V_r	368
b = 166	1 570	366	356	345	334	321	308	1 160	365	1 110	L_u	2 490
t = 11.2	1 150	330	323	315	306	297	285	851	335	1 080	I_x	99.2
	730	294	288	282	274	266	256	540	289	1 030	S_x	634
W310X39	2 420	363	350	336	322	306	290	1 330	356	992	M_r	165
W12X26	2 000	356	344	332	318	304	289	1 330	342	981	V_r	320
b = 165	1 570	333	323	313	301	289	276	1 160	324	966	L_u	2 440
t = 9.7	1 150	298	291	283	274	265	255	851	299	943	I_x	85.1
	730	262	257	252	245	237	228	540	260	903	S_x	549

† No. of studs/beam = 2 x Q_r x percent shear connection/100/q_r (per stud)
* Units — M_r — kN•m L_u — mm   b — mm
  V_r — kN I_x — $10^6\,mm^4$ t — mm
  S_x — $10^3\,mm^3$

The Imperial designation for each steel beam is listed below the SI designation to assist designers involved with drawings using Imperial designations.

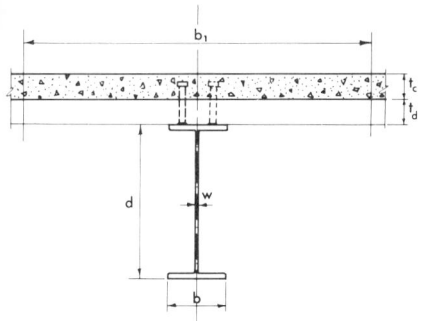

COMPOSITE BEAMS
Trial Selection Tables

G40.21-M 300W
20 MPa Concrete

76 mm Deck with 65 mm Slab
$\varnothing = 0.90$, $\varnothing_c = 0.67$, $\varnothing_{sc} = 0.80$

Steel Shape	Composite Beam											Steel Shape Data*	
		Factored Resistances								Properties			
	b_1	M_{rc} in kilonewton metres for various percentages of shear connection						Q_r† for 100%	I_1	S_{s_1}		
	mm	100%	90%	80%	70%	60%	50%	kN	10^6mm^4	10^3mm^3		
W250X101	2 510	652	635	616	596	575	552	1 860	598	2 210	M_r	378
W10X68	2 070	612	598	582	566	548	529	1 530	561	2 170	V_r	560
b = 257	1 630	572	560	548	535	520	503	1 210	515	2 110	L_u	4 950
t = 19.6	1 190	531	522	513	501	488	474	881	457	2 030	I_x	164
	750	486	478	470	461	451	440	555	379	1 890	S_x	1 240
W250X89	2 510	596	580	562	543	522	499	1 860	540	1 970	M_r	332
W10X60	2 070	558	544	529	512	495	476	1 530	509	1 940	V_r	496
b = 256	1 630	518	507	495	482	468	453	1 210	469	1 890	L_u	4 690
t = 17.3	1 190	478	470	461	451	439	425	881	417	1 820	I_x	143
	750	436	429	421	413	403	393	555	347	1 700	S_x	1 100
W250X80	2 510	551	535	518	499	478	456	1 860	491	1 770	M_r	294
W10X54	2 070	513	500	485	469	452	434	1 530	464	1 740	V_r	429
b = 255	1 630	475	464	452	439	426	411	1 210	429	1 700	L_u	4 520
t = 15.6	1 190	435	427	418	409	398	385	881	383	1 640	I_x	126
	750	395	389	382	374	365	355	555	320	1 540	S_x	982
W250X73	2 510	517	501	484	465	445	424	1 860	453	1 620	M_r	266
W10X49	2 070	480	466	452	436	420	402	1 530	429	1 590	V_r	388
b = 254	1 630	442	431	419	407	393	379	1 210	398	1 560	L_u	4 390
t = 14.2	1 190	403	395	386	377	367	355	881	356	1 510	I_x	113
	750	363	358	351	344	335	325	555	298	1 420	S_x	891
W250X67	2 460	493	478	461	443	423	401	1 820	429	1 500	M_r	243
W10X45	2 030	457	444	429	414	397	379	1 500	407	1 480	V_r	408
b = 204	1 600	419	409	397	385	371	357	1 180	378	1 440	L_u	3 570
t = 15.7	1 170	381	373	364	355	345	333	866	340	1 400	I_x	104
	740	342	336	329	321	313	303	548	285	1 310	S_x	806
W250X58	2 460	450	435	419	401	381	361	1 820	377	1 300	M_r	208
W10X39	2 030	414	402	388	373	356	339	1 500	359	1 290	V_r	359
b = 203	1 600	378	368	356	344	331	317	1 180	335	1 260	L_u	3 410
t = 13.5	1 170	341	333	324	315	306	294	866	303	1 220	I_x	87.3
	740	302	297	291	284	275	266	548	255	1 150	S_x	693
W250X49	2 460	396	381	366	349	331	311	1 690	322	1 100	M_r	171
W10X33	2 030	371	359	346	331	315	298	1 500	308	1 090	V_r	326
b = 202	1 600	336	326	315	303	290	277	1 180	289	1 060	L_u	3 240
t = 11.0	1 170	299	292	284	275	265	255	866	263	1 030	I_x	70.6
	740	262	257	251	245	237	228	548	224	982	S_x	572

† No. of studs/beam = 2 x Q_r x percent shear connection/100/q_r (per stud)

* Units — M_r — kN•m L_u — mm   b — mm
  　　　　　 V_r — kN I_x — 10^6mm^4 t — mm
  　　　　　　　　　　　　　　　　　　　S_x — 10^3mm^3

The Imperial designation for each steel beam is listed below the SI designation to assist designers involved with drawings using Imperial designations.

COMPOSITE BEAMS
Trial Selection Tables

G40.21-M 300W
20 MPa Concrete

76 mm Deck with 65 mm Slab
$\emptyset = 0.90$, $\emptyset_c = 0.67$, $\emptyset_{sc} = 0.80$

Steel Shape		Composite Beam										Steel Shape Data*	
		Factored Resistances							Properties				
	b_1	M_{rc} in kilonewton metres for various percentages of shear connection						Q_r† for 100%	I_1	S_{s_1}			
	mm	100%	90%	80%	70%	60%	50%	kN	10^6mm^4	10^3mm^3		
W250X45	2 400	380	366	351	335	318	300	1 540	325	1 040	M_r	163
W10X30	1 980	364	353	339	325	310	293	1 470	311	1 030	V_r	360
b = 148	1 560	330	320	309	298	285	272	1 150	293	1 010	L_u	2 360
t = 13.0	1 140	294	286	278	270	260	249	844	267	979	I_x	71.1
	720	257	252	246	239	231	222	533	228	929	S_x	534
W250X39	2 400	329	316	303	288	273	257	1 330	283	898	M_r	139
W10X26	1 980	322	311	298	285	271	255	1 330	272	887	V_r	308
b = 147	1 560	299	290	279	268	256	243	1 150	258	872	L_u	2 280
t = 11.2	1 140	264	257	249	240	231	221	844	236	850	I_x	60.1
	720	228	223	218	212	205	196	533	204	810	S_x	459
W250X33	2 400	281	269	257	244	231	217	1 130	243	761	M_r	114
W10X22	1 980	276	265	254	242	229	216	1 130	234	752	V_r	280
b = 146	1 560	268	259	249	238	226	214	1 130	222	740	L_u	2 180
t = 9.1	1 140	236	229	222	213	204	195	844	205	723	I_x	48.9
	720	201	196	191	186	179	171	533	178	692	S_x	379
W200X100	2 470	580	563	544	524	502	479	1 830	481	1 980	M_r	310
W8X67	2 030	539	525	509	492	474	455	1 500	449	1 940	V_r	592
b = 210	1 600	499	487	474	461	446	430	1 180	410	1 880	L_u	5 020
t = 23.7	1 170	458	449	439	428	416	401	866	361	1 800	I_x	113
	740	413	406	398	389	380	370	548	296	1 660	S_x	989
W200X86	2 470	525	508	490	471	450	428	1 830	424	1 740	M_r	265
W8X58	2 030	486	472	457	440	423	404	1 500	398	1 700	V_r	514
b = 209	1 600	447	435	423	410	396	381	1 180	365	1 660	L_u	4 620
t = 20.6	1 170	407	398	389	379	367	354	866	323	1 590	I_x	94.7
	740	365	358	350	342	333	323	548	265	1 470	S_x	853
W200X71	2 460	461	446	429	410	390	368	1 820	360	1 450	M_r	217
W8X48	2 030	425	411	397	381	364	346	1 500	340	1 420	V_r	393
b = 206	1 600	387	376	364	352	338	324	1 180	314	1 390	L_u	4 150
t = 17.4	1 170	348	340	331	322	312	301	866	280	1 340	I_x	76.6
	740	309	303	297	290	282	273	548	232	1 250	S_x	709
W200X59	2 460	412	397	380	362	343	322	1 820	305	1 210	M_r	176
W8X40	2 030	376	363	349	334	318	301	1 500	290	1 190	V_r	341
b = 205	1 600	340	329	318	306	293	279	1 180	269	1 160	L_u	3 780
t = 14.2	1 170	302	294	286	277	267	257	866	242	1 120	I_x	61.1
	740	264	259	253	247	239	231	548	202	1 060	S_x	582

† No. of studs/beam = 2 x Q_r x percent shear connection/100/q_r (per stud)

* Units — M_r — kN•m L_u — mm   b — mm
  V_r — kN I_x — 10^6mm^4 t — mm
  S_x — 10^3mm^3

The Imperial designation for each steel beam is listed below the SI designation to assist designers involved with drawings using Imperial designations.

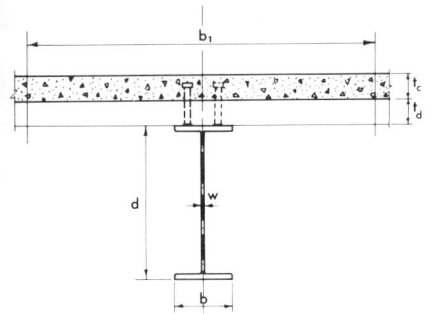

COMPOSITE BEAMS
Trial Selection Tables

G40.21-M 300W
20 MPa Concrete

76 mm Deck with 65 mm Slab
$\emptyset = 0.90$, $\emptyset_c = 0.67$, $\emptyset_{sc} = 0.80$

Steel Shape	b_1 mm	\multicolumn{6}{c}{M_{rc} in kilonewton metres for various percentages of shear connection}	$Q_r^\dagger$ for 100% kN	I_1 $10^6 mm^4$	S_{s1} $10^3 mm^3$	Steel Shape Data*	
		100%	90%	80%	70%	60%	50%					
W200X52	2 460	381	367	351	333	314	294	1 800	273	1 070	M_r	154
W8X35	2 030	348	335	322	307	291	274	1 500	259	1 050	V_r	290
b = 204	1 600	312	302	291	279	266	253	1 180	242	1 030	L_u	3 620
t = 12.6	1 170	275	268	259	250	241	231	866	219	999	I_x	52.7
	740	238	233	227	221	215	207	548	184	943	S_x	512
W200X46	2 460	339	325	310	294	277	258	1 580	244	945	M_r	134
W8X31	2 030	324	312	298	284	268	251	1 500	233	932	V_r	260
b = 203	1 600	288	279	268	256	243	230	1 180	218	914	L_u	3 460
t = 11.0	1 170	252	245	237	228	219	209	866	198	887	I_x	45.5
	740	215	210	205	199	193	186	548	168	841	S_x	448
W200X42	2 420	312	299	284	269	253	236	1 430	226	861	M_r	120
W8X28	2 000	304	292	279	265	250	234	1 430	216	849	V_r	263
b = 166	1 570	273	263	252	241	229	215	1 160	203	833	L_u	2 850
t = 11.8	1 150	237	230	222	214	204	194	851	185	810	I_x	40.9
	730	201	196	191	185	179	172	540	158	769	S_x	399
W200X36	2 420	271	259	246	232	218	202	1 240	197	746	M_r	103
W8X24	2 000	265	254	242	229	215	201	1 240	189	736	V_r	222
b = 165	1 570	250	241	231	219	207	194	1 160	179	723	L_u	2 730
t = 10.2	1 150	216	209	201	192	183	174	851	164	704	I_x	34.4
	730	180	175	170	165	159	152	540	141	671	S_x	342
W200X31	2 390	244	233	221	209	196	182	1 080	184	664	M_r	90.4
W8X21	1 970	240	229	218	207	194	181	1 080	177	656	V_r	240
b = 134	1 550	233	224	214	203	192	179	1 080	168	645	L_u	2 150
t = 10.2	1 140	205	198	190	182	173	163	844	155	629	I_x	31.4
	720	169	165	159	154	148	141	533	134	601	S_x	299
W200X27	2 390	208	198	188	177	166	154	915	158	566	M_r	75.3
W8X18	1 970	205	196	186	175	165	153	915	153	558	V_r	214
b = 133	1 550	200	192	183	173	163	152	915	145	549	L_u	2 050
t = 8.4	1 130	185	179	171	163	155	145	837	135	536	I_x	25.8
	720	152	147	142	137	131	125	533	118	515	S_x	249

$\dagger$ No. of studs/beam = 2 x Q_r x percent shear connection/100/q_r (per stud)

* Units — M_r — kN•m L_u — mm   b — mm
          V_r — kN I_x — $10^6 mm^4$ t — mm
                              S_x — $10^3 mm^3$

The Imperial designation for each steel beam is listed below the SI designation to assist designers involved with drawings using Imperial designations.

COMPOSITE BEAMS
Trial Selection Tables

G40.21-M 300W
25 MPa Concrete

51 mm Deck with 85 mm Slab
$\varnothing = 0.90$, $\varnothing_c = 0.67$, $\varnothing_{sc} = 0.80$

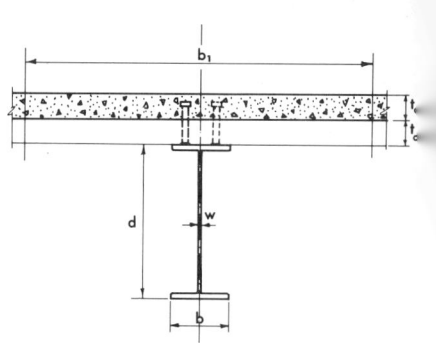

Steel Shape		Composite Beam										Steel Shape Data*	
		Factored Resistances							Properties#				
	b_1	M_{rc} in kilonewton metres for various percentages of shear connection						Q_r† for 100%	I_1	S_{s_1}			
	mm	100%	90%	80%	70%	60%	50%	kN	$10^6 mm^4$	$10^3 mm^3$			
W610X241	2 510	2 850	2 820	2 780	2 740	2 680	2 600	3 040	4 100	8 710	M_r	2 070
W24X162	2 070	2 780	2 740	2 700	2 650	2 590	2 530	2 510	3 870	8 550	V_r	2 030
b = 329	1 630	2 680	2 640	2 600	2 550	2 500	2 440	1 970	3 600	8 350	L_u	5 200
t = 31.0	1 190	2 550	2 520	2 480	2 440	2 390	2 350	1 440	3 300	8 090	I_x	2 150
	750	2 390	2 370	2 340	2 310	2 280	2 250	908	2 940	7 740	S_x	6 780
W610X217	2 500	2 580	2 560	2 530	2 490	2 430	2 370	3 030	3 750	7 880	M_r	1 850
W24X146	2 070	2 520	2 490	2 460	2 410	2 360	2 290	2 510	3 540	7 750	V_r	1 850
b = 328	1 630	2 430	2 400	2 360	2 320	2 270	2 210	1 970	3 300	7 570	L_u	5 080
t = 27.7	1 190	2 320	2 280	2 250	2 210	2 170	2 120	1 440	3 010	7 330	I_x	1 910
	750	2 170	2 140	2 110	2 090	2 060	2 020	908	2 670	7 010	S_x	6 070
W610X195	2 500	2 340	2 310	2 290	2 250	2 200	2 140	3 030	3 410	7 080	M_r	1 640
W24X131	2 060	2 270	2 250	2 220	2 180	2 130	2 070	2 490	3 220	6 950	V_r	1 710
b = 327	1 630	2 200	2 170	2 140	2 100	2 050	1 990	1 970	3 000	6 800	L_u	4 940
t = 24.4	1 190	2 090	2 060	2 030	1 990	1 950	1 910	1 440	2 740	6 590	I_x	1 680
	750	1 950	1 930	1 900	1 870	1 840	1 810	908	2 420	6 300	S_x	5 400
W610X174	2 500	2 100	2 080	2 060	2 030	1 990	1 930	3 030	3 090	6 330	M_r	1 450
W24X117	2 060	2 040	2 030	2 000	1 970	1 920	1 870	2 490	2 920	6 220	V_r	1 540
b = 325	1 630	1 980	1 960	1 930	1 890	1 850	1 790	1 970	2 720	6 080	L_u	4 830
t = 21.6	1 190	1 880	1 860	1 830	1 790	1 750	1 710	1 440	2 480	5 890	I_x	1 470
	750	1 750	1 730	1 700	1 680	1 650	1 620	908	2 180	5 630	S_x	4 780
W610X155	2 500	1 890	1 870	1 850	1 820	1 790	1 740	3 030	2 810	5 650	M_r	1 280
W24X104	2 060	1 840	1 820	1 800	1 770	1 730	1 680	2 490	2 650	5 550	V_r	1 380
b = 324	1 630	1 780	1 760	1 730	1 700	1 660	1 610	1 970	2 480	5 440	L_u	4 740
t = 19.0	1 190	1 700	1 670	1 640	1 610	1 570	1 530	1 440	2 250	5 270	I_x	1 290
	750	1 570	1 550	1 530	1 500	1 470	1 440	908	1 970	5 030	S_x	4 220
W610X140	2 410	1 750	1 730	1 700	1 680	1 640	1 590	2 920	2 560	5 050	M_r	1 120
W24X94	1 980	1 690	1 670	1 650	1 620	1 580	1 520	2 400	2 420	4 960	V_r	1 440
b = 230	1 560	1 630	1 610	1 580	1 540	1 500	1 450	1 890	2 250	4 840	L_u	3 320
t = 22.2	1 140	1 540	1 510	1 480	1 450	1 410	1 370	1 380	2 040	4 680	I_x	1 120
	720	1 410	1 390	1 370	1 340	1 310	1 280	871	1 780	4 450	S_x	3 630
W610X125	2 410	1 580	1 560	1 540	1 510	1 480	1 440	2 920	2 330	4 510	M_r	991
W24X84	1 980	1 520	1 510	1 490	1 460	1 430	1 380	2 400	2 200	4 440	V_r	1 300
b = 229	1 560	1 470	1 450	1 430	1 400	1 360	1 310	1 890	2 050	4 340	L_u	3 250
t = 19.6	1 140	1 390	1 370	1 340	1 310	1 280	1 240	1 380	1 860	4 200	I_x	985
	720	1 270	1 250	1 230	1 210	1 180	1 150	871	1 620	3 990	S_x	3 220

† No. of studs/beam = 2 x Q_r x percent shear connection/100/q_r (per stud)   #Concrete density = 1850 kg/m³

* Units — M_r — kN•m L_u — mm   b — mm
         V_r — kN I_x — $10^6 mm^4$ t — mm
                          S_x — $10^3 mm^3$

The Imperial designation for each steel beam is listed below the SI designation to assist designers involved with drawings using Imperial designations.

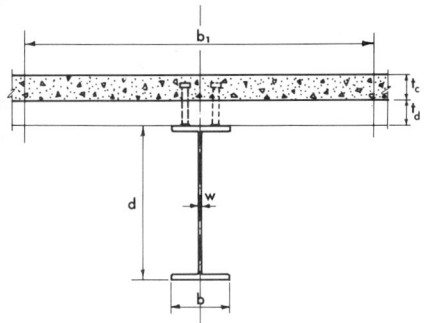

COMPOSITE BEAMS
Trial Selection Tables

G40.21-M 300W
25 MPa Concrete

51 mm Deck with 85 mm Slab
$\varnothing = 0.90, \varnothing_c = 0.67, \varnothing_{sc} = 0.80$

Steel Shape	b_1	M_{rc} in kilonewton metres for various percentages of shear connection						$Q_r^†$ for 100%	I_1	S_{s_1}	Steel Shape Data*	
		100%	90%	80%	70%	60%	50%	kN	$10^6\,mm^4$	$10^3\,mm^3$		
	mm											
W610X113	2 400	1 450	1 430	1 410	1 380	1 360	1 320	2 900	2 130	4 090	M_r	888
W24X76	1 980	1 400	1 380	1 360	1 340	1 310	1 270	2 400	2 020	4 020	V_r	1 210
b = 228	1 560	1 340	1 330	1 310	1 280	1 250	1 200	1 890	1 880	3 930	L_u	3 180
t = 17.3	1 140	1 270	1 250	1 230	1 200	1 170	1 130	1 380	1 710	3 810	I_x	875
	720	1 160	1 140	1 120	1 100	1 070	1 050	871	1 480	3 620	S_x	2 880
W610X101	2 400	1 330	1 310	1 290	1 270	1 240	1 200	2 900	1 940	3 670	M_r	783
W24X68	1 980	1 280	1 260	1 240	1 220	1 190	1 150	2 400	1 840	3 610	V_r	1 130
b = 228	1 560	1 220	1 210	1 190	1 170	1 140	1 090	1 890	1 720	3 530	L_u	3 110
t = 14.9	1 140	1 160	1 140	1 120	1 090	1 060	1 020	1 380	1 560	3 420	I_x	764
	720	1 060	1 040	1 020	993	968	941	871	1 350	3 250	S_x	2 530
W530X138	2 390	1 560	1 540	1 510	1 490	1 450	1 400	2 890	2 060	4 490	M_r	975
W21X93	1 970	1 500	1 480	1 460	1 430	1 390	1 350	2 380	1 940	4 410	V_r	1 440
b = 214	1 550	1 440	1 420	1 400	1 360	1 320	1 280	1 880	1 800	4 300	L_u	3 180
t = 23.6	1 140	1 360	1 340	1 310	1 280	1 250	1 210	1 380	1 630	4 150	I_x	861
	720	1 240	1 220	1 200	1 180	1 150	1 130	871	1 410	3 930	S_x	3 140
W530X123	2 390	1 420	1 400	1 370	1 350	1 320	1 280	2 890	1 870	4 040	M_r	867
W21X83	1 970	1 360	1 340	1 320	1 300	1 270	1 220	2 380	1 770	3 970	V_r	1 270
b = 212	1 550	1 300	1 290	1 270	1 240	1 200	1 160	1 880	1 640	3 870	L_u	3 100
t = 21.2	1 130	1 230	1 210	1 190	1 160	1 130	1 090	1 370	1 490	3 740	I_x	761
	720	1 130	1 110	1 090	1 060	1 040	1 010	871	1 290	3 550	S_x	2 800
W530X109	2 390	1 280	1 260	1 240	1 210	1 190	1 150	2 890	1 700	3 600	M_r	764
W21X73	1 970	1 230	1 210	1 190	1 170	1 140	1 110	2 380	1 610	3 540	V_r	1 110
b = 211	1 550	1 170	1 160	1 140	1 120	1 090	1 050	1 880	1 490	3 460	L_u	3 040
t = 18.8	1 130	1 110	1 090	1 070	1 050	1 020	984	1 370	1 350	3 340	I_x	667
	720	1 020	998	979	957	934	909	871	1 170	3 180	S_x	2 480
W530X101	2 390	1 200	1 190	1 170	1 140	1 110	1 080	2 890	1 600	3 350	M_r	707
W21X68	1 970	1 150	1 140	1 120	1 100	1 070	1 040	2 380	1 520	3 300	V_r	1 040
b = 210	1 550	1 100	1 090	1 070	1 050	1 020	988	1 880	1 410	3 230	L_u	2 990
t = 17.4	1 130	1 040	1 030	1 010	984	956	924	1 370	1 280	3 130	I_x	617
	720	954	937	919	898	876	851	871	1 110	2 970	S_x	2 300
W530X92	2 390	1 120	1 100	1 080	1 060	1 030	1 000	2 890	1 470	3 060	M_r	637
W21X62	1 970	1 070	1 050	1 040	1 020	993	964	2 380	1 400	3 020	V_r	969
b = 209	1 550	1 020	1 000	990	972	947	914	1 880	1 310	2 950	L_u	2 930
t = 15.6	1 130	962	949	932	910	883	852	1 370	1 180	2 860	I_x	552
	720	880	865	847	827	805	781	871	1 030	2 720	S_x	2 070

† No. of studs/beam = 2 x Q_r x percent shear connection/100/q_r (per stud) #Concrete density = 1850 kg/m³

* Units — M_r — kN•m L_u — mm   b — mm
             V_r — kN I_x — $10^6\,mm^4$ t — mm
                                 S_x — $10^3\,mm^3$

The Imperial designation for each steel beam is listed below the SI designation to assist designers involved with drawings using Imperial designations.

COMPOSITE BEAMS
Trial Selection Tables

G40.21-M 300W
25 MPa Concrete

51 mm Deck with 85 mm Slab
$\emptyset = 0.90$, $\emptyset_c = 0.67$, $\emptyset_{sc} = 0.80$

Steel Shape	b$_1$	Composite Beam									Steel Shape Data*	
		Factored Resistances							Properties#			
		M$_{rc}$ in kilonewton metres for various percentages of shear connection						Q$_r$† for 100%	I$_1$	S$_{s1}$		
	mm	100%	90%	80%	70%	60%	50%	kN	10^{6}mm^4	10^{3}mm^3		
W530X82	2 390	1 020	999	980	957	932	903	2 830	1 330	2 720	M$_r$	559
W21X55	1 970	970	956	939	920	898	871	2 380	1 260	2 680	V$_r$	894
b = 209	1 550	920	908	894	878	856	826	1 880	1 180	2 630	L$_u$	2 860
t = 13.3	1 130	867	856	841	821	797	767	1 370	1 070	2 550	I$_x$	479
	720	793	778	762	743	721	698	871	929	2 420	S$_x$	1 810
W460X106	2 370	1 120	1 100	1 080	1 060	1 030	996	2 870	1 310	3 140	M$_r$	645
W18X71	1 960	1 070	1 050	1 030	1 010	988	956	2 370	1 240	3 080	V$_r$	1 050
b = 194	1 540	1 010	1 000	985	965	938	905	1 860	1 150	3 010	L$_u$	2 910
t = 20.6	1 130	957	943	925	903	877	847	1 370	1 040	2 910	I$_x$	488
	710	871	856	839	821	800	778	859	893	2 750	S$_x$	2 080
W460X97	2 370	1 040	1 020	1 000	979	952	921	2 870	1 220	2 880	M$_r$	589
W18X65	1 950	990	975	957	936	913	885	2 360	1 160	2 830	V$_r$	947
b = 193	1 540	938	925	910	893	870	841	1 860	1 080	2 770	L$_u$	2 870
t = 19.0	1 130	883	872	857	837	814	786	1 370	975	2 680	I$_x$	445
	710	807	794	778	760	741	720	859	836	2 540	S$_x$	1 910
W460X89	2 370	981	964	944	920	894	864	2 870	1 150	2 680	M$_r$	543
W18X60	1 950	931	916	898	878	856	830	2 360	1 090	2 640	V$_r$	866
b = 192	1 540	880	867	852	836	816	789	1 860	1 010	2 580	L$_u$	2 830
t = 17.7	1 120	825	815	802	784	762	736	1 360	917	2 500	I$_x$	410
	710	757	744	729	713	694	673	859	788	2 370	S$_x$	1 770
W460X82	2 370	911	895	875	852	827	798	2 810	1 060	2 450	M$_r$	494
W18X55	1 950	866	851	834	815	793	768	2 360	1 010	2 420	V$_r$	812
b = 191	1 540	816	804	790	773	755	731	1 860	941	2 370	L$_u$	2 770
t = 16.0	1 120	762	753	742	726	706	681	1 360	853	2 290	I$_x$	370
	710	700	688	675	659	641	621	859	734	2 180	S$_x$	1 610
W460X74	2 370	834	817	798	776	751	724	2 550	976	2 240	M$_r$	445
W18X50	1 950	803	790	773	755	733	709	2 360	929	2 200	V$_r$	733
b = 190	1 540	755	743	730	714	697	675	1 860	871	2 160	L$_u$	2 730
t = 14.5	1 120	703	694	683	670	652	629	1 360	791	2 100	I$_x$	333
	710	645	635	622	607	590	571	859	682	1 990	S$_x$	1 460
W460X67	2 370	769	753	734	713	690	664	2 340	903	2 050	M$_r$	405
W18X45	1 950	752	738	723	704	683	660	2 340	862	2 020	V$_r$	688
b = 190	1 540	705	694	681	665	648	628	1 860	809	1 990	L$_u$	2 660
t = 12.7	1 120	654	645	635	622	605	583	1 360	736	1 930	I$_x$	300
	710	598	588	576	561	544	525	859	636	1 830	S$_x$	1 320

† No. of studs/beam = 2 x Q$_r$ x percent shear connection/100/q$_r$ (per stud)

\#Concrete density = 1850 kg/m^3

* Units — M$_r$ — kN•m   L$_u$ — mm   b — mm
  V$_r$ — kN   I$_x$ — 10^{6}mm^4 t — mm
  S$_x$ — 10^{3}mm^3

The Imperial designation for each steel beam is listed below the SI designation to assist designers involved with drawings using Imperial designations.

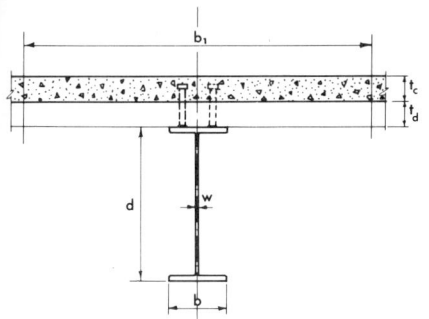

COMPOSITE BEAMS
Trial Selection Tables

G40.21-M 300W
25 MPa Concrete

51 mm Deck with 85 mm Slab
$$\varnothing = 0.90,\ \varnothing_c = 0.67,\ \varnothing_{sc} = 0.80$$

Steel Shape	b_1	Composite Beam — Factored Resistances M_{rc} in kilonewton metres for various percentages of shear connection						Q_r for 100%	I_1	S_{s_1}	Steel Shape Data*	
	mm	100%	90%	80%	70%	60%	50%	kN	$10^6\,mm^4$	$10^3\,mm^3$		
W460X61	2 370	691	675	657	637	616	592	2 100	812	1 830	M_r	354
W18X41	1 950	677	664	648	630	610	589	2 100	776	1 800	V_r	650
b = 189	1 540	645	635	622	607	590	571	1 860	731	1 770	L_u	2 580
t = 10.8	1 120	595	587	577	566	550	528	1 360	667	1 720	I_x	259
	710	542	533	522	508	491	472	859	577	1 640	S_x	1 150
W410X85	2 360	875	859	839	816	790	761	2 860	930	2 360	M_r	467
W16X57	1 940	826	811	794	774	752	727	2 350	881	2 320	V_r	810
b = 181	1 530	775	763	749	732	714	690	1 850	821	2 270	L_u	2 730
t = 18.2	1 120	722	713	701	686	667	643	1 360	743	2 200	I_x	315
	710	661	650	637	622	605	586	859	637	2 080	S_x	1 510
W410X74	2 360	784	768	748	726	702	675	2 580	838	2 100	M_r	408
W16X50	1 940	752	738	722	703	681	657	2 350	796	2 070	V_r	714
b = 180	1 530	703	691	677	662	644	624	1 850	744	2 020	L_u	2 670
t = 16.0	1 120	651	642	632	619	602	581	1 360	675	1 960	I_x	275
	710	595	586	574	560	544	526	859	580	1 860	S_x	1 330
W410X67	2 360	712	695	676	655	632	607	2 320	767	1 900	M_r	367
W16X45	1 940	694	681	665	647	626	603	2 320	731	1 870	V_r	643
b = 179	1 530	648	637	623	608	591	572	1 850	685	1 830	L_u	2 610
t = 14.4	1 120	598	589	579	567	553	533	1 360	624	1 780	I_x	246
	710	545	537	526	514	499	482	859	537	1 690	S_x	1 200
W410X60	2 350	632	616	598	579	557	535	2 050	689	1 680	M_r	321
W16X40	1 940	619	605	590	572	553	531	2 050	659	1 660	V_r	558
b = 178	1 530	589	579	566	551	535	516	1 850	620	1 630	L_u	2 580
t = 12.8	1 120	541	532	522	511	498	482	1 360	567	1 590	I_x	216
	710	489	483	475	464	451	435	859	490	1 510	S_x	1 060
W410X54	2 350	570	554	538	519	500	478	1 840	620	1 500	M_r	283
W16X36	1 940	559	546	531	514	496	476	1 840	594	1 480	V_r	539
b = 177	1 530	543	533	520	506	490	472	1 840	560	1 460	L_u	2 480
t = 10.9	1 120	496	488	478	467	455	440	1 360	514	1 420	I_x	186
	710	446	440	432	422	409	393	859	445	1 350	S_x	924
W410X46	2 320	498	484	468	452	434	415	1 590	546	1 300	M_r	239
W16X31	1 910	490	477	463	448	431	413	1 590	524	1 280	V_r	503
b = 140	1 510	478	467	455	442	426	410	1 590	496	1 260	L_u	1 930
t = 11.2	1 100	444	437	427	417	405	390	1 330	456	1 230	I_x	156
	690	395	389	382	373	361	346	835	395	1 170	S_x	773

† No. of studs/beam = 2 x Q_r x percent shear connection/100/q_r (per stud)
\# Concrete density = 1850 kg/m³

* Units — M_r — kN•m L_u — mm   b — mm
        V_r — kN I_x — $10^6\,mm^4$ t — mm
                S_x — $10^3\,mm^3$

The Imperial designation for each steel beam is listed below the SI designation to assist designers involved with drawings using Imperial designations.

COMPOSITE BEAMS
Trial Selection Tables

G40.21-M 300W
25 MPa Concrete

51 mm Deck with 85 mm Slab
$\emptyset = 0.90$, $\emptyset_c = 0.67$, $\emptyset_{sc} = 0.80$

Steel Shape	b_1	Composite Beam — Factored Resistances — M_{rc} in kilonewton metres for various percentages of shear connection						$Q_r^\dagger$ for 100%	Properties# I_1	S_{s_1}	Steel Shape Data*	
	mm	100%	90%	80%	70%	60%	50%	kN	$10^6\,mm^4$	$10^3\,mm^3$		
W410X39	2 320	425	411	397	383	367	351	1 350	468	1 100	M_r	197
W16X26	1 910	419	407	394	380	365	349	1 350	451	1 090	V_r	448
b = 140	1 510	410	399	388	375	362	347	1 350	428	1 070	L_u	1 860
t = 8.8	1 100	393	386	377	367	355	342	1 330	396	1 040	I_x	127
	690	345	340	334	326	315	301	835	345	995	S_x	634
W360X79	2 380	744	727	708	685	660	632	2 730	704	2 020	M_r	386
W14X53	1 960	704	690	673	654	632	608	2 370	668	1 990	V_r	593
b = 205	1 550	655	643	629	613	595	576	1 880	624	1 950	L_u	3 270
t = 16.8	1 130	602	593	582	570	557	539	1 370	563	1 890	I_x	227
	710	547	540	531	520	506	490	859	480	1 790	S_x	1 280
W360X72	2 380	676	659	640	618	595	569	2 460	642	1 830	M_r	346
W14X48	1 960	652	639	623	604	583	559	2 370	610	1 800	V_r	536
b = 204	1 550	604	593	579	564	547	528	1 880	571	1 770	L_u	3 190
t = 15.1	1 130	553	544	534	522	509	493	1 370	517	1 710	I_x	201
	710	499	493	485	475	462	447	859	442	1 620	S_x	1 150
W360X64	2 380	609	592	574	554	531	507	2 200	583	1 640	M_r	308
W14X43	1 960	594	580	564	546	526	504	2 200	556	1 620	V_r	476
b = 203	1 550	556	545	532	517	500	482	1 880	522	1 590	L_u	3 110
t = 13.5	1 130	506	497	487	476	463	449	1 370	474	1 540	I_x	178
	710	453	448	441	432	421	407	859	406	1 470	S_x	1 030
W360X57	2 350	557	541	524	505	484	462	1 950	548	1 480	M_r	273
W14X38	1 940	545	532	516	499	480	459	1 950	524	1 460	V_r	504
b = 172	1 530	522	511	499	484	468	450	1 850	493	1 430	L_u	2 550
t = 13.1	1 120	474	465	456	444	432	418	1 360	450	1 390	I_x	161
	700	422	416	409	400	388	374	847	386	1 320	S_x	897
W360X51	2 350	501	485	469	451	432	412	1 740	495	1 320	M_r	241
W14X34	1 940	491	478	463	447	429	410	1 740	475	1 310	V_r	455
b = 171	1 530	476	466	453	439	424	406	1 740	448	1 280	L_u	2 500
t = 11.6	1 110	434	426	416	406	393	380	1 340	409	1 250	I_x	141
	700	384	378	372	364	354	341	847	353	1 190	S_x	796
W360X45	2 350	447	433	417	401	384	365	1 550	444	1 180	M_r	210
W14X30	1 940	439	426	412	397	381	363	1 550	426	1 160	V_r	433
b = 171	1 530	428	417	405	391	377	361	1 550	403	1 140	L_u	2 430
t = 9.8	1 110	398	390	381	370	358	345	1 340	370	1 110	I_x	122
	700	349	343	337	330	320	308	847	321	1 060	S_x	691

† No. of studs/beam = 2 x Q_r x percent shear connection/100/q_r (per stud)   #Concrete density = 1850 kg/m³

* Units — M_r — kN•m L_u — mm   b — mm
  V_r — kN I_x — $10^6\,mm^4$ t — mm
  S_x — $10^3\,mm^3$

The Imperial designation for each steel beam is listed below the SI designation to assist designers involved with drawings using Imperial designations.

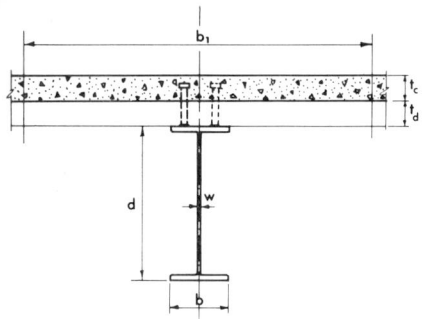

COMPOSITE BEAMS
Trial Selection Tables

G40.21-M 300W
25 MPa Concrete

51 mm Deck with 85 mm Slab
$\emptyset = 0.90$, $\emptyset_c = 0.67$, $\emptyset_{sc} = 0.80$

Steel Shape		Composite Beam										Steel Shape Data*	
		Factored Resistances							Properties#				
	b_1	M_{rc} in kilonewton metres for various percentages of shear connection						$Q_r^\dagger$ for 100%	I_1	S_{s_1}			
	mm	100%	90%	80%	70%	60%	50%	kN	10^6 mm⁴	10^3 mm³			
W360X39	2 300	393	379	365	351	335	319	1 340	392	1 020	M_r	179
W14X26	1 900	387	375	362	348	333	317	1 340	377	1 010	V_r	409
b = 128	1 500	378	367	356	343	330	315	1 340	358	989	L_u	1 790
t = 10.7	1 090	361	353	344	334	323	310	1 320	330	963	I_x	102
	690	314	308	302	295	286	274	835	287	921	S_x	580
W360X33	2 300	330	319	306	293	280	266	1 130	332	855	M_r	146
W14X22	1 900	326	315	304	291	278	265	1 130	321	844	V_r	361
b = 127	1 500	320	310	300	288	276	263	1 130	306	830	L_u	1 720
t = 8.5	1 090	309	301	292	283	272	261	1 130	284	810	I_x	82.7
	690	274	269	263	256	249	238	835	249	777	S_x	474
W310X129	2 480	983	963	941	915	886	854	3 000	868	2 980	M_r	583
W12X87	2 050	929	912	892	871	846	820	2 480	816	2 930	V_r	742
b = 308	1 610	872	858	842	825	805	784	1 950	752	2 850	L_u	5 580
t = 20.6	1 180	814	804	792	779	762	741	1 430	673	2 740	I_x	308
	750	754	745	734	722	707	690	908	573	2 580	S_x	1 940
W310X118	2 480	913	894	873	848	820	788	3 000	800	2 720	M_r	526
W12X79	2 050	860	844	825	804	781	754	2 480	753	2 670	V_r	666
b = 307	1 610	805	791	776	759	740	719	1 950	695	2 600	L_u	5 390
t = 18.7	1 180	749	738	727	714	699	680	1 430	623	2 510	I_x	275
	740	689	681	671	659	645	629	896	527	2 360	S_x	1 750
W310X107	2 480	850	832	811	787	759	729	3 000	740	2 490	M_r	478
W12X72	2 050	799	783	765	744	721	695	2 480	698	2 440	V_r	604
b = 306	1 610	744	731	716	700	681	661	1 950	645	2 380	L_u	5 220
t = 17.0	1 180	689	679	668	656	642	625	1 430	579	2 300	I_x	248
	740	631	625	616	605	592	577	896	490	2 170	S_x	1 590
W310X97	2 480	792	774	754	730	703	674	3 000	681	2 260	M_r	389
W12X65	2 050	741	726	708	688	666	641	2 480	644	2 220	V_r	543
b = 305	1 610	688	675	661	645	627	607	1 950	596	2 170	L_u	5 410
t = 15.4	1 180	634	624	614	601	588	572	1 430	537	2 100	I_x	222
	740	577	571	563	554	542	527	896	455	1 980	S_x	1 440
W310X86	2 430	735	719	699	676	650	621	2 940	628	2 040	M_r	383
W12X58	2 000	686	671	654	634	612	588	2 420	594	2 010	V_r	503
b = 254	1 580	635	623	609	593	575	555	1 910	553	1 960	L_u	4 250
t = 16.3	1 150	581	572	561	549	536	521	1 390	497	1 900	I_x	199
	730	527	521	514	505	493	479	883	423	1 790	S_x	1 280

† No. of studs/beam = 2 x Q_r x percent shear connection/100/q_r (per stud)   #Concrete density = 1850 kg/m³

* Units — M_r — kN•m L_u — mm   b — mm
  V_r — kN I_x — 10^6 mm⁴   t — mm
                     S_x — 10^3 mm³

The Imperial designation for each steel beam is listed below the SI designation to assist designers involved with drawings using Imperial designations.

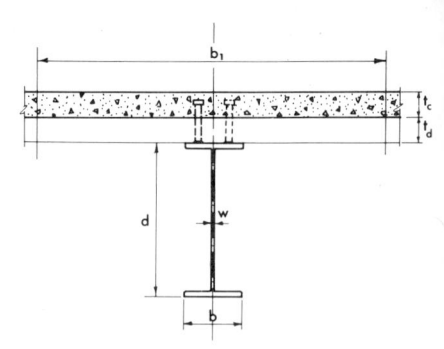

COMPOSITE BEAMS
Trial Selection Tables

G40.21-M 300W
25 MPa Concrete

51 mm Deck with 85 mm Slab
$\varnothing = 0.90$, $\varnothing_c = 0.67$, $\varnothing_{sc} = 0.80$

Steel Shape	b₁	\multicolumn{6}{c}{M_{rc} in kilonewton metres for various percentages of shear connection}	Q_r for 100%	I_1	S_{s_1}	Steel Shape Data*
	mm	100%	90%	80%	70%	60%	50%	kN	$10^6\,mm^4$	$10^3\,mm^3$	
W310X79	2 430	681	664	644	622	597	569	2 730	578	1 870	M_r 346
W12X53	2 000	643	629	612	593	572	548	2 420	548	1 840	V_r 480
b = 254	1 580	594	582	568	552	535	516	1 910	510	1 800	L_u 4 140
t = 14.6	1 150	541	532	521	510	496	482	1 390	460	1 740	I_x 177
	730	487	481	474	466	454	441	883	392	1 650	S_x 1 160
W310X74	2 380	649	632	613	591	567	540	2 560	554	1 760	M_r 321
W12X50	1 960	619	605	589	570	549	525	2 370	525	1 730	V_r 519
b = 205	1 550	570	559	545	530	512	493	1 880	490	1 690	L_u 3 380
t = 16.3	1 130	519	509	499	487	474	459	1 370	442	1 630	I_x 165
	710	464	458	451	441	430	416	859	375	1 540	S_x 1 060
W310X67	2 380	586	569	551	530	507	482	2 300	502	1 580	M_r 286
W12X45	1 960	569	556	540	522	501	478	2 300	477	1 550	V_r 463
b = 204	1 550	526	515	502	487	470	451	1 880	446	1 520	L_u 3 280
t = 14.6	1 130	475	467	457	445	432	418	1 370	404	1 470	I_x 145
	710	422	417	410	402	391	378	859	343	1 400	S_x 949
W310X60	2 380	527	511	493	473	452	430	2 050	456	1 420	M_r 254
W12X40	1 960	514	500	485	467	448	426	2 050	435	1 400	V_r 405
b = 203	1 550	486	475	462	448	431	412	1 880	408	1 370	L_u 3 200
t = 13.1	1 130	436	428	418	407	394	380	1 370	371	1 330	I_x 129
	710	384	379	372	365	356	344	859	317	1 260	S_x 849
W310X52	2 340	482	466	450	431	412	391	1 800	433	1 270	M_r 226
W12X35	1 930	471	458	443	426	408	389	1 800	414	1 260	V_r 429
b = 167	1 520	455	445	433	419	403	385	1 800	389	1 230	L_u 2 570
t = 13.2	1 110	410	402	392	381	369	355	1 340	355	1 200	I_x 118
	700	360	354	348	340	331	319	847	304	1 140	S_x 747
W310X45	2 340	414	400	384	368	351	333	1 540	376	1 090	M_r 191
W12X30	1 930	406	394	380	364	348	331	1 540	361	1 080	V_r 368
b = 166	1 520	395	384	372	359	344	328	1 540	341	1 060	L_u 2 490
t = 11.2	1 110	366	358	349	338	327	313	1 340	313	1 030	I_x 99.2
	700	317	312	305	298	291	281	847	270	984	S_x 634
W310X39	2 340	361	348	334	320	304	288	1 330	332	954	M_r 165
W12X26	1 930	356	344	331	317	302	287	1 330	319	942	V_r 320
b = 165	1 520	347	337	325	313	299	285	1 330	303	926	L_u 2 440
t = 9.7	1 110	332	324	315	305	294	281	1 330	279	903	I_x 85.1
	700	285	279	273	267	259	250	847	243	864	S_x 549

† No. of studs/beam = 2 x Q_r x percent shear connection/100/q_r (per stud)

\# Concrete density = 1850 kg/m³

* Units — M_r — kN•m L_u — mm   b — mm
         V_r — kN I_x — $10^6\,mm^4$ t — mm
                  S_x — $10^3\,mm^3$

The Imperial designation for each steel beam is listed below the SI designation to assist designers involved with drawings using Imperial designations.

COMPOSITE BEAMS
Trial Selection Tables

G40.21-M 300W
25 MPa Concrete

51 mm Deck with 85 mm Slab
$$\phi = 0.90, \; \phi_c = 0.67, \; \phi_{sc} = 0.80$$

Steel Shape	b_1	Composite Beam — Factored Resistances — M_{rc} in kilonewton metres for various percentages of shear connection						$Q_r^\dagger$ for 100%	Properties# I_1	S_{s_1}	Steel Shape Data*	
	mm	100%	90%	80%	70%	60%	50%	kN	$10^6\,mm^4$	$10^3\,mm^3$		
W250X101	2 430	734	716	695	671	644	614	2 940	554	2 110	M_r	378
W10X68	2 010	683	668	650	629	606	581	2 430	521	2 070	V_r	560
b = 257	1 580	630	617	602	585	567	546	1 910	480	2 010	L_u	4 950
t = 19.6	1 160	575	566	554	542	528	512	1 400	428	1 940	I_x	164
	730	518	511	504	494	483	469	883	358	1 810	S_x	1 240
W250X89	2 430	675	658	638	615	589	560	2 940	500	1 880	M_r	332
W10X60	2 010	626	611	594	574	552	527	2 430	472	1 850	V_r	496
b = 256	1 580	574	562	547	531	513	494	1 910	436	1 800	L_u	4 690
t = 17.3	1 160	521	512	501	489	475	460	1 400	390	1 730	I_x	143
	730	465	459	452	444	433	421	883	327	1 630	S_x	1 100
W250X80	2 430	617	601	581	559	533	505	2 750	454	1 690	M_r	294
W10X54	2 010	580	565	549	529	508	483	2 430	430	1 660	V_r	429
b = 255	1 580	529	517	503	487	470	450	1 910	398	1 620	L_u	4 520
t = 15.6	1 150	476	467	456	445	431	417	1 390	356	1 560	I_x	126
	730	422	416	409	402	393	381	883	300	1 470	S_x	982
W250X73	2 430	567	550	531	509	485	459	2 510	418	1 540	M_r	266
W10X49	2 000	543	529	513	495	473	450	2 420	396	1 520	V_r	388
b = 254	1 580	494	483	470	454	437	418	1 910	368	1 480	L_u	4 390
t = 14.2	1 150	443	434	423	412	399	385	1 390	331	1 430	I_x	113
	730	390	384	377	370	361	351	883	280	1 350	S_x	891
W250X67	2 380	532	515	497	476	453	428	2 310	396	1 430	M_r	243
W10X45	1 960	515	502	486	467	447	424	2 310	376	1 410	V_r	408
b = 204	1 550	471	460	447	432	415	396	1 880	350	1 380	L_u	3 570
t = 15.7	1 130	420	412	402	390	377	363	1 370	315	1 330	I_x	104
	710	367	362	355	347	339	328	859	266	1 250	S_x	806
W250X58	2 380	466	449	432	412	392	369	2 000	348	1 240	M_r	208
W10X39	1 960	453	439	424	406	387	366	2 000	331	1 220	V_r	359
b = 203	1 550	428	417	404	390	373	355	1 880	310	1 200	L_u	3 410
t = 13.5	1 130	378	370	360	349	337	323	1 370	280	1 160	I_x	87.3
	710	327	321	315	307	299	289	859	237	1 100	S_x	693
W250X49	2 380	396	381	365	347	329	309	1 690	297	1 050	M_r	171
W10X33	1 960	387	373	359	343	326	307	1 690	284	1 030	V_r	326
b = 202	1 550	373	363	350	336	321	304	1 690	267	1 010	L_u	3 240
t = 11.0	1 130	336	328	318	308	296	282	1 370	243	984	I_x	70.6
	710	286	280	274	267	259	250	859	207	933	S_x	572

† No. of studs/beam = 2 x Q_r x percent shear connection/100/q_r (per stud)

#Concrete density = 1850 kg/m³

* Units — M_r — kN•m L_u — mm   b — mm
  V_r — kN I_x — $10^6\,mm^4$ t — mm
  S_x — $10^3\,mm^3$

The Imperial designation for each steel beam is listed below the SI designation to assist designers involved with drawings using Imperial designations.

COMPOSITE BEAMS
Trial Selection Tables

G40.21-M 300W
25 MPa Concrete

51 mm Deck with 85 mm Slab
$\emptyset = 0.90$, $\emptyset_c = 0.67$, $\emptyset_{SC} = 0.80$

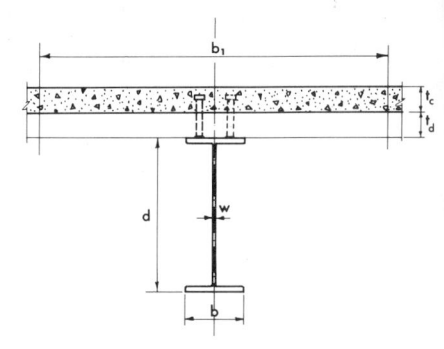

Steel Shape	b_1	Composite Beam M_{rc} in kilonewton metres for various percentages of shear connection						Q_r for 100%	I_1	S_{s_1}	Steel Shape Data*
	mm	100%	90%	80%	70%	60%	50%	kN	$10^6\,mm^4$	$10^3\,mm^3$	
W250X45	2 320	379	365	350	333	316	298	1 540	300	994	M_r 163
W10X30	1 920	372	359	345	330	313	296	1 540	288	980	V_r 360
b = 148	1 510	360	349	337	324	309	293	1 540	271	960	L_u 2 360
t = 13.0	1 100	330	322	313	302	290	277	1 330	247	932	I_x 71.1
	700	282	276	270	263	255	245	847	212	886	S_x 534
W250X39	2 320	328	315	301	286	271	255	1 330	262	860	M_r 139
W10X26	1 920	322	310	297	284	269	254	1 330	252	848	V_r 308
b = 147	1 510	314	303	292	279	266	251	1 330	238	832	L_u 2 280
t = 11.2	1 100	298	291	282	272	260	247	1 330	218	809	I_x 60.1
	700	252	247	240	234	226	217	847	189	772	S_x 459
W250X33	2 320	279	267	255	242	229	215	1 130	225	731	M_r 114
W10X22	1 920	275	264	253	240	227	214	1 130	216	720	V_r 280
b = 146	1 510	269	259	249	237	225	212	1 130	205	707	L_u 2 180
t = 9.1	1 100	258	250	242	232	221	210	1 130	189	688	I_x 48.9
	700	224	219	213	206	199	191	847	165	658	S_x 379
W200X100	2 390	662	644	623	599	572	541	2 890	441	1 880	M_r 310
W8X67	1 970	611	595	577	556	533	507	2 380	413	1 840	V_r 592
b = 210	1 550	557	544	529	512	494	473	1 880	378	1 780	L_u 5 020
t = 23.7	1 130	502	492	480	467	453	438	1 370	334	1 700	I_x 113
	720	445	438	431	421	410	398	871	277	1 580	S_x 989
W200X86	2 390	603	586	567	544	517	488	2 890	388	1 650	M_r 265
W8X58	1 970	554	539	522	502	480	455	2 380	365	1 610	V_r 514
b = 209	1 550	502	490	476	460	442	422	1 880	335	1 570	L_u 4 620
t = 20.6	1 130	449	439	428	416	402	387	1 370	297	1 500	I_x 94.7
	720	394	388	380	372	362	350	871	247	1 400	S_x 853
W200X71	2 380	511	494	475	454	430	404	2 460	329	1 370	M_r 217
W8X48	1 970	489	475	459	440	419	395	2 380	311	1 350	V_r 393
b = 206	1 550	440	428	415	399	382	363	1 880	288	1 310	L_u 4 150
t = 17.4	1 130	388	379	369	357	344	330	1 370	257	1 260	I_x 76.6
	710	334	328	322	314	306	296	859	213	1 180	S_x 709
W200X59	2 380	430	414	396	377	356	333	2 040	279	1 150	M_r 176
W8X40	1 960	417	404	388	370	351	330	2 040	264	1 130	V_r 341
b = 205	1 550	390	379	366	351	335	316	1 880	246	1 100	L_u 3 780
t = 14.2	1 130	340	332	322	311	298	284	1 370	221	1 060	I_x 61.1
	710	288	283	276	269	261	252	859	185	997	S_x 582

† No. of studs/beam = 2 x Q_r x percent shear connection/100/q_r (per stud)

\# Concrete density = 1850 kg/m³

* Units — M_r — kN•m L_u — mm   b — mm
  V_r — kN I_x — $10^6\,mm^4$ t — mm
  S_x — $10^3\,mm^3$

The Imperial designation for each steel beam is listed below the SI designation to assist designers involved with drawings using Imperial designations.

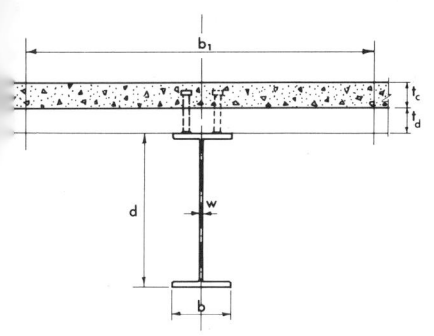

COMPOSITE BEAMS
Trial Selection Tables

G40.21-M 300W
25 MPa Concrete

51 mm Deck with 85 mm Slab
$\emptyset = 0.90$, $\emptyset_c = 0.67$, $\emptyset_{sc} = 0.80$

Steel Shape	b_1	\multicolumn{6}{c}{M_{rc} in kilnewton metres for various percentages of shear connection}						Q_r† for 100%	I_1	S_{s_1}	\multicolumn{2}{c}{Steel Shape Data*}
		100%	90%	80%	70%	60%	50%	kN	10^6mm^4	10^3mm^3		
	mm											
W200X52	2 380	382	367	350	332	312	292	1 800	249	1 020	M_r	154
W8X35	1 960	372	358	343	327	309	289	1 800	237	998	V_r	290
b = 204	1 550	357	346	333	319	303	286	1 800	221	976	L_u	3 620
t = 12.6	1 130	312	304	295	284	272	258	1 370	200	944	I_x	52.7
	710	262	256	250	243	235	226	859	168	890	S_x	512
W200X46	2 380	339	324	309	292	275	256	1 580	222	900	M_r	134
W8X31	1 960	331	318	304	288	272	254	1 580	212	884	V_r	260
b = 203	1 550	319	308	296	282	267	251	1 580	199	865	L_u	3 460
t = 11.0	1 130	288	280	271	261	249	235	1 370	181	838	I_x	45.5
	710	239	233	227	220	212	204	859	153	793	S_x	448
W200X42	2 340	311	297	283	267	251	234	1 430	207	820	M_r	120
W8X28	1 930	305	292	279	264	249	232	1 430	197	806	V_r	263
b = 166	1 520	294	284	272	259	245	230	1 430	185	789	L_u	2 850
t = 11.8	1 110	273	265	256	246	234	221	1 340	169	765	I_x	40.9
	700	224	219	213	206	198	190	847	144	725	S_x	399
W200X36	2 340	270	257	244	230	216	200	1 240	180	712	M_r	103
W8X24	1 930	265	253	241	228	214	199	1 240	173	700	V_r	222
b = 165	1 520	257	247	236	224	211	197	1 240	163	686	L_u	2 730
t = 10.2	1 110	244	236	228	218	206	194	1 240	149	665	I_x	34.4
	700	203	198	192	185	177	169	847	128	633	S_x	342
W200X31	2 310	243	231	219	207	194	180	1 080	169	636	M_r	90.4
W8X21	1 910	239	228	217	205	193	179	1 080	162	626	V_r	240
b = 134	1 500	233	223	213	202	190	178	1 080	153	613	L_u	2 150
t = 10.2	1 100	223	215	207	197	187	176	1 080	141	595	I_x	31.4
	690	191	186	180	174	166	158	835	122	567	S_x	299
W200X27	2 310	206	196	186	175	164	152	915	145	542	M_r	75.3
W8X18	1 900	204	194	184	174	163	152	915	140	534	V_r	214
b = 133	1 500	200	191	182	172	161	151	915	133	523	L_u	2 050
t = 8.4	1 100	192	185	177	168	159	149	915	123	509	I_x	25.8
	690	173	168	162	156	149	141	835	107	486	S_x	249

† No. of studs/beam = 2 x Q_r x percent shear connection/100/q_r (per stud)

Concrete density = 1850 kg/m^3

* Units — M_r — kN•m L_u — mm   b — mm
         V_r — kN I_x — 10^6mm^4 t — mm
                        S_x — 10^3mm^3

The Imperial designation for each steel beam is listed below the SI designation to assist designers involved with drawings using Imperial designations.

COMPOSITE BEAMS
Trial Selection Tables

G40.21-M 300W
25 MPa Concrete

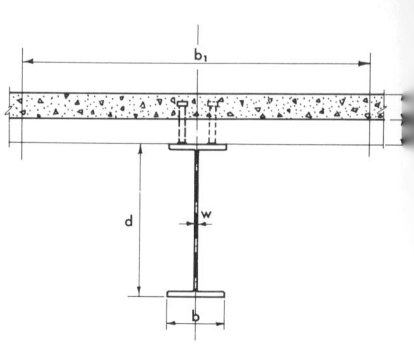

76 mm Deck with 85 mm Slab
$\emptyset = 0.90$, $\emptyset_c = 0.67$, $\emptyset_{sc} = 0.80$

Steel Shape	b_1 (mm)	100%	90%	80%	70%	60%	50%	Q_r† for 100% (kN)	I_1 (10^6 mm⁴)	S_{s_1} (10^3 mm³)	Steel Shape Data*	
W610X241	2 910	2 990	2 950	2 910	2 860	2 790	2 710	3 520	4 550	9 180	M_r	2 070
W24X162	2 400	2 900	2 870	2 820	2 770	2 700	2 620	2 900	4 280	9 000	V_r	2 030
b = 329	1 890	2 800	2 760	2 710	2 650	2 590	2 520	2 290	3 960	8 770	L_u	5 200
t = 31.0	1 380	2 650	2 610	2 570	2 520	2 470	2 410	1 670	3 590	8 470	I_x	2 150
	870	2 470	2 430	2 400	2 370	2 330	2 290	1 050	3 150	8 040	S_x	6 780
W610X217	2 900	2 730	2 690	2 650	2 610	2 550	2 470	3 510	4 170	8 320	M_r	1 850
W24X146	2 400	2 640	2 610	2 570	2 520	2 460	2 390	2 900	3 930	8 170	V_r	1 850
b = 328	1 890	2 550	2 510	2 470	2 420	2 360	2 290	2 290	3 640	7 960	L_u	5 080
t = 27.7	1 380	2 410	2 380	2 330	2 290	2 240	2 180	1 670	3 300	7 690	I_x	1 910
	870	2 240	2 210	2 170	2 140	2 100	2 060	1 050	2 880	7 300	S_x	6 070
W610X195	2 900	2 480	2 440	2 400	2 360	2 310	2 240	3 510	3 800	7 480	M_r	1 640
W24X131	2 390	2 390	2 360	2 330	2 290	2 230	2 160	2 890	3 580	7 340	V_r	1 710
b = 327	1 890	2 310	2 270	2 240	2 190	2 130	2 070	2 290	3 320	7 160	L_u	4 940
t = 24.4	1 380	2 180	2 150	2 110	2 070	2 020	1 970	1 670	3 010	6 920	I_x	1 680
	870	2 020	1 990	1 960	1 920	1 890	1 850	1 050	2 610	6 570	S_x	5 400
W610X174	2 900	2 240	2 210	2 170	2 130	2 090	2 030	3 510	3 450	6 690	M_r	1 450
W24X117	2 390	2 160	2 130	2 100	2 060	2 020	1 950	2 890	3 250	6 570	V_r	1 540
b = 325	1 890	2 080	2 050	2 020	1 980	1 930	1 870	2 290	3 020	6 420	L_u	4 830
t = 21.6	1 380	1 970	1 940	1 910	1 870	1 820	1 770	1 670	2 730	6 200	I_x	1 470
	870	1 820	1 790	1 760	1 730	1 690	1 660	1 050	2 370	5 890	S_x	4 780
W610X155	2 900	2 030	2 000	1 960	1 920	1 880	1 830	3 510	3 130	5 970	M_r	1 280
W24X104	2 390	1 950	1 920	1 890	1 860	1 820	1 760	2 890	2 960	5 870	V_r	1 380
b = 324	1 890	1 870	1 850	1 820	1 780	1 740	1 680	2 290	2 750	5 740	L_u	4 740
t = 19.0	1 380	1 780	1 750	1 720	1 680	1 640	1 590	1 670	2 490	5 550	I_x	1 290
	870	1 640	1 610	1 580	1 550	1 520	1 480	1 050	2 150	5 270	S_x	4 220
W610X140	2 810	1 890	1 850	1 820	1 780	1 740	1 680	3 400	2 870	5 360	M_r	1 120
W24X94	2 310	1 810	1 780	1 750	1 710	1 670	1 610	2 800	2 710	5 260	V_r	1 440
b = 230	1 820	1 720	1 700	1 670	1 630	1 580	1 530	2 200	2 520	5 130	L_u	3 320
t = 22.2	1 330	1 630	1 600	1 560	1 520	1 480	1 430	1 610	2 270	4 950	I_x	1 120
	840	1 480	1 450	1 420	1 390	1 360	1 320	1 020	1 950	4 680	S_x	3 630
W610X125	2 810	1 710	1 680	1 650	1 610	1 570	1 520	3 400	2 610	4 790	M_r	991
W24X84	2 310	1 640	1 610	1 580	1 550	1 510	1 460	2 800	2 470	4 710	V_r	1 300
b = 229	1 820	1 560	1 540	1 510	1 480	1 430	1 380	2 200	2 290	4 600	L_u	3 250
t = 19.6	1 330	1 470	1 450	1 420	1 380	1 340	1 290	1 610	2 070	4 450	I_x	985
	840	1 340	1 310	1 290	1 260	1 220	1 190	1 020	1 780	4 210	S_x	3 220

† No. of studs/beam = 2 x Q_r x percent shear connection/100/q_r (per stud)

\#Concrete density = 1850 kg/m³

* Units — M_r — kN•m L_u — mm   b — mm
V_r — kN I_x — 10^6 mm⁴   t — mm
S_x — 10^3 mm³

The Imperial designation for each steel beam is listed below the SI designation to assist designers involved with drawings using Imperial designations.

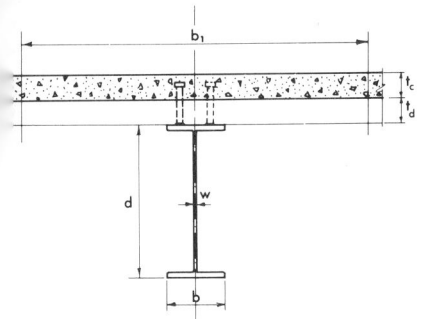

COMPOSITE BEAMS
Trial Selection Tables

G40.21-M 300W
25 MPa Concrete

76 mm Deck with 85 mm Slab
$\phi = 0.90$, $\phi_c = 0.67$, $\phi_{sc} = 0.80$

Steel Shape	b_1	\multicolumn{6}{c}{M_{rc} in kilonewton metres for various percentages of shear connection}					$Q_r^\dagger$ for 100%	I_1	S_{s1}	Steel Shape Data*	
		100%	90%	80%	70%	60%	50%	kN	$10^6\,mm^4$	$10^3\,mm^3$		
	mm											
W610X113	2 800	1 580	1 550	1 520	1 480	1 440	1 400	3 390	2 390	4 340	M_r	888
W24X76	2 310	1 510	1 480	1 450	1 420	1 390	1 340	2 800	2 270	4 270	V_r	1 210
b = 228	1 820	1 430	1 410	1 390	1 360	1 320	1 270	2 200	2 110	4 180	L_u	3 180
t = 17.3	1 330	1 350	1 330	1 300	1 270	1 230	1 180	1 610	1 910	4 040	I_x	875
	840	1 230	1 200	1 180	1 150	1 120	1 080	1 020	1 640	3 830	S_x	2 880
W610X101	2 800	1 460	1 430	1 400	1 360	1 320	1 280	3 390	2 180	3 900	M_r	783
W24X68	2 310	1 390	1 360	1 340	1 310	1 270	1 230	2 800	2 070	3 840	V_r	1 130
b = 228	1 820	1 310	1 290	1 270	1 240	1 210	1 160	2 200	1 930	3 760	L_u	3 110
t = 14.9	1 330	1 230	1 210	1 190	1 160	1 120	1 080	1 610	1 750	3 640	I_x	764
	840	1 120	1 090	1 070	1 040	1 010	978	1 020	1 500	3 440	S_x	2 530
W530X138	2 790	1 700	1 660	1 630	1 590	1 550	1 490	3 380	2 330	4 800	M_r	975
W21X93	2 300	1 620	1 590	1 560	1 530	1 480	1 430	2 780	2 200	4 710	V_r	1 440
b = 214	1 810	1 540	1 510	1 480	1 450	1 400	1 350	2 190	2 030	4 590	L_u	3 180
t = 23.6	1 330	1 440	1 420	1 380	1 350	1 310	1 260	1 610	1 830	4 420	I_x	861
	840	1 300	1 280	1 250	1 230	1 200	1 160	1 020	1 560	4 160	S_x	3 140
W530X123	2 790	1 550	1 520	1 490	1 450	1 410	1 360	3 380	2 120	4 310	M_r	867
W21X83	2 300	1 470	1 450	1 420	1 390	1 350	1 300	2 780	2 010	4 240	V_r	1 270
b = 212	1 810	1 390	1 370	1 350	1 320	1 280	1 230	2 190	1 860	4 130	L_u	3 100
t = 21.2	1 320	1 310	1 290	1 260	1 230	1 190	1 140	1 600	1 680	3 990	I_x	761
	840	1 190	1 160	1 140	1 110	1 080	1 050	1 020	1 440	3 760	S_x	2 800
W530X109	2 790	1 410	1 380	1 350	1 310	1 270	1 230	3 380	1 920	3 840	M_r	764
W21X73	2 300	1 340	1 310	1 280	1 250	1 220	1 180	2 780	1 820	3 780	V_r	1 110
b = 211	1 810	1 260	1 240	1 220	1 190	1 160	1 110	2 190	1 690	3 690	L_u	3 040
t = 18.8	1 320	1 180	1 160	1 140	1 110	1 070	1 030	1 600	1 530	3 570	I_x	667
	840	1 070	1 050	1 030	1 000	975	945	1 020	1 310	3 380	S_x	2 480
W530X101	2 790	1 340	1 310	1 280	1 240	1 200	1 160	3 380	1 810	3 580	M_r	707
W21X68	2 300	1 260	1 240	1 210	1 180	1 150	1 110	2 780	1 720	3 530	V_r	1 040
b = 210	1 810	1 190	1 170	1 140	1 120	1 090	1 050	2 190	1 600	3 450	L_u	2 990
t = 17.4	1 320	1 110	1 090	1 070	1 040	1 010	974	1 600	1 450	3 340	I_x	617
	840	1 010	990	968	943	916	886	1 020	1 240	3 160	S_x	2 300
W530X92	2 790	1 230	1 210	1 180	1 140	1 100	1 060	3 190	1 670	3 280	M_r	637
W21X62	2 300	1 180	1 150	1 130	1 100	1 070	1 030	2 780	1 590	3 230	V_r	969
b = 209	1 810	1 100	1 080	1 060	1 040	1 010	973	2 190	1 480	3 160	L_u	2 930
t = 15.6	1 320	1 030	1 010	993	969	938	902	1 600	1 340	3 060	I_x	552
	840	934	916	895	871	845	816	1 020	1 150	2 900	S_x	2 070

$\dagger$ No. of studs/beam = 2 x Q_r x percent shear connection/100/q_r (per stud)

\# Concrete density = 1850 kg/m^3

* Units — M_r — kN•m L_u — mm   b — mm
       V_r — kN I_x — $10^6\,mm^4$ t — mm
                S_x — $10^3\,mm^3$

The Imperial designation for each steel beam is listed below the SI designation to assist designers involved with drawings using Imperial designations.

COMPOSITE BEAMS
Trial Selection Tables

G40.21-M 300W
25 MPa Concrete

76 mm Deck with 85 mm Slab
$\phi = 0.90$, $\phi_c = 0.67$, $\phi_{sc} = 0.80$

Steel Shape	b_1	Composite Beam — Factored Resistances — M_{rc} in kilonewton metres for various percentages of shear connection						$Q_r^\dagger$ for 100%	Properties # — I_1	S_{s_1}	Steel Shape Data*	
	mm	100%	90%	80%	70%	60%	50%	kN	$10^6\,mm^4$	$10^3\,mm^3$		
W530X82	2 790	1 100	1 080	1 050	1 020	980	942	2 830	1 500	2 910	M_r	559
W21X55	2 300	1 080	1 060	1 030	1 000	969	934	2 780	1 430	2 870	V_r	894
b = 209	1 810	1 010	987	966	942	916	883	2 190	1 340	2 810	L_u	2 860
t = 13.3	1 320	931	916	900	878	850	815	1 600	1 220	2 730	I_x	479
	840	845	828	808	786	760	732	1 020	1 050	2 590	S_x	1 810
W460X106	2 770	1 250	1 220	1 190	1 150	1 110	1 070	3 350	1 510	3 380	M_r	645
W18X71	2 290	1 180	1 150	1 130	1 100	1 060	1 020	2 770	1 430	3 320	V_r	1 050
b = 194	1 800	1 100	1 080	1 060	1 030	1 000	965	2 180	1 320	3 240	L_u	2 910
t = 20.6	1 320	1 020	1 010	987	962	931	895	1 600	1 190	3 130	I_x	488
	830	925	907	886	864	839	811	1 000	1 010	2 940	S_x	2 080
W460X97	2 770	1 170	1 140	1 110	1 070	1 040	993	3 320	1 400	3 100	M_r	589
W18X65	2 280	1 100	1 080	1 050	1 020	985	949	2 760	1 330	3 050	V_r	947
b = 193	1 800	1 030	1 010	983	958	931	897	2 180	1 240	2 980	L_u	2 870
t = 19.0	1 320	949	933	916	893	866	832	1 600	1 120	2 890	I_x	445
	830	858	842	823	802	778	752	1 000	949	2 720	S_x	1 910
W460X89	2 770	1 090	1 060	1 030	996	959	919	3 080	1 310	2 890	M_r	543
W18X60	2 280	1 040	1 020	989	960	927	891	2 760	1 250	2 840	V_r	866
b = 192	1 800	967	947	925	901	875	844	2 180	1 160	2 780	L_u	2 830
t = 17.7	1 310	890	875	858	838	813	781	1 590	1 050	2 690	I_x	410
	830	806	791	774	753	731	705	1 000	897	2 540	S_x	1 770
W460X82	2 770	998	971	942	910	875	837	2 810	1 220	2 640	M_r	494
W18X55	2 280	973	950	924	896	864	829	2 760	1 160	2 600	V_r	812
b = 191	1 800	902	883	862	838	812	783	2 180	1 080	2 550	L_u	2 770
t = 16.0	1 310	826	812	795	777	754	725	1 590	980	2 470	I_x	370
	830	747	734	717	698	677	652	1 000	837	2 340	S_x	1 610
W460X74	2 770	911	886	858	827	795	760	2 550	1 120	2 410	M_r	445
W18X50	2 280	894	871	846	819	788	755	2 550	1 070	2 380	V_r	733
b = 190	1 800	840	822	801	778	753	725	2 180	1 000	2 330	L_u	2 730
t = 14.5	1 310	766	752	736	719	698	672	1 590	910	2 260	I_x	333
	830	690	678	664	646	625	602	1 000	780	2 140	S_x	1 460
W460X67	2 770	840	815	788	760	729	697	2 340	1 040	2 210	M_r	405
W18X45	2 280	825	803	779	752	724	693	2 340	990	2 180	V_r	688
b = 190	1 800	790	772	752	729	704	677	2 180	931	2 140	L_u	2 660
t = 12.7	1 310	717	703	687	670	651	625	1 590	848	2 080	I_x	300
	830	642	631	617	599	579	555	1 000	729	1 980	S_x	1 320

† No. of studs/beam = 2 x Q_r x percent shear connection/100/q_r (per stud)

* Units — M_r — kN•m L_u — mm   b — mm
         V_r — kN I_x — $10^6\,mm^4$ t — mm
                 S_x — $10^3\,mm^3$

Concrete density = 1850 kg/m³

The Imperial designation for each steel beam is listed below the SI designation to assist designers involved with drawings using Imperial designations.

COMPOSITE BEAMS
Trial Selection Tables

G40.21-M 300W
25 MPa Concrete

76 mm Deck with 85 mm Slab
$\emptyset = 0.90$, $\emptyset_c = 0.67$, $\emptyset_{sc} = 0.80$

Steel Shape	b₁	M_{rc} in kilonewton metres for various percentages of shear connection						Q_r for 100%	I_1	S_{s_1}	Steel Shape Data*
	mm	100%	90%	80%	70%	60%	50%	kN	10⁶mm⁴	10³mm³	
W460X61	2 770	753	730	705	678	650	621	2 100	932	1 970	M_r 354
W18X41	2 280	741	720	697	672	646	618	2 100	893	1 940	V_r 650
b = 189	1 800	723	705	686	664	640	613	2 100	842	1 910	L_u 2 580
t = 10.8	1 310	658	644	629	612	594	569	1 590	769	1 860	I_x 259
	830	585	575	561	545	526	503	1 000	663	1 770	S_x 1 150
W410X85	2 760	969	942	913	880	844	805	2 920	1 080	2 560	M_r 467
W16X57	2 270	933	910	884	855	823	788	2 750	1 020	2 520	V_r 810
b = 181	1 790	862	843	821	797	771	742	2 170	954	2 460	L_u 2 730
t = 18.2	1 310	787	772	755	737	714	686	1 590	862	2 380	I_x 315
	830	707	694	678	660	639	616	1 000	733	2 250	S_x 1 510
W410X74	2 760	863	837	809	779	746	710	2 580	971	2 270	M_r 408
W16X50	2 270	845	822	797	770	739	706	2 580	924	2 240	V_r 714
b = 180	1 790	788	770	749	726	700	672	2 170	865	2 190	L_u 2 670
t = 16.0	1 310	715	701	685	667	647	622	1 590	784	2 130	I_x 275
	830	639	628	614	597	578	556	1 000	669	2 010	S_x 1 330
W410X67	2 760	781	757	730	702	671	639	2 320	888	2 060	M_r 367
W16X45	2 270	766	745	721	694	666	635	2 320	848	2 030	V_r 643
b = 179	1 790	733	715	694	672	647	619	2 170	796	1 990	L_u 2 610
t = 14.4	1 310	661	647	631	614	595	573	1 590	725	1 930	I_x 246
	830	586	577	565	550	532	511	1 000	621	1 830	S_x 1 200
W410X60	2 750	692	669	645	619	591	562	2 050	798	1 830	M_r 321
W16X40	2 270	681	660	638	613	587	560	2 050	765	1 800	V_r 558
b = 178	1 790	664	646	627	605	581	555	2 050	720	1 770	L_u 2 580
t = 12.8	1 310	603	590	574	558	539	519	1 590	659	1 720	I_x 216
	830	530	521	510	498	482	463	1 000	568	1 640	S_x 1 060
W410X54	2 750	623	602	579	555	530	503	1 840	718	1 630	M_r 283
W16X36	2 270	614	594	573	550	526	501	1 840	690	1 610	V_r 539
b = 177	1 790	600	583	564	544	521	498	1 840	652	1 580	L_u 2 480
t = 10.9	1 310	558	545	530	513	495	476	1 590	598	1 540	I_x 186
	830	486	477	467	455	440	421	1 000	517	1 470	S_x 924
W410X46	2 720	544	524	504	482	460	436	1 590	633	1 410	M_r 239
W16X31	2 240	537	519	499	479	457	434	1 590	609	1 390	V_r 503
b = 140	1 770	526	510	492	474	453	432	1 590	578	1 370	L_u 1 930
t = 11.2	1 290	505	493	478	462	445	425	1 560	532	1 340	I_x 156
	810	434	425	416	405	390	373	980	461	1 280	S_x 773

† No. of studs/beam = 2 x Q_r x percent shear connection/100/q_r (per stud)   #Concrete density = 1850 kg/m³

* Units — M_r — kN•m L_u — mm   b — mm
  V_r — kN I_x — 10⁶mm⁴   t — mm
  S_x — 10³mm³

The Imperial designation for each steel beam is listed below the SI designation to assist designers involved with drawings using Imperial designations.

COMPOSITE BEAMS
Trial Selection Tables

G40.21-M 300W
25 MPa Concrete

76 mm Deck with 85 mm Slab
$\emptyset = 0.90$, $\emptyset_c = 0.67$, $\emptyset_{sc} = 0.80$

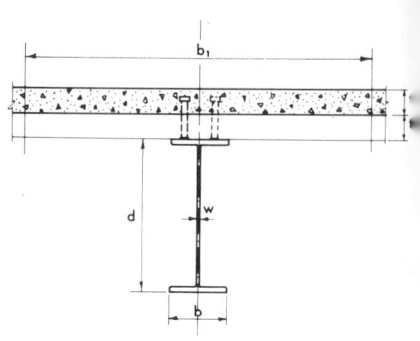

Steel Shape	Composite Beam										Steel Shape Data*	
		Factored Resistances							Properties#			
	b_1	M_{rc} in kilonewton metres for various percentages of shear connection						Q_r† for 100%	I_1	S_{s_1}		
	mm	100%	90%	80%	70%	60%	50%	kN	10^6mm⁴	10^3mm³		
W410X39	2 720	462	445	427	408	389	368	1 350	542	1 190	M_r	197
W16X26	2 240	457	441	424	406	387	367	1 350	523	1 180	V_r	448
b = 140	1 770	450	435	419	402	384	365	1 350	498	1 160	L_u	1 860
t = 8.8	1 290	436	424	410	395	379	362	1 350	462	1 130	I_x	127
	810	384	376	366	356	343	327	980	404	1 090	S_x	634
W360X79	2 780	828	801	772	741	707	670	2 730	827	2 210	M_r	386
W14X53	2 290	808	785	760	731	700	665	2 730	786	2 180	V_r	593
b = 205	1 810	741	722	701	677	652	624	2 190	734	2 130	L_u	3 270
t = 16.8	1 320	666	652	635	618	598	577	1 600	662	2 060	I_x	227
	830	588	579	568	554	537	518	1 000	560	1 950	S_x	1 280
W360X72	2 780	750	725	697	668	636	602	2 460	754	2 000	M_r	346
W14X48	2 290	734	711	687	660	630	598	2 460	718	1 970	V_r	536
b = 204	1 810	690	671	651	628	603	575	2 190	673	1 930	L_u	3 190
t = 15.1	1 320	616	602	586	569	550	530	1 600	609	1 870	I_x	201
	830	540	530	520	508	493	474	1 000	517	1 770	S_x	1 150
W360X64	2 780	674	650	624	597	568	537	2 200	685	1 790	M_r	308
W14X43	2 290	661	640	616	591	563	534	2 200	654	1 770	V_r	476
b = 203	1 810	641	623	603	581	556	529	2 190	615	1 740	L_u	3 110
t = 13.5	1 320	569	555	540	523	504	484	1 600	559	1 690	I_x	178
	830	494	485	475	463	450	433	1 000	477	1 600	S_x	1 030
W360X57	2 750	614	592	568	543	517	489	1 950	643	1 620	M_r	273
W14X38	2 270	604	584	562	538	513	486	1 950	615	1 590	V_r	504
b = 172	1 790	588	571	551	530	507	482	1 950	580	1 570	L_u	2 550
t = 13.1	1 310	536	523	508	491	472	453	1 590	530	1 520	I_x	161
	820	462	453	443	431	418	401	992	454	1 450	S_x	897
W360X51	2 750	551	530	508	485	461	436	1 740	580	1 450	M_r	241
W14X34	2 270	543	523	503	481	458	433	1 740	557	1 430	V_r	455
b = 171	1 790	530	513	495	475	453	430	1 740	527	1 400	L_u	2 500
t = 11.6	1 300	495	482	468	451	434	414	1 570	483	1 370	I_x	141
	820	424	415	405	394	382	366	992	416	1 300	S_x	796
W360X45	2 750	491	472	451	431	409	386	1 550	520	1 290	M_r	210
W14X30	2 270	484	466	447	427	406	384	1 550	501	1 270	V_r	433
b = 171	1 790	474	458	441	422	403	382	1 550	475	1 250	L_u	2 430
t = 9.8	1 300	457	444	430	414	396	377	1 550	437	1 220	I_x	122
	820	388	380	370	360	348	333	992	379	1 160	S_x	691

† No. of studs/beam = 2 x Q_r x percent shear connection/100/q_r (per stud)

#Concrete density = 1850 kg/m³

* Units — M_r — kN•m L_u — mm   b — mm
         V_r — kN I_x — 10^6mm⁴   t — mm
                        S_x — 10^3mm³

The Imperial designation for each steel beam is listed below the SI designation to assist designers involved with drawings using Imperial designations.

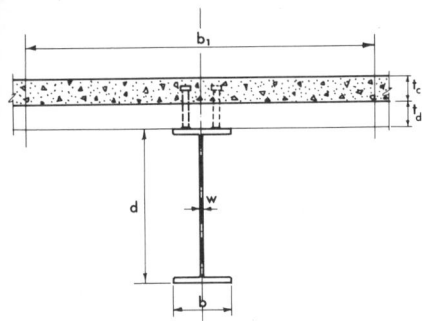

COMPOSITE BEAMS
Trial Selection Tables

G40.21-M 300W
25 MPa Concrete

76 mm Deck with 85 mm Slab
$\varnothing = 0.90$, $\varnothing_c = 0.67$, $\varnothing_{sc} = 0.80$

Steel Shape		Composite Beam										Steel Shape Data*	
		Factored Resistances							Properties#				
	b_1	M_{rc} in kilonewton metres for various percentages of shear connection						$Q_r^\dagger$ for 100%	I_1	S_{s_1}			
	mm	100%	90%	80%	70%	60%	50%	kN	$10^6\,mm^4$	$10^3\,mm^3$		
W360X39	2 700	430	413	395	376	357	336	1 340	460	1 120	M_r	179
W14X26	2 230	425	409	392	374	355	335	1 340	443	1 100	V_r	409
b = 128	1 760	418	403	387	370	352	333	1 340	422	1 080	L_u	1 790
t = 10.7	1 280	404	392	378	363	347	330	1 340	390	1 060	I_x	102
	810	353	344	335	324	313	299	980	340	1 010	S_x	580
W360X33	2 700	361	346	331	314	298	281	1 130	390	937	M_r	146
W14X22	2 230	358	343	328	313	297	280	1 130	377	926	V_r	361
b = 127	1 760	352	339	325	310	295	278	1 130	360	911	L_u	1 720
t = 8.5	1 280	343	331	319	305	291	276	1 130	336	890	I_x	82.7
	810	312	304	295	285	274	262	980	296	855	S_x	474
W310X129	2 880	1 120	1 090	1 050	1 020	975	930	3 490	1 030	3 280	M_r	583
W12X87	2 380	1 040	1 020	987	955	920	882	2 880	969	3 220	V_r	742
b = 308	1 870	962	941	917	891	863	833	2 260	890	3 130	L_u	5 580
t = 20.6	1 370	881	865	847	828	807	782	1 660	792	3 010	I_x	308
	870	798	787	774	758	739	718	1 050	664	2 810	S_x	1 940
W310X118	2 880	1 050	1 020	985	948	908	863	3 490	951	2 990	M_r	526
W12X79	2 380	973	948	919	888	854	817	2 880	895	2 940	V_r	666
b = 307	1 870	894	874	851	825	798	768	2 260	824	2 860	L_u	5 390
t = 18.7	1 370	815	799	782	763	742	719	1 660	735	2 750	I_x	275
	860	732	722	709	695	677	657	1 040	614	2 580	S_x	1 750
W310X107	2 880	984	955	923	887	847	803	3 490	880	2 730	M_r	478
W12X72	2 380	910	886	858	827	794	757	2 880	830	2 690	V_r	604
b = 306	1 870	833	813	790	766	739	710	2 260	767	2 620	L_u	5 220
t = 17.0	1 370	755	740	723	704	684	662	1 660	686	2 530	I_x	248
	860	673	663	652	639	623	604	1 040	573	2 370	S_x	1 590
W310X97	2 880	912	883	852	817	778	737	3 320	810	2 490	M_r	389
W12X65	2 380	852	828	801	771	738	702	2 880	766	2 450	V_r	543
b = 305	1 870	776	756	734	710	684	655	2 260	710	2 390	L_u	5 410
t = 15.4	1 370	700	684	668	650	630	608	1 660	637	2 310	I_x	222
	860	619	609	598	586	572	554	1 040	534	2 170	S_x	1 440
W310X86	2 830	829	802	772	739	703	664	2 970	748	2 240	M_r	383
W12X58	2 330	794	771	745	716	684	649	2 820	708	2 210	V_r	503
b = 254	1 840	722	703	681	658	632	603	2 230	659	2 160	L_u	4 250
t = 16.3	1 340	646	631	615	597	578	557	1 620	591	2 090	I_x	199
	850	569	559	548	536	522	505	1 030	499	1 970	S_x	1 280

† No. of studs/beam = 2 x Q_r x percent shear connection/100/q_r (per stud)   #Concrete density = 1850 kg/m^3

* Units — M_r — kN•m L_u — mm   b — mm

  V_r — kN I_x — $10^6\,mm^4$ t — mm

  S_x — $10^3\,mm^3$

The Imperial designation for each steel beam is listed below the SI designation to assist designers involved with drawings using Imperial designations.

COMPOSITE BEAMS
Trial Selection Tables

G40.21-M 300W
25 MPa Concrete

76 mm Deck with 85 mm Slab
$\emptyset = 0.90$, $\emptyset_c = 0.67$, $\emptyset_{sc} = 0.80$

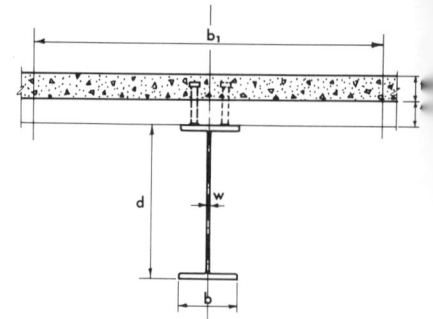

Steel Shape	b_1	\multicolumn{6}{c}{Composite Beam — Factored Resistances — M_{rc} in kilonewton metres for various percentages of shear connection}						Q_r† for 100%	I_1	S_{s_1}	Steel Shape Data*	
	mm	100%	90%	80%	70%	60%	50%	kN	10^6mm^4	10^3mm^3		
W310X79	2 830	764	737	708	677	643	607	2 730	689	2 060	M_r	346
W12X53	2 330	744	721	696	667	636	602	2 730	654	2 020	V_r	480
b = 254	1 840	680	661	640	617	591	563	2 230	609	1 980	L_u	4 140
t = 14.6	1 340	605	591	575	557	538	517	1 620	548	1 920	I_x	177
	850	529	519	509	497	483	467	1 030	463	1 810	S_x	1 160
W310X74	2 780	727	701	673	643	610	575	2 560	660	1 940	M_r	321
W12X50	2 290	709	687	662	634	604	571	2 560	627	1 910	V_r	519
b = 205	1 810	656	638	617	594	568	540	2 190	585	1 860	L_u	3 380
t = 16.3	1 320	582	568	552	535	515	495	1 600	528	1 800	I_x	165
	830	505	496	485	474	459	442	1 000	445	1 700	S_x	1 060
W310X67	2 780	655	630	604	576	546	514	2 300	599	1 740	M_r	286
W12X45	2 290	641	619	595	569	541	510	2 300	570	1 710	V_r	463
b = 204	1 810	611	593	573	550	525	498	2 190	534	1 680	L_u	3 280
t = 14.6	1 320	539	525	509	492	473	453	1 600	483	1 630	I_x	145
	830	463	454	443	432	419	403	1 000	409	1 540	S_x	949
W310X60	2 780	587	564	540	514	486	457	2 050	543	1 560	M_r	254
W12X40	2 290	576	555	532	508	482	455	2 050	519	1 540	V_r	405
b = 203	1 810	559	541	522	500	476	450	2 050	488	1 510	L_u	3 200
t = 13.1	1 320	499	485	470	453	435	415	1 600	444	1 470	I_x	129
	830	425	415	405	394	383	368	1 000	378	1 390	S_x	849
W310X52	2 740	534	513	490	466	442	416	1 800	513	1 400	M_r	226
W12X35	2 260	525	505	484	462	438	413	1 800	492	1 380	V_r	429
b = 167	1 780	511	494	476	455	433	410	1 800	464	1 360	L_u	2 570
t = 13.2	1 300	472	458	444	427	409	390	1 570	424	1 320	I_x	118
	820	399	391	381	370	358	344	992	363	1 260	S_x	747
W310X45	2 740	458	438	418	398	376	353	1 540	446	1 200	M_r	191
W12X30	2 260	451	433	414	394	374	352	1 540	429	1 190	V_r	368
b = 166	1 780	441	425	408	390	370	349	1 540	406	1 170	L_u	2 490
t = 11.2	1 300	424	411	397	381	364	345	1 540	373	1 140	I_x	99.2
	820	356	348	338	328	316	304	992	323	1 090	S_x	634
W310X39	2 740	399	381	364	345	326	306	1 330	393	1 050	M_r	165
W12X26	2 260	394	378	360	343	324	305	1 330	379	1 040	V_r	320
b = 165	1 780	386	371	356	339	321	303	1 330	360	1 020	L_u	2 440
t = 9.7	1 300	373	361	347	333	317	300	1 330	333	997	I_x	85.1
	820	324	315	306	296	284	272	992	291	955	S_x	549

† No. of studs/beam = 2 x Q_r x percent shear connection/100/q_r (per stud)

\# Concrete density = 1850 kg/m^3

* Units — M_r — kN•m L_u — mm b — mm
  V_r — kN I_x — 10^6mm^4 t — mm
  S_x — 10^3mm^3

The Imperial designation for each steel beam is listed below the SI designation to assist designers involved with drawings using Imperial designations.

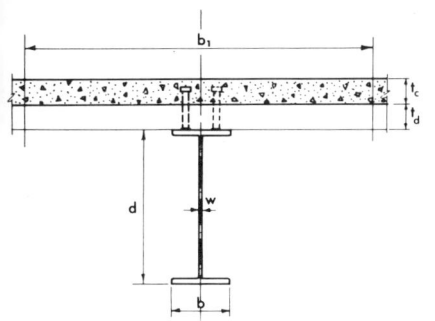

COMPOSITE BEAMS
Trial Selection Tables

G40.21-M 300W
25 MPa Concrete

76 mm Deck with 85 mm Slab
$\phi = 0.90$, $\phi_C = 0.67$, $\phi_{SC} = 0.80$

Steel Shape	b₁	\multicolumn{6}{c}{Composite Beam — Factored Resistances — M_rc in kilonewton metres for various percentages of shear connection}	Q_r† for 100%	I₁	S_s₁	\multicolumn{2}{c}{Steel Shape Data*}
	mm	100%	90%	80%	70%	60%	50%	kN	10⁶ mm⁴	10³ mm³		
W250X101	2 830	866	838	806	770	731	688	3 420	674	2 360	M_r	378
W10X68	2 340	794	769	742	712	679	642	2 830	635	2 310	V_r	560
b = 257	1 840	718	698	676	651	624	595	2 230	584	2 250	L_u	4 950
t = 19.6	1 350	641	626	609	590	570	548	1 630	520	2 160	I_x	164
	850	560	550	539	527	512	495	1 030	430	2 020	S_x	1 240
W250X89	2 830	778	751	720	686	650	610	3 080	608	2 100	M_r	332
W10X60	2 340	735	712	685	656	623	588	2 830	575	2 060	V_r	496
b = 256	1 840	661	642	620	596	570	542	2 230	531	2 010	L_u	4 690
t = 17.3	1 350	586	571	555	537	517	496	1 630	475	1 940	I_x	143
	850	507	497	486	475	461	446	1 030	394	1 810	S_x	1 100
W250X80	2 830	702	675	646	614	580	544	2 750	553	1 890	M_r	294
W10X54	2 340	682	659	633	605	573	539	2 750	524	1 860	V_r	429
b = 255	1 840	615	596	575	552	526	498	2 230	486	1 810	L_u	4 520
t = 15.6	1 340	540	526	510	492	473	452	1 620	435	1 750	I_x	126
	850	464	454	443	432	420	405	1 030	364	1 650	S_x	982
W250X73	2 830	642	617	589	559	527	493	2 510	509	1 720	M_r	266
W10X49	2 330	626	603	578	551	521	489	2 510	483	1 700	V_r	388
b = 254	1 840	581	562	541	518	493	465	2 230	450	1 660	L_u	4 390
t = 14.2	1 340	506	492	476	459	440	420	1 620	404	1 600	I_x	113
	850	431	422	411	400	388	374	1 030	339	1 510	S_x	891
W250X67	2 780	601	576	550	522	492	460	2 310	483	1 600	M_r	243
W10X45	2 290	587	565	541	515	486	456	2 310	459	1 570	V_r	408
b = 204	1 810	556	538	518	495	470	443	2 190	428	1 540	L_u	3 570
t = 15.7	1 320	484	470	454	437	418	398	1 600	386	1 490	I_x	104
	830	408	399	388	377	365	351	1 000	323	1 400	S_x	806
W250X58	2 780	524	501	477	452	425	396	2 000	424	1 390	M_r	208
W10X39	2 290	513	493	470	446	421	394	2 000	404	1 370	V_r	359
b = 203	1 810	497	479	460	438	415	390	2 000	379	1 340	L_u	3 410
t = 13.5	1 320	441	427	412	396	377	357	1 600	343	1 300	I_x	87.3
	830	367	358	348	337	325	312	1 000	290	1 230	S_x	693
W250X49	2 780	444	424	402	380	356	332	1 690	362	1 180	M_r	171
W10X33	2 290	436	417	397	376	354	330	1 690	347	1 160	V_r	326
b = 202	1 810	425	408	390	370	349	327	1 690	327	1 140	L_u	3 240
t = 11.0	1 320	398	385	370	354	336	316	1 600	298	1 100	I_x	70.6
	830	325	317	307	296	285	272	1 000	254	1 050	S_x	572

† No. of studs/beam = 2 x Q_r x percent shear connection/100/q_r (per stud)

Concrete density = 1850 kg/m³

* Units — M_r — kN•m L_u — mm b — mm
V_r — kN I_x — 10⁶ mm⁴ t — mm
S_x — 10³ mm³

The Imperial designation for each steel beam is listed below the SI designation to assist designers involved with drawings using Imperial designations.

COMPOSITE BEAMS
Trial Selection Tables

G40.21-M 300W
25 MPa Concrete

76 mm Deck with 85 mm Slab
$\emptyset = 0.90$, $\emptyset_c = 0.67$, $\emptyset_{sc} = 0.80$

Steel Shape	b_1	Composite Beam Factored Resistances M_{rc} in kilonewton metres for various percentages of shear connection						Q_r for 100%	I_1	S_{s_1}	Steel Shape Data*	
	mm	100%	90%	80%	70%	60%	50%	kN	10^6 mm^4	10^3 mm^3		
W250X45 W10X30 b = 148 t = 13.0	2 720 2 250 1 770 1 290 820	423 417 407 389 321	404 399 391 376 312	384 380 373 362 303	363 360 355 346 292	341 339 335 329 280	318 317 314 310 268	1 540 1 540 1 540 1 540 992	364 349 329 301 259	1 110 1 090 1 070 1 040 992	M_r V_r L_u I_x S_x	163 360 2 360 71.1 534
W250X39 W10X26 b = 147 t = 11.2	2 720 2 250 1 770 1 290 820	365 360 353 340 291	348 344 338 327 282	330 327 322 314 273	312 309 306 299 263	292 291 288 283 251	272 271 269 266 239	1 330 1 330 1 330 1 330 992	317 305 289 267 231	959 946 929 905 865	M_r V_r L_u I_x S_x	139 308 2 280 60.1 459
W250X33 W10X22 b = 146 t = 9.1	2 720 2 250 1 770 1 290 820	310 307 301 292 263	295 292 288 280 255	279 277 274 268 245	263 262 259 254 235	247 246 244 240 224	230 229 228 225 212	1 130 1 130 1 130 1 130 992	272 262 250 231 203	815 804 790 770 738	M_r V_r L_u I_x S_x	114 280 2 180 48.9 379
W200X100 W8X67 b = 210 t = 23.7	2 790 2 300 1 810 1 320 840	793 721 645 567 487	765 696 625 552 477	733 669 603 535 466	698 639 578 516 453	658 605 551 496 439	615 569 522 474 423	3 380 2 780 2 190 1 600 1 020	549 515 472 416 341	2 130 2 090 2 020 1 930 1 790	M_r V_r L_u I_x S_x	310 592 5 020 113 989
W200X86 W8X58 b = 209 t = 20.6	2 790 2 300 1 810 1 320 840	702 662 589 513 436	675 639 570 498 426	645 613 548 482 415	611 584 524 464 403	575 551 498 444 390	536 516 470 423 374	3 000 2 780 2 190 1 600 1 020	485 456 420 372 306	1 870 1 830 1 780 1 710 1 590	M_r V_r L_u I_x S_x	265 514 4 620 94.7 853
W200X71 W8X48 b = 206 t = 17.4	2 780 2 300 1 810 1 320 830	585 569 525 452 375	560 547 507 437 366	532 522 486 422 355	503 495 463 404 344	471 466 438 385 332	438 434 410 365 319	2 460 2 460 2 190 1 600 1 000	411 389 361 322 266	1 560 1 530 1 490 1 440 1 340	M_r V_r L_u I_x S_x	217 393 4 150 76.6 709
W200X59 W8X40 b = 205 t = 14.2	2 780 2 290 1 810 1 320 830	490 479 462 403 328	467 458 444 389 319	443 436 425 374 309	417 411 403 357 299	390 385 379 339 287	361 358 354 319 274	2 040 2 040 2 040 1 600 1 000	348 331 309 278 232	1 300 1 280 1 250 1 210 1 140	M_r V_r L_u I_x S_x	176 341 3 780 61.1 582

† No. of studs/beam = 2 x Q_r x percent shear connection/100/q_r (per stud)

\# Concrete density = 1850 kg/m^3

* Units — M_r — kN•m L_u — mm   b — mm
  V_r — kN I_x — 10^6 mm^4 t — mm
  S_x — 10^3 mm^3

The Imperial designation for each steel beam is listed below the SI designation to assist designers involved with drawings using Imperial designations.

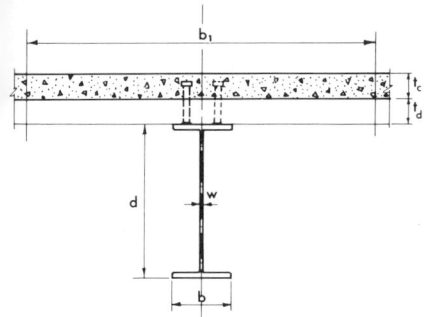

COMPOSITE BEAMS
Trial Selection Tables

G40.21-M 300W
25 MPa Concrete

76 mm Deck with 85 mm Slab
$\phi = 0.90$, $\phi_c = 0.67$, $\phi_{sc} = 0.80$

Steel Shape	b_1	M_{rc} in kilonewton metres for various percentages of shear connection						Q_r† for 100%	I_1	S_{s_1}	Steel Shape Data*	
		100%	90%	80%	70%	60%	50%	kN	$10^6\,mm^4$	$10^3\,mm^3$		
	mm											
W200X52	2 780	434	413	390	367	342	316	1 800	311	1 150	M_r	154
W8X35	2 290	425	405	384	362	339	314	1 800	296	1 130	V_r	290
b = 204	1 810	412	395	376	356	334	311	1 800	278	1 110	L_u	3 620
t = 12.6	1 320	374	361	346	330	312	292	1 600	251	1 080	I_x	52.7
	830	301	293	283	272	260	248	1 000	212	1 020	S_x	512
W200X46	2 780	384	364	344	322	300	277	1 580	278	1 020	M_r	134
W8X31	2 290	377	359	339	319	298	276	1 580	265	1 000	V_r	260
b = 203	1 810	367	350	333	314	294	273	1 580	250	984	L_u	3 460
t = 11.0	1 320	349	336	321	305	288	268	1 580	227	955	I_x	45.5
	830	278	269	260	249	238	225	1 000	193	906	S_x	448
W200X42	2 740	351	333	314	295	274	253	1 430	258	930	M_r	120
W8X28	2 260	346	329	311	292	272	252	1 430	247	916	V_r	263
b = 166	1 780	337	322	305	288	269	249	1 430	233	897	L_u	2 850
t = 11.8	1 300	322	310	296	280	264	246	1 430	213	871	I_x	40.9
	820	263	255	245	235	224	211	992	182	828	S_x	399
W200X36	2 740	304	287	271	253	235	217	1 240	225	808	M_r	103
W8X24	2 260	300	284	268	251	234	216	1 240	216	795	V_r	222
b = 165	1 780	293	279	264	248	231	214	1 240	204	780	L_u	2 730
t = 10.2	1 300	282	270	257	243	227	211	1 240	188	758	I_x	34.4
	820	242	233	224	214	203	191	992	162	723	S_x	342
W200X31	2 710	272	258	243	227	211	195	1 080	209	720	M_r	90.4
W8X21	2 240	269	255	240	225	210	194	1 080	202	709	V_r	240
b = 134	1 760	264	251	237	223	208	193	1 080	191	695	L_u	2 150
t = 10.2	1 290	256	244	232	219	205	190	1 080	177	677	I_x	31.4
	810	229	221	212	202	191	179	980	154	647	S_x	299
W200X27	2 710	231	219	205	192	178	164	915	180	614	M_r	75.3
W8X18	2 230	229	217	204	191	177	164	915	174	605	V_r	214
b = 133	1 760	225	214	202	189	176	163	915	166	593	L_u	2 050
t = 8.4	1 290	219	209	198	186	174	161	915	154	578	I_x	25.8
	810	206	198	189	180	169	158	915	135	554	S_x	249

† No. of studs/beam = 2 x Q_r x percent shear connection/100/q_r (per stud)

\#Concrete density = 1850 kg/m³

* Units — M_r — kN•m L_u — mm   b — mm
  V_r — kN I_x — $10^6\,mm^4$ t — mm
  S_x — $10^3\,mm^3$

The Imperial designation for each steel beam is listed below the SI designation to assist designers involved with drawings using Imperial designations.

DEFLECTION OF FLEXURAL MEMBERS

Deflection seldom has been, in the past, a governing factor in the design of flexural members in buildings. "Rules of thumb" which establish approximate relationships between depth and span were usually satisfactory and minimize the need for refined deflection calculations.

More recently, the use of high strength steels, composite construction, and the trend towards longer clear spans in buildings have created a situation in which deflection considerations may be of more importance than was formerly the case.

With CSA Standard CAN3-S16.1-M78, "Steel Structures for Buildings — Limit States Design", deflection is one of the serviceability limit states to be accounted for in the design. The calculations to determine deflection are based on the specified loads. Appendix I of CAN3-S16.1-M78 provides some guidance to designers on the recommended maximum values for deflection for industrial and all other buildings. Several methods of dealing with deflection are summarized as follows:

1. Before a beam size is selected compute the minimum moment of inertia, $I_{req'd}$, to satisfy the deflection constraint where

   $$I_{req'd} = W \cdot C_d \cdot B_d$$

   where

   $I_{req'd}$ = required value of moment of inertia ($10^6 \, mm^4$).

   W = specified load value as described in Table 5—4 (kilonewtons).

   C_d = value of deflection constant obtained from the graph, Fig. 5—1, for the appropriate span, L, and span/deflection ratio, $n = L/\Delta$, and equals $13 \, nL^2/E$, where E = 200 000 MPa. ($10^6 \, mm^4/kN$).

   B_d = a number to relate the actual load and support condition to a uniformly distributed load (udl) on a simply supported beam on which the graph is based. The values of B_d are computed for the maximum deflection within the span without regard to its location. For a udl, $B_d = 1.0$.

   The actual deflection of a beam can be computed as follows:

   $$\Delta = \frac{I_{req'd}}{I} \times \Delta_m$$

   where

   Δ = actual deflection (millimetres).

   I = moment of inertia of beam ($10^6 \, mm^4$).

   Δ_m = maximum deflection permitted (millimetres).

   $I_{req'd}$ = moment of inertia required to meet Δ_m ($10^6 \, mm^4$).

2. Formulas for deflection of single and multispan, simple, fixed and cantilever beams, subject to various loading conditions are provided in the Beam Diagrams and Formulas, pages 5—132 to 5—144.

3. For CSA G40.21-M 300W steel, approximate total deflections in inches are listed for various steel sections, spans and total factored loads in the beam load tables, pages 5—110 to 5—125. This deflection has been computed assuming that the total factored load would result in a stress, at specified load, of 215 MPa. Deflections for live load only or for total loads which result in stresses of other than 215 MPa can be determined by multiplying the tabulated deflection by the ratio of actual stress/assumed stress (215 MPa). Since the moment of inertia is listed for each section method 1 could also be used.

The three methods, as described, are applicable only to symmetrical sections.

Examples

Given:

A W410×85 section has been chosen for a single span, simply supported floor beam subjected to a uniformly distributed specified load of 15 kN/m live and 7 kN/m dead on a 10 m span. The compression flange is laterally supported. Check for live load deflection. Steel is G40.21-M 300W. $\Delta_m = L/300 = 33$ mm.

Solutions:

(1) For a span/deflection ratio, 300, determine C_d from Table 5—4.

B_d = 1.0 (standard case, udl)

C_d = 1.95 (from graph for Δ/L = 300, Figure 5—1)

$$I_{req'd} = W \cdot C_d \cdot B_d$$

$$= (15 \times 10) \times 1.95 \times 10^6 \times 1.0$$

$$= 293 \times 10^6 \, \text{mm}^4$$

For W410×85, $I_x = 315 \times 10^6 \, \text{mm}^4$ (page 6—44)

Actual deflection, $\Delta = \dfrac{I_{req'd}}{I} \times \Delta_m$

$$= \frac{293}{315} \times 33 = 31 \text{ mm}$$

(2) From Beam Diagrams and Formulas, page 5—132

$\Delta = \dfrac{5wL^4}{384 \, EI}$ $I = 315 \times 10^6 \, \text{mm}^4$

$E = 200\,000$ MPa

Therefore $\Delta = \dfrac{5 \times 15 \times 10^3 \times 10 \times (10 \times 10^3)^3}{384 \times 200\,000 \times 315 \times 10^6}$

$$= 31 \text{ mm}$$

(3) From the tables, page 5—119, approximate deflection for beam fully loaded to a stress of 215 MPa = 55 mm

Stress due to live load $= \dfrac{M}{S} = \dfrac{wL}{8S} = \dfrac{15 \times 10^3 \times 10 \times 10\,000}{8 \times 1\,510 \times 10^3}$

$$= 124 \text{ MPa}$$

Live load deflection $= \dfrac{124}{215} \times 55 = 32$ mm

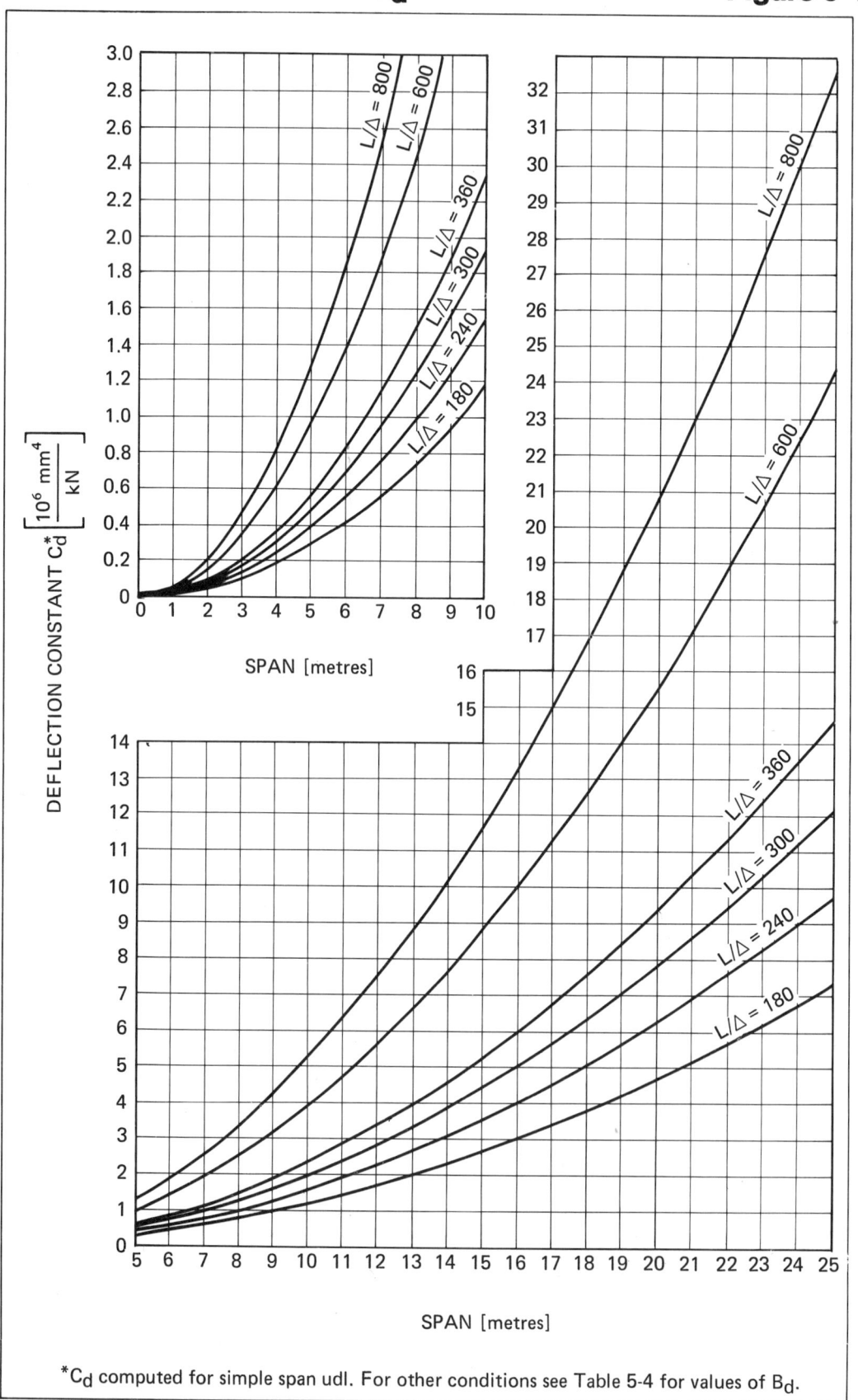

*C$_d$ computed for simple span udl. For other conditions see Table 5-4 for values of B$_d$.

Table 5-4

Values of B_d for Various Loadings & Support Conditions

LOADING CONDITION	a/L	B_d	LOADING CONDITION	a/L	B_d	LOADING CONDITION	B_d	LOADING CONDITION	B_d
Cantilever, point load (a, w, L)	1.	0.0	Fixed both ends, point load (a, w, L)	1.	0.0	Simple span, udl (w)	1.0	Fixed ends, udl (w)	.20
	.8	.91		.8	.16				
	.6	1.5		.6	.37				
	.5	1.6		.5	.40	Propped cantilever, udl (w)	.42	Cantilever, udl (w)	9.6
	.4	1.5		.4	.37				
	.2	.91		.2	.16				
Point loads near left (a, w, L)	1.	1.0	Propped, point loads near left (a, w, L)	1.	.20	L/4 w L/4	1.4	LW/4 WL/4	2.2
	.8	1.13		.8	.24				
	.6	1.10		.6	.23	Triangular load (w)	1.0	Triangular peak load (w)	1.3
	.4	.86		.4	.16				
	.2	.48		.2	.057				
Point loads (a, w, L)	1.	.415	Point loads (w, a, L)	1.	.415				
	.8	.452		.8	.500				
	.6	.390		.6	.539	Two point loads (w w)	.72	Single point load (w)	1.2
	.4	.242		.4	.463				
	.2	.079		.2	.268				
Cantilever fixed left (a, w, L)	1.	0.0	Propped, point load (a, w, L)	1.	25.6	w w w w	.93	w w	1.9
	.8	.51		.8	17.8				
	.6	.75		.6	10.9				
	.5	.72		.4	5.27	www www	1.6	www	2.7
	.4	.59		.2	1.41				
	.2	.22							

$$I\ \text{REQUIRED} = W \cdot C_d \cdot B_d$$

Where
I — 10^6 mm^4
W — kN
C_d — from graph
B_d — from this table
= 1.0 for simple span, udl.

LOADING CONDITION	B_d	LOADING CONDITION	B_d
udl (w w) simply supported	.42	point load (w)	.71
udl (w w w)	.53	two point loads (w w)	.77
three point loads (w w w)	.89	two point loads (w w)	1.24
6 × w	1.44	2 × w 2 × w	2.1
9 × w	2.1	3 × w 3 × w	2.9

LOADING CONDITION	n	B_d	LOADING CONDITION	n	B_d
n no. of spaces $(n-1) \cdot W$	2	1.60	n no. of spaces $(n-1) \cdot W$	2	.40
	3	2.72		3	.55
	4	3.80		4	.80
	5	4.84		5	1.0
	6	6.14		6	1.2
	7	6.87		7	1.4

FACTORED RESISTANCES OF BEAMS

General

The tables on page 5—98 to 5—109 are provided to facilitate the proportioning of flexural members subject to forces and moments determined by elastic analysis. Certain values in these tables may also be used to facilitate the selection of Class 1 flexural members for which the moments and forces have been determined by plastic analysis. In using these tables, the factored moment or force must be equal to or less than the appropriate factored resistances, V_r, M_r or M_r', shown in the tables or modified as appropriate.

Beam Selection Tables

Table

In this table WWF, W, S, C shapes and the MC460 shapes for G40.21-M 300W steel have been listed in order of decreasing factored moment resistance (M_r) beginning with the shape with the largest M_r (eg. WWF1200 × 487 on page 5—98) and ending with the shape with the smallest M_r (e.g. C75 × 6 on page 5—108).

Shapes which are not available from Canadian mills are identified by an asterisk in the table.

The values of M_r listed take into account whether the section is Class 1, 2 or 3. Class 3 sections are identified. The table contains no section which is Class 4 in pure bending. (Class 1 was formerly known as a plastic design section, Class 2 as a compact section and Class 3 as a non-compact section. Class 4 is a slender section). Pages 5—5 to 5—7 contain tables listing the Classes of the sections for various steel grades.

In the tables, the shapes are listed in groups. The shape situated at the top of each group, shown in bold-face type, has the largest M_r in that group and, in general, is the lightest shape in that group. In a few cases the W shape produced in Canada is shown in bold-face type at the top of the group while, within the group, lighter WWF shapes or lighter imported W shapes may have a similar factored moment resistance. Both of the alternatives generally have a larger unit price; therefore, in spite of their lower mass, they are, in general, a more costly substitute for the W shape produced in Canada.

Symbols:

The following items are included in the table:

J = St. Venant torsional constant, 10^3 mm^4

C_w = Warping torsion constant, 10^9 mm^6

b = Flange width, millimetres

L_u = Length of span, in millimetres, up to which the tabulated loads are applicable with or without lateral support

V_r = factored shear resistance for an unstiffened web. $V_r = \phi A_w F_s$, kilonewtons

I_x = moment of inertia about the X—X axis, 10^6 mm^4

M_r = factored moment resistance, $M_r = \phi Z_x F_y$ for Class 1 and 2 sections and $\phi S_x F_y$ for Class 3 sections, kilonewton metres

M_r' = factored moment resistance for a beam for a given unbraced length greater than L_u. M_r is computed according to Clause 13.6 using the expression

$$\frac{\pi}{L}\sqrt{EI_y \, GJ + \left(\frac{\pi E}{L}\right)^2 I_y C_w} \text{ to determine } M_u, \text{ kilonewton metres}$$

(ω is taken as 1.0)

Design

Compute the maximum bending moment in the beam, M_f, under factored loads and the required moment of inertia, $I_{req'd}$, to meet the deflection limit using the specified loads, (For $I_{req'd}$ see also Deflection page 5–88)

For a laterally supported beam, proceed up the M_r column until a value of $M_r > M_f$ is obtained. Any beam above will satisfy the factored moment requirement. Check to insure that $V_r > V_f$ (the maximum factored beam shear), $I_x > I_{req'd}$ and $L_u >$ maximum unsupported length of the compression flange.

For a laterally unsupported beam, proceed up the M_r column until a value of $M_r > M_f$ is reached. Then move to the right across the table to the column headed by the required length (or the first listed length greater than that required) to obtain a value of M_r'. Generally, M_r' will be less than M_f. Now proceed up this column comparing a few beams that have an $M_r' > M_f$ and choose the lightest section. Check $V_r > V_f$ and $I_x > I_{req'd}$ if deflection check is necessary.

Other Steel Grades

Beams not available from Canadian mills are identified by an asterisk in the tables. These beams are also commonly available in other steel grades. To use the Beam Selection Tables for beams of a steel grade with an F_y less than 300 MPa multiply M_r, M_r' and V_r by the ratio of $F_y/300$ where F_y is expressed in megapascals.

For beams of a steel grade with an F_y greater than 300 MPa, the use of the tabulated values is conservative.

Plastic Analysis

For beams analysed plastically (Clause 8.5, CAN3-S16.1-M78), the Beam Selection Tables may be used to assist in the selection of a beam shape.

1. Proceed up the M_r column until a value of $M_r > M_f$ is obtained.

2. Any beam above will satisfy the factored moment requirement provided the beam meets the requirements of Class 1. Table 5–1 on pages 5–5 to 5–7 give the Class of steel shapes used as beams for various steel grades, including G40.21-M grade 300W steel.

3. Check to insure that $0.83\ V_r > V_f$ (the maximum factored beam shear). See Clause 13.4.2 of CAN3-S16.1-M78.

4. Provide lateral bracing. (Clause 13.7, CAN3-S16.1-M78)

Beam Load Tables — CSA G40.21-M 300W Steel

Loads

The tables listing total uniformly distributed factored loads for laterally supported beams, pages 5–110 to 5–125, are based on CSA G40.21-M 300W steel and only WWF and W and S shapes produced by Canadian mills are listed. The loads listed in the tables are the total uniformly distributed factored loads, in kilonewtons, for ordinary, simply supported spans where the top flange is laterally supported. The loads include the dead load of the beam which should be deducted from the tabulated loads if the net load which the beam is permitted to support is required.

The loads also are applicable to other cases of loading (provided that the compression flange of the beam is laterally supported). For these cases, the loads listed in the tables may be divided by the Equivalent Tabular Load value appearing in the pages entitled "Beam Diagrams and Formulae". Thus, for a simple beam, laterally supported, carrying a concentrated load at the centre of the span (Loading Condition No. 7), the concentrated load is one-half of the tabulated, uniformly distributed load for the same span.

Class 3 sections are identified in the tables.

For steel grades where F_y is less than 300 MPa multiply the tabular values by the ratio of $F_y/300$, where F_y is in megapascals. For steel grades where F_y is greater than 300 MPa the tabulated values are conservative.

Web Shear

With relatively short spans, the loads for beams may be limited by the shear capability of the web instead of by the bending capacity of the section. In the tables beams of spans shorter than the span for which the largest uniformly distributed factored load is listed are limited by the maximum shear capacity rather than bending capacity. The factored shear resistance of the web, V_r (kilonewtons), is listed in the tables.

Vertical Deflection

The columns headed "Approximate Deflection" list the approximate theoretical mid-span deflection, at an assumed stress level due to specified loads, for beams of various spans designed for the tabulated factored loads.

These approximate deflections are based on the nominal depth of the beam, and were calculated using the formula

$$\Delta = \frac{5}{384} \frac{WL^2}{EI}$$

where

Δ = deflection, in millimetres,

W = total uniform specified load including the dead load of the beam, in kilonewtons,

L = span, in millimetres

E = modulus of elasticity, in megapascals

I = moment of inertia of beams, in millimetres to the fourth,

For E = 200 000 MPa and an assumed bending unit stress of 215 MPa formula reduces

to $\Delta = \dfrac{224 \times 10^{-6} L^2}{d}$ where L = span, in millimetres

d = depth of beam or girder, in millimetres

Approximate deflections listed assume that the factored loads tabulated result from specified loads inducing a bending unit stress in the beam of 215 MPa. (This is approximately the level of stress in many laterally supported Class 1 or 2 beams where the ratio of specified live load to specified dead load is about 2.) More precise values of deflection can be determined by multiplying the approximate deflection listed by the ratio of the actual stress/215 MPa. This procedure is applicable to deflections due either to total load or live load only. (See also page 5—88).

Web Crippling

Flexural members should be proportioned so that the factored compressive resistance, B_r, of the web at the web toe of the flange-to-web fillets, resulting from factored concentrated loads or reactions not supported by bearing stiffeners, does not exceed, for

end reaction (R)

$B_r = 1.25 \, \phi \, w \, (N + k) \, F_y$

interior loads

$B_r = 1.25 \, \phi \, w \, (N + 2k) \, F_y$

ϕ = performance factor, 0.90

w = web thickness, millimetres,

k = distance from outer face of flange to web toe of fillet, millimetres,

N = length of bearing or length of interior load, millimetres.

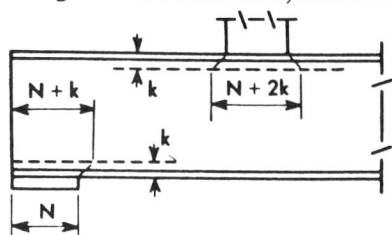

If the above values are exceeded, the web of the beam should be reinforced, or the length of bearing should be increased. Proper lateral support must be provided for the top flanges of beams at the reaction point to ensure that the crippling strength of the web is not decreased.

Values of R, maximum factored end reaction (kilonewtons) for 100 mm of bearing, and values of N, the length of end bearing (millimetres) required to develop the factored shear resistance of the web, V_r, are listed in the tables. Values of G, the increase in R (kilonewtons) for each additional millimetre of bearing also are listed. For steels other than CSA G40.21-M 300W (F_y = 300 MPa), values of R and G can be computed by multiplying the values listed by the ratio $F_y/300$. N is the same for all grades of steel.

Values of R, N and G are not listed for WWF shapes since the web slenderness of these shapes exceeds 63, and bearing stiffeners would be required (Clause 15.5.1, CAN3-S16.1-M78).

Symbols:

S_x = elastic section modulus, $10^3 \, mm^3$

Z_x = plastic section modulus, $10^3 \, mm^3$

I_x = moment of inertia about the X—X axis, $10^6 \, mm^4$

J = St. Venant torsional constant, $10^3 \, mm^4$

C_w = Warping torsion constant, $10^9 \, mm^6$

L_u = Length of span, in millimetres, up to which the tabulated loads are applicable with or without lateral support,

V_r = factored shear resistance of the web, kilonewtons

R = maximum factored end reaction, in kilonewtons, for 100 mm of bearing

N = length of bearing, in millimetres, to develop $V_r \simeq 0.528d$-k.

Beam Load Tables — HSS

Loads

The tables listing total factored uniformly distributed loads for laterally supported beams, pages 5—126 to 5—131, are based on CSA G40.21-M 350W steel and Rectangular Hollow Structural Sections (HSS). The loads listed are the total uniformly distributed factored loads, in kilonewtons, for HSS bent about their strong axis only, where the top flange receives sufficient lateral support. As with the Beam Load Tables for W shapes the Equivalent Tabular Load Factors may be used for other cases of loading. Class 3 sections for X—X bending are identified in the table.

The approximate deflections listed are calculated based on an assumed bending stress of 240 MPa, due to specified loads. More precise values of deflection can be determined by multiplying the approximate deflection tabulated by the ratio of actual stress under specified load to 240 MPa.

Symbols

S_x = Elastic section modulus about the strong (X—X) axis, $10^3\,mm^3$

Z_x = Plastic section modulus about the strong (X—X) axis, $10^3\,mm^3$

I_x = Moment of inertia about the strong (X—X) axis, $10^6\,mm^4$

C = Shear constant. For rectangular tubes this is equal to total area of webs. The factored web shear is obtained by multiplying the value of C by the factored web shear stress.

V_r = Maximum factored web shear. Beam loads above a value producing this shear are not listed in the tables, kilonewtons.

Examples

1. **Given:**

   Design a simply supported beam to span 8 m carrying a uniformly distributed load of 15 kN/m specified live load and 7 kN/m specified dead load. The dead load includes an assumed dead load of the beam of 0.7 kN/m. Assume the compression flange is laterally supported, and the beam frames into a girder. Live load deflection is limited to L/300. Use G40.21-M 300W steel.

   Solutions:

   (a) Using the Beam Selection Tables — Elastic Analysis

   Factored load = $\alpha_D D + \alpha_L L$ = 1.25 × 7 + 1.50 × 15 = 31.3 kN/m

   M_f (factored load moment) = $\dfrac{wL^2}{8}$ = $\dfrac{31.3 \times 8^2}{8}$ = 250 kN·m

   M (specified load moment) = $\dfrac{(15 + 7) \times 8^2}{8}$ = 176 kN·m

   R = V_f = $\dfrac{wL}{2}$ = 31.3 × $\dfrac{8}{2}$ = 125 kN

   Compute $I_{req'd}$ to meet deflection limit, see page 5—88 for udl

   B_d = 1.0, from graph in Figure 5—1, C_d = 1.25 × 10^6

   $I_{req'd}$ = W · C_d · B_d = (15 × 8) × 1.25 × 10^6 × 1.0 = 150 × $10^6\,mm^4$

   From the tables; page 5—104, select a W410 × 54

   M_r = 283 > 250 kN·m — OK

   V_r = 539 > 125 kN — OK

   I_x = 186 × $10^6\,mm^4$ > 150 × $10^6\,mm^4$ — OK

   Use W410 × 54

   (b) Using Beam Load Tables

   Total factored load = 31.3 × 8 = 250 kN

R = 250/2 = 125 kN

From tables on page 5—119, select a W410 × 54.

W_f = 250 kN < 283 kN — OK

V_r = 539 kN > 125 kN — OK

(If the beam did not frame into a girder, but was supported on a bearing plate instead, it would be necessary to ensure that R listed in the tables ⩾ R computed).

Approximate deflection listed (total for specified load) = 35 mm.

S_x = 924 × 10^3 mm^3 (from bottom of table)

Live load stress at specified load

$$\frac{M_{Live}}{S_x} = \frac{15}{22} \times \frac{176 \text{ kN·m} \times 10^6}{924 \times 10^3} = 130 \text{ MPa}$$

Live load deflection = $\frac{130}{215} \times 35 = 21$ mm

L/300 = 8 000/300 = 27 mm > 21 mm — OK

Use W410 × 54

2. **Given:**

Same as in (1), except assume that compression flange is braced only at $^1\!/_4$ points, midspan and ends.

Solution:

As in (1), select a W410 × 54

L_u = 2 480 mm > 8 000/4 = 2 000 mm — OK

Use W410 × 54

3. **Given:**

Same as in (1), except assume that compression flange is braced only at midpoint and ends.

Solution:

As in (1), select W410 × 54 (on basis of M_r). From the tables, page 5—105, for a W410 × 54 with an unbraced length of 8 000/2 = 4 000 mm,

M_r' for 4 000 mm = 225 kN·m < 250 kN·m

Therefore the W410 × 54 is inadequate. Checking further up the table; choose a W410 × 60 (This is the lightest beam with an M_r' greater than that required for an unbraced length of 4 000 mm).

M_r' (4 000) = 264 kN·m > 250 kN·m — OK

V_r = 558 kN > 125 kN

I_x = 216 × 10^6 mm^4 > 187 × 10^6 mm^4

Use W410 × 60

Shape #	J	C_W	b	L_u	V_r	I_x	M_r	M'_r (kN·m) Unbraced Length in Millimetres			
	10^3mm^4	10^9mm^6	mm	mm	kN	10^6mm^4	kN·m	4 000	4 500	5 000	5 500
WWF1200X487	25 000	373 000	550	8 370	2 670	16 700	**8 260**	....	....	....	....
WWF1100X458	24 400	312 000	550	8 600	2 050	13 600	**7 290**	....	....	....	....
WWF1200X403	11 500	285 000	550	7 980	2 670	13 300	**6 640**	....	....	....	....
WWF1000X447	24 300	256 000	550	8 770	2 050	11 100	6 510	....	....	....	....
WWF1100X388	15 200	207 000	500	7 570	2 050	11 200	**6 050**	....	....	....	....
WWF1200X364	8 880	200 000	500	7 090	2 670	11 700	**5 860**	....	....	....	....
WWF900X417	23 800	205 000	550	9 080	1 260	8 670	5 620	....	....	....	....
WWF1000X377	15 100	170 000	500	7 700	2 050	9 120	5 400	....	....	....	....
W920X446*	26 800	107 000	423	6 650	3 860	8 470	5 380	....	....	....	....
WWF1100X335	8 270	168 000	500	7 300	2 050	9 410	**5 100**	....	....	....	....
W920X417*	21 900	98 700	422	6 560	3 600	7 880	5 010	....	....	....	....
WWF900X347	14 700	136 000	500	7 970	1 260	7 100	4 620	....	....	....	....
WWF1200X302	5 740	92 200	400	5 390	2 670	8 970	**4 620**	....	....	....	4 590
W920X387*	17 300	88 500	420	5 430	3 380	7 180	4 590	....	....	....	....
WWF1000X324	8 180	138 000	500	7 420	2 050	7 620	4 540	....	....	....	....
W920X365*	14 400	81 900	419	6 350	3 200	6 710	4 310	....	....	....	....
WWF1100X291	6 810	85 900	400	5 690	2 050	7 800	**4 290**	....	....	....	....
W840X359*	15 000	67 400	403	6 210	3 150	5 910	4 020	....	....	....	....
W920X342*	11 900	75 500	418	6 280	3 030	6 250	4 020	....	....	....	....
WWF800X332	14 500	107 000	500	8 210	1 040	5 470	4 000	....	....	....	....
WWF900X293	7 690	111 000	500	7 690	1 260	5 900	3 830	....	....	....	....
WWF1200X263	4 700	39 000	300	3 850	2 670	7 250	**3 830**	3 790	3 630	3 460	3 270
WWF1000X280	6 720	70 600	400	5 790	2 050	6 300	3 810	....	....	....	....
W920X313*	11 600	34 300	309	4 390	3 500	5 480	3 670	....	3 650	3 530	3 400
W840X329*	11 500	60 000	401	6 090	2 930	5 350	3 650	....	....	....	....
WWF1100X255	3 810	68 200	400	5 450	2 050	6 520	**3 640**	....	....	....	3 630
W920X289*	9 230	31 300	308	4 330	3 200	5 040	3 400	....	3 360	3 250	3 130
W760X314*	11 600	44 700	384	5 860	2 760	4 270	3 320	....	....	....	....
WWF800X279	7 570	86 900	500	7 890	1 040	4 530	3 290	....	....	....	....
W840X299*	8 560	53 200	400	5 990	2 680	4 790	3 290	....	....	....	....
WWF1000X244	3 710	56 200	400	5 550	2 050	5 260	**3 210**	....	....	....	....
W920X271*	7 690	28 900	307	4 280	3 030	4 720	3 190	....	3 140	3 030	2 910
WWF900X249	6 230	56 800	400	6 030	1 260	4 830	3 190	....	....	....	....
WWF1100X220	3 100	28 800	300	3 900	2 050	5 240	**3 000**	2 980	2 860	2 720	2 580
W760X284*	8 580	39 300	382	5 750	2 500	3 810	2 970	....	....	....	....
W920X253*	6 260	26 500	306	4 230	2 830	4 370	2 970	....	2 920	2 810	2 700
W920X238*	5 140	24 300	305	4 190	2 690	4 060	2 750	....	2 700	2 600	2 490
WWF800X235	6 100	44 500	400	6 200	1 040	3 700	2 730	....	....	....	....
W760X257*	6 380	34 800	381	5 650	2 290	3 420	2 680	....	....	....	....
WWF900X213	3 220	45 200	400	5 810	1 260	3 990	**2 650**	....	....	....	....
W920X223*	4 220	22 100	304	4 120	2 580	3 770	2 580	....	2 510	2 410	2 300
W690X265*	8 110	26 400	358	5 480	2 310	2 900	2 510	....	....	....	....

*Not available from Canadian mills.

\# The SI designation is shown for each shape and is the preferred designation for use in Canada.

Nominal Mass per Metre (kg)	M'_r (kN•m) Unbraced Length of Compression Flange, in mm										Imperial Designation
	6 000	7 000	8 000	9 000	10 000	12 000	14 000	16 000	18 000	20 000	
487	....	....	....	8 090	7 790	7 140	6 440	5 690	4 800	4 090	WWF(M)47X326
458	....	....	....	7 200	6 950	6 420	5 850	5 240	4 550	3 900	WWF(M)43X307
403	....	....	....	6 390	6 110	5 500	4 820	4 000	3 280	2 760	WWF(M)47X270
447	....	....	....	6 460	6 250	5 810	5 340	4 840	4 340	3 730	WWF(M)39X300
388	....	....	5 950	5 710	5 450	4 890	4 280	3 550	2 960	2 530	WWF(M)43X260
364	....	....	5 630	5 360	5 060	4 390	3 580	2 850	2 340	1 980	WWF(M)47X244
417	....	....	....	....	5 460	5 120	4 750	4 370	3 990	3 550	WWF(M)35X279
377	....	....	5 340	5 140	4 920	4 440	3 940	3 360	2 810	2 420	WWF(M)39X253
446	....	5 300	5 090	4 860	4 630	4 160	3 680	3 120	2 690	2 360	W36X300
335	....	....	4 960	4 730	4 490	3 950	3 330	2 660	2 190	1 850	WWF(M)43X225
417	....	4 920	4 710	4 490	4 260	3 800	3 310	2 770	2 380	2 090	W36X280
347	....	....	4 610	4 450	4 280	3 920	3 530	3 130	2 660	2 290	WWF(M)35X233
302	4 460	4 170	3 840	3 490	3 100	2 250	1 730	1 390	1 150	978	WWF(M)47X203
387	....	4 480	4 280	4 070	3 840	3 380	2 870	2 390	2 040	1 790	W36X260
324	....	....	4 430	4 240	4 030	3 580	3 080	2 490	2 060	1 750	WWF(M)39X217
365	....	4 180	3 990	3 780	3 560	3 100	2 580	2 140	1 830	1 600	W36X245
291	4 220	3 980	3 720	3 430	3 120	2 380	1 840	1 490	1 240	1 060	WWF(M)43X195
359	....	3 880	3 690	3 500	3 300	2 890	2 410	2 020	1 730	1 520	W33X241
342	....	3 890	3 700	3 490	3 280	2 830	2 310	1 910	1 630	1 420	W36X230
332	....	....	....	3 890	3 760	3 470	3 170	2 870	2 520	2 190	WWF(M)31X223
293	....	....	3 790	3 640	3 480	3 130	2 750	2 300	1 910	1 630	WWF(M)35X197
263	3 070	2 640	2 100	1 710	1 430	1 060	834	684	578	500	WWF(M)47X176
280	3 770	3 560	3 340	3 090	2 830	2 220	1 730	1 410	1 180	1 020	WWF(M)39X188
313	3 270	3 000	2 720	2 410	2 070	1 600	1 310	1 110	962	850	W36X210
329	....	3 500	3 320	3 130	2 940	2 530	2 060	1 710	1 470	1 280	W33X221
255	3 530	3 310	3 050	2 770	2 470	1 790	1 370	1 100	907	769	WWF(M)43X171
289	3 000	2 740	2 450	2 130	1 820	1 400	1 140	963	833	734	W36X194
314	3 300	3 140	2 980	2 810	2 630	2 270	1 860	1 560	1 350	1 190	W30X211
279	....	....	3 280	3 160	3 030	2 760	2 460	2 140	1 790	1 540	WWF(M)31X187
299	....	3 130	2 960	2 780	2 590	2 190	1 740	1 440	1 230	1 070	W33X201
244	3 130	2 940	2 730	2 500	2 240	1 660	1 280	1 030	853	727	WWF(M)39X163
271	2 790	2 530	2 250	1 930	1 640	1 260	1 020	859	741	653	W36X182
249	....	3 040	2 860	2 680	2 480	2 040	1 600	1 310	1 100	953	WWF(M)35X167
220	2 420	2 090	1 670	1 360	1 130	836	654	535	450	389	WWF(M)43X147
284	2 940	2 790	2 630	2 470	2 300	1 930	1 550	1 300	1 120	978	W30X191
253	2 580	2 320	2 050	1 730	1 470	1 120	905	758	652	573	W36X170
238	2 370	2 130	1 860	1 550	1 310	998	802	669	575	504	W36X160
235	....	2 630	2 490	2 340	2 190	1 870	1 500	1 230	1 040	908	WWF(M)31X157
257	2 640	2 490	2 340	2 180	2 020	1 640	1 310	1 090	931	814	W30X173
213	2 620	2 480	2 320	2 140	1 950	1 500	1 160	936	779	665	WWF(M)35X142
223	2 190	1 950	1 680	1 380	1 170	884	707	589	504	441	W36X150
265	2 440	2 320	2 180	2 040	1 900	1 590	1 300	1 090	946	835	W27X178

Shape #	Properties J	Cw	b	Lu	Vr	Ix	Mr	M'r (kN•m) Unbraced Length in Millimetres 3 000	3 500	4 000	4 500	5 000
	10^3mm^4	10^9mm^6	mm	mm	kN	10^6mm^4	kN•m	3 000	3 500	4 000	4 500	5 000
WWF1000X200	2 480	21 700	300	3 910	2 050	3 940	**2 480**	....	....	2 460	2 360	2 250
W840X226*	5 140	19 300	294	4 130	2 440	3 400	2 470	....	....	....	2 410	2 320
WWF900X192	3 500	21 600	300	4 310	1 260	3 460	**2 320**	....	....	....	2 290	2 210
WWF700X222	6 010	33 700	400	6 410	846	2 740	2 290	....	....	....	....	....
W840X210*	4 050	17 300	293	4 060	2 320	3 110	2 280	....	....	....	2 200	2 120
W690X240*	6 090	23 400	356	5 370	2 100	2 610	2 270	....	....	....	....	....
W920X201*	2 910	18 400	304	4 000	2 450	3 250	2 260	....	....	....	2 170	2 080
WWF800X198	3 090	35 500	400	5 970	1 040	3 040	2 250	....				
WWF700X203	4 320	30 400	400	6 280	846	2 500	2 090	....				
W610X241	7 700	16 800	329	5 200	2 030	2 150	**2 070**	....	....			
W840X193*	3 050	15 100	292	3 970	2 200	2 780	2 060	....	....	2 050	1 980	1 890
W690X217*	4 560	20 800	355	5 290	1 910	2 340	2 040	....	....			
WWF900X169	1 980	17 400	300	4 130	1 260	2 930	1 990	....	....	....	1 940	1 860
W760X196*	4 040	11 300	268	3 770	2 140	2 400	1 940	....	....	1 900	1 830	1 740
WWF700X185	3 000	27 000	400	6 140	846	2 250	1 880	....				
W610X217	5 600	14 700	328	5 080	1 850	1 910	**1 850**	....	....			
W840X176*	2 220	13 000	292	3 880	2 080	2 460	1 840	....	....	1 820	1 750	1 670
W760X185*	3 330	10 300	267	3 720	2 030	2 230	1 810	....	....	1 770	1 690	1 610
WWF800X164	2 380	15 000	300	4 350	1 040	2 380	1 780	....	....	....	1 770	1 700
W760X173*	2 690	9 420	267	3 670	1 960	2 060	1 680	....	....	1 630	1 560	1 480
WWF800X154	1 850	13 700	300	4 270	1 040	2 210	1 670	....	....	....	1 640	1 580
W530X219*	6 420	11 000	318	5 140	1 830	1 510	1 650	....				
W610X195	3 970	12 700	327	4 940	1 710	1 680	**1 640**	....	....	....	....	1 630
WWF700X164	3 280	12 800	300	4 610	846	1 930	1 630	....	....	....	....	1 590
W760X161*	2 070	8 280	266	3 590	1 860	1 860	1 530	....	....	1 480	1 410	1 330
W690X170*	3 050	7 410	256	3 650	1 790	1 700	1 520	....	....	1 480	1 410	1 350
WWF700X151	2 290	11 400	300	4 500	846	1 740	1 480	....	....	....	....	1 430
W530X196*	4 700	9 640	316	5 000	1 630	1 340	1 470	....				
W610X174	2 800	10 900	325	4 830	1 540	1 470	**1 450**	....	....	....	....	1 430
W760X147*	1 560	7 160	265	3 510	1 770	1 660	1 380	....	....	1 320	1 250	1 180
WWF700X141	1 760	10 400	300	4 420	846	1 620	1 380	....	....	....	1 370	1 320
W530X182*	3 740	8 820	315	4 910	1 490	1 240	1 360	....	....	....	....	1 350
S610X180*	5 330	3 070	204	2 790	2 250	1 310	1 360	1 330	1 270	1 200	1 130	1 070
W690X152*	2 200	6 420	254	3 570	1 610	1 510	1 350	....	....	1 300	1 240	1 180
W610X155	1 950	9 450	324	4 740	1 380	1 290	**1 280**	....	....	....		1 260
S610X158*	4 210	2 860	200	2 780	1 740	1 220	1 240	1 210	1 150	1 090	1 030	961
W530X165*	2 830	7 790	313	4 810	1 360	1 110	1 230	....	....	....		1 220
W690X140*	1 670	5 720	254	3 520	1 510	1 360	1 230	....	....	1 180	1 120	1 060
W460X177*	4 410	5 440	286	4 730	1 430	910	1 160	....	....	....		1 140
W530X150*	2 160	7 030	312	4 730	1 230	1 010	1 120	....	....	....		1 100
W610X140	2 180	3 990	230	3 320	1 440	1 120	**1 120**	....	1 100	1 050	1 000	946
W690X125*	1 180	4 830	253	3 430	1 410	1 190	1 080	....	....	1 030	975	918
S610X149*	3 150	1 730	184	2 330	2 050	996	1 060	977	910	841	771	698
W460X158*	3 120	4 670	284	4 560	1 270	796	1 020	....	....	....		996

* Not available from Canadian mills.
\# The SI designation is shown for each shape and is the preferred designation for use in Canada.

Nominal Mass per Metre (kg)	M'r (kN·m) Unbraced Length of Compression Flange, in mm											Imperial Designation
	5 500	6 000	7 000	8 000	9 000	10 000	12 000	14 000	16 000	18 000	20 000	
200	2 130	2 010	1 730	1 390	1 130	945	699	549	449	379	328	WWF(M)39X134
226	2 220	2 120	1 900	1 670	1 400	1 190	914	741	623	537	473	W33X152
192	2 120	2 030	1 820	1 600	1 330	1 120	842	670	555	473	412	WWF(M)35X128
222	....	....	2 240	2 130	2 020	1 910	1 670	1 400	1 160	993	867	WWF(M)28X149
210	2 020	1 920	1 710	1 480	1 220	1 040	792	639	535	461	404	W33X141
240	2 250	2 190	2 070	1 940	1 800	1 660	1 340	1 090	914	788	694	W27X161
201	1 980	1 870	1 640	1 370	1 120	941	707	561	464	396	345	W36X135
198	....	2 240	2 130	2 000	1 860	1 720	1 380	1 070	867	726	623	WWF(M)31X133
203	....	....	2 020	1 920	1 810	1 700	1 460	1 180	972	826	718	WWF(M)28X136
241	2 040	1 990	1 880	1 770	1 660	1 540	1 300	1 070	911	795	705	W24X162
193	1 800	1 710	1 500	1 260	1 040	877	666	534	445	382	334	W33X130
217	2 020	1 970	1 850	1 720	1 590	1 450	1 140	920	769	660	579	W27X146
169	1 770	1 680	1 480	1 240	1 010	845	625	491	402	339	293	WWF(M)35X113
196	1 660	1 570	1 380	1 160	973	835	650	532	451	391	346	W30X132
185	....	....	1 810	1 710	1 600	1 490	1 250	982	803	677	585	WWF(M)28X124
217	1 810	1 760	1 660	1 550	1 440	1 320	1 070	878	745	647	573	W24X146
176	1 580	1 490	1 300	1 060	868	731	551	439	364	311	271	W33X118
185	1 530	1 440	1 260	1 040	867	743	576	470	397	344	304	W30X124
164	1 640	1 560	1 410	1 240	1 040	872	654	520	430	366	319	WWF(M)31X109
173	1 400	1 320	1 140	924	770	657	506	411	346	299	264	W30X116
154	1 510	1 440	1 290	1 120	920	771	575	454	374	317	275	WWF(M)31X103
219	1 620	1 580	1 500	1 410	1 330	1 240	1 060	880	754	659	587	W21X147
195	1 590	1 540	1 440	1 340	1 230	1 120	870	709	598	518	457	W24X131
164	1 540	1 490	1 370	1 240	1 110	955	733	593	498	429	378	WWF(M)28X110
161	1 260	1 170	988	793	658	560	429	347	291	251	220	W30X108
170	1 280	1 200	1 050	875	737	635	497	409	347	302	268	W27X114
151	1 380	1 330	1 210	1 080	942	797	605	485	404	347	303	WWF(M)28X101
196	1 440	1 400	1 320	1 230	1 150	1 060	873	721	615	537	477	W21X132
174	1 390	1 350	1 250	1 150	1 040	924	709	574	482	415	365	W24X117
147	1 110	1 030	840	671	555	470	358	288	241	207	181	W30X99
141	1 270	1 220	1 100	981	831	700	527	420	348	297	259	WWF(M)28X95
182	1 320	1 280	1 200	1 120	1 030	949	759	625	531	463	410	W21X122
180	1 000	932	778	662	577	511	418	353	307	271	243	S24X121
152	1 120	1 040	898	728	610	523	406	332	281	244	216	W27X102
155	1 220	1 180	1 080	988	886	762	579	465	388	333	291	W24X104
158	896	830	682	578	502	444	362	305	265	234	209	S24X106
165	1 180	1 140	1 070	987	905	822	641	525	445	386	342	W21X111
140	998	931	778	628	523	447	345	280	236	204	180	W27X94
177	1 110	1 080	1 020	956	894	833	695	581	500	439	392	W18X119
150	1 070	1 030	960	881	801	709	548	446	377	326	288	W21X101
140	888	829	695	573	486	422	334	277	237	207	184	W24X94
125	857	793	641	514	426	362	277	224	188	162	142	W27X84
149	615	549	453	385	336	298	244	206	179	158	142	S24X100
158	967	937	877	816	754	692	556	463	397	348	310	W18X106

Shape #	Properties							M'r (kN·m)				
	J	Cw	b	Lu	Vr	Ix	Mr	Unbraced Length in Millimetres				
	10^3mm⁴	10^9mm⁶	mm	mm	kN	10^6mm⁴	kN·m	2 500	3 000	3 500	4 000	4 500
W610X125	1 540	3 450	229	3 250	1 300	985	**991**	...	...	970	923	873
S610X134*	2 520	1 640	181	2 320	1 730	939	985	965	904	839	772	703
W530X138	2 500	2 670	214	3 180	1 440	861	975	...	...	948	906	861
W460X144*	2 440	4 230	283	4 490	1 140	726	931	...	...	...	...	...
S610X119*	2 030	1 540	178	2 330	1 380	879	907	889	832	771	707	641
W610X113	1 120	2 990	228	3 180	1 210	875	**888**	...	...	862	818	770
S510X143*	3 570	1 280	183	2 520	1 870	702	880	...	839	796	751	706
W410X149*	3 220	3 200	265	4 450	1 140	619	877	...	...	...	...	875
W530X123	1 800	2 310	212	3 100	1 270	761	867	...	...	836	794	751
W360X162*	2 940	5 430	371	6 540	863	516	848	...	...	...	...	...
W460X128*	1 720	3 670	282	4 380	1 020	637	823	...	...	...	...	817
S510X128*	2 830	1 190	179	2 480	1 540	660	815	814	772	729	684	640
W610X101	781	2 550	228	3 110	1 130	764	**783**	...	...	754	713	668
W410X132*	2 260	2 730	263	4 290	1 010	538	769	...	...	...	...	760
W360X147*	2 230	4 840	370	6 350	789	463	767	...	...	...	...	...
W530X109	1 260	2 000	211	3 040	1 110	667	764	...	...	731	692	651
W460X113*	1 180	3 150	280	4 270	891	556	721	...	...	...	...	710
W530X101	1 020	1 820	210	2 990	1 040	617	**707**	...	...	672	635	595
W610X92*	710	1 250	179	2 340	1 170	646	678	664	618	566	510	448
S510X112*	1 910	745	162	2 120	1 460	532	675	644	600	554	508	461
W410X114*	1 490	2 300	261	4 140	868	462	664	...	...	...	...	649
W460X106	1 460	1 260	194	2 910	1 050	488	645	...	...	640	610	546
W530X92	762	1 590	209	2 930	969	552	**637**	...	633	601	565	526
† W360X134*	1 680	4 310	369	6 570	711	415	629	...	...	...	...	...
S510x98.2*	1 490	698	159	2 120	1 160	497	618	588	546	502	457	411
W360X122*	2 110	1 790	257	4 420	841	365	613	...	...	...	...	610
W610X82*	488	1 040	178	2 270	1 070	560	594	576	533	484	429	364
W460X97	1 130	1 140	193	2 870	947	445	589	...	581	553	522	490
W310X129	2 130	2 220	308	5 580	742	308	583	...	...	...	...	...
W410X100*	994	1 960	260	4 040	740	398	575	...	...	...	...	557
W530X85*	737	849	166	2 270	982	485	567	551	512	469	422	373
W530X82	530	1 340	209	2 860	894	479	**559**	...	551	521	487	451
W360X110*	1 610	1 610	256	4 300	731	331	556	...	...	...	...	550
S460X104*	1 740	495	159	2 060	1 470	387	553	524	488	452	416	380
W460X89	907	1 040	192	2 830	866	410	543	...	534	506	477	446
W310X118	1 600	1 970	307	5 390	666	275	526	...	...	...	...	...
W360X101*	1 260	1 450	255	4 200	668	302	508	...	...	...	...	499
W460X82	691	918	191	2 770	812	370	**494**	...	482	456	427	396
W530X74*	480	692	166	2 200	914	411	489	469	432	391	346	293
W310X107	1 220	1 760	306	5 220	604	248	478	...	...	...	...	...
W410X85	926	717	181	2 730	810	315	467	...	455	431	406	380
S460X81.4*	986	423	152	2 000	953	335	464	433	399	363	327	285
W360X91*	916	1 270	254	4 080	598	267	454	...	...	...	...	442
W460X74	517	813	190	2 730	733	333	**445**	...	433	407	380	351
W530X66*	320	565	165	2 130	833	351	421	399	364	326	283	232
W410X74	637	614	180	2 670	714	275	**408**	...	394	371	348	323

*Not available from Canadian mills.
† Class 3 Section.
\# The SI designation is shown for each shape and is the preferred designation for use in Canada.

Nominal Mass per Metre (kg)	M'r (kN•m)											Imperial Designation
	Unbraced Length of Compression Flange, in mm											
	5 000	5 500	6 000	7 000	8 000	9 000	10 000	12 000	14 000	16 000	18 000	
125	821	765	708	575	470	396	342	269	222	189	165	W24X84
134	625	548	488	401	340	295	262	213	180	156	138	S24X90
138	815	768	720	616	515	444	390	314	263	227	200	W21X93
144	904	876	847	789	729	668	602	478	396	339	297	W18X97
119	564	493	437	357	302	262	231	188	158	137	121	S24X80
113	719	666	610	481	391	328	282	220	180	153	133	W24X76
143	662	618	569	474	407	357	318	262	223	194	172	S20X96
149	852	828	804	755	707	658	610	502	421	364	320	W16X100
123	706	660	613	505	421	361	316	253	211	182	160	W21X83
162	...	...	...	834	804	773	743	681	621	558	488	W14X109
128	792	765	738	680	621	562	490	386	318	271	237	W18X86
128	595	551	496	412	353	309	275	226	192	167	148	S20X86
101	619	568	512	396	320	267	228	176	144	121	105	W24X68
132	738	715	691	644	596	548	496	398	333	287	252	W16X89
147	...	...	...	748	718	688	658	597	536	467	407	W14X99
109	608	563	517	413	342	291	254	202	168	144	126	W21X73
113	686	661	635	580	522	458	394	307	252	213	185	W18X76
101	553	509	462	365	301	255	222	176	146	125	109	W21X68
92	376	322	281	222	183	156	135	107	88.9	76.1	66.5	W24X62
112	406	360	323	269	230	202	180	148	126	109	96.7	S20X75
114	627	605	582	536	488	439	383	305	254	218	191	W16X77
106	512	478	444	366	308	266	235	190	160	138	122	W18X71
92	486	444	393	309	253	214	185	146	120	103	89.6	W21X62
134	...	...	...	619	595	571	546	497	447	392	341	W14X90
98.2	356	315	282	234	200	174	155	127	108	93.7	82.9	S20X66
122	594	578	561	529	496	463	431	357	301	260	229	W14X82
82	304	260	225	177	145	123	106	83.4	68.9	58.7	51.2	W24X55
97	457	424	389	314	264	227	200	161	135	117	103	W18X65
129	...	...	573	550	527	504	481	435	390	336	296	W12X87
100	537	516	494	449	403	349	302	238	197	168	147	W16X67
85	316	273	240	193	162	139	122	97.8	81.9	70.6	62.0	W21X57
82	412	371	321	251	204	172	148	115	94.8	80.5	70.0	W21X55
110	534	518	502	470	437	404	372	301	252	218	192	W14X74
104	338	301	271	227	196	172	154	127	108	94.2	83.4	S18X70
89	414	381	343	276	231	198	174	140	117	101	88.6	W18X60
118	...	524	513	490	467	444	421	375	324	279	245	W12X79
101	483	468	452	420	388	356	319	256	215	185	163	W14X68
82	365	332	292	234	195	167	146	117	97.3	83.7	73.5	W18X55
74	247	212	186	148	123	105	91.7	73.2	61.0	52.4	46.0	W21X50
107	...	472	461	438	415	393	370	324	272	234	205	W12X72
85	354	328	297	243	205	178	157	127	107	92.9	82.0	W16X57
81.4	248	219	196	163	140	122	109	89.2	75.7	65.9	58.3	S18X54.7
91	427	412	396	365	333	300	262	209	175	150	132	W14X61
74	320	285	249	198	164	140	122	96.9	80.6	69.1	60.6	W18X50
66	195	167	145	115	94.9	80.6	70.0	55.5	46.0	39.4	34.5	W21X44
74	297	271	239	194	163	140	124	99.8	83.8	72.4	63.7	W16X50

Shape #	Properties							M'_r (kN•m)				
	J	C_W	b	L_u	V_r	I_x	M_r	Unbraced Length in Millimetres				
	$10^3\,mm^4$	$10^9\,mm^6$	mm	mm	kN	$10^6\,mm^4$	kN•m	2 000	2 500	3 000	3 500	4 000
W460X67	412	709	190	2 660	688	300	**405**	...	...	390	366	339
W460X68*	509	463	154	2 170	744	297	402	...	385	355	323	289
†W310X97	912	1 560	305	5 410	543	222	389	...	...	...	...	...
W360X79	814	687	205	3 270	593	227	386	...	...	...	379	364
W310X86	877	961	254	4 250	503	199	383	...	...	...	...	...
W250X101	1 490	829	257	4 950	560	164	378	...	...	...	...	...
W410X67	469	540	179	2 610	643	246	**367**			352	330	307
W460X61	289	588	189	2 580	650	259	**354**	...	...	336	313	288
W310X79	657	847	254	4 140	480	177	346	...	...	...	...	...
W360X72	603	600	204	3 190	536	201	346	...	...	...	337	322
W460X60*	335	388	153	2 130	649	255	346	...	327	300	270	239
S380X74*	884	220	143	1 910	951	203	343	339	316	292	268	243
†MC460X86*	1 190	291	107	2 210	1 450	283	335	...	324	306	287	269
W250X89	1 040	713	256	4 690	496	143	332	...	...	...	...	...
W310X74	745	505	205	3 380	519	165	321	...	...	...	318	307
W410X60	328	468	178	2 580	558	216	**321**	...	...	306	286	264
W200X100	2 090	386	210	5 020	592	113	310	...	...	...	...	...
†MC460X77.2*	856	265	104	2 140	1 240	262	308	...	295	276	257	238
S380X64*	641	204	140	1 900	706	187	308	304	282	259	235	211
W360X64	438	524	203	3 110	476	178	308	...	...	...	297	283
W250X80	757	623	255	4 520	429	126	294	...	...	...	...	...
W460X52*	210	306	152	2 030	609	212	294	...	273	247	219	185
†MC460X68.2*	621	245	102	2 080	1 030	243	286	...	271	252	232	212
W310X67	545	439	204	3 280	463	145	286	...	...	...	281	270
W410X54	226	388	177	2 480	539	186	**283**	...	...	266	246	225
†MC460X63.5*	524	228	100	2 050	928	231	273	...	256	237	217	197
W360X57	334	331	172	2 550	504	161	273	...	...	259	243	225
S310X74*	1 160	137	139	2 150	946	127	270	...	261	248	235	222
W250X73	575	553	254	4 390	388	113	266	...	...	...	...	...
W200X86	1 400	318	209	4 620	514	94.7	265	...	...	...	...	...
W310X60	397	384	203	3 200	405	129	254	...	...	...	248	237
W250X67	625	324	204	3 570	408	104	243	...	...	...	...	237
W360X51	238	285	171	2 500	455	141	**241**	...	...	227	212	195
W410X46	192	197	140	1 930	503	156	**239**	236	217	195	171	142
†C380X74	1 110	131	94	2 040	1 240	168	238	...	226	214	202	189
S310X60.7*	723	118	133	2 010	636	113	235	...	222	208	194	181
W310X52	308	237	167	2 570	429	118	226	...	...	216	203	189
W200X71	818	250	206	4 150	393	76.6	217	...	...	...	...	...
W360X45	160	239	171	2 430	433	122	**210**	...	209	195	181	165
W250X58	409	268	203	3 410	359	87.3	208	...	...	...	207	199
†C380X60	607	109	89	1 860	896	145	205	201	188	174	160	147
S310X52	450	88.2	129	1 800	592	95.8	199	193	179	165	150	136
W410X39	111	154	140	1 860	448	127	**197**	193	175	155	132	105
W310X45	191	195	166	2 490	368	99.2	191	...	...	180	168	155
S310X47	374	83.6	127	1 780	484	91.1	186	181	167	153	138	124
†C380X50	424	95.2	86	1 780	693	131	185	180	166	152	137	123

*Not available from Canadian mills.
†Class 3 Section.
The SI designation is shown for each shape and is the preferred designation for use in Canada.

Nominal Mass per Metre (kg)	M'_r (kN•m)											Imperial Designation
	Unbraced Length of Compression flange, in mm											
	4 500	5 000	5 500	6 000	7 000	8 000	9 000	10 000	12 000	14 000	16 000	
67	311	281	245	214	169	140	119	103	82.0	68.0	58.2	W18X45
68	250	214	186	164	133	112	96.8	85.3	69.0	58.0	50.1	W18X46
97	...	...	387	379	361	342	324	305	268	226	194	W12X65
79	348	331	315	298	264	225	195	172	139	117	101	W14X53
86	378	367	355	344	320	297	273	248	200	167	144	W12X58
101	...	377	369	361	346	330	315	300	270	236	205	W10X68
67	283	258	228	201	161	135	116	102	81.7	68.4	58.9	W16X45
61	261	231	198	172	135	111	93.9	81.3	64.1	53.0	45.2	W18X41
79	338	327	316	305	282	258	235	207	166	139	119	W12X53
72	306	290	274	257	222	186	161	141	114	95.7	82.6	W14X48
60	200	169	147	129	104	86.7	74.4	65.3	52.4	43.9	37.8	W18X40
74	216	190	170	153	129	111	97.8	87.4	72.2	61.5	53.6	S15X50
86	251	232	211	191	160	139	122	109	90.1	76.8	67.0	MC18X58
89	...	327	320	312	296	281	266	250	220	186	161	W10X60
74	295	282	270	258	233	206	179	159	129	109	94.6	W12X50
60	241	217	188	165	131	109	93.2	81.4	65.0	54.2	46.5	W16X40
100	...	...	305	300	289	279	269	258	238	217	194	W8X67
77.2	219	198	177	159	133	115	101	90.0	74.2	63.2	55.0	MC18X51.9
64	183	160	142	128	107	92.2	80.9	72.2	59.5	50.6	44.1	S15X42.9
64	268	252	237	220	183	153	131	115	92.4	77.3	66.6	W14X43
80	...	287	280	272	257	242	227	212	179	151	130	W10X54
52	152	128	110	96.3	76.8	63.7	54.4	47.4	37.9	31.6	27.1	W18X35
68.2	191	167	148	133	111	95.1	83.4	74.3	61.1	51.9	45.2	MC18X45.8
67	258	246	234	222	198	169	147	129	105	88.5	76.6	W12X45
54	203	176	151	132	104	86.1	73.2	63.6	50.5	41.9	35.9	W16X36
63.5	175	152	135	121	100	85.9	75.2	67.0	55.0	46.7	40.6	MC18X42.7
57	207	189	167	147	119	99.8	86.0	75.7	61.1	51.3	44.3	W14X38
74	209	196	184	168	143	124	110	98.5	81.8	69.9	61.0	S12X50
73	264	257	250	242	227	212	198	183	149	126	108	W10X49
86	...	261	256	251	240	230	220	210	190	169	147	W8X58
60	226	214	203	191	166	139	120	106	85.3	71.7	61.9	W12X40
67	229	221	213	205	189	174	157	139	114	96.5	83.8	W10X45
51	178	159	137	121	97.0	81.0	69.5	60.9	48.9	40.9	35.2	W14X34
46	117	99.9	86.7	76.4	61.7	51.8	44.6	39.2	31.6	26.5	22.9	W16X31
74	177	165	151	138	117	101	89.7	80.5	66.8	57.1	49.8	C15X50
60.7	168	154	138	125	106	91.7	80.9	72.5	60.1	51.3	44.8	S12X40.8
52	176	162	146	130	106	89.4	77.4	68.4	55.5	46.8	40.5	W12X35
71	213	208	203	198	188	178	168	158	137	117	101	W8X48
45	148	128	110	96.1	76.5	63.4	54.1	47.2	37.6	31.3	26.9	W14X30
58	191	184	176	168	153	137	119	105	85.7	72.4	62.8	W10X39
60	132	117	105	94.8	80.0	69.3	61.2	54.8	45.3	38.7	33.8	C15X40
52	119	105	94.3	85.4	72.0	62.3	55.0	49.2	40.7	34.7	30.3	S12X35
39	86.7	73.1	63.0	55.2	44.1	36.6	31.3	27.4	21.9	18.2	15.7	W16X26
45	142	128	111	98.2	79.3	66.5	57.3	50.4	40.6	34.1	29.4	W12X30
47	107	94.4	84.5	76.4	64.3	55.6	49.0	43.8	36.2	30.9	26.9	S12X31.8
50	106	93.3	83.4	75.5	63.5	54.9	48.4	43.3	35.7	30.5	26.6	C15X33.9

Shape #	Properties							M_r' (kN•m)				
	J	C_W	b	L_u	V_r	I_x	M_r	Unbraced Length in Millimetres				
	10^3mm^4	10^9mm^6	mm	mm	kN	10^6mm^4	kN•m	1 500	2 000	2 500	3 000	3 500
W360X39	151	110	128	1 790	409	102	**179**	...	173	157	139	120
W200X59	465	196	205	3 780	341	61.1	176	...	...	...	...	...
W250X49	241	211	202	3 240	326	70.6	171	...	...	...	...	167
W310X39	126	164	165	2 440	320	85.1	**165**	...	...	164	153	142
W250X45	261	113	148	2 360	360	71.1	163	...	...	160	151	142
S250X52	541	51.9	126	1 880	683	61.6	158	...	155	147	138	129
W200X52	324	167	204	3 620	290	52.7	154	...	...	...	...	...
W360X33	85.9	84.3	127	1 720	361	82.7	**146**	...	139	124	108	87.6
W250X39	169	93.4	147	2 280	308	60.1	139	...	...	135	126	117
W200X46	221	141	203	3 460	260	45.5	134	...	...	...	...	...
W310X33*	122	43.8	102	1 430	368	65.0	130	128	114	98.4	80.5	64.2
S250X38	251	41.5	118	1 720	358	51.4	126	...	121	111	102	92.7
W200X42	223	84.0	166	2 850	263	40.9	120	...	...	...	119	114
†C310X45	363	39.9	80	1 690	707	67.3	119	...	114	106	98.2	90.2
W250X33	98.5	73.2	146	2 180	280	48.9	**114**	...	...	110	102	93.1
W310X28*	75.7	35.6	102	1 390	330	54.3	110	107	94.4	79.6	61.9	48.8
†C310X37	224	34.6	77	1 590	533	59.9	106	...	99.3	90.6	81.9	73.2
W200X36	146	69.6	165	2 730	222	34.4	103	...	...	...	100	95.3
W250X28*	96.7	27.7	102	1 480	297	40.0	95.3	95.0	85.7	75.5	64.9	52.6
†C310X31	153	29.3	74	1 510	391	53.5	**94.8**	...	86.6	77.7	68.7	58.5
†C250X45*	511	20.5	76	1 850	774	42.8	91.0	...	89.6	85.2	80.8	76.4
W200X31	119	40.9	134	2 150	240	31.4	**90.4**	...	...	86.7	81.1	75.3
W310X24*	42.5	25.7	101	1 300	304	42.7	88.6	84.5	72.5	58.1	42.8	33.5
S200X34	229	16.8	106	1 620	405	27.0	85.3	...	81.0	75.4	69.8	64.3
W150X37	193	40.0	154	2 910	234	22.2	83.7	...	...	...	83.2	80.2
W250X25*	65.2	23.0	102	1 430	279	34.2	82.9	81.8	72.9	63.0	51.6	41.2
†C250X37	290	18.2	73	1 630	607	37.9	80.7	...	77.0	71.9	66.9	62.0
W310X21*	29.4	21.7	101	1 270	275	37.0	77.5	73.3	62.0	47.9	35.0	27.2
W200X27	71.3	32.5	133	2 050	214	25.8	**75.3**	...	...	70.8	65.4	59.7
S200X27	140	14.7	102	1 540	250	24.0	**73.4**	...	68.2	62.5	56.8	51.2
W250X22*	43.4	18.7	102	1 380	263	28.9	71.0	69.3	61.0	51.6	40.3	31.9
†C250X30	154	15.0	69	1 460	435	32.7	69.4	69.0	63.4	57.7	52.0	46.4
W150X30	101	30.3	153	2 680	185	17.2	65.9	...	...	...	64.1	61.2
S180X30*	188	9.44	98	1 570	362	17.8	64.3	...	60.8	56.7	52.7	48.8
†C230X30	180	10.5	67	1 500	465	25.5	59.9	...	55.7	51.6	47.4	43.4
W200X22*	56.6	13.9	102	1 500	228	20.0	59.9	...	54.4	48.4	42.2	35.0
†C250X23	86.8	11.7	65	1 340	276	27.8	**59.1**	57.3	51.4	45.2	38.9	32.1
W250X18*	22.4	13.8	101	1 320	215	22.4	55.9	53.7	46.3	37.6	27.8	21.7
S180X22.8*	101	7.88	93	1 440	203	15.4	53.7	53.2	48.9	44.6	40.4	36.2
W150X24*	92.9	10.2	102	1 780	188	13.4	51.8	...	50.5	47.2	44.0	40.7
W200X19*	36.2	11.1	102	1 440	210	16.6	50.5	49.9	44.7	39.0	32.7	26.2
†C230X22	86.9	8.33	63	1 330	294	21.3	**50.2**	48.7	44.0	39.2	34.5	29.1
†C200X28	183	6.67	64	1 540	449	18.2	48.6	...	45.8	42.9	40.0	37.1

*Not available from Canadian mills.
†Class 3 Section.
The SI designation is shown for each shape and is the preferred designation for use in Canada.

| Nominal Mass per Metre (kg) | M'_r (kN•m) | | | | | | | | | | | Imperial Designation |
| | Unbraced Length of Compression Flange, in mm | | | | | | | | | | | |
	4 000	4 500	5 000	5 500	6 000	7 000	8 000	9 000	10 000	12 000	14 000	
39	97.2	81.3	69.8	61.1	54.2	44.3	37.5	32.5	28.8	23.4	19.7	W14X26
59	174	169	164	159	154	144	134	124	114	93.4	79.3	W8X40
49	160	153	146	138	130	115	97.2	84.0	74.1	60.0	50.5	W10X33
39	130	117	103	88.5	77.7	62.2	51.8	44.3	38.8	31.1	25.9	W12X26
45	132	122	112	101	90.6	75.2	64.4	56.3	50.1	41.1	34.9	W10X30
52	120	111	102	92.1	83.9	71.3	62.0	54.9	49.3	40.9	35.0	S10X35
52	150	145	140	135	131	121	111	101	89.7	73.4	62.2	W8X35
33	70.3	58.4	49.7	43.2	38.1	30.8	25.9	22.3	19.6	15.8	13.3	W14X22
39	108	98.6	88.0	77.5	69.2	57.0	48.6	42.3	37.6	30.7	26.0	W10X26
46	129	124	119	114	109	99.8	90.1	78.6	69.6	56.7	48.0	W8X31
33	53.3	45.5	39.7	35.3	31.7	26.4	22.7	19.9	17.7	14.6	12.4	W12X22
38	83.3	72.4	64.1	57.5	52.2	44.1	38.2	33.8	30.2	25.0	21.4	S10X25.4
42	109	104	98.6	93.5	88.4	77.7	66.7	58.4	52.1	42.8	36.4	W8X28
45	82.3	73.0	64.9	58.5	53.3	45.2	39.3	34.8	31.2	25.9	22.1	C12X30
33	84.0	74.1	63.6	55.6	49.4	40.3	34.1	29.6	26.1	21.2	17.9	W10X22
28	40.2	34.1	29.5	26.1	23.4	19.4	16.5	14.5	12.8	10.5	8.9	W12X19
37	63.1	54.9	48.6	43.7	39.7	33.5	29.1	25.7	23.0	19.1	16.3	C12X25
36	90.4	85.5	80.5	75.5	70.6	59.2	50.6	44.2	39.3	32.2	27.3	W8X24
28	44.0	37.8	33.1	29.5	26.6	22.3	19.2	16.9	15.1	12.4	10.6	W10X19
31	49.5	42.9	37.9	33.9	30.7	25.9	22.4	19.8	17.7	14.7	12.5	C12X20.7
45	72.1	67.8	63.5	58.7	53.6	45.8	40.0	35.5	31.9	26.5	22.7	C10X30
31	69.5	63.6	57.0	50.6	45.6	38.0	32.7	28.7	25.6	21.0	17.9	W8X21
24	27.3	23.0	19.8	17.4	15.5	12.8	10.9	9.4	8.4	6.8	5.8	W12X16
34	58.9	52.5	46.8	42.3	38.6	32.9	28.6	25.4	22.8	18.9	16.2	S8X23
37	77.2	74.2	71.3	68.3	65.4	59.7	53.3	47.0	42.1	34.8	29.7	W6X25
25	34.2	29.2	25.5	22.7	20.4	17.0	14.6	12.8	11.4	9.4	8.0	W10X17
37	57.0	51.6	46.1	41.7	38.1	32.5	28.3	25.1	22.5	18.7	16.0	C10X25
21	22.0	18.4	15.8	13.8	12.3	10.0	8.5	7.4	6.5	5.3	4.5	W12X14
27	54.0	47.5	41.2	36.4	32.6	27.1	23.1	20.2	18.0	14.7	12.5	W8X18
27	44.7	39.2	34.8	31.4	28.6	24.3	21.1	18.7	16.8	13.9	11.9	S8X18.4
22	26.3	22.4	19.5	17.2	15.4	12.8	11.0	9.6	8.5	7.0	5.9	W10X15
30	39.9	34.9	31.1	28.1	25.6	21.7	18.9	16.7	15.0	12.5	10.7	C10X20
30	58.3	55.4	52.5	49.7	46.8	40.4	34.8	30.6	27.3	22.5	19.1	W6X20
30	44.8	40.4	36.1	32.7	29.9	25.5	22.2	19.7	17.7	14.7	12.6	S7X20
30	39.1	34.5	30.8	27.9	25.4	21.7	18.9	16.8	15.1	12.5	10.7	C9X20
22	29.4	25.3	22.3	19.9	18.0	15.1	13.0	11.5	10.3	8.5	7.2	W8X15
23	27.4	23.9	21.2	19.1	17.3	14.7	12.7	11.3	10.1	8.4	7.1	C10X15.3
18	17.7	14.9	12.8	11.3	10.0	8.2	7.0	6.1	5.4	4.4	3.7	W10X12
22.8	31.3	27.5	24.5	22.2	20.2	17.2	15.0	13.3	11.9	9.9	8.5	S7X15.3
24	37.6	34.3	30.5	27.5	25.0	21.3	18.5	16.4	14.7	12.2	10.4	W6X16
19	21.9	18.7	16.4	14.6	13.2	11.0	9.5	8.3	7.4	6.1	5.2	W8X13
22	24.9	21.9	19.5	17.6	16.0	13.6	11.8	10.5	9.4	7.8	6.7	C9X15
28	34.2	31.0	27.8	25.2	23.0	19.7	17.2	15.2	13.7	11.4	9.8	C8X18.75

Shape #	Properties							M_r' (kN·m)				
	J	C_w	b	L_u	V_r	I_x	M_r	Unbraced Length in Millimetres				
	10^3mm^4	10^9mm^6	mm	mm	kN	10^6mm^4	kN•m	1 500	2 000	2 500	3 000	3 500
†C230X20	69.7	7.35	61	1 280	241	19.8	**46.7**	44.7	39.9	35.0	29.8	24.7
S150X26	155	5.01	91	1 580	320	10.9	46.7	...	44.4	41.7	39.0	36.3
†W150X22	41.8	20.4	152	2 590	157	12.1	42.9	...	...	...	41.2	39.0
†C200X21	77.8	5.04	59	1 290	279	14.9	39.7	38.2	34.6	31.1	27.6	23.6
W200X15*	17.6	8.24	100	1 390	153	12.7	39.1	38.2	33.6	28.4	22.1	17.4
S150X19	70.1	3.96	85	1 360	160	9.19	**37.5**	36.7	33.7	30.7	27.7	24.7
W150X18*	37.3	6.70	102	1 610	158	9.16	36.7	...	34.4	31.4	28.3	25.2
†C200X17	54.2	4.34	57	1 210	203	13.5	**35.9**	33.8	30.1	26.3	22.3	18.6
†C180X22*	111	3.47	58	1 420	336	11.3	34.3	33.9	31.6	29.3	27.1	24.9
S130X22	133	2.43	83	1 640	283	6.33	32.7	...	31.5	29.8	28.1	26.5
†C180X18	67.3	2.90	55	1 250	254	10.0	30.5	29.2	26.6	24.1	21.6	18.7
W150X14*	17.0	4.79	100	1 500	115	6.87	27.8	...	25.2	22.3	19.3	15.8
†C180X15	41.6	2.46	53	1 150	168	8.86	**26.9**	25.0	22.2	19.5	16.4	13.8
†C150X19	100	1.84	54	1 470	301	7.12	25.3	25.2	23.7	22.2	20.8	19.3
S130X15	47.4	1.79	76	1 280	122	5.12	**25.1**	24.2	22.2	20.2	18.2	16.2
†C150X16	54.3	1.53	51	1 240	217	6.22	22.1	21.2	19.4	17.7	16.0	14.2
†C150X12	31.0	1.21	48	1 080	138	5.36	**19.1**	17.4	15.5	13.6	11.5	9.7
†C130X17	97.2	1.02	52	1 690	272	4.36	18.5	...	18.0	17.1	16.2	15.4
S100X14.1*	49.9	0.842	71	1 380	151	2.85	18.0	17.7	16.5	15.4	14.3	13.2
S100X11	29.9	0.724	68	1 230	87.2	2.55	**15.6**	14.9	13.7	12.5	11.3	10.1
†C130X13	45.7	0.746	47	1 270	188	3.66	15.6	15.0	13.9	12.9	11.8	10.8
†C130X10	22.8	0.580	44	1 050	109	3.09	**13.1**	12.0	10.7	9.4	8.1	6.9
S75X11	38.2	0.299	64	1 590	121	1.22	10.4	...	10.0	9.5	9.0	8.4
†C100X11	34.6	0.320	43	1 340	149	1.91	10.1	9.9	9.3	8.6	8.0	7.4
†C100X9	23.4	0.293	42	1 180	115	1.77	**9.34**	8.9	8.2	7.5	6.9	6.2
S75X8	18.3	0.228	59	1 230	58.2	1.04	**8.61**	8.3	7.7	7.1	6.5	5.9
†C100X8	16.8	0.246	40	1 050	85.4	1.61	**8.53**	7.8	7.1	6.4	5.6	4.8
†C75X9	30.1	0.118	40	1 680	122	0.846	6.02	...	5.8	5.6	5.3	5.0
†C75X7	17.7	0.093	37	1 320	89.4	0.749	**5.32**	5.2	4.9	4.6	4.2	3.9
†C75X6	11.0	0.077	35	1 080	58.2	0.670	**4.75**	4.4	4.1	3.7	3.4	2.9

*Not available from Canadian mills.
†Class 3 Section.
The SI designation is shown for each shape and is the preferred designation for use in Canada.

Nominal Mass per Metre (kg)	M_r (kN•m) Unbraced Length of Compression Flange, in mm											Imperial Designation
	4 000	4 500	5 000	5 500	6 000	7 000	8 000	9 000	10 000	12 000	14 000	
20	21.2	18.5	16.5	14.9	13.5	11.5	10.0	8.8	7.9	6.6	5.6	C9X13.4
26	33.7	31.0	27.8	25.2	23.1	19.7	17.2	15.3	13.7	11.4	9.8	S6X17.25
22	36.8	34.5	32.2	29.9	27.3	22.6	19.3	16.8	15.0	12.3	10.4	W6X15
21	20.4	17.9	16.0	14.5	13.2	11.3	9.8	8.7	7.8	6.5	5.6	C8X13.75
15	14.4	12.2	10.6	9.3	8.3	6.9	5.9	5.2	4.6	3.8	3.2	W8X10
19	21.4	18.8	16.8	15.2	13.9	11.9	10.3	9.2	8.2	6.8	5.9	S6X12.5
18	21.6	18.7	16.6	14.8	13.5	11.4	9.8	8.7	7.8	6.4	5.5	W6X12
17	16.0	14.1	12.5	11.3	10.3	8.8	7.6	6.8	6.1	5.1	4.3	C8X11.5
22	22.6	20.0	17.9	16.2	14.8	12.7	11.1	9.8	8.8	7.4	6.3	C7X14.75
22	24.8	23.2	21.5	19.5	17.8	15.3	13.3	11.8	10.7	8.9	7.6	S5X14.75
18	16.2	14.3	12.8	11.6	10.6	9.1	7.9	7.0	6.3	5.2	4.5	C7X12.25
14	13.2	11.3	9.9	8.9	8.0	6.7	5.8	5.1	4.5	3.7	3.2	W6X9
15	11.9	10.5	9.4	8.5	7.7	6.6	5.8	5.1	4.6	3.8	3.3	C7X9.8
19	17.9	16.3	14.6	13.3	12.1	10.4	9.1	8.1	7.2	6.0	5.2	C6X13
15	14.0	12.4	11.1	10.1	9.2	7.8	6.9	6.1	5.5	4.5	3.9	S5X10
16	12.4	11.0	9.8	8.9	8.1	7.0	6.1	5.4	4.9	4.0	3.5	C6X10.5
12	8.4	7.4	6.7	6.0	5.5	4.7	4.1	3.6	3.3	2.7	2.3	C6X8.2
17	14.5	13.6	12.8	11.8	10.8	9.2	8.1	7.2	6.4	5.4	4.6	C5X11.5
14.1	12.1	10.8	9.7	8.8	8.1	6.9	6.0	5.3	4.8	4.0	3.4	S4X9.5
11	8.8	7.8	7.0	6.3	5.8	5.0	4.3	3.8	3.5	2.9	2.5	S4X7.7
13	9.5	8.4	7.6	6.9	6.3	5.4	4.7	4.2	3.8	3.1	2.7	C5X9
10	6.0	5.3	4.7	4.3	3.9	3.4	2.9	2.6	2.3	1.9	1.7	C5X6.7
11	7.9	7.4	6.9	6.2	5.7	4.9	4.3	3.8	3.4	2.8	2.4	S3X7.5
11	6.8	6.1	5.5	5.0	4.5	3.9	3.4	3.0	2.7	2.3	1.9	C4X7.25
9	5.4	4.8	4.3	3.9	3.6	3.1	2.7	2.4	2.1	1.8	1.5	C4X6.25
8	5.2	4.6	4.2	3.8	3.5	3.0	2.6	2.3	2.1	1.7	1.5	S3X5.7
8	4.2	3.7	3.3	3.0	2.8	2.4	2.1	1.8	1.7	1.4	1.2	C4X5.4
9	4.7	4.5	4.2	3.9	3.6	3.0	2.7	2.4	2.1	1.8	1.5	C3X6
7	3.6	3.2	2.9	2.6	2.4	2.1	1.8	1.6	1.4	1.2	1.0	C3X5
6	2.6	2.3	2.1	1.9	1.7	1.5	1.3	1.1	1.0	0.9	0.7	C3X4.1

Total Uniformly Distributed Factored
Loads for Laterally Supported Beams — kilonewtons

Designation		WWF1200					Approx. Deflection (mm)
Mass (kg/m)		487	403	364	302	263	
Span in millimetres	5 000						5
	5 500					5 350	6
	6 000					5 110	7
	6 500				5 350	4 720	8
	7 000				5 280	4 380	9
	7 500				4 920	4 090	11
	8 000				4 620	3 830	12
	8 500			5 350	4 340	3 610	13
	9 000			5 210	4 100	3 410	15
	9 500		5 350	4 930	3 890	3 230	17
	10 000		5 310	4 690	3 690	3 070	19
	10 500		5 060	4 460	3 520	2 920	21
	11 000		4 830	4 260	3 360	2 790	23
	11 500		4 620	4 080	3 210	2 670	25
	12 000	5 350	4 430	3 910	3 080	2 560	27
	12 500	5 290	4 250	3 750	2 960	2 450	29
	13 000	5 080	4 090	3 610	2 840	2 360	32
	13 500	4 900	3 940	3 470	2 740	2 270	34
	14 000	4 720	3 800	3 350	2 640	2 190	37
	14 500	4 560	3 660	3 230	2 550	2 120	39
	15 000	4 410	3 540	3 120	2 460	2 040	42
	15 500	4 260	3 430	3 020	2 380	1 980	45
	16 000	4 130	3 320	2 930	2 310	1 920	48
	16 500	4 010	3 220	2 840	2 240	1 860	51
	17 000	3 890	3 130	2 760	2 170	1 800	54
	17 500	3 780	3 040	2 680	2 110	1 750	57
	18 000	3 670	2 950	2 600	2 050	1 700	60
	18 500	3 570	2 870	2 530	2 000	1 660	64
	19 000	3 480	2 800	2 470	1 940	1 610	67
	19 500	3 390	2 720	2 400	1 890	1 570	71
	20 000	3 300	2 660	2 340	1 850	1 530	75
	20 500	3 220	2 590	2 290	1 800	1 500	78
	21 000	3 150	2 530	2 230	1 760	1 460	82
	21 500	3 070	2 470	2 180	1 720	1 430	86
	22 000	3 000	2 420	2 130	1 680	1 390	90

PROPERTIES AND DESIGN DATA

	487	403	364	302	263	
$S_x \ 10^3 mm^3$	27 900	22 200	19 400	15 000	12 100	
$Z_x \ 10^3 mm^3$	30 600	24 600	21 700	17 100	14 200	
$I_x \ 10^6 mm^4$	16 700	13 300	11 700	8 970	7 250	
$J \ 10^3 mm^4$	25 000	11 500	8 880	5 740	4 700	
$C_w \ 10^9 mm^6$	373 000	285 000	200 000	92 200	39 000	
$L_u \ mm$	8 370	7 980	7 090	5 390	3 850	
$V_r \ kN$	2 670	2 670	2 670	2 670	2 670	

IMPERIAL SIZE AND MASS

Mass (lb./ft.)	326	270	244	203	176	
Nominal Depth (in.)			47			

BEAM LOAD TABLES
Welded Wide Flange Beams

Total Uniformly Distributed Factored
Loads for Laterally Supported Beams — kilonewtons

Designation		WWF1100						Approx. Deflection (mm)
Mass (kg/m)		458	388	335	291	255	220	
Span in millimetres	5 000							5
	5 500						4 090	6
	6 000						4 000	7
	6 500						3 690	9
	7 000					4 090	3 420	10
	7 500					3 890	3 200	11
	8 000				4 090	3 640	3 000	13
	8 500				4 040	3 430	2 820	15
	9 000				3 820	3 240	2 660	16
	9 500			4 090	3 620	3 070	2 520	18
	10 000			4 080	3 430	2 920	2 400	20
	10 500			3 890	3 270	2 780	2 280	22
	11 000			3 710	3 120	2 650	2 180	25
	11 500		4 090	3 550	2 990	2 540	2 080	27
	12 000		4 030	3 400	2 860	2 430	2 000	29
	12 500		3 870	3 270	2 750	2 330	1 920	32
	13 000		3 720	3 140	2 640	2 240	1 840	34
	13 500		3 580	3 020	2 540	2 160	1 780	37
	14 000	4 090	3 460	2 920	2 450	2 080	1 710	40
	14 500	4 020	3 340	2 820	2 370	2 010	1 650	43
	15 000	3 890	3 230	2 720	2 290	1 940	1 600	46
	15 500	3 760	3 120	2 630	2 220	1 880	1 550	49
	16 000	3 640	3 020	2 550	2 150	1 820	1 500	52
	16 500	3 540	2 930	2 470	2 080	1 770	1 450	55
	17 000	3 430	2 850	2 400	2 020	1 720	1 410	59
	17 500	3 330	2 760	2 330	1 960	1 670	1 370	62
	18 000	3 240	2 690	2 270	1 910	1 620	1 330	66
	18 500	3 150	2 620	2 210	1 860	1 580	1 300	70
	19 000	3 070	2 550	2 150	1 810	1 540	1 260	74
	19 500	2 990	2 480	2 090	1 760	1 500	1 230	77
	20 000	2 920	2 420	2 040	1 720	1 460	1 200	81
	20 500	2 840	2 360	1 990	1 680	1 420	1 170	86
	21 000	2 780	2 300	1 940	1 640	1 390	1 140	90
	21 500	2 710	2 250	1 900	1 600	1 360	1 120	94
	22 000	2 650	2 200	1 860	1 560	1 320	1 090	99

PROPERTIES AND DESIGN DATA

	458	388	335	291	255	220	
$S_x \ 10^3 mm^3$	24 800	20 400	17 100	14 200	11 900	9 530	
$Z_x \ 10^3 mm^3$	27 000	22 400	18 900	15 900	13 500	11 100	
$I_x \ 10^6 mm^4$	13 600	11 200	9 410	7 800	6 520	5 240	
$J \ 10^3 mm^4$	24 400	15 200	8 270	6 810	3 810	3 100	
$C_w 10^9 mm^6$	312 000	207 000	168 000	85 900	68 200	28 800	
L_u mm	8 600	7 570	7 300	5 690	5 450	3 900	
V_r kN	2 050	2 050	2 050	2 050	2 050	2 050	

IMPERIAL SIZE AND MASS

Mass (lb./ft.)	307	260	225	195	171	147	
Nominal Depth (in.)			43				

BEAM LOAD TABLES
Welded Wide Flange Beams

G40.21-M 300W
$\emptyset = 0.90$

Total Uniformly Distributed Factored
Loads for Laterally Supported Beams — kilonewtons

Designation								Approx. Deflection (mm)
		WWF1000						
Mass (kg/m)		447	377	324	280	244	200	
Span in millimetres	4 000							4
	4 500						4 090	5
	5 000						3 960	6
	5 500						3 600	7
	6 000					4 090	3 300	8
	6 500					3 950	3 050	9
	7 000				4 090	3 670	2 830	11
	7 500				4 060	3 430	2 640	13
	8 000				3 810	3 210	2 480	14
	8 500			4 090	3 580	3 020	2 330	16
	9 000			4 030	3 380	2 860	2 200	18
	9 500			3 820	3 210	2 710	2 080	20
	10 000			3 630	3 050	2 570	1 980	22
	10 500		4 090	3 460	2 900	2 450	1 890	25
	11 000		3 930	3 300	2 770	2 340	1 800	27
	11 500		3 760	3 160	2 650	2 240	1 720	30
	12 000		3 600	3 020	2 540	2 140	1 650	32
	12 500	4 090	3 460	2 900	2 440	2 060	1 580	35
	13 000	4 000	3 320	2 790	2 340	1 980	1 520	38
	13 500	3 860	3 200	2 690	2 260	1 900	1 470	41
	14 000	3 720	3 090	2 590	2 180	1 840	1 420	44
	14 500	3 590	2 980	2 500	2 100	1 770	1 370	47
	15 000	3 470	2 880	2 420	2 030	1 710	1 320	50
	15 500	3 360	2 790	2 340	1 960	1 660	1 280	54
	16 000	3 250	2 700	2 270	1 900	1 610	1 240	57
	16 500	3 160	2 620	2 200	1 850	1 560	1 200	61
	17 000	3 060	2 540	2 140	1 790	1 510	1 160	65
	17 500	2 980	2 470	2 070	1 740	1 470	1 130	69
	18 000	2 890	2 400	2 020	1 690	1 430	1 100	73
	18 500	2 810	2 340	1 960	1 650	1 390	1 070	77
	19 000	2 740	2 270	1 910	1 600	1 350	1 040	81
	19 500	2 670	2 220	1 860	1 560	1 320	1 020	85
	20 000	2 600	2 160	1 810	1 520	1 280	990	90
	20 500	2 540	2 110	1 770	1 490	1 250	966	94
	21 000	2 480	2 060	1 730	1 450	1 220	943	99

PROPERTIES AND DESIGN DATA

	447	377	324	280	244	200	
$S_x \ 10^3 \text{mm}^3$	22 200	18 200	15 200	12 600	10 500	7 890	
$Z_x \ 10^3 \text{mm}^3$	24 100	20 000	16 800	14 100	11 900	9 170	
$I_x \ 10^6 \text{mm}^4$	11 100	9 120	7 620	6 300	5 260	3 940	
$J \ 10^3 \text{mm}^4$	24 300	15 100	8 180	6 720	3 710	2 480	
$C_w 10^9 \text{mm}^6$	256 000	170 000	138 000	70 600	56 200	21 700	
L_u mm	8 770	7 700	7 420	5 790	5 550	3 910	
V_r kN	2 050	2 050	2 050	2 050	2 050	2 050	

IMPERIAL SIZE AND MASS

Mass (lb./ft.)	300	253	217	188	163	134	
Nominal Depth (in.)				39			

Total Uniformly Distributed Factored
Loads for Laterally Supported Beams — kilonewtons

Designation		WWF900							Approx. Deflection (mm)
Mass (kg/m)		417	347	393	249	213	192	169	
Span in millimetres	6 000							2 530	9
	6 500							2 450	11
	7 000						2 530	2 270	12
	7 500						2 480	2 120	14
	8 000					2 530	2 320	1 990	16
	8 500					2 490	2 180	1 870	18
	9 000					2 350	2 060	1 770	20
	9 500					2 230	1 960	1 680	22
	10 000				2 530	2 120	1 860	1 590	25
	10 500				2 430	2 020	1 770	1 520	27
	11 000				2 320	1 920	1 690	1 450	30
	11 500				2 220	1 840	1 620	1 380	33
	12 000			2 530	2 120	1 760	1 550	1 330	36
	12 500			2 450	2 040	1 690	1 490	1 270	39
	13 000			2 360	1 960	1 630	1 430	1 220	42
	13 500			2 270	1 890	1 570	1 380	1 180	45
	14 000			2 190	1 820	1 510	1 330	1 140	49
	14 500		2 530	2 120	1 760	1 460	1 280	1 100	52
	15 000		2 460	2 040	1 700	1 410	1 240	1 060	56
	15 500		2 380	1 980	1 640	1 370	1 200	1 030	60
	16 000		2 310	1 920	1 590	1 320	1 160	995	64
	16 500		2 240	1 860	1 540	1 280	1 130	965	68
	17 000		2 170	1 800	1 500	1 240	1 090	936	72
	17 500	2 530	2 110	1 750	1 460	1 210	1 060	910	76
	18 000	2 500	2 050	1 700	1 420	1 180	1 030	884	81
	18 500	2 430	2 000	1 660	1 380	1 140	1 000	860	85
	19 000	2 360	1 940	1 610	1 340	1 110	978	838	90
	19 500	2 300	1 890	1 570	1 310	1 090	953	816	95
	20 000	2 250	1 850	1 530	1 270	1 060	929	796	100
	20 500	2 190	1 800	1 500	1 240	1 030	906	777	105
	21 000	2 140	1 760	1 460	1 210	1 010	885	758	110
	21 500	2 090	1 720	1 430	1 180	985	864	740	115
	22 000	2 040	1 680	1 390	1 160	962	844	724	120
	22 500	2 000	1 640	1 360	1 130	941	826	708	126
	23 000	1 950	1 610	1 330	1 110	920	808	692	132

PROPERTIES AND DESIGN DATA

	417	347	393	249	213	192	169	
$S_x\ 10^3\,mm^3$	19 300	15 800	13 100	10 700	8 870	7 680	6 510	
$Z_x\ 10^3\,mm^3$	20 800	17 100	14 200	11 800	9 800	8 600	7 370	
$I_x\ 10^6\,mm^4$	8 670	7 100	5 900	4 830	3 990	3 460	2 930	
$J\ 10^3\,mm^4$	23 800	14 700	7 690	6 230	3 220	3 500	1 980	
$C_w\ 10^9\,mm^6$	205 000	136 000	111 000	56 800	45 200	21 600	17 400	
$L_u\ mm$	9 080	7 970	7 690	6 030	5 810	4 310	4 130	
$V_r\ kN$	1 260	1 260	1 260	1 260	1 260	1 260	1 260	

IMPERIAL SIZE AND MASS

Mass (lb./ft.)	279	233	197	167	142	128	113
Nominal Depth (in.)				35			

Total Uniformly Distributed Factored
Loads for Laterally Supported Beams — kilonewtons

Designation			WWF800					Approx. Deflection (mm)
Mass (kg/m)		332	279	235	198	164	154	
Span in millimetres	6 000						2 090	10
	6 500					2 090	2 050	12
	7 000					2 040	1 900	14
	7 500					1 900	1 780	16
	8 000					1 780	1 670	18
	8 500				2 090	1 680	1 570	20
	9 000				2 000	1 590	1 480	23
	9 500				1 890	1 500	1 400	25
	10 000			2 090	1 800	1 430	1 330	28
	10 500			2 080	1 710	1 360	1 270	31
	11 000			1 980	1 630	1 300	1 210	34
	11 500			1 900	1 560	1 240	1 160	37
	12 000			1 820	1 500	1 190	1 110	40
	12 500		2 090	1 740	1 440	1 140	1 070	44
	13 000		2 030	1 680	1 380	1 100	1 020	47
	13 500		1 950	1 620	1 330	1 060	987	51
	14 000		1 880	1 560	1 280	1 020	952	55
	14 500		1 820	1 500	1 240	985	919	59
	15 000	2 090	1 760	1 450	1 200	952	888	63
	15 500	2 060	1 700	1 410	1 160	921	860	67
	16 000	2 000	1 650	1 360	1 120	892	833	72
	16 500	1 940	1 600	1 320	1 090	865	808	76
	17 000	1 880	1 550	1 280	1 060	840	784	81
	17 500	1 830	1 510	1 250	1 030	816	762	86
	18 000	1 780	1 460	1 210	998	793	740	91
	18 500	1 730	1 420	1 180	971	772	720	96
	19 000	1 680	1 390	1 150	946	751	701	101
	19 500	1 640	1 350	1 120	922	732	683	106
	20 000	1 600	1 320	1 090	899	714	666	112
	20 500	1 560	1 280	1 060	877	696	650	118
	21 000	1 520	1 260	1 040	856	680	635	123
	21 500	1 490	1 230	1 020	836	664	620	129
	22 000	1 450	1 200	992	817	649	606	136
	22 500	1 420	1 170	970	799	635	592	142
	23 000	1 390	1 150	949	781	621	579	148

PROPERTIES AND DESIGN DATA

	332	279	235	198	164	154	
S_x 10^3mm^3	13 700	11 300	9 250	7 600	5 940	5 520	
Z_x 10^3mm^3	14 800	12 200	10 100	8 320	6 610	6 170	
I_x 10^6mm^4	5 470	4 530	3 700	3 040	2 380	2 210	
J 10^3mm^4	14 500	7 570	6 100	3 090	2 380	1 850	
C_w 10^9mm^6	107 000	86 900	44 500	35 500	15 000	13 700	
L_u mm	8 210	7 890	6 200	5 970	4 350	4 270	
V_r kN	1 040	1 040	1 040	1 040	1 040	1 040	

IMPERIAL SIZE AND MASS

Mass (lb./ft.)	223	187	157	133	109	103	
Nominal Depth (in.)			31				

Total Uniformly Distributed Factored
Loads for Laterally Supported Beams — kilonewtons

Designation	WWF 700						Approx. Deflection (mm)
Mass (kg/m)	222	203	185	164	151	141	
6 000							12
6 500					1 690	1 690	14
7 000					1 690	1 570	16
7 500				1 690	1 580	1 470	18
8 000				1 630	1 480	1 380	20
8 500			1 690	1 540	1 390	1 300	23
9 000			1 680	1 450	1 320	1 220	26
9 500		1 690	1 590	1 380	1 250	1 160	29
10 000		1 670	1 510	1 310	1 180	1 100	32
10 500	1 690	1 590	1 440	1 240	1 130	1 050	35
11 000	1 670	1 520	1 370	1 190	1 080	1 000	39
11 500	1 600	1 450	1 310	1 140	1 030	958	42
12 000	1 530	1 390	1 260	1 090	986	918	46
12 500	1 470	1 340	1 210	1 040	947	881	50
13 000	1 410	1 290	1 160	1 000	911	847	54
13 500	1 360	1 240	1 120	968	877	816	58
14 000	1 310	1 190	1 080	933	845	787	63
14 500	1 270	1 150	1 040	901	816	760	67
15 000	1 220	1 120	1 000	871	789	734	72
15 500	1 180	1 080	973	843	764	711	77
16 000	1 150	1 040	942	817	740	688	82
16 500	1 110	1 010	914	792	717	668	87
17 000	1 080	983	887	769	696	648	92
17 500	1 050	955	862	747	676	629	98
18 000	1 020	929	838	726	658	612	104
18 500	992	904	815	706	640	595	110
19 000	966	880	794	688	623	580	116
19 500	942	857	773	670	607	565	122
20 000	918	836	754	653	592	551	128
20 500	896	816	735	637	577	537	134
21 000	874	796	718	622	564	525	141
21 500	854	778	701	608	551	512	148
22 000	835	760	685	594	538	501	155

Span in millimetres

PROPERTIES AND DESIGN DATA

	222	203	185	164	151	141
$S_x \ 10^3 \text{mm}^3$	7 840	7 140	6 420	5 510	4 980	4 620
$Z_x \ 10^3 \text{mm}^3$	8 500	7 740	6 980	6 050	5 480	5 100
$I_x \ 10^6 \text{mm}^4$	2 740	2 500	2 250	1 930	1 740	1 620
$J \ 10^3 \text{mm}^4$	6 010	4 320	3 000	3 280	2 290	1 760
$C_w 10^9 \text{mm}^6$	33 700	30 400	27 000	12 800	11 400	10 400
L_u mm	6 410	6 280	6 140	4 610	4 500	4 420
V_r kN	846	846	846	846	846	846

IMPERIAL SIZE AND MASS

Mass (lb./ft.)	149	136	124	110	101	95
Nominal Depth (in.)			28			

Total Uniformly Distributed Factored
Loads for Laterally Supported Beams — kilonewtons

Designation					W610						Approx. Deflection (mm)
Mass (kg/m)		241	217	195	174	155	140	125	113	101	
Span in millimetres	2 000										1
	2 500								2 430	2 260	2
	3 000						2 880	2 600	2 370	2 090	3
	3 500			3 410	3 070	2 770	2 560	2 260	2 030	1 790	4
	4 000	4 050	3 690	3 280	2 890	2 550	2 240	1 980	1 780	1 570	6
	4 500	3 680	3 290	2 910	2 570	2 270	1 990	1 760	1 580	1 390	7
	5 000	3 310	2 960	2 620	2 320	2 040	1 790	1 580	1 420	1 250	9
	5 500	3 010	2 690	2 380	2 100	1 860	1 630	1 440	1 290	1 140	11
	6 000	2 760	2 470	2 180	1 930	1 700	1 490	1 320	1 180	1 040	13
	6 500	2 550	2 280	2 020	1 780	1 570	1 380	1 220	1 090	964	16
	7 000	2 370	2 110	1 870	1 650	1 460	1 280	1 130	1 020	895	18
	7 500	2 210	1 970	1 750	1 540	1 360	1 200	1 060	948	835	21
	8 000	2 070	1 850	1 640	1 450	1 280	1 120	991	888	783	24
	8 500	1 950	1 740	1 540	1 360	1 200	1 060	933	836	737	27
	9 000	1 840	1 640	1 460	1 290	1 140	996	881	790	696	30
	9 500	1 740	1 560	1 380	1 220	1 080	944	834	748	659	33
	10 000	1 660	1 480	1 310	1 160	1 020	896	793	711	626	37
	10 500	1 580	1 410	1 250	1 100	973	854	755	677	597	40
	11 000	1 510	1 340	1 190	1 050	929	815	721	646	569	44
	11 500	1 440	1 290	1 140	1 010	888	779	689	618	545	49
	12 000	1 380	1 230	1 090	965	851	747	661	592	522	53
	12 500	1 320	1 180	1 050	926	817	717	634	569	501	57
	13 000	1 270	1 140	1 010	891	786	690	610	547	482	62
	13 500	1 230	1 100	971	858	757	664	587	526	464	67
	14 000	1 180	1 060	937	827	730	640	566	508	447	72
	14 500	1 140	1 020	904	798	705	618	547	490	432	77
	15 000	1 100	986	874	772	681	598	528	474	418	83
	15 500	1 070	955	846	747	659	578	511	458	404	88
	16 000	1 040	925	819	724	639	560	495	444	391	94
	16 500	1 000	897	795	702	619	543	480	431	380	100
	17 000	975	870	771	681	601	527	466	418	368	106
	17 500	947	845	749	662	584	512	453	406	358	112
	18 000	920	822	728	643	568	498	440	395	348	119
	18 500	896	800	709	626	552	485	428	384	339	126
	19 000	872	779	690	609	538	472	417	374	330	133

PROPERTIES AND DESIGN DATA

	241	217	195	174	155	140	125	113	101	
S_x 10^3 mm^3	6 780	6 070	5 400	4 780	4 220	3 630	3 220	2 880	2 530	
Z_x 10^3 mm^3	7 670	6 850	6 070	5 360	4 730	4 150	3 670	3 290	2 900	
I_x 10^6 mm^4	2 150	1 910	1 680	1 470	1 290	1 120	985	875	764	
J 10^3 mm^4	7 700	5 600	3 970	2 800	1 950	2 180	1 540	1 120	781	
C_w 10^9 mm^6	16 800	14 700	12 700	10 900	9 450	3 990	3 450	2 990	2 550	
L_u mm	5 200	5 080	4 940	4 830	4 740	3 320	3 250	3 180	3 110	
V_r kN	2 030	1 850	1 710	1 540	1 380	1 440	1 300	1 210	1 130	
R kN	906	819	748	666	592	628	558	518	475	
G kN	6.04	5.57	5.20	4.72	4.29	4.42	4.02	3.78	3.54	
N mm	285	285	284	284	285	284	284	284	284	

IMPERIAL SIZE AND MASS

Mass (lb./ft.)	162	146	131	117	104	94	84	76	68	
Nominal Depth (in.)					24					

Total Uniformly Distributed Factored
Loads for Laterally Supported Beams — kilonewtons

Designation		W530						Approx. Deflection (mm)
Mass (kg/m)		138	123	109	101	92	82	
2 000							1 790	2
2 500		2 880	2 540	2 230	2 090	1 940	1 790	3
3 000		2 600	2 310	2 040	1 890	1 700	1 490	4
3 500		2 230	1 980	1 750	1 620	1 460	1 280	5
4 000		1 950	1 730	1 530	1 420	1 270	1 120	7
4 500		1 730	1 540	1 360	1 260	1 130	994	9
5 000		1 560	1 390	1 220	1 130	1 020	894	11
5 500		1 420	1 260	1 110	1 030	927	813	13
6 000		1 300	1 160	1 020	943	850	745	15
6 500		1 200	1 070	940	871	784	688	18
7 000		1 110	991	873	808	728	639	21
7 500		1 040	924	815	755	680	596	24
8 000		975	867	764	707	637	559	27
8 500		917	816	719	666	600	526	31
9 000		866	770	679	629	566	497	34
9 500		821	730	643	596	537	471	38
10 000		780	693	611	566	510	447	42
10 500		743	660	582	539	485	426	47
11 000		709	630	556	514	463	406	51
11 500		678	603	532	492	443	389	56
12 000		650	578	509	472	425	373	61
12 500		624	555	489	453	408	358	66
13 000		600	533	470	435	392	344	71
13 500		578	514	453	419	378	331	77
14 000		557	495	437	404	364	319	83
14 500		538	478	422	390	352	308	89
15 000		520	462	408	377	340	298	95
15 500		503	447	394	365	329	288	102
16 000		487	433	382	354	319	279	108

(Span in millimetres)

PROPERTIES AND DESIGN DATA

	138	123	109	101	92	82	
S_x 10^3mm^3	3 140	2 800	2 480	2 300	2 070	1 810	
Z_x 10^3mm^3	3 610	3 210	2 830	2 620	2 360	2 070	
I_x 10^6mm^4	861	761	667	617	552	479	
J 10^3mm^4	2 500	1 800	1 260	1 020	762	530	
C_w 10^9mm^6	2 670	2 310	2 000	1 820	1 590	1 340	
L_u mm	3 180	3 100	3 040	2 990	2 930	2 860	
V_r kN	1 440	1 270	1 110	1 040	969	894	
R kN	704	615	536	497	461	414	
G kN	4.96	4.42	3.91	3.68	3.44	3.21	
N mm	248	248	248	249	247	250	

IMPERIAL SIZE AND MASS

Mass (lb./ft.)	93	83	73	68	62	55	
Nominal Depth (in.)			21				

Total Uniformly Distributed Factored
Loads for Laterally Supported Beams — kilonewtons

Designation		W460							Approx. Deflection (mm)
Mass (kg/m)		106	97	89	82	74	67	61	
Span in millimetres	2 000	2 110	1 890		1 620	1 470	1 380	1 300	2
	2 500	2 060	1 880	1 730	1 580	1 430	1 300	1 130	3
	3 000	1 720	1 570	1 450	1 320	1 190	1 080	943	4
	3 500	1 480	1 340	1 240	1 130	1 020	926	808	6
	4 000	1 290	1 180	1 080	988	891	810	707	8
	4 500	1 150	1 050	965	878	792	720	629	10
	5 000	1 030	942	868	791	713	648	566	12
	5 500	939	856	789	719	648	589	514	15
	6 000	860	785	724	659	594	540	472	18
	6 500	794	724	668	608	548	498	435	21
	7 000	737	673	620	565	509	463	404	24
	7 500	688	628	579	527	475	432	377	27
	8 000	645	589	543	494	445	405	354	31
	8 500	607	554	511	465	419	381	333	35
	9 000	574	523	482	439	396	360	314	39
	9 500	543	496	457	416	375	341	298	44
	10 000	516	471	434	395	356	324	283	49
	10 500	492	448	413	376	339	309	269	54
	11 000	469	428	395	359	324	295	257	59
	11 500	449	409	378	344	310	282	246	64
	12 000	430	392	362	329	297	270	236	70
	12 500	413	377	347	316	285	259	226	76
	13 000	397	362	334	304	274	249	218	82
	13 500	382	349	322	293	264	240	210	89
	14 000	369	336	310	282	255	231	202	95

PROPERTIES AND DESIGN DATA

	106	97	89	82	74	67	61
S_x 10^3mm^3	2 080	1 910	1 770	1 610	1 460	1 320	1 150
Z_x 10^3mm^3	2 390	2 180	2 010	1 830	1 650	1 500	1 310
I_x 10^6mm^4	488	445	410	370	333	300	259
J 10^3mm^4	1 460	1 130	907	691	517	412	289
C_W 10^9mm^6	1 260	1 140	1 040	918	813	709	588
L_u mm	2 910	2 870	2 830	2 770	2 730	2 660	2 580
V_r kN	1 050	947	866	812	733	688	650
R kN	587	523	478	444	401	373	350
G kN	4.25	3.85	3.54	3.34	3.04	2.87	2.73
N mm	210	210	209	210	209	210	210

IMPERIAL SIZE AND MASS

Mass (lb./ft.)	71	65	60	55	50	45	41
Nominal Depth (in.)				18			

Total Uniformly Distributed Factored
Loads for Laterally Supported Beams — kilonewtons

Designation		W410							Approx. Deflection (mm)
Mass (kg/m)		85	74	67	60	54	46	39	
	1 000								1
	1 500						1 000	895	1
	2 000	1 620	1 430	1 290	1 120	1 080	956	788	2
	2 500	1 500	1 300	1 180	1 030	907	765	631	3
	3 000	1 250	1 090	979	857	756	637	526	5
	3 500	1 070	932	839	734	648	546	451	7
	4 000	934	815	734	643	567	478	394	9
	4 500	830	725	653	571	504	425	350	11
	5 000	747	652	588	514	454	382	315	14
	5 500	679	593	534	467	412	348	287	17
	6 000	623	544	490	428	378	319	263	20
	6 500	575	502	452	395	349	294	243	23
	7 000	534	466	420	367	324	273	225	27
	7 500	498	435	392	343	302	255	210	31
	8 000	467	408	367	321	283	239	197	35
	8 500	440	384	346	302	267	225	186	39
	9 000	415	362	326	286	252	212	175	44
	9 500	393	343	309	271	239	201	166	49
	10 000	374	326	294	257	227	191	158	55
	10 500	356	311	280	245	216	182	150	60
	11 000	340	297	267	234	206	174	143	66
	11 500	325	284	255	224	197	166	137	72
	12 000	311	272	245	214	189	159	131	79
	12 500	299	261	235	206	181	153	126	85
	13 000	287	251	226	198	174	147	121	92

Span in millimetres

PROPERTIES AND DESIGN DATA

		85	74	67	60	54	46	39
S_x	$10^3 mm^3$	1 510	1 330	1 200	1 060	924	773	634
Z_x	$10^3 mm^3$	1 730	1 510	1 360	1 190	1 050	885	730
I_x	$10^6 mm^4$	315	275	246	216	186	156	127
J	$10^3 mm^4$	926	637	469	328	226	192	111
C_W	$10^9 mm^6$	717	614	540	468	388	197	154
L_u	mm	2 730	2 670	2 610	2 580	2 480	1 930	1 860
V_r	kN	810	714	643	558	539	503	448
R	kN	497	435	392	338	324	302	272
G	kN	3.68	3.27	2.97	2.60	2.53	2.36	2.16
N	mm	185	185	184	185	185	185	185

IMPERIAL SIZE AND MASS

Mass (lb./ft.)	57	50	45	40	36	31	26
Nominal Depth (in.)				16			

Total Uniformly Distributed Factored
Loads for Laterally Supported Beams — kilonewtons

Designation				W360						Approx. Deflection (mm)
Mass (kg/m)		79	72	64	57	51	45	39	33	
Span in millimetres	1 000									1
	1 500						866	818	721	1
	2 000				1 010	911	841	715	585	2
	2 500	1 190	1 070	952	873	772	673	572	468	4
	3 000	1 030	922	821	727	644	561	477	390	6
	3 500	883	790	704	623	552	481	409	334	8
	4 000	772	691	616	545	483	421	357	293	10
	4 500	686	614	547	485	429	374	318	260	13
	5 000	618	553	492	436	386	337	286	234	16
	5 500	562	503	448	397	351	306	260	213	19
	6 000	515	461	410	364	322	280	238	195	22
	6 500	475	425	379	336	297	259	220	180	26
	7 000	441	395	352	312	276	240	204	167	30
	7 500	412	369	328	291	257	224	191	156	35
	8 000	386	346	308	273	241	210	179	146	40
	8 500	363	325	290	257	227	198	168	138	45
	9 000	343	307	274	242	215	187	159	130	50
	9 500	325	291	259	230	203	177	151	123	56
	10 000	309	276	246	218	193	168	143	117	62
	10 500	294	263	235	208	184	160	136	111	69
	11 000	281	251	224	198	176	153	130	106	75

PROPERTIES AND DESIGN DATA

	79	72	64	57	51	45	39	33
S_x 10^3mm^3	1 280	1 150	1 030	897	796	691	580	474
Z_x 10^3mm^3	1 430	1 280	1 140	1 010	894	779	662	542
I_x 10^6mm^4	227	201	178	161	141	122	102	82.7
J 10^3mm^4	814	603	438	334	238	160	151	85.9
C_w 10^9mm^6	687	600	524	331	285	239	110	84.3
L_u mm	3 270	3 190	3 110	2 550	2 500	2 430	1 790	1 720
V_r kN	593	536	476	504	455	433	409	361
R kN	431	389	346	347	313	296	281	247
G kN	3.17	2.90	2.60	2.67	2.43	2.33	2.19	1.96
N mm	151	151	150	159	158	159	158	158

IMPERIAL SIZE AND MASS

Mass (lb./ft.)	53	48	43	38	34	30	26	22
Nominal Depth (in.)				14				

Total Uniformly Distributed Factored
Loads for Laterally Supported Beams — kilonewtons

Designation						W310							Approx. Deflection (mm)
Mass (kg/m)	129	118	107	†97	86	79	74	67	60	52	45	39	
2 000							1 040	927		859	736	641	3
2 500				1 090		960	1 030	916	810	723	612	527	5
3 000	1 480	1 330	1 210	1 040	1 000	922	857	763	678	603	510	439	7
3 500	1 330	1 200	1 090	889	876	790	734	654	581	517	437	376	9
4 000	1 170	1 050	956	778	767	691	643	572	508	452	382	329	12
4 500	1 040	936	850	691	682	614	571	509	452	402	340	293	15
5 000	933	842	765	622	613	553	514	458	407	362	306	264	18
5 500	848	766	695	566	558	503	467	416	370	329	278	240	22
6 000	778	702	637	518	511	461	428	382	339	301	255	220	26
6 500	718	648	588	479	472	425	395	352	313	278	235	203	31
7 000	667	602	546	444	438	395	367	327	290	258	218	188	35
7 500	622	562	510	415	409	369	343	305	271	241	204	176	41
8 000	583	526	478	389	383	346	321	286	254	226	191	165	46
8 500	549	496	450	366	361	325	302	269	239	213	180	155	52
9 000	518	468	425	346	341	307	286	254	226	201	170	146	59
9 500	491	443	402	327	323	291	271	241	214	190	161	139	65
10 000	467	421	382	311	307	276	257	229	203	181	153	132	72

Span in millimetres

PROPERTIES AND DESIGN DATA

	129	118	107	†97	86	79	74	67	60	52	45	39	
S_x 10^3mm^3	1 940	1 750	1 590	1 440	1 280	1 160	1 060	949	849	747	634	549	
Z_x 10^3mm^3	2 160	1 950	1 770	1 590	1 420	1 280	1 190	1 060	941	837	708	610	
I_x 10^6mm^4	308	275	248	222	199	177	165	145	129	118	99.2	85.1	
J 10^3mm^4	2 130	1 600	1 220	912	877	657	745	545	397	308	191	126	
C_w 10^9mm^6	2 220	1 970	1 760	961	1 560	847	847	439	384	237	195	164	
L_u mm	5 580	5 390	5 220	5 410	4 250	4 140	3 380	3 280	3 200	2 570	2 490	2 440	
V_r kN	742	666	604	543	503	480	519	463	405	429	368	320	
R kN	610	546	493	444	412	392	425	379	329	333	285	249	
G kN	4.42	4.02	3.68	3.34	3.07	2.97	3.17	2.87	2.53	2.56	2.23	1.96	
N mm	130	130	130	130	130	130	130	130	130	137	137	137	

IMPERIAL SIZE AND MASS

Mass (lb./ft.)	87	79	72	65	58	53	50	45	40	35	30	26	
Nominal Depth (in.)						12							

† Class 3 section.

Total Uniformly Distributed Factored
Loads for Laterally Supported Beams — kilonewtons

Designation						W250						Approx. Deflection (mm)
Mass (kg/m)		101	89	80	73	67	58	49	45	39	33	
	1 000											1
	1 500								720	616	561	2
	2 000					815	719	651	650	554	458	4
	2 500	1 120	992	858	775	778	665	547	520	443	366	6
	3 000	1 010	886	785	709	649	554	456	433	369	305	8
	3 500	864	759	673	608	556	475	391	372	317	262	11
	4 000	756	664	589	532	487	416	342	325	277	229	14
	4 500	672	590	523	473	432	370	304	289	246	204	18
	5 000	605	531	471	426	389	333	273	260	222	183	22
	5 500	550	483	428	387	354	302	249	236	201	167	27
	6 000	504	443	392	355	324	277	228	217	185	153	32
	6 500	465	409	362	327	299	256	210	200	170	141	38
	7 000	432	380	336	304	278	238	195	186	158	131	44
	7 500	403	354	314	284	259	222	182	173	148	122	50
	8 000	378	332	294	266	243	208	171	163	139	114	57

Span in millimetres

PROPERTIES AND DESIGN DATA

	101	89	80	73	67	58	49	45	39	33	
S_x 10^3mm^3	1 240	1 100	982	891	806	693	572	534	459	379	
Z_x 10^3mm^3	1 400	1 230	1 090	985	901	770	633	602	513	424	
I_x 10^6mm^4	164	143	126	113	104	87.3	70.6	71.1	60.1	48.9	
J 10^3mm^4	1 490	1 040	757	575	625	409	241	261	169	98.5	
C_w 10^9mm^6	829	713	623	553	324	268	211	113	93.4	73.2	
L_u mm	4 950	4 690	4 520	4 390	3 570	3 410	3 240	2 360	2 280	2 180	
V_r kN	560	496	429	388	408	359	326	360	308	280	
R kN	550	488	422	380	399	354	320	315	270	245	
G kN	4.02	3.61	3.17	2.90	3.00	2.70	2.50	2.56	2.23	2.06	
N mm	102	102	102	103	103	102	102	117	117	117	

IMPERIAL SIZE AND MASS

Mass (lb./ft.)	68	60	54	49	45	39	33	30	26	22	
Nominal Depth (in.)					10						

Total Uniformly Distributed Factored
Loads for Laterally Supported Beams — kilonewtons

Designation		W200										Approx. Deflection (mm)
Mass (kg/m)		100	86	71	59	52	46	42	36	31	27	
	1 000										428	1
	1 500							526	444	479	402	3
	2 000	1 180	1 030	785	681	580	521	482	410	362	301	4
	2 500	994	848	694	564	492	429	385	328	289	241	7
	3 000	828	706	578	470	410	357	321	274	241	201	10
	3 500	710	605	496	403	352	306	275	235	207	172	14
	4 000	621	530	434	353	308	268	241	205	181	151	18
	4 500	552	471	385	313	274	238	214	182	161	134	23
	5 000	497	424	347	282	246	214	193	164	145	121	28
	5 500	452	385	315	256	224	195	175	149	132	110	34
	6 000	414	353	289	235	205	179	161	137	121	100	40
	6 500	382	326	267	217	189	165	148	126	111	93	47
	7 000	355	303	248	201	176	153	138	117	103	86	55

Span in millimetres

PROPERTIES AND DESIGN DATA

S_x 10^3mm^3		989	853	709	582	512	448	399	342	299	249	
Z_x 10^3mm^3		1 150	981	803	653	570	496	446	380	335	279	
I_x 10^6mm^4		113	94.7	76.6	61.1	52.7	45.5	40.9	34.4	31.4	25.8	
J 10^3mm^4		2 090	1 400	818	465	324	221	223	146	119	71.3	
C_w 10^9mm^6		386	318	250	196	167	141	84.0	69.6	40.9	32.5	
L_u mm		5 020	4 620	4 150	3 780	3 620	3 460	2 850	2 730	2 150	2 050	
V_r kN		592	514	393	341	290	260	263	222	240	214	
R kN		666	584	448	390	333	301	304	257	259	231	
G kN		4.89	4.39	3.44	3.07	2.67	2.43	2.43	2.09	2.16	1.96	
N mm		84.9	84.2	84.0	83.9	83.8	83.2	83.2	83.1	90.9	91.3	

IMPERIAL SIZE AND MASS

Mass (lb./ft.)		67	58	48	40	35	31	28	24	21	18	
Nominal Depth (in.)		8										

Total Uniformly Distributed Factored
Loads for Laterally Supported Beams — kilonewtons

Designation	S310		Approx. Deflection (mm)	S250		Approx. Deflection (mm)	S200		Approx. Deflection (mm)
Mass (kg/m)	52	47		52	38		34	27	
1 000	1 180		1	1 260	715	1	683	499	1
1 500	1 060	967	2	841	670	2	455	392	3
2 000	795	745	3	631	502	4	341	294	4
2 500	636	596	5	505	402	6	273	235	7
3 000	530	497	7	420	335	8	228	196	10
3 500	454	426	9	360	287	11	195	168	14
4 000	397	373	12	315	251	14	171	147	18
4 500	353	331	15	280	223	18	152	131	23
5 000	318	298	18	252	201	22	137	118	28
5 500	289	271	22	229	183	27	124	107	34
6 000	265	248	26	210	167	32	114	98	40
6 500	245	229	31	194	155	38	105	90	47
7 000	227	213	35	180	143	44	98	84	55
7 500	212	199	41	168	134	50	91	78	63
8 000	199	186	46	158	126	57	85	73	72
8 500	187	175	52	148	118	65	80	69	81
9 000	177	166	59	140	112	73	76	65	91
9 500	167	157	65	133	106	81	72	62	101
10 000	159	149	72	126	100	90	68	59	112

Span in millimetres

PROPERTIES AND DESIGN DATA

$S_x \ 10^3 mm^3$	629	597		485	405		266	237	
$Z_x \ 10^3 mm^3$	736	690		584	465		316	272	
$I_x \ 10^6 mm^4$	95.8	91.1		61.6	51.4		27.0	24.0	
$J \ 10^3 mm^4$	450	374		541	251		229	140	
$C_w 10^9 mm^6$	88.2	83.6		51.9	41.5		16.8	14.7	
$L_u \ mm$	1 800	1 780		1 880	1 720		1 620	1 540	
$V_r \ kN$	592	484		683	358		405	250	
$R \ kN$	475	387		647	339		469	289	
$G \ kN$	3.68	3.00		5.10	2.67		3.78	2.33	
$N \ mm$	132	132		107	107		83.2	83.2	

IMPERIAL SIZE AND MASS

Mass (lb./ft.)	35	31.8		35	25.4		23	18.4	
Nominal Depth (in.)	12			10			8		

Total Uniformly Distributed Factored
Loads for Laterally Supported Beams — kilonewtons

Designation	S150		Approx. Deflection (mm)	S130		Approx. Deflection (mm)	S100	Approx. Deflection (mm)
Mass (kg/m)	26	19		22	15		11	
500	639	320	0	523	244	0	174	1
1 000	374	300	1	261	200	2	125	2
1 500	249	200	3	174	134	4	83	5
2 000	187	150	6	131	100	7	62	9
2 500	149	120	9	105	80	11	50	14
3 000	125	100	13	87	67	16	42	20
3 500	107	86	18	75	57	21	36	27
4 000	93	75	24	65	50	28	31	36
4 500	83	67	30	58	45	35	28	45
5 000	75	60	37	52	40	43	25	56

Span in millimetres

PROPERTIES AND DESIGN DATA

$S_x \ 10^3 mm^3$	144	121		99.6	80.6		50.1	
$Z_x \ 10^3 mm^3$	173	139		121	92.8		57.7	
$I_x \ 10^6 mm^4$	10.9	9.19		6.33	5.12		2.55	
$J \ 10^3 mm^4$	155	70.1		133	47.4		29.9	
$C_w \ 10^9 mm^6$	5.01	3.96		2.43	1.79		0.724	
L_u mm	1 580	1 360		1 640	1 280		1 230	
V_r kN	320	160		283	122		87.2	
R kN	478	239		502	217		190	
G kN	3.98	1.99		4.22	1.82		1.62	
N mm	60.3	60.3		48.1	48.1		36.9	

IMPERIAL SIZE AND MASS

Mass (lb./ft.)	17.25	12.5		14.75	10		7.7	
Nominal Depth (in.)	6			5			4	

BEAM LOAD TABLES[1]
Rectangular HSS

G40.21-M 350W
$\emptyset = 0.90$

Total Uniformly Distributed Factored
Loads for Laterally Supported Beams — kN

Size (mm)	304.8 x 203.2					Approx. Deflection (mm)	254 x 152.4					Approx. Deflection (mm)
Thickness (mm)	12.7	11.13	9.53	7.95	6.35		12.7	11.13	9.53	7.95	6.35	
Mass (kg/m)	93	82.4	71.3	60.1	48.6		12.7	64.6	56.1	47.5	38.4	
Span in millimetres												
500							2 150	1 940	1 710	1 470	1 210	
1 000	2 680	2 410	2 110	1 800	1 480	1	1 880	1 690	1 480	1 270	1 040	1
1 500	2 000	1 780	1 550	1 320	1 080	2	1 250	1 130	990	845	690	2
2 000	1 500	1 340	1 160	992	806	3	940	845	742	634	518	4
2 500	1 200	1 070	932	793	645	5	752	676	594	507	414	6
3 000	1 000	890	777	661	538	8	627	564	495	423	345	9
3 500	857	763	666	567	461	10	537	483	424	362	296	13
4 000	750	668	583	496	403	14	470	423	371	317	259	16
4 500	666	594	518	441	358	17	418	376	330	282	230	21
5 000	600	534	466	397	323	21	376	338	297	254	207	26
5 500	545	486	424	361	293	26	342	307	270	230	188	31
6 000	500	445	388	331	269	31	313	282	247	211	173	37
6 500	461	411	359	305	248	36	289	260	228	195	159	43
7 000	428	382	333	283	230	42	269	242	212	181	148	50
7 500	400	356	311	264	215	48	251	225	198	169	138	58
8 000	375	334	291	248	202	55	235	211	186	158	129	66
8 500	353	314	274	233	190	62	221	199	175	149	122	74
9 000	333	297	259	220	179	69	209	188	165	141	115	83
9 500	316	281	245	209	170	77	198	178	156	133	109	93
10 000	300	267	233	198	161	86	188	169	148	127	104	103

PROPERTIES AND DESIGN DATA

	304.8 x 203.2						254 x 152.4					
S_x $10^3 mm^3$	964	867	762	652	535		592	537	475	409	338	
Z_x $10^3 mm^3$	1 190	1 060	925	787	640		746	671	589	503	411	
I_x $10^6 mm^4$	147	132	116	99.4	81.5		75.2	68.2	60.3	52.0	42.9	
C mm^2	6 450	5 790	5 080	4 340	3 550		5 160	4 660	4 110	3 530	2 900	
V_r kN	1 340	1 200	1 060	902	738		1 070	969	855	735	604	

IMPERIAL SIZE AND MASS

	304.8 x 203.2						254 x 152.4					
Mass (lb./ft.)	62.5	55.4	47.9	40.4	32.6		48.9	43.4	37.7	31.9	25.8	
Thickness (in.)	.500	.438	.375	.313	.250		.500	.438	.375	.313	.250	
Size (in.)	12 x 8						10 x 6					

[1] For strong axis bending only.

G40.21-M 350W
$\phi = 0.90$

Total Uniformly Distributed Factored
Loads for Laterally Supported Beams — kN

Size (mm)	203.2 x 152.4						203.2 x 101.6						Approx. Deflection (mm)
Thickness (mm)	12.7	11.13	9.53	7.95	6.35	4.78	12.7	11.13	9.53	7.95	6.53	4.78	
Mass (kg/m)	62.6	55.7	48.5	41.1	33.4	25.5	52.4	46.9	40.9	34.8	28.3	21.7	
500	1 610	1 470	1 310	1 130	939	732	1 610	1 470	1 310	1 130	939	732	
1 000	1 330	1 200	1 060	907	743	575	1 020	925	819	708	585	454	1
1 500	887	800	704	605	496	383	680	617	546	472	390	302	3
2 000	665	600	528	454	372	287	510	462	409	354	292	227	5
2 500	532	480	422	363	297	230	408	370	328	283	234	181	8
3 000	444	400	352	302	248	192	340	308	273	236	195	151	12
3 500	380	343	302	259	212	164	292	264	234	202	167	130	16
4 000	333	300	264	227	186	144	255	231	205	177	146	113	21
4 500	296	267	235	202	165	128	227	206	182	157	130	101	26
5 000	266	240	211	181	149	115	204	185	164	142	117	91	32
5 500	242	218	192	165	135	104	186	168	149	129	106	82	39
6 000	222	200	176	151	124	96	170	154	136	118	97	76	46
6 500	205	185	162	140	114	88	157	142	126	109	90	70	54
7 000	190	171	151	130	106	82	146	132	117	101	84	65	63

Span in millimetres

PROPERTIES AND DESIGN DATA

S_x 10^3mm^3	423	385	343	297	246	192	307	282	253	221	185	145	
Z_x 10^3mm^3	528	476	419	360	295	228	405	367	325	281	232	180	
I_x 10^6mm^4	43.0	39.1	34.8	30.2	25.0	19.5	31.2	28.7	25.8	22.5	18.8	14.7	
C mm^2	3 870	3 530	3 150	2 730	2 260	1 760	3 870	3 530	3 150	2 730	2 260	1 760	
V_r kN	805	734	654	567	469	366	805	734	654	567	469	366	

IMPERIAL SIZE AND MASS

Mass (lb./ft.)	42.1	37.5	32.6	27.6	22.4	17.1	35.2	31.5	27.5	23.4	19.0	14.6	
Thickness (in.)	.500	.438	.375	.313	.250	.188	.500	.438	.375	.313	.250	.188	
Size (in.)	8 x 6						8 x 4						

[1] For strong axis bending only.

Total Uniformly Distributed Factored
Loads for Laterally Supported Beams — kN

Size (mm)	177.8 x 127.#						Approx. Deflection (mm)
Thickness (mm)	12.7	11.13	9.53	7.95	6.35	4.78	
Mass (kg/m)	52.4	46.9	40.9	34.8	28.3	21.7	
500	1 340	1 230	1 110	965	805	631	
1 000	950	862	764	658	544	421	1
1 500	633	575	509	438	363	281	3
2 000	475	431	382	329	272	210	6
2 500	380	345	305	263	218	168	9
3 000	317	287	255	219	181	140	13
3 500	271	246	218	188	156	120	18
4 000	238	215	191	164	136	105	23
4 500	211	192	170	146	121	94	30
5 000	190	172	153	132	109	84	37
5 500	173	157	139	120	99	77	44
6 000	158	144	127	110	91	70	53

Span in millimetres

PROPERTIES AND DESIGN DATA

S_x 10^3mm^3	297	272	244	213	178	140	
Z_x 10^3mm^3	377	342	303	261	216	167	
I_x 10^6mm^4	26.4	24.2	21.7	18.9	15.8	12.4	
C mm^2	3 230	2 970	2 660	2 320	1 940	1 520	
V_r kN	671	617	553	483	402	315	

IMPERIAL SIZE AND MASS

Mass (lb./ft.)	35.2	31.5	27.5	23.4	19.0	14.6	
Thickness (in.)	.500	.438	.375	.313	.250	.188	
Size (in.)	7 x 5 #						

#Check manufacturer for current availability.
[1]For strong axis bending only.

Total Uniformly Distributed Factored
Loads for Laterally Supported Beams — kN

Size (mm)	152.4 x 101.6					Approx. Deflection (mm)	127 x 76.2				Approx. Deflection (mm)
Thickness (mm)	11.13	9.53	7.95	6.35	4.78		9.53	7.95	6.35	4.78	
Mass (kg/m)	38	33.3	28.4	23.2	17.9		25.7	22.1	18.2	14.1	
500	999	906	797	671	530		635	559	470	372	1
1 000	580	517	449	373	292	2	318	280	235	186	2
1 500	386	344	299	249	195	4	212	186	157	124	5
2 000	290	258	224	186	146	7	159	140	118	93	8
2 500	232	207	179	149	117	11	127	112	94	74	13
3 000	193	172	150	124	97	15	106	93	78	62	19
3 500	166	148	128	107	84	21	91	80	67	53	25
4 000	145	129	112	93	73	28	79	70	59	46	33
4 500	129	115	100	83	65	35	71	62	52	41	42
5 000	116	103	90	75	58	43	64	56	47	37	51

Span in millimetres

PROPERTIES AND DESIGN DATA

S_x $10^3 mm^3$	179	162	143	121	95.6		96.4	86.4	74.0	59.5	
Z_x $10^3 mm^3$	230	205	178	148	116		126	111	93.3	73.8	
I_x $10^6 mm^4$	13.6	12.4	10.9	9.18	7.28		6.12	5.49	4.70	3.78	
C mm^2	2 400	2 180	1 920	1 610	1 270		1 690	1 510	1 290	1 030	
V_r kN	499	453	399	335	265		352	315	268	214	

IMPERIAL SIZE AND MASS

Mass (lb./ft.)	25.5	22.4	19.1	15.6	12.0		17.3	14.9	12.2	9.45	
Thickness (in.)	.438	.375	.313	.250	.188		.375	.313	.250	.188	
Size (in.)	6 x 4						5 x 3				

[1] For strong axis bending only.

BEAM LOAD TABLES[1]
Rectangular HSS

G40.21-M 350W
$\emptyset = 0.90$

Total Uniformly Distributed Factored
Loads for Laterally Supported Beams — kN

Size (mm)	127 x 63.5				127 x 50.8				Approx. Deflection (mm)
Thickness (mm)	9.53	7.95	6.35	4.78	9.53	7.95	6.35	4.78	
Mass (kg/m)	23.8	20.5	16.9	13.1	21.9	18.9	15.6	12.2	
500	564	498	421	334	492	438	372	297	1
1 000	282	249	211	167	246	219	186	148	2
1 500	188	166	140	111	164	146	124	99	5
2 000	141	125	105	84	123	109	93	74	8
2 500	113	100	84	67	98	88	74	59	13
3 000	94	83	70	56	82	73	62	49	19
3 500	81	71	60	48	70	63	53	42	25
4 000	71	62	53	42	62	55	46	37	33

Span in millimetres

PROPERTIES AND DESIGN DATA

S_x 10^3mm^3	83.2	75.1	64.8	52.4	70.0	63.8	55.5	45.3	
Z_x 10^3mm^3	112	98.9	83.6	66.3	97.7	86.9	73.8	58.9	
I_x 10^6mm^4	5.28	4.77	4.11	3.33	4.45	4.05	3.53	2.87	
C mm^2	1 690	1 510	1 290	1 030	1 690	1 510	1 290	1 030	
V_r kN	352	315	268	214	352	315	268	214	

IMPERIAL SIZE AND MASS

Mass (lb./ft.)	16.0	13.8	11.4	8.81	14.7	12.7	10.5	8.17	
Thickness (in.)	.375	.313	.250	.188	.375	.313	.250	.188	
Size (in.)	5 x 2½				5 x 2				

[1] For strong axis bending only.

Total Uniformly Distributed Factored
Loads for Laterally Supported Beams — kN

Size (mm)	101.6 x 76.2				101.6 x 50.8					Approx. Deflection (mm)
Thickness (mm)	9.53	7.95	6.35	4.78	7.95	6.35	4.78	3.81	3.18	
Mass (kg/m)	21.9	18.9	15.6	12.2	15.8	13.1	10.3	8.37	7.09	
500	442	392	332	265	296	255	206	171	146	1
1 000	221	196	166	132	148	128	103	85	73	3
1 500	147	131	111	88	99	85	69	57	49	6
2 000	110	98	83	66	74	64	51	43	37	10
2 500	88	78	66	53	59	51	41	34	29	16
3 000	74	65	55	44	49	43	34	28	24	23
3 500	63	56	47	38	42	36	29	24	21	31
4 000	55	49	42	33	37	32	26	21	18	41

Span in millimetres

PROPERTIES AND DESIGN DATA

S_x 10^3mm^3	67.2	61.0	52.8	43.0	43.5	38.4	31.8	26.8	23.1	
Z_x 10^3mm^3	87.6	77.7	65.9	52.5	58.8	50.6	40.8	33.9	29.0	
I_x 10^6mm^4	3.41	3.10	2.68	2.18	2.21	1.95	1.61	1.36	1.17	
C mm^2	1 210	1 110	968	789	1 110	968	789	658	565	
V_r kN	252	231	201	164	231	201	164	137	118	

IMPERIAL SIZE AND MASS

Mass (lb./ft.)	14.7	12.7	10.5	8.17	10.6	8.81	6.89	5.62	4.76	
Thickness (in.)	.375	.313	.250	.188	.313	.250	.188	.150	.125	
Size (in.)	4 x 3				4 x 2					

[1] For strong axis bending only.

BEAM DIAGRAMS AND FORMULAE

Equivalent Tabular Load is the uniformly
distributed factored load given in the Beam Load Tables

---

1 SIMPLE BEAM—UNIFORMLY DISTRIBUTED LOAD

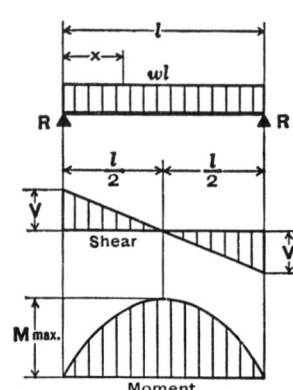

Equivalent Tabular Load . . . $= wl$

$R = V$ . . . . $= \dfrac{wl}{2}$

V_x . . . . $= w\left(\dfrac{l}{2} - x\right)$

M max. (at center) . . . . $= \dfrac{wl^2}{8}$

M_x . . . . $= \dfrac{wx}{2}(l - x)$

Δmax. (at center) . . . . $= \dfrac{5\,wl^4}{384\,EI}$

$Δ_x$ . . . . $= \dfrac{wx}{24EI}(l^3 - 2lx^2 + x^3)$

---

2 SIMPLE BEAM—LOAD INCREASING UNIFORMLY TO ONE END

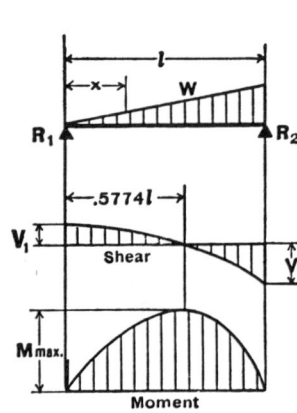

Equivalent Tabular Load . . . $= \dfrac{16W}{9\sqrt{3}} = 1.0264W$

$R_1 = V_1$ . . . . $= \dfrac{W}{3}$

$R_2 = V_2$ max. . . . . $= \dfrac{2W}{3}$

V_x . . . . $= \dfrac{W}{3} - \dfrac{Wx^2}{l^2}$

M max. $\left(\text{at } x = \dfrac{l}{\sqrt{3}} = .5774l\right)$ . . $= \dfrac{2Wl}{9\sqrt{3}} = .1283\,Wl$

M_x . . . . $= \dfrac{Wx}{3l^2}(l^2 - x^2)$

Δmax. $\left(\text{at } x = l\sqrt{1 - \sqrt{\dfrac{8}{15}}} = .5193l\right) = .01304\,\dfrac{Wl^3}{EI}$

$Δ_x$ . . . . $= \dfrac{Wx}{180EI\,l^2}(3x^4 - 10l^2x^2 + 7l^4)$

---

3 SIMPLE BEAM—LOAD INCREASING UNIFORMLY TO CENTER

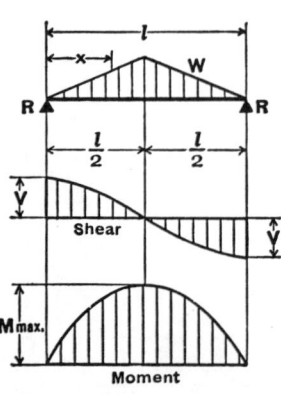

Equivalent Tabular Load . . . $= \dfrac{4W}{3}$

$R = V$ . . . . $= \dfrac{W}{2}$

V_x $\left(\text{when } x < \dfrac{l}{2}\right)$ . . . . . $= \dfrac{W}{2l^2}(l^2 - 4x^2)$

M max. (at center) . . . . $= \dfrac{Wl}{6}$

M_x $\left(\text{when } x < \dfrac{l}{2}\right)$ . . . . $= Wx\left(\dfrac{1}{2} - \dfrac{2x^2}{3l^2}\right)$

Δmax. (at center) . . . . $= \dfrac{Wl^3}{60EI}$

$Δ_x$ . . . . $= \dfrac{Wx}{480\,EI\,l^2}(5l^2 - 4x^2)^2$

Note: For deflection calculations, use specified loads.

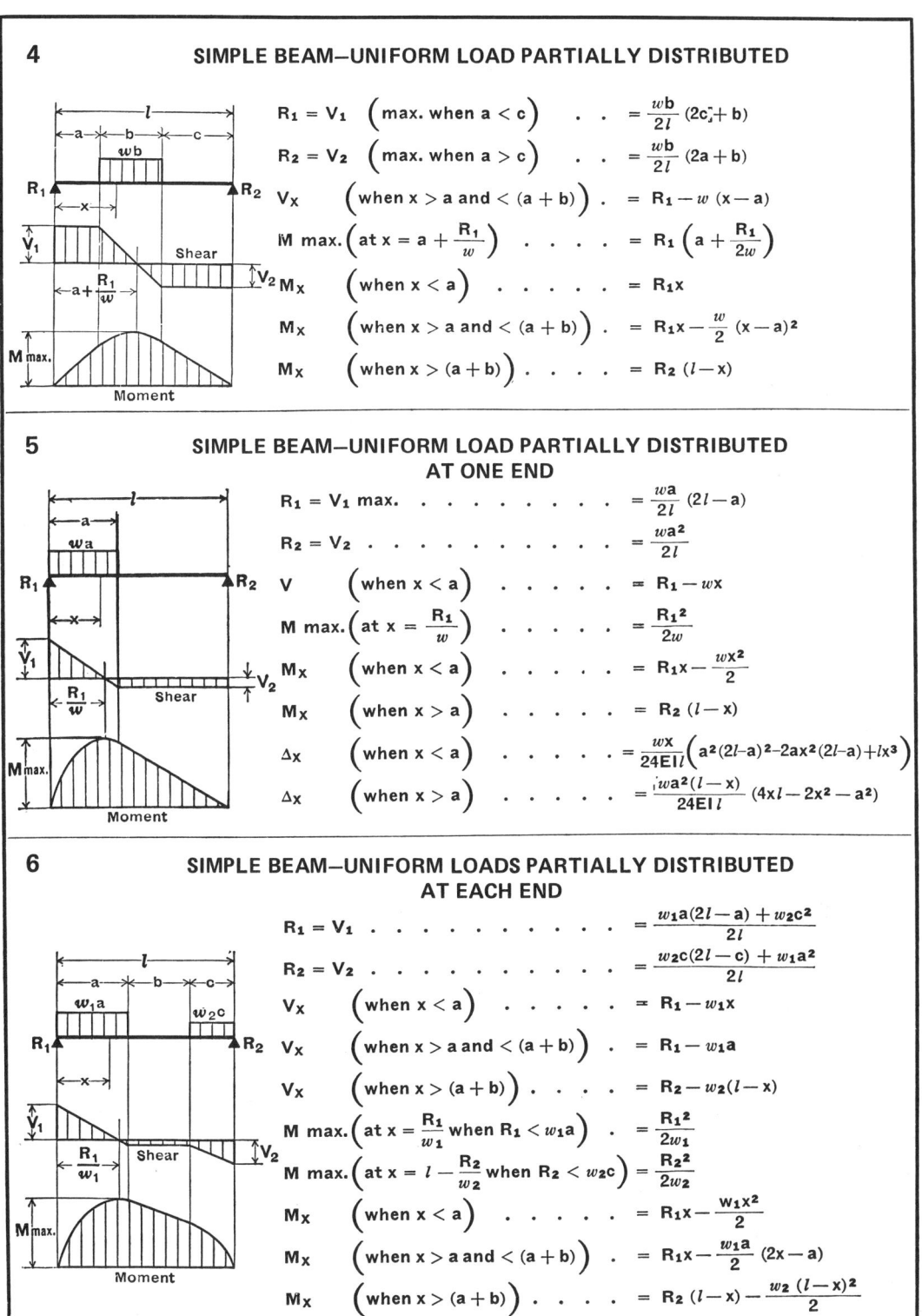

4   **SIMPLE BEAM—UNIFORM LOAD PARTIALLY DISTRIBUTED**

$$R_1 = V_1 \left(\text{max. when } a < c \right) \quad \cdots \quad = \frac{wb}{2l}(2c + b)$$

$$R_2 = V_2 \left(\text{max. when } a > c \right) \quad \cdots \quad = \frac{wb}{2l}(2a + b)$$

$$V_x \left(\text{when } x > a \text{ and} < (a+b) \right) \cdot \quad = R_1 - w(x-a)$$

$$M \text{ max.} \left(\text{at } x = a + \frac{R_1}{w} \right) \quad \cdots \quad = R_1 \left(a + \frac{R_1}{2w} \right)$$

$$M_x \left(\text{when } x < a \right) \quad \cdots \quad \cdots \quad = R_1 x$$

$$M_x \left(\text{when } x > a \text{ and} < (a+b) \right) \cdot \quad = R_1 x - \frac{w}{2}(x-a)^2$$

$$M_x \left(\text{when } x > (a+b) \right) \cdot \quad \cdots \quad = R_2 (l - x)$$

---

5   **SIMPLE BEAM—UNIFORM LOAD PARTIALLY DISTRIBUTED AT ONE END**

$$R_1 = V_1 \text{ max.} \quad \cdots \cdots \cdots \quad = \frac{wa}{2l}(2l - a)$$

$$R_2 = V_2 \quad \cdots \cdots \cdots \cdots \quad = \frac{wa^2}{2l}$$

$$V \left(\text{when } x < a \right) \quad \cdots \cdots \quad = R_1 - wx$$

$$M \text{ max.} \left(\text{at } x = \frac{R_1}{w} \right) \quad \cdots \cdots \quad = \frac{R_1^2}{2w}$$

$$M_x \left(\text{when } x < a \right) \quad \cdots \cdots \quad = R_1 x - \frac{wx^2}{2}$$

$$M_x \left(\text{when } x > a \right) \quad \cdots \cdots \quad = R_2 (l - x)$$

$$\Delta_x \left(\text{when } x < a \right) \quad \cdots \cdots \quad = \frac{wx}{24EIl}\left(a^2(2l-a)^2 - 2ax^2(2l-a) + lx^3 \right)$$

$$\Delta_x \left(\text{when } x > a \right) \quad \cdots \cdots \quad = \frac{wa^2(l-x)}{24EIl}(4xl - 2x^2 - a^2)$$

---

6   **SIMPLE BEAM—UNIFORM LOADS PARTIALLY DISTRIBUTED AT EACH END**

$$R_1 = V_1 \quad \cdots \cdots \cdots \quad = \frac{w_1 a(2l - a) + w_2 c^2}{2l}$$

$$R_2 = V_2 \quad \cdots \cdots \cdots \cdots \quad = \frac{w_2 c(2l - c) + w_1 a^2}{2l}$$

$$V_x \left(\text{when } x < a \right) \quad \cdots \cdots \quad = R_1 - w_1 x$$

$$V_x \left(\text{when } x > a \text{ and} < (a+b) \right) \cdot \quad = R_1 - w_1 a$$

$$V_x \left(\text{when } x > (a+b) \right) \quad \cdots \cdots \quad = R_2 - w_2 (l - x)$$

$$M \text{ max.} \left(\text{at } x = \frac{R_1}{w_1} \text{ when } R_1 < w_1 a \right) \cdot \quad = \frac{R_1^2}{2w_1}$$

$$M \text{ max.} \left(\text{at } x = l - \frac{R_2}{w_2} \text{ when } R_2 < w_2 c \right) = \frac{R_2^2}{2w_2}$$

$$M_x \left(\text{when } x < a \right) \quad \cdots \cdots \quad = R_1 x - \frac{w_1 x^2}{2}$$

$$M_x \left(\text{when } x > a \text{ and} < (a+b) \right) \cdot \quad = R_1 x - \frac{w_1 a}{2}(2x - a)$$

$$M_x \left(\text{when } x > (a+b) \right) \quad \cdots \cdots \quad = R_2 (l - x) - \frac{w_2 (l-x)^2}{2}$$

Note: For deflection calculations, use specified loads.

BEAM DIAGRAMS AND FORMULAE

Equivalent Tabular Load is the uniformly
distributed factored load given in the Beam Load Tables

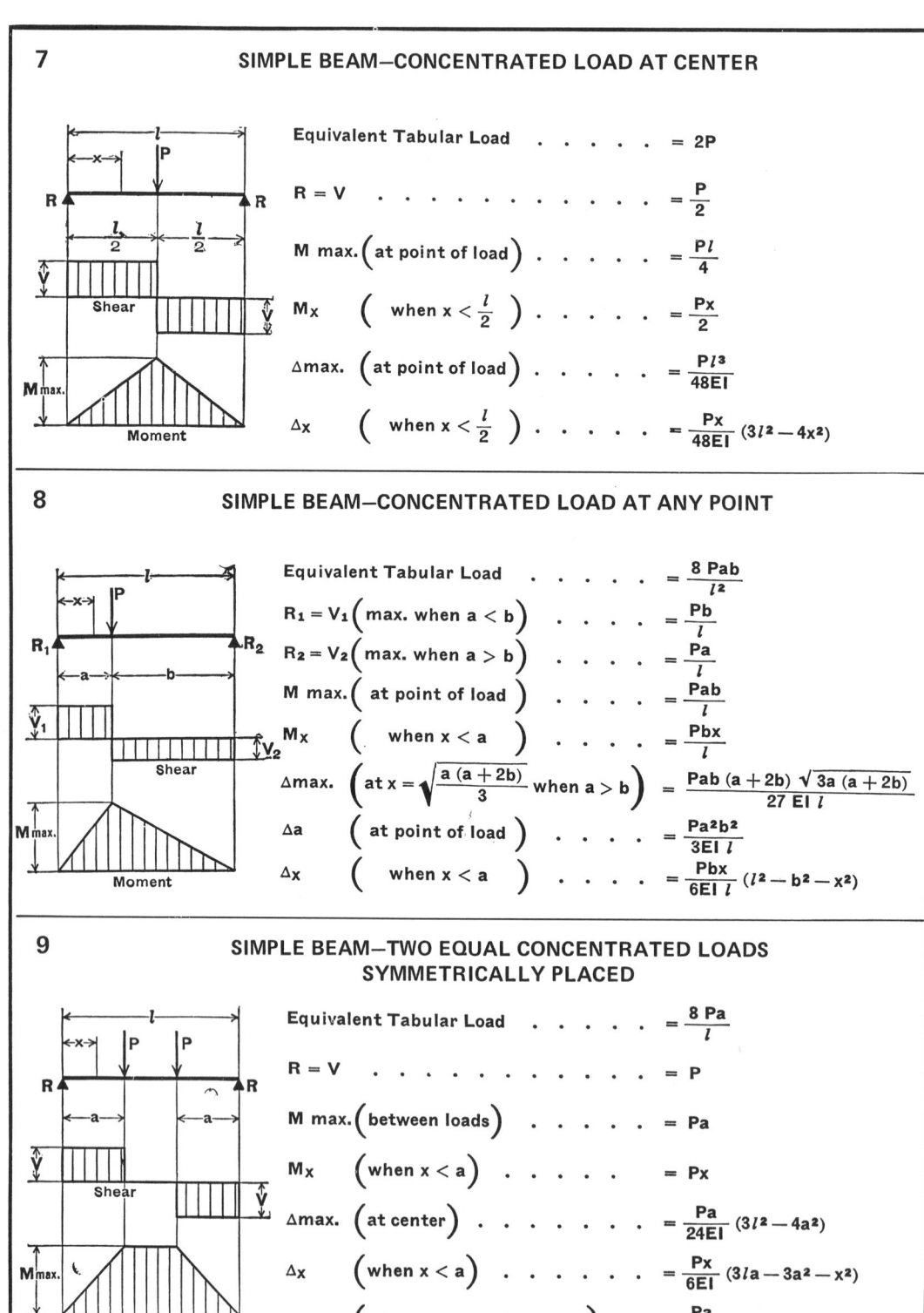

7   **SIMPLE BEAM—CONCENTRATED LOAD AT CENTER**

Equivalent Tabular Load . . . . . . $= 2P$

$R = V$ . . . . $= \dfrac{P}{2}$

M max. $\left(\text{at point of load}\right)$ . . . . . $= \dfrac{Pl}{4}$

M_x $\left(\text{when } x < \dfrac{l}{2}\right)$ . . . . . $= \dfrac{Px}{2}$

Δmax. $\left(\text{at point of load}\right)$ . . . . . $= \dfrac{Pl^3}{48EI}$

Δ_x $\left(\text{when } x < \dfrac{l}{2}\right)$ . . . . . . $= \dfrac{Px}{48EI}(3l^2 - 4x^2)$

---

8   **SIMPLE BEAM—CONCENTRATED LOAD AT ANY POINT**

Equivalent Tabular Load . . . . . . $= \dfrac{8\,Pab}{l^2}$

$R_1 = V_1 \left(\text{max. when } a < b\right)$ . . . . $= \dfrac{Pb}{l}$

$R_2 = V_2 \left(\text{max. when } a > b\right)$ . . . . $= \dfrac{Pa}{l}$

M max. $\left(\text{at point of load}\right)$ . . . . $= \dfrac{Pab}{l}$

M_x $\left(\text{when } x < a\right)$ . . . . . $= \dfrac{Pbx}{l}$

Δmax. $\left(\text{at } x = \sqrt{\dfrac{a(a+2b)}{3}} \text{ when } a > b\right)$ $= \dfrac{Pab(a+2b)\sqrt{3a(a+2b)}}{27\,EI\,l}$

Δa $\left(\text{at point of load}\right)$ . . . . $= \dfrac{Pa^2b^2}{3EI\,l}$

Δ_x $\left(\text{when } x < a\right)$ . . . . $= \dfrac{Pbx}{6EI\,l}(l^2 - b^2 - x^2)$

---

9   **SIMPLE BEAM—TWO EQUAL CONCENTRATED LOADS**
SYMMETRICALLY PLACED

Equivalent Tabular Load . . . . . . $= \dfrac{8\,Pa}{l}$

$R = V$ . . . . $= P$

M max. $\left(\text{between loads}\right)$ . . . . . $= Pa$

M_x $\left(\text{when } x < a\right)$ . . . . . $= Px$

Δmax. $\left(\text{at center}\right)$ . . . . $= \dfrac{Pa}{24EI}(3l^2 - 4a^2)$

Δ_x $\left(\text{when } x < a\right)$ . . . . . . $= \dfrac{Px}{6EI}(3la - 3a^2 - x^2)$

Δ_x $\left(\text{when } x > a \text{ and } < (l-a)\right)$ . . $= \dfrac{Pa}{6EI}(3lx - 3x^2 - a^2)$

Note: For deflection calculations, use specified loads.

Equivalent Tabular Load is the uniformly
distributed factored load given in the Beam Load Tables

---

10   SIMPLE BEAM—TWO EQUAL CONCENTRATED LOADS UNSYMMETRICALLY PLACED

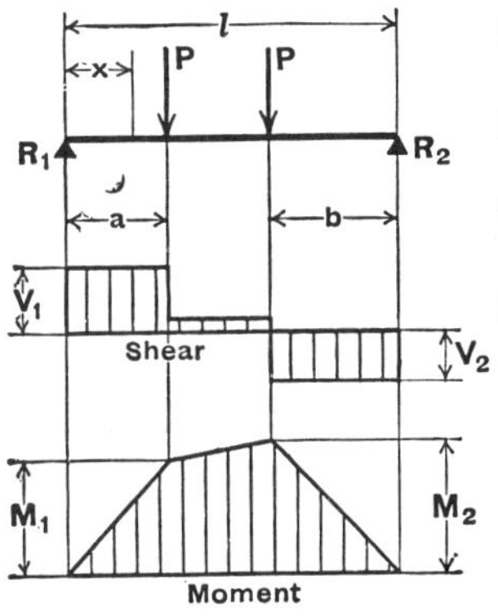

$R_1 = V_1 \left(\text{max. when } a < b \right)$ . . . . . $= \dfrac{P}{l}(l - a + b)$

$R_2 = V_2 \left(\text{max. when } a > b \right)$ . . . . . $= \dfrac{P}{l}(l - b + a)$

$V_x \quad \left(\text{when } x > a \text{ and } < (l - b) \right)$ . . $= \dfrac{P}{l}(b - a)$

$M_1 \quad \left(\text{max. when } a > b \right)$ . . . . . $= R_1 a$

$M_2 \quad \left(\text{max. when } a < b \right)$ . . . . . $= R_2 b$

$M_x \quad \left(\text{when } x < a \right)$ . . . . . . $= R_1 x$

$M_x \quad \left(\text{when } x > a \text{ and } < (l - b) \right)$ . . $= R_1 x - P(x - a)$

---

11   SIMPLE BEAM—TWO UNEQUAL CONCENTRATED LOADS UNSYMMETRICALLY PLACED

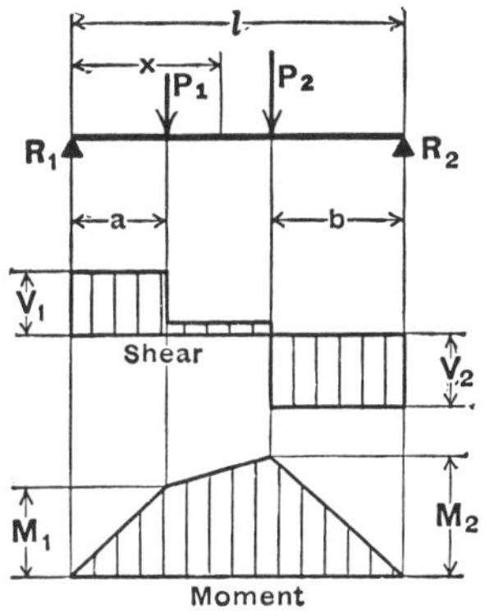

$R_1 = V_1$ . . . . $= \dfrac{P_1(l - a) + P_2 b}{l}$

$R_2 = V_2$ . . . . $= \dfrac{P_1 a + P_2(l - b)}{l}$

$V_x \quad \left(\text{when } x > a \text{ and } < (l - b) \right)$ . . $= R_1 - P_1$

$M_1 \quad \left(\text{max. when } R_1 < P_1 \right)$ . . . $= R_1 a$

$M_2 \quad \left(\text{max. when } R_2 < P_2 \right)$ . . . $= R_2 b$

$M_x \quad \left(\text{when } x < a \right)$ . . . . . . $= R_1 x$

$M_x \quad \left(\text{when } x > a \text{ and } < (l - b) \right)$ . . $= R_1 x - P_1(x - a)$

---

12   BEAM FIXED AT ONE END, SUPPORTED AT OTHER— UNIFORMLY DISTRIBUTED LOAD

Equivalent Tabular Load . . . . . $= wl$

$R_1 = V_1$ . . . . $= \dfrac{3wl}{8}$

$R_2 = V_2$ max. . . . . $= \dfrac{5wl}{8}$

V_x . . . . $= R_1 - wx$

M max. . . . . $= \dfrac{wl^2}{8}$

$M_1 \quad \left(\text{at } x = \dfrac{3}{8}l \right)$ . . . . . . $= \dfrac{9}{128} wl^2$

M_x . . . . $= R_1 x - \dfrac{wx^2}{2}$

Δmax. $\left(\text{at } x = \dfrac{l}{16}(1 + \sqrt{33}) = .4215l \right)$. $= \dfrac{wl^4}{185EI}$

Δ_x . . . . $= \dfrac{wx}{48EI}(l^3 - 3lx^2 + 2x^3)$

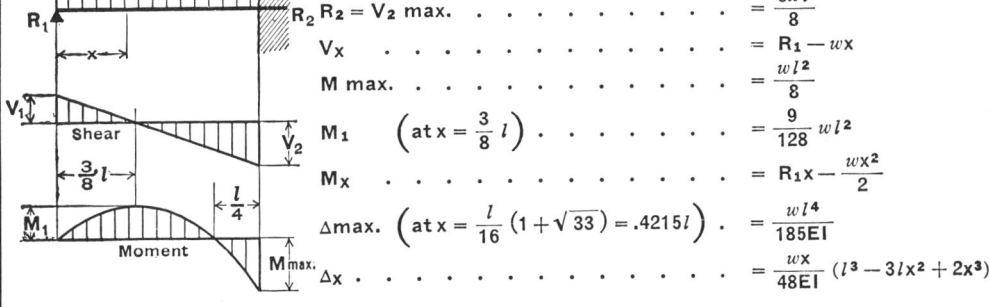

Note: For deflection calculations, use specified loads.

BEAM DIAGRAMS AND FORMULAE

Equivalent Tabular Load is the uniformly
distributed factored load given in the Beam Load Tables

13 BEAM FIXED AT ONE END, SUPPORTED AT OTHER—
CONCENTRATED LOAD AT CENTER

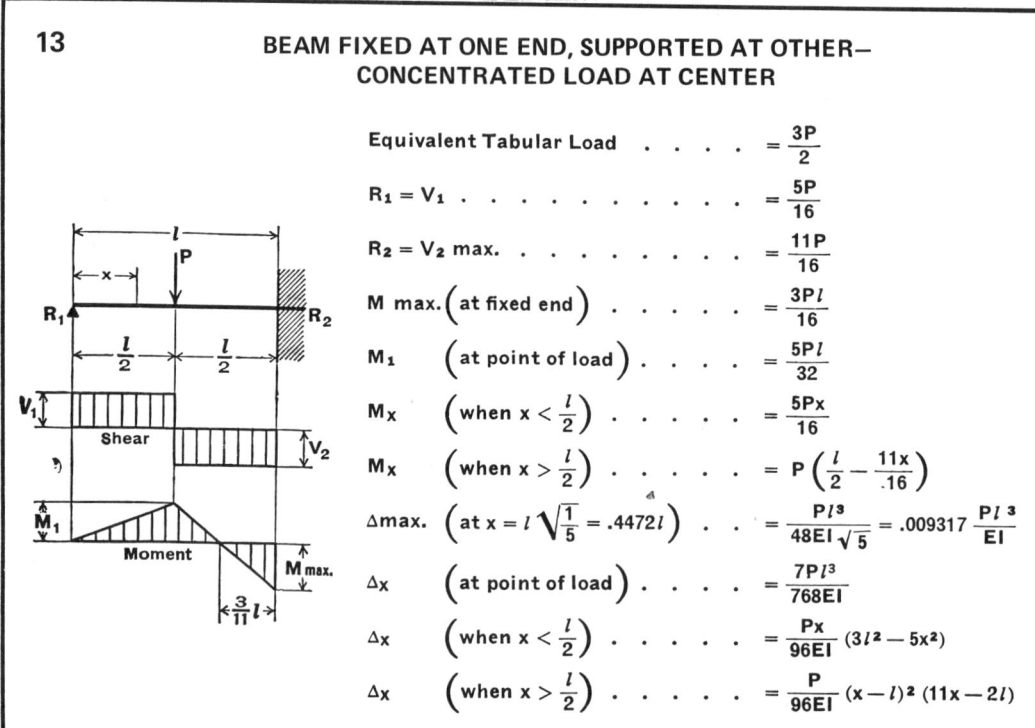

Equivalent Tabular Load . . . . $= \dfrac{3P}{2}$

$R_1 = V_1$ . . . . $= \dfrac{5P}{16}$

$R_2 = V_2$ max. . . . . $= \dfrac{11P}{16}$

M max. $\left(\text{at fixed end}\right)$ . . . . . $= \dfrac{3Pl}{16}$

$M_1 \quad \left(\text{at point of load}\right)$ . . . . $= \dfrac{5Pl}{32}$

$M_x \quad \left(\text{when } x < \dfrac{l}{2}\right)$ . . . . $= \dfrac{5Px}{16}$

$M_x \quad \left(\text{when } x > \dfrac{l}{2}\right)$ . . . . . $= P\left(\dfrac{l}{2} - \dfrac{11x}{.16}\right)$

Δmax. $\left(\text{at } x = l\sqrt{\dfrac{1}{5}} = .4472l\right)$ . . $= \dfrac{Pl^3}{48EI\sqrt{5}} = .009317\dfrac{Pl^3}{EI}$

$\Delta_x \quad \left(\text{at point of load}\right)$ . . . . $= \dfrac{7Pl^3}{768EI}$

$\Delta_x \quad \left(\text{when } x < \dfrac{l}{2}\right)$ . . . . . $= \dfrac{Px}{96EI}(3l^2 - 5x^2)$

$\Delta_x \quad \left(\text{when } x > \dfrac{l}{2}\right)$ . . . . . $= \dfrac{P}{96EI}(x-l)^2(11x - 2l)$

14 BEAM FIXED AT ONE END, SUPPORTED AT OTHER—
CONCENTRATED LOAD AT ANY POINT

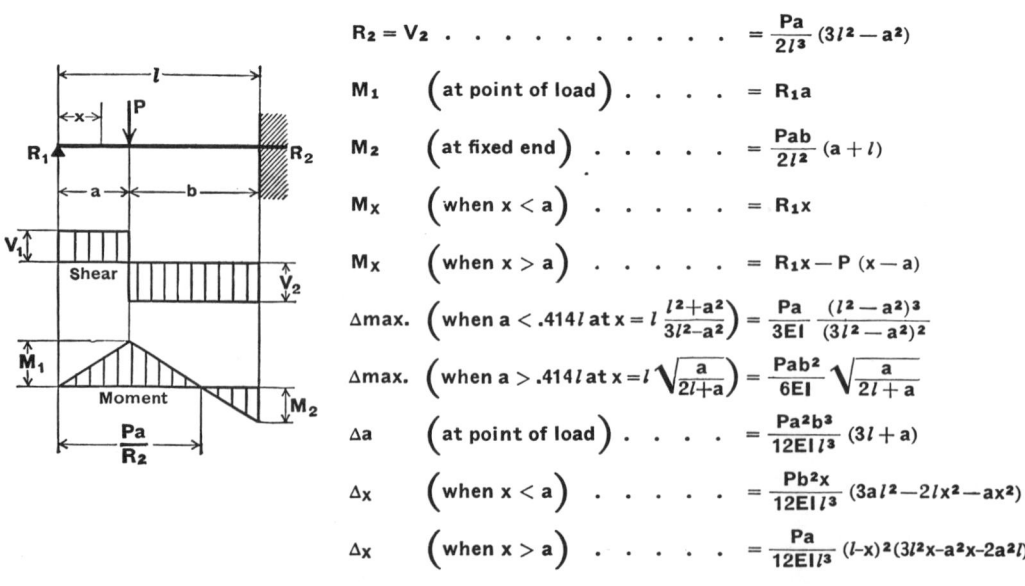

$R_1 = V_1$ . . . . $= \dfrac{Pb^2}{2l^3}(a + 2l)$

$R_2 = V_2$ . . . . $= \dfrac{Pa}{2l^3}(3l^2 - a^2)$

$M_1 \quad \left(\text{at point of load}\right)$ . . . . $= R_1a$

$M_2 \quad \left(\text{at fixed end}\right)$ . . . . . $= \dfrac{Pab}{2l^2}(a + l)$

$M_x \quad \left(\text{when } x < a\right)$ . . . . . $= R_1x$

$M_x \quad \left(\text{when } x > a\right)$ . . . . . $= R_1x - P(x - a)$

Δmax. $\left(\text{when } a < .414l \text{ at } x = l\dfrac{l^2+a^2}{3l^2-a^2}\right) = \dfrac{Pa}{3EI}\dfrac{(l^2-a^2)^3}{(3l^2-a^2)^2}$

Δmax. $\left(\text{when } a > .414l \text{ at } x = l\sqrt{\dfrac{a}{2l+a}}\right) = \dfrac{Pab^2}{6EI}\sqrt{\dfrac{a}{2l+a}}$

$\Delta_a \quad \left(\text{at point of load}\right)$ . . . . $= \dfrac{Pa^2b^3}{12EIl^3}(3l + a)$

$\Delta_x \quad \left(\text{when } x < a\right)$ . . . . . $= \dfrac{Pb^2x}{12EIl^3}(3al^2 - 2lx^2 - ax^2)$

$\Delta_x \quad \left(\text{when } x > a\right)$ . . . . . $= \dfrac{Pa}{12EIl^3}(l-x)^2(3l^2x - a^2x - 2a^2l)$

Note: For deflection calculations, use specified loads.

15   BEAM FIXED AT BOTH ENDS—UNIFORMLY DISTRIBUTED LOADS

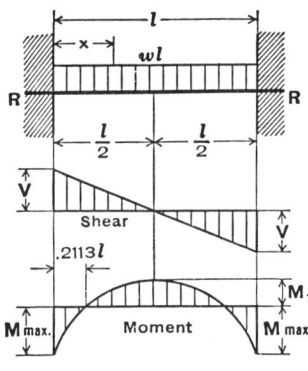

Equivalent Tabular Load $\quad \ldots \quad = \dfrac{2wl}{3}$

$R = V \quad \ldots \ldots \ldots \ldots = \dfrac{wl}{2}$

$V_x \quad \ldots \ldots \ldots \ldots = w\left(\dfrac{l}{2} - x\right)$

$M \text{ max.}\left(\text{at ends}\right) \quad \ldots \ldots = \dfrac{wl^2}{12}$

$M_1 \quad \left(\text{at center}\right) \quad \ldots \ldots = \dfrac{wl^2}{24}$

$M_x \quad \ldots \ldots \ldots \ldots = \dfrac{w}{12}(6lx - l^2 - 6x^2)$

$\Delta\text{max.}\left(\text{at center}\right) \quad \ldots \ldots = \dfrac{wl^4}{384EI}$

$\Delta_x \quad \ldots \ldots \ldots \ldots = \dfrac{wx^2}{24EI}(l - x)^2$

16   BEAM FIXED AT BOTH ENDS—CONCENTRATED LOAD AT CENTER

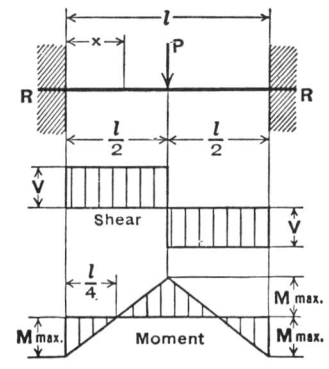

Equivalent Tabular Load $\quad \ldots \ldots = P$

$R = V \quad \ldots \ldots \ldots = \dfrac{P}{2}$

$M \text{ max.}\left(\text{at center and ends}\right) \ldots = \dfrac{Pl}{8}$

$M_x \quad \left(\text{when } x < \dfrac{l}{2}\right) \ldots \ldots = \dfrac{P}{8}(4x - l)$

$\Delta\text{max.}\left(\text{at center}\right) \ldots \ldots = \dfrac{Pl^3}{192EI}$

$\Delta_x \quad \ldots \ldots \ldots \ldots = \dfrac{Px^2}{48EI}(3l - 4x)$

17   BEAM FIXED AT BOTH ENDS—CONCENTRATED LOAD AT ANY POINT

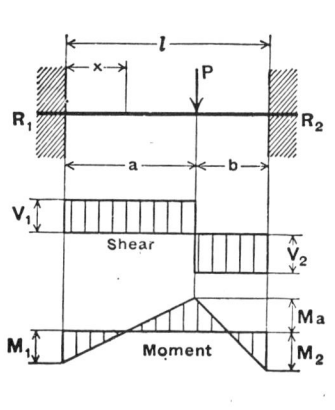

$R_1 = V_1\left(\text{max. when } a < b\right) \quad \ldots = \dfrac{Pb^2}{l^3}(3a + b)$

$R_2 = V_2\left(\text{max. when } a > b\right) \quad \ldots = \dfrac{Pa^2}{l^3}(a + 3b)$

$M_1 \quad \left(\text{max. when } a < b\right) \quad \ldots = \dfrac{Pab^2}{l^2}$

$M_2 \quad \left(\text{max. when } a > b\right) \quad \ldots = \dfrac{Pa^2b}{l^2}$

$M_a \quad \left(\text{at point of load}\right) \quad \ldots = \dfrac{2Pa^2b^2}{l^3}$

$M_x \quad \left(\text{when } x < a\right) \quad \ldots \ldots = R_1x - \dfrac{Pab^2}{l^2}$

$\Delta\text{max.}\left(\text{when } a > b \text{ at } x = \dfrac{2al}{3a + b}\right) = \dfrac{2Pa^3b^2}{3EI(3a + b)^2}$

$\Delta_a \quad \left(\text{at point of load}\right) \quad \ldots = \dfrac{Pa^3b^3}{3EIl^3}$

$\Delta_x \quad \left(\text{when } x < a\right) \quad \ldots \ldots = \dfrac{Pb^2x^2}{6EIl^3}(3al - 3ax - bx)$

Note: For deflection calculations, use specified loads.

BEAM DIAGRAMS AND FORMULAE

Equivalent Tabular Load is the uniformly
distributed factored load given in the Beam Load Tables

---

18   CANTILEVER BEAM—LOAD INCREASING UNIFORMLY TO FIXED END

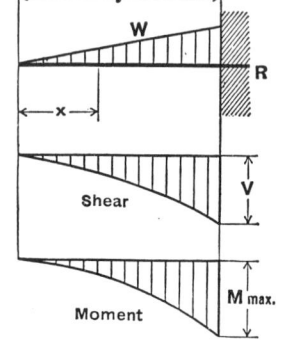

Equivalent Tabular Load $\ldots\ldots = \dfrac{8}{3} W$

$R = V \ldots\ldots\ldots\ldots = W$

$V_x \ldots\ldots\ldots\ldots = W \dfrac{x^2}{l^2}$

M max. $\left(\text{at fixed end}\right) \ldots\ldots = \dfrac{Wl}{3}$

$M_x \ldots\ldots\ldots\ldots = \dfrac{Wx^3}{3l^2}$

Δmax. $\left(\text{at free end}\right) \ldots\ldots = \dfrac{Wl^3}{15EI}$

$\Delta_x \ldots\ldots\ldots\ldots = \dfrac{W}{60EI\,l^2}(x^5 - 5l^4x + 4l^5)$

---

19   CANTILEVER BEAM—UNIFORMLY DISTRIBUTED LOAD

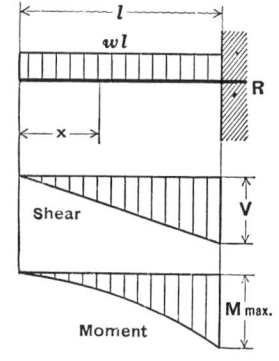

Equivalent Tabular Load $\ldots\ldots = 4wl$

$R = V \ldots\ldots\ldots\ldots = wl$

$V_x \ldots\ldots\ldots\ldots = wx$

M max. $\left(\text{at fixed end}\right) \ldots\ldots = \dfrac{wl^2}{2}$

$M_x \ldots\ldots\ldots\ldots = \dfrac{wx^2}{2}$

Δmax. $\left(\text{at free end}\right) \ldots\ldots = \dfrac{wl^4}{8EI}$

$\Delta_x \ldots\ldots\ldots\ldots = \dfrac{w}{24EI}(x^4 - 4l^3x + 3l^4)$

---

20   BEAM FIXED AT ONE END, FREE BUT GUIDED AT OTHER—UNIFORMLY DISTRIBUTED LOAD

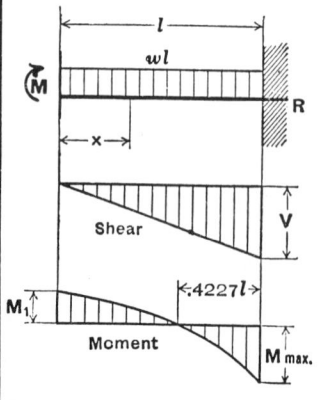

Equivalent Tabular Load $\ldots\ldots = \dfrac{8}{3} wl$

$R = V \ldots\ldots\ldots\ldots = wl$

$V_x \ldots\ldots\ldots\ldots = wx$

M max. $\left(\text{at fixed end}\right) \ldots\ldots = \dfrac{wl^2}{3}$

$M_1 \left(\text{at deflected end}\right) \ldots\ldots = \dfrac{wl^2}{6}$

$M_x \ldots\ldots\ldots\ldots = \dfrac{w}{6}(l^2 - 3x^2)$

Δmax. $\left(\text{at deflected end}\right) \ldots\ldots = \dfrac{wl^4}{24EI}$

$\Delta_x \ldots\ldots\ldots\ldots = \dfrac{w(l^2 - x^2)^2}{24EI}$

Note: For deflection calculations, use specified loads.

21   CANTILEVER BEAM—CONCENTRATED LOAD AT ANY POINT

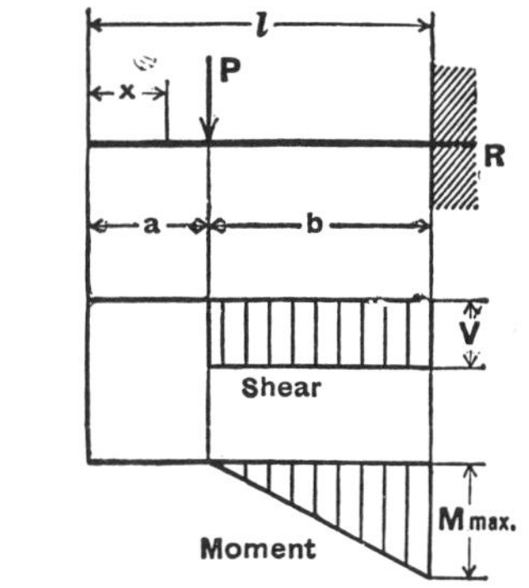

Equivalent Tabular Load $\dots = \dfrac{8Pb}{l}$

$R = V \left(\text{when } x < a\right) \dots = P$

$M \text{ max.} \left(\text{at fixed end}\right) \dots = Pb$

$M_x \left(\text{when } x > a\right) \dots = P(x - a)$

$\Delta \text{max.} \left(\text{at free end}\right) \dots = \dfrac{Pb^2}{6EI}(3l - b)$

$\Delta a \left(\text{at point of load}\right) \dots = \dfrac{Pb^3}{3EI}$

$\Delta x \left(\text{when } x < a\right) \dots = \dfrac{Pb^2}{6EI}(3l - 3x - b)$

$\Delta x \left(\text{when } x > a\right) \dots = \dfrac{P(l - x)^2}{6EI}(3b - l + x)$

Shear

Moment

22   CANTILEVER BEAM—CONCENTRATED LOAD AT FREE END

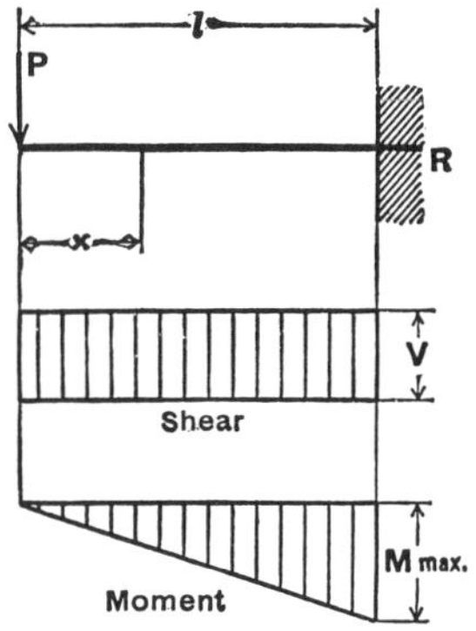

Equivalent Tabular Load $\dots = 8P$

$R = V \dots = P$

$M \text{ max.} \left(\text{at fixed end}\right) \dots = Pl$

$M_x \dots = Px$

$\Delta \text{max.} \left(\text{at free end}\right) \dots = \dfrac{Pl^3}{3EI}$

$\Delta x \dots = \dfrac{P}{6EI}(2l^3 - 3l^2x + x^3)$

Shear

Moment

23   BEAM FIXED AT ONE END, FREE BUT GUIDED AT OTHER— CONCENTRATED LOAD AT GUIDED END

Equivalent Tabular Load $\dots = 4P$

$R = V \dots = P$

$M \text{ max.} \left(\text{at both ends}\right) \dots = \dfrac{Pl}{2}$

$M_x \dots = P\left(\dfrac{l}{2} - x\right)$

$\Delta \text{max.} \left(\text{at deflected end}\right) \dots = \dfrac{Pl^3}{12EI}$

$\Delta x \dots = \dfrac{P(l - x)^2}{12EI}(l + 2x)$

Shear

Moment

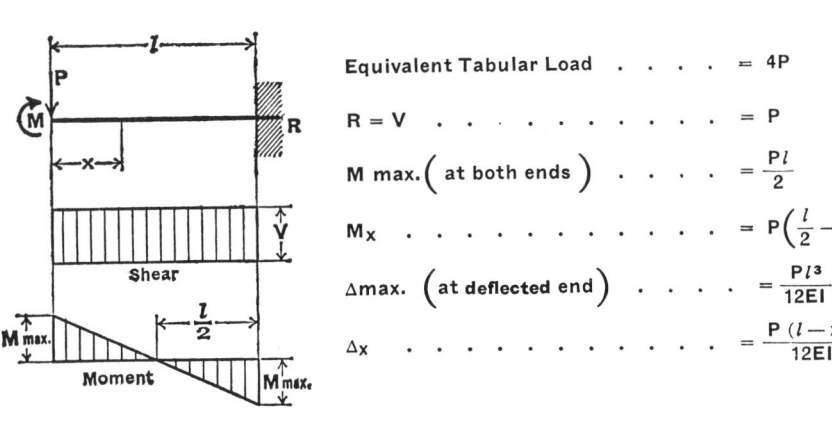

Note: For deflection calculations, use specified loads.

BEAM DIAGRAMS AND FORMULAE

Equivalent Tabular Load is the uniformly
distributed factored load given in the Beam Load Tables

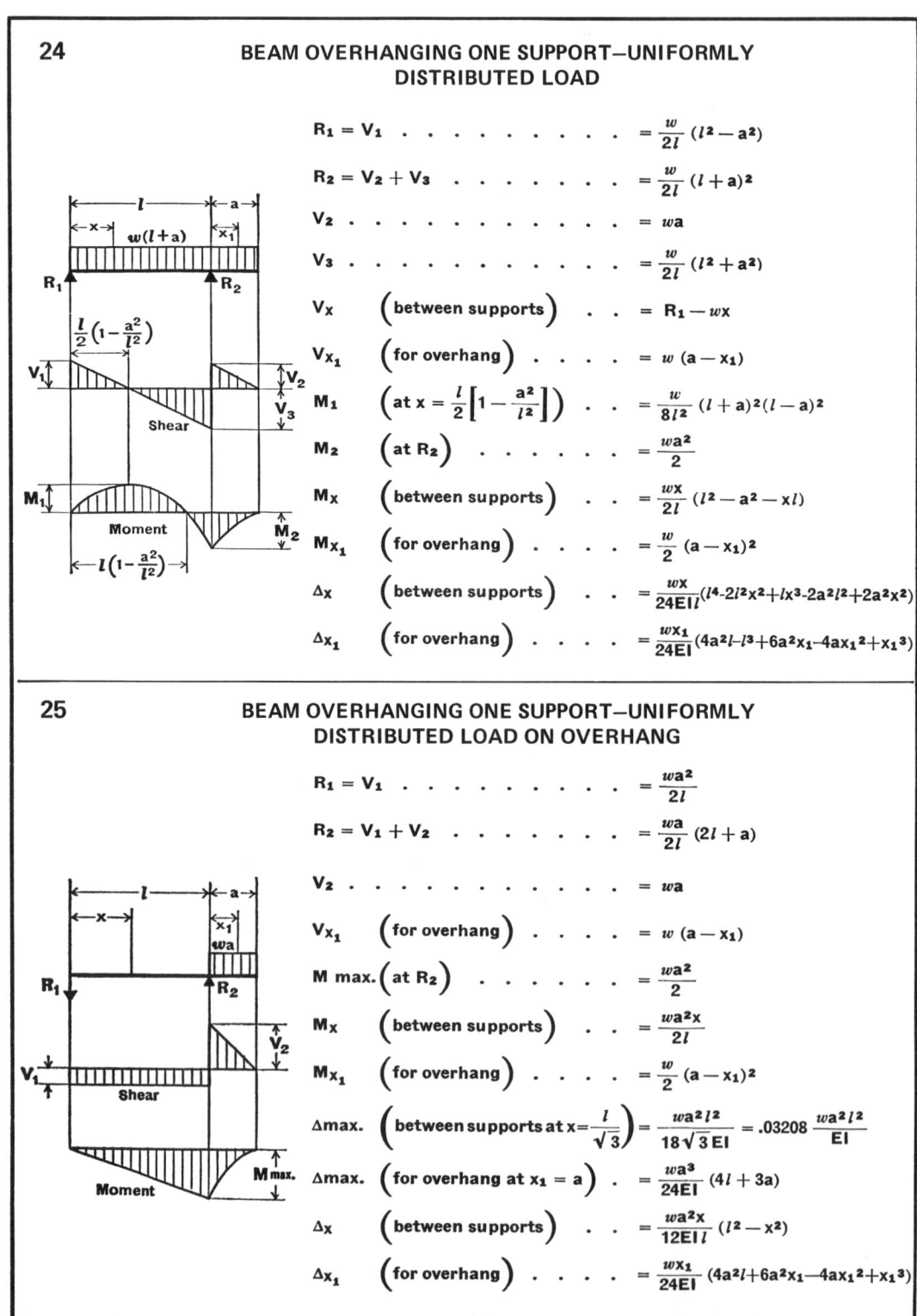

24   **BEAM OVERHANGING ONE SUPPORT—UNIFORMLY
DISTRIBUTED LOAD**

$R_1 = V_1$ . . . . $= \dfrac{w}{2l}(l^2 - a^2)$

$R_2 = V_2 + V_3$ . . . . $= \dfrac{w}{2l}(l + a)^2$

V_2 . . . . $= wa$

V_3 . . . . $= \dfrac{w}{2l}(l^2 + a^2)$

V_x $\left(\text{between supports}\right)$ . . $= R_1 - wx$

V_{x_1} $\left(\text{for overhang}\right)$ . . . . $= w(a - x_1)$

M_1 $\left(\text{at } x = \dfrac{l}{2}\left[1 - \dfrac{a^2}{l^2}\right]\right)$ . . $= \dfrac{w}{8l^2}(l + a)^2(l - a)^2$

M_2 $\left(\text{at } R_2\right)$ . . . . $= \dfrac{wa^2}{2}$

M_x $\left(\text{between supports}\right)$ . . $= \dfrac{wx}{2l}(l^2 - a^2 - xl)$

M_{x_1} $\left(\text{for overhang}\right)$ . . . . $= \dfrac{w}{2}(a - x_1)^2$

Δ_x $\left(\text{between supports}\right)$ . . $= \dfrac{wx}{24EIl}(l^4 - 2l^2x^2 + lx^3 - 2a^2l^2 + 2a^2x^2)$

Δ_{x_1} $\left(\text{for overhang}\right)$ . . . . $= \dfrac{wx_1}{24EI}(4a^2l - l^3 + 6a^2x_1 - 4ax_1^2 + x_1^3)$

---

25   **BEAM OVERHANGING ONE SUPPORT—UNIFORMLY
DISTRIBUTED LOAD ON OVERHANG**

$R_1 = V_1$ . . . . $= \dfrac{wa^2}{2l}$

$R_2 = V_1 + V_2$ . . . . $= \dfrac{wa}{2l}(2l + a)$

V_2 . . . . $= wa$

V_{x_1} $\left(\text{for overhang}\right)$ . . . . $= w(a - x_1)$

M max. $\left(\text{at } R_2\right)$ . . . . . . $= \dfrac{wa^2}{2}$

M_x $\left(\text{between supports}\right)$ . . $= \dfrac{wa^2x}{2l}$

M_{x_1} $\left(\text{for overhang}\right)$ . . . . $= \dfrac{w}{2}(a - x_1)^2$

Δmax. $\left(\text{between supports at } x = \dfrac{l}{\sqrt{3}}\right) = \dfrac{wa^2l^2}{18\sqrt{3}EI} = .03208\dfrac{wa^2l^2}{EI}$

Δmax. $\left(\text{for overhang at } x_1 = a\right)$. $= \dfrac{wa^3}{24EI}(4l + 3a)$

Δ_x $\left(\text{between supports}\right)$ . . $= \dfrac{wa^2x}{12EIl}(l^2 - x^2)$

Δ_{x_1} $\left(\text{for overhang}\right)$ . . . . $= \dfrac{wx_1}{24EI}(4a^2l + 6a^2x_1 - 4ax_1^2 + x_1^3)$

Note: For deflection calculations, use specified loads.

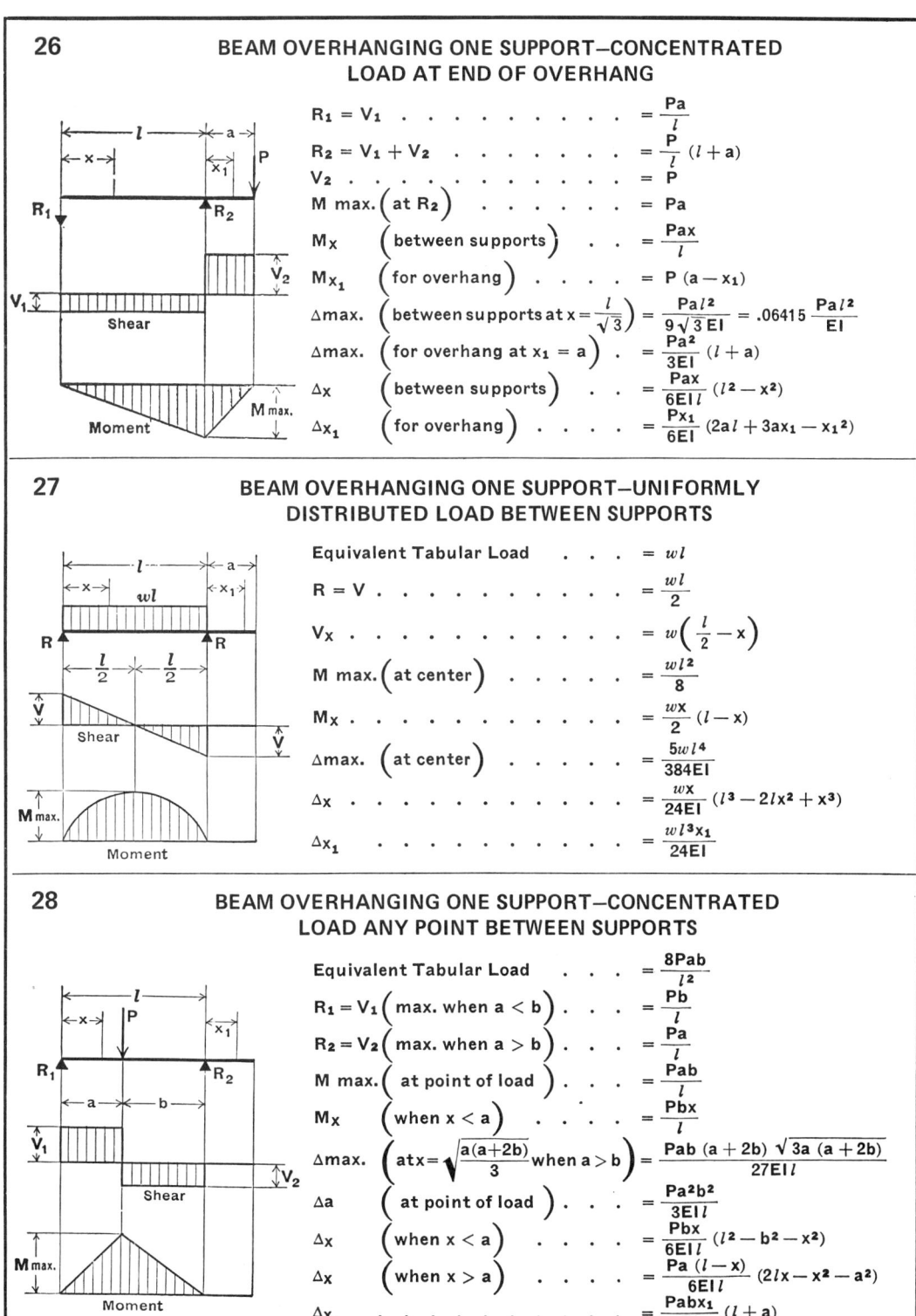

26   **BEAM OVERHANGING ONE SUPPORT—CONCENTRATED LOAD AT END OF OVERHANG**

$R_1 = V_1$ . . . . $= \dfrac{Pa}{l}$

$R_2 = V_1 + V_2$ . . . . $= \dfrac{P}{l}(l + a)$

V_2 . . . . $= P$

M max. $\left(\text{at } R_2\right)$ . . . . . . $= Pa$

M_x $\left(\text{between supports}\right)$ . . $= \dfrac{Pax}{l}$

M_{x_1} $\left(\text{for overhang}\right)$ . . . . $= P(a - x_1)$

Δmax. $\left(\text{between supports at } x = \dfrac{l}{\sqrt{3}}\right) = \dfrac{Pal^2}{9\sqrt{3}\,EI} = .06415\dfrac{Pal^2}{EI}$

Δmax. $\left(\text{for overhang at } x_1 = a\right)$. $= \dfrac{Pa^2}{3EI}(l + a)$

Δ_x $\left(\text{between supports}\right)$ . . $= \dfrac{Pax}{6EIl}(l^2 - x^2)$

Δ_{x_1} $\left(\text{for overhang}\right)$ . . . . $= \dfrac{Px_1}{6EI}(2al + 3ax_1 - x_1^2)$

27   **BEAM OVERHANGING ONE SUPPORT—UNIFORMLY DISTRIBUTED LOAD BETWEEN SUPPORTS**

Equivalent Tabular Load . . . . $= wl$

$R = V$ . . . . $= \dfrac{wl}{2}$

V_x . . . . $= w\left(\dfrac{l}{2} - x\right)$

M max. $\left(\text{at center}\right)$ . . . . . $= \dfrac{wl^2}{8}$

M_x . . . . $= \dfrac{wx}{2}(l - x)$

Δmax. $\left(\text{at center}\right)$ . . . . . $= \dfrac{5wl^4}{384EI}$

Δ_x . . . . $= \dfrac{wx}{24EI}(l^3 - 2lx^2 + x^3)$

Δ_{x_1} . . . . $= \dfrac{wl^3x_1}{24EI}$

28   **BEAM OVERHANGING ONE SUPPORT—CONCENTRATED LOAD ANY POINT BETWEEN SUPPORTS**

Equivalent Tabular Load . . . . $= \dfrac{8Pab}{l^2}$

$R_1 = V_1\left(\text{max. when } a < b\right)$ . . . $= \dfrac{Pb}{l}$

$R_2 = V_2\left(\text{max. when } a > b\right)$ . . . $= \dfrac{Pa}{l}$

M max. $\left(\text{at point of load}\right)$ . . . $= \dfrac{Pab}{l}$

M_x $\left(\text{when } x < a\right)$ . . . . $= \dfrac{Pbx}{l}$

Δmax. $\left(\text{at } x = \sqrt{\dfrac{a(a+2b)}{3}}\text{ when } a > b\right) = \dfrac{Pab(a + 2b)\sqrt{3a(a + 2b)}}{27EIl}$

Δa $\left(\text{at point of load}\right)$ . . . $= \dfrac{Pa^2b^2}{3EIl}$

Δ_x $\left(\text{when } x < a\right)$ . . . . $= \dfrac{Pbx}{6EIl}(l^2 - b^2 - x^2)$

Δ_x $\left(\text{when } x > a\right)$ . . . . $= \dfrac{Pa(l - x)}{6EIl}(2lx - x^2 - a^2)$

Δ_{x_1} . . . . $= \dfrac{Pabx_1}{6EIl}(l + a)$

Note: For deflection calculations, use specified loads.

BEAM DIAGRAMS AND FORMULAE

Equivalent Tabular Load is the uniformly
distributed factored load given in the Beam Load Tables

---

29   BEAM—UNIFORMLY DISTRIBUTED LOAD AND VARIABLE END MOMENTS

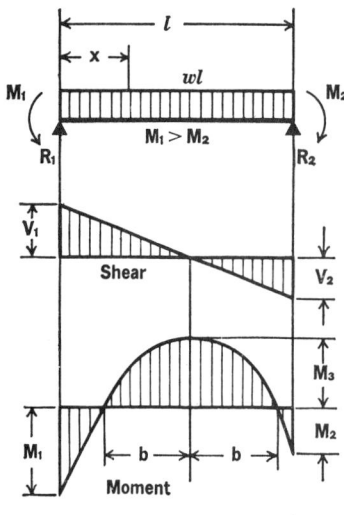

$$R_1 = V_1 = \frac{wl}{2} + \frac{M_1 - M_2}{l}$$

$$R_2 = V_2 = \frac{wl}{2} - \frac{M_1 - M_2}{l}$$

$$V_x = w\left(\frac{l}{2} - x\right) + \frac{M_1 - M_2}{l}$$

$$M_3 \left(\text{at } x = \frac{l}{2} + \frac{M_1 - M_2}{wl}\right)$$

$$= \frac{wl^2}{8} - \frac{M_1 + M_2}{2} + \frac{(M_1 - M_2)^2}{2wl^2}$$

$$M_x = \frac{wx}{2}(l - x) + \left(\frac{M_1 - M_2}{l}\right)x - M_1$$

$$b\left(\begin{array}{l}\text{To locate}\\ \text{inflection points}\end{array}\right) = \sqrt{\frac{l^2}{4} - \left(\frac{M_1 + M_2}{w}\right) + \left(\frac{M_1 - M_2}{wl}\right)^2}$$

$$\Delta_x = \frac{wx}{24EI}\left[x^3 - \left(2l + \frac{4M_1}{wl} - \frac{4M_2}{wl}\right)x^2 + \frac{12M_1}{w}x + l^3 - \frac{8M_1 l}{w} - \frac{4M_2 l}{w}\right]$$

---

30   BEAM—CONCENTRATED LOAD AT CENTER AND VARIABLE END MOMENTS

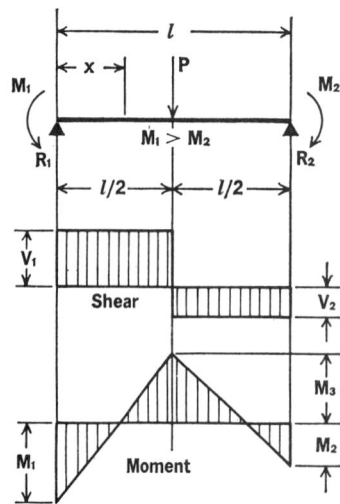

$$R_1 = V_1 = \frac{P}{2} + \frac{M_1 - M_2}{l}$$

$$R_2 = V_2 = \frac{P}{2} - \frac{M_1 - M_2}{l}$$

$$M_3 \text{ (At center)} = \frac{Pl}{4} - \frac{M_1 + M_2}{2}$$

$$M_x \left(\text{When } x < \frac{l}{2}\right) = \left(\frac{P}{2} + \frac{M_1 - M_2}{l}\right)x - M_1$$

$$M_x \left(\text{When } x > \frac{l}{2}\right) = \frac{P}{2}(l - x) + \frac{(M_1 - M_2)x}{l} - M_1$$

$$\Delta_x \left(\text{When } x < \frac{l}{2}\right) = \frac{Px}{48EI}\left(3l^2 - 4x^2 - \frac{8(l - x)}{Pl}[M_1(2l - x) + M_2(l + x)]\right)$$

Note: For deflection calculations, use specified loads.

---

31   SIMPLE BEAM—ONE CONCENTRATED MOVING LOAD

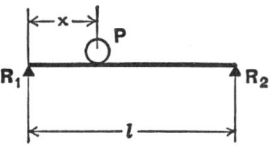

$$R_1 \text{ max.} = V_1 \text{ max.} \left(\text{at } x = 0 \right) \quad \ldots \ldots = P$$

$$M \text{ max.} \left(\text{at point of load, when } x = \frac{l}{2} \right) \quad . \quad = \frac{Pl}{4}$$

---

32   SIMPLE BEAM—TWO EQUAL CONCENTRATED MOVING
LOADS

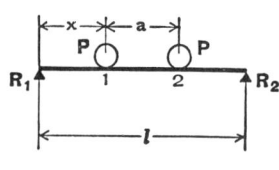

$$R_1 \text{ max.} = V_1 \text{ max.} \left(\text{at } x = 0 \right) \quad \ldots \ldots = P \left(2 - \frac{a}{l} \right)$$

$$M \text{ max.} \begin{cases} \left[\begin{array}{l} \text{when } a < (2 - \sqrt{2})\, l = .586l \\ \text{under load 1 at } x = \frac{1}{2} \left(l - \frac{a}{2} \right) \end{array} \right] = \frac{P}{2l} \left(l - \frac{a}{2} \right)^2 \\[4ex] \left[\begin{array}{l} \text{when } a > (2 - \sqrt{2})\, l = .586l \\ \text{with one load at center of span} \\ \text{(case 31)} \end{array} \right] = \frac{Pl}{4} \end{cases}$$

---

33   SIMPLE BEAM—TWO UNEQUAL CONCENTRATED MOVING
LOADS

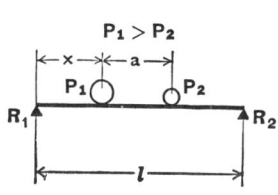

$$R_1 \text{ max.} = V_1 \text{ max.} \left(\text{at } x = 0 \right) \quad \ldots \ldots = P_1 + P_2 \frac{l - a}{l}$$

$$M \text{ max.} \begin{cases} \left[\text{under } P_1, \text{ at } x = \frac{1}{2} \left(l - \frac{P_2 a}{P_1 + P_2} \right) \right] = \left(P_1 + P_2 \right) \frac{x^2}{l} \\[3ex] \left[\begin{array}{l} \text{M max. may occur with larger} \\ \text{load at center of span and other} \\ \text{load off span (case 31)} \end{array} \right] = \frac{P_1 l}{4} \end{cases}$$

GENERAL RULES FOR SIMPLE BEAMS CARRYING MOVING
CONCENTRATED LOADS

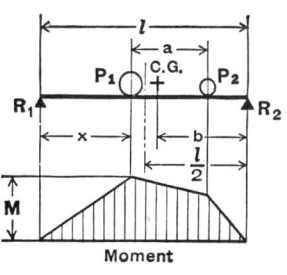

The maximum shear due to moving concentrated loads occurs at one support when one of the loads is at that support. With several moving loads, the location that will produce maximum shear must be determined by trial.

The maximum bending moment produced by moving concentrated loads occurs under one of the loads when that load is as far from one support as the center of gravity of all the moving loads on the beam is from the other support.

In the accompanying diagram, the maximum bending moment occurs under load P_1 when $x = b$. It should also be noted that this condition occurs when the center line of the span is midway between the center of gravity of loads and the nearest concentrated load.

Note: For deflection calculations, use specified loads.

BEAM DIAGRAMS AND FORMULAE

Equivalent Tabular Load is the uniformly
distributed factored load given in the Beam Load Tables

34

CONTINUOUS BEAM—TWO EQUAL SPANS—UNIFORM LOAD ON ONE SPAN

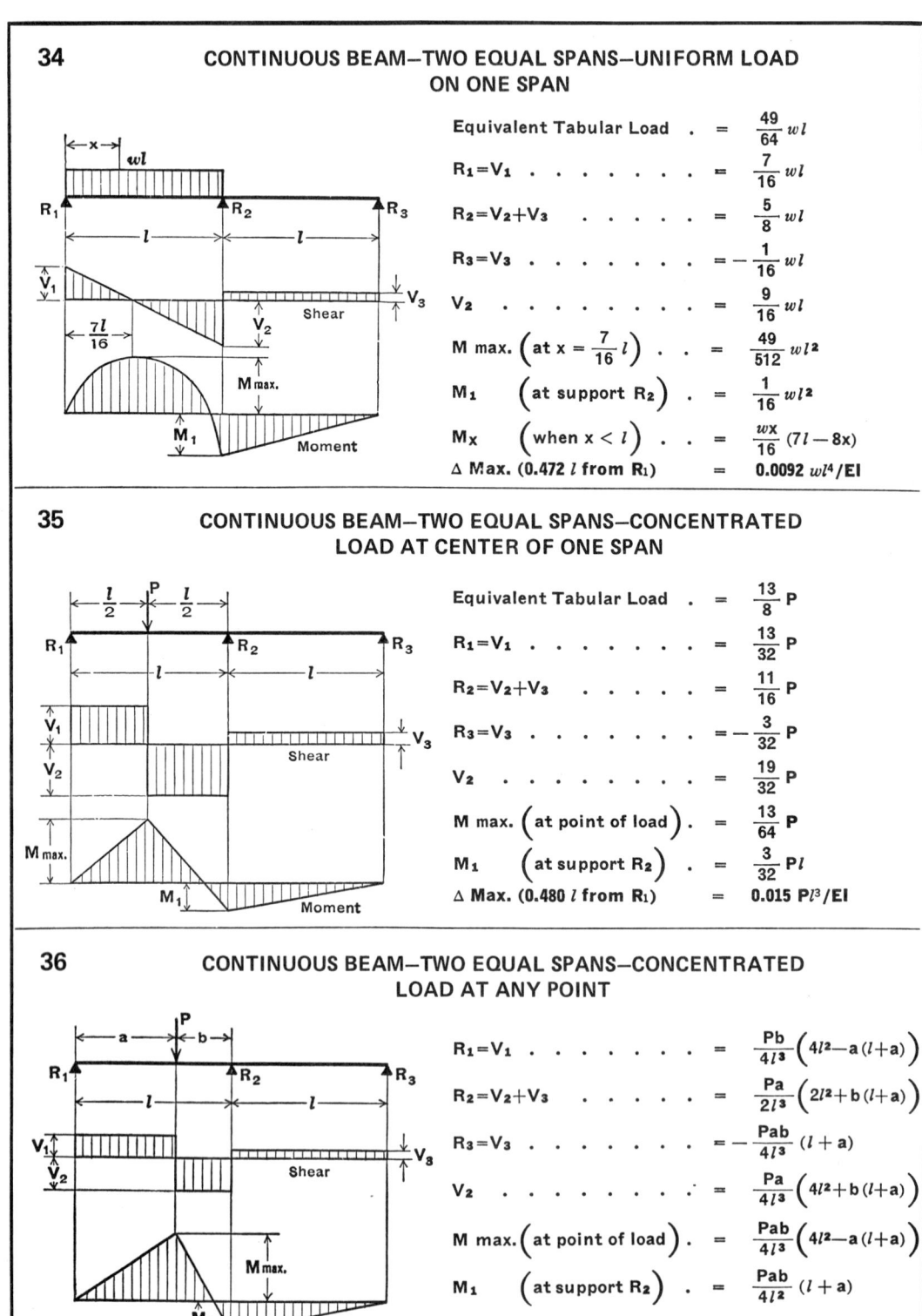

Equivalent Tabular Load $\quad = \dfrac{49}{64}\,wl$

$R_1 = V_1 \quad \ldots \ldots \ldots \ldots = \dfrac{7}{16}\,wl$

$R_2 = V_2 + V_3 \quad \ldots \ldots = \dfrac{5}{8}\,wl$

$R_3 = V_3 \quad \ldots \ldots \ldots \ldots = -\dfrac{1}{16}\,wl$

$V_2 \quad \ldots \ldots \ldots \ldots = \dfrac{9}{16}\,wl$

$M \text{ max.} \left(\text{at } x = \dfrac{7}{16}\,l\right) \ldots = \dfrac{49}{512}\,wl^2$

$M_1 \quad \left(\text{at support } R_2\right) \ldots = \dfrac{1}{16}\,wl^2$

$M_x \quad \left(\text{when } x < l\right) \ldots = \dfrac{wx}{16}\,(7l - 8x)$

$\Delta \text{ Max. (0.472 } l \text{ from } R_1) \quad = \mathbf{0.0092}\ wl^4/\mathbf{EI}$

35

CONTINUOUS BEAM—TWO EQUAL SPANS—CONCENTRATED LOAD AT CENTER OF ONE SPAN

Equivalent Tabular Load $\quad = \dfrac{13}{8}\,P$

$R_1 = V_1 \quad \ldots \ldots \ldots \ldots = \dfrac{13}{32}\,P$

$R_2 = V_2 + V_3 \quad \ldots \ldots = \dfrac{11}{16}\,P$

$R_3 = V_3 \quad \ldots \ldots \ldots \ldots = -\dfrac{3}{32}\,P$

$V_2 \quad \ldots \ldots \ldots \ldots = \dfrac{19}{32}\,P$

$M \text{ max.} \left(\text{at point of load}\right) = \dfrac{13}{64}\,P$

$M_1 \quad \left(\text{at support } R_2\right) \ldots = \dfrac{3}{32}\,Pl$

$\Delta \text{ Max. (0.480 } l \text{ from } R_1) \quad = \mathbf{0.015}\ Pl^3/\mathbf{EI}$

36

CONTINUOUS BEAM—TWO EQUAL SPANS—CONCENTRATED LOAD AT ANY POINT

$R_1 = V_1 \quad \ldots \ldots \ldots \ldots = \dfrac{Pb}{4l^3}\left(4l^2 - a(l+a)\right)$

$R_2 = V_2 + V_3 \quad \ldots \ldots = \dfrac{Pa}{2l^3}\left(2l^2 + b(l+a)\right)$

$R_3 = V_3 \quad \ldots \ldots \ldots \ldots = -\dfrac{Pab}{4l^3}\,(l+a)$

$V_2 \quad \ldots \ldots \ldots \ldots = \dfrac{Pa}{4l^3}\left(4l^2 + b(l+a)\right)$

$M \text{ max.} \left(\text{at point of load}\right) = \dfrac{Pab}{4l^3}\left(4l^2 - a(l+a)\right)$

$M_1 \quad \left(\text{at support } R_2\right) \ldots = \dfrac{Pab}{4l^2}\,(l+a)$

Note: For deflection calculations, use specified loads.

Moment = Coefficient x W x L
Reaction = Coefficient x W
Where: W = Total uniformly distributed load on one span
L = Length of one span

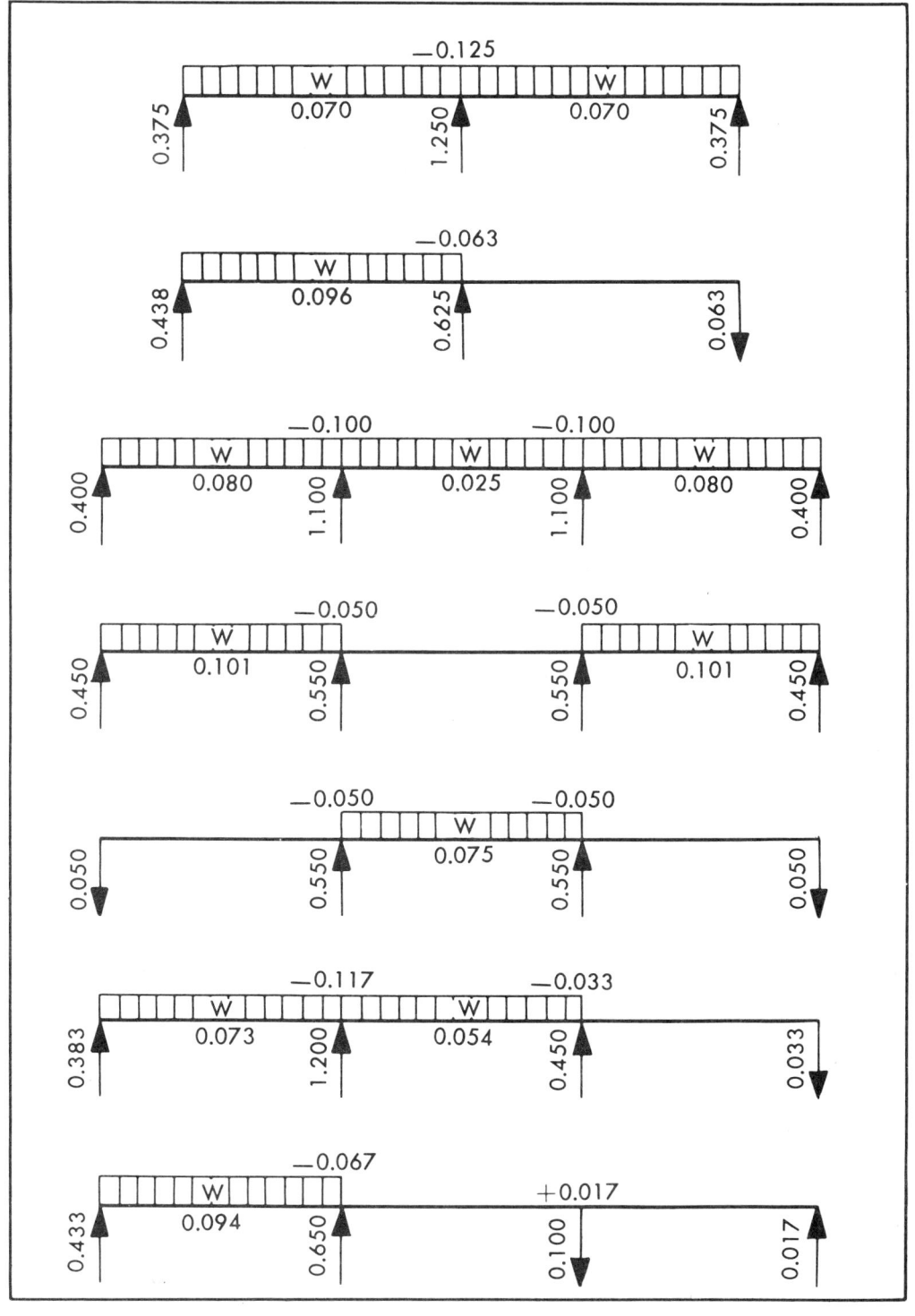

MOMENTS, REACTIONS
Equal Span Continuous Beams
UNIFORMLY DISTRIBUTED LOADS

Moment = Coefficient x W x L
Reaction = Coefficient x W
Where: W = Total uniformly distributed load on one span
          L = Length of one span

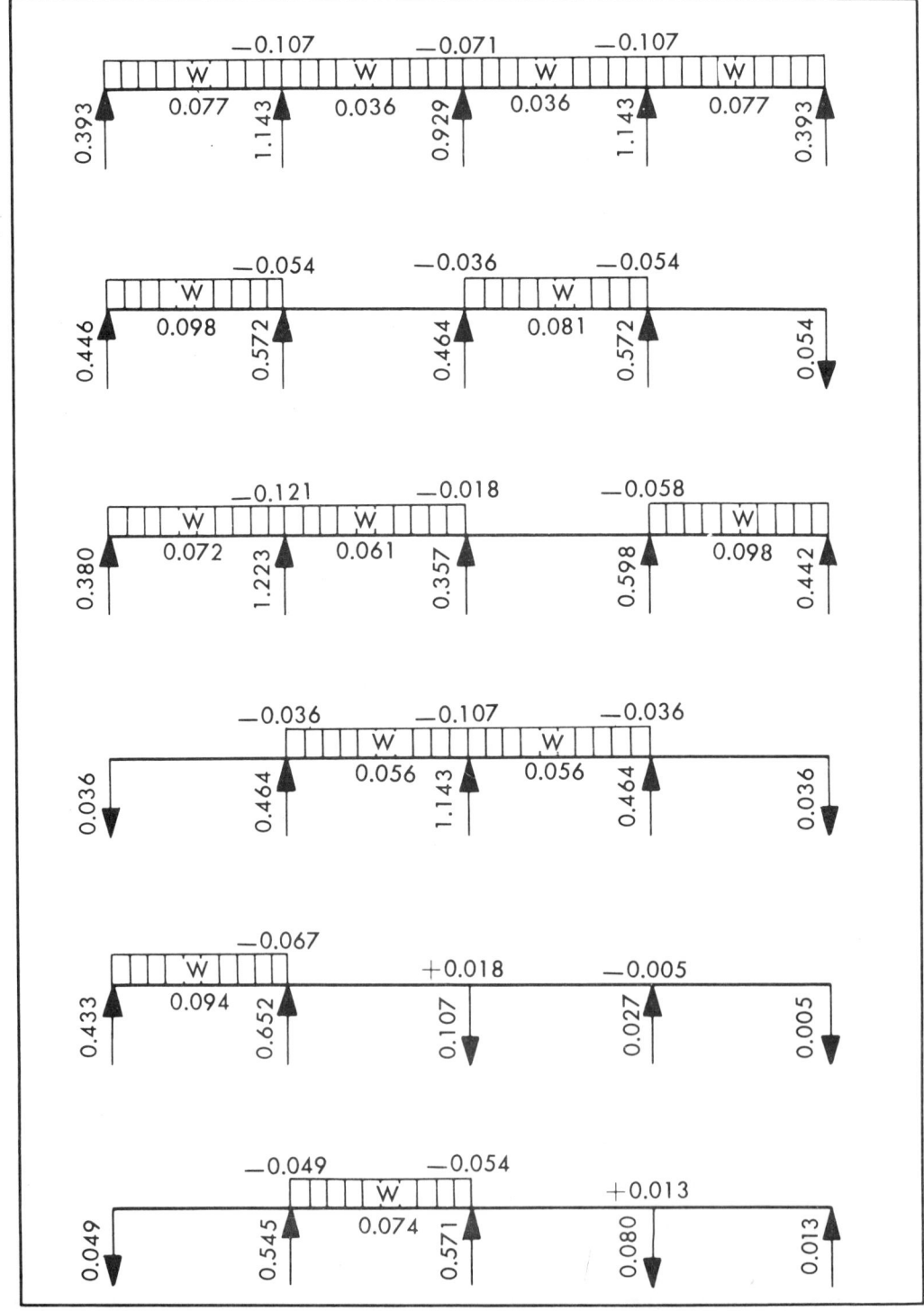

MOMENTS, REACTIONS
Equal Span Continuous Beams
CENTRAL POINT LOADS

Moment = Coefficient x W x L
Reaction = Coefficient x W
Where: W = The concentrated load on one span
       L = Length of one span

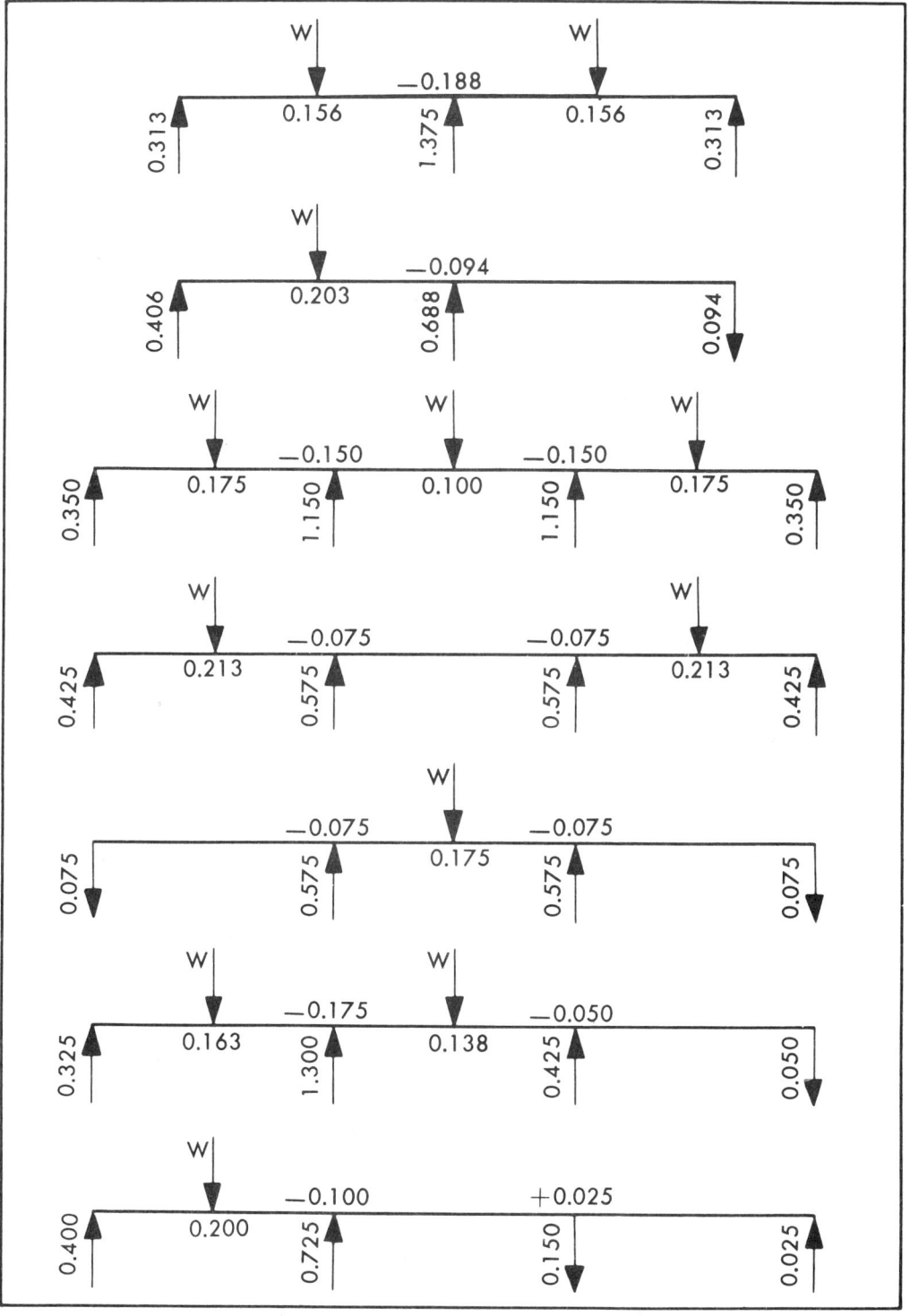

MOMENTS, REACTIONS
Equal Span Continuous Beams
CENTRAL POINT LOADS

Moment = Coefficient x W x L
Reaction = Coefficient x W
Where: W = The concentrated load on one span
       L = Length of one span

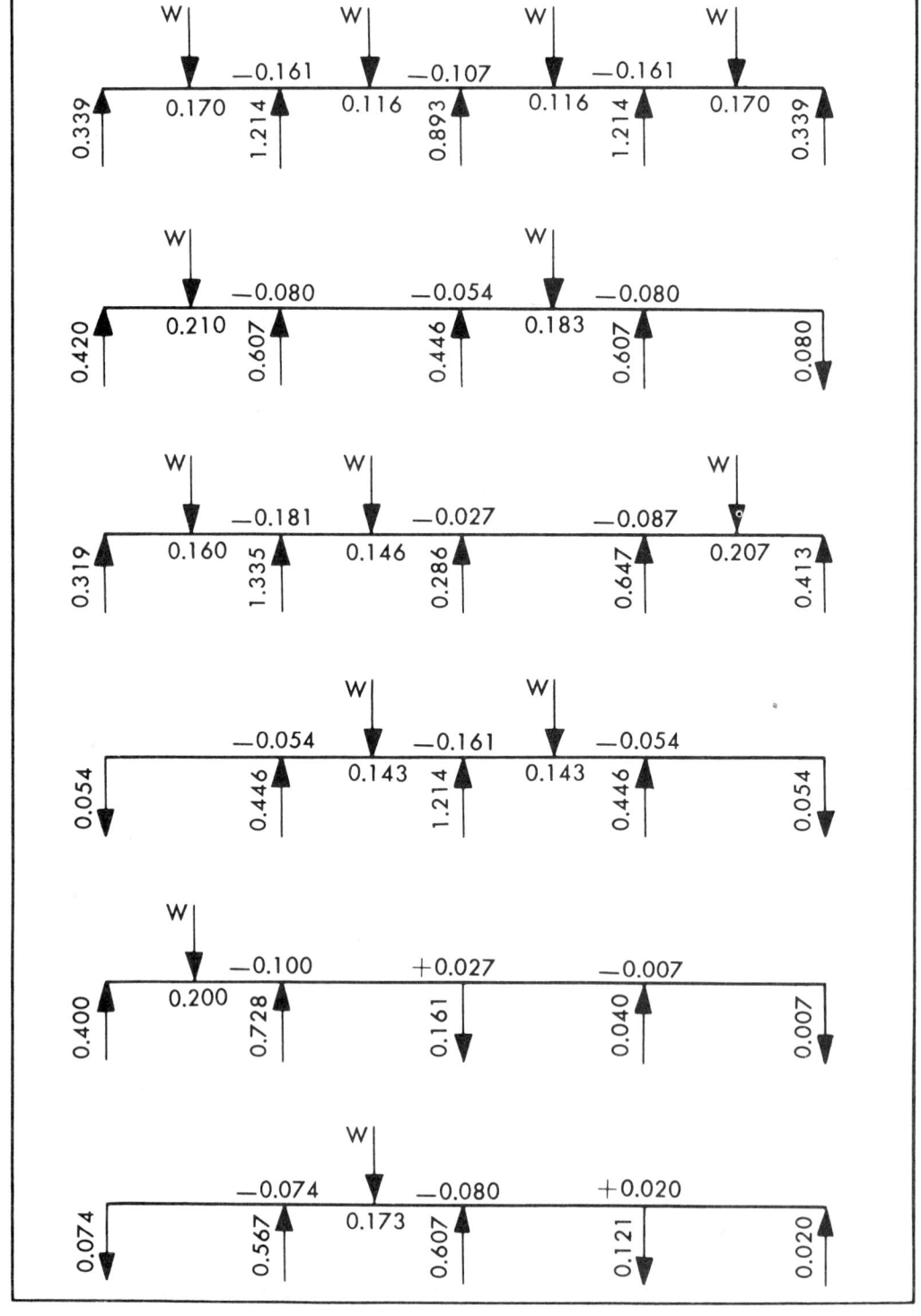

MOMENTS, REACTIONS
Equal Span Continuous Beams

POINT LOADS AT THIRD POINTS OF SPAN

Moment = Coefficient x W x L
Reaction = Coefficient x W
Where: W = The total load on one span
L = Length of one span

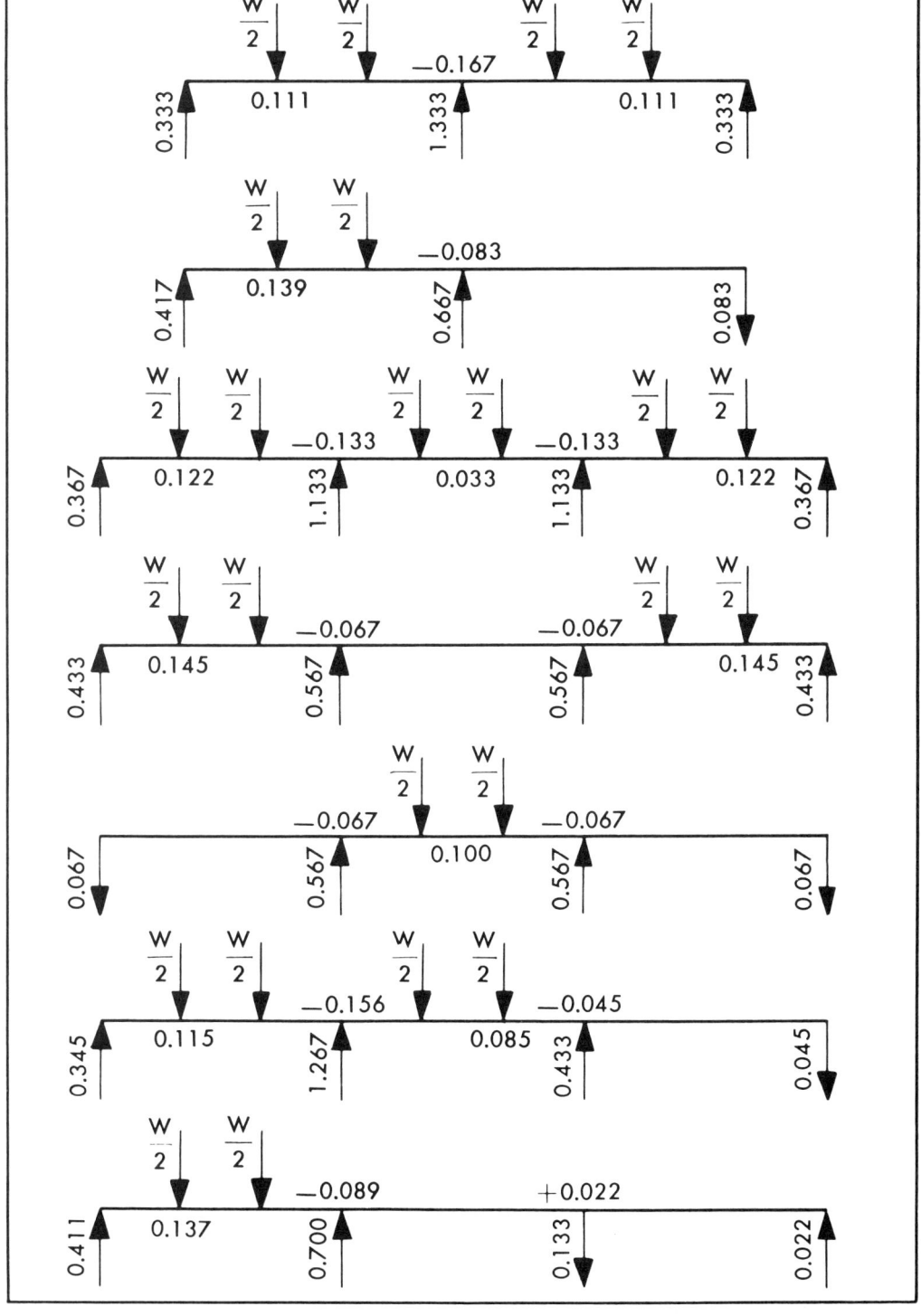

MOMENTS, REACTIONS
Equal Span Continuous Beams

POINT LOADS AT THIRD POINTS OF SPAN

Moment = Coefficient x W x L
Reaction = Coefficient x W
Where: W = The total load on one span
L = Length of one span

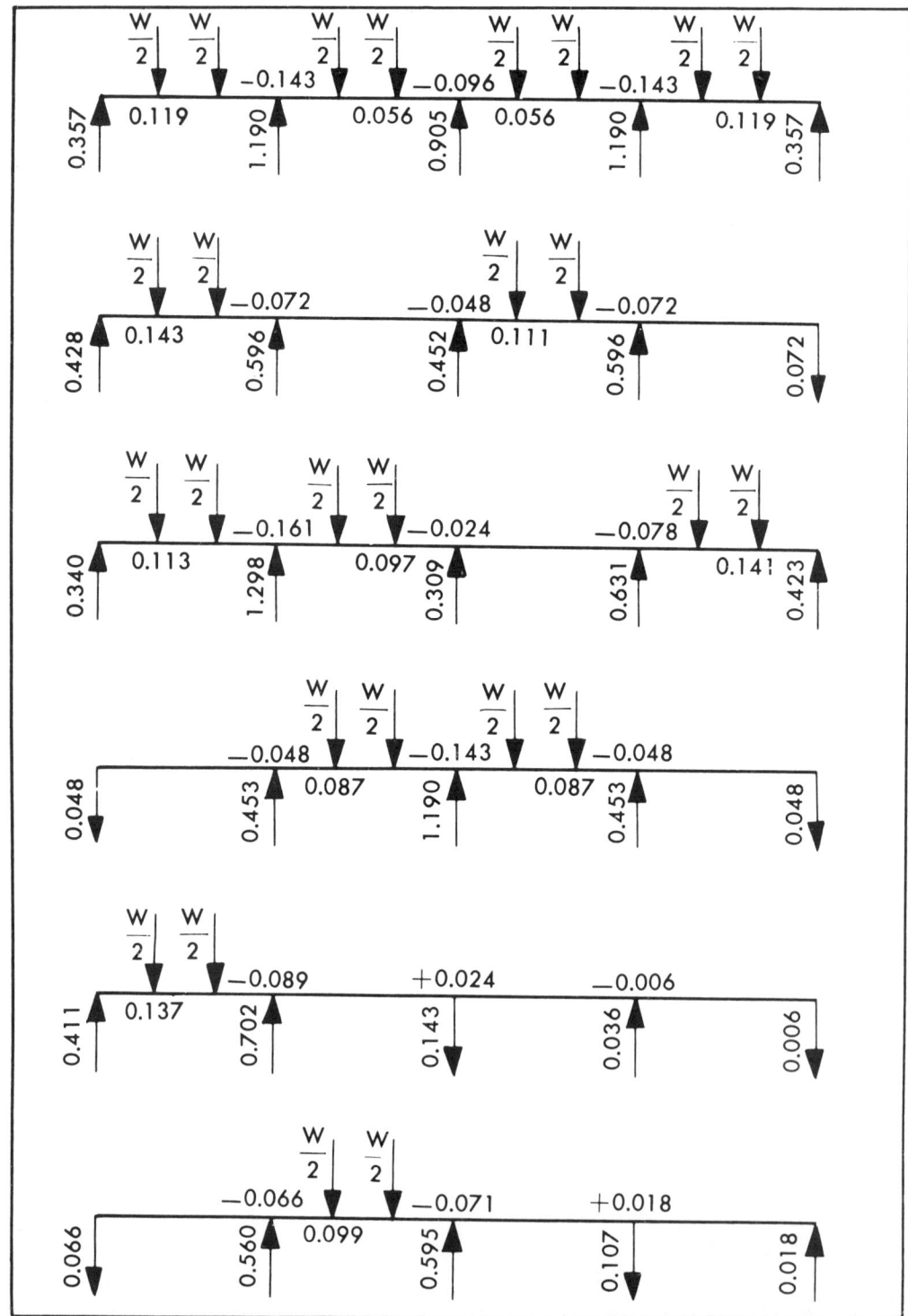

BEAM BEARING PLATES

When a flexural member is supported by a masonry wall or pier, the beam reaction must be distributed over an area sufficient in size to keep from exceeding the bearing capacity of the masonry or concrete. Steel bearing plates generally are used for this purpose.

Traditional practice has been to limit the bearing pressure to the allowable limits set in the various structural design standards in order to size the bearing plate. With the introduction of CSA Standard S16.1—1974 "Steel Structures for Buildings — Limit States Design" allowable stresses for steel members were replaced by factored member resistances.

The design chart, Figure 5—2, on page 5—153 provides a graphical means of determining the minimum thickness of bearing plates for beams having no web stiffeners over the bearing plate. The following assumptions are made:

1. The beam reaction, R, is uniformly distributed upon the bearing plate over an area, the width of which is 2k;

2. The bearing pressure between the concrete or masonry support and the bearing plate is uniform over the area of the plate;

3. The bearing plate projecting beyond a distance k from the centre line of the beam web acts as a cantilever subjected to the calculated bearing pressure. (This assumption does not take into account any bending resistance of the beam flange, since in practice the flange may be slightly "curled" thus making the degree of additional bending resistance difficult to evaluate).

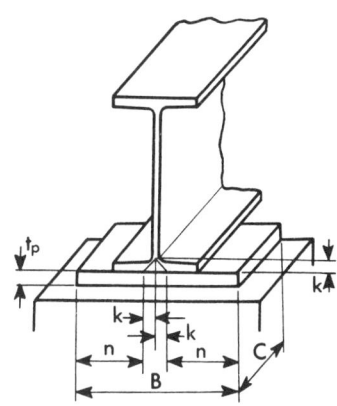

Where F_y = specified minimum yield point of the bearing plate steel, megapascals;

A = B x C = Area of plate, square millimetres;

t_p = Required thickness of bearing plate, millimetres;

k = Distance from outer face of beam flange to web toe of fillet, millimetres;

n = Distance ½B-k, millimetres;

b = Width of beam flange, millimetres;

Design Chart

Figure 5—2 shows the minimum thickness of bearing plate, t_p, for unit factored bearing resistance, B_r/A, from 1 to 20 MPa and length of cantilever arm, n, from 30 to 300 mm, for G40.21-M grade 300W steel.

$$t_p = \sqrt{\frac{2\, B_r\, n^2}{A\, \phi\, F_y}}$$

This formula was derived by equating the factored moment acting on the portion of the plate taken as a cantilever to the factored moment resistance of the plate, (M_r = $\phi Z F_y$), and solving for the plate thickness, t_p.

In addition, in order to minimize deflection of the bearing plate, the thickness generally should not be less than approximately ⅕ of the overhang $\frac{B\text{-}b}{2}$; that is $t_p \geqslant (B\text{-}b)/10$.

Use

1. Determine the required area

   A = Reaction of beam due to factored loads divided by the unit factored bearing resistance. The unit factored bearing resistance for concrete is assumed to be $0.85\ \phi_c f'_c$ where $\phi_c = 0.63$ in bearing. (ϕ_c has been adjusted from that given in CSA A23.3—1973 to account for the different load factors used in A23.3 and S16.1).

2. Determine C and solve for B. (The length of bearing C usually is governed by the available wall thickness or some other structural consideration);

3. Determine n and enter Figure 5—2 to determine t_p

Example

Given:

A W610 × 140 has an end reaction, under factored load, of 850 kN. One end of the beam rests on a concrete pier with a 28 day compressive strength of 20 MPa. The length of bearing, C, is limited to 300 mm. Design the bearing plate for G40.21-M grade 300W steel.

Solution:

Unit factored bearing resistance of concrete
$$= 0.85\ \phi_c f'_c = 0.85 \times 0.63 \times 20 = 10.7\ \text{MPa}$$

$$\text{Area required} = \frac{850 \times 10^3}{10.7} = 79\ 400\ \text{mm}^2$$

$$\text{Therefore required B} = \frac{79\ 400}{300} = 265\ \text{mm} - \text{Use 270 mm}$$

For a W610 × 140, b = 230 mm, k = 41 mm, w = 13.1 mm

n = (B/2) − k = (270/2) − 41 = 94 mm

From Figure 5—2, for unit factored bearing resistance = 10.7 MPa and n = 94 mm select t_p of 30 mm.

Use plate 30 × 300 × 270

Check for web crippling on length C + k,

$B_r = 1.25\ \phi\ w\ (N + k)\ F_{yb}$ (Clause 15.8(b), CAN3-S16.1-M78) (N = C)

$\qquad = 1.25 \times 0.9 \times 13.1\ (300 + 41)\ 300\ \text{MPa}$

$\qquad = 1\ 510\ 000\ \text{N} = 1\ 510\ \text{kN} > 850\ \text{kN} - \text{OK}$

SPECIAL CASE

In cases where the bearing capacity of the material upon which the bearing plate rests is given only in allowable stress terms. Figure 5—2, can still be used as follows:

1. Divide the allowable stress of the material by the approximate ratio of specified to factored load determined from Table 3—1, page 3—4 for the appropriate dead to live load ratio.

2. Then proceed as outlined previously, but use stress obtained in step 1 above.

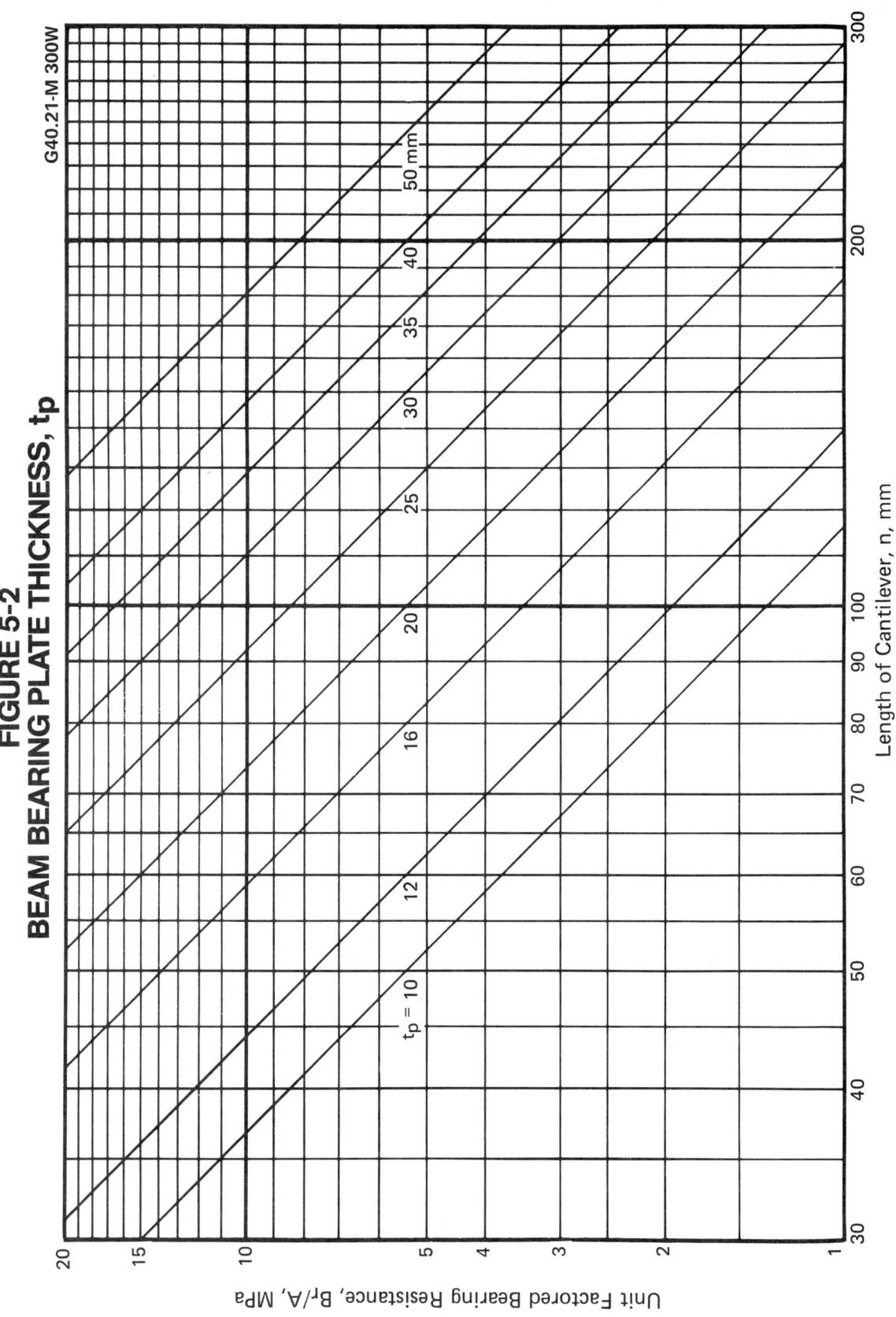

FIGURE 5-2
BEAM BEARING PLATE THICKNESS, t_p

G40.21-M 300W

$t_p = 10$ 12   16   20   25   30   35   40   50 mm

Length of Cantilever, n, mm

Unit Factored Bearing Resistance, B_r/A, MPa

Example

Given:

A W610 × 140 has an end reaction of 360 kN due to factored loads. One end of the beam rests on a masonry wall for which the allowable bearing stress is 1.78 MPa. The length of bearing is limited to 300 mm and the bearing plate will be from G40.21-M grade 300W steel. The dead-to-live load ratio is 1.0.

Solution:

From Table 3-1, page 3-4, for D/L = 1.0, approximate specified/factored load ratio is 0.727 (α_D = 1.25)

Unit factored bearing resistance = 1.78/0.727 = 2.45 MPa

$$\text{Area required} = \frac{360 \times 10^3}{2.45} = 147\ 000 \text{ mm}^2$$

$$\text{Compute B} = \frac{147\ 000}{300} = 490 \text{ mm}$$

$$n = \frac{490}{2} - 41 = 209 \text{ mm}$$

From Figure 5-2, for unit factored bearing resistance = 2.45 MPa, and n = 209 mm, select t_p = 30 mm.

General

Bearing plates are generally set in place and grouted level at the required elevation prior to positioning the beam in place. Since they facilitate erection, beam bearing plates are useful even when the flange of the beam has sufficient bearing area to distribute adequately the reaction.

Generally, some form of anchorage is used to ensure that the beam will not pull away longitudinally from the pier or wall or be subject to uplift.

One method is to weld or bolt angles or a plate to the end of the beam.

BEAMS WITH WEB HOLES

General

Most structures support a variety of piping, ducting, conduit, etc. and efforts to reduce floor heights have led to these items being placed in the same plane as the structural floor members. Structural systems, such as stub girders, trusses and open web steel joists all provide openings for structural/mechanical integration; however, when beams with solid webs are used it is sometimes necessary to cut openings in the webs. The following section describes a method whereby these openings can be accounted for in the design of the member.

Recent research work is summarized by Redwood and Shrivastava in "Design Recommendation for Steel Beams with Web Holes". The material presented in this part of the Handbook is based on that paper.

If it becomes necessary to cut holes in beam webs after construction is complete, special precautions may be required.

Design

The formulas are applicable for beams of Class 1 and Class 2 sections with openings between 0.3 and 0.7 times the depth of the beam with the hole length up to three times the hole height. The steel should meet the requirements of Clause 8.5(a) of CAN3-S16.1-M78 and exhibit the characteristics necessary to achieve moment redistribution, such as G40.21-M grade 300W.

The hole corner should have a radius at least equal to the larger of 16 mm or twice the web thickness. Fatigue loading considerations have not been accounted for in the formulas of this section and if holes are necessary in a member subjected to fatigue, some guidance is available in Frost & Leffler (Reference 3).

Special design considerations are required if concentrated loads are to be located within the hole length or within one beam depth from either end of a hole.

The width-to-thickness ratio of outstanding reinforcing plates should meet Class 1 requirements.

Web Stability

For Class 1 Sections	For Class 2 Sections
$V_f \leqslant 0.67 \, V_r$ and in addition for rectangular holes $a/H \leqslant 3.0$ $(a/H) + 6(2H/d) \leqslant 5.6$	$V_f \leqslant 0.45 \, V_r$ and in addition for rectangular holes $a/H \leqslant 2.2$ $(a/H) + 6(2H/d) \leqslant 5.6$

When these values are exceeded, refer to the paper by Redwood and Shrivastava.

Deflections

One or two small circular holes normally give negligible additional deflections. Deflections of beams with large holes will be increased due to the local deformations caused by the following:

(a) Effect of rotation produced by change in length of the tees above and below the hole.

(b) Local bending over the length of the hole.

(c) Shear deformations.

Multiple Holes

To avoid interaction effects between two holes which may occur when the shear force is high, it is necessary that the length of the web between the holes, s, should satisfy the following:

Rectangular holes:

$$s \geqslant 2H$$

$$s \geqslant 2a \left(\frac{V_f/V_r}{1 - V_f/V_r} \right)$$

Circular holes:

$$s \geqslant 3R$$

$$s \geqslant 2R \left(\frac{V_f/V_r}{1 - V_f/V_r} \right)$$

where in each case the length, height or radius refers to that of the larger of the two holes.

Lateral Buckling

The presence of a hole has only a minor effect on the lateral stability of a beam, providing the strength of the beam, calculated without considering lateral buckling, is governed by the resistance of a section remote from the hole. For members that may be susceptible to lateral buckling, refer to the paper by Redwood and Shrivastava.

Nomenclature

In this section the following nomenclature is used in addition to that given on page viii.

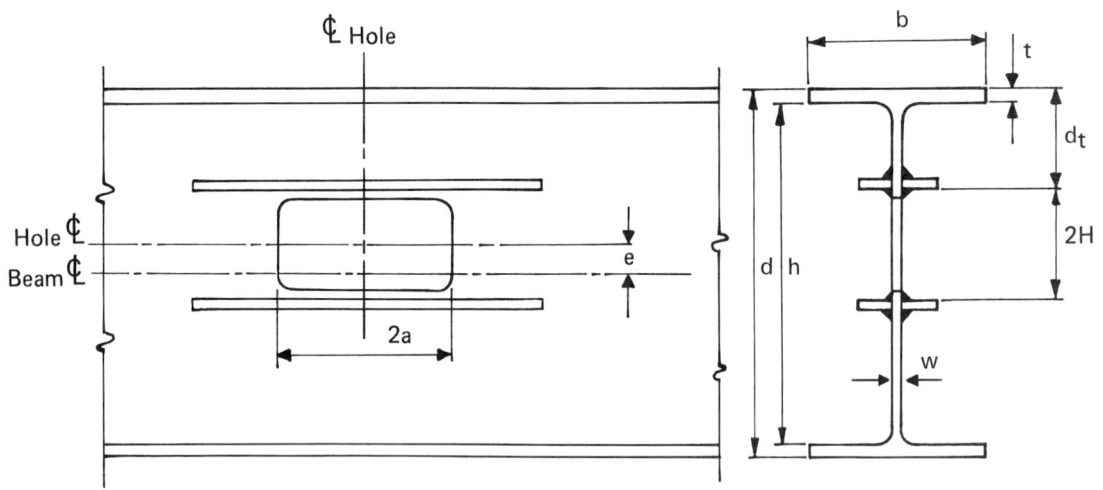

A_f	area of one flange (bt)
A_r	area of reinforcement along top or bottom edge of hole
A_w	area of web (dw)
e	eccentricity of centerline of hole above or below beam centerline — always positive.
M_f	bending moment due to factored loads at centerline of hole
M_r	factored moment resistance of an unperforated beam

M_o, M_1	values of moment resistance defined in web hole formulas
R	radius of a circular hole
s	length of web between adjacent holes
V_f	shear force due to factored loads at centerline of hole
V_r	factored shear resistance of an unperforated beam = $0.55\,\phi\,w\,d\,F_y$ (can be obtained by multiplying tabulated values of V_r given in beam load tables or beam selection table by 0.833)
V_o, V_1	values of shear resistance defined in web hole formulas

Unreinforced Holes

According to Clause 15.10.2 of CAN3-S16.1-M78 (see Part 2), unreinforced circular openings may be used under stipulated conditions. Round holes that are not covered by Clause 15.10.2 may be checked using the reinforced hole formulas below by equating 'a' and 'H' to hole radius 'R' as follows:

$2a = .9R$
$2H = 1.8R$

Compression zone stability of the Tee section should be checked when $2a > 4\,d_t$.

The factored applied shear force V_f and factored applied moment M_f applied to the web centerline must satisfy:

$$V_f \leqslant V_1 \tag{1}$$

$$M_f \leqslant M_o - (M_o - M_1)\,V_f/V_1 \tag{2}$$

in which

$$\frac{M_o}{M_r} = 1 - \frac{\dfrac{A_w}{4A_f}\left[\left(\dfrac{2H}{d}\right)^2 + \left(\dfrac{4e}{d}\right)\left(\dfrac{2H}{d}\right)\right]}{1 + \dfrac{A_w}{4A_f}} \tag{3}$$

$$\frac{M_1}{M_r} = \frac{1 - \dfrac{2}{\sqrt{3}}\left(\dfrac{A_w}{A_f}\right)\left(\dfrac{a}{d}\right)\sqrt{\dfrac{\alpha_2}{1+\alpha_2}}}{1 + \dfrac{A_w}{4A_f}} \tag{4}$$

$$\frac{V_1}{V_r} = \frac{2}{\sqrt{3}}\left(\frac{a}{d}\right)\left[\frac{\alpha_1}{\sqrt{1+\alpha_1}} + \frac{\alpha_2}{\sqrt{1+\alpha_2}}\right] \tag{5}$$

where

$$\alpha_1 = \frac{3}{16}\left(\frac{d}{a}\right)^2\left(1 - \frac{2H}{d} - \frac{2e}{d}\right)^2 \tag{6}$$

$$\alpha_2 = \frac{3}{16}\left(\frac{d}{a}\right)^2\left(1 - \frac{2H}{d} + \frac{2e}{d}\right)^2 \tag{7}$$

Table 5—5, page 5—164, and Table 5—6, page 5—165, provide a means of evaluating equations (1) and (2). For further explanation of these tables, see page 5—159.

Reinforced Holes — Horizontal Bars Only

Equal areas of reinforcement should be placed above and below the hole, with the reinforcement as close as possible to the edges of the hole. Welds attaching the reinforcement to the beam web should be continuous and may be placed on one side only of the reinforcing bar. Within the legnth of the hole, the welds should develop twice the factored tensile resistance of the reinforcement except that the weld capacity need not exceed 1.15 a w F_y. The reinforcement should extend past the hole far enough for the weld to develop the factored tensile resistance of the reinforcement but not less than a distance of 'a/2'.

For Class 1 sections only it is often more economical to place reinforcement on one side of the web only. This can be done providing the following conditions are satisfied:

$A_r \leqslant 0.333 \ A_f$

$M_f \leqslant 20 \ V_f d$ at the hole centreline

$a/H \leqslant 2.5$

$d_t/w \leqslant 370/\sqrt{F_y}$ (F_y in MPa)

The compression zone stability of the reinforced tee should be checked by treating the member as an axially loaded column with effective length equal to '2a'. If it is determined that web instability could be a problem, then vertical reinforcing at the ends of the hole will be required. Attachment of both vertical and horizontal bars is generally more economical when the horizontal bars are welded on only one side of the web with the vertical bars on the other side.

Round holes may be checked using the reinforced hole formulas by relating 'a' and 'H' to radius 'R' as follows:

$2a = .9R \quad$ and $\quad 2H = 2R$

Once it is established that hole reinforcement is required, Table 5—7 on page 5—167 provides a means of checking the resistance of a beam with a reinforced hole for an assumed area of reinforcement. To determine minimum reinforcement requirements, a flow chart for writing programs for a programmable calculator is shown on page 5—160.

Beam Resistance — Holes with Horizontal Reinforcing Bars

Web stability and compression zone stability must be checked in addition to the following strength requirements. The factored shear force V_f and factored moment M_f applied at the web hole centerline must satisfy the following where A_r is less than A_f:

$$V_f \leqslant V_l \tag{8a}$$

$$V_f/V_r \leqslant 1 - \frac{2H}{d} \tag{8b}$$

$$M_f \leqslant M_o - (M_o - M_l) \ V_f/V_l \tag{9a}$$

$$M_f \leqslant M_r \tag{9b}$$

in which

$$\left(\frac{M_o}{M_r}\right)_a = 1 + \frac{\dfrac{A_r}{A_f}\left(\dfrac{2H}{d}\right) - \dfrac{A_w}{4A_f}\left[\left(\dfrac{2H}{d}\right)^2 + 4\left(\dfrac{2H}{d}\right)\left(\dfrac{2e}{d}\right) - 4\left(\dfrac{2e}{d}\right)^2\right]}{1 + \dfrac{A_w}{4A_f}} \quad \text{for } \left|\dfrac{e}{d}\right| \leqslant \dfrac{A_r}{A_w} \tag{10a}$$

$$\left(\frac{M_o}{M_r}\right)_b = \left(\frac{M_o}{M_r}\right)_a - \frac{\dfrac{A_w}{A_f}\left[\dfrac{e}{d} - \dfrac{A_r}{A_w}\right]^2}{1 + \dfrac{A_w}{4A_f}} \qquad \text{for } \left|\frac{e}{d}\right| > \frac{A_r}{A_w} \qquad (10b)$$

$$\frac{M_l}{M_r} = \frac{1 - A_r/A_f}{1 + \dfrac{A_w}{4A_f}} \qquad (11)$$

$$\frac{V_l}{V_r} = \sqrt{3}\left(\frac{d}{a}\right)\left(\frac{A_r}{A_w}\right)\left(1 - \frac{2H}{d}\right) \qquad (12)$$

Flow Chart

The flow chart on page 5—160 is provided as a guide in developing programs for programmable calculators and other computers. The logic provided determines the minimum A_r which will satisfy equation 9a. It is anticipated that the person implementing the program will modify it to his own needs.

References

1. Part 2 of the Handbook.

2. Redwood, R. G. and Shrivastava, S. C., "Design Recommendations for Steel Beams with Web Holes". (To be published in Can. J. Civ. Eng. Dec. 1980).

3. Frost, R. W. and Leffler, R. E., 1971, "Fatigue Tests of Beams with Rectangular Web Holes," ASCE, Journal of the Structural Division, 97(ST2), pp. 509-527.

4. Redwood, R. G., 1971, "Simplified Plastic Analysis for Reinforced Web Holes." AISC Engineering Journal, 8(3) pp. 128-131.

5. Redwood, R. G., 1973, "Design of Beams with Web Holes," Canadian Steel Construction Council.

6. Redwood, R. G., 1974. The Influence of Web Holes on the Design of Steel Beams, Proceedings, 4th Canadian Structural Engineering Conference, Toronto. Canadian Steel Construction Council.

Tables

(a) *Unreinforced Holes*

Table 5—5 page 5—164 gives the values of the constants C_1 and C_2 for unreinforced holes where,

$$C_1 = \frac{M_o}{M_r} \text{ and } C_2 = \frac{M_o/M_r - M_l/M_r}{V_l/V_r}$$

where M_o, M_r, M_l, V_l and V_r are defined in equations (3) to (5), and Table 5—6, page 5—165, gives the value of C_3 taken as V_l/V_r. A_w/A_f varies from 0.5 to 2.25, $2H/d$ from 0.3 to 0.6, a/H from 1.0 to 2.4 and $e/d = 0$.

Written in terms of the constants C_1 and C_2, equation (2) becomes

$$\frac{M_f}{M_r} \leqslant C_1 - C_2\left(\frac{V_f}{V_r}\right) \qquad (13)$$

and equation (1) becomes

$$\frac{V_f}{V_r} \leqslant C_3 \qquad (14)$$

REINFORCED HOLE PROGRAM FLOWCHART

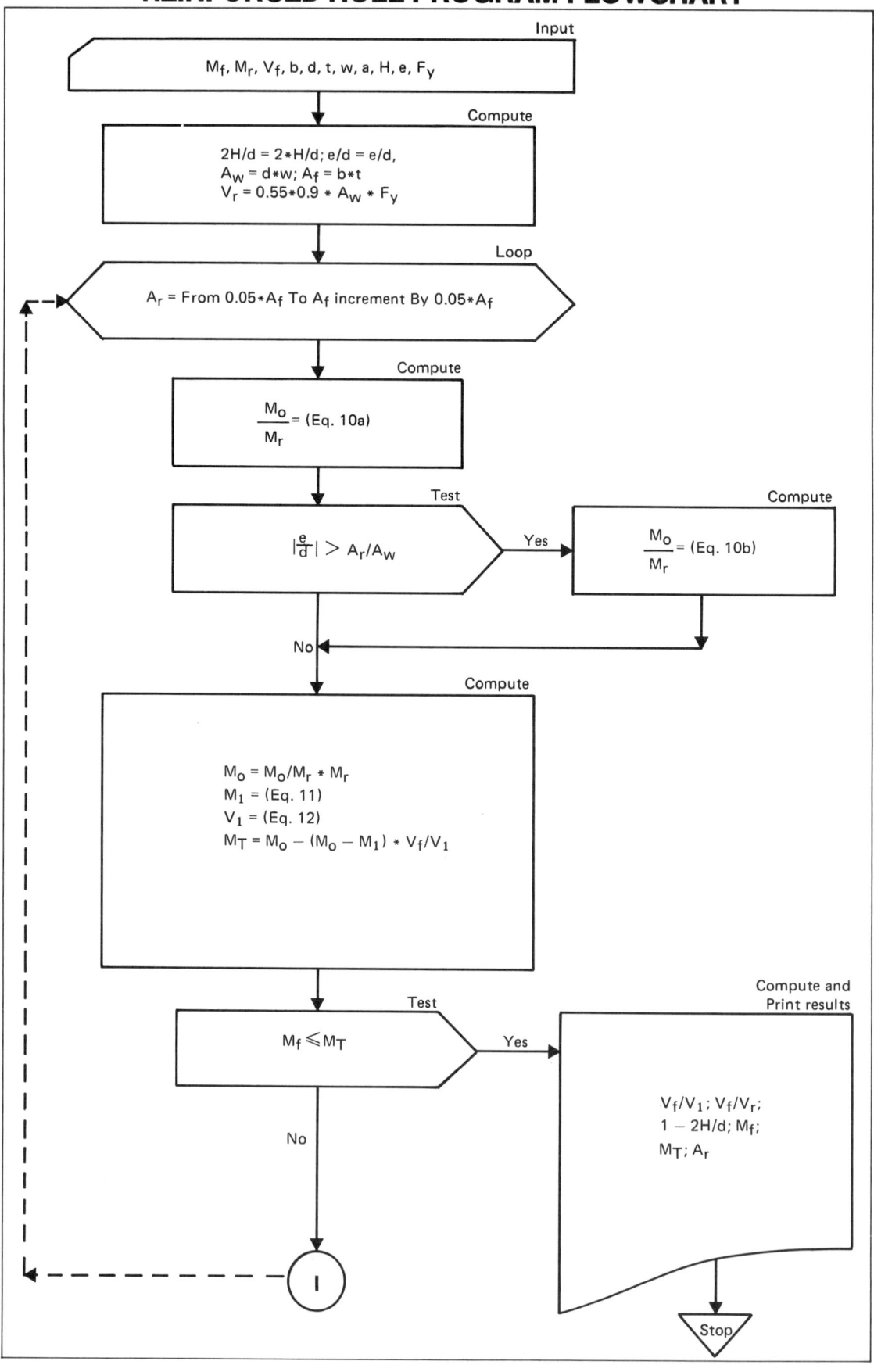

Input

$M_f, M_r, V_f, b, d, t, w, a, H, e, F_y$

Compute

$2H/d = 2*H/d; e/d = e/d,$
$A_w = d*w; A_f = b*t$
$V_r = 0.55*0.9 * A_w * F_y$

Loop

A_r = From $0.05*A_f$ To A_f increment By $0.05*A_f$

Compute

$\dfrac{M_o}{M_r}$ = (Eq. 10a)

Test

$|\dfrac{e}{d}| > A_r/A_w$

Yes

Compute

$\dfrac{M_o}{M_r}$ = (Eq. 10b)

No

Compute

$M_o = M_o/M_r * M_r$
$M_1 =$ (Eq. 11)
$V_1 =$ (Eq. 12)
$M_T = M_o - (M_o - M_1) * V_f/V_1$

Test

$M_f \leqslant M_T$

Yes

Compute and Print results

$V_f/V_1; V_f/V_r;$
$1 - 2H/d; M_f;$
$M_T; A_r$

No

1

Stop

Use

For concentric (e/d = 0) unreinforced holes compute A_w/A_f, $2H/d$ and a/H. Determine C_1, C_2 and C_3 with the aid of Tables 5—5 and 5—6 for use in equations (13) and (14).

(b) *Reinforced Holes*

Table 5—7, pages 5—166 to 5—168, gives the values of the constants C_4 and C_5 for reinforced holes where

$$C_4 = \frac{M_o}{M_r} \text{ and } C_5 = \frac{M_o/M_r - M_l/M_r}{V_l/V_r}$$

where M_o, M_r, M_l, V_l and V_r are defined in equations (10) to (12) for concentric holes (e/d = 0). A_w/A_f varies from 0.5 to 2.25, $2H/d$ from 0.3 to 0.6 and a/H from 1.0 to 2.4, for three values of A_r/A_f, 0.33, 0.67 and 1.0.

Written in terms of the constants C_4 and C_5, equation (10) becomes

$$\frac{M_f}{M_r} \leqslant C_4 - C_5 \left(\frac{V_f}{V_r}\right) \tag{15}$$

Use

For concentric (e/d = 0) reinforced holes, compute A_w/A_f, $2H/d$, and a/H. Determine C_4 and C_5, for one of the assumed values of A_r/A_f, for use in equation (15).

Then check Equation (8a), (8b) and (9b).

Example

Given:

A simple span W610 × 101 beam spanning 12 m supports a total uniformly distributed load of 420 kN (35 kN/m). Check the adequacy of the section for 2 rectangular holes located as shown. Steel G40.21-M 300W. Lateral support to compression flange is provided.

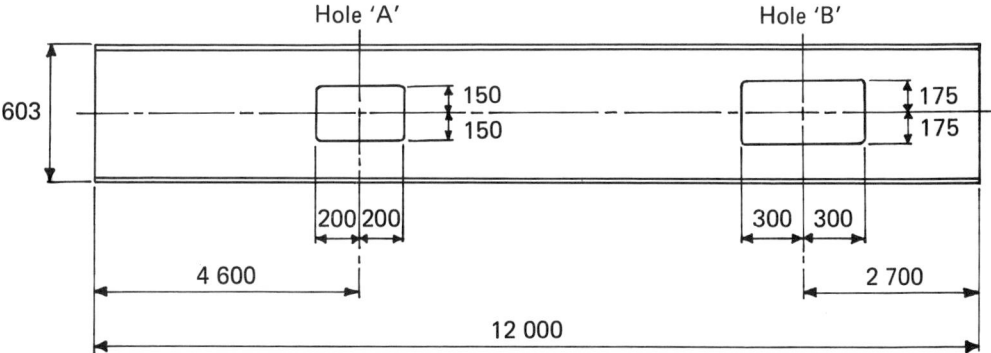

1. Solution for Hole 'A'

Check Class. From page 5—6, for G40.21-M. 300W steel, W610 × 101 is Class 1 — OK

From page 5—116, $M_r = 784 \text{ kN·m}$

$$V_r = 1\ 130 \text{ kN}$$

For use in formulae for holes in beam webs V_r must be reduced to the value of V_r used for plastically analysed beams.

Therefore $V_r = 0.833 \times 1\ 130 = 941 \text{ kN}$

$$\frac{A_w}{A_f} = \frac{10.5 \times 603}{228 \times 14.9} = 1.86$$

$$a/H = \frac{200}{150} = 1.33 < 3.0 - OK$$

$$\frac{2H}{d} = \frac{300}{603} = 0.50 < .70 - OK$$

At centre line of hole

$$M_f = 35 \text{ kN/m} \times 4.6 \text{ m } (12 - 4.6)/2 = 596 \text{ kN·m}$$

$$V_f = 35 \text{ kN/m } (\frac{12}{2} - 4.6) = 49 \text{ kN}$$

Therefore $\frac{M_f}{M_r} = \frac{596}{784} = 0.76$

$$\frac{V_f}{V_r} = \frac{49}{941} = 0.052$$

Check for web stability

$$a/H = 1.33 < 3.0 \text{ (limit for Class 1 beam)} - OK$$

$$\frac{V_f}{V_r} = 0.052 < 0.67 - OK$$

$$a/H + 6 (\frac{2H}{d}) = 1.33 + 6 (0.50) = 4.33 < 5.6 - OK$$

Compression zone stability

$$4d_t = 4 (\frac{603}{2} - 150) = 606 \text{ mm}$$

$$2a = 400 \text{ mm}$$

Since $4d_t > 2a$, compression zone stability not critical.

Check for unreinforced hole

For $A_w/A_f = 1.86$ and $\frac{2H}{d} = 0.50,$

$C_1 = 0.92$ from Table 5—5, page 5—164 by interpolation.

For $a/H = 1.33$ use 1.4

$C_2 = 1.9$ from Table 5—5, page 5—164 by interpolation.

$C_3 = 0.263$ (Table 5—6)

$$\frac{M_f}{M_r} \leqslant C_1 - C_2(\frac{V_f}{V_r}) = 0.92 - 1.9 \times 0.052 = 0.82$$

$$M_f/M_r = 0.76 < 0.82 - OK$$

and $\frac{V_f}{V_r} = 0.052 < 0.263 - OK$

2. Solution for Hole 'B'

$$\frac{a}{H} = \frac{300}{175} = 1.7 < 3.0 - OK$$

$$\frac{2H}{d} = \frac{350}{603} = 0.58 < 0.7 - OK$$

e = 0 therefore e/d = 0

At centre line of hole

$$M_f = 35 \text{ kN·m} \times 2.7 \text{ m } (\frac{12 - 2.7}{2}) = 440 \text{ kN·m}$$

$$V_f = 35 \text{ kN·m} \times (12/2 - 2.7) = 116 \text{ kN}$$

Therefore

$$\frac{M_f}{M_r} = \frac{440}{784} = 0.561$$

$$\frac{V_f}{V_r} = \frac{116}{941} = 0.123$$

Check spacing between holes. Use 2H of larger hole.

S ⩾ 2H

12 000 − (2 700 + 4 600) ⩾ 2 × 175

4 700 ⩾ 300 − OK

Check for web stability

a/H = 1.7 < 3.0 (limit for Class 1 beam) − OK

$$\frac{V_f}{V_r} = 0.123 < 0.67 - OK$$

$$a/H + 6 \left(\frac{2H}{d}\right) = 1.7 + 6 (0.58) = 5.18 < 5.6 - OK$$

Check if unreinforced hole would be acceptable

From Table 5—5, page 5—164 for A_w/A_f = 1.86 use 2.0

and $\frac{2H}{d}$ = 0.58 use 0.60

C_1 = 0.88

For a/H = 1.7 use 1.8, C_2 = 3.83

$$C_1 - C_2 \frac{V_f}{V_r} = 0.88 - 3.83 \times 0.123$$

$$= 0.409 < 0.561 - \text{Reinforcement required.}$$

Assume A_r/A_f = 0.33 (maximum permitted for single sided reinforcement)

From Table 5—7, page 5—166

for $\frac{A_r}{A_f}$ = 0.33; $\frac{A_w}{A_f}$ = 2.0, $\frac{2H}{d}$ = 0.60

C_4 = 1.013

for $\frac{a}{H}$ = 1.7, C_5 = 2.51 by interpolation

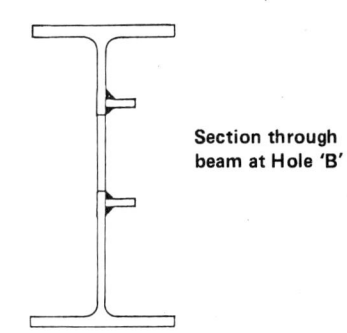

Section through
beam at Hole 'B'

VALUES OF C_1 AND C_2
For Unreinforced Concentric Holes in Beam Webs

Table 5-5

$\dfrac{A_w}{A_f}$	$\dfrac{2H}{d}$	C_1	C_2 — For following a/H values							
			1.0	1.2	1.4	1.6	1.8	2.0	2.2	2.4†
.50	.30	.990	.271	.300	.330	.360	.391	.423	.455	.488
	.35	.986	.315	.353	.392	.433	.474	.516	.558	.601
	.40	.982	.367	.417	.468	.520	.574	.628	.682	.737
	.45	.978	.432	.495	.561	.628	.696	.764	.833	.903
	.50	.972	.511	.593	.676	.761	.846	.933	1.020	1.107
	.55	.966	.612	.715	.820	.927	1.035	1.143	1.252	1.361
	.60	.960	740	.872	1.005	1.140	1.275	1.411	*	*
.75	.30	.986	.385	.426	.468	.512	.556	.601	.647	.694
	.35	.981	.447	.502	.557	.615	.673	.733	.793	.854
	.40	.975	.522	.593	.665	.740	.815	.892	.970	1.048
	.45	.968	.613	.704	.797	.892	.989	1.086	1.184	1.283
	.50	.961	.726	.842	.961	1.081	1.203	1.325	1.449	1.573
	.55	.952	.869	1.016	1.166	1.317	1.470	1.624	1.779	1.934
	.60	.943	1.052	1.239	1.428	1.619	1.812	2.005	*	*
1.00	.30	.982	.488	.540	.593	.648	.705	.762	.820	.879
	.35	.976	.567	.635	.706	.779	.853	.928	1.005	1.082
	.40	.968	.661	.751	.843	.937	1.033	1.130	1.228	1.327
	.45	.960	.777	.892	1.010	1.130	1.252	1.376	1.500	1.626
	.50	.950	.920	1.067	1.217	1.369	1.523	1.679	1.835	1.992
	.55	.940	1.101	1.287	1.477	1.669	1.862	2.057	2.253	2.450
	.60	.928	1.333	1.569	1.809	2.051	2.295	2.539	*	*
1.25	.30	.979	.581	.643	.706	.772	.839	.907	.976	1.046
	.35	.971	.675	.756	.841	.927	1.015	1.105	1.196	1.288
	.40	.962	.787	.894	1.003	1.115	1.229	1.345	1.462	1.580
	.45	.952	.925	1.062	1.202	1.346	1.491	1.638	1.786	1.935
	.50	.940	1.095	1.270	1.449	1.630	1.813	1.999	2.185	2.372
	.55	.928	1.310	1.532	1.758	1.987	2.217	2.449	2.682	2.916
	.60	.914	1.587	1.868	2.154	2.442	2.732	3.023	*	*
1.50	.30	.975	.666	.736	.809	.884	.961	1.039	1.118	1.198
	.35	.967	.773	.866	.963	1.062	1.163	1.266	1.370	1.475
	.40	.956	.902	1.024	1.149	1.278	1.408	1.541	1.675	1.810
	.45	.945	1.059	1.216	1.377	1.541	1.708	1.876	2.046	2.217
	.50	.932	1.255	1.455	1.659	1.867	2.077	2.289	2.502	2.717
	.55	.918	1.501	1.755	2.014	2.276	2.540	2.805	3.072	3.340
	.60	.902	1.817	2.140	2.467	2.797	3.129	3.463	*	*
1.75	.30	.973	.743	.822	.903	.987	1.072	1.159	1.248	1.337
	.35	.963	.862	.967	1.075	1.185	1.298	1.413	1.529	1.646
	.40	.951	1.006	1.142	1.282	1.426	1.572	1.719	1.869	2.020
	.45	.938	1.182	1.357	1.537	1.720	1.906	2.094	2.283	2.474
	.50	.924	1.400	1.624	1.852	2.084	2.318	2.555	2.793	3.032
	.55	.908	1.675	1.959	2.247	2.539	2.834	3.131	3.429	3.728
	.60	.890	2.028	2.388	2.753	3.122	3.492	3.864	*	*
2.00	.30	.970	.813	.900	.989	1.081	1.174	1.270	1.366	1.465
	.35	.959	.944	1.059	1.177	1.298	1.421	1.547	1.674	1.803
	.40	.947	1.102	1.251	1.405	1.561	1.721	1.883	2.047	2.212
	.45	.933	1.295	1.486	1.683	1.884	2.087	2.293	2.500	2.709
	.50	.917	1.534	1.778	2.028	2.282	2.539	2.798	3.059	3.321
	.55	.899	1.835	2.145	2.461	2.781	3.104	3.429	3.755	4.083
	.60	.880	2.221	2.616	3.016	3.419	3.825	4.232	*	*
2.25	.30	.968	.878	.972	1.068	1.167	1.268	1.371	1.476	1.582
	.35	.956	1.020	1.144	1.271	1.402	1.535	1.671	1.808	1.947
	.40	.942	1.190	1.351	1.517	1.686	1.859	2.034	2.211	2.389
	.45	.927	1.398	1.605	1.818	2.034	2.254	2.476	2.700	2.926
	.50	.910	1.656	1.920	2.190	2.465	2.742	3.022	3.303	3.586
	.55	.891	1.981	2.317*	2.658	3.004	3.352	3.703	4.056	4.409
	.60	.870	2.399	2.825	3.257	3.692	4.131	4.571	*	*

*a/H plus 6 (2H/d) exceeds 5.6.
†Exceeds web stability limit for Class 2 sections.

5-164

$$\frac{M_f}{M_r} \leqslant C_4 - C_5 \left(\frac{V_f}{V_r}\right) = 1.013 - 2.51 \,(0.123)$$
$$= 0.70 > 0.561 - OK$$

Further refinement of A_r/A_f can be accomplished by using the expressions previously given.

Try single sided reinforcement

$M_f \leqslant 20 \; V_f d$ at hole centreline

$20 \; V_f d = 20 \times 116 \times 603 = 1\,400\,000 \; kN \cdot mm$
$$= 1\,400 \; kN \cdot m$$

$M_f = 440 \; kN \cdot m < 1\,400 \; kN \cdot m - OK$

$a/H = 1.7 < 2.5 - OK$

$$\frac{d_t}{w} = \frac{603/2 - 175}{10.5} = 12.0 < 21.4 \left(\frac{370}{\sqrt{F_y}}\right) - OK$$

Therefore use single sided reinforcement,

$A_r = 0.33 \; A_f = 0.33 \times 228 \times 14.9 = 1\,121 \; mm^2$

Check shear

$$V_l = \sqrt{3} \left(\frac{d}{a}\right) \left(\frac{A_r}{A_w}\right) \left(1 - \frac{2H}{d}\right) V_r$$

$$= \sqrt{3} \left(\frac{603}{300}\right) \left(\frac{1\,121}{10.5 \times 603}\right) (1 - 0.58)\,941$$

$$= 243 > 116 - OK$$

$$\frac{V_f}{V_r} \leqslant 1 - \frac{2H}{d} = 0.42 > 0.123 - OK$$

Try 16×70 reinforcement

Check $\dfrac{b}{t} \leqslant \dfrac{145}{\sqrt{F_y}}$

$$\frac{b}{t} = \frac{70}{16} = 4.3 < 8.37 \left(\frac{145}{\sqrt{F_y}}\right) - OK$$

Therefore use 16×70 one sided reinforcement.

VALUES OF C₃   Table 5-6
For Unreinforced Concentric Holes in Beam Webs

$\dfrac{2H}{d}$	a/H							
	1.0	1.2	1.4	1.6	1.8	2.0	2.2	2.4
0.30	.627	.602	.575	.549	.523	.498	.474	.451
0.35	.552	.521	.490	.461	.433	.407	.384	.362
0.40	.475	.441	.408	.378	.351	.327	.305	.286
0.45	.400	.364	.332	.303	.279	.257	.238	.222
0.50	.327	.293	.263	.238	.217	.199	.183	.170
0.55	.260	.229	.203	.182	.165	.150	.138	.127
0.60	.200	.173	.152	.136	.122	.111	.102	.094

VALUES OF C_4 AND C_5
For Reinforced Concentric Holes in Beam Webs

Table 5-7
$A_r/A_f = 0.33$

$\dfrac{A_w}{A_f}$	$\dfrac{2H}{d}$	C_4	C_5 For following a/H values							
			1.0	1.2	1.4	1.6	1.8	2.0	2.2	2.4†
.50	.30	1.079	.090	.108	.126	.144	.162	.180	.199	.217
	.35	1.090	.116	.139	.162	.186	.209	.232	.255	.278
	.40	1.101	.147	.176	.205	.235	.264	.293	.323	.352
	.45	1.111	.184	.220	.257	.294	.330	.367	.404	.441
	.50	1.120	.229	.274	.320	.366	.411	.457	.503	.548
	.55	1.129	.284	.341	.398	.455	.511	.568	.625	.682
	.60	1.138	.354	.425	.496	.567	.637	.708	*	*
.75	.30	1.070	.142	.170	.198	.227	.255	.283	.311	.340
	.35	1.079	.181	.217	.253	.290	.326	.362	.398	.434
	.40	1.087	.228	.273	.319	.364	.410	.455	.501	.546
	.45	1.094	.283	.340	.397	.453	.510	.566	.623	.680
	.50	1.101	.350	.420	.491	.561	.631	.701	.771	.841
	.55	1.107	.433	.519	.606	.693	.779	.866	.952	1.039
	.60	1.112	.536	.643	.750	.858	.965	1.072	*	*
1.00	.30	1.062	.196	.235	.275	.314	.353	.392	.432	.471
	.35	1.069	.250	.300	.350	.400	.449	.499	.549	.599
	.40	1.075	.313	.375	.438	.500	.563	.625	.688	.750
	.45	1.080	.387	.464	.542	.619	.697	.774	.851	.929
	.50	1.083	.476	.572	.667	.762	.857	.953	1.048	1.143
	.55	1.086	.585	.702	.819	.936	1.053	1.170	1.287	1.404
	.60	1.088	.721	.865	1.009	1.153	1.297	1.441	*	*
1.25	.30	1.055	.254	.304	.355	.406	.457	.507	.558	.609
	.35	1.060	.322	.386	.450	.515	.579	.643	.708	.772
	.40	1.063	.401	.481	.561	.642	.722	.802	.882	.962
	.45	1.066	.494	.593	.692	.791	.890	.989	1.088	1.186
	.50	1.067	.606	.727	.848	.969	1.090	1.211	1.333	1.454
	.55	1.068	.741	.889	1.037	1.185	1.333	1.481	1.629	1.777
	.60	1.067	.907	1.089	1.270	1.452	1.633	1.815	*	*
1.50	.30	1.048	.314	.376	.439	.502	.565	.627	.690	.753
	.35	1.051	.396	.476	.555	.634	.713	.793	.872	.951
	.40	1.053	.492	.591	.689	.788	.886	.985	1.083	1.182
	.45	1.054	.605	.726	.847	.968	1.089	1.210	1.331	1.451
	.50	1.053	.738	.886	1.033	1.181	1.329	1.476	1.624	1.771
	.55	1.051	.899	1.078	1.258	1.438	1.618	1.797	1.977	2.157
	.60	1.047	1.096	1.315	1.534	1.753	1.973	2.192	*	*
1.75	.30	1.042	.376	.451	.526	.601	.676	.751	.827	.902
	.35	1.044	.473	.568	.663	.757	.852	.947	1.041	1.136
	.40	1.044	.586	.704	.821	.938	1.055	1.173	1.290	1.407
	.45	1.043	.718	.861	1.005	1.149	1.292	1.436	1.579	1.723
	.50	1.040	.873	1.048	1.222	1.397	1.572	1.746	1.921	2.095
	.55	1.035	1.059	1.271	1.483	1.694	1.906	2.118	2.330	2.542
	.60	1.030	1.286	1.543	1.801	2.058	2.315	2.572	*	*
2.00	.30	1.037	.440	.528	.615	.703	.791	.879	.967	1.055
	.35	1.037	.553	.663	.774	.884	.995	1.105	1.216	1.326
	.40	1.036	.683	.819	.956	1.092	1.229	1.365	1.502	1.638
	.45	1.033	.833	1.000	1.167	1.333	1.500	1.667	1.833	2.000
	.50	1.028	1.010	1.212	1.415	1.617	1.819	2.021	2.223	2.425
	.55	1.021	1.221	1.466	1.710	1.954	2.198	2.443	2.687	2.931
	.60	1.013	1.478	1.774	2.069	2.365	2.660	2.956	*	*
2.25	.30	1.032	.505	.606	.707	.808	.909	1.010	1.111	1.212
	.35	1.031	.634	.760	.887	1.014	1.141	1.267	1.394	1.521
	.40	1.028	.781	.937	1.093	1.249	1.405	1.562	1.718	1.874
	.45	1.023	.951	1.141	1.331	1.521	1.712	1.902	2.092	2.282
	.50	1.017	1.150	1.380	1.610	1.839	2.069	2.299	2.529	2.759
	.55	1.008	1.386	1.663	1.940	2.217	2.494	2.771	3.048	3.325
	.60	.998	1.671	2.005	2.340	2.674	3.008	3.342	*	*

*a/H plus 6 (2H/d) exceeds 5.6.
†Exceeds web stability limit for Class 2 sections.

VALUES OF C_4 AND C_5
For Reinforced Concentric Holes in Beam Webs

$A_r/A_f = 0.67$

$\dfrac{A_w}{A_f}$	$\dfrac{2H}{d}$	C_4	C_5 For following a/H values							
			1.0	1.2	1.4	1.6	1.8	2.0	2.2	2.4†
.50	.30	1.168	.081	.097	.113	.129	.146	.162	.178	.194
	.35	1.194	.105	.126	.146	.167	.188	.209	.230	.251
	.40	1.219	.133	.160	.187	.213	.240	.266	.293	.320
	.45	1.244	.168	.201	.235	.269	.302	.336	.369	.403
	.50	1.269	.210	.253	.295	.337	.379	.421	.463	.505
	.55	1.292	.264	.316	.369	.422	.474	.527	.580	.633
	.60	1.316	.331	.397	.463	.530	.596	.662	*	*
.75	.30	1.154	.122	.146	.170	.195	.219	.243	.267	.292
	.35	1.177	.157	.188	.219	.251	.282	.314	.345	.376
	.40	1.199	.199	.239	.278	.318	.358	.398	.438	.477
	.45	1.221	.250	.300	.350	.400	.450	.500	.549	.599
	.50	1.241	.312	.374	.437	.499	.561	.624	.686	.749
	.55	1.261	.389	.467	.545	.623	.700	.778	.856	.934
	.60	1.280	.487	.584	.682	.779	.876	.974	*	*
1.00	.30	1.142	.162	.195	.227	.260	.292	.325	.357	.390
	.35	1.162	.209	.251	.292	.334	.376	.418	.459	.501
	.40	1.181	.264	.317	.370	.422	.475	.528	.581	.634
	.45	1.200	.330	.397	.463	.529	.595	.661	.727	.793
	.50	1.217	.411	.494	.576	.658	.740	.823	.905	.987
	.55	1.233	.511	.614	.716	.818	.920	1.023	1.125	1.227
	.60	1.248	.637	.765	.892	1.020	1.147	1.275	*	*
1.25	.30	1.131	.203	.244	.285	.325	.366	.407	.448	.488
	.35	1.149	.261	.313	.365	.417	.469	.521	.574	.626
	.40	1.165	.329	.395	.460	.526	.592	.658	.723	.789
	.45	1.180	.410	.492	.574	.656	.738	.821	.903	.985
	.50	1.194	.509	.611	.713	.814	.916	1.018	1.120	1.222
	.55	1.207	.631	.757	.883	1.009	1.135	1.261	1.388	1.514
	.60	1.219	.784	.940	1.097	1.254	1.410	1.567	*	*
1.50	.30	1.121	.245	.293	.342	.391	.440	.489	.538	.587
	.35	1.136	.313	.375	.438	.500	.563	.625	.688	.750
	.40	1.150	.393	.472	.550	.629	.708	.786	.865	.943
	.45	1.163	.489	.587	.685	.783	.881	.978	1.076	1.174
	.50	1.174	.605	.726	.847	.968	1.089	1.210	1.332	1.453
	.55	1.184	.748	.897	1.047	1.196	1.346	1.495	1.645	1.794
	.60	1.193	.926	1.111	1.296	1.481	1.667	1.852	*	*
1.75	.30	1.112	.286	.343	.400	.457	.514	.571	.629	.686
	.35	1.125	.364	.437	.510	.583	.656	.729	.802	.875
	.40	1.137	.457	.549	.640	.731	.823	.914	1.006	1.097
	.45	1.147	.567	.681	.794	.908	1.021	1.135	1.248	1.362
	.50	1.156	.700	.840	.980	1.120	1.260	1.400	1.540	1.680
	.55	1.163	.862	1.035	1.207	1.380	1.552	1.725	1.897	2.070
	.60	1.169	1.065	1.278	1.491	1.704	1.917	2.130	*	*
2.00	.30	1.103	.327	.392	.458	.523	.589	.654	.719	.785
	.35	1.115	.416	.499	.583	.666	.749	.832	.916	.999
	.40	1.124	.521	.625	.729	.833	.938	1.042	1.146	1.250
	.45	1.133	.645	.774	.903	1.032	1.161	1.290	1.419	1.548
	.50	1.139	.794	.953	1.111	1.270	1.429	1.588	1.746	1.905
	.55	1.144	.975	1.170	1.365	1.560	1.755	1.951	2.146	2.341
	.60	1.147	1.201	1.441	1.681	1.921	2.162	2.402	*	*
2.25	.30	1.096	.368	.442	.516	.589	.663	.737	.810	.884
	.35	1.105	.468	.561	.655	.749	.842	.936	1.029	1.123
	.40	1.113	.584	.701	.818	.935	1.052	1.169	1.286	1.403
	.45	1.119	.722	.866	1.011	1.155	1.300	1.444	1.588	1.733
	.50	1.123	.887	1.064	1.241	1.419	1.596	1.773	1.951	2.128
	.55	1.126	1.087	1.304	1.521	1.738	1.956	2.173	2.390	2.608
	.60	1.126	1.334	1.601	1.868	2.135	2.402	2.669	*	*

*a/H plus 6 (2H/d) exceeds 5.6.
†Exceeds web stability limit for Class 2 sections.

VALUES OF C₄ AND C₅
For Reinforced Concentric Holes in Beam Webs

Table 5-7
$A_r/A_f = 1.00$

$\frac{A_w}{A_f}$	$\frac{2H}{d}$	C_4	C_5 For following a/H values							
			1.0	1.2	1.4	1.6	1.8	2.0	2.2	2.4†
.50	.30	1.257	.078	.093	.109	.124	.140	.155	.171	.187
	.35	1.298	.101	.121	.141	.161	.182	.202	.222	.242
	.40	1.338	.129	.154	.180	.206	.232	.257	.283	.309
	.45	1.378	.163	.195	.228	.260	.293	.325	.358	.390
	.50	1.417	.204	.245	.286	.327	.368	.409	.450	.491
	.55	1.455	.257	.308	.359	.411	.462	.513	.565	.616
	.60	1.493	.323	.388	.453	.517	.582	.647	*	*
.75	.30	1.238	.115	.138	.161	.184	.207	.230	.253	.276
	.35	1.275	.149	.178	.208	.238	.268	.297	.327	.357
	.40	1.312	.189	.227	.265	.303	.341	.379	.416	.454
	.45	1.347	.239	.286	.334	.382	.429	.477	.525	.573
	.50	1.382	.299	.359	.419	.479	.538	.598	.658	.718
	.55	1.415	.375	.449	.524	.599	.674	.749	.824	.899
	.60	1.448	.470	.564	.659	.753	.847	.941	*	*
1.00	.30	1.222	.151	.181	.212	.242	.272	.302	.333	.363
	.35	1.256	.195	.234	.273	.312	.351	.390	.429	.468
	.40	1.288	.248	.297	.347	.397	.446	.496	.545	.595
	.45	1.320	.312	.374	.436	.499	.561	.623	.686	.748
	.50	1.350	.390	.468	.546	.624	.701	.779	.857	.935
	.55	1.380	.487	.584	.681	.779	.876	.973	1.071	1.168
	.60	1.408	.610	.732	.854	.975	1.097	1.219	*	*
1.25	.30	1.207	.187	.224	.261	.299	.336	.373	.411	.448
	.35	1.238	.240	.289	.337	.385	.433	.481	.529	.577
	.40	1.267	.305	.366	.427	.488	.548	.609	.670	.731
	.45	1.295	.382	.459	.535	.612	.688	.764	.841	.917
	.50	1.321	.477	.572	.668	.763	.858	.954	1.049	1.144
	.55	1.347	.594	.713	.832	.951	1.069	1.188	1.307	1.426
	.60	1.371	.742	.891	1.039	1.188	1.336	1.485	*	*
1.50	.30	1.194	.222	.266	.310	.354	.399	.443	.487	.532
	.35	1.221	.285	.342	.399	.456	.512	.569	.626	.683
	.40	1.247	.360	.432	.504	.576	.648	.720	.792	.864
	.45	1.272	.451	.541	.631	.721	.811	.901	.991	1.082
	.50	1.295	.561	.673	.785	.898	1.010	1.122	1.234	1.346
	.55	1.318	.697	.837	.976	1.116	1.255	1.395	1.534	1.673
	.60	1.338	.869	1.043	1.217	1.391	1.565	1.738	*	*
1.75	.30	1.181	.256	.307	.358	.409	.460	.512	.563	.614
	.35	1.206	.328	.394	.459	.525	.591	.656	.722	.787
	.40	1.230	.414	.497	.580	.663	.745	.828	.911	.994
	.45	1.251	.517	.621	.724	.828	.931	1.034	1.138	1.241
	.50	1.272	.642	.771	.899	1.028	1.156	1.285	1.413	1.542
	.55	1.291	.797	.956	1.116	1.275	1.434	1.594	1.753	1.912
	.60	1.308	.991	1.189	1.387	1.586	1.784	1.982	*	*
2.00	.30	1.170	.289	.347	.405	.463	.521	.579	.637	.695
	.35	1.193	.371	.445	.519	.593	.667	.741	.816	.890
	.40	1.213	.467	.560	.654	.747	.841	.934	1.027	1.121
	.45	1.233	.582	.699	.815	.932	1.048	1.164	1.281	1.397
	.50	1.250	.722	.866	1.010	1.155	1.299	1.443	1.588	1.732
	.55	1.266	.893	1.072	1.251	1.429	1.608	1.786	1.965	2.144
	.60	1.280	1.109	1.330	1.552	1.774	1.995	2.217	*	*
2.25	.30	1.160	.323	.387	.452	.516	.581	.646	.710	.775
	.35	1.180	.413	.495	.578	.660	.743	.825	.908	.990
	.40	1.198	.519	.623	.726	.830	.934	1.038	1.142	1.245
	.45	1.215	.646	.775	.904	1.033	1.162	1.291	1.421	1.550
	.50	1.230	.799	.959	1.118	1.278	1.438	1.598	1.758	1.917
	.55	1.243	.987	1.184	1.382	1.579	1.776	1.974	2.171	2.368
	.60	1.254	1.222	1.467	1.711	1.955	2.200	2.444	*	*

*a/H plus 6 (2H/d) exceeds 5.6.
†Exceeds web stability limit for Class 2 sections.
5-168

Guide for Floor Vibrations**

G1. Recent developments of floors of lighter construction, longer spans and less inherent damping have sometimes resulted in problems of objectionable floor vibrations during normal human activity.

G2. Two types of vibration problems arise in floor construction. Continuous vibrations arise due to the periodic forces of machinery, vehicles or certain human activities such as dancing. These vibrations can be considerably amplified when the periodic forces are synchronized with a floor frequency — a condition called resonance. Transient vibrations, which decay as shown in Figure G1, arise due to footsteps or other impact.

G3. The most important floor characteristics affecting vibration problems are natural frequency in hertz (cycles per second), usually that corresponding to the lowest mode of vibration, and damping. The relation between damping, expressed in per cent of critical damping,* and decay of free vibration is shown in Figure G2. Other characteristics affecting transient vibration problems are mass, especially for heavy long span floors, and stiffness under point load, especially for light short span floors.

Refer to Clause G11.1, References.

G4. Thresholds of Annoyance

G4.1 Generally people do not like floors to vibrate. For continuous sinusoidal vibration lasting more than about ten cycles an average threshold of definite perception is shown in Figure G3 in terms of peak acceleration; the threshold levels for different people range from about one-half to twice the level shown. In the frequency range 2—8 Hz, where people are most sensitive to vibration, the threshold corresponds to 0.5 per cent g approximately, where g is the acceleration due to gravity. The threshold of definite perception shown in Figure G3 can be used to approximate a design threshold of annoyance for residential, school and office occupancies; the design level will be lower for sensitive occupancies (e.g., operating rooms, special laboratories) and greater for industrial occupancies.

G4.2 For transient vibrations, the design threshold in terms of initial peak acceleration of a decaying vibration, as shown in Figure G1, increases with an increase in damping. This is because people find continuous vibration much more annoying than vibration which quickly dies out.

G4.3 Design thresholds equivalent to that for continuous vibration are shown in Figure G3 for transient vibrations due to footsteps for different levels of damping.

G5. Continuous Vibrations — Resonance

G5.1 Continuous vibrations caused by machines can be reduced by special design provisions* such as vibration isolation. Care should be taken at the planning stage to locate such machinery away from sensitive occupancies such as offices.

**Appendix G of CAN3-S16.1-M78

G5.2   Floor vibrations can also arise from heavy street traffic on bumpy pavement over soft subgrade. The annoyance increases considerably when repetitive vehicles such as buses create ground vibrations which synchronize with the floor frequency.

G5.3   Continuous vibrations caused by human activities may be a problem for light residential floors, or for long span floors used for special purposes such as dancing or sports. People alone or in union can create periodic forces in the frequency range 1—4 Hz approximately, and therefore for such occupancies, natural frequencies less than 5 Hz should be avoided. For very repetitive activities such as dancing, it is possible to get some resonance when the beat is on every second cycle of floor vibration and it is therefore recommended that the frequency of such floors be 10 Hz or more unless there is a large amount of damping.

Refer to Clause G11.1, References.

G6.   Transient Vibrations

G6.1   Objectionable vibration due to footstep impact can occur in floor systems with light damping in residential, school, office and similar occupancies. Since this is the most common source of annoyance, the remainder of this guide will be concerned with this problem. Types of construction which may give transient vibration problems include open web steel joists or steel beams with concrete deck and light wood deck floors using steel joists.

G7.   Performance Test for Floor Vibration

G7.1   The vibration acceptability of a floor system to human activity can be evaluated by a performance test. Partitions, rug and furnishings, finishes, etc., contribute to reduce vibration annoyance and should therefore be considered in setting up the test floor. A measuring device, which filters out frequencies greater than approximately 1.5 times the fundamental frequency, should be located near mid-span. A person who will give a subjective evaluation of the floor should also be sitting close to the measuring device.

G7.2   One test is for a person of average weight with softsoled shoes to rise up on his toes and drop on his heels near the location of measurement. Fundamental frequency, damping from the decay record (see Figure G2) and peak acceleration are obtained from the measurement and the peak acceleration is plotted on Figure G3 to see how it compares with the threshold of annoyance. Another test is to check floor comfort when different persons walk down the floor; the average peak acceleration can then be compared with the annoyance threshold for steady motion given in Figure G3.

G8.   Long Span Steel Floors With Concrete Deck

G8.1   Transient vibrations may be a problem for open web steel joists or steel beams with concrete deck, composite or non-composite, generally of spans 7000—20 000 mm and frequencies in the range 4—15 Hz. For such floors, partitions, if properly located, provide more than enough damping to avoid excessive vibrations. On the other hand transient vibrations may be serious for bare floors with very low inherent damping, as is the case for fully composite construction. Figure G3 shows that the threshold of annoyance is roughly 10 times greater for 12 per cent damping than for 3 per cent damping.

G8.2   To assess vibration acceptability requires a knowledge of frequency, damping and peak acceleration from heel impact. If design by performance testing is not feasible, these parameters should be estimated by calculation as follows:

(a)   **Frequency** can be estimated by assuming full composite action, even for non-composite construction. For a simply-supported one-way system, the frequency f_1 is given by:

$$f_1 = 156 \sqrt{\frac{EI_T}{wL^4}} \tag{1}$$

where E is the modulus of elasticity of steel (200 000 MPa), I_T the moment of inertia (mm⁴) of the transformed T section (concrete transformed to steel) assuming a concrete flange of width equal to the spacing of steel joists or beams, L the span in millimetres and w the dead load of T-section in N/mm of span. Often one-way systems are supported on steel beams, and this can reduce the frequency calculated for a one-way system.

In this case the frequency can be approximated by:

$$\frac{1}{f^2} = \frac{1}{f_1^2} + \frac{1}{f_2^2} \tag{2}$$

where f_2 is the frequency of floor supported on steel beam perpendicular to joists. Continuous beams should be treated as simply-supported since adjacent spans vibrate in opposite directions;

(b)   **Damping** is generally more difficult to estimate than frequency. A bare steel and concrete deck floor has a damping of approximately 3—4 per cent critical for non-composite construction, about 2 per cent for fully composite construction. The addition of components such as floor finishing, rug and furnishings, ceiling, fireproofing and ducts increases the damping by about 3 per cent or more. Partitions, either above or below the floor, provide the most effective damping especially when they are located in both directions. Even light partitions which do not extend to the ceiling provide considerable damping. Partitions along with supports, or parallel to the floor joists and further apart than approximately 6000 mm, however, may not be effective because the nodal lines of vibration form under the partitions. Human beings also provide damping but this is less effective for heavy long span floors than for lighter short span floors. The following values are suggested for design calculation:

	Damping in Per Cent Critical
Bare floor	3
Finished floor — ceiling, ducts, flooring, furniture	6
Finished floor with partitions	12

(c)   **Peak acceleration from heel drop** for floors greater than 7000 mm span and frequencies less than about 10 Hz, can be estimated by assuming an impulse of 70 N·s suddenly applied to a simple spring and mass system, whose mass corresponds to half that of a floor panel bounded by the nodal lines of vibration. For a one-way system this can be approximated by a floor panel whose width is 60 times the effective thickness of concrete deck. (For concrete on ribbed deck, determine effective thickness from the average weight of concrete, including ribs.) The peak acceleration, a_o in per cent g, can then be approximated by:

$$a_o = \frac{70\ 000f}{Lt_c(t_c + 25)} \quad \text{for normal density concrete; or}$$

$$a_o = \frac{90\ 000f}{Lt_c(t_c + 25)} \quad \text{for structural low density concrete.}$$

(3)

Where f is the frequency in hertz, L the span in metres, and t_c the effective thickness of concrete deck in millimetres. Equation (3) shows that increasing concrete thickness is more effective in reducing transient floor vibrations than increasing the stiffness (i.e., the span to depth ratio) of joists or beams. Lateral stiffness of the deck is also important; non-continuity in the slab deck, in particular the use of unconnected precast planks, should therefore be avoided. Cross-bracing has not been shown to increase lateral load distribution significantly beyond that provided by a continuous concrete deck.

G8.3   For floor spans less than 7000 mm, the deflection limitations given in Clause 6.2.1.2 in this Standard are recommended, where, for non-composite construction, stiffness should be based on non-composite action. In any case, care should be taken to avoid low damping.

G9.   **Light Wood Deck Floors Using Steel Joists**

G9.1   Transient vibrations may be objectionable for light wood deck floors using steel joists with small rolled or cold formed sections, generally with frequencies in the range 10—25 Hz. Although the same principles applying to long span floors can be used for lighter floors with higher frequencies, the motion can no longer be represented by a simple impulse applied to the floor system. This is because the persons involved — the one causing and the one receiving the motion interact with the floor to damp out the motion of the floor.

G9.2   Research carried out so far on steel joist floors with wood deck indicates that, in general, their characteristics for vibration acceptability are similar to those for wood joist floors. Evaluation tests of wood floors indicate that stiffness under point loading is the most important parameter affecting vibration comfort. Such a stiffness requirement also helps to prevent cabinet swaying, china rattling, etc. Until research under way provides a more suitable criterion a joist deflection limitation of L/360 under 2 kPa loading is recommended. This criterion applies only when sufficient lateral stiffness is provided either in the deck or by cross-bridging.

G9.3   Floor damping is less important for light floors than for long span floors since the main source of damping is provided by the persons on the floor. Also adding mass does not improve vibration comfort since an increase in mass corresponds to a decrease in effective damping. Spans continuous over a support which is a party wall between housing units should be avoided, since people are more annoyed by vibrations originating outside their units than from within. For cold formed C joists, ceiling boards or straps should be attached to the bottom flange to prevent annoying high frequency torsional vibrations in the joists.

G10. Corrective Measures for Unacceptable Floors

G10.1 Measures for correcting floors with annoying vibrations will depend on whether the vibrations are continuous or transient.

G10.2 For transient vibrations usually the most effective measure is to increase the damping. This can be done by adding partitions or damper posts in the floor below. If these methods are not suitable, special devices such as vibration absorbers or damping materials can be incorporated into the floor system. For light floors a rug is effective in reducing walking impact as well as in cushioning the sway of china cabinets.

G10.3 Corrective measures for continuous vibrations include vibration isolation, smoothing of road surface and alteration of floor frequency to reduce resonance.

G11. References

(1) Thomson, W.T. "Vibration Theory and Applications". Prentice-Hall.

(2) Steffens, R.J. "Some Aspects of Structural Vibration". Building Research Current Paper Engineering Series 37, Building Research Station, Ministry of Technology, Great Britain.

(3) Lenzen, K.H. "Vibration of Steel Joists-Concrete Slab Floors". AISC Engineering Journal, Vol. 3, No. 3, July 1966, p. 133.

(4) Lenzen, K.H. "Vibration of Floor Systems of Tall Buildings". Proceedings of ASCE-IABSE International Conference on the Planning and Design of Tall Buildings, 1972, Vol. II, p. 667.

(5) Allen, D.L. "Vibrational Behaviour of Long-Span Floor Slabs". Proceedings of the Canadian Structural Engineering Conference, 1974.

(6) Allen, D.E. and H. Rainer. "Vibration Criteria for Long Span Steel Floors". Can. J. Civ. Eng., Vol. 3, No. 2, June 1976.

(7) Wright, D.T. and R. Green. "Human Sensitivity to Vibrations". Department of Civil Engineering, Report No. 7, Queen's University, February 1959.

(8) Funk, P. "Stiffness Requirements in Terms of Human Comfort (Dynamic Criteria)". Proceedings of ASCE-IABSE International Conference on Planning and Design of Tall Buildings, 1972, Vol. III, p. 705.

(9) Onysko, D.M. "Performance of Wood-Joist Floor Systems—A Literature Review". Forest Products Laboratory Information Report OP-X-24, Canadian Forestry Service, Department of Fisheries and Forestry, January 1970.

(10) Nelson, F.C. "The Use of Viscoelastic Material to Damp Vibrations in Buildings and Large Structures". AISC Engineering Journal, Vol. 5, No. 2, April 1968, p. 72.

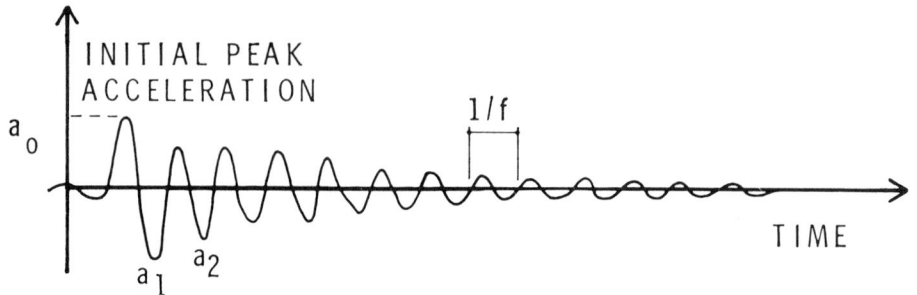

ACCELERATION, %g

INITIAL PEAK
ACCELERATION

a_0

1/f

a_1 a_2

TIME

Figure G1
Typical Transient Vibration From Heel Drop
(High Frequencies Filtered Out)

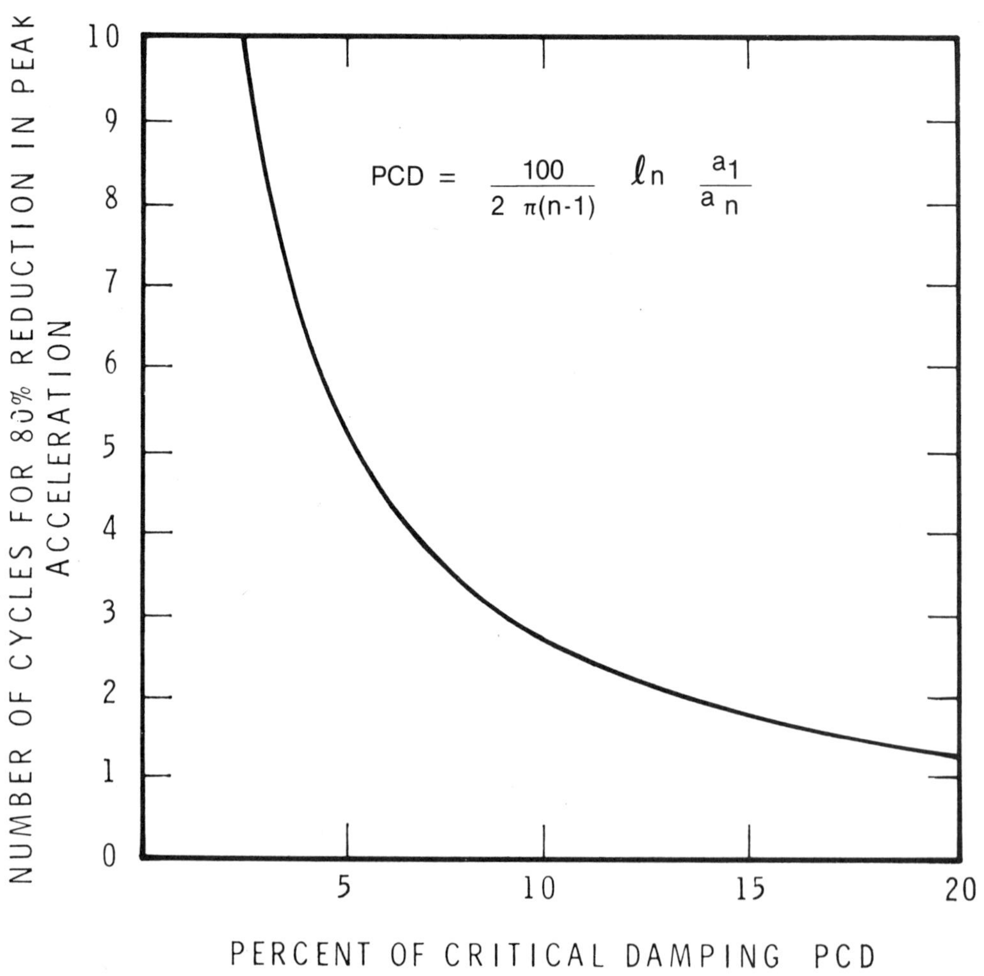

$$PCD = \frac{100}{2\pi(n-1)} \ell n \frac{a_1}{a_n}$$

NUMBER OF CYCLES FOR 80% REDUCTION IN PEAK ACCELERATION

PERCENT OF CRITICAL DAMPING PCD

Figure G2
Relation Between Damping and Decay

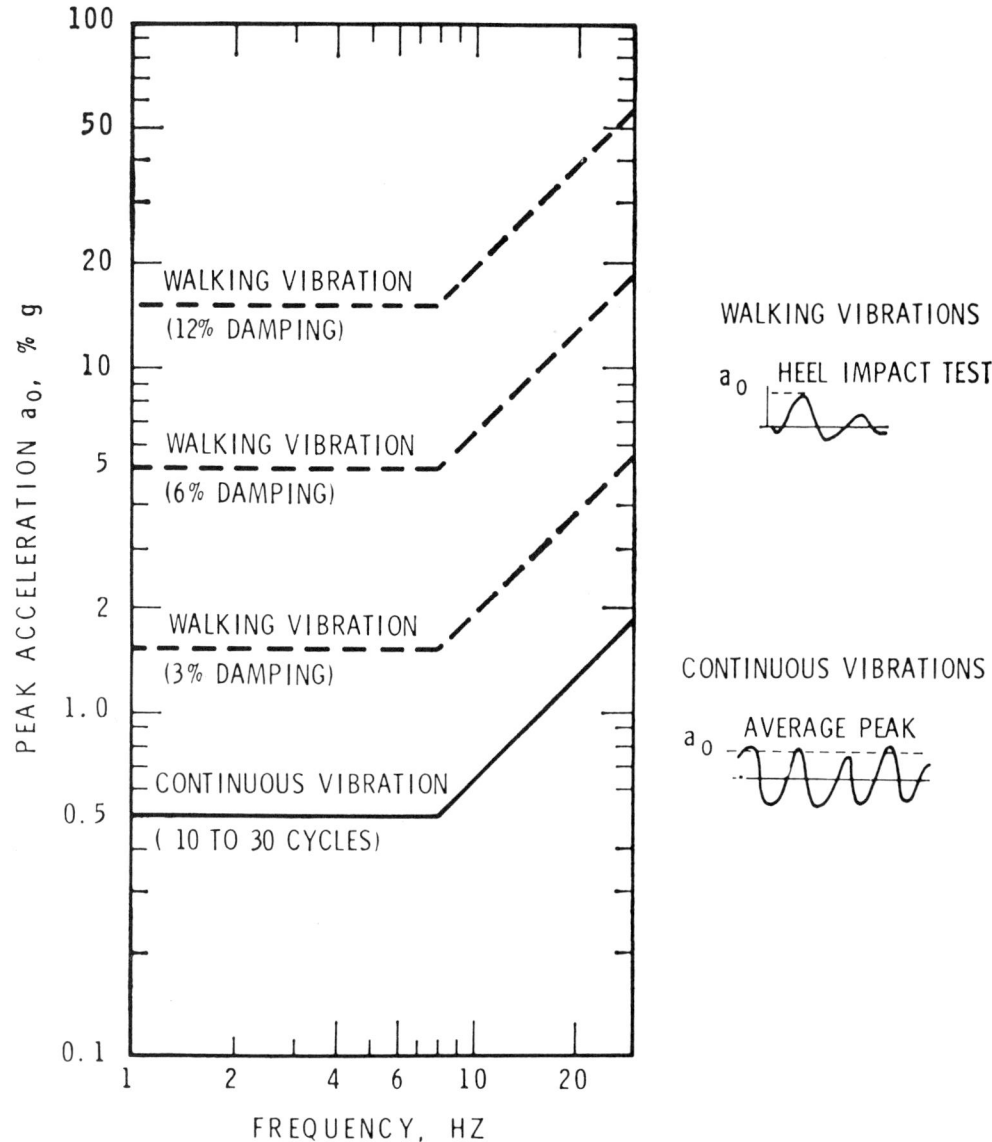

Figure G3
Annoyance Thresholds for Floor Vibrations Due to Footstep
(Residential, School, Office Occupancies)

PART SIX
PROPERTIES AND DIMENSIONS

Structural Steels . . . .   6—3

Standard Mill Practice . . . .   6—11

Principal Sources of Structural Steel Sections . . . .   6—17

Comparison Tables . . . .   6—22

Welded Wide Flange Shapes (WWF) . . . .   6—33

Rolled Structural Shapes . . . .   6—38

    W Shapes . . . .   6—40

    HP Shapes . . . .   6—54

    M Shapes . . . .   6—56

    S Shapes . . . .   6—58

    Standard Channels (C) . . . .   6—62

    Miscellaneous Channels (MC) . . . .   6—64

    Equal Leg Angles (L) . . . .   6—68

    Unequal Leg Angles (L) . . . .   6—70

Double Angles . . . .   6—72

Welded Wide Flange Tees (WWT) . . . .   6—78

Structural Tees (WT) . . . .   6—79

Hollow Structural Sections (HSS) . . . .   6—85

Built-Up Sections . . . .   6—95

Bars and Plates . . . .   6—103

Crane Rails . . . .   6—111

Fasteners . . . .   6—116

Welds . . . .   6—127

STRUCTURAL STEELS

General

The Canadian Standards Association Technical Committee on Structural Steel introduced Standards G40.20 and G40.21 in 1973 to rationalize Canada's structural steel material standards. The introduction of the International System of Units (SI) in Canada has resulted in a number of standards being revised to incorporate the new metric units. Accordingly CSA G40.20-M and CSA G40.21-M are versions reflecting the changes made necessary by the adoption of SI, as well as recent technological advances.

The steel industry, in making the change to SI, took the opportunity to rationalize the range and dimensions of rolled W sections for more efficient usage, and this too has been taken into account. The resulting new series is standard in North America and supplying mills are listed under "Principal Sources of Structural Steel Sections" page 6-17 of this Handbook. More information is available in the Canadian Standards Association Standard CAN3-G312.3-M78.

CSA G40.20-M, "General Requirements for Rolled or Welded Structural Quality Steel", sets out the general requirements governing the delivery of structural quality steels. This includes: Definitions, Variation in Dimensions, Chemical Composition, Method and Frequency of Testing Requirements, Heat Treating, Repairs of Defects, Marking, etc.

CSA G40.21-M, "Structural Quality Steels", governs the chemical and mechanical properties of the normally available 8 types and 8 strength levels of structural steel. The selection of the proper type and strength level (230 — 700 MPa) is important but for most structural purposes CSA G40.21-M 300W and either CSA G40.21-M 350AT or CSA G40.21-M 350A will be specified. The first is the standard weldable steel (W) used in most building construction. The second two are atmospheric corrosion resistant structural steels either with or without specified Charpy V-notch impact requirements, which are used in bridge construction.

The 8 types covered in G40.21-M are:

(a) **Type G — General Construction Steel.** Steels of this type meet minimum strength requirements, however, the chemical control is not such that all of these steels may be welded satisfactorily under normal field conditions. They are primarily designed for applications involving bolted connections, or for welding under carefully controlled shop conditions.

(b) **Type W — Weldable Steels.** Steels of this type meet minimum strength requirements, and are suitable for general welded construction where notch toughness at low temperatures is not a design requirement. Applications may include buildings, compression members of bridges, etc.;

(c) **Type WT — Weldable Notch Tough Steels.** Steels of this type meet specified strength and Charpy V-Notch impact requirements and are suitable for welded construction where notch toughness at low temperature is a design requirement. The purchaser, in addition to specifying the grade, also must specify the category of steel required which establishes the Charpy V-Notch test temperature and energy level. Applications may include primary tension members in bridges and similar elements;

(d) **Type R — Atmospheric Corrosion Resistant Steel.** Steels of this type meet specified strength requirements and display an atmospheric corrosion resistance approximately 4 times that of plain carbon steels.* These steels may be readily welded up to the maximum thickness covered by this Standard. Applications include unpainted siding, unpainted light structural members, etc., where notch toughness at low temperature is not a design requirement,

*Copper content not exceeding 0.02 per cent.

(e) **Type A — Atmospheric Corrosion Resistant Weldable Steel.** Steels of this type meet specified strength requirements and display an atmospheric corrosion resistance approximately 4 times that of plain carbon steels.* These steels are suitable for welded construction where notch toughness at low temperature is not a design requirement and are often used in structures in the unpainted condition. Applications are similar to those for Type "W";

(f) **Type AT — Atmospheric Corrosion Resistant Weldable Notch Tough Steel.** Steels of this type meet specified strength and Charpy V-Notch impact requirements and display an atmospheric corrosion resistance of approximately 4 times that of plain carbon steels.* These steels are suitable for welded construction where notch toughness at low temperature is a design requirement and are often used in structures in the unpainted condition. The purchaser, in addition to specifying the grade, also must specify the category of steel required which establishes the Charpy V-Notch test temperature and energy level. Applications may include primary tension members in bridges, and similar elements;

(g) **Type Q — Quenched and Tempered Low Alloy Steel Plate.** Steels of this type meet specified strength requirements. While these steels may be readily welded, the welding and fabrication techniques are of fundamental importance and must not adversely affect the properties of the plate, especially the head-affected zone. Applications may include bridges and similar structures,

(h) **Type QT — Quenched and Tempered Low Alloy Notch Tough Steel Plate.** Steels of this type meet specified strength and Charpy V-Notch impact requirements. They provide good resistance to brittle fracture and are suitable for structures where notch toughness at low temperature is a design requirement. The purchaser, in addition to specifying the grade, also must specify the category of steel required which establishes the Charpy V-Notch test temperature and energy level. While these steels may be readily welded, the welding and fabrication techniques are of fundamental importance and must not adversely affect the properties of the plate, especially the heat-affected zone. Applications may include primary tension members in bridges and similar elements.

Tables

Table 6-1, "Grades, Types, Strength Levels", page 6-6 gives the grade designation of various types of steel and strength levels according to the requirements of CAN3-G40.21-M81. (At the time of printing this Handbook, December 1980, this standard had been approved by CSA for publication in 1981.)

The availability of any type, grade and shape combination should be kept in mind when designing so as to ensure the economy of the overall structure. The listing of producers of structural sections is shown on pages 6-18 to 6-21 but this does not mean a specified product will be available in the tonnage and time frame contemplated. Local availability should be checked when the product, timing, etc. warrant.

The yield strength, tensile strength and grade levels available are tabulated in Table 6-3, "Mechanical Properties Summary", on page 6-7 according to plates, bars and welded shapes, rolled shapes and sheet piling, and hollow structural sections. Table 6-2 "Shape Size Groupings for Tensile Property Classification", page 6-6, summarizes the size groupings for rolled shapes.

Table 6-4 "Chemical Compositions", page 6-8 lists the chemical composition of many of the steel grades covered by G40.21-M.

Before leaving the Mill the steel is marked as to the type and grade. The method commonly used is that employing the colour code as shown in Tables 6—5.

*Copper content not exceeding 0.02 per cent.

Normally one end of each piece is marked with the appropriate colour code. In cases where products are bundled or are shipped as 'secured lifts' a top or outside piece may be marked, or a substantial tag used.

For more detail it is recommended that CSA G40.20-M and CAN3-G40.21-M be consulted.

GRADES, TYPES, STRENGTH LEVELS **

Table 6-1

Type	Yield Strength, MPa							
	230	260	300	350	380	400	480	700
G	230G	–	–	350G	–	400G	–	–
W	–	260W	300W	350W	380W*	400W	480W	–
WT	–	260WT	300WT	350WT	380WT*	400WT	480WT	–
R	–	–	–	350R	–	–	–	–
A	–	–	–	350A	–	400A	480A	–
AT	–	–	–	350AT	–	400AT	480AT	–
Q	–	–	–	–	–	–	–	700Q
QT	–	–	–	–	–	–	–	700QT

*These grades are available in hollow structural sections and angles only.
** See CAN3-G40.21-M81

SHAPE SIZE GROUPINGS FOR TENSILE PROPERTY CLASSIFICATION *

Table 6

Shape Type	Group 1	Group 2	Group 3	Group 4	Group 5
W Shapes	W610 x 82 & 92 W530 x 66–85 incl. W460 x 52–106 incl. W410 x 39–85 incl. W360 x 33–79 incl. W310 x 21–86 incl. W250 x 18–67 incl. W200 x 15–71 incl. W150 x 13–37 incl. W130 x 24 & 28 W100 x 19	W920 x 201–313 incl. W840 x 176–226 incl. W760 x 147–314 incl. W690 x 125–265 incl. W610 x 101–241 incl. W530 x 92–219 incl. W460 x 113–117 incl. W410 x 100–149 incl. W360 x 91–196 incl. W310 x 97–158 incl. W250 x 73–167 incl. W200 x 86 & 100	W920 x 342–446 incl. W840 x 299–359 incl. W360 x 216–314 incl. W310 x 179–283 incl.	W360 x 347–818 incl. W310 x 313–500 incl.	W360 x 900–1086 in
M Shapes S Shapes HP Shapes C Shapes MC Shapes L Shapes	To 56 kg/m incl. To 52 kg/m incl. To 30.8 kg/m incl. To 42.4 kg/m incl. To 13 mm incl.	Over 52 kg/m To 152 kg/m incl. Over 30.8 kg/m Over 42.4 kg/m Over 13–20 mm incl.	Over 152 kg/m Over 20 mm		

Note: Tees cut from W, M, and S shapes fall in the same group as the shape from which they are cut.
* See CSA G40.20-M

Table 6-3   MECHANICAL PROPERTIES SUMMARY

CSA G40.21-M* Type	Grade	Tensile Strength F_u (MPa)	Plates, Bars and Welded Shapes — Nominal Maximum Thickness t (mm)	F_y (MPa) min. t≤40	40<t≤65	65<t	Rolled Shapes and Sheet Piling — Usual Maximum Shape Size Group	F_y (MPa) min. Groups 1 and 2	Groups 3 and 4	Group 5	Hollow Structural Sections — Usual Maximum Wall Thickness (mm)	F_y (MPa) min.
G	230G	380-500[1]	300	230	230	230	5	230	230	230		
	350G	480-690	30	350[3]			3	350	350			
	400G	550-720	30	400[3]			3	400	400			
W	260W	410-590	100	260	260	250	4	260	260			
	300W	450-620[4]	100	300	290	280	3	300	290		16	300
	350W	450-650[2]	100	350	330	320	2	350			16	350
	380W	480-650									16	380
	400W	520-690	20	400			1	400				
	480W	590-790	20	480			1	480				
WT	260WT	410-590	100	260	260	250	5	260	260	250		
	300WT	450-620	100	300	290	280	5	300	290	280		
	350WT	480-650	60	350	330		4	350	330		16	350
	380WT	480-650									16	380
	400WT	520-690	20	400			2	400				
	480WT	590-790	20	480			1	480				
R	350R	480-650	14	350			1	350				
A	350A	480-650	100	350	350	350	5	350	350	320	16	350
	400A	520-690	40	400			2	400				
	480A	590-790	20	480								
AT	350AT	480-650	100	350	350	350	5	350	350	320	16	350
	400AT	520-690	40	400			2	400				
	480AT	590-790	20	480								
Q	700Q	800-950	50	700	700							
QT	700QT	800-950	50	700	700							

[1] Upper bound F_u = 520 MPa for rolled shapes and sheet piling.
[2] Upper bound F_u = 620 MPa for rolled shapes, sheet piling and HSS.
[3] Bar size shapes only.
[4] 410-590 for HSS only.
* See CAN3-G40.21-M81

CSA G40.21-M* Grade	Chemical Composition (Heat Analysis) Per Cent[14] All percentages are maxima unless otherwise indicated								
	C	Mn	P	S	Si[12,13]	Other[2]	Cr	Ni	Cu[9]
230G	0.26	1.20[3]	0.05	0.05	0.40	0.10	—	—	—
350G } 400G }	0.28[4]	1.65	0.04	0.05	0.40	0.10	—	—	—
260W	0.20	0.50/1.50	0.04	0.05	0.40	0.10	—	—	—
300W	0.22[5]	0.50/1.50[5]	0.04	0.05	0.40	0.10	—	—	—
350W	0.23	0.50/1.50	0.04	0.05	0.40	0.10	—	—	—
380W[6]	0.23	0.50/1.50	0.04	0.05	0.40	0.10	—	—	—
400W	0.23	0.50/1.50	0.04	0.05	0.40	0.10	—	—	—
480W	0.26	0.50/1.50	0.04	0.05	0.40	0.10	—	—	—
260WT	0.20	0.80/1.50	0.03	0.04	0.15/0.40	0.10	—	—	—
300WT	0.22	0.80/1.50	0.03	0.04	0.15/0.40	0.10	—	—	—
350WT	0.22	0.80/1.50[7]	0.03	0.04	0.15/0.40	0.10[8]	—	—	—
380WT[6]	0.22	0.80/1.50	0.03	0.04	0.15/0.40	0.10	—	—	—
400WT	0.22	0.80/1.50[7]	0.03	0.04	0.15/0.40	0.10[8]	—	—	—
480WT	0.26	0.80/1.50[7]	0.03	0.04	0.15/0.40	0.10[8]	—	—	—
350R	0.16	0.75	0.05/0.15	0.04	0.75	0.10	0.30/1.25[10]	0.90[10]	0.20/0.60[10]
350A	0.20	0.75/1.35	0.03	0.04	0.15/0.40	0.10	0.70[11]	0.90[11]	0.20/0.60
400A	0.20	0.75/1.35	0.03	0.04	0.15/0.40	0.10	0.70[11]	0.90[11]	0.20/0.60
480A	0.20	1.00/1.60	0.025	0.035	0.15/0.40	0.12	0.70[11]	0.25/0.50[11]	0.20/0.60
350AT	0.20	0.75/1.35[7]	0.03	0.04	0.15/0.40	0.10	0.70[11]	0.90[11]	0.20/0.60
400AT	0.20	0.75/1.35[7]	0.03	0.04	0.15/0.40	0.10	0.70[11]	0.90[11]	0.20/0.60
480AT	0.20	1.00/1.60[7]	0.025	0.035	0.15/0.40	0.12	0.70[11]	0.25/0.50[11]	0.20/0.60
700Q	0.20	1.50	0.03	0.04	0.15/0.35	—	Boron 0.0005/0.005		—
700QT	0.20	1.50	0.03	0.04	0.15/0.35	—	Boron 0.0005/0.005		—

*See CAN3-G40.21-M81

Notes:
1. Actual standard should be consulted for full details.
2. Elements (C_b, V) may be used singly or in combination. Al, when used, is not included in summation.
3. May have 1.50% Mn.
4. May have 0.32% C for thicknesses over 20 mm.
5. For HSS 0.26% C and 0.30/1.20% Mn.
6. HSS only.
7. With prior agreement Mn may be increased. See CSA G40.21-M.
8. 0.01/0.02% N may be used but N ≯ ¼V.
9. Copper content of 0.20% minimum may be specified.
10. Cr + Ni + Cu ≮ 1.00%.
11. Cr + Ni ≮ 0.40%.
12. Si content of 0.15% to 0.40% is required for W and WT type steel over 40 mm thickness or bar diameter except as noted in footnote 13.
13. By purchaser's request or producer's option no minimum Si content is required so long as 0.02% of aluminum content is used.
14. Additional alloying elements may be used when approved.

Table 6-5

Steel Grade	Primary Colour	Secondary Colour
230G 350G 400G	Orange Blue Black	Orange Orange Orange
260W 300W 350W 380W 400W 480W	White Green Blue Brown Black Yellow	Green Green Green Green Green Green
260WT 300WT 350WT 380WT 400WT 480WT	White Green Blue Brown Black Yellow	White White White White White White
350R	Blue	Blue
350A 400A 480A	Blue Black Yellow	Yellow Yellow Yellow
350AT 400AT 480AT	Blue Black Yellow	Brown Brown Brown
700Q	Red	Red
700QT	Red	Purple

In this Code the following colour system applies:

Strength Level	Primary Colour	Type	Secondary Colour
260	White	G	Orange
300	Green	W	Green
350	Blue	WT	White
380	Brown	R	Blue
400	Black	A	Yellow
480	Yellow	AT	Brown
700	Red	Q	Red
		QT	Purple

Note: See also page 6—4.

NOTES

STANDARD MILL PRACTICE

General

Rolled structural shapes are produced by passing hot blooms, billets or slabs of steel through a series of grooved rolls. Wear on the rolls may cause the dimensions of the finished product to vary slightly from the theoretical, published dimensions. Standard rolling tolerances have been established to make maximum allowance for roll wear, and other factors. These tolerances are contained in CSA Standard G40.20-M for shapes supplied in grades of steel covered by CSA material standards, and in ASTM Standard A6 for shapes supplied in grades of steel covered by ASTM material standards.

Letter symbols representing dimensions on sketches shown herein are in accordance with CSA G40.20-M, ASTM A6 and mill catalogs and not necessarily as defined by the general nomenclature of this manual.

Methods of increasing areas and mass by spreading rolls

Almost every nominal size group of rolled shapes contains several specific shapes, each of which is slightly different in mass, area and properties from the other members of the same size group. The following illustrations and explanations describe the method of increasing areas and mass of shapes from the minimum nominal sizes by spreading the rolls.

For W Shapes (Fig. 1), the thickness of both flange and web is changed, resulting in a corresponding increase in beam depth and flange width, the distance between inside faces of flanges remaining unchanged.

For S Shapes and Channels (Fig. 2 and 3), the web thickness and flange width are increased by equal amounts, all other dimensions remaining unchanged.

For Angles (Fig. 4) the thickness of each leg is increased an equal amount, resulting in a corresponding slight increase in the leg length.

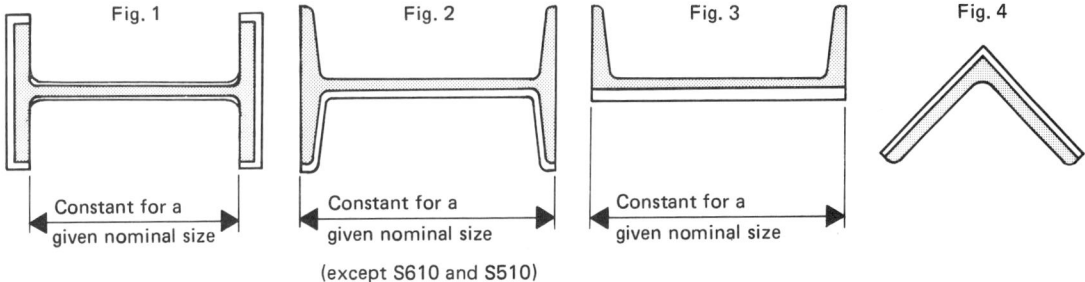

Fig. 1 — Constant for a given nominal size

Fig. 2 — Constant for a given nominal size (except S610 and S510)

Fig. 3 — Constant for a given nominal size

Fig. 4

Cambering of rolled sections

After the section has been rolled it is cold straightened to meet the sweep and camber tolerances as specified below. The following table lists the permissible variations in straightness for standard and wide-flange shapes, bars, and bar-size shapes.

Shapes	Maximum Permissible Variation in Straightness mm	Shape	Maximum Permissible Variation in Straightness, mm
Standard shapes (camber)	$\dfrac{\text{Length in mm}}{500}$	Wide-flange beams when ordered as columns (camber or sweep):	
Wide-flange beams (camber or sweep)	$\dfrac{\text{Length in mm}}{1000}$		
Bars and bar-size shapes*	$\dfrac{\text{Length in mm}}{250}$	Lengths of 14 000 and under	$\dfrac{\text{Length in mm}}{1000}$, but not more than 10 mm
Steel sheet piling	$\dfrac{\text{Length in mm}}{1000}$	Lengths over 14 000 mm	$10\text{ mm} + \dfrac{\text{length} - 14\,000}{1000}$

*Permissible variations do not apply to hot rolled bars if any subsequent heating operation has been performed.

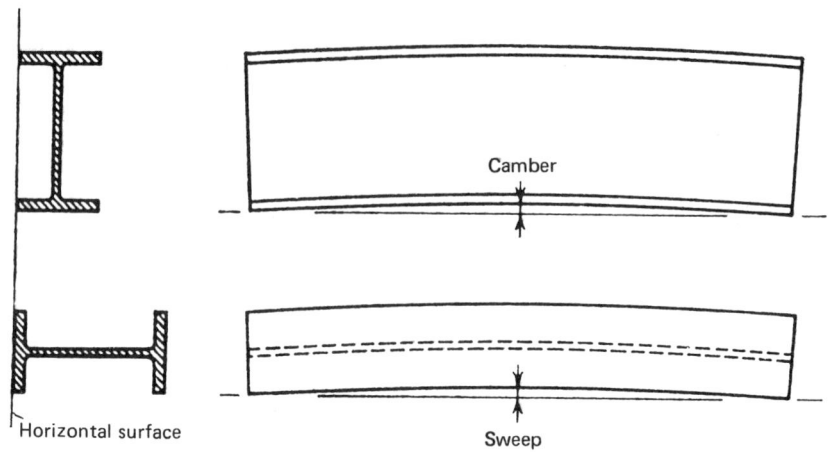

Positions for measuring camber and sweep

Camber is a deflection along the depth of a section approximating a simple regular curve and is usually measured half way between any two specified points along the section. The length for purposes of determining the maximum permissible variation is the distance between the two specified points.

Sweep is similar to camber but is measured along the width of the section.

WELDED WIDE FLANGE SECTIONS

Notes:

(1) "A" is measured at the centre-line of the web.
(2) "B" is the actual flange width and is measured parallel to the flange.

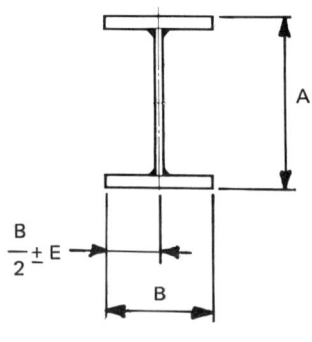

MANUFACTURING TOLERANCES

Depth A mm		Width of Flange B mm		Web Off-Centre, E mm
Over	Under	Over	Under	Not over
4	3	6	5	5

Warpage & Tilt: The combined warpage and tilt of the flange shall not exceed 1/200 of the total width of the flange, or 3 mm, whichever is greater, when measured from the toe of the flange to a line normal to the plane of the web through the intersection of the centreline of the web with the outside surface of the flange plate.

Web Flatness: The deviation from flatness of the web as measured in a length of the web equal to the total depth of the beam shall not exceed 1/150 of the total depth of the beam.

W SHAPES†

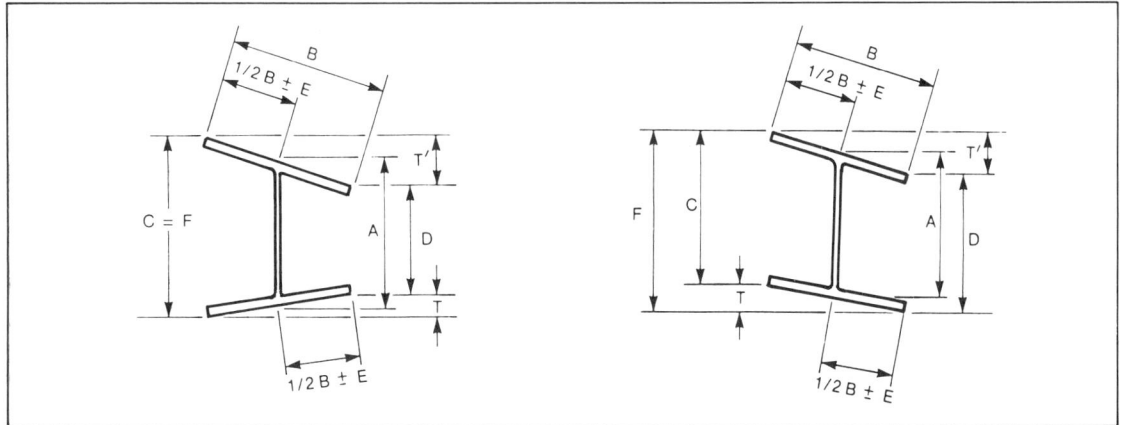

NOTE:
"A" is measured at centreline of web.
"B" is the actual flange width and is measured parallel to the flange.
"F" is measured parallel to the web.

Nominal Depth mm	A Depth mm		B Flange Width mm		T+T' Out-of-Square mm	C - D Out-of-Parallel mm	E Web Off-Centre mm	F Max. Overall Depth at any Cross-Section mm
	Over	Under	Over	Under	Not Over	Not Over	Not Over	Over Nominal
300 and under* Over 300	4 4	3 3	6 6	5 5	5 6	5 6	5 5	6 6

*Includes all H-beams rolled on mills having vertical rolls.

PERMISSIBLE VARIATIONS IN LENGTH
FOR STANDARD AND WIDE FLANGE SHAPES

Shapes	Variations from Specified Length for Lengths Given, mm									
	To 9 000 incl.		Over 9000 to 12 000 incl.		Over 12 000 to 15 000 incl.		Over 15 000 to 20 000 incl.		Over 20 000	
	Over	Under	Over	Under	Over	Under	Over	Under	Over	Under
All standard sections	13	6	19	6	25	6	29	6	32	6
Wide-flange shapes: Beams 610 mm and under in nominal depth.	10	10	13	10	16	10	21	10	24	10
Beams over 610 mm in nominal depth and all columns.	13	13	16	13	19	13	24	13	27	13

When wide flange sections are used as bearing piles, the length tolerance is plus 120 mm, minus 0 mm. See page 6-14 for other tolerances.
†includes HP sections.

S and C SHAPES

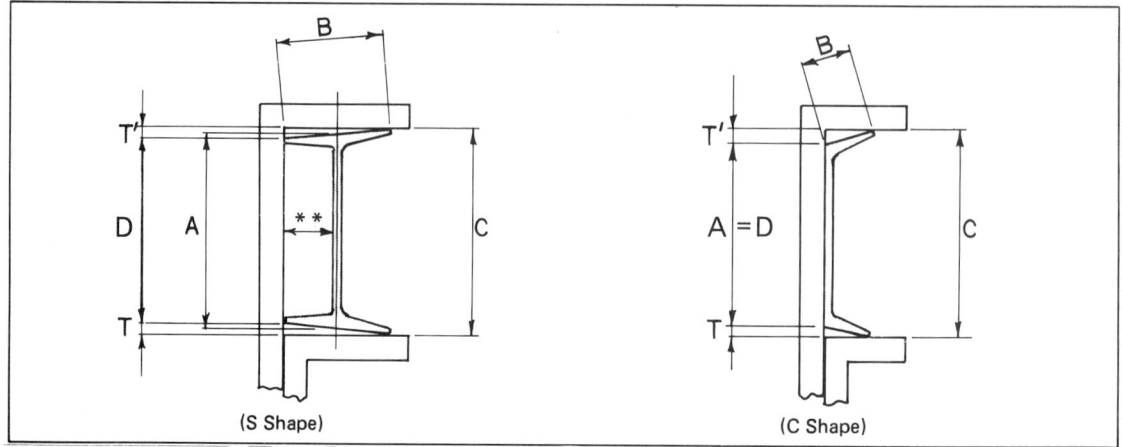

(S Shape)   (C Shape)

**Back of square and centreline of web to be parallel when measuring out-of-square

Shape	Nominal Specified Size, mm	Depth, A* mm		Flange Width B mm		Out-of-Square $\frac{T + T'}{B}$	Out-of-Parallel $\frac{C-D}{B}$
		Over	Under	Over	Under		
S Shapes	75 to 180 incl.	2	2	4	3	0.03	0.03
	over 180 to 360 incl.	4	2	4	4	0.03	0.03
	over 360 to 610 incl.	5	3	5	5	0.03	0.03
Channels	75 to 180 incl.	2	2	4	3	0.03	0.03
	over 180 to 360 incl.	3	2	3	4	0.03	0.03
	over 360	5	3	3	5	0.03	0.03

*A is measured at centreline of web for beams and at back of web for channels.

CUTTING TOLERANCES

Section	Variations from Specified Length for Lengths Giving mm									
	to 9 000 mm inclusive		Over 9 000 to 12 000 mm inclusive		Over 12 000 to 15 000 mm inclusive		Over 15 000 to 20 000 mm inclusive		Over 20 000 mm	
	Over	Under	Over	Under	Over	Under	Over	Under	Over	Under
S Shapes and American Standard Channels	13	6	19	6	25	6	29	6	32	6

OTHER TOLERANCES FOR W, S & C SHAPES

Area and Mass Variation: ± 2.5% theoretical or specified amount.
Ends Out-of-Square: S shapes and channels 0.016 mm per mm of depth.

ANGLES

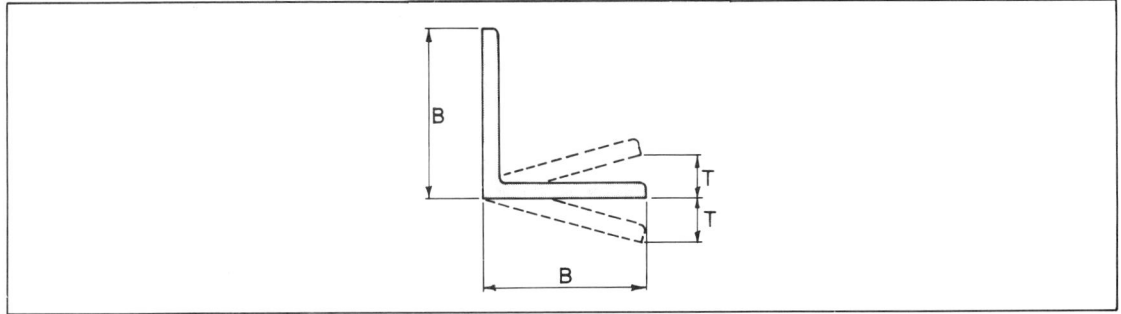

BAR SIZE⁺   **STRUCTURAL SIZE**

Specified Length of Leg mm	Variations from Thickness for Thicknesses Given over and under mm			Variations from Length of Leg Over and Under mm	Shape	Specified size mm	Length of Leg B, mm		Out-of-Square T/B
	5 and under	Over 5 to 10 incl.	Over 10				Over	Under	
50 and under	0.2	0.3	0.3	1	Angles*	75 to 100 incl.	4	2	0.024
Over 50	0.3	0.4	0.4	2		Over 100 to 150 incl.	4	3	0.024
						Over 150	5	3	0.024

Notes:
1. The longer leg of an unequal angle determines the size for permissible variation.
2. Permissible out-of-square in either direction, 1-1/2 degrees.

Notes:
*For unequal leg angles, longer leg determines classification.

Other Angle Tolerances

Area and Mass Variation: ± 2.5% theoretical or specified amount.

Ends Out-of-Square: 0.024 mm per mm of leg length or 1½ degrees. Tolerances are based on the longer leg of an unequal angle.

+Bar size shape means rolled angles having a maximum dimension of cross-section less than 75 mm.

HOLLOW STRUCTURAL SECTIONS

Cross-Sectional Dimensions

Outside dimensions measured across the flats or diameter positions at least 50 mm from either end of a piece, including an allowance for convexity or concavity, shall not vary from the specified dimensions of the section by more than the prescribed tolerances.

Tolerance includes allowance for convexity or concavity. Tolerance may be increased 50 per cent when applied to the smaller dimension of rectangular sections whose ratio of cross-sectional dimensions is between 1.5 and 3, and 100 per cent when this ratio exceeds 3.

Largest Outside Dimension Across Flats or Diameter mm	Tolerance* mm
To 65	± 0.5
Over 65 – 90 incl.	± 0.8
Over 90 – 140 incl.	± 1.0
Over 140	± 1 per cent

Corner Squareness

For rectangular sections, corners shall be square (90°) within ±1° for hot formed sections and 2° for cold formed sections. Squareness shall be determined with a protractor or other suitable measuring device and the average slope of the sides shall be the basis for determination.

Straightness Variation

Deviation from straightness in millimetres shall not exceed total length in millimetres divided by 500.

Maximum Outside Corner Radii

Wall Thickness mm	Maximum Outside Corner Radii, mm	
	Perimeter to 700 mm Incl.	Perimeter Over 700 mm
To 3 incl.	6	—
Over 3 — 4 incl.	8	—
Over 4 — 5 incl.	15	—
Over 5 — 6 incl.	18	
Over 6 — 8 incl.	21	18
		24
Over 8 — 10 incl.	27	30
Over 10 — 13 incl.	36	39
Over 13	—	3 x wall thickness

Wall Thickness

Not more than ±10 per cent from the nominal wall thickness specified, except the weld seam. (See G40.20-M)

Classes of Section

Class H means hollow sections made by: (i) A seamless or furnace-buttwelded (continuous-welded) or automatic electric-welding process, and hot formed to final shape; or (ii) A seamless or automatic electric-welding process producing a continuous weld, and cold formed to final shape; subsequently stress-relieved by heating to a temperature of 450°C of higher; followed by cooling in air.

Class C means hollow sections that are cold formed from a section produced either by a seamless process or by an automatic electric-welding process producing a continuous weld.

Mass Variation

On the basis that the density of rolled steel is 7850 kg/m³, the actual mass of an individual length of hollow structural section shall not deviate from the published mass by more than -3.5 or +10 per cent.

Permissible Twist

Tolerances for twist for rectangular or other non-circular profiles are prescribed as follows: Twist of a rectangular section may be measured by holding down the side of one end of the section on a flat surface and noting how high above the surface is either corner at the opposite end of that side.

Largest Outside Dimension mm	Maximum Twist per 1000 mm of Length mm
To 65 incl.	0.8
Over 65 — 105 incl.	1.0
Over 105 — 155 incl.	1.1
Over 155 — 205 incl.	1.2
Over 205	1.4

Cutting Tolerances

Tolerances in millimetres on ordered cold cut lengths are:
+12 and —6 for lengths 7500 and under;
+18 and —6 for lengths over 7500.

Tolerances in millimetres on ordered hot cut lengths of hot rolled sections area:
±25 for lengths 7500 and under;
±50 for lengths over 7500.

PRINCIPAL SOURCES OF STRUCTURAL STEEL SECTIONS

General

Canadian steel mills produce a wide range of structural sections, varying from light angles to deep welded wide flange beams and heavy welded wide flange columns. Some structural sections, particularly the larger rolled wide flange shapes and certain lighter rolled beams, are not produced in Canada but are imported from other countries and are usually readily available.

Structural sections that must be imported are identified as being "not available from Canadian mills" in various tables in this book. The following four pages provide detailed information on some of the more common sources (for Canada) of structural sections. A summary of the majority of structural sections available from Canadian mills is provided below. For information on other shapes used occasionally in construction, reference should be made to the various producers' catalogues.

STRUCTURAL SECTIONS AVAILABLE FROM CANADIAN MILLS		
[3]W610 x 241 − 101	WWF1200	S310 x 52−47
[1]W530 x 138−82	WWF1100	S250 x 52−38
[1]W460 x 106−61	WWF1000	S200 x 34−27
W410 x 85−39	WWF900	S150 x 26−19
W360 x 79−33	WWF800	S130 x 22−15
W310 x 283−39	WWF700	S100 x 11
W250 x 167−33	WWF550	S75 x 11−8
W200 x 100−27	WWF500	
W150 x 37−22	WWF450	C380 x 74−50
	WWF400	C310 x 45−31
[1]HP310 x 174−79	WWF350	C250 x 37−23
HP250 x 85−62		C230 x 30−20
HP200 x 54	M100 x 19	C200 x 28−17
		C180 x 18−15
		C150 x 19−12
		C130 x 17−10
		C100 x 11−8
		C75 x 9−6

ANGLES − all sizes except 200 x 150, 200 x 100.
HOLLOW STRUCTURAL SECTIONS[2]
Square   − 25.4 x 25.4, 31.8 x 31.8, 38.1 x 38.1, 50.8 x 50.8, 63.5 x 63.5,
           76.2 x 76.2, 88.9 x 88.9, 101.6 x 101.6, 127.0 x 127.0, 152.4 x 152.4,
           177.8 x 177.8, 203.2 x 203.2, 254.0 x 254.0, 304.8 x 304.8
Rectangular − 50.8 x 25.4, 76.2 x 50.8, 88.9 x 63.5, 101.6 x 50.8, 101.6 x 76.2,
           127.0 x 50.8, 127.0 x 63.5, 127.0 x 76.2, 152.4 x 101.6, 177.8 x 127.0
           203.2 x 101.6, 203.2 x 152.4, 254.0 x 152.4, 304.8 x 203.2
Round − All sizes
PIPE − All Standard Sizes

Notes:
1. W530 x 85, W460 x 68 and HP310 x 125 are not produced in Canada.
2. HSS Sizes listed are those given in CAN3-G312.3-M78.
3. W610 x 241−101 denotes all sections from W610 x 241 to W610 x 101 inclusive. Other designations are similar.

SOURCES OF STRUCTURAL SHAPES

Designation	Source	Designation	Source	Designation	Source
W920 x 446–201	BOU	W150 x 37–22	ABCINORU	C130 x 13	A[1]BCDIJLNSU
		W150 x 24–18	BINR	C130 x 10	A[1]BCDIJLNSUW
W840 x 359–299	BU	W150 x 14	BIJNRU		
W840 x 226–176	BOU			C100 x 11 & 8	A[1]BCDIJLNRSUW
		W130 x 28–24	BIR	C100 x 9	DLS
W760 x 314–257	BU				
W760 x 196–147	BOU	W100 x 19	BNR	C75 x 9	CDJLNRS
				C75 x 7	BCDIJLNORSUW
W690 x 265–217	BU	WWF all sizes listed on previous page	A	C75 x 6	BCDIJLNRSUW
W690 x 170–125	BOU				
				MC460 x 86–63.5	BU
W610 x 241–155	ABIRU			MC330 x 74–47.3	BU
W610 x 140–101	ABIORU	HP360 x 174–108	BOU	MC310 x 74–46	BU
W610 x 92–82	BIRU	HP330 x 149–89	IR	MC310 x 15.8	J
		HP310 x 174–132	A	MC250 x 61.2–32.6	BU
W530 x 219–150	BIRU	HP310 x 125	IOR	MC250 x 12.5–9.7	J
W530 x 138–82	ABIORU	HP310 x 110 & 79	ABIORU		
W530 x 85–66	BIRU	HP310 x 94	AIOR	MC230 x 37.8–35.6	B
		HP250 x 85–62	ABINORU	MC200 x 33.9–27.8	BU
W460 x 177–113	BIRU	HP200 x 54	ABINORU	MC200 x 12.6	J
W460 x 106–74	ABINORU			MC180 x 33.8–28.4	BU
W460 x 67	AO			MC180 x 26.2	U
W460 x 61	A	S610 x 180–119	B		
W460 x 68–52	BINORU	S510 x 143–98	B	MC150 x 26.8	B
		S460 x 104–81.4	BU	MC150 x 22.8	BDU
W410 x 149–100	BIRU	S380 x 74–64	BU	MC150 x 24.3	BOU
W410 x 85	ABINRU	S310 x 74–60.7	BIU	MC150 x 22.5–17.9	BU
W410 x 74–39	ABCINORU				
		S310 x 52–47	ABIU	M310 x 17.6	J
W360 x 1086–677	RU	S250 x 52	ABCIU	M250 x 13.4	J
W360 x 634–347	ORU	S250 x 38	ABCIOU	M200 x 9.7	J
W360 x 314	RU	S200 x 34–27	ABCIU	M150 x 29.8	U
W360 x 287–134	ORU	S180 x 30	C	M150 x 6.5	J
W360 x 122–91	BIRU	S180 x 22.8	BCIU	M130 x 28.1	B
W360 x 79–64	ABCIRU			M100 x 19	AIU
W360 x 57–45	ABCINORU	S150 x 26–19	ABCIU		
W360 x 39–33	ABCINRU	S130 x 22	AC		
		S130 x 15	ABCIU		
W310 x 500–313	IR	S100 x 14.1	B[1] CIU		
W310 x 283–97	ABIORU	S100 x 11	ABCIU		
W310 x 86–79	ABIRU	S75 x 11	ABCI		
W310 x 74–60	ABCIRU	S75 x 8	ABCIU		
W310 x 52–39	ABCINORU				
W310 x 33–24	BCINORU				
W310 x 21	BCINRU				
		C380 x 74–50	ABCINU		
W250 x 167–115	ABIORU	C310 x 45–31	ABCINU		
W250 x 101–73	ABINORU	C250 x 45	BINU		
W250 x 67–49	ABCINRU	C250 x 37–23	ABCINU		
W250 x 45–33	ABCINORU	C230 x 30	AC		
W250 x 28–22	BCINORU	C230 x 22–20	ABCIU		
W250 x 18	BCINR	C200 x 28–17	ABCIJLNU		
		C180 x 22	CL		
W200 x 100–71	ABCIORU	C180 x 18–15	ABCILNU		
W200 x 59–46	ABCINORU				
W200 x 42–36	ABCINRU	C150 x 19	A[1]BCDIJLNSU		
W200 x 31–27	ABCINORU	C150 x 16	A[1]BCDIJLNU		
W200 x 22–19	BCINRU	C150 x 12	A[1]BCDIJLNSUW		
W200 x 15	BCINR	C130 x 17	DL		

SOURCE KEY:

A The Algoma Steel Corporation, Limited.

B Bethlehem Steel Export Co. of Canada Ltd.

C CF & I Steel Corporation

D Sidbec – Dosco

I Inland Steel Corporation

J Jones & Laughlin Steel Corp.

L Lake Ontario Steel Company Limited

M Manitoba Rolling Mills (Canada) Limited

N Northwestern Steel and Wire Company

O British Steel Corporation

R Armco Inc.

S Stelco, Inc.

U United States Steel International, Ltd.

W Western Canada Steel Limited

[1] Check current availability.

Size	Source															Size	Source													
	A	B	C	D	I	J	L	M	N	O	R	S	U	W			A	B	C	D	I	J	L	M	N	O	R	S	U	W
200 x 200 x 30	○	○		○										○		200 x 150 x 25*		○	○	○									○	
25	○	○		○										○		20*		○	○	○									○	
20	○	○		○						●				○		16*			○											
16	○	○		○						●				○		13*		○	○	○									○	
13	○	○		○										○		200 x 100 x 20*		○											○	
10																16*		○												
150 x 150 x 20	○	○	○	■	○									○		13*		○											○	
16	○	○	○	●	○									○		10*										●				
13	○	○	○	●	○									○		150 x 100 x 16	○	○	○	■	○			○	○	●				
10	○	○	○	●	○					●				○		13	○	○	○	●	○			○	○				○	
125 x 125 x 16	○		○	■	○		○		○					○		10	○	○	○	●	○			○	○				○	
13	○	○	○	●	○		○		○					○		8	○	□	○	●	○			○	○				○	
10	○	○	○	●	○		○		○					○		125 x 90 x 16	□	□	○	■	○		○	○	○					
8	○	○	○	●	○		○		○					○		13	□	○	○	●	○		○	○	○	○				
100 x 100 x 16	□	○	○	■	○	○	○	○	○			○		○		10	□	○	○	●	○		○	○	○	○			○	
13	□	○	○	●	○	○	○	○	○		○	○	○	○		8	□	○	○	●	○		○	○	○	○			○	
10	□	○	○	●	○	○	○	○	○	■	○	○	○	○		125 x 75 x 13	□	○	○	●	○		○	○	○	○			○	
8	□	○	○	●	○	○	○	○	○	●	○	○	○	○		10	□	○	○	●	○		○	○	○	○	●		○	
6	□	○	○	●	○	○	○	○	○	○	○	○	○	○		8	□	○	○	●	○		○	○	○	○	●		○	
90 x 90 x 13	□		○	●	○	○	○	○	○		○	○				6	□	○	○	●			○	○	○	○			○	
10	□	○	○	●	○	○	○	○	○		○	○				100 x 90 x 13	□	○	○	●	○		○	○	○		○		○	
8	□	○	○	●	○	○	○	○	○	●	○	○				10	□	○	○	●	○		○	○	○		○		○	
6	□	○	○	●	○	○	○	○	○	●	○	○				8	□	○	○	●	○		○	○	○		○		○	
75 x 75 x 13	□	○	○	●	○	○	○	○	○		○	○	○			6	□	○	○	●	○		○	○	○		○		○	
10	□	○	○	●	○	○	○	○	○		○	○	○			100 x 75 x 13	□	○	○	●	○		○	○	○	○	○	○	○	
8	□	○	○	●	○	○	○	○	○		○	○	○			10	□	○	○	●	○		○	○	○	○	●	○	○	
6	□	○	○	●	○	○	○	○	○		○	○	○			8	□	○	○	●	○		○	○	○	○	●	○	○	
5	□	○	○	●		○	○	○	○		○	○	○			6	□	○	○	●			○	○	○	○	○	○	○	
65 x 65 x 10	□	○	○	●	○		○	○	○		○	○	○			90 x 75 x 13	□			●			○	○	○		○		○	
8	□	○	○	●	○		○	○	○		○	○	○			10		○		●			○	○	○		○		○	
6	□	○	○	●	○		○	○	○		○	○	○			8	□	○		●			○	○	○		○		○	
5	□	○	○	●			○	○	○		○	○	○			6	□	○		●			○	○	○		○		○	
55 x 55 x 10	□	○	○	●	○		○	○	○		○	○	○			5				●										
8	□	○	○	●	○		○	○	○		○	○	○			90 x 65 x 10	□	○	○	●			○	○	○		○	○	○	
6	□	○	○	●	○		○	○	○		○	○	○			8	□	○	○	●			○	○	○		○	○	○	
5	□	○	○	●			○	○	○		○	○	○			6	□	○	○	●			○	○	○		○	○	○	
4				■												5				●										
3		○	○	■			○	○	○		○	○	○			80 x 60 x 10				●										
45 x 45 x 8				●			○	○				○				8				●							●			
6		○		●			○	○			○	○				6				●							●			
5		○		●			○	○	●		○	○				5				●										
4				■			○	○	●			○				75 x 50 x 8	□	○	○	●	○		○	○	○	○	●	○	○	
3		○		■			○	○	●							6	□	○	○	●	○		○	○	○	○	●	○	○	○
35 x 35 x 6		○		●			○	○			○	○				5	□	□	○	●	○		○	○	○	○		○	○	○
5		○		●			○	○			○	○				65 x 50 x 8	□	○		●			○	○	○	○	●	○	○	
4		○		■			○	○				○				6	□	○		●	○		○	○	○	○	●	○	○	
3		○		■			○	○								5				●			○	○	○	○	●	○	○	
25 x 25 x 5		○		X			○	○	●							4				■										
4				X			○	○	●							55 x 35 x 6		○		X			○	○				○		
3		○		X			○	○	●							5		○		X			○	○						
																4				X			○	○						
																3		○		X			○	○						
																45 x 30 x 6		○		X			○	○						
																5		○		X			○	○						
																4				X										
																3		○		X			○	○						

KEY TO SYMBOLS:
- ● Produces listed size.
- ○ Produces comparable Imperial size. See pages 6-28 and 6-29. Check manufacturer's catalog for properties and dimensions.
- ■ Check availability of listed product.
- □ Check availability of comparable Imperial size.
- X Produces cold formed product. See pages 6-68 to 6-77.
- * Not available from Canadian mills.

Note: During the period of metric conversion, designers specifying metric angles should be prepared to accept substitutions of Imperial angles. See pages 6—28 and 6—29 for comparison tables of metric and Imperial series equal and unequal leg angles.

SOURCES OF HOLLOW STRUCTURAL SECTIONS

Size	Source	Size	Source	Size	Source
SQUARE		38.1 x 38.1 x 4.78	OST	101.6 x 76.2 x 9.53	OPST
304.8 x 304.8 x 12.70	S	3.81	OST	7.95	OPST
11.13	S	3.18	IOST	6.35	IOPST
9.53	ST	2.54	IOST	4.78	IOPST
7.95	ST				
6.35	ST	31.8 x 31.8 x 3.81	ST	101.6 x 50.8 x 7.95	OPST
		3.18	IOST	6.35	IOPST
254.0 x 254.0 x 12.70	S	2.54	IOST	4.78	IOPST
11.13	S			3.81	IOPST
9.53	ST	25.4 x 25.4 x 3.18	IOST	3.18	IOPST
7.95	ST	2.54	IOST		
6.35	ST			88.9 x 63.5 x 7.95	OPS
		RECTANGULAR		6.35	OPST
203.2 x 203.2 x 12.70	PS	304.8 x 203.2 x 12.70	S	4.78	OPST
11.13	S	11.13	S	3.81	OPST
9.53	PST	9.53	ST	3.18	OPST
7.95	PST	7.95	ST		
6.35	PST	6.35	ST	76.2 x 50.8 x 7.95	ST
				6.35	OPST
177.8 x 177.8 x 12.70	PS	254.0 x 152.4 x 12.70	PS	4.78	OPST
11.13	S	11.13	S	3.81	OPST
9.53	OPST	9.53	PST		
7.95	OPST	7.95	PST	50.8 x 25.4 x 3.18	IOST
6.35	OPST	6.35	PST	2.54	IOST
4.78	OPST				
		203.2 x 152.4 x 12.70	PS	**ROUND**	
152.4 x 152.4 x 12.70	PS	11.13	S	406.4 x 12.70	S
11.13	S	9.53	OPST	11.13	S
9.53	OPST	7.95	OPST	9.53	S
7.95	OPST	6.35	OPST	7.95	S
6.35	OPST	4.78	OPST	6.35	S
4.78	OPST				
		203.2 x 101.6 x 12.70	PS	355.6 x 12.70	S
127.0 x 127.0 x 11.13	S	11.13	S	11.13	S
9.53	OPST	9.53	OPST	9.53	S
7.95	IOPST	7.95	OPST	7.95	S
6.35	IOPST	6.35	OPST	6.35	S
4.78	IOPST	4.78	OPST		
				323.9 x 12.70	S
101.6 x 101.6 x 9.53	OPST	177.8 x 127.0 x 12.70	PS[1]	11.13	S
7.95	OPST	11.13	S[1]	9.53	S
6.35	IOPST	9.53	OPS[1]T	7.95	S
4.78	IOPST	7.95	OPS[1]T	6.35	S
		6.35	OPS[1]T		
88.9 x 88.9 x 9.53	OPST	4.78	OPS[1]T	273.1 x 12.70	PS
7.95	OPST			11.13	PS
6.35	IOPST	152.4 x 101.6 x 11.13	S	9.53	S
4.78	IOPST	9.53	OPST	7.95	S
		7.95	IOPST	6.35	PS
76.2 x 76.2 x 7.95	OPST	6.35	IOPST		
6.35	IOPST	4.78	IOPS[1]T	219.1 x 12.70	PS
4.78	IOPST			11.13	S
		127.0 x 76.2 x 9.53	OPST	9.53	PS
63.5 x 63.5 x 6.35	OPST	7.95	OPST	7.95	PS
4.78	IOPST	6.35	OPST	6.35	PS
3.81	IOPST	4.78	OPST	4.78	PS
3.18	IOPST				
		127.0 x 63.5 x 9.53	ST	168.3 x 9.53	PS
50.8 x 50.8 x 6.35	OPST	7.95	ST	7.95	PS
4.78	OPST	6.35	ST	6.35	PS
3.81	IOPST	4.78	ST	4.78	PS
3.18	IOPST				
2.79	IOST	127.0 x 50.8 x 9.53	OPST	141.3 x 9.53	PS
		7.95	OPST	7.95	PS
		6.35	IOPST	6.35	S
		4.78	IOPST	4.78	PS

Size	Source	KEY TO SOURCES:
114.3 x 7.95	OPS	
6.35	OPST	D Sidbec — Dosco
4.78	OPST	I Interprovincial Steel and Pipe Corporation Ltd.
101.6 x 7.95	OPS	P Prudential Steel
6.35	OPST	
4.78	OPST	O Sonco
3.81	OPST	
		S Stelco, Inc.
88.9 x 7.95	OPS	
6.35	OPST	T Standard Tube Canada Limited
4.78	DOPST	
3.81	OST	

Size	Source	NOTES
73.0 x 6.35	ST	1. Check current availability
4.78	DPST	
3.81	DST	2. Most of the companies listed produce sections in addition to those listed. For complete details, company product catalogues should be consulted.
3.18	PS	
60.3 x 6.35	OPST	3. Some of the companies listed as sources for sections shown above produce sections with wall thicknesses which differ slightly from those shown, but are close enough usually to be considered equivalent to the sections listed.
4.78	OPST	
3.81	DOS	
3.18	DOPST	
48.3 x 4.78	ST	4. The shapes listed are those given in CAN3-G312.3
3.81	DST	
3.18	DOST	5. HSS produced to CSA G40.20-M will be manufactured either to Class H or to Class C requirements (see page 6-16). Since different factored axial compressive resistances are ascribed to each Class of HSS used as columns (see page 1-35), the Class description should be part of the HSS designation, as shown on page vii, to clearly indicate the material assumed in the design. For the availability of each Class, consult the manufacturer.
2.79	OST	
42.2 x 3.18	DOST	
2.54	DOST	
33.4 x 3.18	DOST	
2.54	DOST	
26.7 x 3.18	DST	
2.54	DST	

COMPARISON TABLES

The comparison tables, pages 6—23 to 6—32, list, for WWF, M, S, C and MC shapes, angles and HSS, the old designation, which was based upon the Imperial system of units, and the corresponding metric designation. For W and HP shapes, the comparison tables list the old series designations (Imperial units) — for W and HP shapes produced prior to September 1, 1978 — the Canadian metric designation, and the ASTM Imperial designation (currently common in the USA), for the new series W and HP shapes.

The metric designation is the preferred designation for all steel design and orders in Canada.

All shapes marked with an asterisk (*) are not available from Canadian mills.

For angles, the comparison tables list comparable Imperial size angles for most metric size angles. All angles are listed in descending order of size. During the period of metric conversion, designers specifying metric angles should be prepared to accept substitutions from Imperial angles. See also page 6—19 for the sources of equal and unequal leg angles.

COMPARISON TABLE FOR WWF SHAPES

Old Designation (in. x lb./ft.)	Metric Designation† (mm x kg/m)	Old Designation (in. x lb./ft.)	Metric Designation† (mm x kg/m)
WWF(M)47	WWF1200	WWF(M)22	WWF550
X326	X487	X484	X721
X270	X403	X416	X620
X244	X364	X338	X503
X203	X302	X282	X420
X176	X263	X146	X217
WWF(M)43	WWF1100	WWF(M)20	WWF500
X307	X458	X437	X651
X260	X388	X377	X561
X225	X335	X306	X456
X195	X291	X256	X381
X171	X255	X230	X343
X147	X220	X205	X306
		X185	X276
WWF(M)39	WWF1000	X170	X254
X300	X447	X150	X223
X253	X377	X132	X197
X217	X324		
X188	X280	WWF(M)18	WWF450
X163	X244	X337	X503
X134	X200	X275	X409
		X229	X342
WWF(M)35	WWF900	X207	X308
X279	X417	X184	X274
X233	X347	X166	X248
X197	X293	X152	X228
X167	X249	X134	X201
X142	X213	X119	X177
X128	X192		
X113	X169	WWF(M)16	WWF400
		X298	X444
WWF(M)31	WWF800	X243	X362
X223	X332	X203	X303
X187	X279	X183	X273
X157	X235	X163	X243
X133	X198	X147	X220
X109	X164	X135	X202
X103	X154	X119	X178
		X105	X157
WWF(M)28	WWF700		
X149	X222	WWF(M)14	WWF350
X136	X203	X258	X385
X124	X185	X211	X315
X110	X164	X177	X263
X101	X151	X159	X238
X95	X141	X142	X212
		X128	X192
		X118	X176
		X104	X155
		X92	X137

†Nominal depth in millimetres and mass in kilograms per metre.

COMPARISON TABLE FOR W SHAPES

OLD W SERIES # Designation (in. x lb./ft.)	Nominal Flange Width (in.)	NEW W SERIES Canadian Metric Designation† (mm x kg/m)	Nominal Flange Width (mm)	ASTM Imperial Designation (in. x lb./ft.)	Nominal Flange Width (in.)
W36x300	16½	W920x446*	420	W36x300	16½
x280		x417*		x280	
x260		x387*		x260	
x245		x365*		x245	
x230		x342*		x230	
—	12	W920x313*	305	W36x210	12
W36x194		x289*		x194	
x182		x271*		x182	
x170		x253*		x170	
x160		x238*		x160	
x150		x223*		x150	
x135		x201*		x135	
W33x240	15¾	W840x359*	400	W33x241	15¾
x220		x329*		x221	
x200		x299*		x201	
W33x152	11½	W840x226*	290	W33x152	11½
x141		x210*		x141	
x130		x193*		x130	
x118		x176*		x118	
W30x210	15	W760x314*	380	W30x211	15
x190		x284*		x191	
x172		x257*		x173	
W30x132	10½	W760x196*	265	W30x132	10½
x124		x185*		x124	
x116		x173*		x116	
x108		x161*		x108	
x99		x147*		x99	
W27x177	14	W690x265*	355	W27x178	14
x160		x240*		x161	
x145		x217*		x146	
W27x114	10	W690x170*	255	W27x114	10
x102		x152*		x102	
x94		x140*		x94	
x84		x125*		x84	
W24x160	14	W610x241	325	W24x162	12¾
x145		x217		x146	
x130		x195		x131	
x120		x174		x117	
x110		—			
x100		x155		x104	
W24x94	9	W610x140	230	W24x94	9
x84		x125		x84	
x76		x113		x76	
x68		x101		x68	
W24x61	7	W610x92*	180	W24x62	7
x55		x82*		x55	

OLD W SERIES # Designation (in. x lb./ft.)	Nominal Flange Width (in.)	NEW W SERIES Canadian Metric Designation† (mm x kg/m)	Nominal Flange Width (mm)	ASTM Imperial Designation (in. x lb./ft.)	Nominal Flange Width (in.)
W21x142	13	W530x219*	315	W21x147	12¼
x127		x196*		x132	
—		x182*		x122	
x112		x165*		x111	
—		x150*		x101	
W21x96	9	W530x138	210	W21x93	8¼
x82		x123		x83	
x73	8¼	x109		x73	
x68		x101		x68	
x62		x92		x62	
x55		x82¹		—	
W21x55	8¼	W530x85*	165	W21x57	6½
x49	6½	x74*		x50	
x44		x66*		x44	
W18x114	11¾	W460x177*	285	W18x119	11
x105		x158*		x106	
x96		x144*		x97	
x85	8¾	x128*		x86	
x77		x113*		x76	
W18x70	8¾	W460x106	190	W18x71	7½
x64		x97		x65	
x60	7½	x89		x60	
x55		x82		x55	
x50		x74		x50	
x45		x67¹		—	
x40		x61¹		—	
W18x45	7½	W460x68*	150	W18x46	6
x40	6	x60*		x40	
x35		x52*		x35	
W16x96	11½	W410x149*	260	W16x100	10¼
x88		x132*		x89	
x78	8½	x114*		x77	
x71		x100*		x67	
x64		—		—	
W16x58	8½	W410x85	180	W16x57	7
x50	7	x74		x50	
x45		x67		x45	
x40		x60		x40	
x36		x54		x36	
W16x31	5½	W410x46	140	W16x31	5½
x26		x39		x26	

†Nominal depth in millimetres and mass in kilograms per metre.
#North American mills discontinued this W series on 1978 09 01.
*Not available from Canadian Mills.
¹Produced only by Algoma. Only the W18 x 40 underwent a major change (W18 x 41 in Imperial)

OLD W SERIES #		NEW W SERIES				OLD W SERIES #		NEW W SERIES			
Designation (in. x lb./ft.)	Nominal Flange Width (in.)	Canadian Metric Designation† (mm x kg/m)	Nominal Flange Width (mm)	ASTM Imperial Designation (in. x lb./ft.)	Nominal Flange Width (in.)	Designation (in. x lb./ft.)	Nominal Flange Width (in.)	Canadian Metric Designation† (mm x kg/m)	Nominal Flange Width (mm)	ASTM Imperial Designation (in. x lb./ft.)	Nominal Flange Width (in.)
W14x730	16	W360x1086*	405	W14x730	16	W12x85	12	W310x129	310	W12x87	12
x665		x990*		x665		x79		x118		x79	
x605		x900*		x605		x72		x107		x72	
x550		x818*		x550		x65		x97		x65	
x500		x744*		x500		W12x58	10	W310x86	255	W12x58	10
x455		x677*		x455		x53		x79		x53	
x426		x634*		x426		W12x50	8	W310x74	200	W12x50	8
x398		x592*		x398		x45		x67		x45	
x370		x551*		x370		x40		x60		x40	
x342		x509*		x342		W12x36	6½	W310x52	165	W12x35	6½
x320		—		—		x31		x45		x30	
x314		x463*		x311		x27		x39		x26	
x287		x421*		x283		W12x22	4	W310x33*	100	W12x22	4
x264		—		—		x19		x28*		x19	
—		x382*		x257		x16.5		x24*		x16	
x246		—		—		x14		x21*		x14	
x237		x347*		x233		W10x112	10	W250x167	255	W10x112	10
x228		—		—		x100		x149		x100	
x219		—		—		x89		x131		x88	
x211		x314*		x211		x77		x115		x77	
x202		—		—		x72		—		—	
x193		x287*		x193		x66		x101		x68	
x184		—		—		x60		x89		x60	
x176		x262*		x176		x54		x80		x54	
x167		—		—		x49		x73		x49	
x158		x237*		x159		W10x45	8	W250x67	200	W10x45	8
x150		—		—		x39		x58		x39	
x142		x216*		x145		x33		x49		x33	
W14x136	14½	W360x196*	370	W14x132	14½	W10x29	5¾	W250x45	145	W10x30	5¾
x127		—		—		x25		x39		x26	
x119		x179*		x120		x21		x33		x22	
x111		x162*		x109		W10x19	4	W250x28*	100	W10x19	4
x103		—		—		x17		x25*		x17	
x95		x147*		x99		x15		x22*		x15	
x87		x134*		x90		x11.5		x18*		x12	
W14x84	12	W360x122*	255	W14x82	10	W8x67	8	W200x100	200	W8x67	8
x78		—		—		x58		x86		x58	
x74	10	x110*		x74		x48		x71		x48	
x68		x101*		x68		x40		x59		x40	
x61		x91*		x61		x35		x52		x35	
W14x53	8	W360x79	205	W14x53	8	x31		x46		x31	
x48		x72		x48		W8x28	6½	W200x42	165	W8x28	6½
x43		x64		x43		x24		x36		x24	
W14x38	6¾	W360x57	170	W14x38	6¾	W8x20	5¼	W200x31	135	W8x21	5¼
x34		x51		x34		x17		x27		x18	
x30		x45		x30		W8x15	4	W200x22*	100	W8x15	4
W14x26	5	W360x39	130	W14x26	5	x13		x19*		x13	
x22		x33		x22		x10		x15*		x10	
—		W310x500*	330	W12x336	13	W6x25	6	W150x37	150	W6x25	6
—		x454*		x305		x20		x30		x20	
—		x415*		x279		x15.5		x22		x15	
—		x375*		x252		W6x16	4	W150x24*	100	W6x16	4
—		x342*		x230		x12		x18*		x12	
—		x313*		x210		x8.5		x14*		x9	
W12x190	12	W310x283	310	W12x190	12	W5x18.5	5	W130x28*	125	W5x19	5
—		x253		x170		x16		x24*		x16	
x161		—		—		W4x13	4	W100x19*	100	#W4x13	4
—		x226		x152							
x133		x202		x136							
x120		x179		x120							
x106		x158		x106							
x99		x143		x96							
x92		—		—							

†Normal depth in millimetres and mass in kilograms per metre.
#North American mills discontinued this W series on 1978 09 01.

*Not available from Canadian Mills.
#M4 x 13 is available from Canadian mills; see next page.

COMPARISON TABLE FOR HP SHAPES

Old HP Series #	NEW HP SERIES	
Designation (in. x lb./ft.)	Canadian Metric Designation† (mm x kg/m)	ASTM Imperial Designation (in. x lb./ft.)
HP14x117	HP360x174*	HP14x117
x102	x152*	x102
x89	x132*	x89
x73	x108*	x73
—	HP330x149*	HP13x100
—	x129*	x87
—	x109*	x73
—	x89*	x60
HP12x117	HP310x174[1]	—
x102	x152[1]	—
x89	x132[1]	—
—	x125*	HP12x84
x74	x110	x74
—	x94	x63
x53	x79	x53
HP10x57	HP250x85	HP10x57
x42	x62	x42
HP8x36	HP200x54	HP8x36

†Nominal depth in millimetres and mass in kilograms per metre.
#North American mills discontinued this HP series on 1978 09 01.
*Not available from Canadian mills.
[1] Produced only by Algoma.

COMPARISON TABLE FOR M SHAPES

Old Designation (in. x lb./ft.)	Metric Designation† (mm x kg/m)
M12x11.8	M310x17.6*
M10x9	M250x13.4*
M8x6.5	M200x9.7*
M6x20	M150x29.8*
M6x4.4	M150x6.5*
M5x18.9	M130x28.1*
M4x13	M100x19

†Nominal depth in millimetres and mass in kilograms per metre.
*Not available from Canadian Mills.

Note: These shapes have been soft converted from Imperial to SI dimensions.

COMPARISON TABLE FOR S SHAPES

Old Designation (in. x lb./ft.)	Metric Designation† (mm x kg/m)
S24x121	S610x180*
x106	x158*
S24x100	S610x149*
x90	x134*
x80	x119*
S20x96	S510x143*
x86	x128*
S20x75	S510x112*
x66	x98*
S18x70	S460x104*
x54.7	x81.4*
S15x50	S380x74*
x42.9	x64*
S12x50	S310x74*
x40.8	x60.7*
S12x35	S310x52
x31.8	x47
S10x35	S250x52
x25.4	x38
S8x23	S200x34
x18.4	x27
S7x20	S180x30*
x15.3	x22.8*
S6x17.25	S150x26
x12.5	x19
S5x14.75	S130x22
x10	x15
S4x9.5	S100x14.1*
x7.7	x11
S3x7.5	S75x11
x5.7	x8

†Nominal depth in millimetres and mass in kilograms per metre.
*Not available from Canadian Mills.

Note: These shapes have been soft converted from Imperial to SI dimensions.

COMPARISON TABLE FOR C SHAPES

Old Designation (in. x lb./ft.)	Metric Designation† (mm x kg/m)
C15x50	C380x74
x40	x60
x33.9	x50
C12x30	C310x45
x25	x37
x20.7	x31
C10x30	C250x45*
x25	x37
x20	x30
x15.3	x23
C9x20	C230x30
x15	x22
x13.4	x20
C8x18.75	C200x28
x13.75	x21
x11.5	x17
C7x14.75	C180x22*
x12.25	x18
x9.8	x15
C6x13	C150x19
x10.5	x16
x8.2	x12
C5x9	C130x13
x6.7	x10
C4x7.25	C100x11
x5.4	x8
C3x6	C75x9
x5	x7
x4.1	x6

†Nominal depth in millimetres and mass in kilograms per metre.
*Not available from Canadian Mills.

Note: These shapes have been soft converted from Imperial to SI dimensions.

COMPARISON TABLE FOR MC SHAPES

Old Designation (in. x lb./ft.)	Metric Designation† (mm x kg/m)
MC18x58	MC460x86 *
x51.9	x77.2 *
x45.8	x68.2 *
x42.7	x63.5 *
MC13x50	MC330x74 *
x40	x60 *
x35	x52 *
x31.8	x47.3 *
MC12x50	MC310x74 *
x45	x67 *
x40	x60 *
x35	x52 *
MC12x37	MC310x55 *
x32.9	x49 *
x30.9	x46 *
MC12x10.6	MC310x15.8 *
MC10x41.1	MC250x61.2 *
x33.6	x50 *
x28.5	x42.4 *
MC10x28.3	MC250x42.1 *
x25.3	x37.7 *
x24.9	x37.1 *
x21.9	x32.6 *
MC10x8.4	MC250x12.5 *
MC10x6.5	MC250x9.7 *
MC9x25.4	MC230x37.8 *
x23.9	x35.6 *
MC8x22.8	MC200x33.9 *
x21.4	x31.8 *
MC8x20	MC200x29.8 *
x18.7	x27.8 *
MC8x8.5	MC200x12.6 *
MC7x22.7	MC180x33.8 *
x19.1	x28.4 *
MC7x17.6	MC180x26.2 *
MC6x18	MC150x26.8 *
x15.3	x22.8
MC6x16.3	MC150x24.3 *
x15.1	x22.5 *
MC6x12	MC150x17.9 *

†Nominal depth in millimetres and mass in kilograms per metre.
*Not available from Canadian Mills.

Note: These shapes have been soft converted from Imperial to SI dimensions.

COMPARISON TABLE FOR EQUAL LEG ANGLES

OLD SERIES		NEW METRIC SERIES	
Size	Thickness	Size	Thickness
in.	in.	mm	mm
8x8	1⅛	200x200	30
	1		25
	7/8		—
	3/4		20
	5/8		16
	9/16		—
	1/2		13
	—		10
6x6	1	150x150	—
	7/8		—
	3/4		20
	5/8		16
	9/16		—
	1/2		13
	7/16		—
	3/8		10
	5/16		—
5x5	7/8	125x125	—
	3/4		—
	5/8		16
	1/2		13
	7/16		—
	3/8		10
	5/16		8
4x4	3/4	100x100	—
	5/8		16
	1/2		13
	7/16		—
	3/8		10
	5/16		8
	1/4		6
3½x3½	1/2	90x90	13
	7/16		—
	3/8		10
	5/16		8
	1/4		6

OLD SERIES		NEW METRIC SERIES	
Size	Thickness	Size	Thickness
in.	in.	mm	mm
3x3	1/2	75x75	13
	7/16		—
	3/8		10
	5/16		8
	1/4		6
	3/16		5
2½x2½	1/2	65x65	—
	3/8		10
	5/16		8
	1/4		6
	3/16		5
2x2	3/8	55x55	10
	5/16		8
	1/4		6
	3/16		5
	—		4
	1/8		3
1¾x1¾	—	45x45	8
	1/4		6
	3/16		5
	—		4
	1/8		3
1½x1½	5/16	—	—
	1/4		—
	3/16		—
	1/8		—
—	—	35x35	6
	—		5
	—		4
	—		3
1¼x1¼	1/4	—	—
	3/16		—
	1/8		—
1x1	1/4	25x25	—
	3/16		5
	—		4
	1/8		3

COMPARISON TABLE FOR UNEQUAL LEG ANGLES

OLD SERIES		NEW METRIC SERIES		OLD SERIES		NEW METRIC SERIES	
Size	Thickness	Size	Thickness	Size	Thickness	Size	Thickness
in.	in.	mm	mm	in.	in.	mm	mm
9x4	All	–	–	4x3	5/8	100x75	–
8x6	1	200x150*	25		1/2		13
	7/8		–		7/16		–
	3/4		20		3/8		10
	5/8		16		5/16		8
	9/16		–		1/4		6
	1/2		13	3½x3	1/2	90x75	13
	7/16		–		7/16		–
8x4	1	200x100*	–		3/8		10
	7/8		–		5/16		8
	3/4		20		1/4		6
	5/8		16		–		5
	9/16		–	3½x2½	1/2	90x65	–
	1/2		13		7/16		–
	7/16		–		3/8		10
	–		10		5/16		8
7x4	All	–	–		1/4		6
6x4	7/8	150x100	–		–		5
	3/4		–	–	–	80x60	10
	5/8		16		–		8
	9/16		–		–		6
	1/2		13		–		5
	7/16		–	3x2½	All	–	–
	3/8		10	3x2	1/2	75x50	–
	5/16		8		7/16		–
	1/4		–		3/8		–
6x3½	All	–	–		5/16		8
5x3½	3/4	125x90	–		1/4		6
	5/8		16		3/16		5
	1/2		13	2½x2	3/8	65x50	–
	7/16		–		5/16		8
	3/8		10		1/4		6
	5/16		8		3/16		5
	1/4		–		–		4
5x3	1/2	125x75	13	2½x1½	All	–	–
	7/16		–	–	–	55x35	6
	3/8		10		–		5
	5/16		8		–		4
	1/4		6		–		3
4x3½	5/8	100x90	–	2x1½	All	–	–
	1/2		13	2x1¼	All	–	–
	7/16		–	1¾x1¼	1/4	45x30	6
	3/8		10		3/16		5
	5/16		8		–		4
	1/4		6		1/8		3

*Not available from Canadian Mills.

COMPARISON TABLE FOR RECTANGULAR HSS

IMPERIAL		METRIC		IMPERIAL		METRIC	
Size	Thickness	Size	Thickness	Size	Thickness	Size	Thickness
in.	in.	mm	mm	in.	in.	mm	mm
2x1	.100	50.8x25.4	2.54	6x4	.188	152.4x101.6	4.78
	.125		3.18		.250		6.35
					.313		7.95
3x2	.150	76.2x50.8	3.81		.375		9.53
	.188		4.78		.438		11.13
	.250		6.35	7x5	.188	177.8x127.0#	4.78
	.313		7.95		.250		6.35
3½x2½	.125	88.9x63.5	3.18		.313		7.95
	.150		3.81		.375		9.53
	.188		4.78		.438		11.13
	.250		6.35		.500		12.70
	.313		7.95	8x4	.188	203.2x101.6	4.78
4x2	.125	101.6x50.8	3.18		.250		6.35
	.150		3.81		.313		7.95
	.188		4.78		.375		9.53
	.250		6.35		.438		11.13
	.313		7.95		.500		12.70
4x3	.188	101.6x76.2	4.78	8x6	.188	203.2x152.4	4.78
	.250		6.35		.250		6.35
	.313		7.95		.313		7.95
	.375		9.53		.375		9.53
					.438		11.13
5x2	.188	127.0x50.8	4.78		.500		12.70
	.250		6.35	10x6	.250	254.0x152.4	6.35
	.313		7.95		.313		7.95
	.375		9.53		.375		9.53
					.438		11.13
5x2½	.188	127.0x63.5	4.78		.500		12.70
	.250		6.35	12x8	.250	304.8x203.2	6.35
	.313		7.95		.313		7.95
	.375		9.53		.375		9.53
5x3	.188	127.0x76.2	4.78		.438		11.13
	.250		6.35		.500		12.70
	.313		7.95				
	.375		9.53				

#Check manufacturer for current availability.

COMPARISON TABLE FOR SQUARE HSS

IMPERIAL		METRIC		IMPERIAL		METRIC	
Size	Thickness	Size	Thickness	Size	Thickness	Size	Thickness
in.	in.	mm	mm	in.	in.	mm	mm
1x1	.100	25.4x25.4	2.54	5x5	.188	127.0x127.0	4.78
	.125		3.18		.250		6.35
					.313		7.95
1¼x1¼	.100	31.8x31.8	2.54		.375		9.53
	.125		3.18		.438		11.13
	.150		3.81	6x6	.188	152.4x152.4	4.78
1½x1½	.100	38.1x38.1	2.54		.250		6.35
	.125		3.18		.313		7.95
	.150		3.81		.375		9.53
	.188		4.78		.438		11.13
2x2	.110	50.8x50.8	2.79		.500		12.70
	.125		3.18	7x7	.188	177.8x177.8	4.78
	.150		3.81		.250		6.35
	.188		4.78		.313		7.95
	.250		6.35		.375		9.53
2½x2½	.125	63.5x63.5	3.18		.438		11.13
	.150		3.81		.500		12.70
	.188		4.78	8x8	.250	203.2x203.2	6.35
	.250		6.35		.313		7.95
3x3	.188	76.2x76.2	4.78		.375		9.53
	.250		6.35		.438		11.13
	.313		7.95		.500		12.70
				10x10	.250	254.0x254.0	6.35
3½x3½	.188	88.9x88.9	4.78		.313		7.95
	.250		6.35		.375		9.53
	.313		7.95		.438		11.13
	.375		9.53		.500		12.70
4x4	.188	101.6x101.6	4.78	12x12	.250	304.8x304.8	6.35
	.250		6.35		.313		7.95
	.313		7.95		.375		9.53
	.375		9.53		.438		11.13
					.500		12.70

COMPARISON TABLE FOR ROUND HSS

IMPERIAL		METRIC		IMPERIAL		METRIC	
Size	Thickness	Size	Thickness	Size	Thickness	Size	Thickness
in.	in.	mm	mm	in.	in.	mm	mm
1.05	.100	26.7	2.54	6.625	.188	168.3	4.78
	.125		3.18		.250		6.35
1.315	.100	33.4	2.54		.313		7.95
	.125		3.18		.375		9.53
1.66	.100	42.4	2.54	8.625	.188	219.1	4.78
	.125		3.18		.250		6.35
1.9	.110	48.3	2.79		.313		7.95
	.125		3.18		.375		9.53
	.150		3.81		.438		11.13
	.188		4.78		.500		12.70
2.375	.125	60.3	3.18	10.75	.250	273.1	6.35
	.150		3.81		.313		7.95
	.188		4.78		.375		9.53
	.250		6.35		.438		11.13
2.875	.125	73.0	3.18		.500		12.70
	.150		3.81	12.75	.250	323.9	6.35
	.188		4.78		.313		7.95
	.250		6.35		.375		9.53
3.50	.150	88.9	3.81		.438		11.13
	.188		4.78		.500		12.70
	.250		6.35	14	.250	355.6	6.35
	.313		7.95		.313		7.95
4	.150	101.6	3.81		.375		9.53
	.188		4.78		.438		11.13
	.250		6.35		.500		12.70
	.313		7.95	16	.250	406.4	6.35
4.5	.188	114.3	4.78		.313		7.95
	.250		6.35		.375		9.53
	.313		7.95		.438		11.13
5.562	.188	141.3	4.78		.500		12.70
	.250		6.35				
	.313		7.95				
	.375		9.53				

WELDED WIDE FLANGE SHAPES

General

Welded wide flange (WWF) shapes are produced in accordance with the requirements of CSA Standard G40.20-M from plate meeting the requirements of CSA Standard G40. 21-M grade 300W by the Algoma Steel Corporation, Limited. If the use of other grades of steel is contemplated, the manufacturer should be consulted.

Manufacture

Automated production methods are used throughout. Hot rolled plates are flame-cut automatically to required widths. The assembly machine holds a web plate and two flange plates in correct relationship by means of rolls. The main rolls force the plates into intimate contact and propel them at uniform speed under the automatic welding heads, which are adjacent to the pressure rolls.

For all welded beams, and for columns with webs up to, and including, 20 mm thick, the actual strength of the welds will be adequate to develop the full capacity of the flange-to-web junction. For heavy columns with web thickness greater than 20 mm, web-to-flange welds may be proportioned so as to develop the specified minimum tensile strength of a 20 mm web only. This partial web weld is considered adequate to join flanges and web for most applications, but additional welding by the purchaser may be required at major connection points. The column sections with the partial web weld are identified in the tables of dimensions and properties with the following note "welding does not fully develop web strength for these sections".

Products

WWF beams range in depth from 700 mm to 1200 mm and meet the requirements of CSA Standard CAN3-S16.1-M78 for Class 2 sections. The overall depths of all welded WWF beams are constant for the full mass range of each section, while the flange width dimensions vary in multiples of 50 mm.

Column shapes are available in five depths, from 350 mm to 550 mm in 50 mm increments, with a maximum mass of 721 kg/m. Both the depth and the flange width are constant in each size range while the web and flange thicknesses vary according to the preferred thicknesses of plate.

WELDED WIDE FLANGE SHAPES
WWF1200-WWF700

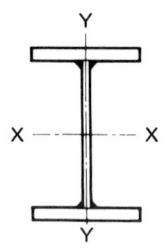

PROPERTIES

Designation[‡]	Dead Load	Total Area	Axis X-X				Axis Y-Y				Torsional Constant	Warping Constant
			I_x	S_x	r_x	Z_x	I_y	S_y	r_y	Z_y	J	C_w
	kN/m	mm^2	10^6mm^4	10^3mm^3	mm	10^3mm^3	10^6mm^4	10^3mm^3	mm	10^3mm^3	10^3mm^4	10^9mm^6
WWF1200												
X487	4.77	62 000	16 700	27 900	519	30 600	1 110	4 030	134	6 120	25 000	373 000
X403	3.95	51 400	13 300	22 200	509	24 600	832	3 030	127	4 610	11 500	285 000
X364	3.57	46 400	11 700	19 400	502	21 700	584	2 330	112	3 570	8 880	200 000
X302	2.96	38 500	8 970	15 000	483	17 100	267	1 340	83.3	2 070	5 740	92 200
X263	2.58	33 500	7 250	12 100	465	14 200	113	753	58.1	1 200	4 700	39 000
WWF1100												
X458	4.49	58 400	13 600	24 800	483	27 000	1 110	4 030	138	6 100	24 400	312 000
X388	3.81	49 500	11 200	20 400	476	22 400	729	2 920	121	4 430	15 200	207 000
X335	3.29	42 700	9 410	17 100	469	18 900	584	2 330	117	3 550	8 270	168 000
X291	2.85	37 100	7 800	14 200	459	15 900	299	1 490	89.8	2 290	6 810	85 900
X255	2.50	32 500	6 520	11 900	448	13 500	235	1 170	85.0	1 810	3 810	68 200
X220	2.16	28 100	5 240	9 530	432	11 100	99.3	662	59.4	1 040	3 100	28 800
WWF1000												
X447	4.38	57 000	11 100	22 200	441	24 100	1 110	4 030	140	6 100	24 300	256 000
X377	3.70	48 100	9 120	18 200	435	20 000	729	2 920	123	4 420	15 100	170 000
X324	3.18	41 300	7 620	15 200	430	16 800	584	2 330	119	3 550	8 180	138 000
X280	2.75	35 700	6 300	12 600	420	14 100	299	1 490	91.5	2 290	6 720	70 600
X244	2.39	31 100	5 260	10 500	411	11 900	235	1 170	86.9	1 810	3 710	56 200
X200	1.96	25 600	3 940	7 890	392	9 170	90.2	602	59.4	948	2 480	21 700
WWF900												
X417	4.09	53 100	8 670	19 300	404	20 800	1 110	4 030	145	6 080	23 800	205 000
X347	3.40	44 300	7 100	15 800	400	17 100	729	2 920	128	4 400	14 700	136 000
X293	2.88	37 400	5 900	13 100	397	14 200	583	2 330	125	3 530	7 690	111 000
X249	2.44	31 800	4 830	10 700	390	11 800	299	1 490	97.0	2 270	6 230	56 800
X213	2.08	27 100	3 990	8 870	384	9 800	235	1 170	93.1	1 790	3 220	45 200
X192	1.88	24 500	3 460	7 680	376	8 600	113	751	67.9	1 150	3 500	21 600
X169	1.66	21 600	2 930	6 510	368	7 370	90.1	601	64.6	927	1 980	17 400
WWF800												
X332	3.26	42 400	5 470	13 700	359	14 800	729	2 920	131	4 390	14 500	107 000
X279	2.73	35 600	4 530	11 300	357	12 200	583	2 330	128	3 520	7 570	86 900
X235	2.30	30 000	3 700	9 250	351	10 100	299	1 490	99.8	2 260	6 100	44 500
X198	1.94	25 300	3 040	7 600	347	8 320	235	1 170	96.4	1 780	3 090	35 500
X164	1.60	20 900	2 380	5 940	337	6 610	99.1	660	68.9	1 010	2 380	15 000
X154	1.51	19 700	2 210	5 520	335	6 170	90.1	600	67.6	920	1 850	13 700
WWF700												
X222	2.18	28 300	2 740	7 840	311	8 500	299	1 490	103	2 250	6 010	33 700
X203	2.00	26 000	2 500	7 140	310	7 740	267	1 330	101	2 010	4 320	30 400
X185	1.81	23 600	2 250	6 420	309	6 980	235	1 170	99.8	1 770	3 000	27 000
X164	1.61	21 000	1 930	5 510	303	6 050	113	750	73.4	1 140	3 280	12 800
X151	1.48	19 200	1 740	4 980	301	5 480	99.0	660	71.8	1 000	2 290	11 400
X141	1.39	18 100	1 620	4 620	299	5 100	90.0	600	70.5	914	1 760	10 400

‡ Nominal depth in millimetres and mass in kilograms per metre.

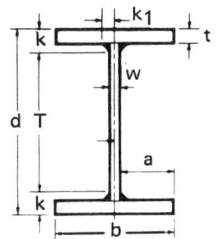

DIMENSIONS AND SURFACE AREAS

Nominal Mass	Depth d	Flange Width b	Flange Thickness t	Web Thickness w	a	T	k	k_1	d-2t	Surface Area (m²) per metre of length Total	Minus Top of Top Flange
kg/m	mm	mm	mm	mm	mm	mm	mm	mm	mm		
487	1 200	550	40.0	16.0	267	1 102	49	16	1 120	4.61	4.06
403	1 200	550	30.0	16.0	267	1 122	39	16	1 140	4.57	4.02
364	1 200	500	28.0	16.0	242	1 126	37	16	1 144	4.36	3.86
302	1 200	400	25.0	16.0	192	1 132	34	16	1 150	3.95	3.55
263	1 200	300	25.0	16.0	142	1 132	34	16	1 150	3.55	3.25
458	1 100	550	40.0	14.0	268	1 002	49	15	1 020	4.42	3.87
388	1 100	500	35.0	14.0	243	1 012	44	15	1 030	4.20	3.70
335	1 100	500	28.0	14.0	243	1 026	37	15	1 044	4.17	3.67
291	1 100	400	28.0	14.0	193	1 026	37	15	1 044	3.77	3.37
255	1 100	400	22.0	14.0	193	1 038	31	15	1 056	3.74	3.34
220	1 100	300	22.0	14.0	143	1 038	31	15	1 056	3.34	3.04
447	1 000	550	40.0	14.0	268	902	49	15	920	4.22	3.67
377	1 000	500	35.0	14.0	243	912	44	15	930	4.00	3.50
324	1 000	500	28.0	14.0	243	926	37	15	944	3.97	3.47
280	1 000	400	28.0	14.0	193	926	37	15	944	3.57	3.17
244	1 000	400	22.0	14.0	193	938	31	15	956	3.54	3.14
200	1 000	300	20.0	14.0	143	942	29	15	960	3.14	2.84
417	900	550	40.0	11.0	270	802	49	14	820	4.02	3.47
347	900	500	35.0	11.0	245	812	44	14	830	3.80	3.30
293	900	500	28.0	11.0	245	826	37	14	844	3.78	3.28
249	900	400	28.0	11.0	195	826	37	14	844	3.38	2.98
213	900	400	22.0	11.0	195	838	31	14	856	3.35	2.95
192	900	300	25.0	11.0	145	832	34	14	850	2.96	2.66
169	900	300	20.0	11.0	145	842	29	14	860	2.94	2.64
332	800	500	35.0	10.0	245	712	44	13	730	3.62	3.12
279	800	500	28.0	10.0	245	726	37	13	744	3.59	3.09
235	800	400	28.0	10.0	195	726	37	13	744	3.19	2.79
198	800	400	22.0	10.0	195	738	31	13	756	3.16	2.76
164	800	300	22.0	10.0	145	738	31	13	756	2.76	2.46
154	800	300	20.0	10.0	145	742	29	13	760	2.76	2.46
222	700	400	28.0	9.0	196	626	37	13	644	3.00	2.60
203	700	400	25.0	9.0	196	632	34	13	650	2.99	2.59
185	700	400	22.0	9.0	196	638	31	13	656	2.98	2.58
164	700	300	25.0	9.0	146	632	34	13	650	2.59	2.29
151	700	300	22.0	9.0	146	638	31	13	656	2.58	2.28
141	700	300	20.0	9.0	146	642	29	13	660	2.57	2.27

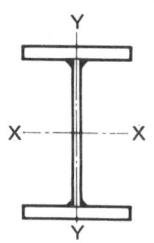

WELDED WIDE FLANGE SHAPES
WWF550-WWF350

PROPERTIES

Designation ‡	Dead Load	Total Area	Axis X-X				Axis Y-Y				Torsional Constant	Warping Constant
			I_x	S_x	r_x	Z_x	I_y	S_y	r_y	Z_y	J	C_w
	kN/m	mm²	10^6mm⁴	10^3mm³	mm	10^3mm³	10^6mm³	10^3mm³	mm	10^3mm³	10^3mm⁴	10^9mm⁶
WWF550												
X721**	7.08	92 000	4 390	16 000	218	19 000	1 670	6 080	135	9 470	110 000	100 000
X620**	6.08	79 100	4 190	15 200	230	17 600	1 660	6 050	145	9 180	83 100	99 900
X503	4.94	64 200	3 610	13 100	237	14 800	1 390	5 040	147	7 610	47 000	86 700
X420	4.12	53 600	3 050	11 100	239	12 400	1 110	4 030	144	6 100	24 700	72 100
X217	2.13	27 700	1 680	6 090	246	6 580	555	2 020	142	3 040	3 160	39 000
WWF500												
X651**	6.38	83 000	3 200	12 800	196	15 400	1 260	5 030	123	7 850	99 400	60 800
X561**	5.51	71 600	3 070	12 300	207	14 300	1 250	5 000	132	7 590	75 400	60 500
X456	4.47	58 200	2 660	10 600	214	12 100	1 040	4 170	134	6 290	42 700	52 700
X381	3.74	48 600	2 250	9 010	215	10 100	834	3 330	131	5 040	22 500	44 100
X343	3.37	43 800	2 040	8 140	216	9 100	729	2 920	129	4 420	15 400	39 400
X306	3.00	39 000	1 810	7 240	215	8 060	625	2 500	127	3 800	10 200	34 500
X276	2.71	35 200	1 680	6 740	218	7 420	583	2 330	129	3 530	7 920	32 500
X254	2.48	32 300	1 540	6 160	218	6 780	521	2 080	127	3 160	5 820	29 400
X223	2.19	28 500	1 370	5 500	219	6 010	458	1 830	127	2 770	3 970	26 200
X197	1.93	25 200	1 250	4 990	223	5 410	417	1 670	129	2 510	2 870	24 000
WWF450												
X503**	4.93	64 100	2 160	9 620	184	11 400	912	4 050	119	6 150	67 800	34 700
X409	4.01	52 200	1 890	8 380	190	9 640	760	3 380	121	5 100	38 400	30 400
X342	3.35	43 600	1 610	7 150	192	8 100	608	2 700	118	4 090	20 200	25 500
X308	3.02	39 300	1 460	6 480	193	7 290	532	2 360	116	3 580	13 900	22 900
X274	2.69	35 000	1 300	5 770	193	6 470	456	2 030	114	3 080	9 140	20 100
X248	2.43	31 600	1 210	5 380	196	5 960	425	1 890	116	2 860	7 120	18 900
X228	2.23	29 000	1 110	4 920	196	5 450	380	1 690	114	2 560	5 230	17 200
X201	1.97	25 600	991	4 400	197	4 840	334	1 490	114	2 250	3 570	15 300
X177	1.74	22 600	901	4 000	200	4 360	304	1 350	116	2 040	2 580	14 000
WWF400												
X444**	4.35	56 600	1 460	7 300	161	8 770	641	3 200	106	4 870	60 100	18 500
X362	3.55	46 200	1 280	6 410	166	7 480	534	2 670	108	4 030	34 100	16 300
X303	2.97	38 600	1 100	5 500	169	6 300	427	2 130	105	3 230	17 900	13 800
X273	2.67	34 800	1 000	5 000	170	5 680	374	1 870	104	2 840	12 300	12 400
X243	2.38	31 000	894	4 470	170	5 050	320	1 600	102	2 440	8 110	11 000
X220	2.15	28 000	834	4 170	173	4 660	299	1 490	103	2 260	6 320	10 300
X202	1.98	25 700	765	3 830	173	4 260	267	1 330	102	2 020	4 640	9 380
X178	1.74	22 700	686	3 430	174	3 790	235	1 170	102	1 780	3 170	8 390
X157	1.54	20 100	625	3 120	176	3 420	213	1 070	103	1 610	2 290	7 700
WWF350												
X385**	3.77	49 100	928	5 300	137	6 510	429	2 450	93.5	3 730	52 500	9 030
X315	3.09	40 200	824	4 710	143	5 580	357	2 040	94.2	3 090	29 800	8 040
X263	2.58	33 600	712	4 070	146	4 730	286	1 630	92.3	2 480	15 700	6 870
X238	2.33	30 300	650	3 720	146	4 280	250	1 430	90.8	2 170	10 800	6 210
X212	2.07	27 000	583	3 330	147	3 810	215	1 230	89.2	1 870	7 070	5 490
X192	1.88	24 400	546	3 120	150	3 520	200	1 140	90.5	1 740	5 520	5 190
X176	1.72	22 400	502	2 870	150	3 220	179	1 020	89.4	1 550	4 060	4 720
X155	1.52	19 800	451	2 580	151	2 870	157	899	89.0	1 360	2 760	4 230
X137	1.35	17 500	412	2 350	153	2 590	143	817	90.4	1 240	2 000	3 890

‡ Nominal depth in millimetres and mass in kilograms per metre.
**Welding does not fully develop the web strength for these sections.

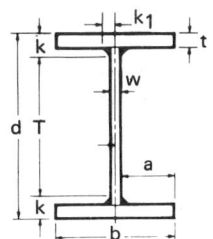

DIMENSIONS AND SURFACE AREAS

Nominal Mass	Depth d	Flange Width b	Flange Thickness t	Web Thickness w	a	T	k	k_1	d-2t	Surface Area (m^2) per metre of length Total	Surface Area (m^2) per metre of length Minus Top of Top Flange
kg/m	mm	mm	mm	mm	mm	mm	mm	mm	mm		
721	550	550	60.0	60.0	245	408	71	40	430	3.24	2.69
620	550	550	60.0	30.0	260	408	71	25	430	3.30	2.75
503	550	550	50.0	20.0	265	428	61	20	450	3.28	2.73
420	550	550	40.0	20.0	265	448	51	20	470	3.24	2.69
217	550	550	20.0	11.0	270	492	29	14	510	3.17	2.62
651	500	500	60.0	60.0	220	358	71	40	380	2.97	2.47
561	500	500	60.0	30.0	235	358	71	25	380	3.03	2.53
456	500	500	50.0	20.0	240	378	61	20	400	3.01	2.51
381	500	500	40.0	20.0	240	398	51	20	420	2.97	2.47
343	500	500	35.0	20.0	240	408	46	20	430	2.95	2.45
306	500	500	30.0	20.0	240	418	41	20	440	2.93	2.43
276	500	500	28.0	16.0	242	426	37	16	444	2.93	2.43
254	500	500	25.0	16.0	242	432	34	16	450	2.92	2.42
223	500	500	22.0	14.0	243	438	31	15	456	2.91	2.41
197	500	500	20.0	11.0	245	442	29	14	460	2.91	2.41
503	450	450	60.0	30.0	210	308	71	25	330	2.74	2.29
409	450	450	50.0	20.0	215	328	61	20	350	2.72	2.27
342	450	450	40.0	20.0	215	348	51	20	370	2.68	2.23
308	450	450	35.0	20.0	215	358	46	20	380	2.66	2.21
274	450	450	30.0	20.0	215	368	41	20	390	2.64	2.19
248	450	450	28.0	16.0	217	376	37	16	394	2.64	2.19
228	450	450	25.0	16.0	217	382	34	16	400	2.63	2.18
201	450	450	22.0	14.0	218	388	31	15	406	2.62	2.17
177	450	450	20.0	11.0	220	392	29	14	410	2.62	2.17
444	400	400	60.0	30.0	185	258	71	25	280	2.44	2.04
362	400	400	50.0	20.0	190	278	61	20	300	2.42	2.02
303	400	400	40.0	20.0	190	298	51	20	320	2.38	1.98
273	400	400	35.0	20.0	190	308	46	20	330	2.36	1.96
243	400	400	30.0	20.0	190	318	41	20	340	2.34	1.94
220	400	400	28.0	16.0	192	326	37	16	344	2.34	1.94
202	400	400	25.0	16.0	192	332	34	16	350	2.33	1.93
178	400	400	22.0	14.0	193	338	31	15	356	2.32	1.92
157	400	400	20.0	11.0	195	342	29	14	360	2.32	1.92
385	350	350	60.0	30.0	160	208	71	25	230	2.14	1.79
315	350	350	50.0	20.0	165	228	61	20	250	2.12	1.77
263	350	350	40.0	20.0	165	248	51	20	270	2.08	1.73
238	350	350	35.0	20.0	165	258	46	20	280	2.06	1.71
212	350	350	30.0	20.0	165	268	41	20	290	2.04	1.69
192	350	350	28.0	16.0	167	276	37	16	294	2.04	1.69
176	350	350	25.0	16.0	167	282	34	16	300	2.03	1.68
155	350	350	22.0	14.0	168	288	31	15	306	2.02	1.67
137	350	350	20.0	11.0	170	292	29	14	310	2.02	1.67

ROLLED STRUCTURAL SHAPES

General

Rolled structural shapes are available in Canada from several sources (see "Principal Sources of Structural Steel Sections", page 6-17). In Canada they are produced according to CSA Standard G40.20-M in grades of steel meeting CSA Standard G40.21-M. See pages 6-3 to 6-9 for more information on grades of steel and availability and pages 6-11 to 6-16 for information on standard mill practice.

The tables of properties and dimensions, pages 6-40 to 6-83, cover the most frequently used rolled structural shapes. Shapes not rolled by Canadian mills (as of June 1980) are identified in the tables with the note "not available from Canadian mills".

Special shapes, such as rolled Tees, Zees, Bulb Angles and Carbuilding and Shipbuilding Channels, can be produced by various mills. Since these shapes are generally rolled at irregular intervals, and often only by special arrangement, their use should be avoided unless the quantity of any one size is sufficient to warrant a rolling. The dimensions, weights and properties of these shapes may be obtained from the appropriate mill catalogues.

Properties and Dimensions

The basic theoretical metric dimensions used in the computation of the properties and dimensions of the rolled steel shapes are taken either from CAN3-G312.3-M78, "Preferred Metric Dimensions for Structural Steel W and HP Shapes, Angles and Hollow Structural Sections", or, for those shapes not listed in CAN3-G312.3-M78, from ASTM Standard A6.

W shapes rolled in Canada, and by most other mills supplying the Canadian market, have essentially parallel flange surfaces. Certain other non-Canadian mills offer W shapes with flanges whose inner surfaces have approximately a 3° taper. Furthermore, the radius of the flange web fillet may vary slightly from mill to mill. The properties for W shapes are calculated using the smallest theoretical fillet radius while the dimensions for detailing are adjusted for the largest theoretical fillet radius produced in North America.

HP (H-Pile) shapes have essentially parallel flange surfaces and equal web and flange thickness.

S shapes and Standard channels (C shapes) have a slope of approximately 16 2/3% (2 in 12) on the inside face of flange. The flange thickness tabulated is the mean thickness.

M and MC shapes are essentially shapes that cannot be classified as W, HP, S or C shapes. Only the M100X19 is rolled in Canada, and since the other M and MC shapes are available only from a limited number of producers, or are infrequently rolled, users should check upon their availability before specifying these shapes. In addition, they have either parallel or sloping flange faces of various slopes. The dimensions and properties shown in the tables of this book should be suitable for general use, in spite of the slight variations in actual dimensions that are possible.

Tees listed in this book are those obtained by splitting the webs of WWF or W shapes, generally with the aid of rotary shears, and subsequently straightening to meet established tolerances. The dimensions and properties of WWT and WT shapes are based on the depth of the Tee equal to one-half the published shape depth. Detail dimensions will be the same as those of the beams from which the Tees are cut. An asterisk (*) denotes Tees cut from shapes not available from Canadian mills.

Hollow structural section (HSS) properties are based on an outer corner radius equal to twice the thickness.

For W, HP, S, M, C and MC shapes two values of flange and web thickness are tabulated. The first is the theoretical dimension and the second, rounded value is the detailing dimension.

Calculations

In keeping with industry standards, the theoretical mass and the properties of shapes listed in this book are calculated including fillets and roundings, except for angles. All values are rounded to three significant figures in accordance with the rules for rounding in Standard CAN3-Z234.1-1976, "Canadian Metric Practice Guide". In view of the dimensional tolerances permitted, it is felt that a greater degree of accuracy is unwarranted.

The theoretical mass of rolled steel shapes is computed on the basis that one cubic metre of steel has a mass of 7 850 kilograms.

W SHAPES
W920 - W690

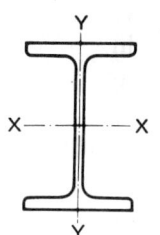

PROPERTIES

Designation‡	Dead Load	Total Area	Axis X-X				Axis Y-Y				Torsional Constant	Warping Constant
			I_x	S_x	r_x	Z_x	I_y	S_y	r_y	Z_y	J	C_w
	kN/m	mm²	10^6mm⁴	10^3mm³	mm	10^3mm³	10^6mm⁴	10^3mm³	mm	10^3mm³	10^3mm⁴	10^9mm⁶
W920												
X446*	4.38	57 000	8 470	18 200	385	20 600	540	2 550	97.3	3 950	26 800	107 000
X417*	4.10	53 300	7 880	17 000	385	19 200	501	2 370	97.0	3 670	21 900	98 700
X387*	3.79	49 300	7 180	15 600	382	17 600	453	2 160	95.9	3 330	17 300	88 500
X365*	3.57	46 400	6 710	14 600	380	16 500	421	2 010	95.3	3 110	14 400	81 900
X342*	3.35	43 600	6 250	13 700	379	15 400	390	1 870	94.6	2 880	11 900	75 500
W920												
X313*	3.06	39 800	5 480	11 800	371	13 600	170	1 100	65.4	1 750	11 600	34 300
X289*	2.83	36 800	5 040	10 900	370	12 600	156	1 020	65.1	1 600	9 230	31 300
X271*	2.66	34 600	4 720	10 200	369	11 800	145	946	64.7	1 490	7 690	28 900
X253*	2.48	32 300	4 370	9 520	368	11 000	134	874	64.4	1 370	6 260	26 500
X238*	2.33	30 400	4 060	8 880	365	10 200	123	806	63.6	1 270	5 140	24 300
X223*	2.19	28 600	3 770	8 270	363	9 540	112	738	62.6	1 160	4 220	22 100
X201*	1.97	25 600	3 250	7 200	356	8 360	94.4	621	60.7	982	2 910	18 400
W840												
X359*	3.52	45 800	5 910	13 600	359	15 400	389	1 930	92.2	2 980	15 000	67 400
X329*	3.23	42 000	5 350	12 400	357	14 000	349	1 740	91.2	2 690	11 500	60 000
X299*	2.93	38 100	4 790	11 200	355	12 600	312	1 560	90.5	2 410	8 560	53 200
W840												
X226*	2.22	28 900	3 400	7 990	343	9 160	114	774	62.8	1 210	5 140	19 300
X210*	2.06	26 800	3 110	7 340	341	8 430	103	700	62.0	1 100	4 050	17 300
X193*	1.89	24 700	2 780	6 630	335	7 620	90.3	618	60.5	971	3 050	15 100
X176*	1.72	22 400	2 460	5 900	331	6 810	78.2	536	59.1	844	2 220	13 000
W760												
X314*	3.08	40 100	4 270	10 900	326	12 300	316	1 640	88.8	2 540	11 600	44 700
X284*	2.78	36 200	3 810	9 790	324	11 000	280	1 470	87.9	2 260	8 580	39 300
X257*	2.52	32 800	3 420	8 840	323	9 930	250	1 310	87.3	2 020	6 380	34 800
W760												
X196*	1.93	25 100	2 400	6 240	309	7 170	81.7	610	57.1	959	4 040	11 300
X185*	1.81	23 500	2 230	5 820	308	6 690	75.1	563	56.5	884	3 330	10 300
X173*	1.70	22 100	2 060	5 400	305	6 210	68.7	515	55.8	810	2 690	9 420
X161*	1.57	20 400	1 860	4 900	302	5 660	60.7	457	54.5	720	2 070	8 280
X147*	1.44	18 700	1 660	4 410	298	5 100	52.9	399	53.2	631	1 560	7 160
W690												
X265*	2.59	33 700	2 900	8 220	293	9 290	231	1 290	82.8	1 990	8 110	26 400
X240*	2.35	30 600	2 610	7 450	292	8 390	206	1 160	82.0	1 780	6 090	23 400
X217*	2.13	27 700	2 340	6 740	291	7 570	185	1 040	81.7	1 600	4 560	20 800
W690												
X170*	1.66	21 600	1 700	4 910	281	5 620	66.2	517	55.4	809	3 050	7 410
X152*	1.49	19 400	1 510	4 380	279	5 000	57.8	455	54.6	710	2 200	6 420
X140*	1.37	17 800	1 360	3 980	276	4 550	51.7	407	53.9	636	1 670	5 720
X125*	1.23	16 000	1 190	3 500	273	4 010	44.1	349	52.5	546	1 180	4 830

‡ Nominal depth in millimetres and mass in kilograms per metre.

* Not available from Canadian mills.

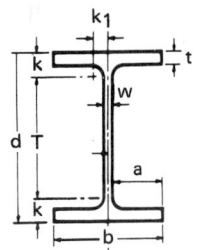

DIMENSIONS AND SURFACE AREAS

Nominal Mass kg/m	Theo-retical Mass kg/m	Depth d mm	Flange Width b mm	Flange Mean Thickness t mm		Web Thickness w mm		Distances a mm	T mm	k mm	k₁ mm	d-2t mm	Surface Area (m²) per metre of length Total	Minus Top of Top Flange
446	447.2	933	423	42.7	43	24.0	24	200	792	70	38	848	3.51	3.09
417	418.1	928	422	39.9	40	22.5	22	200	793	67	37	848	3.50	3.08
387	387.0	921	420	36.6	37	21.3	21	200	792	64	36	848	3.48	3.06
365	364.6	916	419	34.3	34	20.3	20	200	793	61	36	848	3.47	3.05
342	342.4	912	418	32.0	32	19.3	19	200	793	59	35	848	3.46	3.04
313	312.7	932	309	34.5	34	21.1	21	144	820	56	31	863	3.06	2.75
289	288.6	927	308	32.0	32	19.4	19	145	819	54	30	863	3.05	2.74
271	271.7	923	307	30.0	30	18.4	18	145	819	52	29	863	3.04	2.73
253	253.7	919	306	27.9	28	17.3	17	145	819	50	29	863	3.03	2.72
238	238.3	915	305	25.9	26	16.5	16	145	819	48	28	863	3.02	2.71
223	224.2	911	304	23.9	24	15.9	16	144	819	46	28	863	3.01	2.70
201	201.3	903	304	20.1	20	15.2	15	145	819	42	28	863	2.99	2.69
359	359.4	868	403	35.6	36	21.1	21	191	755	57	30	797	3.31	2.90
329	329.4	862	401	32.4	32	19.7	20	191	757	53	29	797	3.29	2.88
299	299.3	855	400	29.2	29	18.2	18	191	756	50	28	797	3.27	2.87
226	226.6	851	294	26.8	27	16.1	16	139	756	48	27	797	2.85	2.55
210	210.8	846	293	24.4	24	15.4	15	139	757	45	27	797	2.83	2.54
193	193.5	840	292	21.7	22	14.7	15	139	755	43	27	797	2.82	2.53
176	176.0	835	292	18.8	19	14.0	14	139	756	40	26	797	2.81	2.52
314	314.4	786	384	33.4	33	19.7	20	182	681	52	28	719	3.07	2.68
284	283.9	779	382	30.1	30	18.0	18	182	680	49	27	719	3.05	2.67
257	257.6	773	381	27.1	27	16.6	17	182	680	46	26	719	3.04	2.65
196	196.8	770	268	25.4	25	15.6	16	126	681	44	26	719	2.58	2.31
185	184.8	766	267	23.6	24	14.9	15	126	679	43	25	719	2.57	2.30
173	173.6	762	267	21.6	22	14.4	14	127	679	41	25	719	2.57	2.30
161	160.4	758	266	19.3	19	13.8	14	126	681	38	25	719	2.55	2.28
147	147.1	753	265	17.0	17	13.2	13	126	680	36	24	719	2.54	2.27
265	264.5	706	358	30.2	30	18.4	18	170	610	48	26	646	2.81	2.45
240	239.9	701	356	27.4	27	16.8	17	170	611	45	25	646	2.79	2.43
217	217.8	695	355	24.8	25	15.4	15	170	609	43	24	646	2.78	2.43
170	169.9	693	256	23.6	24	14.5	14	121	609	42	24	646	2.38	2.13
152	152.1	688	254	21.1	21	13.1	13	121	610	39	23	646	2.37	2.11
140	139.8	684	254	18.9	19	12.4	12	121	610	37	23	646	2.36	2.11
125	125.6	678	253	16.3	16	11.7	12	121	610	34	23	646	2.34	2.09

W SHAPES
W610 - W530

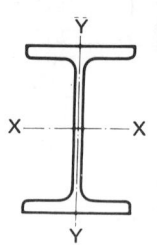

PROPERTIES

Designation ‡	Dead Load	Total Area	Axis X-X				Axis Y-Y				Torsional Constant	Warping Constant
			I_x	S_x	r_x	Z_x	I_y	S_y	r_y	Z_y	J	C_w
	kN/m	mm²	10^6 mm⁴	10^3 mm³	mm	10^3 mm³	10^6 mm⁴	10^3 mm³	mm	10^3 mm³	10^3 mm⁴	10^9 mm⁶
W610												
X241	2.37	30 800	2 150	6 780	264	7 670	184	1 120	77.3	1 730	7 700	16 800
X217	2.13	27 800	1 910	6 070	262	6 850	163	995	76.6	1 530	5 600	14 700
X195	1.91	24 900	1 680	5 400	260	6 070	142	871	75.5	1 340	3 970	12 700
X174	1.70	22 200	1 470	4 780	257	5 360	124	761	74.7	1 170	2 800	10 900
X155	1.51	19 700	1 290	4 220	256	4 730	108	666	74.0	1 020	1 950	9 450
W610												
X140	1.37	17 900	1 120	3 630	250	4 150	45.1	392	50.2	613	2 180	3 990
X125	1.22	15 900	985	3 220	249	3 670	39.3	343	49.7	535	1 540	3 450
X113	1.11	14 400	875	2 880	247	3 290	34.3	300	48.8	469	1 120	2 990
X101	0.997	13 000	764	2 530	242	2 900	29.5	259	47.6	404	781	2 550
W610												
X92*	0.905	11 800	646	2 140	234	2 510	14.4	161	34.9	258	710	1 250
X82*	0.803	10 400	560	1 870	232	2 200	12.1	136	34.1	218	488	1 040
W530												
X219*	2.14	27 900	1 510	5 390	233	6 110	157	986	75.0	1 520	6 420	11 000
X196*	1.92	25 000	1 340	4 840	232	5 460	139	877	74.6	1 350	4 700	9 640
X182*	1.78	23 100	1 240	4 480	232	5 040	127	808	74.1	1 240	3 740	8 820
X165*	1.62	21 100	1 110	4 060	229	4 550	114	726	73.5	1 110	2 830	7 790
X150*	1.47	19 200	1 010	3 710	229	4 150	103	659	73.2	1 010	2 160	7 030
W530												
X138	1.35	17 600	861	3 140	221	3 610	38.7	362	46.9	569	2 500	2 670
X123	1.20	15 700	761	2 800	220	3 210	33.8	319	46.4	499	1 800	2 310
X109	1.06	13 900	667	2 480	219	2 830	29.5	280	46.1	437	1 260	2 000
X101	0.995	12 900	617	2 300	219	2 620	26.9	256	45.7	400	1 020	1 820
X92	0.907	11 800	552	2 070	216	2 360	23.8	228	44.9	355	762	1 590
X82	0.808	10 500	479	1 810	214	2 070	20.3	194	44.0	303	530	1 340
W530												
X85*	0.830	10 800	485	1 810	212	2 100	12.6	152	34.2	242	737	849
X74*	0.733	9 520	411	1 550	208	1 810	10.4	125	33.1	200	480	692
X66*	0.644	8 370	351	1 340	205	1 560	8.57	104	32.0	166	320	565

‡ Nominal depth in millimetres and mass in kilograms per metre.
* Not available from Canadian mills.

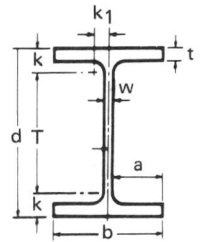

DIMENSIONS AND SURFACE AREAS

Nominal Mass	Theo-retical Mass	Depth d	Flange Width b	Flange Mean Thickness t		Web Thickness w		a	T	k	k$_1$	d-2t	Surface Area (m^2) per metre of length Total	Surface Area (m^2) per metre of length Minus Top of Top Flange
kg/m	kg/m	mm	mm	mm	mm	mm	mm	mm	mm	mm	mm	mm		
241	241.7	635	329	31.0	31	17.9	18	156	534	50	27	573	2.55	2.22
217	217.9	628	328	27.7	28	16.5	16	156	533	47	26	573	2.54	2.21
195	195.6	622	327	24.4	24	15.4	15	156	535	43	25	573	2.52	2.19
174	174.3	616	325	21.6	22	14.0	14	156	533	41	25	573	2.51	2.18
155	154.9	611	324	19.0	19	12.7	13	156	534	38	24	573	2.49	2.17
140	140.1	617	230	22.2	22	13.1	13	109	534	41	24	573	2.13	1.90
125	125.1	612	229	19.6	20	11.9	12	109	533	39	24	573	2.12	1.89
113	113.4	608	228	17.3	17	11.2	11	109	535	36	23	573	2.10	1.88
101	101.7	603	228	14.9	15	10.5	10	109	534	34	23	573	2.10	1.87
92	92.3	603	179	15.0	15	10.9	11	84	534	34	23	573	1.90	1.72
82	81.9	599	178	12.8	13	10.0	10	84	534	32	23	573	1.89	1.71
219	218.9	560	318	29.2	29	18.3	18	150	466	47	26	502	2.36	2.04
196	196.5	554	316	26.3	26	16.5	16	150	466	44	25	502	2.34	2.02
182	181.7	551	315	24.4	24	15.2	15	150	467	42	24	502	2.33	2.01
165	165.3	546	313	22.2	22	14.0	14	150	466	40	24	502	2.32	2.00
150	150.6	543	312	20.3	20	12.7	13	150	467	38	23	502	2.31	1.99
138	138.3	549	214	23.6	24	14.7	15	100	465	42	24	502	1.93	1.71
123	123.2	544	212	21.2	21	13.1	13	100	466	39	23	502	1.91	1.70
109	109.0	539	211	18.8	19	11.6	12	100	465	37	23	502	1.90	1.69
101	101.4	537	210	17.4	17	10.9	11	100	467	35	22	502	1.89	1.68
92	92.5	533	209	15.6	16	10.2	10	100	465	34	22	502	1.88	1.67
82	82.4	528	209	13.3	13	9.5	10	100	471	29	19	502	1.87	1.66
85	84.7	535	166	16.5	16	10.3	10	78	467	34	22	502	1.71	1.55
74	74.7	529	166	13.6	14	9.7	10	78	465	32	22	502	1.70	1.54
66	65.7	525	165	11.4	11	8.9	9	78	467	29	21	502	1.69	1.52

W SHAPES
W460 - W410

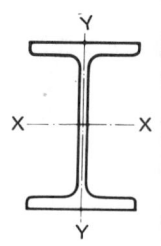

PROPERTIES

Designation‡	Dead Load	Total Area	Axis X-X				Axis Y-Y				Torsional Constant	Warping Constant
			I_x	S_x	r_x	Z_x	I_y	S_y	r_y	Z_y	J	C_w
	kN/m	mm²	10^6mm⁴	10^3mm³	mm	10^3mm³	10^6mm⁴	10^3mm³	mm	10^3mm³	10^3mm⁴	10^9mm⁶
W460												
X177*	1.73	22 600	910	3 780	201	4 280	105	735	68.2	1 130	4 410	5 440
X158*	1.54	20 100	796	3 350	199	3 780	91.4	643	67.4	989	3 120	4 670
X144*	1.41	18 400	726	3 080	199	3 450	83.6	591	67.4	906	2 440	4 230
X128*	1.26	16 400	637	2 730	197	3 050	73.3	520	66.9	796	1 720	3 670
X113*	1.10	14 400	556	2 400	196	2 670	63.3	452	66.3	691	1 180	3 150
W460												
X106	1.03	13 500	488	2 080	190	2 390	25.1	259	43.1	405	1 460	1 260
X97	0.947	12 300	445	1 910	190	2 180	22.8	237	43.1	368	1 130	1 140
X89	0.876	11 400	410	1 770	190	2 010	20.9	218	42.8	339	907	1 040
X82	0.804	10 400	370	1 610	189	1 830	18.6	195	42.3	303	691	918
X74	0.728	9 450	333	1 460	188	1 650	16.6	175	41.9	271	517	813
X67	0.668	8 680	300	1 320	186	1 500	14.6	153	41.0	239	412	709
X61	0.598	7 760	259	1 150	183	1 310	12.2	129	39.7	202	289	588
W460												
X68*	0.672	8 730	297	1 290	184	1 490	9.41	122	32.8	192	509	463
X60*	0.584	7 590	255	1 120	183	1 280	7.96	104	32.4	163	335	388
X52*	0.510	6 630	212	943	179	1 090	6.34	83.4	30.9	131	210	306
W410												
X149*	1.46	19 000	619	2 870	180	3 250	77.7	586	63.9	900	3 220	3 200
X132*	1.29	16 800	538	2 530	179	2 850	67.4	512	63.3	785	2 260	2 730
X114*	1.12	14 600	462	2 200	178	2 460	57.2	439	62.6	671	1 490	2 300
X100*	0.977	12 700	398	1 920	177	2 130	49.5	381	62.4	581	994	1 960
W410												
X85	0.833	10 800	315	1 510	171	1 730	18.0	199	40.8	310	926	717
X74	0.735	9 550	275	1 330	170	1 510	15.6	173	40.4	269	637	614
X67	0.662	8 600	246	1 200	169	1 360	13.8	154	40.1	239	469	540
X60	0.584	7 580	216	1 060	169	1 190	12.0	135	39.8	209	328	468
X54	0.524	6 810	186	924	165	1 050	10.1	114	38.5	177	226	388
W410												
X46	0.453	5 890	156	773	163	885	5.14	73.4	29.5	115	192	197
X39	0.384	4 990	127	634	160	730	4.04	57.7	28.5	90.6	111	154

‡ Nominal depth in millimetres and mass in kilograms per metre.
* Not available from Canadian mills.

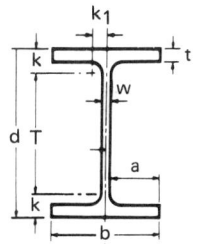

DIMENSIONS AND SURFACE AREAS

Nominal Mass	Theo-retical Mass	Depth d	Flange Width b	Flange Mean Thickness t		Web Thickness w		Distances a	T	k	k₁	d-2t	Surface Area (m²) per metre of length Total	Minus Top of Top Flange
kg/m	kg/m	mm	mm	mm	mm	mm	mm	mm	mm	mm	mm	mm		
177	177.3	482	286	26.9	27	16.6	17	135	395	44	24	428	2.07	1.79
158	157.7	476	284	23.9	24	15.0	15	135	395	41	23	428	2.06	1.77
144	144.6	472	283	22.1	22	13.6	14	135	395	39	22	428	2.05	1.76
128	128.4	467	282	19.6	20	12.2	12	135	394	37	21	428	2.04	1.76
113	113.1	463	280	17.3	17	10.8	11	135	396	34	21	428	2.02	1.74
106	105.8	469	194	20.6	21	12.6	13	91	393	38	22	428	1.69	1.50
97	96.6	466	193	19.0	19	11.4	11	91	394	36	21	428	1.68	1.49
89	89.3	463	192	17.7	18	10.5	10	91	393	35	21	428	1.68	1.48
82	81.9	460	191	16.0	16	9.9	10	91	394	33	21	428	1.66	1.47
74	74.2	457	190	14.5	14	9.0	9	91	395	31	20	428	1.65	1.46
67	68.1	454	190	12.7	13	8.5	8	91	394	30	20	428	1.65	1.46
61	60.9	450	189	10.8	11	8.1	8	91	394	28	20	428	1.64	1.45
68	68.5	459	154	15.4	15	9.1	9	73	396	32	20	428	1.51	1.36
60	59.6	455	153	13.3	13	8.0	8	73	396	30	19	428	1.50	1.35
52	52.0	450	152	10.8	11	7.6	8	72	395	28	19	428	1.49	1.34
149	149.3	431	265	25.0	25	14.9	15	125	348	42	23	381	1.89	1.63
132	132.1	425	263	22.2	22	13.3	13	125	348	39	22	381	1.88	1.61
114	114.5	420	261	19.3	19	11.6	12	125	349	36	21	381	1.86	1.60
100	99.6	415	260	16.9	17	10.0	10	125	348	34	20	381	1.85	1.59
85	85.0	417	181	18.2	18	10.9	11	85	347	35	21	381	1.54	1.35
74	74.9	413	180	16.0	16	9.7	10	85	347	33	21	381	1.53	1.35
67	67.5	410	179	14.4	14	8.8	9	85	348	31	20	381	1.52	1.34
60	59.5	407	178	12.8	13	7.7	8	85	347	30	20	381	1.51	1.33
54	53.4	403	177	10.9	11	7.5	8	85	347	28	20	381	1.50	1.32
46	46.2	403	140	11.2	11	7.0	7	67	347	28	19	381	1.35	1.21
39	39.2	399	140	8.8	9	6.4	6	67	347	26	19	381	1.35	1.21

W SHAPES
W360

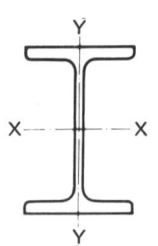

PROPERTIES

Designation ‡	Dead Load	Total Area	Axis X-X				Axis Y-Y				Torsional Constant	Warping Constant
			I_x	S_x	r_x	Z_x	I_y	S_y	r_y	Z_y	J	C_w
	kN/m	mm²	10^6mm⁴	10^3mm³	mm	10^3mm³	10^6mm⁴	10^3mm³	mm	10^3mm³	10^3mm⁴	10^9mm⁶
W360												
X1086*	10.6	139 000	5 960	20 900	207	27 200	1 960	8 650	119	13 400	605 000	96 700
X990*	9.71	126 000	5 190	18 900	203	24 300	1 730	7 740	117	12 000	469 000	82 000
X900*	8.84	115 000	4 500	17 000	198	21 600	1 530	6 940	115	10 700	364 000	69 200
X818*	8.03	104 000	3 920	15 300	194	19 300	1 360	6 200	114	9 560	279 000	58 900
X744*	7.29	94 800	3 420	13 700	190	17 200	1 200	5 550	113	8 550	214 000	50 200
X677*	6.64	86 300	2 990	12 400	186	15 300	1 070	4 990	111	7 680	165 000	43 100
W360												
X634*	6.22	80 800	2 740	11 600	184	14 200	983	4 630	110	7 120	138 000	38 700
X592*	5.81	75 500	2 500	10 800	182	13 100	902	4 280	109	6 570	114 000	34 800
X551*	5.40	70 100	2 260	9 940	180	12 100	825	3 950	108	6 050	92 500	31 000
X509*	4.99	64 900	2 050	9 170	178	11 000	754	3 630	108	5 550	74 000	27 700
X463*	4.53	59 000	1 800	8 280	175	9 880	670	3 250	107	4 980	56 500	23 900
X421*	4.13	53 700	1 600	7 510	173	8 880	601	2 940	106	4 490	43 400	20 800
X382*	3.75	48 700	1 410	6 790	170	7 970	536	2 640	105	4 030	32 900	18 200
X347*	3.40	44 200	1 250	6 140	168	7 140	481	2 380	104	3 630	24 800	15 900
X314*	3.07	39 900	1 100	5 530	166	6 370	426	2 120	103	3 240	18 500	13 800
X287*	2.82	36 600	997	5 070	165	5 810	388	1 940	103	2 960	14 500	12 300
X262*	2.57	33 500	894	4 620	163	5 260	350	1 760	102	2 680	11 100	11 000
X237*	2.31	30 100	788	4 150	162	4 690	310	1 570	101	2 390	8 190	9 500
X216*	2.12	27 600	712	3 790	161	4 260	283	1 430	101	2 180	6 330	8 520
W360												
X196*	1.92	25 000	636	3 420	159	3 840	229	1 220	95.7	1 860	5 140	6 830
X179*	1.75	22 800	575	3 120	159	3 480	207	1 110	95.3	1 680	3 910	6 120
X162*	1.58	20 600	516	2 830	158	3 140	186	1 000	95.0	1 520	2 940	5 430
X147*	1.44	18 800	463	2 570	157	2 840	167	904	94.2	1 370	2 230	4 840
X134*	1.31	17 100	415	2 330	156	2 560	151	817	94.0	1 240	1 680	4 310
W360												
X122*	1.19	15 500	365	2 010	153	2 270	61.5	478	63.0	732	2 110	1 790
X110*	1.08	14 000	331	1 840	154	2 060	55.7	435	63.1	664	1 610	1 610
X101*	0.993	12 900	302	1 690	153	1 880	50.6	397	62.6	606	1 260	1 450
X91*	0.891	11 600	267	1 510	152	1 680	44.8	353	62.1	538	916	1 270
W360												
X79	0.777	10 100	227	1 280	150	1 430	24.2	236	48.9	362	814	687
X72	0.701	9 110	201	1 150	149	1 280	21.4	210	48.5	322	603	600
X64	0.627	8 140	178	1 030	148	1 140	18.8	186	48.1	284	438	524
W360												
X57	0.556	7 220	161	897	149	1 010	11.1	129	39.2	200	334	331
X51	0.496	6 450	141	796	148	894	9.68	113	38.7	174	238	285
X45	0.441	5 730	122	691	146	779	8.18	95.7	37.8	148	160	239
W360												
X39	0.384	4 980	102	580	143	662	3.75	58.6	27.4	91.7	151	110
X33	0.321	4 170	82.7	474	141	542	2.91	45.8	26.4	71.8	85.9	84.3

‡ Nominal depth in millimetres and mass in kilograms per metre.
* Not available from Canadian mills.

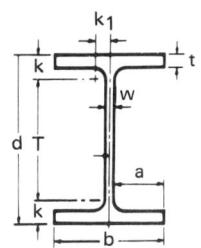

DIMENSIONS AND SURFACE AREAS

Nominal Mass	Theo- retical Mass	Depth d	Flange Width b	Flange Mean Thickness t		Web Thickness w		a	T	k	k₁	d-2t	Surface Area (m²) per metre of length Total	Surface Area (m²) per metre of length Minus Top of Top Flange
kg/m	kg/m	mm	mm	mm	mm	mm	mm	mm	mm	mm	mm	mm		
1086	1087.9	569	454	125	125	78.0	78	188	286	142	54	320	2.80	2.35
990	991.0	550	448	115	115	71.9	72	188	287	132	51	320	2.75	2.30
900	902.2	531	442	106	106	65.9	66	188	286	123	48	320	2.70	2.26
818	819.0	514	437	97.0	97	60.5	60	189	287	114	45	320	2.66	2.22
744	744.3	498	432	88.9	89	55.6	56	188	287	106	43	320	2.61	2.18
677	677.8	483	428	81.5	82	51.2	51	189	286	99	41	320	2.58	2.15
634	634.3	474	424	77.1	77	47.6	48	188	287	94	39	320	2.55	2.12
592	592.6	465	421	72.3	72	45.0	45	188	288	89	38	320	2.52	2.10
551	550.6	455	418	67.6	68	42.0	42	188	286	85	36	320	2.50	2.08
509	509.5	446	416	62.7	63	39.1	39	189	287	80	35	320	2.48	2.06
463	462.8	435	412	57.4	57	35.8	36	188	288	74	33	320	2.44	2.03
421	421.7	425	409	52.6	53	32.8	33	188	286	70	32	320	2.42	2.01
382	382.4	416	406	48.0	48	29.8	30	188	287	65	30	320	2.40	1.99
347	347.0	407	404	43.7	44	27.2	27	189	286	61	29	320	2.38	1.97
314	313.4	399	401	39.6	40	24.9	25	188	286	57	28	320	2.35	1.95
287	287.6	393	399	36.6	37	22.6	23	188	286	54	27	320	2.34	1.94
262	262.7	387	398	33.3	33	21.1	21	189	288	50	26	320	2.32	1.92
237	236.3	380	395	30.2	30	18.9	19	188	287	47	25	320	2.30	1.91
216	216.3	375	394	27.7	28	17.3	17	189	286	45	24	320	2.29	1.90
196	196.5	372	374	26.2	26	16.4	16	179	287	43	23	320	2.21	1.83
179	179.2	368	373	23.9	24	15.0	15	179	287	41	23	320	2.20	1.82
162	162.0	364	371	21.8	22	13.3	13	179	287	39	22	320	2.19	1.81
147	147.5	360	370	19.8	20	12.3	12	179	287	37	21	320	2.18	1.81
134	134.0	356	369	18.0	18	11.2	11	179	287	35	21	320	2.17	1.80
122	121.7	363	257	21.7	22	13.0	13	122	280	41	24	320	1.73	1.47
110	110.2	360	256	19.9	20	11.4	11	123	281	39	23	320	1.72	1.47
101	101.2	357	255	18.3	18	10.5	10	123	282	37	23	320	1.71	1.46
91	90.8	353	254	16.4	16	9.5	10	122	282	35	23	320	1.70	1.45
79	79.3	354	205	16.8	17	9.4	9	98	281	36	22	320	1.51	1.30
72	71.5	350	204	15.1	15	8.6	9	98	281	34	22	320	1.50	1.29
64	63.9	347	203	13.5	14	7.7	8	98	280	33	22	320	1.49	1.29
57	56.7	358	172	13.1	13	7.9	8	82	298	30	20	332	1.39	1.22
51	50.6	355	171	11.6	12	7.2	7	82	297	29	19	332	1.38	1.21
45	45.0	352	171	9.8	10	6.9	7	82	298	27	19	332	1.37	1.20
39	39.1	353	128	10.7	11	6.5	6	61	297	28	19	332	1.21	1.08
33	32.8	349	127	8.5	8	5.8	6	61	299	25	19	332	1.19	1.06

W SHAPES
W310

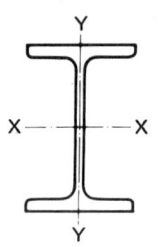

PROPERTIES

Designation‡	Dead Load	Total Area	Axis X-X				Axis Y-Y				Torsional Constant	Warping Constant
			I_x	S_x	r_x	Z_x	I_y	S_y	r_y	Z_y	J	C_w
	kN/m	mm²	10^6mm⁴	10^3mm³	mm	10^3mm³	10^6mm⁴	10^3mm³	mm	10^3mm³	10^3mm⁴	10^9mm⁶
W310												
X500*	4.90	63 700	1 690	7 910	163	9 880	494	2 910	88.1	4 490	101 000	15 300
X454*	4.45	57 800	1 480	7 130	160	8 820	436	2 600	86.9	4 000	77 200	13 100
X415*	4.07	52 900	1 300	6 450	157	7 900	391	2 340	86.0	3 610	59 500	11 300
X375*	3.67	47 700	1 130	5 760	154	7 000	343	2 080	84.8	3 200	44 700	9 560
X342*	3.36	43 700	1 010	5 260	152	6 330	310	1 890	84.2	2 910	34 900	8 420
X313*	3.07	39 900	896	4 790	150	5 720	277	1 700	83.3	2 620	27 000	7 350
W310												
X283	2.77	36 000	787	4 310	148	5 100	246	1 530	82.7	2 340	20 400	6 330
X253	2.48	32 200	682	3 830	146	4 490	215	1 350	81.7	2 060	14 800	5 370
X226	2.22	28 900	596	3 420	144	3 980	189	1 190	80.9	1 830	10 800	4 620
X202	1.98	25 800	520	3 050	142	3 510	166	1 050	80.2	1 610	7 740	3 960
X179	1.75	22 800	445	2 680	140	3 050	144	919	79.5	1 400	5 380	3 340
X158	1.54	20 100	386	2 360	139	2 670	125	805	78.9	1 220	3 780	2 840
X143	1.40	18 200	348	2 150	138	2 420	113	729	78.8	1 110	2 870	2 540
X129	1.27	16 500	308	1 940	137	2 160	100	652	77.8	991	2 130	2 220
X118	1.15	15 000	275	1 750	135	1 950	90.2	588	77.5	893	1 600	1 970
X107	1.04	13 600	248	1 590	135	1 770	81.2	531	77.3	806	1 220	1 760
X97	0.950	12 300	222	1 440	134	1 590	72.9	478	77.0	725	912	1 560
W310												
X86	0.847	11 000	199	1 280	135	1 420	44.5	351	63.6	533	877	961
X79	0.774	10 100	177	1 160	132	1 280	39.9	314	62.9	478	657	847
W310												
X74	0.730	9 490	165	1 060	132	1 190	23.4	229	49.7	350	745	505
X67	0.655	8 510	145	949	131	1 060	20.7	203	49.3	310	545	439
X60	0.585	7 590	129	849	130	941	18.3	180	49.1	275	397	384
W310												
X52	0.513	6 670	118	747	133	837	10.3	123	39.3	189	308	237
X45	0.438	5 690	99.2	634	132	708	8.55	103	38.8	158	191	195
X39	0.380	4 940	85.1	549	131	610	7.27	88.1	38.4	135	126	164
W310												
X33*	0.321	4 180	65.0	415	125	480	1.92	37.6	21.4	59.6	122	43.8
X28*	0.278	3 610	54.3	351	123	407	1.58	31.0	20.9	49.2	75.7	35.6
X24*	0.234	3 040	42.7	280	119	328	1.16	22.9	19.5	36.7	42.5	25.7
X21*	0.207	2 690	37.0	244	117	287	0.983	19.5	19.1	31.2	29.4	21.7

‡ Nominal depth in millimetres and mass in kilograms per metre.
* Not available from Canadian mills.

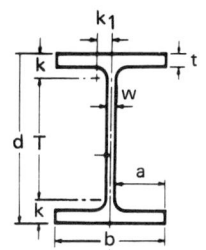

DIMENSIONS AND SURFACE AREAS

Nominal Mass	Theoretical Mass	Depth d	Width b	Flange Mean Thickness t		Web Thickness w		a	T	k	k₁	d-2t	Surface Area (m²) per metre of length Total	Minus Top of Top Flange
kg/m	kg/m	mm	mm	mm	mm	mm	mm	mm	mm	mm	mm	mm		
500	500.4	427	340	75.1	75	45.1	45	148	244	92	38	277	2.12	1.78
454	454.0	415	336	68.7	69	41.3	41	148	244	86	36	277	2.09	1.76
415	415.1	403	334	62.7	63	38.9	39	148	244	80	35	277	2.06	1.73
375	374.3	391	330	57.1	57	35.4	35	148	244	74	33	277	2.03	1.70
342	343.3	382	328	52.6	53	32.6	33	148	243	70	32	277	2.01	1.68
313	313.3	374	325	48.3	48	30.0	30	148	245	65	30	277	1.99	1.66
283	283.0	365	322	44.1	44	26.9	27	148	243	61	29	277	1.96	1.64
253	252.9	356	319	39.6	40	24.4	24	148	242	57	28	277	1.94	1.62
226	226.8	348	317	35.6	36	22.1	22	148	242	53	27	277	1.92	1.60
202	202.6	341	315	31.8	32	20.1	20	148	243	49	26	277	1.90	1.59
179	178.8	333	313	28.1	28	18.0	18	148	243	45	25	277	1.88	1.57
158	157.4	327	310	25.1	25	15.5	16	147	243	42	24	277	1.86	1.55
143	143.1	323	309	22.9	23	14.0	14	148	243	40	23	277	1.85	1.54
129	129.6	318	308	20.6	21	13.1	13	148	242	38	22	277	1.84	1.54
118	117.5	314	307	18.7	19	11.9	12	148	242	36	22	277	1.83	1.53
107	106.9	311	306	17.0	17	10.9	11	148	243	34	21	277	1.82	1.52
97	96.8	308	305	15.4	15	9.9	10	148	244	32	21	277	1.81	1.51
86	86.4	310	254	16.3	16	9.1	9	123	244	33	20	277	1.62	1.36
79	78.9	306	254	14.6	15	8.8	9	123	242	32	20	277	1.61	1.36
74	74.5	310	205	16.3	16	9.4	9	98	244	33	20	277	1.42	1.21
67	66.8	306	204	14.6	15	8.5	8	98	242	32	20	277	1.41	1.21
60	59.6	303	203	13.1	13	7.5	8	98	243	30	20	277	1.40	1.20
52	52.3	317	167	13.2	13	7.6	8	80	257	30	20	291	1.29	1.12
45	44.6	313	166	11.2	11	6.6	7	80	257	28	19	291	1.28	1.11
39	38.7	310	165	9.7	10	5.8	6	80	256	27	19	291	1.27	1.10
33	32.8	313	102	10.8	11	6.6	7	48	269	22	13	291	1.02	0.918
28	28.4	309	102	8.9	9	6.0	6	48	269	20	12	291	1.01	0.912
24	23.8	305	101	6.7	7	5.6	6	48	269	18	12	291	1.00	0.901
21	21.1	303	101	5.7	6	5.1	5	48	269	17	12	291	1.00	0.899

W SHAPES
W250 - W200

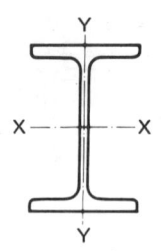

PROPERTIES

Designation‡	Dead Load	Total Area	Axis X-X				Axis Y-Y				Torsional Constant	Warping Constant
			I_x	S_x	r_x	Z_x	I_y	S_y	r_y	Z_y	J	C_w
	kN/m	mm²	10^6mm⁴	10^3mm³	mm	10^3mm³	10^6mm⁴	10^3mm³	mm	10^3mm³	10^3mm⁴	10^9mm⁶
W250												
X167	1.64	21 300	300	2 080	119	2 430	98.8	746	68.1	1 140	6 310	1 630
X149	1.46	19 000	259	1 840	117	2 130	86.2	656	67.4	1 000	4 510	1 390
X131	1.28	16 700	221	1 610	115	1 850	74.5	571	66.8	870	3 120	1 160
X115	1.12	14 600	189	1 410	114	1 600	64.1	495	66.3	753	2 130	976
X101	0.992	12 900	164	1 240	113	1 400	55.5	432	65.6	656	1 490	829
X89	0.878	11 400	143	1 100	112	1 230	48.4	378	65.2	574	1 040	713
X80	0.786	10 200	126	982	111	1 090	43.1	338	65.0	513	757	623
X73	0.715	9 280	113	891	110	985	38.8	306	64.7	463	575	553
W250												
X67	0.658	8 550	104	806	110	901	22.2	218	51.0	332	625	324
X58	0.571	7 420	87.3	693	108	770	18.8	186	50.3	283	409	268
X49	0.481	6 250	70.6	572	106	633	15.1	150	49.2	228	241	211
W250												
X45	0.440	5 720	71.1	534	111	602	7.03	95.1	35.1	146	261	113
X39	0.379	4 920	60.1	459	111	513	5.94	80.8	34.7	124	169	93.4
X33	0.321	4 170	48.9	379	108	424	4.73	64.7	33.7	99.5	98.5	73.2
W250												
X28*	0.279	3 630	40.0	307	105	353	1.78	34.8	22.1	54.7	96.7	27.7
X25*	0.249	3 230	34.2	266	103	307	1.49	29.2	21.5	46.2	65.2	23.0
X22*	0.219	2 850	28.9	227	101	263	1.23	24.0	20.8	38.1	43.4	18.7
X18*	0.175	2 270	22.4	179	99.3	207	0.913	18.1	20.1	28.6	22.4	13.8
W200												
X100	0.976	12 700	113	989	94.3	1 150	36.6	349	53.7	533	2 090	386
X86	0.851	11 100	94.7	853	92.4	981	31.4	300	53.2	458	1 400	318
X71	0.701	9 110	76.6	709	91.7	803	25.4	246	52.8	375	818	250
X59	0.582	7 560	61.1	582	89.9	653	20.4	199	51.9	303	465	196
X52	0.513	6 660	52.7	512	89.0	570	17.8	175	51.7	266	324	167
X46	0.451	5 860	45.5	448	88.1	496	15.3	151	51.1	230	221	141
W200												
X42	0.409	5 310	40.9	399	87.8	446	9.00	108	41.2	165	223	84.0
X36	0.352	4 580	34.4	342	86.7	380	7.64	92.6	40.8	141	146	69.6
W200												
X31	0.308	4 000	31.4	299	88.6	335	4.10	61.1	32.0	93.8	119	40.9
X27	0.261	3 390	25.8	249	87.2	279	3.30	49.6	31.2	76.1	71.3	32.5
W200												
X22*	0.220	2 860	20.0	194	83.6	222	1.42	27.8	22.3	43.7	56.6	13.9
X19*	0.191	2 480	16.6	163	81.8	187	1.15	22.6	21.5	35.6	36.2	11.1
X15*	0.147	1 900	12.7	127	81.8	145	0.869	17.4	21.4	27.1	17.6	8.24

‡ Nominal depth in millimetres and mass in kilograms per metre.
* Not available from Canadian mills.

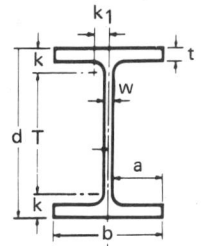

DIMENSIONS AND SURFACE AREAS

Nominal Mass	Theo-retical Mass	Depth d	Flange Width b	Flange Mean Thickness t		Web Thickness w		Distances a	T	k	k_1	d-2t	Surface Area (m²) per metre of length Total	Minus Top of Top Flange
kg/m	kg/m	mm	mm	mm	mm	mm	mm	mm	mm	mm	mm	mm		
167	167.4	289	265	31.8	32	19.2	19	123	191	49	25	225	1.60	1.33
149	148.9	282	263	28.4	28	17.3	17	123	192	45	24	225	1.58	1.32
131	131.1	275	261	25.1	25	15.4	15	123	191	42	23	225	1.56	1.30
115	114.8	269	259	22.1	22	13.5	14	123	191	39	23	225	1.55	1.29
101	101.2	264	257	19.6	20	11.9	12	123	190	37	22	225	1.53	1.28
89	89.6	260	256	17.3	17	10.7	11	123	192	34	21	225	1.52	1.26
80	80.1	256	255	15.6	16	9.4	9	123	190	33	20	225	1.52	1.26
73	72.9	253	254	14.2	14	8.6	9	123	191	31	20	225	1.50	1.25
67	67.1	257	204	15.7	16	8.9	9	98	191	33	20	225	1.31	1.11
58	58.2	252	203	13.5	14	8.0	8	98	190	31	20	225	1.30	1.10
49	49.0	247	202	11.0	11	7.4	7	98	191	28	19	225	1.29	1.09
45	44.9	266	148	13.0	13	7.6	8	70	220	23	12	240	1.11	0.960
39	38.7	262	147	11.2	11	6.6	7	70	220	21	12	240	1.10	0.951
33	32.7	258	146	9.1	9	6.1	6	70	220	19	11	240	1.09	0.942
28	28.5	260	102	10.0	10	6.4	6	48	221	20	11	240	0.916	0.814
25	25.3	257	102	8.4	8	6.1	6	48	222	18	11	240	0.908	0.806
22	22.4	254	102	6.9	7	5.8	6	48	221	17	11	240	0.904	0.802
18	17.9	251	101	5.3	5	4.8	5	48	222	15	11	240	0.894	0.793
100	99.5	229	210	23.7	24	14.5	14	98	156	37	18	181	1.27	1.06
86	86.7	222	209	20.6	21	13.0	13	98	155	34	18	181	1.26	1.05
71	71.5	216	206	17.4	17	10.2	10	98	157	30	16	181	1.23	1.03
59	59.4	210	205	14.2	14	9.1	9	98	157	27	16	181	1.22	1.01
52	52.3	206	204	12.6	13	7.9	8	98	155	26	15	181	1.21	1.01
46	46.0	203	203	11.0	11	7.2	7	98	156	24	15	181	1.20	1.00
42	41.7	205	166	11.8	12	7.2	7	80	156	25	15	181	1.06	0.894
36	35.9	201	165	10.2	10	6.2	6	80	156	23	14	181	1.05	0.885
31	31.4	210	134	10.2	10	6.4	6	64	171	20	11	190	0.944	0.810
27	26.6	207	133	8.4	8	5.8	6	64	172	18	11	190	0.932	0.799
22	22.4	206	102	8.0	8	6.2	6	48	171	18	11	190	0.808	0.706
19	19.4	203	102	6.5	6	5.8	6	48	172	16	11	190	0.800	0.698
15	15.0	200	100	5.2	5	4.3	4	48	171	15	10	190	0.792	0.692

W SHAPES
W150 - W100

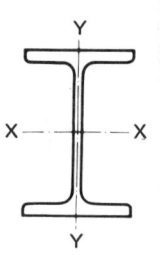

PROPERTIES

Designation ‡	Dead Load	Total Area	Axis X-X				Axis Y-Y				Torsional Constant	Warping Constant
			I_x	S_x	r_x	Z_x	I_y	S_y	r_y	Z_y	J	C_w
	kN/m	mm²	10^6mm⁴	10^3mm³	mm	10^3mm³	10^6mm⁴	10^3mm³	mm	10^3mm³	10^3mm⁴	10^9mm⁶
W150												
X37	0.364	4 730	22.2	274	68.5	310	7.07	91.8	38.7	140	193	40.0
X30	0.292	3 790	17.2	219	67.4	244	5.56	72.6	38.3	111	101	30.3
X22	0.219	2 850	12.1	159	65.2	176	3.87	50.9	36.8	77.6	41.8	20.4
W150												
X24*	0.235	3 060	13.4	168	66.2	192	1.83	35.8	24.5	55.3	92.9	10.2
X18*	0.176	2 290	9.16	120	63.2	136	1.26	24.7	23.5	38.2	37.3	6.70
X14*	0.133	1 730	6.87	91.5	63.0	103	0.918	18.4	23.0	28.3	17.0	4.79
W130												
X28*	0.275	3 580	10.9	167	55.2	190	3.81	59.6	32.6	90.8	128	13.8
X24*	0.232	3 010	8.80	139	54.1	156	3.11	49.0	32.1	74.6	76.7	10.8
W100												
X19*	0.190	2 470	4.76	89.9	43.9	103	1.61	31.2	25.5	48.0	63.4	3.79

‡ Nominal depth in millimetres and mass in kilograms per metre.

* Not available from Canadian mills.

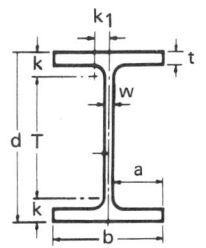

DIMENSIONS AND SURFACE AREAS

Nominal Mass kg/m	Theoretical Mass kg/m	Depth d mm	Flange Width b mm	Flange Mean Thickness t mm		Web Thickness w mm		Distances a mm	Distances T mm	Distances k mm	Distances k₁ mm	Distances d-2t mm	Surface Area (m²) per metre of length Total	Surface Area (m²) per metre of length Minus Top of Top Flange
37	37.1	162	154	11.6	12	8.1	8	73	122	20	10	139	0.926	0.772
30	29.8	157	153	9.3	9	6.6	7	73	123	17	10	139	0.912	0.759
22	22.3	152	152	6.6	7	5.8	6	73	122	15	9	139	0.902	0.750
24	24.0	160	102	10.3	10	6.6	7	48	124	18	10	139	0.712	0.610
18	18.0	153	102	7.1	7	5.8	6	48	123	15	9	139	0.702	0.600
14	13.6	150	100	5.5	6	4.3	4	48	122	14	8	139	0.694	0.594
28	28.1	131	128	10.9	11	6.9	7	61	93	19	10	109	0.760	0.632
24	23.6	127	127	9.1	9	6.1	6	61	93	17	9	109	0.750	0.623
19	19.4	106	103	8.8	9	7.1	7	48	72	17	10	88	0.610	0.507

HP SHAPES

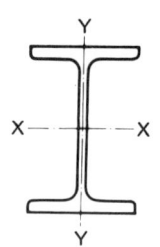

PROPERTIES

Designation‡	Dead Load	Total Area	Axis X-X				Axis Y-Y				Torsional Constant	Warping Constant
			I_x	S_x	r_x	Z_x	I_y	S_y	r_y	Z_y	J	C_w
	kN/m	mm²	10^6mm⁴	10^3mm³	mm	10^3mm³	10^6mm⁴	10^3mm³	mm	10^3mm³	10^3mm⁴	10^9mm⁶
HP360												
X174*	1.70	22 200	508	2 820	151	3 180	184	973	91.0	1 490	3 310	5 330
X152*	1.49	19 400	439	2 470	150	2 770	159	845	90.5	1 290	2 240	4 540
X132*	1.29	16 800	375	2 140	149	2 380	135	724	89.6	1 110	1 490	3 800
X108*	1.06	13 800	303	1 750	148	1 940	108	585	88.5	891	832	3 000
HP330												
X149*	1.45	18 900	368	2 200	140	2 500	122	727	80.3	1 120	2 590	3 010
X129*	1.26	16 400	315	1 910	139	2 150	104	626	79.6	960	1 720	2 540
X109*	1.07	14 000	263	1 620	137	1 810	86.3	523	78.5	801	1 070	2 070
X89*	0.872	11 300	211	1 320	137	1 460	68.9	420	78.1	641	583	1 630
HP310												
X174†	1.70	22 200	394	2 430	133	2 800	138	843	78.8	1 300	4 470	3 110
X152†	1.48	19 300	338	2 120	132	2 420	115	716	77.2	1 100	3 040	2 550
X132†	1.28	16 700	287	1 830	131	2 070	93.7	599	74.9	922	2 050	2 050
X125*	1.22	15 900	270	1 730	130	1 960	88.2	566	74.5	870	1 760	1 910
X110	1.08	14 100	237	1 540	130	1 730	77.1	497	73.9	763	1 240	1 650
X94	0.916	11 900	196	1 300	128	1 450	63.9	415	73.3	635	764	1 340
X79	0.768	9 980	163	1 090	128	1 210	52.6	344	72.6	525	460	1 090
HP250												
X85	0.837	10 900	123	968	106	1 090	42.3	325	62.3	500	829	606
X62	0.614	7 980	87.5	711	105	792	30.0	234	61.3	358	339	415
HP200												
X54	0.525	6 820	49.8	488	85.5	552	16.7	162	49.5	249	321	155

‡ Nominal depth in millimetres and mass in kilograms per metre.
* Not available from Canadian mills.
† Produced exclusively by Algoma Steel.

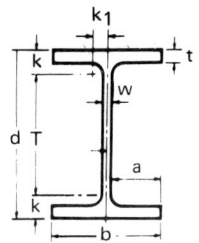

DIMENSIONS AND SURFACE AREAS

Nominal Mass	Theo-retical Mass	Depth d	Flange			Web Thickness w		Distances					Surface Area (m²) per metre of length	
			Width b	Mean Thickness t				a	T	k	k₁	d-2t	Total	Minus Top of Top Flange
kg/m	kg/m	mm	mm	mm	mm	mm	mm	mm	mm	mm	mm	mm		
174	173.9	361	378	20.4	20	20.4	20	179	289	36	25	320	2.19	1.81
152	152.2	356	376	17.9	18	17.9	18	179	288	34	24	320	2.18	1.80
132	132.1	351	373	15.6	16	15.6	16	179	287	32	23	320	2.16	1.79
108	108.1	346	370	12.8	13	12.8	13	179	288	29	22	320	2.15	1.78
149	148.5	334	335	19.4	19	19.4	19	158	263	36	25	295	1.97	1.63
129	129.1	329	333	16.9	17	16.9	17	158	262	34	24	295	1.96	1.62
109	109.5	324	330	14.4	14	14.4	14	158	263	31	23	295	1.94	1.61
89	89.0	319	328	11.7	12	11.7	12	158	262	29	22	295	1.93	1.60
174	174.0	324	327	23.6	24	23.6	24	152	243	41	28	277	1.91	1.58
152	151.7	319	321	20.8	21	20.8	21	150	244	38	26	277	1.88	1.56
132	131.3	314	313	18.3	18	18.3	18	148	245	35	25	277	1.84	1.53
125	124.7	312	312	17.4	17	17.4	17	148	245	34	24	277	1.84	1.52
110	110.5	308	310	15.5	16	15.4	15	148	243	33	23	277	1.83	1.52
94	93.4	303	308	13.1	13	13.1	13	148	244	30	22	277	1.81	1.50
79	78.3	299	306	11.0	11	11.0	11	148	244	28	21	277	1.80	1.49
85	85.3	254	260	14.4	14	14.4	14	123	193	31	23	225	1.52	1.26
62	62.6	246	256	10.7	11	10.5	10	123	191	28	21	225	1.50	1.24
54	53.5	204	207	11.3	11	11.3	11	98	158	23	17	181	1.21	1.00

M SHAPES

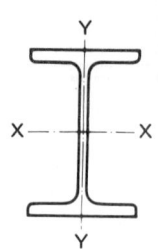

PROPERTIES

Designation ‡	Dead Load	Total Area	Axis X-X				Axis Y-Y				Torsional Constant	Warping Constant
			I_x	S_x	r_x	Z_x	I_y	S_y	r_y	Z_y	J	C_w
	kN/m	mm²	10^6mm⁴	10^3mm³	mm	10^3mm³	10^6mm⁴	10^3mm³	mm	10^3mm³	10^3mm⁴	10^9mm⁶
M310 X17.6*	0.171	2 230	29.7	195	115	232	0.394	10.2	13.3	17.3	21.8	8.82
M250 X13.4*	0.131	1 700	16.1	126	97.3	150	0.248	7.30	12.1	12.3	13.7	3.84
M200 X9.7*	0.094	1 220	7.56	74.5	78.7	87.5	0.136	4.78	10.6	7.93	7.92	1.34
M150 X29.8*	0.292	3 790	16.1	212	65.2	237	4.87	63.5	35.8	103	121	24.7
M150 X6.5*	0.063	821	2.92	38.4	59.6	44.8	0.065	2.81	8.88	4.63	4.17	0.353
M130 X28.1*	0.276	3 580	10.0	158	52.9	181	3.31	51.2	30.4	82.6	142	11.2
M100 X19	0.190	2 460	4.41	86.4	42.3	99.8	1.41	28.1	23.9	44.8	78.5	3.02

‡ Nominal depth in millimetres and mass in kilograms per metre.
* Not available from Canadian mills.
Note: These shapes have been soft converted from Imperial to SI dimensions.

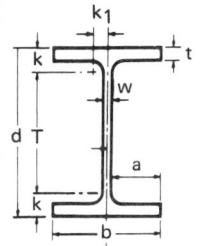

DIMENSIONS AND SURFACE AREAS

Nominal Mass	Theo-retical Mass	Depth d	Flange			Web Thickness w		Distances				Surface Area (m²) per metre of length	
			Width b	Mean Thickness t				a	T	k	k₁	Total	Minus Top of Top Flange
kg/m	kg/m	mm	mm	mm	mm	mm	mm	mm	mm	mm	mm		
17.6	17.5	305	77	5.7	6	4.5	4	37	277	14	8	0.910	0.833
13.4	13.4	254	68	5.2	5	4.0	4	32	230	12	7	0.772	0.704
9.7	9.6	203	57	4.8	5	3.4	3	27	181	11	6	0.628	0.571
29.8	29.8	152	151	9.6	10	6.4	6	73	111	21	11	0.896	0.745
6.5	6.5	152	46	4.3	4	2.9	3	22	134	9	5	0.482	0.436
28.1	28.1	127	127	10.6	11	8.0	8	60	84	22	12	0.746	0.619
19	19.3	102	100	9.4	9	6.5	6	47	63	19	11	0.592	0.492

S SHAPES
S610 - S180

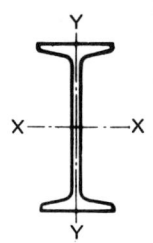

PROPERTIES

Designation #	Dead Load	Total Area	Axis X-X				Axis Y-Y				Torsional Constant	Warping Constant
			I_x	S_x	r_x	Z_x	I_y	S_y	r_y	Z_y	J	C_w
	kN/m	mm^2	$10^6 mm^4$	$10^3 mm^3$	mm	$10^3 mm^3$	$10^6 mm^4$	$10^3 mm^3$	mm	$10^3 mm^3$	$10^3 mm^4$	$10^9 mm^6$
S610												
X180*	1.76	22 900	1 310	4 220	239	5 020	34.7	340	38.9	591	5 330	3 070
X158*	1.54	20 100	1 220	3 940	246	4 580	32.4	324	40.1	544	4 210	2 860
S610												
X149*	1.45	18 900	996	3 270	230	3 930	20.1	218	32.6	392	3 150	1 730
X134*	1.31	17 100	939	3 080	234	3 650	18.9	209	33.2	366	2 520	1 640
X119*	1.16	15 200	879	2 880	240	3 360	17.9	201	34.3	341	2 030	1 540
S510												
X143*	1.40	18 300	702	2 720	196	3 260	21.1	231	34.0	409	3 570	1 280
X128*	1.26	16 400	660	2 560	201	3 020	19.6	219	34.6	377	2 830	1 190
S510												
X112*	1.09	14 200	532	2 090	194	2 500	12.5	155	29.7	273	1 910	745
X98.2*	0.965	12 500	497	1 960	199	2 290	11.7	148	30.6	252	1 490	698
S460												
X104*	1.02	13 300	387	1 690	171	2 050	10.3	129	27.8	237	1 740	495
X81.4*	0.800	10 400	335	1 470	179	1 720	8.77	115	29.0	198	986	423
S380												
X74*	0.731	9 500	203	1 060	146	1 270	6.60	92.3	26.4	163	884	220
X64*	0.627	8 150	187	980	151	1 140	6.11	87.3	27.4	149	641	204
S310												
X74*	0.729	9 470	127	833	116	1 000	6.60	94.9	26.4	168	1 160	137
X60.7*	0.595	7 730	113	744	121	869	5.67	85.3	27.1	144	723	118
S310												
X52	0.512	6 650	95.8	629	120	736	4.16	64.5	25.0	111	450	88.2
X47	0.465	6 040	91.1	597	123	690	3.94	62.1	25.5	105	374	83.6
S250												
X52	0.513	6 660	61.6	485	96.2	584	3.56	56.5	23.1	102	541	51.9
X38	0.371	4 820	51.4	405	103	465	2.84	48.2	24.3	81.1	251	41.5
S200												
X34	0.336	4 370	27.0	266	78.6	316	1.81	34.2	20.4	60.2	229	16.8
X27	0.270	3 500	24.0	237	82.8	272	1.59	31.1	21.3	52.2	140	14.7
S180												
X30*	0.293	3 800	17.8	200	68.4	238	1.34	27.3	18.8	48.4	188	9.44
X22.8*	0.224	2 910	15.4	173	72.7	199	1.12	24.0	19.6	40.2	101	7.88

*Not available from Canadian mills.
For sections available from Canadian mills, the nominal mass has been rounded to the nearest kg/m. Designation consists of nominal depth in millimetres by nominal mass in kilograms per metre.
Note: These shapes have been soft converted from Imperial to SI dimension.

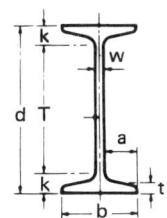

DIMENSIONS AND SURFACE AREAS

Nominal Mass	Theo- retical Mass	Depth d	Flange Width b	Flange Mean Thickness t		Web Thickness w		Distances a	Distances T	Distances k	Surface Area (m²) per metre of length Total	Surface Area (m²) per metre of length Minus Top of Top Flange
kg/m	kg/m	mm	mm	mm	mm	mm	mm	mm	mm	mm		
180	180.0	622	204	27.7	28	20.3	20	92	522	50	2.02	1.82
158	157.8	622	200	27.7	28	15.7	16	92	522	50	2.01	1.81
149	148.7	610	184	22.1	22	18.9	19	83	524	43	1.92	1.73
134	134.4	610	181	22.1	22	15.9	16	83	524	43	1.91	1.73
119	119.1	610	178	22.1	22	12.7	13	83	524	43	1.91	1.73
143	143.3	516	183	23.4	23	20.3	20	82	424	46	1.72	1.54
128	128.9	516	179	23.4	23	16.8	17	81	424	46	1.71	1.53
112	111.4	508	162	20.2	20	16.1	16	73	428	40	1.63	1.47
98.2	98.4	508	159	20.2	20	12.8	13	73	428	40	1.63	1.47
104	104.7	457	159	17.6	18	18.1	18	71	383	37	1.51	1.35
81.4	81.6	457	152	17.6	18	11.7	12	70	383	37	1.50	1.35
74	74.6	381	143	15.8	16	14.0	14	65	314	34	1.31	1.16
64	63.9	381	140	15.8	16	10.4	10	65	314	34	1.30	1.16
74	74.4	305	139	16.7	17	17.4	17	61	235	35	1.13	0.993
60.7	60.6	305	133	16.7	17	11.7	12	61	235	35	1.12	0.985
52	52.2	305	129	13.8	14	10.9	11	59	246	29	1.10	0.975
47	47.4	305	127	13.8	14	8.9	9	59	246	29	1.10	0.973
52	52.3	254	126	12.5	12	15.1	15	56	201	26	0.982	0.856
38	37.8	254	118	12.5	12	7.9	8	55	202	26	0.964	0.846
34	34.3	203	106	10.8	11	11.2	11	48	155	24	0.808	0.702
27	27.5	203	102	10.8	11	6.9	7	48	155	24	0.800	0.698
30	29.9	178	98	10.0	10	11.4	11	44	134	22	0.726	0.628
22.8	22.9	178	93	10.0	10	6.4	6	44	134	22	0.716	0.623

S SHAPES
S150 - S75

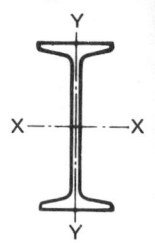

PROPERTIES

Designation #	Dead Load	Total Area	Axis X-X				Axis Y-Y				Torsional Constant	Warping Constant
			I_x	S_x	r_x	Z_x	I_y	S_y	r_y	Z_y	J	C_w
	kN/m	mm²	10^6 mm⁴	10^3 mm³	mm	10^3 mm³	10^6 mm⁴	10^3 mm³	mm	10^3 mm³	10^3 mm⁴	10^9 mm⁶
S150												
X26	0.252	3 270	10.9	144	57.7	173	0.981	21.6	17.3	38.7	155	5.01
X19	0.183	2 370	9.19	121	62.3	139	0.776	18.2	18.1	30.5	70.1	3.96
S130												
X22	0.215	2 790	6.33	99.6	47.6	121	0.690	16.6	15.7	30.3	133	2.43
X15	0.146	1 890	5.12	80.6	52.0	92.8	0.508	13.4	16.4	22.2	47.4	1.79
S100												
X14.1*	0.139	1 800	2.85	55.8	39.8	66.5	0.376	10.6	14.5	18.3	49.9	0.842
X11	0.112	1 450	2.55	50.1	41.9	57.7	0.324	9.52	14.9	15.8	29.9	0.724
S75												
X11	0.110	1 430	1.22	32.0	29.2	38.7	0.249	7.77	13.2	13.5	38.2	0.299
X8	0.083	1 070	1.04	27.4	31.2	31.9	0.190	6.43	13.3	10.6	18.3	0.228

*Not available from Canadian mills.

For sections available from Canadian mills, the nominal mass has been rounded to the nearest kg/m. Designation consists of nominal depth in millimetres by nominal mass in kilograms per metre.

Note: These shapes have been soft converted from Imperial to SI dimension.

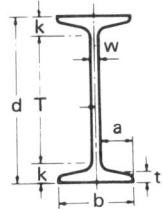

DIMENSIONS AND SURFACE AREAS

Nominal Mass	Theo-retical Mass	Depth d	Flange			Web Thickness w		Distances			Surface Area (m²) per metre of length	
			Width b	Mean Thickness t				a	T	k	Total	Minus Top of Top Flange
kg/m	kg/m	mm	mm	mm	mm	mm	mm	mm	mm	mm		
26	25.7	152	91	9.1	9	11.8	12	40	111	20	0.644	0.553
19	18.6	152	85	9.1	9	5.9	6	40	111	20	0.632	0.547
22	21.9	127	83	8.3	8	12.5	12	36	90	19	0.562	0.479
15	14.8	127	76	8.3	8	5.4	5	36	90	19	0.548	0.472
14.1	14.2	102	71	7.4	7	8.3	8	32	68	17	0.472	0.401
11	11.4	102	68	7.4	7	4.8	5	32	68	17	0.466	0.398
11	11.2	76	64	6.6	7	8.9	9	28	44	16	0.390	0.326
8	8.4	76	59	6.6	7	4.3	4	28	44	16	0.380	0.321

STANDARD CHANNELS (C SHAPES)

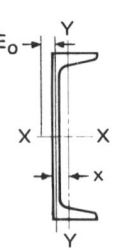

PROPERTIES

Designation#	Dead Load	Total Area	Axis X-X			Axis Y-Y				Shear Centre	Torsional Constant	Warping Constant
			I_x	S_x	r_x	I_y	S_y	r_y	x	E_o	J	C_w
	kN/m	mm^2	$10^6\,mm^4$	$10^3\,mm^3$	mm	$10^6\,mm^4$	$10^3\,mm^3$	mm	mm	mm	$10^3\,mm^4$	$10^9\,mm^6$
C380												
X74	0.730	9 480	168	881	133	4.60	62.4	22.0	20.3	23.7	1 110	131
X60	0.583	7 570	145	760	138	3.84	55.5	22.5	19.7	25.9	607	109
X50	0.495	6 430	131	687	143	3.39	51.4	23.0	20.0	27.6	424	95.2
C310												
X45	0.438	5 690	67.3	442	109	2.12	33.6	19.3	17.0	21.9	363	39.9
X37	0.363	4 720	59.9	393	113	1.85	30.9	19.8	17.1	23.7	224	34.6
X31	0.302	3 920	53.5	351	117	1.59	28.2	20.1	17.5	25.3	153	29.3
C250												
X45*	0.437	5 670	42.8	337	86.9	1.60	26.8	16.8	16.3	17.5	511	20.5
X37	0.365	4 750	37.9	299	89.3	1.40	24.3	17.2	15.7	19.1	290	18.2
X30	0.291	3 780	32.7	257	93.0	1.16	21.5	17.5	15.3	20.8	154	15.0
X23	0.221	2 880	27.8	219	98.2	0.922	18.8	17.9	15.9	22.8	86.8	11.7
C230												
X30	0.292	3 800	25.5	222	81.9	1.01	19.3	16.3	14.8	18.6	180	10.5
X22	0.219	2 840	21.3	186	86.6	0.806	16.8	16.8	14.9	20.9	86.9	8.33
X20	0.195	2 530	19.8	173	88.5	0.716	15.6	16.8	15.1	21.5	69.7	7.35
C200												
X28	0.274	3 560	18.2	180	71.5	0.825	16.6	15.2	14.4	17.0	183	6.67
X21	0.200	2 600	14.9	147	75.7	0.627	13.9	15.5	14.0	19.0	77.8	5.04
X17	0.167	2 170	13.5	133	78.9	0.544	12.8	15.8	14.5	20.3	54.2	4.34
C180												
X22*	0.214	2 780	11.3	127	63.8	0.568	12.8	14.3	13.5	16.4	111	3.47
X18	0.178	2 310	10.0	113	65.8	0.476	11.4	14.4	13.2	17.3	67.3	2.90
X15	0.142	1 850	8.86	99.6	69.2	0.405	10.3	14.8	13.8	19.1	41.6	2.46
C150												
X19	0.189	2 450	7.12	93.7	53.9	0.425	10.3	13.2	12.9	14.9	100	1.84
X16	0.152	1 980	6.22	81.9	56.0	0.351	9.13	13.3	12.6	16.0	54.3	1.53
X12	0.118	1 540	5.36	70.6	59.0	0.279	7.93	13.5	12.8	17.4	31.0	1.21
C130												
X17	0.168	2 190	4.36	68.7	44.6	0.346	8.85	12.6	12.9	14.0	97.2	1.02
X13	0.131	1 700	3.66	57.6	46.4	0.252	7.20	12.2	11.9	14.5	45.7	0.746
X10	0.097	1 260	3.09	48.6	49.5	0.195	6.14	12.4	12.2	16.2	22.8	0.580
C100												
X11	0.106	1 370	1.91	37.4	37.3	0.174	5.52	11.3	11.5	13.5	34.6	0.320
X9	0.092	1 190	1.77	34.6	38.6	0.158	5.18	11.5	11.6	14.5	23.4	0.293
X8	0.079	1 020	1.61	31.6	39.7	0.132	4.65	11.4	11.6	14.9	16.8	0.246
C75												
X9	0.087	1 120	0.85	22.3	27.5	0.123	4.31	10.5	11.4	12.5	30.1	0.118
X7	0.072	933	0.75	19.7	28.3	0.096	3.67	10.1	10.8	12.7	17.7	0.093
X6	0.059	763	0.67	17.6	29.6	0.077	3.21	10.1	10.9	13.5	11.0	0.077

* Not available from Canadian mills.

\# For sections available from Canadian mills, the nominal mass has been rounded to the nearest kg/m. Designation consists of nominal depth in millimetres by nominal mass in kilograms per metre.

Note: These shapes have been soft converted from Imperial to SI dimensions.

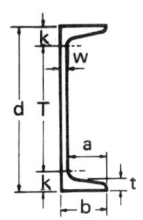

STANDARD CHANNELS (C SHAPES)

Nominal Mass	Theoretical Mass	Depth d	Flange			Web		Distances			Surface Area (m²) per metre of length	
			Width b	Mean Thickness t		Web Thickness w		a	T	k	Total	Minus Top of Top Flange
kg/m	kg/m	mm	mm	mm	mm	mm	mm	mm	mm	mm		
74	74.4	381	94	16.5	16	18.2	18	76	312	34	1.10	1.01
60	59.4	381	89	16.5	16	13.2	13	76	312	34	1.09	1.00
50	50.5	381	86	16.5	16	10.2	10	76	312	34	1.09	1.00
45	44.7	305	80	12.7	13	13.0	13	67	250	28	0.904	0.824
37	37.1	305	77	12.7	13	9.8	10	67	250	28	0.898	0.821
31	30.8	305	74	12.7	13	7.2	7	67	250	28	0.892	0.818
45	44.5	254	76	11.1	11	17.1	17	59	206	24	0.778	0.702
37	37.3	254	73	11.1	11	13.4	13	60	206	24	0.774	0.701
30	29.6	254	69	11.1	11	9.6	10	59	206	24	0.764	0.695
23	22.6	254	65	11.1	11	6.1	6	59	206	24	0.756	0.691
30	29.8	229	67	10.5	10	11.4	11	56	184	23	0.704	0.637
22	22.3	229	63	10.5	10	7.2	7	56	184	23	0.696	0.633
20	19.8	229	61	10.5	10	5.9	6	55	184	23	0.690	0.629
28	27.9	203	64	9.9	10	12.4	12	52	159	22	0.638	0.574
21	20.4	203	59	9.9	10	7.7	8	51	159	22	0.626	0.567
17	17.0	203	57	9.9	10	5.6	6	51	159	22	0.622	0.565
22	21.9	178	58	9.3	9	10.6	11	47	137	20	0.566	0.508
18	18.2	178	55	9.3	9	8.0	8	47	137	20	0.560	0.505
15	14.5	178	53	9.3	9	5.3	5	48	137	21	0.558	0.505
19	19.2	152	54	8.7	9	11.1	11	43	112	20	0.498	0.444
16	15.5	152	51	8.7	9	8.0	8	43	112	20	0.492	0.441
12	12.1	152	48	8.7	9	5.1	5	43	112	20	0.486	0.438
17	17.2	127	52	8.1	8	12.0	12	40	90	18	0.438	0.386
13	13.3	127	47	8.1	8	8.3	8	39	90	18	0.426	0.379
10	9.9	127	44	8.1	8	4.8	5	39	90	18	0.420	0.376
11	10.8	102	43	7.5	8	8.2	8	35	66	18	0.360	0.317
9	9.4	102	42	7.5	8	6.3	6	36	66	18	0.360	0.318
8	8.0	102	40	7.5	8	4.7	5	35	66	18	0.354	0.314
9	8.8	76	40	6.9	7	9.0	9	31	44	16	0.294	0.254
7	7.3	76	37	6.9	7	6.6	7	30	44	16	0.286	0.249
6	6.0	76	35	6.9	7	4.3	4	31	44	16	0.284	0.249

MISCELLANEOUS CHANNELS
MC460 - MC 200

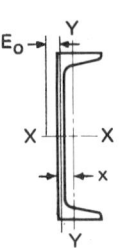

PROPERTIES

Designation#	Dead Load	Total Area	Axis X-X			Axis Y-Y				Shear Centre	Torsional Constant	Warping Constant
			I_x	S_x	r_x	I_y	S_y	r_y	x	E_o	J	C_W
	kN/m	mm^2	10^6 mm^4	10^3 mm^3	mm	10^6 mm^4	10^3 mm^3	mm	mm	mm	10^3 mm^4	10^9 mm^6
MC460												
X86*	0.851	11 100	283	1 240	160	7.45	87.6	25.9	22.0	26.7	1 190	291
X77.2*	0.759	9 860	262	1 150	163	6.81	82.8	26.3	21.8	27.9	856	265
X68.2*	0.672	8 730	243	1 060	167	6.35	79.5	27.0	22.1	29.6	621	245
X63.5*	0.625	8 120	231	1 010	169	5.94	76.3	27.0	22.2	30.2	524	228
MC330												
X74*	0.731	9 490	131	793	117	6.92	79.4	27.0	24.8	30.7	1 240	150
X60*	0.583	7 570	113	687	122	5.73	70.4	27.5	24.5	33.3	649	123
X52*	0.511	6 640	105	635	126	5.14	65.8	27.8	24.9	34.8	475	110
X47.3*	0.465	6 040	99.8	605	129	4.86	63.7	28.4	25.7	36.6	394	103
MC310												
X74*	0.732	9 510	113	739	109	7.25	92.4	27.6	26.6	29.4	1 360	111
X67*	0.658	8 540	105	690	111	6.60	87.2	27.8	26.3	30.6	982	101
X60*	0.584	7 590	97.5	639	113	5.80	80.5	27.6	26.0	31.3	716	88.7
X52*	0.512	6 660	90.8	595	117	5.31	76.8	28.2	26.8	33.3	527	81.2
X46*	0.455	5 900	84.7	555	120	4.69	71.5	28.2	27.4	34.3	426	71.8
MC310												
X15.8*	0.153	1 990	23.0	151	108	0.159	5.11	8.94	6.8	9.6	24.6	3.11
MC250												
X61.2*	0.603	7 830	66.1	520	91.9	6.73	81.9	29.3	27.8	32.2	952	73.1
X50*	0.493	6 400	58.3	459	95.4	5.57	73.0	29.5	27.7	34.2	509	60.5
X42.4*	0.418	5 430	53.0	417	98.8	4.79	66.9	29.7	28.4	36.1	335	52.0
MC250												
X37*	0.366	4 750	45.8	361	98.2	3.03	48.9	25.3	24.0	30.6	267	33.1
X33*	0.321	4 170	42.8	337	101	2.71	45.9	25.5	25.0	32.1	214	29.7
MC250												
X12.5*	0.122	1 580	13.3	105	91.7	0.138	4.49	9.35	7.2	10.6	17.2	1.87
MC250												
X9.7*	0.095	1 240	9.16	72.2	85.9	0.043	1.82	5.88	4.4	5.9	7.86	0.617
MC230												
X37.8*	0.371	4 830	36.8	322	87.3	3.10	48.7	25.3	24.3	30.4	296	27.5
X35.6*	0.351	4 560	35.7	312	88.5	2.96	47.4	25.5	24.6	31.1	259	26.3
MC200												
X33.9*	0.332	4 310	26.4	260	78.3	2.85	45.4	25.7	25.2	31.5	242	19.7
X31.8*	0.312	4 050	25.6	252	79.5	2.71	44.1	25.9	25.7	32.3	210	18.8
MC200												
X29.8*	0.293	3 800	22.7	223	77.3	1.82	33.1	21.9	21.1	26.1	189	12.6
X27.8*	0.274	3 560	21.9	215	78.4	1.72	32.1	22.0	21.3	26.7	163	11.9
MC200												
X12.6*	0.123	1 600	9.58	94.4	77.4	0.256	7.07	12.6	10.8	15.8	24.1	2.13

* Not available from Canadian mills.

For sections available from Canadian mills, the nominal mass has been rounded to the nearest kg/m. Designation consists of nominal depth in millimetres by nominal mass in kilograms per metre.

Note: These shapes have been soft converted from Imperial to SI dimensions.

DIMENSIONS AND SURFACE AREAS

Nominal Mass	Theo-retical Mass	Depth d	Flange			Web Thickness		Distances			Surface Area (m²) per metre of length	
			Width b	Mean Thickness t				a	T	k	Total	Minus Top of Top Flange
kg/m	kg/m	mm	mm	mm	mm	mm	mm	mm	mm	mm		
86	86.8	457	107	15.9	16	17.8	18	89	387	35	1.31	1.20
77.2	77.4	457	104	15.9	16	15.2	15	89	387	35	1.30	1.20
68.2	68.5	457	102	15.9	16	12.7	13	89	387	35	1.30	1.19
63.5	63.7	457	100	15.9	16	11.4	11	89	387	35	1.29	1.19
74	74.5	330	112	15.5	16	20.0	20	92	261	34	1.07	0.956
60	59.5	330	106	15.5	16	14.2	14	92	261	34	1.06	0.950
52	52.1	330	103	15.5	16	11.4	11	92	261	34	1.05	0.947
47.3	47.4	330	102	15.5	16	9.5	10	92	261	34	1.05	0.946
74	74.7	305	105	17.8	18	21.2	21	84	239	33	0.988	0.883
67	67.0	305	102	17.8	18	18.0	18	84	239	33	0.982	0.880
60	59.6	305	98	17.8	18	15.0	15	83	239	33	0.972	0.874
52	52.3	305	96	17.8	18	11.8	12	84	239	33	0.970	0.874
46	46.3	305	93	17.8	18	9.4	9	84	239	33	0.964	0.871
15.8	15.6	305	38	7.8	8	4.8	5	33	271	17	0.752	0.714
61.2	61.5	254	110	14.6	15	20.2	20	90	189	32	0.908	0.798
50	50.2	254	104	14.6	15	14.6	15	89	189	32	0.894	0.790
42.4	42.6	254	100	14.6	15	10.8	11	89	189	32	0.886	0.786
37	37.3	254	86	14.6	15	9.7	10	76	193	30	0.832	0.746
33	32.8	254	84	14.6	15	7.4	7	77	193	31	0.830	0.746
12.5	12.4	254	38	7.1	7	4.3	4	34	222	16	0.652	0.614
9.7	9.7	254	28	5.1	5	3.9	4	24	233	11	0.612	0.584
37.8	37.9	229	88	14.0	14	11.4	11	77	168	31	0.788	0.700
35.6	35.8	229	87	14.0	14	10.2	10	77	168	31	0.786	0.699
33.9	33.8	203	88	13.3	13	10.8	11	77	145	29	0.736	0.648
31.8	31.8	203	87	13.3	13	9.5	10	77	145	29	0.734	0.647
29.8	29.8	203	76	12.7	13	10.2	10	66	147	28	0.690	0.614
27.8	28.0	203	75	12.7	13	9.0	9	66	147	28	0.688	0.613
12.6	12.5	203	47	7.9	8	4.5	4	43	167	18	0.586	0.539

MISCELLANEOUS CHANNELS
MC180 - MC150

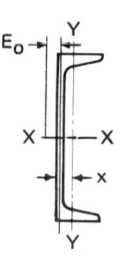

PROPERTIES

Designation#	Dead Load	Total Area	Axis X-X			Axis Y-Y				Shear Centre	Torsional Constant	Warping Constant
			I_x	S_x	r_x	I_y	S_y	r_y	x	E_o	J	C_w
	kN/m	mm²	10^6 mm⁴	10^3 mm³	mm	10^6 mm⁴	10^3 mm³	mm	mm	mm	10^3 mm⁴	10^9 mm⁶
MC180												
X33.8*	0.333	4 320	19.9	223	67.9	2.97	45.8	26.2	26.1	31.8	270	15.6
X28.4*	0.279	3 630	18.0	203	70.4	2.48	41.1	26.1	26.8	33.5	175	13.2
MC180												
X26.2*	0.258	3 350	15.8	178	68.7	1.66	30.9	22.3	22.1	27.3	153	8.79
MC150												
X26.8*	0.263	3 410	12.3	162	60.1	2.43	40.6	26.7	28.2	34.0	160	9.08
X22.8*	0.223	2 900	10.5	138	60.2	2.03	33.0	26.5	26.5	33.5	94.7	7.92
MC150												
X24.3*	0.239	3 110	10.9	143	59.2	1.59	30.2	22.6	23.5	28.3	145	5.97
X22.5*	0.221	2 870	10.3	136	59.9	1.43	28.3	22.3	23.6	28.7	122	5.41
MC150												
X17.9*	0.176	2 280	7.76	102	58.3	0.761	16.8	18.3	17.6	22.1	66.4	2.98

* Not available from Canadian mills.

\# For sections available from Canadian mills, the nominal mass has been rounded to the nearest kg/m. Designation consists of nominal depth in millimetres by nominal mass in kilograms per metre.

Note: These shapes have been soft converted from Imperial to SI dimensions.

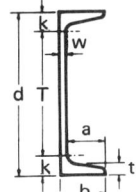

DIMENSIONS AND SURFACE AREAS

Nominal Mass	Theo-retical Mass	Depth d	Flange			Web Thickness w		Distances			Surface Area (m²) per metre of length	
			Width b	Mean Thickness t				a	T	k	Total	Minus Top of Top Flange
kg/m	kg/m	mm	mm	mm	mm	mm	mm	mm	mm	mm		
33.8	33.9	178	91	12.7	13	12.8	13	78	121	29	0.694	0.603
28.4	28.5	178	87	12.7	13	8.9	9	78	121	29	0.686	0.599
26.2	26.3	178	76	12.1	12	9.5	10	66	125	27	0.640	0.564
26.8	26.8	152	88	12.1	12	9.6	10	78	99	27	0.636	0.548
22.8	22.8	152	88	9.8	10	8.6	9	79	107	22	0.638	0.550
24.3	24.4	152	76·	12.1	12	9.5	10	66	99	26	0.588	0.512
22.5	22.5	152	74	12.1	12	8.0	8	66	99	27	0.584	0.510
17.9	17.9	152	63	9.5	10	7.9	8	55	108	22	0.540	0.477

ANGLES
Equal Legs

PROPERTIES AND DIMENSIONS

Size	Thickness t	Mass	Dead Load	Area	Axis X-X and Axis Y-Y				Axis Z-Z
					I	S	r	x or y	r
mmxmm	mm	kg/m	kN/m	mm²	10^6 mm⁴	10^3 mm³	mm	mm	mm
200X200									
	30	87.1	0.855	11 100	40.3	290	60.3	60.9	39.0
	25	73.6	0.722	9 380	34.8	247	60.9	59.2	39.1
	20	59.7	0.585	7 600	28.8	202	61.6	57.4	39.3
	16	48.2	0.473	6 140	23.7	165	62.1	55.9	39.5
	13	39.5	0.387	5 030	19.7	136	62.6	54.8	39.7
	10	30.6	0.300	3 900	15.5	106	63.0	53.7	39.9
150X150									
	20	44.0	0.431	5 600	11.6	110	45.5	44.8	29.3
	16	35.7	0.350	4 540	9.63	90.3	46.0	43.4	29.4
	13	29.3	0.287	3 730	8.05	74.7	46.4	42.3	29.6
	10	22.8	0.223	2 900	6.37	58.6	46.9	41.2	29.8
125X125									
	16	29.4	0.288	3 740	5.41	61.5	38.0	37.1	24.4
	13	24.2	0.237	3 080	4.54	51.1	38.4	36.0	24.5
	10	18.8	0.185	2 400	3.62	40.2	38.8	34.9	24.7
	8	15.2	0.149	1 940	2.96	32.6	39.1	34.2	24.8
100X100									
	16	23.1	0.227	2 940	2.65	38.3	30.0	30.8	19.5
	13	19.1	0.187	2 430	2.24	31.9	30.4	29.8	19.5
	10	14.9	0.146	1 900	1.80	25.2	30.8	28.7	19.7
	8	12.1	0.118	1 540	1.48	20.6	31.1	28.0	19.8
	6	9.14	0.090	1 160	1.14	15.7	31.3	27.2	19.9
90X90									
	13	17.0	0.167	2 170	1.60	25.6	27.2	27.2	17.6
	10	13.3	0.131	1 700	1.29	20.2	27.6	26.2	17.6
	8	10.8	0.106	1 380	1.07	16.5	27.8	25.5	17.7
	6	8.20	0.080	1 040	0.826	12.7	28.1	24.7	17.9
75X75									
	13	14.0	0.137	1 780	0.892	17.3	22.4	23.5	14.6
	10	11.0	0.108	1 400	0.725	13.8	22.8	22.4	14.6
	8	8.92	0.087	1 140	0.602	11.3	23.0	21.7	14.7
	6	6.78	0.066	864	0.469	8.68	23.3	21.0	14.8
	5	5.69	0.056	725	0.398	7.32	23.4	20.6	14.9

Note: The properties of angles currently produced by cold forming are up to 7 percent less than the properties shown in the above tables. Check manufacturers' catalogue for the exact properties and dimensions. See also page 6-19.

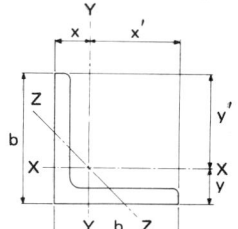

PROPERTIES AND DIMENSIONS

Size	Thickness t	Mass	Dead Load	Area	Axis X-X and Axis Y-Y				Axis Z-Z
					I	S	r	x or y	r
mmxmm	mm	kg/m	kN/m	mm²	10^6mm⁴	10^3mm³	mm	mm	mm
65X65									
	10	9.42	0.092	1 200	0.459	10.2	19.6	19.9	12.7
	8	7.66	0.075	976	0.383	8.36	19.8	19.2	12.7
	6	5.84	0.057	744	0.300	6.44	20.1	18.5	12.8
	5	4.91	0.048	625	0.255	5.45	20.2	18.1	12.9
55X55									
	10	7.85	0.077	1 000	0.268	7.11	16.4	17.4	10.7
	8	6.41	0.063	816	0.225	5.87	16.6	16.7	10.7
	6	4.90	0.048	624	0.177	4.54	16.9	16.0	10.8
	5	4.12	0.040	525	0.152	3.85	17.0	15.6	10.8
	4	3.33	0.033	424	0.125	3.13	17.1	15.2	10.9
	3	2.52	0.025	321	0.096	2.39	17.3	14.9	11.0
45X45									
	8	5.15	0.050	656	0.118	3.82	13.4	14.2	8.76
	6	3.96	0.039	504	0.094	2.98	13.7	13.4	8.79
	5	3.34	0.033	425	0.081	2.53	13.8	13.1	8.82
	4	2.70	0.026	344	0.067	2.07	13.9	12.7	8.87
	3	2.05	0.020	261	0.052	1.58	14.1	12.4	8.93
35X35									
	6	3.01	0.030	384	0.042	1.74	10.5	10.9	6.81
	5	2.55	0.025	325	0.036	1.49	10.6	10.6	6.83
	4	2.07	0.020	264	0.030	1.22	10.7	10.2	6.86
	3	1.58	0.015	201	0.024	0.940	10.8	9.86	6.91
25X25									
	5	1.77	0.017	225	0.012	0.724	7.39	8.06	4.87
	4	1.44	0.014	184	0.010	0.599	7.50	7.71	4.87
	3	1.11	0.011	141	0.008	0.465	7.63	7.35	4.89

Note: The properties of angles currently produced by cold forming are up to 7 percent less than the properties shown in the above tables. Check manufacturers' catalogue for the exact properties and dimensions. See also page 6-19.

ANGLES
Unequal Legs

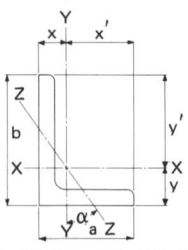

PROPERTIES AND DIMENSIONS

Size	Thick-ness t	Mass	Dead Load	Area	Axis X-X				Axis Y-Y				Axis Z-Z	
					I_x	S_x	r_x	y	I_y	S_y	r_y	x	r_z	Tan α
mmxmm	mm	kg/m	kN/m	mm²	10^6mm⁴	10^3mm³	mm	mm	10^6mm⁴	10^3mm³	mm	mm	mm	
200X150*	25	63.8	0.625	8 120	31.6	236	62.3	66.3	15.1	139	43.2	41.3	32.0	0.543
	20	51.8	0.508	6 600	26.2	193	63.0	64.5	12.7	115	43.8	39.5	32.1	0.549
	16	42.0	0.411	5 340	21.6	158	63.5	63.1	10.5	93.8	44.3	38.1	32.3	0.554
	13	34.4	0.337	4 380	17.9	130	64.0	62.0	8.77	77.6	44.7	37.0	32.5	0.557
200X100*	20	44.0	0.431	5 600	22.6	180	63.6	74.3	3.84	50.8	26.2	24.3	21.3	0.256
	16	35.7	0.350	4 540	18.7	147	64.2	72.8	3.22	41.8	26.6	22.8	21.4	0.262
	13	29.3	0.287	3 730	15.6	121	64.6	71.7	2.72	34.7	27.0	21.7	21.6	0.266
	10	22.8	0.223	2 900	12.3	94.8	65.1	70.5	2.18	27.4	27.4	20.5	21.8	0.271
150X100	16	29.4	0.288	3 740	8.40	84.8	47.4	50.9	3.00	40.4	28.3	25.9	21.6	0.434
	13	24.2	0.237	3 080	7.03	70.2	47.8	49.9	2.53	33.7	28.7	24.9	21.7	0.440
	10	18.8	0.185	2 400	5.58	55.1	48.2	48.8	2.03	26.6	29.1	23.8	21.9	0.445
	8	15.2	0.149	1 940	4.55	44.6	48.5	48.0	1.67	21.6	29.3	23.0	22.0	0.448
125X90	16	25.0	0.245	3 180	4.84	58.5	39.0	42.2	2.09	32.0	25.6	24.7	19.2	0.499
	13	20.6	0.202	2 630	4.07	48.6	39.4	41.2	1.77	26.7	26.0	23.7	19.3	0.505
	10	16.1	0.158	2 050	3.25	38.2	39.8	40.1	1.42	21.1	26.4	22.6	19.5	0.511
	8	13.0	0.127	1 660	2.66	31.1	40.1	39.3	1.18	17.2	26.6	21.8	19.6	0.515
125X75	13	19.1	0.187	2 430	3.82	47.1	39.6	43.9	1.04	18.5	20.7	18.9	16.2	0.356
	10	14.9	0.146	1 900	3.05	37.1	40.0	42.8	0.841	14.7	21.0	17.8	16.3	0.363
	8	12.1	0.118	1 540	2.50	30.1	40.3	42.1	0.697	12.0	21.3	17.1	16.4	0.367
	6	9.14	0.090	1 160	1.92	23.0	40.6	41.3	0.542	9.23	21.6	16.3	16.6	0.372
100X90	13	18.1	0.177	2 300	2.17	31.4	30.7	31.1	1.66	25.9	26.8	26.1	18.4	0.796
	10	14.1	0.139	1 800	1.74	24.9	31.1	30.0	1.33	20.5	27.2	25.0	18.5	0.800
	8	11.4	0.112	1 460	1.43	20.3	31.4	29.3	1.10	16.8	27.5	24.3	18.6	0.802
	6	8.67	0.085	1 100	1.11	15.5	31.7	28.5	0.853	12.8	27.8	23.5	18.7	0.805

*Not available from Canadian mills.

Note: The properties of angles currently produced by cold forming are up to 7 percent less than the properties shown in the above tables. Check manufacturers' catalogue for the exact properties and dimensions. See also page 6-19.

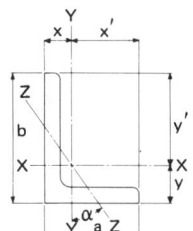

PROPERTIES AND DIMENSIONS

Size	Thickness t	Mass	Dead Load	Area	Axis X-X				Axis Y-Y				Axis Z-Z	
					I_x	S_x	r_x	y	I_y	S_y	r_y	x	r_z	Tan α
mmxmm	mm	kg/m	kN/m	mm²	10^6mm⁴	10^3mm³	mm	mm	10^6mm⁴	10^3mm³	mm	mm	mm	
100X75	13	16.5	0.162	2 110	2.04	30.6	31.1	33.4	0.976	18.0	21.5	20.9	16.0	0.541
	10	13.0	0.127	1 650	1.64	24.2	31.5	32.3	0.791	14.3	21.9	19.8	16.1	0.549
	8	10.5	0.103	1 340	1.35	19.7	31.8	31.5	0.656	11.7	22.2	19.0	16.2	0.554
	6	7.96	0.078	1 010	1.04	15.1	32.1	30.8	0.511	9.01	22.4	18.3	16.3	0.559
90X75	13	15.5	0.152	1 980	1.51	24.8	27.6	29.3	0.946	17.8	21.9	21.8	15.6	0.672
	10	12.2	0.119	1 550	1.22	19.7	28.0	28.2	0.767	14.1	22.2	20.7	15.7	0.679
	8	9.86	0.097	1 260	1.01	16.1	28.3	27.5	0.636	11.6	22.5	20.0	15.8	0.683
	6	7.49	0.073	954	0.779	12.3	28.6	26.8	0.495	8.89	22.8	19.3	15.9	0.687
	5	6.28	0.062	800	0.660	10.4	28.7	26.4	0.421	7.50	22.9	18.9	16.0	0.689
90X65	10	11.4	0.112	1 450	1.16	19.2	28.3	29.8	0.507	10.6	18.7	17.3	13.9	0.506
	8	9.23	0.090	1 180	0.958	15.7	28.5	29.1	0.422	8.72	18.9	16.6	14.0	0.512
	6	7.02	0.069	894	0.743	12.1	28.8	28.4	0.330	6.72	19.2	15.9	14.2	0.518
	5	5.89	0.058	750	0.629	10.2	29.0	28.0	0.281	5.68	19.4	15.5	14.2	0.520
80X60	10	10.2	0.100	1 300	0.808	15.1	24.9	26.5	0.388	8.92	17.3	16.5	12.8	0.543
	8	8.29	0.081	1 060	0.670	12.4	25.2	25.8	0.324	7.33	17.5	15.8	12.9	0.549
	6	6.31	0.062	804	0.522	9.50	25.5	25.1	0.254	5.66	17.8	15.1	13.0	0.555
	5	5.30	0.052	675	0.443	8.02	25.6	24.7	0.217	4.79	17.9	14.7	13.0	0.558
75X50	8	7.35	0.072	936	0.525	10.6	23.7	25.5	0.187	5.06	14.1	13.0	10.8	0.434
	6	5.60	0.055	714	0.410	8.15	24.0	24.7	0.148	3.92	14.4	12.2	10.9	0.441
	5	4.71	0.046	600	0.349	6.88	24.1	24.4	0.127	3.32	14.5	11.9	10.9	0.445
65X50	8	6.72	0.066	856	0.351	8.03	20.2	21.3	0.180	4.97	14.5	13.8	10.6	0.572
	6	5.13	0.050	654	0.275	6.19	20.5	20.6	0.142	3.85	14.7	13.1	10.7	0.580
	5	4.32	0.042	550	0.235	5.24	20.7	20.2	0.122	3.27	14.9	12.7	10.8	0.583
	4	3.49	0.034	444	0.192	4.25	20.8	19.9	0.100	2.66	15.0	12.4	10.8	0.587
55X35	6	3.96	0.039	504	0.152	4.23	17.4	19.0	0.048	1.85	9.77	9.04	7.55	0.396
	5	3.34	0.033	425	0.130	3.59	17.5	18.7	0.041	1.58	9.89	8.68	7.59	0.401
	4	2.70	0.026	344	0.107	2.92	17.7	18.3	0.034	1.29	10.0	8.31	7.65	0.406
	3	2.05	0.020	261	0.083	2.23	17.8	17.9	0.027	0.994	10.2	7.94	7.72	0.411
45X30	6	3.25	0.032	414	0.082	2.79	14.0	15.7	0.029	1.32	8.35	8.22	6.44	0.426
	5	2.75	0.027	350	0.070	2.37	14.2	15.4	0.025	1.13	8.46	7.86	6.47	0.433
	4	2.23	0.022	284	0.058	1.94	14.3	15.0	0.021	0.930	8.58	7.49	6.51	0.439
	3	1.70	0.017	216	0.045	1.49	14.5	14.6	0.016	0.717	8.72	7.12	6.57	0.445

Note: The properties of angles currently produced by cold forming are up to 7 percent less than the properties shown in the above tables. Check manufacturers' catalogue for the exact properties and dimensions. See also page 6-19.

TWO ANGLES EQUAL LEGS
Back to Back

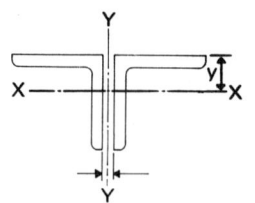

PROPERTIES OF SECTIONS

Size	Thick-ness t	Mass of 2 Angles	Dead Load	Area of 2 Angles	Axis X-X				Radii of Gyration about Axis Y-Y					
					I	S	r	y	back to back of angles, millimetres					
mmxmm	mm	kg/m	kN/m	mm²	10^6mm⁴	10^3mm³	mm	mm	0	8	10	12	16	20
200X200														
	30	174	1.71	22 200	80.6	580	60.3	60.9	85.7	88.6	89.3	90.1	91.6	93.1
	25	147	1.44	18 800	69.5	494	60.9	59.2	84.9	87.7	88.5	89.2	90.7	92.2
	20	119	1.17	15 200	57.6	404	61.6	57.4	84.1	86.9	87.6	88.3	89.8	91.3
	16	96.5	0.946	12 300	47.4	329	62.1	55.9	83.6	86.3	87.0	87.7	89.1	90.6
	13	79.0	0.775	10 100	39.4	271	62.6	54.8	83.2	85.9	86.6	87.2	88.7	90.1
	10	61.2	0.600	7 800	31.0	212	63.0	53.7	82.8	85.4	86.1	86.8	88.2	89.6
150X150														
	20	87.9	0.862	11 200	23.2	221	45.5	44.8	63.9	66.7	67.5	68.2	69.7	71.2
	16	71.3	0.700	9 090	19.3	181	46.0	43.4	63.3	66.1	66.8	67.5	69.0	70.5
	13	58.6	0.574	7 460	16.1	149	46.4	42.3	62.8	65.6	66.3	67.0	68.5	69.9
	10	45.5	0.446	5 800	12.7	117	46.9	41.2	62.4	65.1	65.8	66.5	68.0	69.4
125X125														
	16	58.8	0.576	7 490	10.8	123	38.0	37.1	53.1	56.0	56.7	57.5	59.0	60.5
	13	48.4	0.474	6 160	9.09	102	38.4	36.0	52.7	55.5	56.2	56.9	58.4	60.0
	10	37.7	0.370	4 800	7.23	80.3	38.8	34.9	52.2	55.0	55.7	56.4	57.9	59.4
	8	30.4	0.298	3 870	5.92	65.2	39.1	34.2	52.0	54.7	55.4	56.1	57.6	59.0
100X100														
	16	46.2	0.453	5 890	5.30	76.6	30.0	30.8	43.0	46.0	46.7	47.5	49.1	50.7
	13	38.2	0.374	4 860	4.49	63.9	30.4	29.8	42.5	45.4	46.2	46.9	48.5	50.0
	10	29.8	0.293	3 800	3.60	50.5	30.8	28.7	42.1	44.9	45.6	46.4	47.9	49.4
	8	24.1	0.236	3 070	2.96	41.1	31.1	28.0	41.8	44.6	45.3	46.0	47.5	49.0
	6	18.3	0.179	2 330	2.29	31.4	31.3	27.2	41.5	44.2	45.0	45.7	47.2	48.7
90X 90														
	13	34.1	0.334	4 340	3.21	51.1	27.2	27.2	38.5	41.4	42.2	42.9	44.5	46.1
	10	26.7	0.262	3 400	2.58	40.5	27.6	26.2	38.0	40.9	41.6	42.4	43.9	45.5
	8	21.6	0.212	2 750	2.13	33.0	27.8	25.5	37.7	40.5	41.3	42.0	43.5	45.1
	6	16.4	0.161	2 090	1.65	25.3	28.1	24.7	37.4	40.2	40.9	41.7	43.2	44.7
75X 75														
	13	28.0	0.274	3 560	1.78	34.6	22.4	23.5	32.4	35.4	36.2	37.0	38.6	40.3
	10	22.0	0.216	2 800	1.45	27.6	22.8	22.4	31.9	34.9	35.6	36.4	38.0	39.6
	8	17.8	0.175	2 270	1.20	22.6	23.0	21.7	31.6	34.5	35.2	36.0	37.6	39.2
	6	13.6	0.133	1 730	0.938	17.4	23.3	21.0	31.3	34.1	34.9	35.6	37.2	38.8
	5	11.4	0.112	1 450	0.797	14.6	23.4	20.6	31.2	34.0	34.7	35.5	37.0	38.5

Note: The properties of angles currently produced by cold forming are up to 7 percent less than the properties shown in the above tables. Check manufacturers' catalogue for the exact properties and dimensions. See also page 6-19.

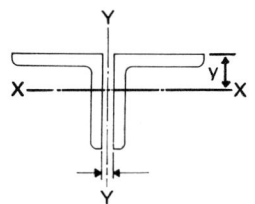

PROPERTIES OF SECTIONS

Size	Thick-ness t	Mass of 2 Angles	Dead Load	Area of 2 Angles	Axis X-X				Radii of Gyration about Axis Y-Y					
					I	S	r	y	back to back of angles, millimetres					
mmxmm	mm	kg/m	kN/m	mm²	10^6mm⁴	10^3mm³	mm	mm	0	8	10	12	16	20
65X 65														
	10	18.8	0.185	2 400	0.917	20.3	19.6	19.9	27.9	30.9	31.7	32.4	34.1	35.7
	8	15.3	0.150	1 950	0.766	16.7	19.8	19.2	27.6	30.5	31.3	32.0	33.6	35.3
	6	11.7	0.115	1 490	0.600	12.9	20.1	18.5	27.3	30.1	30.9	31.6	33.2	34.8
	5	9.81	0.096	1 250	0.511	10.9	20.2	18.1	27.1	30.0	30.7	31.5	33.0	34.6
55X 55														
	10	15.7	0.154	2 000	0.535	14.2	16.4	17.4	23.9	26.9	27.7	28.5	30.2	31.9
	8	12.8	0.126	1 630	0.450	11.7	16.6	16.7	23.5	26.5	27.3	28.1	29.7	31.4
	6	9.80	0.096	1 250	0.355	9.09	16.9	16.0	23.2	26.1	26.9	27.7	29.3	31.0
	5	8.24	0.081	1 050	0.303	7.70	17.0	15.6	23.1	25.9	26.7	27.5	29.1	30.7
	4	6.66	0.065	848	0.249	6.26	17.1	15.2	22.9	25.8	26.5	27.3	28.9	30.5
	3	5.04	0.049	642	0.192	4.78	17.3	14.9	22.8	25.6	26.3	27.1	28.7	30.3
45X 45														
	8	10.3	0.101	1 310	0.236	7.65	13.4	14.2	19.5	22.6	23.4	24.2	25.9	27.6
	6	7.91	0.078	1 010	0.188	5.95	13.7	13.4	19.2	22.2	22.9	23.8	25.4	27.1
	5	6.67	0.065	850	0.161	5.06	13.8	13.1	19.0	22.0	22.7	23.5	25.2	26.9
	4	5.40	0.053	688	0.133	4.13	13.9	12.7	18.9	21.8	22.5	23.3	25.0	26.7
	3	4.10	0.040	522	0.103	3.16	14.1	12.4	18.7	21.6	22.3	23.1	24.7	26.4
35X 35														
	6	6.03	0.059	768	0.084	3.49	10.5	10.9	15.1	18.2	19.1	19.9	21.6	23.4
	5	5.10	0.050	650	0.073	2.98	10.6	10.6	15.0	18.0	18.8	19.7	21.4	23.1
	4	4.14	0.041	528	0.060	2.44	10.7	10.2	14.8	17.8	18.6	19.4	21.1	22.9
	3	3.16	0.031	402	0.047	1.88	10.8	9.86	14.7	17.6	18.4	19.2	20.9	22.6
25X 25														
	5	3.53	0.035	450	0.024	1.45	7.39	8.06	10.9	14.1	15.0	15.9	17.7	19.5
	4	2.89	0.028	368	0.021	1.20	7.50	7.71	10.8	13.9	14.8	15.6	17.4	19.2
	3	2.21	0.022	282	0.016	0.930	7.63	7.35	10.6	13.7	14.5	15.4	17.1	19.0

Note: The properties of angles currently produced by cold forming are up to 7 percent less than the properties shown in the above tables. Check manufacturers' catalogue for the exact properties and dimensions. See also page 6-19.

TWO ANGLES UNEQUAL LEGS
Long Legs Back to Back

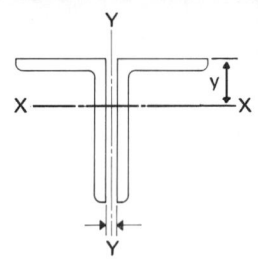

PROPERTIES OF SECTIONS

Size	Thick-ness t	Mass of 2 Angles	Dead Load	Area of 2 Angles	Axis X-X				Radii of Gyration about Axis Y-Y					
					I	S	r	y	\multicolumn{6}{c}{back to back of angles, millimetres}
mmxmm	mm	kg/m	kN/m	mm²	10^6mm⁴	10^3mm³	mm	mm	0	8	10	12	16	20
200X150*														
	25	128	1.25	16 200	63.1	472	62.3	66.3	59.8	62.6	63.3	64.1	65.6	67.1
	20	104	1.02	13 200	52.4	387	63.0	64.5	59.0	61.8	62.5	63.2	64.6	66.1
	16	83.9	0.823	10 700	43.2	315	63.5	63.1	58.4	61.1	61.8	62.5	63.9	65.4
	13	68.8	0.675	8 760	35.9	260	64.0	62.0	58.0	60.7	61.4	62.0	63.4	64.9
200X100*														
	20	87.9	0.862	11 200	45.3	360	63.6	74.3	35.7	38.6	39.3	40.0	41.6	43.1
	16	71.3	0.700	9 090	37.4	294	64.2	72.8	35.1	37.8	38.5	39.2	40.7	42.2
	13	58.6	0.574	7 460	31.1	243	64.6	71.7	34.6	37.2	37.9	38.7	40.1	41.6
	10	45.5	0.446	5 800	24.6	190	65.1	70.5	34.2	36.8	37.4	38.1	39.5	41.0
150X100														
	16	58.8	0.576	7 490	16.8	170	47.4	50.9	38.4	41.2	41.9	42.7	44.2	45.7
	13	48.4	0.474	6 160	14.1	140	47.8	49.9	37.9	40.7	41.4	42.1	43.6	45.1
	10	37.7	0.370	4 800	11.2	110	48.2	48.8	37.5	40.2	40.9	41.6	43.0	44.5
	8	30.4	0.298	3 870	9.11	89.3	48.5	48.0	37.3	39.9	40.6	41.3	42.7	44.2
125X 90														
	16	50.0	0.490	6 370	9.68	117	39.0	42.2	35.6	38.5	39.2	40.0	41.6	43.2
	13	41.2	0.404	5 250	8.15	97.1	39.4	41.2	35.1	37.9	38.7	39.4	40.9	42.5
	10	32.2	0.316	4 100	6.49	76.5	39.8	40.1	34.7	37.4	38.1	38.9	40.4	41.9
	8	26.0	0.255	3 310	5.32	62.1	40.1	39.3	34.4	37.1	37.8	38.5	40.0	41.5
125X 75														
	13	38.2	0.374	4 860	7.63	94.2	39.6	43.9	28.0	30.9	31.6	32.4	34.0	35.6
	10	29.8	0.293	3 800	6.09	74.2	40.0	42.8	27.6	30.3	31.0	31.8	33.3	34.9
	8	24.1	0.236	3 070	5.00	60.3	40.3	42.1	27.3	30.0	30.7	31.4	32.9	34.5
	6	18.3	0.179	2 330	3.84	46.0	40.6	41.3	27.1	29.6	30.3	31.1	32.5	34.0
100X 90														
	13	36.1	0.354	4 600	4.34	62.9	30.7	31.1	37.4	40.3	41.1	41.8	43.4	45.0
	10	28.3	0.277	3 600	3.48	49.7	31.1	30.0	37.0	39.8	40.5	41.3	42.8	44.3
	8	22.9	0.224	2 910	2.87	40.5	31.4	29.3	36.7	39.4	40.2	40.9	42.4	43.9
	6	17.3	0.170	2 210	2.21	31.0	31.7	28.5	36.4	39.1	39.8	40.6	42.0	43.6

*Not available from Canadian mills.

Note: The properties of angles currently produced by cold forming are up to 7 percent less than the properties shown in the above tables. Check manufacturers' catalogue for the exact properties and dimensions. See also page 6-19.

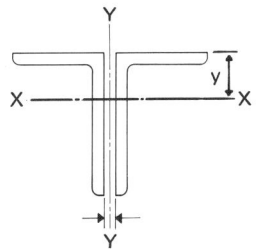

TWO ANGLES UNEQUAL LEGS
Long Legs Back to Back

PROPERTIES OF SECTIONS

Size	Thick-ness t	Mass of 2 Angles	Dead Load	Area of 2 Angles	Axis X-X				Radii of Gyration about Axis Y-Y					
					I	S	r	y	\multicolumn{6}{c}{back to back of angles, millimetres}					
									0	8	10	12	16	20
mmxmm	mm	kg/m	kN/m	mm²	10^6mm⁴	10^3mm³	mm	mm						
100X 75	13	33.1	0.324	4 210	4.07	61.1	31.1	33.4	30.0	32.9	33.6	34.4	36.0	37.6
	10	25.9	0.254	3 300	3.27	48.3	31.5	32.3	29.5	32.3	33.1	33.8	35.4	37.0
	8	21.0	0.206	2 670	2.70	39.4	31.8	31.5	29.2	32.0	32.7	33.4	35.0	36.5
	6	15.9	0.156	2 030	2.08	30.1	32.1	30.8	29.0	31.6	32.4	33.1	34.6	36.1
90X 75	13	31.0	0.304	3 950	3.02	49.7	27.6	29.3	30.9	33.8	34.6	35.4	37.0	38.6
	10	24.3	0.239	3 100	2.43	39.4	28.0	28.2	30.4	33.3	34.0	34.8	36.3	37.9
	8	19.7	0.193	2 510	2.01	32.2	28.3	27.5	30.1	32.9	33.6	34.4	35.9	37.5
	6	15.0	0.147	1 910	1.56	24.6	28.6	26.8	29.8	32.6	33.3	34.0	35.5	37.1
	5	12.6	0.123	1 600	1.32	20.8	28.7	26.4	29.7	32.4	33.1	33.9	35.4	36.9
90X 65	10	22.8	0.223	2 900	2.32	38.5	28.3	29.8	25.5	28.4	29.1	29.9	31.5	33.1
	8	18.5	0.181	2 350	1.92	31.5	28.5	29.1	25.2	28.0	28.7	29.5	31.1	32.7
	6	14.0	0.138	1 790	1.49	24.1	28.8	28.4	24.9	27.6	28.4	29.1	30.6	32.2
	5	11.8	0.115	1 500	1.26	20.3	29.0	28.0	24.8	27.5	28.2	28.9	30.4	32.0
80X 60	10	20.4	0.200	2 600	1.62	30.2	24.9	26.5	23.9	26.8	27.6	28.4	30.0	31.7
	8	16.6	0.163	2 110	1.34	24.7	25.2	25.8	23.6	26.5	27.2	28.0	29.6	31.2
	6	12.6	0.124	1 610	1.04	19.0	25.5	25.1	23.3	26.1	26.8	27.6	29.1	30.8
	5	10.6	0.104	1 350	0.886	16.0	25.6	24.7	23.2	25.9	26.6	27.4	28.9	30.5
75X 50	8	14.7	0.144	1 870	1.05	21.2	23.7	25.5	19.2	22.1	22.9	23.7	25.3	27.0
	6	11.2	0.110	1 430	0.820	16.3	24.0	24.7	18.9	21.7	22.5	23.2	24.8	26.5
	5	9.42	0.092	1 200	0.697	13.8	24.1	24.4	18.8	21.5	22.3	23.0	24.6	26.3
65X 50	8	13.4	0.132	1 710	0.701	16.1	20.2	21.3	20.0	23.0	23.7	24.5	26.2	27.9
	6	10.3	0.101	1 310	0.550	12.4	20.5	20.6	19.7	22.6	23.3	24.1	25.7	27.4
	5	8.63	0.085	1 100	0.469	10.5	20.7	20.2	19.6	22.4	23.1	23.9	25.5	27.2
	4	6.97	0.068	888	0.384	8.51	20.8	19.9	19.5	22.2	23.0	23.7	25.3	26.9
55X 35	6	7.91	0.078	1 010	0.304	8.46	17.4	19.0	13.3	16.3	17.1	17.9	19.6	21.4
	5	6.67	0.065	850	0.261	7.17	17.5	18.7	13.2	16.1	16.9	17.7	19.4	21.1
	4	5.40	0.053	688	0.214	5.84	17.7	18.3	13.0	15.9	16.7	17.5	19.1	20.9
	3	4.10	0.040	522	0.165	4.46	17.8	17.9	12.9	15.7	16.4	17.2	18.9	20.6
45X 30	6	6.50	0.064	828	0.163	5.58	14.0	15.7	11.7	14.8	15.6	16.5	18.2	20.0
	5	5.49	0.054	700	0.141	4.75	14.2	15.4	11.5	14.6	15.4	16.2	18.0	19.8
	4	4.46	0.044	568	0.116	3.88	14.3	15.0	11.4	14.3	15.2	16.0	17.7	19.5
	3	3.39	0.033	432	0.090	2.97	14.5	14.6	11.3	14.1	14.9	15.8	17.5	19.2

Note: The properties of angles currently produced by cold forming are up to 7 percent less than the properties shown in the above tables. Check manufacturers' catalogue for the exact properties and dimensions. See also page 6-19.

TWO ANGLES UNEQUAL LEGS
Short Legs Back to Back

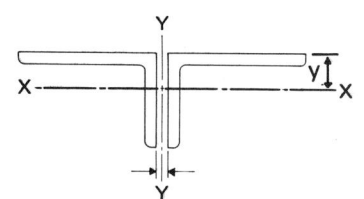

PROPERTIES OF SECTIONS

Size	Thick-ness t	Mass of 2 Angles	Dead Load	Area of 2 Angles	Axis X-X				Radii of Gyration about Axis Y-Y					
					I	S	r	y	back to back of angles, millimetres					
mmxmm	mm	kg/m	kN/m	mm²	10^6mm⁴	10^3mm³	mm	mm	0	8	10	12	16	20
200X150*														
	25	128	1.25	16 200	30.3	279	43.2	41.3	91.0	94.0	94.7	95.5	97.0	98.6
	20	104	1.02	13 200	25.3	229	43.8	39.5	90.2	93.1	93.8	94.6	96.1	97.6
	16	83.9	0.823	10 700	21.0	188	44.3	38.1	89.5	92.4	93.1	93.9	95.4	96.9
	13	68.8	0.675	8 760	17.5	155	44.7	37.0	89.1	91.9	92.6	93.4	94.8	96.3
200X100*														
	20	87.9	0.862	11 200	7.69	102	26.2	24.3	97.8	101	102	102	104	106
	16	71.3	0.700	9 090	6.45	83.5	26.6	22.8	97.0	100	101	102	103	105
	13	58.6	0.574	7 460	5.44	69.4	27.0	21.7	96.5	99.5	100	101	103	104
	10	45.5	0.446	5 800	4.35	54.8	27.4	20.5	95.9	98.9	99.7	100	102	104
150X100														
	16	58.8	0.576	7 490	5.99	80.9	28.3	25.9	69.6	72.5	73.3	74.1	75.6	77.2
	13	48.4	0.474	6 160	5.06	67.3	28.7	24.9	69.0	72.0	72.7	73.5	75.0	76.6
	10	37.7	0.370	4 800	4.05	53.1	29.1	23.8	68.6	71.5	72.2	72.9	74.5	76.0
	8	30.4	0.298	3 870	3.33	43.3	29.3	23.0	68.2	71.1	71.8	72.6	74.1	75.6
125X 90														
	16	50.0	0.490	6 370	4.18	64.0	25.6	24.7	57.5	60.5	61.2	62.0	63.6	65.2
	13	41.2	0.404	5 250	3.54	53.4	26.0	23.7	57.0	59.9	60.7	61.4	63.0	64.6
	10	32.2	0.316	4 100	2.85	42.3	26.4	22.6	56.5	59.4	60.1	60.9	62.4	64.0
	8	26.0	0.255	3 310	2.35	34.5	26.6	21.8	56.2	59.0	59.8	60.5	62.0	63.6
125X 75														
	13	38.2	0.374	4 860	2.08	37.1	20.7	18.9	59.2	62.2	63.0	63.7	65.3	66.9
	10	29.8	0.293	3 800	1.68	29.4	21.0	17.8	58.6	61.6	62.4	63.1	64.7	66.3
	8	24.1	0.236	3 070	1.39	24.1	21.3	17.1	58.3	61.2	62.0	62.8	64.3	65.9
	6	18.3	0.179	2 330	1.08	18.5	21.6	16.3	58.0	60.9	61.6	62.4	63.9	65.5
100X 90														
	13	36.1	0.354	4 600	3.32	51.9	26.8	26.1	43.7	46.6	47.4	48.1	49.7	51.3
	10	28.3	0.277	3 600	2.67	41.1	27.2	25.0	43.2	46.1	46.8	47.6	49.1	50.7
	8	22.9	0.224	2 910	2.20	33.5	27.5	24.3	42.9	45.7	46.5	47.2	48.7	50.3
	6	17.3	0.170	2 210	1.71	25.7	27.8	23.5	42.6	45.4	46.1	46.9	48.4	49.9

*Not available from Canadian mills.

Note: The properties of angles currently produced by cold forming are up to 7 percent less than the properties shown in the above tables. Check manufacturers' catalogue for the exact properties and dimensions. See also page 6-19.

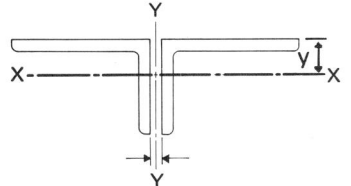

Size	Thick-ness t	Mass of 2 Angles	Dead Load	Area of 2 Angles	Axis X-X				Radii of Gyration about Axis Y-Y					
					I	S	r	y	back to back of angles, millimetres					
mmxmm	mm	kg/m	kN/m	mm²	10⁶mm⁴	10³mm³	mm	mm	0	8	10	12	16	20
100X 75														
	13	33.1	0.324	4 210	1.95	36.1	21.5	20.9	45.6	48.6	49.4	50.2	51.7	53.3
	10	25.9	0.254	3 300	1.58	28.7	21.9	19.8	45.1	48.0	48.8	49.6	51.1	52.7
	8	21.0	0.206	2 670	1.31	23.5	22.2	19.0	44.8	47.7	48.4	49.2	50.7	52.3
	6	15.9	0.156	2 030	1.02	18.0	22.4	18.3	44.5	47.3	48.1	48.8	50.3	51.9
90X 75														
	13	31.0	0.304	3 950	1.89	35.6	21.9	21.8	40.3	43.3	44.0	44.8	46.4	48.0
	10	24.3	0.239	3 100	1.53	28.3	22.2	20.7	39.8	42.7	43.5	44.2	45.8	47.4
	8	19.7	0.193	2 510	1.27	23.1	22.5	20.0	39.5	42.3	43.1	43.9	45.4	47.0
	6	15.0	0.147	1 910	0.991	17.8	22.8	19.3	39.2	42.0	42.7	43.5	45.0	46.6
	5	12.6	0.123	1 600	0.841	15.0	22.9	18.9	39.0	41.8	42.6	43.3	44.8	46.4
90X 65														
	10	22.8	0.223	2 900	1.01	21.3	18.7	17.3	41.1	44.1	44.9	45.6	47.2	48.8
	8	18.5	0.181	2 350	0.844	17.4	18.9	16.6	40.8	43.7	44.5	45.2	46.8	48.4
	6	14.0	0.138	1 790	0.660	13.4	19.2	15.9	40.4	43.3	44.1	44.9	46.4	48.0
	5	11.8	0.115	1 500	0.562	11.4	19.4	15.5	40.3	43.2	43.9	44.7	46.2	47.8
80X 60														
	10	20.4	0.200	2 600	0.776	17.8	17.3	16.5	36.4	39.4	40.2	41.0	42.6	44.2
	8	16.6	0.163	2 110	0.648	14.7	17.5	15.8	36.1	39.0	39.8	40.6	42.2	43.8
	6	12.6	0.124	1 610	0.509	11.3	17.8	15.1	35.8	38.7	39.4	40.2	41.8	43.4
	5	10.6	0.104	1 350	0.434	9.58	17.9	14.7	35.6	38.5	39.2	40.0	41.6	43.2
75X 50														
	8	14.7	0.144	1 870	0.374	10.1	14.1	13.0	34.8	37.8	38.6	39.4	41.0	42.7
	6	11.2	0.110	1 430	0.296	7.84	14.4	12.2	34.4	37.4	38.2	39.0	40.6	42.2
	5	9.42	0.092	1 200	0.253	6.64	14.5	11.9	34.3	37.2	38.0	38.8	40.4	42.0
65X 50														
	8	13.4	0.132	1 710	0.359	9.93	14.5	13.8	29.4	32.4	33.2	34.0	35.6	37.3
	6	10.3	0.101	1 310	0.284	7.70	14.7	13.1	29.1	32.0	32.8	33.6	35.2	36.8
	5	8.63	0.085	1 100	0.243	6.53	14.9	12.7	28.9	31.8	32.6	33.4	35.0	36.6
	4	6.97	0.068	888	0.200	5.32	15.0	12.4	28.8	31.7	32.4	33.2	34.8	36.4
55X 35														
	6	7.91	0.078	1 010	0.096	3.70	9.77	9.04	25.8	28.9	29.7	30.5	32.1	33.8
	5	6.67	0.065	850	0.083	3.16	9.89	8.68	25.6	28.6	29.4	30.3	31.9	33.6
	4	5.40	0.053	688	0.069	2.59	10.0	8.31	25.4	28.4	29.2	30.0	31.7	33.4
	3	4.10	0.040	522	0.054	1.99	10.2	7.94	25.3	28.2	29.0	29.8	31.5	33.1
45X 30														
	6	6.50	0.064	828	0.058	2.65	8.35	8.22	21.1	24.2	25.0	25.9	27.6	29.3
	5	5.49	0.054	700	0.050	2.26	8.46	7.86	20.9	24.0	24.8	25.6	27.3	29.1
	4	4.46	0.044	568	0.042	1.86	8.58	7.49	20.7	23.8	24.6	25.4	27.1	28.8
	3	3.39	0.033	432	0.033	1.43	8.72	7.12	20.6	23.6	24.4	25.2	26.9	28.6

Note: The properties of angles currently produced by cold forming are up to 7 percent less than the properties shown in the above tables. Check manufacturers' catalogue for the exact properties and dimensions. See also page 6-19.

WELDED WIDE FLANGE TEES
Cut from WWF Shapes

PROPERTIES AND DIMENSIONS

Designation	Dead Load	Total Area	Depth of Tee "d"	Flange Width	Flange Aver. Thickness	Stem Thickness "w"	Axis X-X I_x	Axis X-X S_x	Axis X-X r_x	Axis X-X y	Axis Y-Y I_y	Axis Y-Y S_y	Axis Y-Y r_y
	kN/m	mm²	mm	mm	mm	mm	10^6mm⁴	10^3mm³	mm	mm	10^6mm⁴	10^3mm³	mm
WWT275													
X360.5	3.53	46 000	275	550	60.0	60.0	235	1 140	71.5	68.6	836	3 040	135
X310	3.04	39 500	275	550	60.0	30.0	137	615	58.9	52.5	832	3 030	145
X251.5	2.46	32 100	275	550	50.0	20.0	97.8	424	55.2	44.4	693	2 520	147
X210	2.05	26 800	275	550	40.0	20.0	97.8	424	60.4	44.2	555	2 020	144
X108.5	1.06	13 900	275	550	20.0	11.0	57.8	244	64.5	37.9	277	1 010	141
WWT250													
X325.5	3.19	41 500	250	500	60.0	60.0	172	929	64.4	64.4	629	2 510	123
X280.5	2.75	35 800	250	500	60.0	30.0	101	505	53.1	50.0	625	2 500	132
X228	2.23	29 100	250	500	50.0	20.0	72.4	349	49.9	42.3	521	2 080	134
X190.5	1.86	24 300	250	500	40.0	20.0	72.3	347	54.5	41.7	417	1 670	131
X171.5	1.68	21 900	250	500	35.0	20.0	72.3	348	57.5	42.1	365	1 460	129
X153	1.50	19 500	250	500	30.0	20.0	72.0	349	60.8	43.3	313	1 250	127
X138	1.35	17 600	250	500	28.0	16.0	59.8	284	58.3	39.3	292	1 170	129
X127	1.24	16 200	250	500	25.0	16.0	59.5	284	60.6	40.4	261	1 040	127
X111.5	1.09	14 300	250	500	22.0	14.0	52.9	251	60.8	39.1	229	917	127
X98.5	0.966	12 600	250	500	20.0	11.0	43.0	200	58.4	35.2	208	833	128
WWT225													
X251.5	2.46	32 000	225	450	60.0	30.0	72.3	407	47.5	47.5	456	2 030	119
X204.5	2.00	26 100	225	450	50.0	20.0	52.0	281	44.6	40.2	380	1 690	121
X171	1.67	21 800	225	450	40.0	20.0	51.8	279	48.7	39.2	304	1 350	118
X154	1.51	19 600	225	450	35.0	20.0	51.8	279	51.4	39.4	266	1 180	116
X137	1.34	17 500	225	450	30.0	20.0	51.7	280	54.4	40.2	228	1 010	114
X124	1.21	15 800	225	450	28.0	16.0	42.9	228	52.1	36.5	213	945	116
X114	1.11	14 500	225	450	25.0	16.0	42.8	228	54.3	37.4	190	844	114
X100.5	0.986	12 800	225	450	22.0	14.0	38.1	202	54.6	36.0	167	743	114
X88.5	0.868	11 300	225	450	20.0	11.0	31.0	161	52.4	32.5	152	675	116
WWT200													
X222	2.17	28 300	200	400	60.0	30.0	49.8	321	41.9	45.0	320	1 600	106
X181	1.77	23 100	200	400	50.0	20.0	35.9	222	39.4	38.1	267	1 330	108
X151.5	1.48	19 300	200	400	40.0	20.0	35.6	218	42.9	36.7	213	1 070	105
X136.5	1.33	17 400	200	400	35.0	20.0	35.6	218	45.2	36.6	187	934	104
X121.5	1.19	15 500	200	400	30.0	20.0	35.6	218	47.9	37.1	160	801	102
X110	1.07	14 000	200	400	28.0	16.0	29.6	178	46.0	33.7	149	747	103
X101	0.990	12 900	200	400	25.0	16.0	29.5	178	47.8	34.3	133	667	102
X89	0.873	11 400	200	400	22.0	14.0	26.4	158	48.1	33.0	117	587	101
X78.5	0.770	10 000	200	400	20.0	11.0	21.5	126	46.4	29.8	107	533	103
WWT175													
X192.5	1.88	24 500	175	350	60.0	30.0	32.8	248	36.6	42.4	215	1 230	93.7
X157.5	1.54	20 100	175	350	50.0	20.0	23.7	170	34.3	36.0	179	1 020	94.4
X131.5	1.29	16 800	175	350	40.0	20.0	23.3	166	37.2	34.2	143	817	92.3
X119	1.16	15 100	175	350	35.0	20.0	23.3	165	39.3	33.8	125	715	91.0
X106	1.04	13 500	175	350	30.0	20.0	23.3	165	41.5	33.9	107	613	89.0
X96	0.941	12 200	175	350	28.0	16.0	19.4	135	39.9	30.9	100	572	90.5
X88	0.863	11 200	175	350	25.0	16.0	19.4	135	41.6	31.3	89.4	511	89.3
X77.5	0.760	9 900	175	350	22.0	14.0	17.3	119	41.8	30.0	78.6	449	89.1
X68.5	0.672	8 770	175	350	20.0	11.0	14.1	95.6	40.1	27.1	71.5	408	90.3

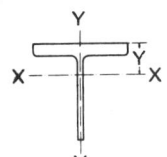

PROPERTIES AND DIMENSIONS

Designation	Dead Load	Total Area	Depth of Tee "d"	Flange Width	Flange Aver. Thickness	Stem Thickness "w"	Axis X-X I_x	Axis X-X S_x	Axis X-X r_x	Axis X-X y	Axis Y-Y I_y	Axis Y-Y S_y	Axis Y-Y r_y
	kN/m	mm^2	mm	mm	mm	mm	10^6mm^4	10^3mm^3	mm	mm	10^6mm^4	10^3mm^3	mm
WT460													
X223*	2.18	28 500	466	423	42.7	24.0	510	1 410	134	105	270	1 280	97.3
X208.5*	2.04	26 600	464	422	39.9	22.5	474	1 310	133	103	250	1 190	96.9
X193.5*	1.89	24 700	460	420	36.6	21.3	439	1 230	133	103	226	1 080	95.7
X182.5*	1.79	23 200	458	419	34.3	20.3	413	1 160	133	102	211	1 010	95.4
X171*	1.67	21 800	456	418	32.0	19.3	389	1 100	134	102	195	933	94.6
WT460													
X156.5*	1.53	19 900	466	309	34.5	21.1	410	1 200	144	124	85.2	551	65.4
X144.5*	1.41	18 400	464	308	32.0	19.4	375	1 100	143	122	78.2	508	65.2
X135.5*	1.32	17 300	462	307	30.0	18.4	352	1 030	143	121	72.6	473	64.8
X126.5*	1.24	16 200	460	306	27.9	17.3	328	967	142	120	66.8	437	64.2
X119*	1.16	15 200	458	305	25.9	16.5	308	915	142	120	61.4	403	63.6
X111.5*	1.09	14 300	456	304	23.9	15.9	291	872	143	122	56.1	369	62.6
X100.5*	0.986	12 800	452	304	20.1	15.2	265	812	144	126	47.2	311	60.7
WT420													
X179.5*	1.76	22 900	434	403	35.6	21.1	363	1 080	126	97.6	195	965	92.3
X164.5*	1.61	21 000	431	401	32.4	19.7	333	997	126	97.0	174	870	91.0
X149.5*	1.46	19 100	428	400	29.2	18.2	302	910	126	96.0	156	780	90.4
WT420													
X113*	1.10	14 400	426	294	26.8	16.1	246	777	131	108	56.9	387	62.9
X105*	1.03	13 400	423	293	24.4	15.4	230	733	131	109	51.3	350	61.9
X96.5*	0.946	12 300	420	292	21.7	14.7	213	688	132	111	45.1	309	60.6
X88*	0.863	11 200	418	292	18.8	14.0	196	644	132	114	39.1	268	59.1
WT380													
X157*	1.54	20 000	393	384	33.4	19.7	254	828	113	86.3	158	822	88.9
X142*	1.39	18 100	390	382	30.1	18.0	228	748	112	84.8	140	733	87.9
X128.5*	1.26	16 400	386	381	27.1	16.6	206	682	112	83.9	125	656	87.3
WT380													
X98*	0.961	12 500	385	268	25.4	15.6	175	613	118	99.0	40.9	305	57.2
X92.5*	0.907	11 800	383	267	23.6	14.9	165	580	118	99.1	37.5	281	56.4
X86.5*	0.848	11 100	381	267	21.6	14.4	156	554	119	100	34.4	257	55.7
X80.5*	0.789	10 200	379	266	19.3	13.8	145	523	119	102	30.4	228	54.6
X73.5*	0.721	9 370	376	265	17.0	13.2	134	492	120	104	26.4	200	53.1
WT345													
X132.5*	1.29	16 900	353	358	30.2	18.4	172	624	101	77.4	116	646	82.8
X120*	1.17	15 300	350	356	27.4	16.8	155	565	101	76.1	103	580	82.0
X108.5*	1.06	13 900	348	355	24.8	15.4	140	512	100	74.8	92.6	522	81.6
WT345													
X85*	0.834	10 800	346	256	23.6	14.5	120	464	105	86.9	33.1	259	55.4
X76*	0.745	9 690	344	254	21.1	13.1	107	415	105	85.8	28.9	227	54.6
X70*	0.686	8 910	342	254	18.9	12.4	99.3	389	106	86.5	25.9	204	53.9
X62.5*	0.613	8 000	339	253	16.3	11.7	90.0	359	106	88.3	22.0	174	52.4
WT305													
X120.5	1.18	15 400	318	329	31.0	17.9	122	490	89.0	68.5	92.1	560	77.3
X108.5	1.06	13 900	314	328	27.7	16.5	110	444	89.0	67.4	81.6	497	76.6
X97.5	0.956	12 500	311	327	24.4	15.4	99.4	408	89.2	67.4	71.2	435	75.5
X87	0.853	11 100	308	325	21.6	14.0	88.3	366	89.2	66.5	61.9	381	74.7
X77.5	0.760	9 860	306	324	19.0	12.7	78.6	328	89.3	65.9	53.9	333	73.9

*Not available from Canadian mills.

STRUCTURAL TEES
Cut from W Shapes

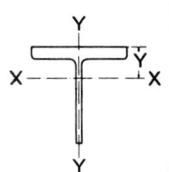

PROPERTIES AND DIMENSIONS

Designation	Dead Load	Total Area	Depth of Tee "d"	Flange Width	Flange Aver. Thickness	Stem Thickness "w"	Axis X-X				Axis Y-Y		
							I_x	S_x	r_x	y	I_y	S_y	r_y
	kN/m	mm²	mm	mm	mm	mm	10^6mm⁴	10^3mm³	mm	mm	10^6mm⁴	10^3mm³	mm
WT305													
X70	0.686	8 930	308	230	22.2	13.1	77.5	333	93.2	76.0	22.6	196	50.3
X62.5	0.613	7 970	306	229	19.6	11.9	69.0	299	93.0	75.4	19.7	172	49.7
X56.5	0.554	7 220	304	228	17.3	11.2	63.2	278	93.6	76.3	17.1	150	48.7
X50.5	0.495	6 480	302	228	14.9	10.5	57.2	255	94.0	77.6	14.7	129	47.6
WT305													
X46*	0.451	5 880	302	179	15.0	10.9	54.6	255	96.4	87.7	7.20	80.5	35.0
X41*	0.402	5 210	300	178	12.8	10.0	48.5	230	96.5	88.9	6.04	67.9	34.0
WT265													
X109.5*	1.07	13 900	280	318	29.2	18.3	85.0	388	78.2	60.8	78.4	493	75.1
X98*	0.961	12 500	277	316	26.3	16.5	75.2	345	77.6	59.0	69.3	438	74.5
X91*	0.892	11 600	276	315	24.4	15.2	68.9	316	77.1	57.7	63.6	404	74.0
X82.5*	0.809	10 500	273	313	22.2	14.0	62.2	288	77.0	56.7	56.8	363	73.5
X75*	0.735	9 590	272	312	20.3	12.7	56.2	260	76.6	55.4	51.4	330	73.2
WT265													
X69	0.677	8 810	274	214	23.6	14.7	59.9	292	82.5	69.4	19.3	181	46.8
X61.5	0.603	7 850	272	212	21.2	13.1	52.6	258	81.9	67.6	16.9	159	46.4
X54.5	0.534	6 940	270	211	18.8	11.6	46.0	226	81.4	66.0	14.8	140	46.2
X50.5	0.495	6 460	268	210	17.4	10.9	42.8	211	81.4	65.7	13.5	128	45.7
X46	0.451	5 890	266	209	15.6	10.2	39.1	195	81.5	65.8	11.9	114	44.9
X41	0.402	5 250	264	209	13.3	9.50	35.1	178	81.8	66.7	10.1	97.0	43.9
WT265													
X42.5*	0.417	5 390	268	166	16.5	10.3	37.6	193	83.5	72.5	6.32	76.1	34.2
X37*	0.363	4 760	264	166	13.6	9.70	33.5	176	83.9	74.5	5.21	62.7	33.1
X33*	0.324	4 190	262	165	11.4	8.90	29.6	159	84.1	75.9	4.29	52.0	32.0
WT230													
X88.5*	0.868	11 300	241	286	26.9	16.6	49.4	260	66.1	51.4	52.5	367	68.2
X79*	0.775	10 000	238	284	23.9	15.0	43.5	231	66.0	50.1	45.7	322	67.6
X72*	0.706	9 210	236	283	22.1	13.6	39.0	208	65.1	48.4	41.8	295	67.4
X64*	0.628	8 180	234	282	19.6	12.2	34.3	184	64.8	47.1	36.7	260	67.0
X56.5*	0.554	7 200	232	280	17.3	10.8	30.0	161	64.5	45.9	31.7	226	66.4
WT230													
X53	0.520	6 740	234	194	20.6	12.6	32.6	184	69.5	57.3	12.6	130	43.2
X48.5	0.476	6 150	233	193	19.0	11.4	29.4	166	69.1	55.8	11.4	118	43.1
X44.5	0.436	5 690	232	192	17.7	10.5	26.8	152	68.6	54.6	10.5	109	43.0
X41	0.402	5 220	230	191	16.0	9.90	24.8	141	68.9	54.8	9.31	97.5	42.2
X37	0.363	4 730	228	190	14.5	9.00	22.3	127	68.7	53.9	8.30	87.4	41.9
X33.5	0.329	4 340	227	190	12.7	8.50	20.5	119	68.7	54.2	7.28	76.6	41.0
X30.5	0.299	3 880	225	189	10.8	8.10	18.7	111	69.4	55.9	6.09	64.5	39.6
WT230													
X34*	0.333	4 360	230	154	15.4	9.10	21.7	127	70.5	59.0	4.70	61.1	32.8
X30*	0.294	3 790	228	153	13.3	8.00	18.7	110	70.2	58.1	3.98	52.0	32.4
X26*	0.255	3 310	225	152	10.8	7.60	16.7	102	71.0	60.8	3.17	41.7	30.9
WT205													
X74.5*	0.731	9 510	216	265	25.0	14.9	32.0	187	58.0	44.7	38.8	293	63.9
X66*	0.647	8 410	212	263	22.2	13.3	27.8	164	57.5	43.1	33.7	256	63.3
X57*	0.559	7 290	210	261	19.3	11.6	23.8	141	57.1	41.6	28.6	219	62.6
X50*	0.490	6 340	208	260	16.9	10.0	20.2	120	56.4	39.7	24.8	191	62.5

*Not available from Canadian mills.

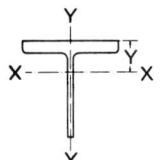

PROPERTIES AND DIMENSIONS

Designation	Dead Load	Total Area	Depth of Tee "d"	Flange Width	Flange Aver. Thickness	Stem Thickness "w"	Axis X-X I_x	Axis X-X S_x	Axis X-X r_x	Axis X-X y	Axis Y-Y I_y	Axis Y-Y S_y	Axis Y-Y r_y
	kN/m	mm^2	mm	mm	mm	mm	10^{6}mm^4	10^{3}mm^3	mm	mm	10^{6}mm^4	10^{3}mm^3	mm
WT205													
X42.5	0.417	5 410	208	181	18.2	10.9	20.2	127	61.1	49.1	9.02	99.6	40.8
X37	0.363	4 770	206	180	16.0	9.70	17.7	112	60.9	48.1	7.79	86.6	40.4
X33.5	0.329	4 300	205	179	14.4	8.80	15.8	100	60.6	47.3	6.90	77.0	40.1
X30	0.294	3 790	204	178	12.8	7.70	13.8	87.4	60.3	45.9	6.02	67.7	39.9
X27	0.265	3 400	202	177	10.9	7.50	12.7	82.9	61.1	47.9	5.05	57.0	38.5
WT205													
X23	0.226	2 940	202	140	11.2	7.00	11.4	76.0	62.3	51.3	2.57	36.7	29.6
X19.5	0.191	2 500	200	140	8.80	6.40	9.89	67.6	62.9	53.3	2.02	28.8	28.4
WT180													
X543*	5.32	69 300	284	454	125	78.0	307	1 560	66.6	88.1	981	4 320	119
X495*	4.85	63 100	275	448	115	71.9	259	1 350	64.1	82.7	867	3 870	117
X450*	4.41	57 500	266	442	106	65.9	218	1 160	61.6	77.4	767	3 470	115
X409*	4.01	52 200	257	437	97.0	60.5	184	997	59.4	72.4	678	3 100	114
X372*	3.64	47 400	249	432	88.9	55.6	156	864	57.4	67.9	600	2 780	113
X338.5*	3.32	43 200	242	428	81.5	51.2	134	751	55.7	63.8	534	2 500	111
WT180													
X317*	3.10	40 400	237	424	77.1	47.6	119	677	54.3	61.0	491	2 320	110
X296*	2.90	37 700	232	421	72.3	45.0	107	618	53.3	58.5	451	2 140	109
X275.5*	2.70	35 100	228	418	67.6	42.0	95.3	555	52.1	55.7	412	1 970	108
X254.5*	2.49	32 500	223	416	62.7	39.1	84.8	499	51.1	53.0	377	1 810	108
X231.5*	2.27	29 500	218	412	57.4	35.8	73.3	438	49.8	50.0	335	1 630	107
X210.5*	2.06	26 900	212	409	52.6	32.8	63.7	386	48.7	47.2	300	1 470	106
X191*	1.87	24 400	208	406	48.0	29.8	55.4	338	47.6	44.5	268	1 320	105
X173.5*	1.70	22 100	204	404	43.7	27.2	48.2	298	46.7	42.0	240	1 190	104
X157*	1.54	20 000	200	401	39.6	24.9	42.2	264	45.9	39.8	213	1 060	103
X143.5*	1.40	18 300	196	399	36.6	22.6	37.3	235	45.1	37.8	194	972	103
X131*	1.28	16 700	194	398	33.3	21.1	33.7	214	44.9	36.3	175	880	102
X118.5*	1.16	15 000	190	395	30.2	18.9	29.1	187	44.0	34.3	155	786	102
X108*	1.05	13 800	188	394	27.7	17.3	26.0	168	43.4	32.8	141	717	101
WT180													
X98*	0.961	12 500	186	374	26.2	16.4	24.0	157	43.8	32.7	114	611	95.5
X89.5*	0.878	11 400	184	373	23.9	15.0	21.6	141	43.5	31.4	103	555	95.1
X81*	0.794	10 300	182	371	21.8	13.3	18.8	124	42.7	29.8	92.8	500	94.9
X73.5*	0.721	9 400	180	370	19.8	12.3	17.0	113	42.5	28.9	83.6	452	94.3
X67*	0.657	8 530	178	369	18.0	11.2	15.2	101	42.2	27.8	75.4	409	94.0
WT180													
X61*	0.598	7 750	182	257	21.7	13.0	17.1	117	47.0	35.3	30.7	239	62.9
X55*	0.539	7 020	180	256	19.9	11.4	15.0	102	46.2	33.5	27.9	218	63.0
X50.5*	0.495	6 450	178	255	18.3	10.5	13.6	93.2	45.9	32.6	25.3	199	62.6
X45.5*	0.446	5 790	176	254	16.4	9.50	12.0	83.0	45.5	31.6	22.4	176	62.2
WT180													
X39.5	0.387	5 050	177	205	16.8	9.40	11.5	81.2	47.7	35.0	12.1	118	48.9
X36	0.353	4 550	175	204	15.1	8.60	10.3	73.1	47.6	34.2	10.7	105	48.5
X32	0.314	4 070	174	203	13.5	7.70	9.09	64.8	47.3	33.2	9.42	92.8	48.1
WT180													
X28.5	0.279	3 610	179	172	13.1	7.90	9.70	69.4	51.8	39.2	5.56	64.7	39.2
X25.5	0.250	3 220	178	171	11.6	7.20	8.66	62.5	51.9	38.8	4.84	56.6	38.8
X22.5	0.221	2 870	176	171	9.80	6.90	7.96	58.6	52.7	40.2	4.09	47.8	37.8

*Not available from Canadian mills.

STRUCTURAL TEES
Cut from W Shapes

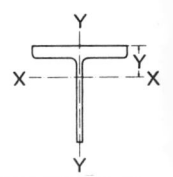

PROPERTIES AND DIMENSIONS

Designation	Dead Load	Total Area	Depth of Tee "d"	Flange Width	Flange Aver. Thickness	Stem Thickness "w"	Axis X-X I_x	Axis X-X S_x	Axis X-X r_x	Axis X-X y	Axis Y-Y I_y	Axis Y-Y S_y	Axis Y-Y r_y
	kN/m	mm^2	mm	mm	mm	mm	10^6mm^4	10^3mm^3	mm	mm	10^6mm^4	10^3mm^3	mm
WT180													
X19.5	0.191	2 490	176	128	10.7	6.50	7.22	54.4	53.8	43.7	1.88	29.3	27.5
X16.5	0.162	2 090	174	127	8.50	5.80	6.14	47.3	54.2	44.6	1.45	22.9	26.3
WT155													
X250*	2.45	31 900	214	340	75.1	45.1	79.2	511	49.8	58.6	247	1 450	88.0
X227*	2.22	28 900	208	336	68.7	41.3	67.7	444	48.4	55.0	218	1 300	86.9
X207.5*	2.03	26 400	202	334	62.7	38.9	59.1	396	47.3	52.1	195	1 170	85.9
X187.5*	1.83	23 800	196	330	57.1	35.4	50.1	341	45.9	48.8	172	1 040	85.0
X171*	1.67	21 900	191	328	52.6	32.6	43.8	302	44.7	46.1	155	946	84.1
X156.5*	1.53	20 000	187	325	48.3	30.0	38.5	269	43.9	43.8	139	852	83.4
WT155													
X141.5	1.38	18 000	182	322	44.1	26.9	32.8	232	42.7	41.0	123	764	82.7
X126.5	1.24	16 100	178	319	39.6	24.4	28.1	202	41.8	38.6	107	673	81.5
X113	1.10	14 400	174	317	35.6	22.1	24.3	176	41.1	36.4	94.6	597	81.1
X101	0.990	12 900	170	315	31.8	20.1	21.2	156	40.5	34.5	82.9	527	80.2
X89.5	0.878	11 400	166	313	28.1	18.0	18.0	134	39.7	32.4	71.9	459	79.4
X79	0.775	10 000	164	310	25.1	15.5	15.1	113	38.9	30.2	62.4	402	79.0
X71.5	0.701	9 120	162	309	22.9	14.0	13.3	101	38.2	28.8	56.3	365	78.6
X64.5	0.633	8 260	159	308	20.6	13.1	12.0	91.8	38.1	27.9	50.2	326	78.0
X59	0.579	7 490	157	307	18.7	11.9	10.7	82.0	37.8	26.8	45.1	294	77.6
X53.5	0.525	6 810	156	306	17.0	10.9	9.61	74.2	37.6	25.9	40.6	265	77.2
X48.5	0.476	6 170	154	305	15.4	9.90	8.59	66.6	37.3	25.0	36.4	239	76.8
WT155													
X43	0.422	5 500	155	254	16.3	9.10	7.93	61.5	38.0	26.1	22.3	175	63.7
X39.5	0.387	5 030	153	254	14.6	8.80	7.38	58.1	38.3	26.1	20.0	157	63.1
WT155													
X37	0.363	4 740	155	205	16.3	9.40	7.81	62.3	40.6	29.7	11.7	114	49.7
X33.5	0.329	4 250	153	204	14.6	8.50	6.88	55.3	40.2	28.7	10.3	101	49.2
X30	0.294	3 800	152	203	13.1	7.50	5.99	48.3	39.7	27.5	9.14	90.1	49.0
WT155													
X26	0.255	3 330	158	167	13.2	7.60	6.60	52.6	44.5	32.9	5.13	61.4	39.2
X22.5	0.221	2 840	156	166	11.2	6.60	5.59	44.9	44.4	32.1	4.27	51.5	38.8
X19.5	0.191	2 470	155	165	9.70	5.80	4.82	39.0	44.2	31.4	3.63	44.0	38.3
WT155													
X16.5*	0.162	2 090	156	102	10.8	6.60	4.88	42.4	48.3	41.5	0.959	18.8	21.4
X14*	0.137	1 810	154	102	8.90	6.00	4.23	37.6	48.3	41.9	0.790	15.5	20.9
X12*	0.118	1 520	152	101	6.70	5.60	3.63	33.6	48.9	44.4	0.578	11.4	19.5
X10.5*	0.103	1 340	152	101	5.70	5.10	3.22	30.2	49.0	44.8	0.491	9.7	19.1
WT125													
X83.5	0.819	10 700	144	265	31.8	19.2	12.0	105	33.5	30.7	49.4	373	67.9
X74.5	0.731	9 490	141	263	28.4	17.3	10.2	91.3	32.8	28.8	43.1	328	67.4
X65.5	0.642	8 350	138	261	25.1	15.4	8.64	78.1	32.2	26.9	37.2	285	66.7
X57.5	0.564	7 310	134	259	22.1	13.5	7.26	66.3	31.5	25.1	32.0	247	66.2
X50.5	0.495	6 440	132	257	19.6	11.9	6.17	57.0	31.0	23.6	27.7	216	65.6
X44.5	0.436	5 700	130	256	17.3	10.7	5.39	50.2	30.8	22.5	24.2	189	65.2
X40	0.392	5 100	128	255	15.6	9.40	4.61	43.2	30.1	21.2	21.6	169	65.1
X36.5	0.358	4 640	126	254	14.2	8.60	4.12	38.9	29.8	20.4	19.4	153	64.7

*Not available from Canadian mills.

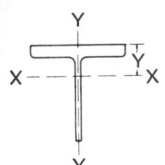

PROPERTIES AND DIMENSIONS

Designation	Dead Load	Total Area	Depth of Tee "d"	Flange Width	Flange Aver. Thickness	Stem Thickness "w"	Axis X-X I_x	Axis X-X S_x	Axis X-X r_x	Axis X-X y	Axis Y-Y I_y	Axis Y-Y S_y	Axis Y-Y r_y
	kN/m	mm²	mm	mm	mm	mm	10^6mm⁴	10^3mm³	mm	mm	10^6mm⁴	10^3mm³	mm
WT125													
X33.5	0.329	4 280	128	204	15.7	8.90	4.29	40.7	31.7	23.1	11.1	109	50.9
X29	0.284	3 710	126	203	13.5	8.00	3.68	35.5	31.5	22.2	9.42	92.8	50.4
X24.5	0.240	3 120	124	202	11.0	7.40	3.21	31.7	32.1	22.1	7.56	74.9	49.2
WT125													
X22.5	0.221	2 860	133	148	13.0	7.60	3.86	36.7	36.7	27.8	3.52	47.5	35.1
X19.5	0.191	2 460	131	147	11.2	6.60	3.26	31.3	36.4	26.7	2.97	40.4	34.7
X16.5	0.162	2 080	129	146	9.10	6.10	2.85	28.1	37.0	27.3	2.36	32.4	33.7
WT125													
X14*	0.137	1 810	130	102	10.0	6.40	2.79	28.7	39.3	32.6	0.888	17.4	22.1
X12.5*	0.123	1 610	128	102	8.40	6.10	2.53	26.6	39.6	33.5	0.746	14.6	21.5
X11*	0.108	1 430	127	102	6.90	5.80	2.27	24.5	39.8	34.6	0.613	12.0	20.7
X9*	0.088	1 140	126	101	5.30	4.80	1.81	19.9	39.8	34.6	0.457	9.0	20.0
WT100													
X50	0.490	6 340	114	210	23.7	14.5	4.55	50.2	26.8	23.8	18.3	174	53.7
X43	0.422	5 530	111	209	20.6	13.0	3.80	42.8	26.2	22.2	15.7	150	53.3
X35.5	0.348	4 550	108	206	17.4	10.2	2.86	32.5	25.1	19.8	12.7	123	52.8
X29.5	0.289	3 780	105	205	14.2	9.10	2.39	27.7	25.1	18.7	10.2	99.5	51.9
X26	0.255	3 330	103	204	12.6	7.90	2.00	23.4	24.5	17.5	8.92	87.4	51.8
X23	0.226	2 930	102	203	11.0	7.20	1.77	20.9	24.6	16.9	7.67	75.6	51.2
WT100													
X21	0.206	2 660	102	166	11.8	7.20	1.76	21.0	25.7	18.6	4.50	54.2	41.1
X18	0.177	2 290	100	165	10.2	6.20	1.46	17.6	25.2	17.5	3.82	46.3	40.8
WT100													
X15.5	0.152	2 000	105	134	10.2	6.40	1.63	19.4	28.5	21.1	2.05	30.6	32.0
X13.5	0.132	1 690	104	133	8.40	5.80	1.41	17.2	28.9	21.1	1.65	24.8	31.2
WT100													
X11*	0.108	1 430	103	102	8.00	6.20	1.36	17.5	30.8	25.3	0.710	13.9	22.3
X9.5*	0.093	1 240	102	102	6.50	5.80	1.20	15.9	31.1	25.9	0.577	11.3	21.6
X7.5*	0.074	952	100	100	5.20	4.30	0.885	11.7	30.5	24.1	0.434	8.7	21.4
WT75													
X18.5	0.181	2 370	81.0	154	11.6	8.10	0.947	14.5	20.0	15.5	3.53	45.9	38.6
X15	0.147	1 900	78.5	153	9.30	6.60	0.725	11.3	19.5	14.2	2.78	36.3	38.3
X11	0.108	1 420	76.0	152	6.60	5.80	0.581	9.4	20.2	14.1	1.93	25.4	36.9
WT75													
X12*	0.118	1 530	80.0	102	10.3	6.60	0.708	11.3	21.5	17.3	0.913	17.9	24.4
X9*	0.088	1 140	76.5	102	7.10	5.80	0.544	9.2	21.8	17.1	0.629	12.3	23.5
X7*	0.069	866	75.0	100	5.50	4.30	0.395	6.7	21.4	15.8	0.459	9.2	23.0
WT65													
X14*	0.137	1 790	65.5	128	10.9	6.90	0.426	8.0	15.4	12.4	1.91	29.8	32.7
X12*	0.118	1 500	63.5	127	9.10	6.10	0.350	6.7	15.3	11.6	1.55	24.5	32.1
WT50													
X9.5*	0.093	1 240	53.0	103	8.80	7.10	0.221	5.3	13.4	11.2	0.803	15.6	25.4

*Not available from Canadian mills.

NOTES

HOLLOW STRUCTURAL SECTIONS

General

The hollow structural sections listed on pages 6-88 to 6-93 are those given in CSA Standard CAN3-G312.3-M78, "Preferred Metric Dimensions of Structural Steel W and HP Shapes, Angles and Hollow Structural Sections." In Canada they are produced according to CSA Standard G40.20-M either to Class H or to Class C from steel meeting CSA Standard G40.21-M. The designation, in Canada, should consist of the symbols HSS, the depth, width, thickness and class (eg. HSS 88.9 x 63.5 x 3.81 — Class H.) In other countries, hollow structural sections may be designated as structural hollow sections, structural tubing, hollow structural tubing and hollow sections. Round sections produced in accordance with common pipe specifications are, of course, designated as pipe. The term "pipe" is used for round sections that are common "pipe" sizes.

Hollow structural sections from non-Canadian mills may be produced in differing sizes and thicknesses.

Manufacture

Steel hollow structural sections are manufactured by two general methods — seamless processes and welding processes — to either Class H or Class C of CSA Standard G40.20-M.

Seamless products may be produced in various ways. In some processes, a heated billet is pierced to produce a hollow bloom, and this bloom is then rolled over a mandrel. In extrusion-type processes, a hot billet is forced through a die. Detailed information on specific processes can be obtained from manufacturers of seamless products.

Welded products are manufactured from flat-rolled steel usually designated as skelp, plate, sheet or strip. Furnace welding, electric resistance welding and electric fusion welding processes are commonly used.

Furnace welding, also known as furnace butt welding or continuous welding, employs pressure on furnace-heated material to achieve fusion. Electric resistance welding also uses heat and pressure, but in this case the heat is generated across the abutting edges of cold-formed material by resistance to the flow of an electric current introduced through electrodes, or by induction.

Electric fusion welding may be used in the manufacture of products with longitudinal seams. The welding is performed manually or by automatic welding equipment with or without the deposit of filler material.

Class H hollow structural sections may be made by any of the above processes and hot formed to final shape or by a seamless or automatic electronic welding process, cold formed to final shape and subsequently stress-relieved.

Separate and distinct column capacities are ascribed to each of Class H and Class C hollow structural section columns. See page 4—8 for more details.

Hollow structural sections are produced in accordance with structural steel material specifications. At present (1980) they are most readily available in material with a specified minimum yield point of 350 MPa, meeting the requirements of CSA Standard G40.21-M.

Pipe

Pipe is usually produced to one of several steel piping material specifications rather than to the commonly used material specifications for structural steel shapes and plates. A class of pipe suitable for general structural purposes is that produced in accordance with ASTM Standard A53 — Welded and Seamless Steel Pipe.

Pipe produced in accordance with this standard is available in three strength levels, with specified minimum yield points of 172, 207 or 241 MPa. These strength levels are lower than the 350 MPa specified minimum yield point generally available for HSS.

Sizes and wall thicknesses of seamless and welded mill pipe up to 323.9 mm outside diameter permit threading the ends for joining lengths with couplings or other connectors. The wall thicknesses of mill pipe have been expressed in terms of "standard wall" (STD), "extra strong" (XS), "double extra strong" (XXS), and more recently in terms of "schedule numbers" (Sch) ranging from 10 to 160, designating ten pipe wall thicknesses. For all sizes up to and including outside diameters of 273.1 mm STD is the same as Sch 40; for all sizes up to and including outside diameters of 219.1 mm XS is the same as Sch 80 and for all sizes up to and including outside diameters of 168.3 mm XXS is always Sch 160. For pipe 305 mm and less there is no Sch 10 size.

In specifying size of pipe, it is recommended that outside (external) diameter and wall thickness be specified (e.g., Pipe — 114.3 O.D. x 8.56 or Pipe 114.3 XS).

Outside Diameter	Thickness	Weight Class[2]	Mass	Dead Load	Area	I	S	r	Z	Shear Constant	J	Surface Area
mm	mm		kg/m	kN/m	mm²	10^6mm⁴	10^3mm³	mm	10^3mm³	mm²	10^6mm⁴	m²/m
21.3	2.77	STD	1.26	0.012 4	161	0.007 11	0.667	6.64	0.962	81.9	0.0142	0.0670
	3.73	XS	1.62	0.015 9	206	0.008 36	0.783	6.36	1.17	106	0.0167	0.0670
	7.47	XXS	2.54	0.025 0	325	0.010 1	0.946	5.57	1.58	191	0.0202	0.0670
26.7	2.87	STD	1.68	0.016 5	215	0.015 4	1.16	8.48	1.63	108	0.0308	0.0838
	3.91	XS	2.19	0.021 5	280	0.018 6	1.40	8.16	2.05	143	0.0373	0.0838
	7.82	XXS	3.63	0.035 6	463	0.024 1	1.81	7.21	2.94	257	0.0482	0.0838
33.4	3.38	STD	2.50	0.024 5	319	0.036 4	2.18	10.7	3.06	161	0.0727	0.105
	4.55	XS	3.23	0.031 7	412	0.044 0	2.63	10.3	3.82	209	0.0879	0.105
	9.09	XXS	5.45	0.053 4	694	0.058 5	3.50	9.18	5.62	378	0.117	0.105
42.2	3.56	STD	3.38	0.033 1	431	0.081 0	3.84	13.7	5.32	217	0.162	0.132
	4.85	XS	4.46	0.043 8	569	0.101	4.77	13.3	6.79	288	0.201	0.132
	9.70	XXS	7.75	0.076 0	969	0.142	6.73	12.0	10.5	523	0.284	0.132
48.3	3.68	STD	4.05	0.039 7	516	0.129	5.35	15.8	7.34	259	0.258	0.152
	5.08	XS	5.40	0.053 0	689	0.163	6.75	15.4	8.52	348	0.326	0.152
	10.16	XXS	9.54	0.093 5	1 220	0.236	9.80	13.9	15.1	636	0.473	0.152
60.3	3.91	STD	5.43	0.053 3	693	0.277	9.19	20.0	12.5	348	0.554	0.190
	5.54	XS	7.47	0.073 3	953	0.361	12.0	19.5	16.7	480	0.723	0.190
	11.07	XXS	13.4	0.132	1 710	0.546	18.1	17.8	27.3	885	1.09	0.190
73.0	5.16	STD	8.62	0.084 5	1 100	0.637	17.4	24.1	23.8	552	1.27	0.229
	7.01	XS	11.4	0.112	1 450	0.801	21.9	23.5	30.7	732	1.60	0.229
	14.02	XXS	20.4	0.200	2 600	1.19	32.7	21.4	49.7	1350	2.39	0.229
88.9	5.49	STD	11.3	0.111	1 440	1.26	28.3	29.6	38.2	721	2.51	0.279
	7.62	XS	15.3	0.150	1 950	1.62	36.5	28.9	50.5	979	3.24	0.279
	15.24	XXS	27.7	0.271	3 530	2.49	56.1	26.6	83.9	1810	4.99	0.279
101.6	5.74	STD	13.6	0.133	1 730	1.99	39.2	34.0	52.8	866	3.99	0.319
	8.08	XS	18.6	0.183	2 370	2.61	51.5	33.2	70.8	1 190	5.23	0.319
114.3	6.02	STD	16.1	0.157	2 050	3.01	52.7	38.3	70.7	1 030	6.02	0.359
	8.56	XS	22.3	0.219	2 840	4.00	70.0	37.5	95.9	1 430	8.00	0.359
	17.12	XXS	40.9	0.402	5 230	6.36	111	34.9	163	2 670	12.7	0.359
141.3	6.55	STD	21.9	0.213	2 770	6.31	89.3	47.7	119	1 390	12.6	0.444
	9.53	XS	30.9	0.303	3 940	8.60	122	46.7	166	1 980	17.2	0.444
	19.05	XXS	57.4	0.563	7 320	14.0	198	43.7	287	3 720	28.0	0.444
168.3	7.11	STD	28.2	0.277	3 600	11.7	139	57.0	185	1 800	23.4	0.529
	10.97	XS	42.5	0.417	5 420	16.9	200	55.7	272	2 720	33.7	0.529
	21.95	XXS	79.1	0.776	10 100	27.6	328	52.3	473	5 120	55.2	0.529
219.1	8.18	STD	42.5	0.417	5 420	30.2	275	74.6	364	2 710	60.3	0.688
	12.70	XS	64.6	0.633	8 230	44.0	402	73.1	542	4 130	88.0	0.688
	22.23	XXS	108.	1.06	13 700	67.4	616	70.0	865	6 930	135	0.688
273.1	9.27	STD	60.2	0.591	7 680	66.9	490	93.3	645	3 840	134	0.858
	12.70	XS	81.5	0.799	10 400	88.2	646	92.2	862	5 200	176	0.858
	25.40	XXS	155.	1.52	19 800	153	1120	88.0	1560	9 950	306	0.858
323.9	9.53	STD	73.8	0.723	9 410	116	718	111	941	4 710	233	1.02
	12.70	XS	97.4	0.955	12 400	150	929	110	1230	6 210	301	1.02
	25.40	XXS	187.	1.83	23 800	267	1650	106	2270	12 000	534	1.02
355.6	9.53	STD	81.2	0.796	10 400	155	873	122	1140	5 940	310	1.12
	12.70	XS	107.	1.05	13 700	201	1130	121	1490	7 860	403	1.12
406.4	9.53	STD	93.1	0.913	11 900	234	1150	140	1500	5 180	468	1.28
	12.70	XS	123.	1.21	15 700	305	1500	139	1970	6 850	609	1.28
457.2	9.53	STD	105.	1.03	13 400	336	1470	158	1910	6 700	671	1.44
	12.70	XS	139.	1.36	17 700	438	1920	157	2510	8 870	877	1.44

1. These dimensions have been soft converted from those specified in ASTM A53.
2. Class refers to: Standard Weight — STD., Extra Strong — XS, Double Extra Strong — XXS.

HOLLOW STRUCTURAL SECTIONS
Rectangular

PROPERTIES AND DIMENSIONS

Outside Dimensions	Wall Thick-ness	Mass	Dead Load	Area	Axis X-X				Axis Y-Y				Torsional Constant J	Shear Constant C_{rt}
					I_x	S_x	r_x	Z_x	I_y	S_y	r_y	Z_y		
mmxmm	mm	kg/m	kN/m	mm²	$10^6 mm^4$	$10^3 mm^3$	mm	$10^3 mm^3$	$10^6 mm^4$	$10^3 mm^3$	mm	$10^3 mm^3$	$10^3 mm^4$	mm²
304.8 X 203.2	12.70	93.0	0.912	11 800	147	964	111	1 190	78.1	769	81.2	896	167 000	6 450
	11.13	82.4	0.808	10 500	132	867	112	1 060	70.5	693	81.9	802	149 000	5 790
	9.53	71.3	0.699	9 090	116	762	113	925	62.1	611	82.7	701	130 000	5 080
	7.95	60.1	0.590	7 660	99.4	652	114	787	53.3	524	83.4	596	111 000	4 340
	6.35	48.6	0.476	6 190	81.5	535	115	640	43.8	431	84.1	486	89 800	3 550
254.0 X 152.4	12.70	72.7	0.713	9 260	75.2	592	90.1	746	33.6	441	60.2	522	78 200	5 160
	11.13	64.6	0.634	8 230	68.2	537	91.0	671	30.6	401	61.0	470	70 200	4 660
	9.53	56.1	0.550	7 150	60.3	475	91.9	589	27.2	357	61.7	413	61 600	4 110
	7.95	47.5	0.465	6 050	52.0	409	92.7	503	23.5	309	62.4	353	52 600	3 530
	6.35	38.4	0.377	4 900	42.9	338	93.6	411	19.5	256	63.1	290	43 000	2 900
203.2 X 152.4	12.70	62.6	0.614	7 970	43.0	423	73.4	528	27.3	358	58.5	432	56 400	3 870
	11.13	55.7	0.547	7 100	39.1	385	74.2	476	24.9	327	59.3	390	50 800	3 530
	9.53	48.5	0.476	6 180	34.8	343	75.1	419	22.3	292	60.0	344	44 600	3 150
	7.95	41.1	0.403	5 240	30.2	297	75.9	360	19.3	254	60.7	295	38 200	2 730
	6.35	33.4	0.327	4 250	25.0	246	76.7	295	16.1	211	61.5	243	31 200	2 260
	4.78	25.5	0.250	3 250	19.5	192	77.5	228	12.6	165	62.2	188	24 100	1 760
203.2 X 101.6	12.70	52.4	0.514	6 680	31.2	307	68.4	405	10.2	201	39.1	246	27 000	3 870
	11.13	46.9	0.460	5 970	28.7	282	69.3	367	9.46	186	39.8	224	24 600	3 530
	9.53	40.9	0.401	5 210	25.8	253	70.3	325	8.56	168	40.5	199	21 900	3 150
	7.95	34.8	0.341	4 430	22.5	221	71.2	281	7.54	148	41.2	172	18 900	2 730
	6.35	28.3	0.278	3 610	18.8	185	72.2	232	6.35	125	42.0	143	15 600	2 260
	4.78	21.7	0.213	2 760	14.7	145	73.1	180	5.03	99.0	42.7	111	12 200	1 760
†† 177.8 x 127.0	12.70	52.4	0.514	6 680	26.4	297	62.8	377	15.5	243	48.1	298	33 600	3 230
	11.13	46.9	0.460	5 970	24.2	272	63.7	342	14.2	224	48.8	270	30 400	2 970
	9.53	40.9	0.401	5 210	21.7	244	64.6	303	12.8	202	49.6	240	26 900	2 660
	7.95	34.8	0.341	4 430	18.9	213	65.4	261	11.2	177	50.3	207	23 100	2 320
	6.35	28.3	0.278	3 610	15.8	178	66.2	216	9.40	148	51.1	171	19 000	1 940
	4.78	21.7	0.213	2 760	12.4	140	67.1	167	7.41	117	51.8	133	14 700	1 520
152.4 X 101.6	11.13	38.0	0.373	4 840	13.6	179	53.1	230	7.13	140	38.4	172	16 300	2 400
	9.53	33.3	0.327	4 240	12.4	162	54.0	205	6.50	128	39.1	154	14 500	2 180
	7.95	28.4	0.279	3 620	10.9	143	54.8	178	5.76	113	39.9	134	12 600	1 920
	6.35	23.2	0.228	2 960	9.18	121	55.7	148	4.88	96.1	40.6	112	10 500	1 610
	4.78	17.9	0.175	2 280	7.28	95.6	56.5	116	3.89	76.6	41.3	87.8	8 160	1 270

††Check with manufacturer for current availability.

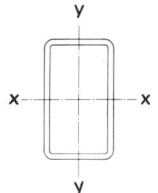

PROPERTIES AND DIMENSIONS

Outside Dimensions	Wall Thickness	Mass	Dead Load	Area	Axis X-X				Axis Y-Y				Torsional Constant J	Shear Constant C_{rt}
					I_x	S_x	r_x	Z_x	I_y	S_y	r_y	Z_y		
mmxmm	mm	kg/m	kN/m	mm^2	$10^6 mm^4$	$10^3 mm^3$	mm	$10^3 mm^3$	$10^6 mm^4$	$10^3 mm^3$	mm	$10^3 mm^3$	$10^3 mm^4$	mm^2
127.0 X 76.2	9.53	25.7	0.252	3 280	6.12	96.4	43.2	126	2.69	70.5	28.6	87.5	6 600	1 690
	7.95	22.1	0.217	2 820	5.49	86.4	44.1	111	2.43	63.8	29.4	77.2	5 810	1 510
	6.35	18.2	0.178	2 320	4.70	74.0	45.1	93.3	2.10	55.1	30.1	65.2	4 890	1 290
	4.78	14.1	0.138	1 790	3.78	59.5	45.9	73.8	1.70	44.7	30.8	51.7	3 860	1 030
127.0 X 63.5	9.53	23.8	0.234	3 030	5.28	83.2	41.7	112	1.70	53.6	23.7	67.4	4 640	1 690
	7.95	20.5	0.201	2 610	4.77	75.1	42.7	98.9	1.56	49.1	24.4	60.0	4 130	1 510
	6.35	16.9	0.166	2 150	4.11	64.8	43.7	83.6	1.36	42.9	25.1	51.0	3 510	1 290
	4.78	13.1	0.129	1 670	3.33	52.4	44.6	66.3	1.12	35.2	25.9	40.7	2 800	1 030
127.0 X 50.8	9.53	21.9	0.215	2 790	4.45	70.0	39.9	97.7	0.961	37.8	18.6	48.9	2 930	1 690
	7.95	18.9	0.186	2 410	4.05	63.8	41.0	86.9	0.897	35.3	19.3	44.0	2 650	1 510
	6.35	15.6	0.153	1 990	3.53	55.5	42.1	73.8	0.798	31.4	20.0	37.9	2 290	1 290
	4.78	12.2	0.119	1 550	2.87	45.3	43.1	58.9	0.665	26.2	20.7	30.5	1 850	1 030
101.6 X 76.2	9.53	21.9	0.215	2 790	3.41	67.2	35.0	87.6	2.15	56.3	27.7	71.3	4 710	1 210
	7.95	18.9	0.186	2 410	3.10	61.0	35.8	77.7	1.96	51.4	28.5	63.5	4 170	1 110
	6.35	15.6	0.153	1 990	2.68	52.8	36.7	65.9	1.71	44.8	29.3	54.0	3 530	968
	4.78	12.2	0.119	1 550	2.18	43.0	37.5	52.5	1.39	36.6	30.0	43.1	2 800	789
101.6 X 50.8	7.95	15.8	0.155	2 010	2.21	43.5	33.2	58.8	0.709	27.9	18.8	35.4	1 950	1 110
	6.35	13.1	0.129	1 670	1.95	38.4	34.2	50.6	0.638	25.1	19.5	30.7	1 690	968
	4.78	10.3	0.101	1 310	1.61	31.8	35.1	40.8	0.536	21.1	20.3	24.9	1 370	789
	3.81	8.37	0.082	1 070	1.36	26.8	35.7	33.9	0.456	18.0	20.7	20.8	1 140	658
	3.18	7.09	0.069	903	1.17	23.1	36.1	29.0	0.397	15.6	21.0	17.9	979	565
88.9 X 63.5	7.95	15.8	0.155	2 010	1.87	42.1	30.5	54.9	1.09	34.3	23.3	43.2	2 450	908
	6.35	13.1	0.129	1 670	1.65	37.1	31.4	47.1	0.966	30.4	24.0	37.2	2 100	806
	4.78	10.3	0.101	1 310	1.36	30.6	32.3	38.0	0.803	25.3	24.8	30.1	1 690	667
	3.81	8.37	0.082	1 070	1.15	25.8	32.8	31.5	0.679	21.4	25.2	25.0	1 400	561
	3.18	7.09	0.069	903	0.990	22.3	33.1	27.0	0.588	18.5	25.5	21.4	1 190	485
76.2 X 50.8	7.95	12.6	0.123	1 600	1.01	26.6	25.1	35.9	0.522	20.5	18.0	26.7	1 270	706
	6.35	10.6	0.104	1 350	0.917	24.1	26.1	31.4	0.477	18.8	18.8	23.5	1 110	645
	4.78	8.35	0.082	1 060	0.774	20.3	27.0	25.7	0.407	16.0	19.6	19.3	911	546
	3.81	6.85	0.067	872	0.660	17.3	27.5	21.6	0.349	13.8	20.0	16.3	762	465
50.8 X 25.4	3.18	3.28	0.032	418	0.122	4.81	17.1	6.33	0.040	3.14	9.77	3.84	106	242
	2.54	2.71	0.026	345	0.105	4.15	17.5	5.35	0.035	2.75	10.1	3.27	89.8	206

HOLLOW STRUCTURAL SECTIONS
Square

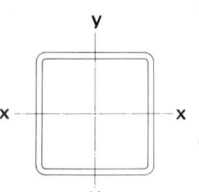

PROPERTIES AND DIMENSIONS

Outside Dimensions	Wall Thick-ness	Mass	Dead Load	Area	I	S	r	Z	Torsional Constant J	Surface Area	Shear Constant C_{rt}
mmxmm	mm	kg/m	kN/m	mm²	10^6mm⁴	10^3mm³	mm	10^3mm³	10^3mm⁴	m²/m	mm²
304.8 X 304.8	12.70	113	1.11	14 400	202	1 330	118	1 560	324 000	1.18	6 450
	11.13	100	0.982	12 800	181	1 190	119	1 390	288 000	1.18	5 790
	9.53	86.5	0.848	11 000	158	1 040	120	1 210	250 000	1.19	5 080
	7.95	72.8	0.714	9 280	135	886	121	1 030	211 000	1.19	4 340
	6.35	58.7	0.576	7 480	110	723	121	833	171 000	1.20	3 550
254.0 X 254.0	12.70	93.0	0.912	11 800	113	888	97.6	1 060	183 000	0.972	5 160
	11.13	82.4	0.808	10 500	102	799	98.4	945	163 000	0.978	4 660
	9.53	71.3	0.699	9 090	89.3	703	99.1	825	142 000	0.983	4 110
	7.95	60.1	0.590	7 660	76.5	602	99.9	702	121 000	0.989	3 530
	6.35	48.6	0.476	6 190	62.7	494	101	571	97 900	0.994	2 900
203.2 X 203.2	12.70	72.7	0.713	9 260	54.7	538	76.8	650	90 700	0.769	3 870
	11.13	64.6	0.634	8 230	49.6	488	77.6	584	81 200	0.775	3 530
	9.53	56.1	0.550	7 150	43.9	432	78.4	513	71 000	0.780	3 150
	7.95	47.5	0.465	6 050	37.9	373	79.2	438	60 500	0.786	2 730
	6.35	38.4	0.377	4 900	31.3	308	79.9	359	49 300	0.791	2 260
177.8 X 177.8	12.70	62.6	0.614	7 970	35.2	396	66.4	484	59 200	0.668	3 230
	11.13	55.7	0.547	7 100	32.1	361	67.2	436	53 200	0.673	2 970
	9.53	48.5	0.476	6 180	28.6	322	68.0	385	46 700	0.678	2 660
	7.95	41.1	0.403	5 240	24.8	279	68.8	330	39 900	0.684	2 320
	6.35	33.4	0.327	4 250	20.6	231	69.6	271	32 700	0.689	1 940
	4.78	25.5	0.250	3 250	16.1	181	70.3	209	25 200	0.695	1 520
152.4 X 152.4	12.70	52.4	0.514	6 680	21.0	275	56.0	341	36 000	0.566	2 580
	11.13	46.9	0.460	5 970	19.3	253	56.8	310	32 500	0.571	2 400
	9.53	40.9	0.401	5 210	17.3	227	57.6	275	28 700	0.577	2 180
	7.95	34.8	0.341	4 430	15.1	198	58.4	237	24 600	0.582	1 920
	6.35	28.3	0.278	3 610	12.6	166	59.2	195	20 300	0.588	1 610
	4.78	21.7	0.213	2 760	9.93	130	59.9	152	15 700	0.593	1 270
127.0 X 127.0	11.13	38.0	0.373	4 840	10.4	164	46.4	205	18 000	0.470	1 840
	9.53	33.3	0.327	4 240	9.47	149	47.2	183	16 000	0.475	1 690
	7.95	28.4	0.279	3 620	8.35	132	48.0	159	13 900	0.481	1 510
	6.35	23.2	0.228	2 960	7.05	111	48.8	132	11 500	0.486	1 290
	4.78	17.9	0.175	2 280	5.60	88.1	49.6	103	8 920	0.492	1 030

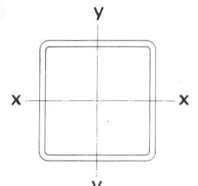

PROPERTIES AND DIMENSIONS

Outside Dimensions	Wall Thickness	Mass	Dead Load	Area	I	S	r	Z	Torsional Constant J	Surface Area	Shear Constant C_{rt}
mmxmm	mm	kg/m	kN/m	mm²	10^6mm⁴	10^3mm³	mm	10^3mm³	10^3mm⁴	m²/m	mm²
101.6 X 101.6	9.53	25.7	0.252	3 280	4.44	87.4	36.8	110	7 740	0.374	1 210
	7.95	22.1	0.217	2 820	3.98	78.4	37.6	96.6	6 780	0.379	1 110
	6.35	18.2	0.178	2 320	3.42	67.3	38.4	81.3	5 670	0.385	968
	4.78	14.1	0.138	1 790	2.75	54.2	39.2	64.3	4 450	0.390	789
88.9 X 88.9	9.53	21.9	0.215	2 790	2.79	62.7	31.6	80.2	4 970	0.323	968
	7.95	18.9	0.186	2 410	2.53	57.0	32.4	71.2	4 390	0.328	908
	6.35	15.6	0.153	1 990	2.20	49.5	33.2	60.5	3 700	0.334	806
	4.78	12.2	0.119	1 550	1.79	40.3	34.0	48.2	2 930	0.339	667
76.2 X 76.2	7.95	15.8	0.155*	2 010	1.49	39.0	27.2	49.7	2 630	0.278	706
	6.35	13.1	0.129	1 670	1.31	34.4	28.0	42.7	2 250	0.283	645
	4.78	10.3	0.101	1 310	1.08	28.5	28.8	34.4	1 800	0.288	546
63.5 X 63.5	6.35	10.6	0.104	1 350	0.701	22.1	22.8	28.0	1 230	0.232	484
	4.78	8.35	0.082	1 060	0.593	18.7	23.6	22.9	1 000	0.238	424
	3.81	6.85	0.067	872	0.506	15.9	24.1	19.2	836	0.241	368
	3.18	5.82	0.057	741	0.441	13.9	24.4	16.5	717	0.243	323
50.8 X 50.8	6.35	8.05	0.079	1 030	0.317	12.5	17.6	16.3	580	0.181	323
	4.78	6.45	0.063	821	0.278	10.9	18.4	13.8	485	0.187	303
	3.81	5.33	0.052	679	0.242	9.54	18.9	11.7	410	0.190	271
	3.18	4.55	0.045	580	0.214	8.42	19.2	10.2	355	0.192	242
	2.79	4.05	0.040	516	0.194	7.64	19.4	9.15	318	0.194	221
38.1 X 38.1	4.78	4.54	0.044	578	0.100	5.27	13.2	6.91	184	0.136	181
	3.81	3.81	0.037	485	0.091	4.77	13.7	6.04	160	0.139	174
	3.18	3.28	0.032	418	0.082	4.31	14.0	5.34	141	0.141	161
	2.54	2.71	0.026	345	0.071	3.71	14.3	4.51	118	0.144	142
31.8 X 31.8	3.81	3.06	0.030	389	0.048	3.01	11.1	3.92	87.0	0.114	126
	3.18	2.65	0.026	338	0.044	2.77	11.4	3.51	77.6	0.116	121
	2.54	2.20	0.022	281	0.039	2.44	11.7	3.01	66.1	0.118	110
25.4 X 25.4	3.18	2.01	0.020	257	0.020	1.56	8.79	2.05	36.3	0.091	80.6
	2.54	1.69	0.017	216	0.018	1.41	9.12	1.79	31.6	0.093	77.4

HOLLOW STRUCTURAL SECTIONS
Round

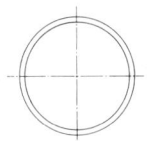

PROPERTIES AND DIMENSIONS

Outside Diameter	Wall Thickness	Mass	Dead Load	Area	I	S	r	Z	J	Surface Area	Shear Constant C_{rt}
mm	mm	kg/m	kN/m	mm²	10⁶mm⁴	10³mm³	mm	10³mm³	10³mm⁴	m²/m	mm²
406.4	12.70	123	1.21	15 700	305	1 500	139	1 970	609 000	1.28	7 860
	11.13	108	1.06	13 800	270	1 330	140	1 740	540 000	1.28	6 910
	9.53	93.3	0.915	11 900	234	1 150	140	1 500	468 000	1.28	5 940
	7.95	78.1	0.766	9 950	198	972	141	1 260	395 000	1.28	4 970
	6.35	62.6	0.614	7 980	160	786	141	1 020	319 000	1.28	3 990
355.6	12.70	107	1.05	13 700	201	1 130	121	1 490	403 000	1.12	6 850
	11.13	94.6	0.927	12 000	179	1 010	122	1 320	358 000	1.12	6 030
	9.53	81.3	0.798	10 400	155	873	122	1 140	310 000	1.12	5 180
	7.95	68.2	0.668	8 680	131	738	123	961	262 000	1.12	4 340
	6.35	54.7	0.536	6 970	106	598	123	775	213 000	1.12	3 480
323.9	12.70	97.5	0.956	12 400	151	930	110	1 230	301 000	1.02	6 210
	11.13	85.9	0.842	10 900	134	827	111	1 090	268 000	1.02	5 470
	9.53	73.9	0.725	9 410	116	719	111	942	233 000	1.02	4 710
	7.95	61.9	0.607	7 890	98.5	608	112	794	197 000	1.02	3 950
	6.35	49.7	0.488	6 330	79.9	493	112	640	160 000	1.02	3 170
273.1	12.70	81.6	0.800	10 400	88.3	646	92.2	862	177 000	0.858	5 200
	11.13	71.9	0.705	9 160	78.7	577	92.7	764	157 000	0.858	4 590
	9.53	61.9	0.607	7 890	68.6	502	93.2	662	137 000	0.858	3 950
	7.95	52.0	0.510	6 620	58.2	427	93.8	559	116 000	0.858	3 310
	6.35	41.8	0.410	5 320	47.4	347	94.3	452	94 700	0.858	2 660
219.1	12.70	64.6	0.634	8 230	44.0	402	73.1	542	88 000	0.688	4 130
	11.13	57.1	0.560	7 270	39.4	360	73.6	482	78 900	0.688	3 640
	9.53	49.3	0.483	6 270	34.5	315	74.2	419	69 000	0.688	3 140
	7.95	41.4	0.406	5 270	29.4	269	74.7	355	58 900	0.688	2 640
	6.35	33.3	0.327	4 240	24.0	219	75.3	288	48 100	0.688	2 120
	4.78	25.3	0.248	3 220	18.5	169	75.8	220	37 000	0.688	1 610
168.3	9.53	37.3	0.366	4 750	15.0	179	56.2	241	30 100	0.529	2 380
	7.95	31.4	0.308	4 000	12.9	153	56.8	205	25 800	0.529	2 010
	6.35	25.4	0.249	3 230	10.6	126	57.3	167	21 200	0.529	1 620
	4.78	19.3	0.189	2 460	8.21	97.6	57.8	128	16 400	0.529	1 230
141.3	9.53	31.0	0.304	3 950	8.61	122	46.7	166	17 200	0.444	1 980
	7.95	26.1	0.256	3 330	7.43	105	47.2	142	14 900	0.444	1 670
	6.35	21.1	0.207	2 690	6.14	86.9	47.8	116	12 300	0.444	1 350
	4.78	16.1	0.158	2 050	4.78	67.7	48.3	89.1	9 560	0.444	1 030

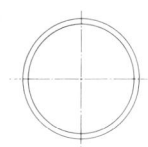

HOLLOW STRUCTURAL SECTIONS
Round

PROPERTIES AND DIMENSIONS

Outside Diameter	Wall Thick-ness	Mass	Dead Load	Area	I	S	r	Z	J	Surface Area	Shear Constant C_{rt}
mm	mm	kg/m	kN/m	mm²	10^6mm⁴	10^3mm³	mm	10^3mm³	10^3mm⁴	m²/m	mm²
114.3	7.95	20.9	0.204	2 660	3.78	66.1	37.7	90.1	7 550	0.359	1 330
	6.35	16.9	0.166	2 150	3.15	55.1	38.2	74.1	6 300	0.359	1 080
	4.78	12.9	0.127	1 640	2.47	43.2	38.8	57.4	4 940	0.359	823
101.6	7.95	18.4	0.180	2 340	2.58	50.8	33.2	69.9	5 170	0.319	1 180
	6.35	14.9	0.146	1 900	2.16	42.6	33.8	57.7	4 330	0.319	954
	4.78	11.4	0.112	1 450	1.71	33.6	34.3	44.8	3 420	0.319	728
	3.81	9.19	0.090	1 170	1.40	27.6	34.6	36.5	2 800	0.319	586
88.9	7.95	15.9	0.156	2 020	1.67	37.6	28.8	52.3	3 340	0.279	1 020
	6.35	12.9	0.127	1 650	1.41	31.7	29.3	43.4	2 820	0.279	828
	4.78	9.92	0.097	1 260	1.12	25.2	29.8	33.9	2 240	0.279	633
	3.81	8.00	0.078	1 020	0.924	20.8	30.1	27.6	1 850	0.279	510
73.0	6.35	10.4	0.102	1 330	0.745	20.4	23.7	28.3	1 490	0.229	670
	4.78	8.04	0.079	1 020	0.599	16.4	24.2	22.3	1 200	0.229	514
	3.81	6.50	0.064	828	0.497	13.6	24.5	18.3	994	0.229	415
	3.18	5.48	0.054	698	0.426	11.7	24.7	15.5	852	0.229	349
60.3	6.35	8.45	0.083	1 080	0.397	13.2	19.2	18.6	794	0.189	545
	4.78	6.54	0.064	834	0.324	10.7	19.7	14.8	647	0.189	420
	3.81	5.31	0.052	676	0.271	8.99	20.0	12.2	542	0.189	339
	3.18	4.48	0.044	571	0.233	7.74	20.2	10.4	467	0.189	286
48.3	4.78	5.13	0.050	654	0.157	6.48	15.5	9.09	313	0.152	331
	3.81	4.18	0.041	533	0.133	5.50	15.8	7.56	265	0.152	268
	3.18	3.54	0.035	451	0.115	4.77	16.0	6.48	231	0.152	226
	2.79	3.13	0.031	399	0.104	4.29	16.1	5.79	207	0.152	200
42.2	3.18	3.06	0.030	390	0.075	3.54	13.8	4.85	149	0.133	196
	2.54	2.48	0.024	316	0.062	2.96	14.1	4.00	125	0.133	159
33.4	3.18	2.37	0.023	302	0.035	2.09	10.7	2.91	69.7	0.105	153
	2.54	1.93	0.019	246	0.029	1.77	10.9	2.42	59.0	0.105	124
26.7	3.18	1.84	0.018	235	0.016	1.24	8.39	1.77	33.1	0.084	120
	2.54	1.51	0.015	193	0.014	1.07	8.59	1.49	28.4	0.084	97.4

NOTES

BUILT-UP SECTIONS

Built-up sections fabricated by means of welding or bolting rolled steel plates and shapes, in various combinations, can be efficient and economical structural members. The possible combinations and resulting sections are virtually limitless. The properties of certain combinations which currently are most frequently used have been tabulated. Other combinations are shown along with the expressions for computing the properties of the section.

Properties of double angles are given immediately following the properties of equal and unequal leg single angles from page 6—72 to 6—77 inclusive. Tables of properties for double channels both toe-to-toe and back-to-back are given on pages 6—96 and 6—97 and for W shapes with channels attached to the top flange on page 6—98. Pages 6—99 to 6—102 give expressions for computing the properties of various other combinations less frequently used.

TWO CHANNELS
Toe to Toe

PROPERTIES OF SECTIONS

Channel Size	For Two Channels			Axis X—X			Axis Y—Y					
							Toe to Toe			c = d		
	Mass	Dead Load	Area	I_x	S_x	r_x	I_y	S_y	r_y	I_y	S_y	r_y
	kg/m	kN/m	mm²	10^6mm⁴	10^3mm³	mm	10^6mm⁴	10^3mm³	mm	10^6mm⁴	10^3mm³	mm
MC460 x 86*	173	1.70	22 000	564	2 480	160	176	1 650	89.5	959	4 200	209
x 77.2*	155	1.52	19 700	522	2 280	163	149	1 430	87.0	861	3 770	209
x 68.2*	137	1.34	17 400	484	2 120	167	126	1 240	85.0	761	3 330	209
x 63.5*	127	1.25	16 200	462	2 020	169	112	1 120	83.2	707	3 090	209
C380 x 74	149	1.46	19 000	336	1 760	133	112	1 190	76.9	558	2 930	172
x 60	119	1.17	15 100	290	1 520	138	80.4	903	72.9	449	2 360	172
x 50	101	0.990	12 900	262	1 370	143	62.8	730	69.9	381	2 000	172
C310 x 45	89.4	0.876	11 400	135	884	109	49.4	618	65.9	213	1 400	137
x 37	74.2	0.726	9 440	120	786	113	37.6	488	63.1	177	1 160	137
x 31	61.6	0.604	7 840	107	702	117	28.2	381	60.0	146	958	136
C250 x 45*	89.0	0.874	11 300	85.6	674	86.9	43.6	574	62.0	142	1 120	112
x 37	74.6	0.730	9 500	75.8	598	89.4	34.0	466	59.8	120	949	113
x 30	59.2	0.582	7 560	65.4	514	93.0	24.1	350	56.5	96.6	761	113
x 23	45.2	0.442	5 760	55.6	438	98.2	15.7	242	52.3	72.9	574	113
C230 x 30	59.6	0.584	7 600	51.0	444	81.9	22.7	339	54.7	77.6	677	101
x 22	44.6	0.438	5 680	42.6	372	86.6	14.8	234	51.0	58.0	506	101
x 20	39.6	0.390	5 060	39.6	346	88.6	12.1	198	48.9	51.4	449	101
C200 x 28	55.8	0.548	7 120	36.4	360	71.6	19.2	299	51.9	55.7	548	88.4
x 21	40.8	0.400	5 200	29.8	294	75.8	11.8	200	47.6	41.1	405	88.9
x 17	34.0	0.167	4 340	27.0	266	78.8	8.93	157	45.4	33.9	334	88.4
C180 x 22*	43.8	0.428	5 560	22.6	254	63.7	12.1	209	46.7	32.8	369	76.8
x 18	36.4	0.356	4 620	20.0	226	65.9	9.02	164	44.2	27.5	309	77.1
x 15	29.0	0.284	3 700	17.7	199	69.3	6.50	123	41.9	21.7	244	76.6
C150 x 19	38.4	0.378	4 900	14.2	187	53.9	9.13	169	43.2	20.4	268	64.5
x 16	31.0	0.304	3 960	12.4	164	56.1	6.54	128	40.6	16.6	219	64.8
x 12	24.2	0.236	3 080	10.7	141	59.1	4.37	91.1	37.7	12.9	169	64.6
C130 x 17	34.2	0.335	4 340	8.66	136	44.7	7.28	140	41.0	11.8	185	52.0
x 13	26.6	0.262	3 400	7.32	115	46.5	4.69	99.8	37.2	9.56	150	53.0
x 10	19.8	0.194	2 520	6.18	97.2	49.5	2.94	66.8	34.1	7.02	111	52.8
C100 x 11	21.6	0.212	2 740	3.82	74.8	37.3	3.07	71.3	33.5	4.62	90.6	41.1
x 9	18.6	0.182	2 340	3.41	67.2	38.1	2.48	59.0	32.5	3.95	77.4	41.1
x 8	16.0	0.158	2 040	3.22	63.2	39.7	1.91	47.7	30.6	3.43	67.3	41.0
C 75 x 9	17.6	0.174	2 240	1.70	44.6	27.4	2.08	52.0	30.5	(1)	(1)	(1)
x 7	14.6	0.144	1 870	1.50	39.4	28.3	1.47	39.8	28.1	1.57	41.4	29.0
x 6	12.0	0.118	1 530	1.34	35.2	29.6	1.04	29.7	26.1	1.27	33.5	28.9

(1) The condition of c = d cannot be met for this section.
* Not available from Canadian Mills.

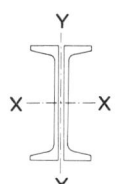

PROPERTIES OF SECTIONS

Channel Size	Mass of 2 Channels	Area of 2 Channels	Axis X—X			Radius of Gyration about Axis Y—Y					
			I_x	S_x	r_x	Back to Back Channels, millimetres					
	kg/m	mm²	10^6 mm⁴	10^3 mm³	mm	0	8	10	12	16	20
MC460 x 86*	173	22 000	564	2 480	160	33.6	36.2	37.0	37.7	39.1	40.7
x 77.2*	155	19 700	522	2 280	163	33.8	36.5	37.2	37.9	39.3	40.8
x 68.2*	137	17 400	484	2 120	167	34.3	36.9	37.6	38.3	39.7	41.2
x 63.5*	127	16 200	462	2 020	169	34.7	37.3	37.9	38.7	40.1	41.6
C380 x 74	149	19 000	336	1 760	133	30.0	32.8	33.5	34.3	35.9	37.5
x 60	119	15 100	290	1 520	138	29.9	32.7	33.4	34.2	35.7	37.3
x 50	101	12 900	262	1 370	143	30.5	33.2	33.9	34.7	36.2	37.8
C310 x 45	89.4	11 400	135	884	109	25.7	28.5	29.3	30.0	31.6	33.2
x 37	74.2	9 440	120	786	113	26.2	28.9	29.7	30.4	32.0	33.6
x 31	61.6	7 840	107	702	117	26.7	29.5	30.2	30.9	32.5	34.1
C250 x 45*	89.0	11 300	85.6	674	86.9	23.4	26.3	27.1	27.9	29.5	31.2
x 37	74.6	9 500	75.8	598	89.4	23.3	26.1	26.9	27.7	29.3	30.9
x 30	59.2	7 560	65.4	514	93.0	23.3	26.1	26.8	27.6	29.2	30.8
x 23	45.2	5 760	55.6	438	98.2	23.9	26.8	27.5	28.3	29.9	31.5
C230 x 30	59.6	7 600	51.0	444	81.9	22.0	24.9	25.6	26.4	28.0	27.9
x 22	44.6	5 680	42.6	372	86.6	22.5	25.3	26.1	26.8	28.4	30.1
x 20	39.6	5 060	39.6	346	88.6	22.6	25.5	26.2	27.0	28.6	30.2
C200 x 28	55.8	7 120	36.4	360	71.6	21.0	23.9	24.7	25.5	27.1	28.8
x 21	40.8	5 200	29.8	294	75.8	20.9	23.8	24.5	25.3	26.9	28.6
x 17	34.0	4 340	27.0	266	78.8	21.5	24.4	25.1	25.9	27.5	29.2
C180 x 22*	43.8	5 560	22.6	254	63.7	19.7	22.6	23.4	24.2	25.8	27.5
x 18	36.4	4 620	20.0	226	65.9	19.5	22.4	23.2	24.0	25.6	27.3
x 15	29.0	3 700	17.7	199	69.3	20.2	23.1	23.9	24.7	26.3	28.0
C150 x 19	38.4	4 900	14.2	187	53.9	18.4	21.4	22.2	23.0	24.7	26.4
x 16	31.0	3 960	12.4	164	56.1	18.3	21.3	22.1	22.9	24.5	26.2
x 12	24.2	3 080	10.7	141	59.1	18.6	21.5	22.3	23.1	24.8	26.5
C130 x 17	34.2	4 340	8.66	136	44.7	18.1	21.1	21.9	22.8	24.5	26.2
x 13	26.6	3 400	7.32	115	46.5	17.0	20.0	20.8	21.6	23.3	25.1
x 10	19.8	2 520	6.18	97.2	49.5	17.4	20.4	21.2	22.0	23.7	25.4
C100 x 11	21.6	2 740	3.82	74.8	37.3	16.1	19.2	20.0	20.8	22.5	24.3
x 9	18.6	2 340	3.41	67.2	38.1	16.5	19.5	20.3	21.2	22.9	24.6
x 8	16.0	2 040	3.22	63.2	39.7	16.2	19.3	20.1	21.0	22.7	24.4
C 75 x 9	17.6	2 240	1.70	44.6	27.4	15.5	18.6	19.5	20.3	22.0	23.8
x 7	14.6	1 870	1.50	39.4	28.3	14.8	17.9	18.8	19.6	21.4	23.1
x 6	12.0	1 530	1.34	35.2	29.6	14.8	18.0	18.8	19.7	21.4	23.2

*Not available from Canadian Mills.

Note: For dead load of two channels refer to table on page 6—96

W SHAPES AND CHANNELS

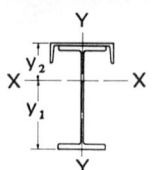

PROPERTIES OF SECTIONS

Beam	Channel	Mass	Dead Load	Total Area	Axis X—X					Axis Y—Y		
					I	$S_1 = \dfrac{I}{Y_1}$	$S_2 = \dfrac{I}{Y_2}$	r	Y_1	I	S	r
		kg/m	kN/m	mm²	$10^6\,mm^4$	$10^3\,mm^3$	$10^3\,mm^3$	mm	mm	$10^6\,mm^4$	$10^3\,mm^3$	mm
W920 x 289*	MC460 x 63.5*	352.2	3.45	44 900	6 410	11 800	16 300	378	545	387	1 690	92.8
	C380 x 50	339.1	3.32	43 200	6 170	11 600	15 200	378	531	287	1 510	81.5
x 271*	MC460 x 63.5*	335.3	3.28	42 700	6 060	11 100	15 700	377	547	376	1 650	93.8
	C380 x 50	322.2	3.20	41 000	5 830	11 000	14 500	377	532	276	1 450	82.0
x 253*	MC460 x 63.5*	317.3	3.10	40 400	5 680	10 300	14 900	375	550	365	1 600	95.1
	C380 x 50	304.2	2.98	38 700	5 460	10 200	13 800	375	534	265	1 390	82.7
x 238*	MC460 x 63.5*	301.9	2.95	38 500	5 350	9 690	14 300	373	552	354	1 550	95.9
	C380 x 50	288.8	2.82	36 800	5 130	9 570	13 200	373	536	254	1 330	83.0
x223*	MC460 x 63.5*	287.8	2.81	36 700	5 030	9 080	13 600	370	554	343	1 500	96.7
	C380 x 50	274.7	2.68	35 000	4 820	8 960	12 500	371	537	243	1 280	83.3
W840 x 226*	MC460 x 63.5*	289.8	2.84	37 000	4 500	8 710	13 000	349	516	345	1 510	96.6
	C380 x 50	277.1	2.72	35 300	4 310	8 600	12 000	349	501	245	1 290	83.3
x 210*	MC460 x 63.5*	274.4	2.68	34 900	4 180	8 050	12 300	346	519	334	1 460	97.8
	C380 x 50	261.3	2.56	33 200	4 000	7 950	11 300	347	503	234	1 230	83.9
x 193*	MC460 x 63.5*	257.1	2.51	32 800	3 810	7 310	11 500	341	521	321	1 410	99.0
	C380 x 50	244.0	2.38	31 100	3 640	7 220	10 500	342	505	221	1 160	84.3
W760 x 196*	MC460 x 63.5*	260.4	2.55	33 200	3 270	6 860	10 700	314	476	313	1 370	97.0
	C380 x 50	247.3	2.42	31 500	3 120	6 770	9 800	315	462	213	1 120	82.1
x 185*	MC460 x 63.5*	248.4	2.43	31 600	3 070	6 420	10 300	312	479	306	1 340	98.4
	C380 x 50	235.3	2.30	29 900	2 940	6 340	9 380	313	463	206	1 080	83.0
x 173*	MC460 x 63.5*	237.2	2.32	30 200	2 880	6 000	9 840	309	481	300	1 310	99.6
	C380 x 50	224.1	2.20	28 500	2 750	5 920	8 940	310	465	200	1 050	83.7
x 161*	MC460 x 63.5*	224.0	2.19	28 500	2 660	5 490	9 300	305	484	292	1 280	101
	C380 x 50	210.9	2.06	26 800	2 530	5 410	8 410	307	467	192	1 010	84.5
W690 x 170*	C380 x 50	220.4	2.16	28 000	2 270	5 350	8 110	284	424	197	1 040	83.9
	C310 x 31	200.7	1.96	25 500	2 080	5 220	6 870	285	398	120	785	68.5
x 152*	C380 x 50	202.6	1.98	25 800	2 050	4 810	7 570	282	427	189	991	85.5
	C310 x 31	182.9	1.79	23 300	1 870	4 690	6 350	284	400	111	730	69.1
x 140*	C380 x 50	190.3	1.86	24 200	1 880	4 380	7 140	279	430	183	959	86.8
	C310 x 31	170.6	1.67	21 700	1 720	4 270	5 930	281	402	105	690	69.6
W610 x 125	C380 x 50	175.6	1.72	22 300	1 390	3 550	6 020	250	391	170	894	87.3
	C310 x 31	155.9	1.52	19 800	1 260	3 460	4 950	252	364	92.8	609	68.4
x 113	C380 x 50	163.9	1.60	20 800	1 260	3 200	5 650	246	395	165	868	89.1
	C310 x 31	144.2	1.41	18 300	1 140	3 110	4 600	250	367	87.8	576	69.2
W530 x 101	C380 x 50	151.9	1.49	19 300	908	2 560	4 710	217	355	158	829	90.4
	C310 x 31	132.2	1.30	16 800	819	2 490	3 800	221	329	80.4	527	69.1
x 92	C380 x 50	143.0	1.40	18 200	830	2 320	4 460	213	357	155	813	92.1
	C310 x 31	123.3	1.21	15 700	747	2 260	3 560	218	330	77.3	507	70.1
W460 x 74	C380 x 50	124.7	1.22	15 900	519	1 640	3 460	181	317	148	775	96.4
	C310 x 31	105.0	1.03	13 400	467	1 600	2 720	187	292	70.1	460	72.4
W410 x 54	C380 x 50	103.9	1.02	13 200	311	1 060	2 620	153	295	141	741	103
	C310 x 31	84.2	0.826	10 700	279	1 030	2 010	161	271	63.6	417	77.0
W360 x 45	C310 x 31	75.8	0.743	9 650	187	771	1 620	139	243	61.7	404	79.9
	C250 x 23	67.6	0.662	8 610	176	759	1 390	143	232	36.0	283	64.6
W310 x 39	C310 x 31	69.5	0.682	8 860	132	605	1 350	122	219	60.8	398	82.8
	C250 x 23	61.3	0.601	7 820	124	597	1 160	126	208	35.1	276	67.0
W250 x 33	C250 x 23	55.3	0.542	7 050	74.0	417	857	102	178	32.5	256	67.9
	C200 x 17	49.7	0.488	6 340	70.0	412	749	105	170	18.2	180	53.6
W200 x 27	C250 x 23	49.2	0.482	6 270	40.4	276	607	80.3	147	31.1	245	70.4
	C200 x 17	43.6	0.428	5 560	38.2	272	529	82.9	140	16.8	166	55.0

*Not available from Canadian Mills.

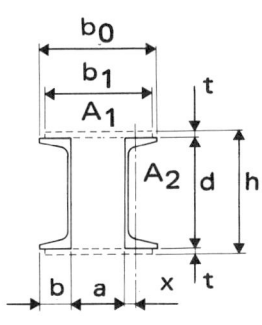

$h \quad = d + 2t \qquad b_o = a + 2b \qquad S_{yy} = 2I_{yy}/b_o \text{ if } b_1 < b_o$

$A_1 \quad = b_1 t \qquad\qquad\qquad S_{yy} = 2I_{yy}/b_1 \text{ if } b_1 \geqslant b_o$

$A \quad = 2(A_1 + A_2)$

$\qquad\qquad\qquad\qquad r_{xx} = \sqrt{I_{yy}/A}$

$I_{xx} = 2I_{xc} + \dfrac{b_1}{12}\left[h^3 - d^3\right]$

$S_{xx} = 2I_{xx}/h$

$r_{xx} = \sqrt{I_{xx}/A}$

$I_{yy} = 2I_{yc} + \dfrac{A_1}{6}\, b_1^2 + 2A_2\,(x + a/2)^2$

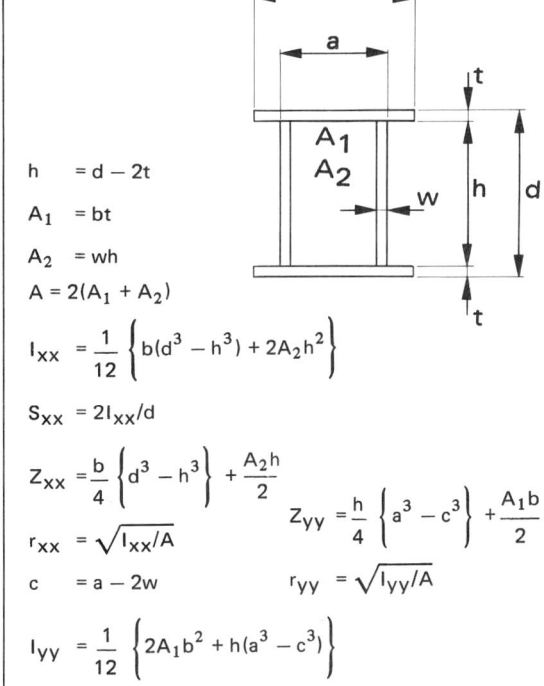

$h \quad = d - 2t$

$A_1 \quad = bt$

$A_2 \quad = wh$

$A = 2(A_1 + A_2)$

$I_{xx} = \dfrac{1}{12}\left\{b(d^3 - h^3) + 2A_2 h^2\right\}$

$S_{xx} = 2I_{xx}/d$

$Z_{xx} = \dfrac{b}{4}\left\{d^3 - h^3\right\} + \dfrac{A_2 h}{2}$

$\qquad\qquad\qquad\qquad\qquad Z_{yy} = \dfrac{h}{4}\left\{a^3 - c^3\right\} + \dfrac{A_1 b}{2}$

$r_{xx} \quad = \sqrt{I_{xx}/A}$

$c \quad = a - 2w \qquad\qquad\qquad r_{yy} = \sqrt{I_{yy}/A}$

$I_{yy} \quad = \dfrac{1}{12}\left\{2A_1 b^2 + h(a^3 - c^3)\right\}$

$S_{yy} \quad = 2I_{yy}/b$

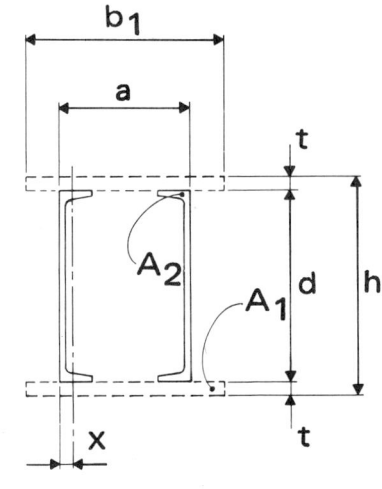

$h \quad = d + 2t$

$A_1 \quad = b_1 t \qquad\qquad I_{yy} = 2I_{yc} + \dfrac{A_1}{6}\, b_1^2 + 2A_2\,(a/2 - x)^2$

$A \quad = 2(A_1 + A_2)$

$I_{xx} = 2I_{xc} + \dfrac{b_1}{12}\,(h^3 - d^3) \quad S_{yy} = 2I_{yy}/b_1 \text{ if } a < b_1$

$\qquad\qquad\qquad\qquad\qquad S_{yy} = 2I_{yy}/a \quad \text{if } a \geqslant b_1$

$S_{xx} = 2I_{xx}/h$

$\qquad\qquad\qquad\qquad r_{yy} = \sqrt{I_{yy}/A}$

$r_{xx} = \sqrt{I_{xx}/A}$

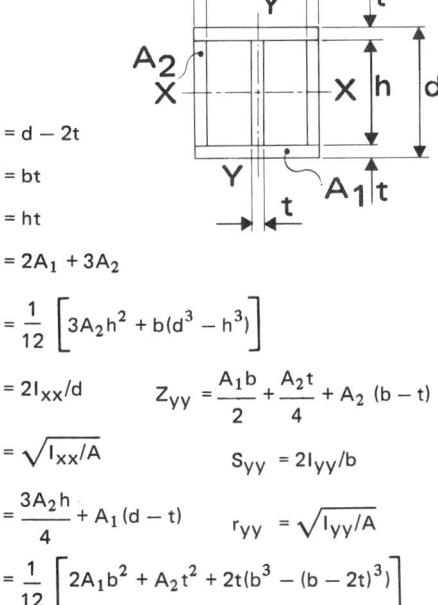

$h \quad = d - 2t$

$A_1 \quad = bt$

$A_2 \quad = ht$

$A \quad = 2A_1 + 3A_2$

$I_{xx} = \dfrac{1}{12}\left[3A_2 h^2 + b(d^3 - h^3)\right]$

$S_{xx} = 2I_{xx}/d \qquad Z_{yy} = \dfrac{A_1 b}{2} + \dfrac{A_2 t}{4} + A_2\,(b - t)$

$r_{xx} = \sqrt{I_{xx}/A} \qquad\qquad S_{yy} = 2I_{yy}/b$

$Z_{xx} = \dfrac{3A_2 h}{4} + A_1\,(d - t) \qquad r_{yy} = \sqrt{I_{yy}/A}$

$I_{yy} = \dfrac{1}{12}\left[2A_1 b^2 + A_2 t^2 + 2t(b^3 - (b - 2t)^3)\right]$

Elements of the shape which are shown in dotted outline are optional and if omitted the variable defining their size should be set equal to zero.

All elements of the shape are assumed to be continuous along the length of the shape.

BUILT-UP SECTIONS

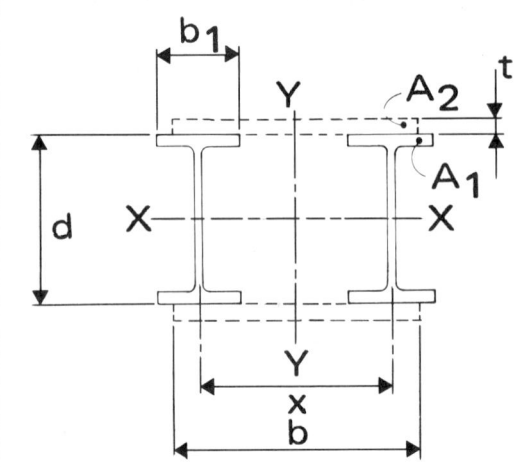

$A_2 = bt$

$A = 2(A_1 + A_2)$

$I_{xx} = 2I_{xw} + \dfrac{1}{12} b \left[(d + 2t)^3 - d^3 \right]$

For $(x + b_1) > b$:

$S_{xx} = 2I_{xx}/(d + 2t)$

$\qquad S_{yy} = 2I_{yy}/(x + b_1)$

For $(x + b_1) \leqslant b$:

$r_{xx} = \sqrt{I_{xx}/A}$

$\qquad S_{yy} = 2I_{yy}/b$

$I_{yy} = 2I_{yw} + \dfrac{1}{6} A_2 t^2 + \dfrac{1}{2} A_1 x^2$

$\qquad\qquad r_{yy} = \sqrt{I_{yy}/A}$

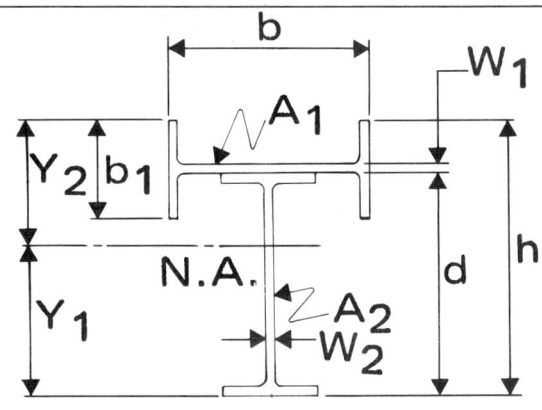

$h = d + \dfrac{1}{2}(b_1 + w_1)$

$Y_1 = \dfrac{A_1(d + W_1/2) + A_2 d/2}{A_1 + A_2}$

$Y_2 = h - Y_1 \qquad I_{yy} = I_{x1} + I_{y2}$

$A = A_1 + A_2 \qquad *I_{yT} = I_{x1} + I_{y2}/2 - (Y_1 - d/2)w^3$

$I_{xx} = I_{y1} + I_{x2} + A_1(Y_2 - b_1/2)^2$

$S_{x1} = I_{xx}/Y_1 \qquad\qquad S_{yy} = 2I_{yy}/b$

$S_{x2} = I_{xx}/Y_2$

$\qquad\qquad\qquad r_{yy} = \sqrt{I_{yy}/A}$

$r_{xx} = \sqrt{I_{xx}/A}$

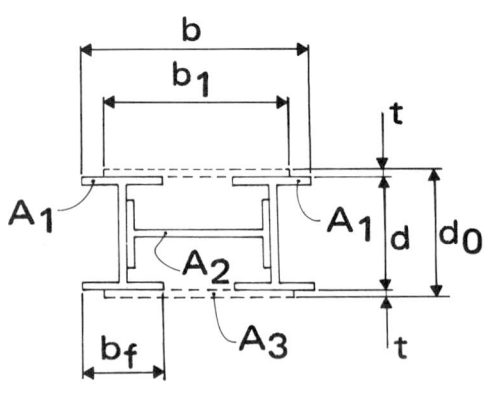

$d_0 = d + 2t \qquad I_{yy} = I_{x2} + 2I_{y1} + \dfrac{A_3}{6} b_1^2 + A_1 b_1^2/2$

$A_3 = b_1 t$

$A = 2(A_1 + A_3) + A_2$

$I_{xx} = 2I_{x1} + I_{y2} + \dfrac{b_1}{12}(d_0^3 - d^3)$

$\qquad\qquad S_{yy} = 2I_{xx}/b \quad$ if $b \geqslant b_1$

$S_{xx} = 2I_{xx}/d_0 \qquad S_{yy} = 2I_{xx}/b_1 \quad$ if $b < b_1$

$r_{xx} = \sqrt{I_{xx}/A} \qquad r_{xx} = \sqrt{I_{xx}/A}$

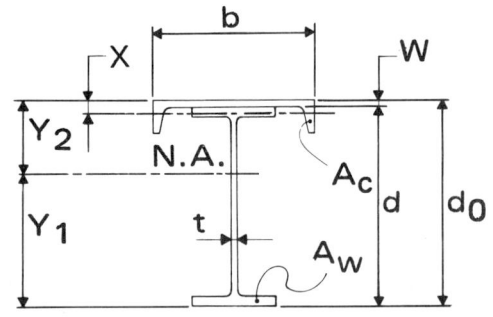

$Y_1 = \dfrac{A_w d/2 + A_c(d_0 - x)}{A} \qquad A = A_c + A_w$

$\qquad\qquad\qquad\qquad\qquad\qquad d_0 = d + w$

$Y_2 = d_0 - Y_1$

$I_{xx} = I_{xw} + I_{yc} + A_w(Y_1 - d/2)^2 + A_c(Y_2 - x)^2$

$S_{x1} = I_{xx}/Y_1 \qquad\qquad I_{yy} = I_{yw} + I_{xc}$

$S_{x2} = I_{xx}/Y_2 \qquad *I_{yT} = I_{xc} + \dfrac{I_{yw}}{2} - (Y_1 - d/2)w^3$

$r_{xx} = \sqrt{I_{xx}/A} \qquad S_{yy} = 2I_{yy}/b$

$\qquad\qquad\qquad\qquad r_{yy} = \sqrt{I_{yy}/A}$

*I_{yT} is the moment of inertia of the T section above the neutral axis.

Note: Centres of gravity of both channels are on the same vertical line.

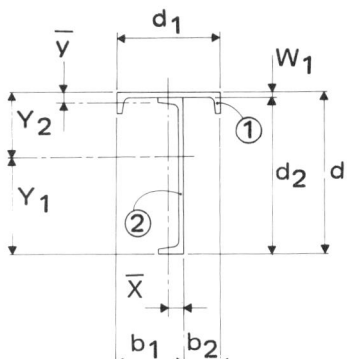

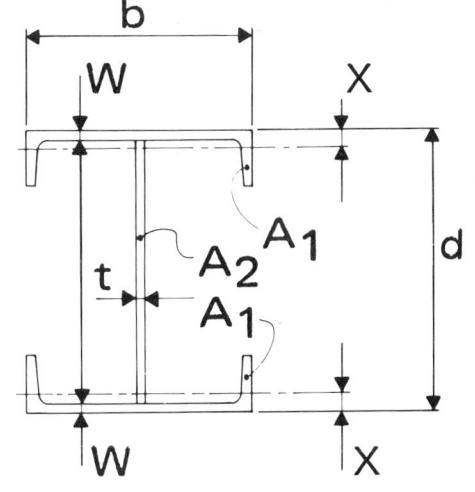

$d = d_2 + w_1$

$A = A_1 + A_2$

$b_1 = (d_1/2) + \bar{x}$

$y_1 = \dfrac{A_1(d - \bar{y}) + \dfrac{A_2}{2}d_2}{A}$

$b_2 = d_1 - b_1$

$I_{xx} = I_{1y} + I_{2x} + A_1(y_2 - \bar{y})^2 + A_2(y_1 - \dfrac{d_2}{2})^2$

$S_1 = \dfrac{I_{xx}}{y_1}$

$y_2 = d - y_1$

$I_{yy} = I_{1x} + I_{zy}$

$S_2 = \dfrac{I_{xx}}{y_2}$

$S_y = 2I_{yy}/d_1$

$r_{xx} = \sqrt{\dfrac{I_{xx}}{A}}$

$r_{yy} = \sqrt{\dfrac{I_{yy}}{A}}$

$h = d - 2w$

$A_2 = ht$

$A = 2A_1 + A_2$

$I_{xx} = 2I_{yc} + \dfrac{1}{12}A_2 h^2 + 2A_1(d/2 - x)^2$

$I_{yy} = 2I_{xc} + \dfrac{1}{12}A_2 t^2$

$S_{xx} = 2I_{xx}/d$

$S_{yy} = 2I_{yy}/b$

$r_{yy} = \sqrt{I_{yy}/A}$

$r_{xx} = \sqrt{I_{xx}/A}$

Note: a and b are the angle leg lengths and b_1 is the width of channel flange.

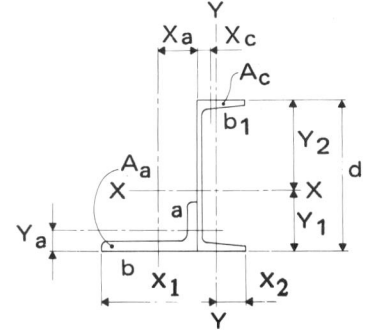

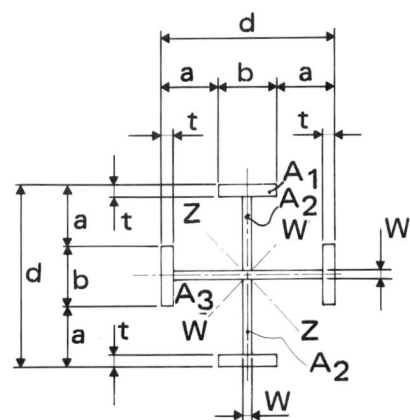

$A = A_a + A_c$

$x_1 = \dfrac{A_a(b - x_a) + A_c(b + x_c)}{A}$; $\quad y_1 = \dfrac{A_a y_a + A_c d/2}{A}$

$x_2 = b_1 \quad b \quad x_1$

$y_2 = d - y_1$

$I_{xx} = I_{ya} + I_{xc} + A_a(y_1 - y_a)^2 + A_c(\dfrac{d}{2} - y_1)^2$

$I_{yy} = I_{xa} + I_{yc} + A_a(x_1 - b + x_a)^2 + A_c(b_1 - x_2 - x_c)^2$

$S_{y1} = I_{yy}/x_1$

$S_{x1} = I_{xx}/y_1$

$S_{y2} = I_{yy}/x_2$

$S_{x2} = I_{xx}/y_2$

$r_{yy} = \sqrt{I_{yy}/A}$

$r_{xx} = \sqrt{I_{xx}/A}$

$A_1 = bt$

$A_3 = 2A_2 + w^2$

$A_2 = (d - w - 2t)w/2$

$A = 4A_1 + 2A_2 + A_3$

$I_x = I_y = \dfrac{1}{12}\left\{ b(d^3 - E^3) + wE^3 + 2tb^3 + Ew^3 - w^4 \right\}$

$S_x = S_y = 2I_x/d$

$E = (d - 2t)$

$r_x = r_y = \sqrt{I_x/A}$

BUILT-UP SECTIONS

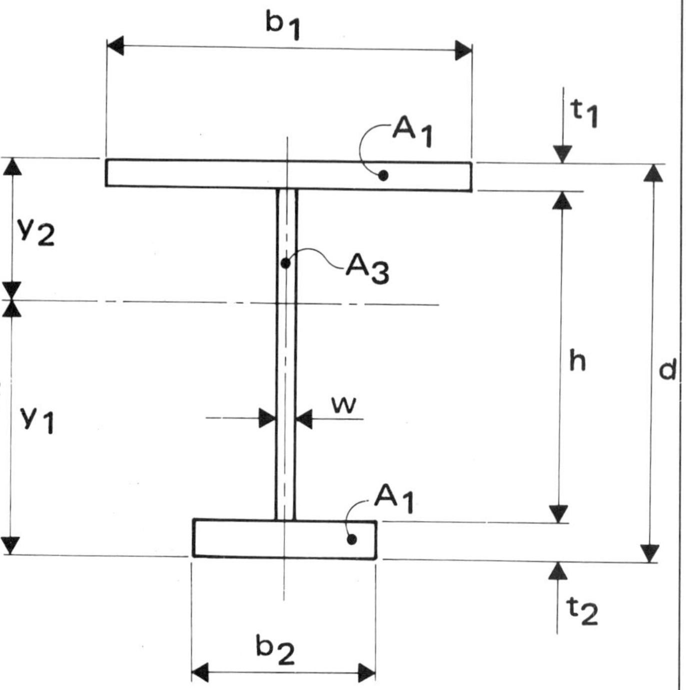

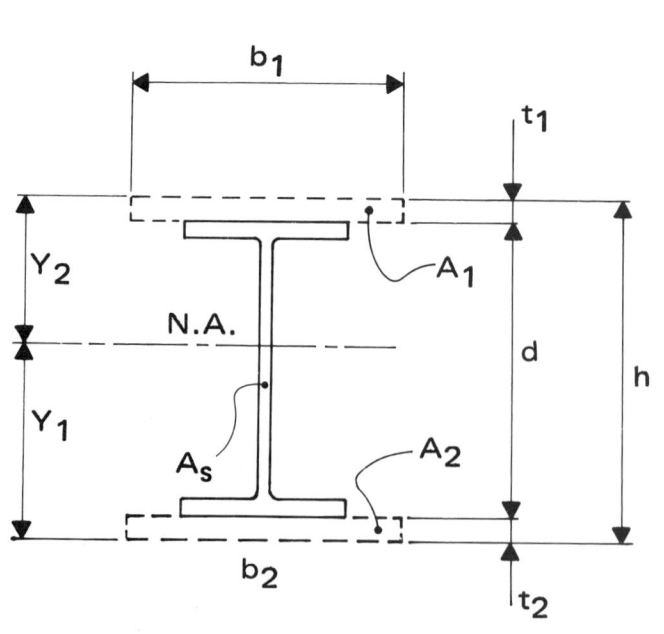

$A_1 = b_1 t_1 \qquad A_2 = b_2 t_2 \qquad A_3 = wh$

$d \quad = h + t_1 + t_2$

$A \quad = A_1 + A_2 + A_3$

$Y_1 \quad = \dfrac{A_1(d - t_1/2) + A_3(t_2 + h/2) + A_2 t_2/2}{A}$

$Y_2 \quad = d - Y_1$

$J \quad = \dfrac{1}{3}\left\{A_1 t_1^2 + A_3 w^2 + A_2 t_2^2\right\}$

$C_w \quad = \dfrac{\left(d - \dfrac{t_1 + t_2}{2}\right)^2 b_1^3 t_1}{12\left[1 + (b_1/b_2)^3 (t_1/t_2)\right]}$

$I_{yy} \quad = \dfrac{1}{12}\left[A_1 b_1^2 + A_2 b_2^2 + A_3 w^2\right]$

$*I_{YT} = \dfrac{1}{12}\left[A_1 b_1^2 + (y_2 - t_1)w^3\right]$

$I_{xx} \quad = \dfrac{1}{12}\left[A_1 t_1^2 + A_2 t_2^2 + A_3 h^2\right] + A_1(y_2 - t_1/2)^2 + A_2(y_1 - t_2/2)^2 + A_3(y_1 - t_2 - h/2)^2$

$S_{x1} = \dfrac{I_{xx}}{y_1} \; ; \qquad S_{x2} = \dfrac{I_{xx}}{y_2} \qquad\qquad S_{yy} = 2I_{yy}/b_1$

$r_{xx} = \sqrt{\dfrac{I_{xx}}{A}} \qquad\qquad r_{yy} = \sqrt{\dfrac{I_{yy}}{A}}$

$A \quad = A_1 + A_2 + A_s \; ; \quad h = d + t_1 + t_2$

$Y_1 \quad = \dfrac{A_1(h - t_1/2) + A_s(t_2 + d/2) + A_2 t_2/2}{A}$

$Y_2 \quad = h - Y_1$

$I_{xx} \quad = I_{xs} + \dfrac{1}{12}(A_1 t_1^2 + A_2 t_2^2)$

$\qquad\qquad + A_1(Y_2 - t_1/2)^2 + A_2(Y_1 - t_2/2)^2$

$S_{x1} = I_{xx}/Y_1 \; ; \quad S_{x2} = I_{xx}/Y_2$

$r_{xx} = \sqrt{I_{xx}/A}$

$I_{yy} \quad = I_{ys} + \dfrac{1}{12}(A_1 b_1^2 + A_2 b_2^2)$

$S_{yy} = I_{yy}/b_1 \quad \text{if } b_1 > b_2$

$S_{yy} = I_{yy}/b_2 \quad \text{if } b_1 \leqslant b_2$

$r_{yy} = \sqrt{I_{yy}/A}$

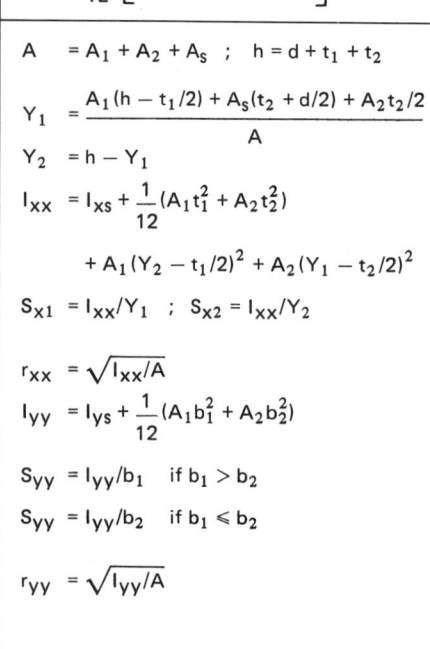

BARS AND PLATES

Bars

The term, "Bars", means:

(a) Rounds, squares and hexagons of all sizes;

(b) Flat-rolled steel,

Up to 200 mm inclusive in width and over 5.0 mm in thickness

Flat bars with thickness up to 6 mm are not produced in widths of 150 mm to 200 mm.

(c) Bar-size shapes under 75 mm in maximum dimension.

Hot-rolled bar mill flats are available from many mills in most thicknesses and widths according to CAN3-G312.2-M and CAN3-G312.1. For more precise information regarding the availability of flats, the various mill catalogues should be consulted.

Plates

The term, "Plates", means flat, hot-rolled steel, when ordered to thickness:

a) Over 200 mm in width and 6.0 mm or over in thickness, and

b) Over 12 000 mm in width and 4.5 mm or over in thickness.

Slabs, sheet, bars, and skelp, although frequently falling in the foregoing ranges, are not classified as plates.

Plates often are further defined as "Universal Mill Plates" or "Sheared Plates". The Shear Plate Mill, having horizontal rolls only, produces a product with uneven edges and ends which, therefore, must be sheared (or sometimes, at the option of the producer, flame cut) on all sides in order to produce a rectangular plate.

Sheared Plates cover a wider range of sizes than Universal Mill Plates.

Universal Mill Plates, on the other hand, are rolled to the ordered width on a Universal Mill. The edges of this product are straight and parallel within the specified tolerance limits for Universal Mill Plate. These plates are sometimes used in lieu of sheared plates where the appearance or the specifications require a finished edge. By this method of rolling, the slab or ingot does not receive cross rolling but is merely elongated in the various passes. When Universal Plates are required, the mill order should so state.

The extreme sizes of plates produced by various mills differ greatly and the individual mills should be consulted for detailed information. Canadian mills can produce sheared and flame cut plate in widths ranging from 650 mm to 3600 mm and in thicknesses ranging from 5.0 to 300 mm. For a list of first and second preference sizes for thickness and width, CAN3-G312.1 should be consulted. (See also pages 6—105 to 6—106).

Standard mill practice is to invoice the purchaser at actual scale weight* at point of shipment. The allowable overweight above theoretical that may be charged for is limited in accordance with either CSA G40.20-M or ASTM A6, depending upon whether the steel is furnished to CSA or ASTM material specifications.

All plates ordered flame cut take extras for flame cutting in addition to all other extras. For example, rolled steel bearing plates are often flame cut to prevent distortion due to shearing and also would take the regular extra for the thickness involved.

Extras for thickness, width, length, cutting, quality and quantity, which are added to the base price of plates, are subject to occasional revision, and should be obtained by inquiry to the producer.

---

*In this book weight is to be used synonymously with mass so as to distinguish it from force as used for design.

Sketch Plates

Sketch Plates, exclusive of those with re-entrant cuts, can be supplied by many mills by shearing. Odd shapes in most instances require flame cutting, for which flame cutting extras are applicable. Full circles also are available, either by shearing, or by flame cutting.

Floor Plates (Raised Patterns)

Different mills offer floor plates in different styles, patterns and extreme dimensions. The nominal or ordered thickness is that of the flat plate exclusive of the raised pattern. The individual producers should be consulted if precise information is desired.

Bearing Plates

Rolled steel bearing plates are extensively used for column bases, wall bearing plates, and a variety of other uses.

The smaller and thinner bearing plates, up to and including 50 mm in thickness, are rolled flat and with surfaces sufficiently smooth to receive, without planing, the milled ends of column shafts. Bearing plates 100 mm and under in thickness often can be straightened by a press to within the required limits of flatness.

Rolled steel bearing plates of thicknesses greater than 100 mm are likely to be slightly dished so that, in order to provide proper bearing surfaces, these plates should be planed on their top surfaces directly under the columns. It usually will not be necessary to plane the bottom surfaces when the plates rest on concrete foundations, as full bearing contact can be provided with a proper grouting technique.

When plates over 100 mm thick rest on steel, the top surfaces should be planed for the column bearing and the bottom surfaces planed over all the bearing area.

STANDARD PRODUCT CLASSIFICATION
of
Flat Rolled Steel Products and Bars
(HOT ROLLED)

Width w \ Thickness, t	t > 6	6 ≥ t > 5	5 ≥ t > 4.5	4.5 ≥ t > 1.2	1.2 ≥ t > 0.9	0.9 ≥ t > 0.65
W ≤ 100	BAR	BAR	STRIP	STRIP	STRIP	STRIP
100 < W ≤ 150	BAR	BAR	STRIP	STRIP	STRIP	
150 < W ≤ 200	BAR	STRIP	STRIP	STRIP		
200 < W ≤ 300	PLATE	STRIP	STRIP	STRIP		
300 < W ≤ 1200	PLATE	SHEET**	SHEET**	SHEET**		
1200 < W	PLATE	PLATE	PLATE	SHEET		

**For alloy steels, sheet begins at widths over 600 mm.

FLAT METAL PRODUCTS* – Sheet & Plate

Nominal Thickness,** mm		Mass† kg/m²	Dead Load kN/m²	Nominal Thickness,** mm		Mass† kg/m²	Dead Load kN/m²
First preference	Second preference			First preference	Second preference		
0.050		0.393	0.003 85		14	110	1.08
0.060		0.471	0.004 62	16		126	1.23
0.080		0.628	0.006 16		18	141	1.39
0.10		0.785	0.007 70	20		157	1.54
0.12		0.942	0.009 24		22	173	1.69
	0.14	1.10	0.010 8	25		196	1.92
0.16		1.26	0.012 3		28	220	2.16
	0.18	1.41	0.013 9	30		236	2.31
0.20		1.57	0.015 4		32	251	2.46
	0.22	1.73	0.016 9	35		275	2.69
0.25		1.96	0.019 2		38	298	2.93
	0.28	2.20	0.021 6	40		314	3.08
0.30		2.36	0.023 1		45	353	3.46
	0.35	2.75	0.026 9	50		393	3.85
0.40		3.14	0.030 8		55	432	4.23
	0.45	3.53	0.034 6	60		471	4.62
0.50		3.93	0.038 5		70	550	5.39
	0.55	4.32	0.042 3	80		628	6.16
0.60		4.71	0.046 2		90	707	6.93
	0.65	5.10	0.050 0	100		785	7.70
	0.70	5.50	0.053 9		110	864	8.47
0.80		6.28	0.061 6	120		942	9.24
	0.90	7.07	0.069 3		130	1020	10.0
1.0		7.85	0.077 0	140		1100	10.8
	1.1	8.64	0.084 7		150	1180	11.5
1.2		9.42	0.092 4	160		1260	12.3
	1.4	11.0	0.108	180		1410	13.9
1.6		12.6	0.123	200		1570	15.4
	1.8	14.1	0.139	250		1960	19.2
2.0		15.7	0.154	300		2360	23.1
	2.2	17.3	0.169				
2.5		19.6	0.192				
	2.8	22.0	0.216				
3.0		23.6	0.231				
	3.2	25.1	0.246				
3.5		27.5	0.269				
	3.8	29.8	0.293				
4.0		31.4	0.308				
	4.2	33.0	0.323				
4.5		35.3	0.346				
	4.8	37.7	0.370				
5.0		39.3	0.385				
	5.5	43.2	0.423				
6.0		47.1	0.462				
7.0		55.0	0.539				
8.0		62.8	0.616				
	9.0	70.7	0.693				
10		78.5	0.770				
	11	86.4	0.847				
12		94.2	0.924				

*Sizes are those listed in CAN3-G312.1-75

**For coated structural sheet, the nominal thickness applies to the base metal. For metric thickness dimensions for zinc coated structural quality sheet steel, see page 7–26.

† Computed using a steel density of 7 850 kg/m³.

MASS (kg/m) for RECTANGULAR STEEL PRODUCTS*

Width millimetres		Thickness, millimetres					14		18		22		28		35	
Second	First	5	6	8	10	12		16		20		25		30		40
	25	0.981	1.18	1.57	1.96	2.36	2.75	3.14	3.53	3.93	4.32					
28		1.10	1.32	1.76	2.20	2.64	3.08	3.52	3.96	4.40	4.84	5.50				
	30	1.18	1.41	1.88	2.36	2.83	3.30	3.77	4.24	4.71	5.18	5.89	6.59			
35		1.37	1.65	2.20	2.75	3.30	3.85	4.40	4.95	5.50	6.04	6.87	7.69	8.24		
	40	1.57	1.88	2.51	3.14	3.77	4.40	5.02	5.65	6.28	6.91	7.85	8.79	9.42	11.0	
45		1.77	2.12	2.83	3.53	4.24	4.95	5.65	6.36	7.07	7.77	8.83	9.89	10.6	12.4	14.1
	50	1.96	2.36	3.14	3.93	4.71	5.50	6.28	7.07	7.85	8.64	9.81	11.0	11.8	13.7	15.7
55		2.16	2.59	3.45	4.32	5.18	6.04	6.91	7.77	8.64	9.50	10.8	12.1	13.0	15.1	17.3
	60	2.36	2.83	3.77	4.71	5.65	6.59	7.54	8.48	9.42	10.4	11.8	13.2	14.1	16.5	18.8
70		2.75	3.30	4.40	5.50	6.59	7.69	8.79	9.89	11.0	12.1	13.7	15.4	16.5	19.2	22.0
	80	3.14	3.77	5.02	6.28	7.54	8.79	10.0	11.3	12.6	13.8	15.7	17.6	18.8	22.0	25.1
90		3.53	4.24	5.65	7.07	8.48	9.89	11.3	12.7	14.1	15.5	17.7	19.8	21.2	24.7	28.3
	100	3.93	4.71	6.28	7.85	9.42	11.0	12.6	14.1	15.7	17.3	19.6	22.0	23.6	27.5	31.4
110		4.32	5.18	6.91	8.64	10.4	12.1	13.8	15.5	17.3	19.0	21.6	24.2	25.9	30.2	34.5
	120	4.71	5.65	7.54	9.42	11.3	13.2	15.1	17.0	18.8	20.7	23.6	26.4	28.3	33.0	37.7
140		5.50	6.59	8.79	11.0	13.2	15.4	17.6	19.8	22.0	24.2	27.5	30.8	33.0	38.5	44.0
	160		7.54	10.0	12.6	15.1	17.6	20.1	22.6	25.1	27.6	31.4	35.2	37.7	44.0	50.2
180			8.48	11.3	14.1	17.0	19.8	22.6	25.4	28.3	31.1	35.3	39.6	42.4	49.5	56.5
	200		9.42	12.6	15.7	18.8	22.0	25.1	28.3	31.4	34.5	39.3	44.0	47.1	55.0	62.8
220			10.4	13.8	17.3	20.7	24.2	27.6	31.1	34.5	38.0	43.2	48.4	51.8	60.4	69.1
	250		11.8	15.7	19.6	23.6	27.5	31.4	35.3	39.3	43.2	49.1	55.0	58.9	68.7	78.5
300			14.1	18.8	23.6	28.3	33.0	37.7	42.4	47.1	51.8	58.9	65.9	70.7	82.4	94.2

Note: The mass has been computed using a steel density of 7 850 kg/m^3.

* Sizes are those listed in Table 2 of CAN3-G312.2-M76

SI WIRE SIZE – WIRE GAUGES COMPARISON

SI Wire Size Preferred Diam*. (mm)	The United States Steel Wire Gauge	American or Brown & Sharpe Wire Gauge	British Imperial or English Legal Standard Wire Gauge	Birmingham or Stubs Iron Wire Gauge
25.0				
24.0				
23.0				
22.0				
21.0				
20.0				
19.0				
18.0				
17.0				
16.0				
15.0				
		6/0's		
14.0				
		5/0's		
13.0				
			7/0's	5/0's
12.5				
	7/0's			
12.0				
11.8				
	6/0's	4/0's	6/0's	4/0's
11.2				
11.0				
	5/0's		5/0's	3/0's
10.6				
		3/0's	4/0's	
10.0	4/0's			
				2/0's
9.5				
	3/0's	2/0's	3/0's	
9.0				
			2/0's	1/0
8.5				
	2/0's	1/0	1/0	
8.0				
	1/0		1	1
7.5				
	1	1	2	2
7.0				
6.7	2			
		2		3
6.5				
			3	
6.3				
	3			4
6.0				

SI Wire Size Preferred Diam*. (mm)	The United States Steel Wire Gauge	American or Brown & Sharpe Wire Gauge	British Imperial or English Legal Standard Wire Gauge	Birmingham or Stubs Iron Wire Gauge
6.0				
	4	3	4	5
5.6				
			5	
5.3	5			
		4		6
5.0				
	6		6	
4.8				
		5		
4.6				
	7		7	7
4.4				
4.2				
	8	6	8	8
4.0				
3.8				
	9	7	9	9
3.6				
	10			
3.4				10
		8	10	
3.2				
	11			11
3.0				
		9	11	
2.8				
	12		12	12
2.6				
		10		13
2.4				
	13	11	13	
2.3				
2.2				
				14
2.1				
	14	12	14	
2.0				
1.90				
	15	13	15	15
1.80				
1.70				
		14	16	16
1.60				
	16			
1.50				

*From CAN3–G312.2-M76.

SI THICKNESS – IMPERIAL GAUGE COMPARISONS†

SI Preferred Thickness		United States Standard Gauge*				New Birmington Sheet Gauge		
		Weight	Ga. No.	Approximate thickness		Gauge Number	Thickness	
First mm	Second mm	Oz. per sq. ft.		Inches	mm		Inches	mm
	18							
						7/0's	0.6666	16.932
16								
						6/0's	0.6250	15.875
						5/0's	0.5883	14.943
	14							
						4/0's	0.5416	13.757
						3/0's	0.5000	12.700
12								
						2/0's	0.4452	11.562
	11							
						0	0.3964	10.069
10								
	9.0							
						1	0.3532	8.971
8.0								
						2	0.3147	7.993
						3	0.2804	7.122
7.0								
		160	3	0.2391	6.073	4	0.2500	6.350
6.0								
		150	4	0.2242	5.695	5	0.2225	5.652
	5.5							
		140	5	0.2092	5.314	6	0.1981	5.032
5.0								
		130	6	0.1943	4.935			
	4.8							
		120	7	0.1793	4.554			
4.5								
						7	0.1764	4.481
	4.2							
		110	8	0.1644	4.176			
4.0								
						8	0.1570	3.988
	3.8	100	9	0.1495	3.797			
						9	0.1398	3.551
3.5								
		90	10	0.1345	3.416			
	3.2							
		80	11	0.1196	3.038	10	0.1250	3.175
3.0								
						11	0.1113	2.827
	2.8							
		70	12	0.1046	2.657	12	0.0991	2.517
2.5								

†Preferred thicknesses are as per CAN3-G312.1-75.
*U.S. Standard Gauge is officially a weight gauge, in oz. per sq. ft. as tabulated. The Approx. thickness shown is the "Manufacturers' Standard" of the AISI based on a steel density of 501.81 lb. per ft.[3]

SI THICKNESS – IMPERIAL GAUGE COMPARISONS†

| SI Preferred Thickness | | United States Standard Gauge* | | | | New Birmington Sheet Gauge | | |
First mm	Second mm	Weight Oz. per sq. ft.	Ga. No.	Approximate thickness Inches	mm	Gauge Number	Thickness Inches	mm
		60	13	0.0897	2.278	13	0.0882	2.240
	2.2							
2.0						14	0.0785	1.994
		50	14	0.0747	1.897			
	1.8							
		45	15	0.0673	1.709	15	0.0699	1.775
1.6								
		40	16	0.0598	1.519	16	0.0625	1.588
						17	0.0556	1.412
	1.4							
		36	17	0.0538	1.367			
		32	18	0.0478	1.214	18	0.0495	1.257
1.2								
						19	0.0440	1.118
	1.1							
		28	19	0.0418	1.062			
1.0						20	0.0392	0.996
		24	20	0.0359	0.912			
	0.90							
		22	21	0.0329	0.836	21	0.0349	0.886
0.80						22	0.0313	0.795
		20	22	0.0299	0.759			
	0.70					23	0.0278	0.706
		18	23	0.0269	0.683			
	0.65							
						24	0.0248	0.630
0.60		16	24	0.0239	0.607			
						25	0.0220	0.559
	0.55							
		14	25	0.0209	0.531			
0.50						26	0.0196	0.498
	0.45	12	26	0.0179	0.455	27	0.0175	0.445
		11	27	0.0164	0.417			
0.40						28	0.0156	0.396
		10	28	0.0149	0.378			
	0.35	9	29	0.0135	0.343	29	0.0139	0.353
						30	0.0123	0.312
0.30		8	30	0.0120	0.305			
	0.28					31	0.0110	0.279
		7	31	0.0105	0.267			
0.25								

†Preferred thicknesses are as per CAN3-G312.1-75.
*U.S. Standard Gauge is officially a weight gauge, in oz. per sq. ft. as tabulated. The Approx. thickness shown is the "Manufacturers' Standard" of the AISI based on a steel density of 501.81 lb. per ft.[3]

MASS OF BARS
Round Bars

Preferred Nominal Size, mm		Mass*	Area	Preferred Nominal Size, mm		Mass*	Area	Preferred Nominal Size, mm		Mass*	Area
First	Second	kg/m	mm²	First	Second	kg/m	mm²	First	Second	kg/m	mm²
3.0		0.055 5	7.07		21	2.72	346		65	26.0	3 320
	3.5	0.075 5	9.62	22		2.98	380		70	30.2	3 850
4.0		0.098 6	12.6		23	3.26	415		72†	32.0	4 070
	4.5	0.125	15.9		24	3.55	452		75	34.7	4 420
5.0		0.154	19.6	25		3.85	491	80		39.5	5 030
	5.5	0.187	23.7		26	4.17	531		90	49.9	6 360
6.0		0.223	28.3		27†	4.49	573	100		61.7	7 850
	6.5	0.260	33.2		28	4.83	616		110	74.6	9 500
	7.0	0.302	38.5	30		5.55	707	120		88.8	11 300
8.0		0.395	50.3		32	6.31	804		130	104	13 300
	9.0	0.499	63.6	35		7.55	962	140		121	15 400
10		0.617	78.5		36†	7.99	1 020		150	139	17 700
	11	0.746	95.0		38	8.90	1 130	160		158	20 100
12		0.888	113	40		9.86	1 260		170	178	22 700
	13	1.04	133		42	10.9	1 390	180		200	25 400
14		1.21	154	45		12.5	1 590		190	223	28 400
	15	1.39	177		48	14.2	1 810	200		247	31 400
16		1.58	201	50		15.4	1 960		220	298	38 000
	17	1.78	227		55	18.7	2 380	250		385	49 100
18		2.00	254		56†	19.3	2 460		280	483	61 600
	19	2.23	284	60		22.2	2 830	300		555	70 700
20		2.47	314		64†	25.3	3 220		320	631	80 400

† Screw Stock, not listed in CAN3-G312.2-M76.

Square Bars

Preferred Nominal Size, mm		Mass*	Area	Preferred Nominal Size, mm		Mass*	Area	Preferred Nominal Size, mm		Mass*	Area
First	Second	kg/m	mm²	First	Second	kg/m	mm²	First	Second	kg/m	mm²
3.0		0.070 6	9.00	25		4.91	625	100		78.5	10 000
4.0		0.126	16.0		28	6.15	784		110	93.0	12 100
5.0		0.196	25.0	30		7.06	900	120		113	14 400
6.0		0.283	36.0		35	9.62	1 220		140	154	19 600
8.0		0.502	64.0	40		12.6	1 600	160		201	25 600
10		0.785	100		45	15.9	2 020		180	254	32 400
12		1.13	144	50		19.6	2 500	200		314	40 000
	14	1.54	196		55	23.7	3 020		220	380	48 400
16		2.01	256	60		28.3	3 600	250		491	62 500
	18	2.54	324		70	38.5	4 900	300		706	90 000
20		3.14	400	80		50.2	6 400				
	22	3.80	484		90	63.6	8 100				

*Computed using a steel density of 7 850 kg/m³

CRANE RAILS

General

Crane rails and their accessories have not to date been converted into metric. The SI dimensions and properties given on the following pages have been soft converted from manufacture's catalogues. Crane rails are specified by their mass in pounds per linear yard Bolt sizes, hole diameters, and washer sizes are dimensioned in inches. Since the ASCE 40, 60 and 85 pound rails require special drilling and punching at time of purchase, substitution of hard metric bolt products could be made. All other rail sizes are predrilled and punched by the manufacturer and therefore the manufacturer should be checked as to the availability of metric fasteners and their appropriate holes.

The rails listed in this handbook are the most popular sizes used for crane runways. If a dimension or property is not given in the tables, consult the manufacturer.

The ASCE 40 and 60 lb. rails are usually supplied in 9 140 mm lengths, the ASCE 60 and 85 pounds rails are available in 10 100 mm lengths and the ASCE 85 pound and heavier rails are available in 11 900 mm lengths. When ordering, the number of required lengths should be specified plus one short length in each run, if bolted rail bar splices are to be used, in order to permit staggering of the joints. When ordering, ensure that the order clearly specifies that "THESE RAILS ARE INTENDED FOR CRANE SERVICE".

Often the ends of the rails are hardened so as to render the metal tougher and better suited to resist rail end batter. Most manufacturer's will chamfer the top and sides of the rail head at the ends, unless it is specified otherwise by the purchaser. Chamferring of the rail ends permits mild deformations to occur thus minimizing chipping of the running surfaces.

When choosing a rail for crane service, the characteristics of operation must be taken under consideration. Some of the more common variables which affect the service life are:

- Frequency of operation
- Crane carriage speed and impacts — rate of loading and unloading
- Corrosion — acidic mill conditions
- Abrasion
- Alignment and integrity of crane and supporting members
- Crane operating procedures

Crane rails are joined together end-to-end by either mechanical fasteners or welding. If bolting is used, special joint bars are employed as shown on page 6—114 and the rails are usually predrilled to 1/16-inch larger than the specified bolt size. If welded, manual arc welding is usually used and joint bars are not required. Welding has the advantage of eliminating mechanical joints and therefore the problems of ensuring that the tops of the rails are flush with each other.

PROPERTIES AND DIMENSIONS

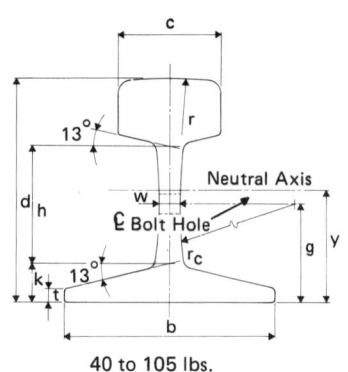

40 to 105 lbs.

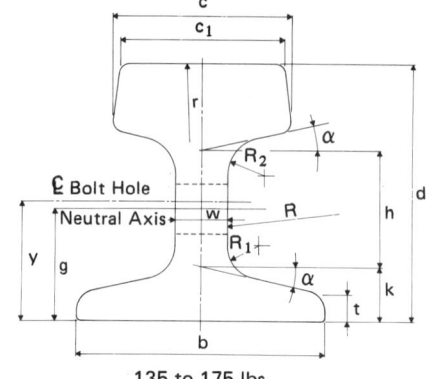

135 to 175 lbs.

Dimensions

Rail Type	Depth d	Head c	Base b	Base t	Web w	Web Gauge g	k	h	r	r_c	R
	mm	mm	mm	mm	mm	mm	mm	mm	mm	mm	mm
ASCE 40	89	48	89	6	10	40	16	47	305	6.4	305
ASCE 60	108	60	108	7	12	52	19	58	305	6.4	305
ASCE 85	132	65	132	8	14	63	23	70	305	6.4	305
BETH 104	127	64	127	13	25	62	27	62	305	12.7	89
USS 105	132	65	132	10	24	56	25	61	305	6.4	305

Dimensions

Rail Type	Depth d	Head c	Head c_1	Base b	Base t	Web w	Web Gauge g	k	h	r	R	R_1	R_2	α
	mm	mm	mm	mm	mm	mm	mm	mm	mm	mm	mm	mm	mm	deg
USS or BETH 135	146	87	76	132	12	32	63	27	71	356	305	19	19	13
BETH 171	152	109	102	152	16	32	67	32	70	FLAT	VERT	19	22	12
USS or BETH 175	152	108	102	152	13	38	68	29	79	457	VERT	29	51	12

Properties

Rail Type	Mass kg/m	Dead Load kN/m	Area mm^2	I_x $10^6 mm^4$	S_x Head $10^3 mm^3$	S_x Base $10^3 mm^3$	y mm
ASCE 40	19.8	0.195	2 540	2.72	58.8	63.7	42.7
60	29.8	0.292	3 830	6.06	108	116	52.1
85	42.2	0.413	5 370	12.5	182	199	62.7
BETH 104	51.6	0.506	6 640	12.4	175	221	56.1
USS 105	52.1	0.511	6 650	14.3	203	234	61.2
USS & BETH 135	67.0	0.657	8 590	21.1	282	295	71.1
BETH 171	84.9	0.832	10 800	30.6	402	400	76.5
USS & BETH 175	86.8	0.851	11 000	29.2	386	381	76.7

RAIL FASTENERS

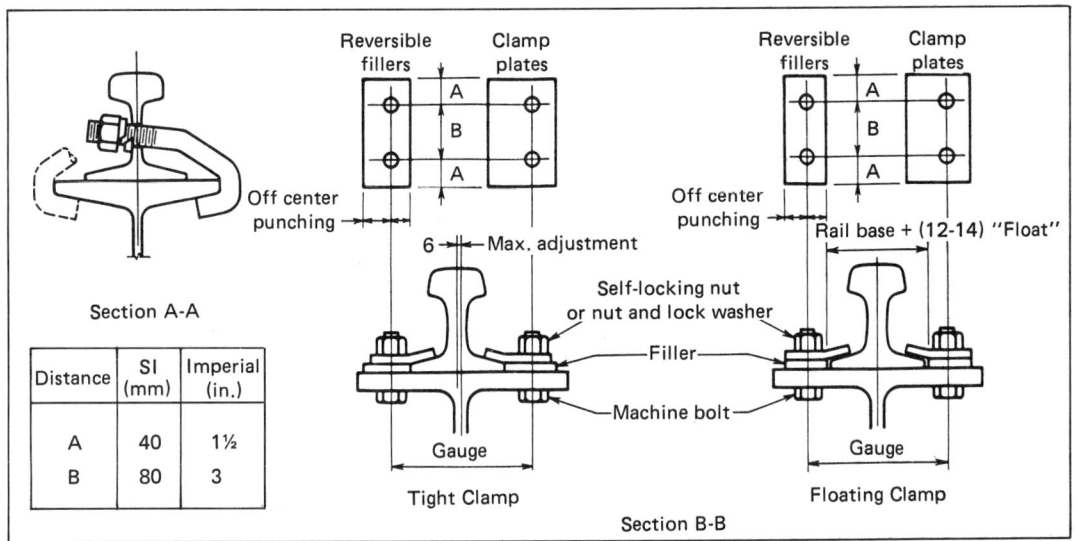

Distance	SI (mm)	Imperial (in.)
A	40	1½
B	80	3

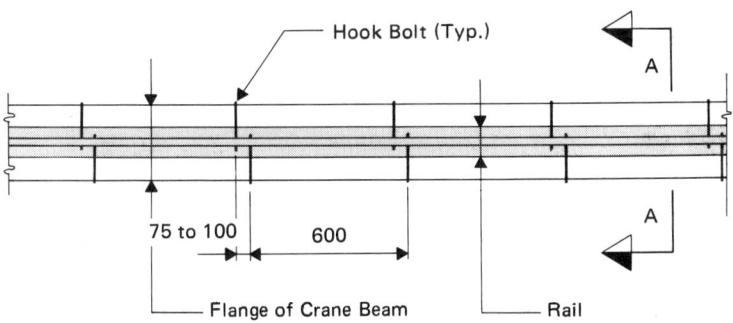

Hook bolts are primarily used when the flange of the crane beam is too narrow to permit the use of rail clamps. These hooks may be adjusted plus or minus 12 mm. Since the hooks are used in groups of 2, 75 to 100 mm apart, at 600 mm centres, the rails require special preparation which is done either in the fabricator's shop or in some instances by the crane rail supplier.

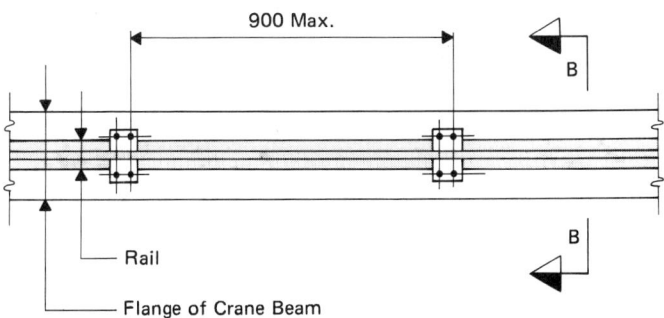

The rail clamp dimensions shown in Section B-B are suggested only. Reference should be made to track accessory manufacturer's catalogues for prefabricated rail clamps. These clamps are available in two primary types; the tight clamp and the floating clamp. The latter is used when longitudinal and controlled transverse movement is required for thermal expansion and alignment. Rail clamps are available fabricated from pressed or forge steel and usually have single or double bolts.

RAIL SPLICES

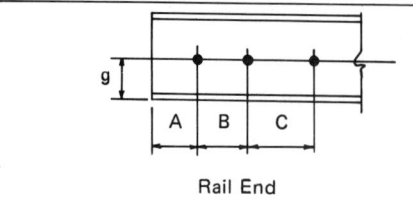

Rail End

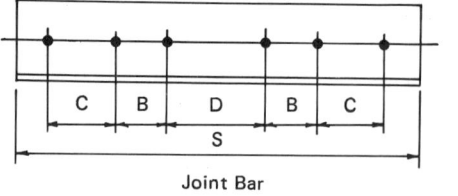

Joint Bar

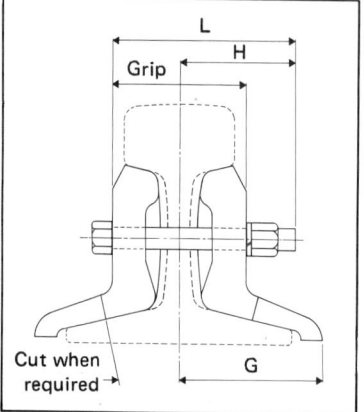

40 to 105 lbs.

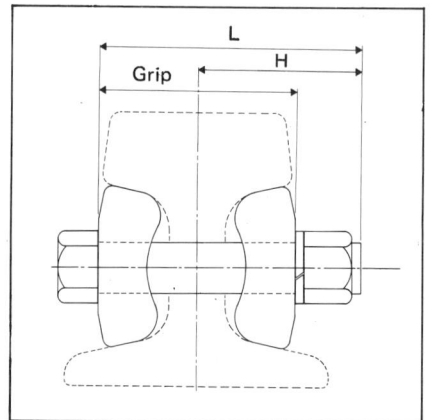

135 to 175 lbs.

Rail Type	Rail						Joint Bar					
	g	Hole dia.	A	B	C		Hole dia.	D	B	C	S	G
	mm	inch.	mm	mm	mm		inch.	mm	mm	mm	mm	mm
40	39.5	*13/16	63.5	127	—		*13/16	125	127	—	508	55.6
60	48.2	*13/16	63.5	127	—		*13/16	125	127	—	610	68.3
85	57.5	*15/16	63.5	127	—		*15/16	125	127	—	610	84.9
104	61.9	1-1/16	102	127	152		1-1/16	202	127	152	864	88.9
105	56.0	15/16	102	127	152		15/16	202	127	152	864	—
135	62.7	1-3/16	102	127	152		1-3/16	202	127	152	864	—
171	66.7	1-3/16	102	127	152		1-3/16	202	127	152	864	—
175	67.5	1-3/16	102	127	152		1-3/16	202	127	152	864	—

*special rail drilling and joint bar punching.

Rail Type	Bolt				Spring Washer		Mass of Ass'y	
	diam.	Grip	L	H	Hole dia.	Thk. & width	With Flg.	Without Flg.
	in.	mm	mm	mm	in.	in. in.	kg.	kg.
40	3/4	49.2	88.9	63.5	13/16	7/16 x 3/8	9.07	7.48
60	3/4	65.9	102	68.3	13/16	7/16 x 3/8	16.56	13.43
85	7/8	80.2	121	81.0	15/16	7/16 x 3/8	25.67	20.55
104	1	88.9	133	88.9	1-1/16	7/16 x 1/2	33.34	25.13
105	7/8	85.7	127	84.1	15/16	7/16 x 3/8	—	27.67
135	1-1/8	92.1	140	93.7	1-3/16	7/16 x 1/2	—	34.16
171	1-1/8	113	159	103	1-3/16	7/16 x 1/2	—	41.19
175	1-1/8	105	152	100	1-3/16	7/16 x 1/2	—	39.78

† For complete description of rail type, see Properties and Dimensions on page 6-112.

Splices

Rail drilling and joint bar punching as supplied for track work is not advised for use in crane runways. The oversized holes used allow too much movement at the rail ends and may eventually result in a failure. For best service it is recommended that tight joints be specified for crane service. This requires special rail and joint bar drilling (see table, page 6—114) and squaring of the rail ends. Light rails are not finished at the mill but are finished at the fabricator's shop or at the erection site. Since the dimensions for the splices have tolerances they may accumulate to the point where reaming of holes may be required to properly fit the bolts.

Joint bars are provided for crane service to match the rails ordered and may be blank, if so ordered. Under no circumstances should these be used as welding straps. Welded straps, regardless of their design, should not be used to splice crane rails. The manufacturer's catalogue should be consulted for joint bar material specifications, dimensions and identification necessary to match the crane rail section.

Joint bar bolts for crane service are easily identified from those for track work as they have straight shanks and are manufactured to ASTM A449 specification. The matching nuts are manufactured to ASTM A563 Grade B. Bolts and nuts manufactured to ASTM A325 are also acceptable for this use. As noted in the sketches, the bolted assembly includes an alloy steel spring washer which is furnished to A.R.E.A. specification.

After the installation of the track, the bolts should be retightened within 30 days and every 3 months thereafter. This is an important procedure in prolonging the life of the runway installation.

FASTENERS

General

The information on fasteners, provided herein, is based on standards, specifications and publications of the following organizations:

The Canadian Standards Association
The American National Standards Institute
The Industrial Fasteners Institute
The Research Council on Structural Connections
(formerly The Research Council on Riveted and Bolted Structural Joints)

Additional information on fasteners can be obtained from the various fastener manufacturers and from the Canadian Fasteners Institute.

Definitions — Terms relating to Bolts and Nuts

Body Length means the distance from the underside of the head bearing surface to either the last scratch of thread or the top of the extrusion angle, whichever is the closest to the head.

Bolt Length means the length from the underside of the head bearing surface to the extreme point.

Finished Fastener means a fastener made to close tolerances and having surfaces other than the threads and bearing surface finished to provide a general high grade appearance.

Grip means the thickness of material or parts which the fastener is designed to secure when fully assembled.

Height of Bolt Head means the overall distance, measured parallel to the fastener axis, from the extreme top (excluding raised identification marks) to the bearing surface and including the thickness of the washer face where provided.

Natural Finish means the as processed finish, unplated or uncoated of the bolt or nut.

Nominal Size means the designation used for the purpose of general identification.

Proof Load means a specified test load which a fastener must withstand without any indication of significant deformation or failure.

Thickness of Nut means the overall distance from the top of the nut to the bearing surface, measured parallel to the axis of the nut.

Thread Length of a Bolt means the distance from the extreme point to the last complete thread.

Transition Thread Length means the distance from the last complete thread to either the last scratch of thread or the top of the extrusion angle, whichever is the closest to the head.

Washer Face means a circular boss on the bearing surface of a bolt or nut.

ASTM A325M AND ASTM A490M**
HIGH STRENGTH BOLTS AND NUTS

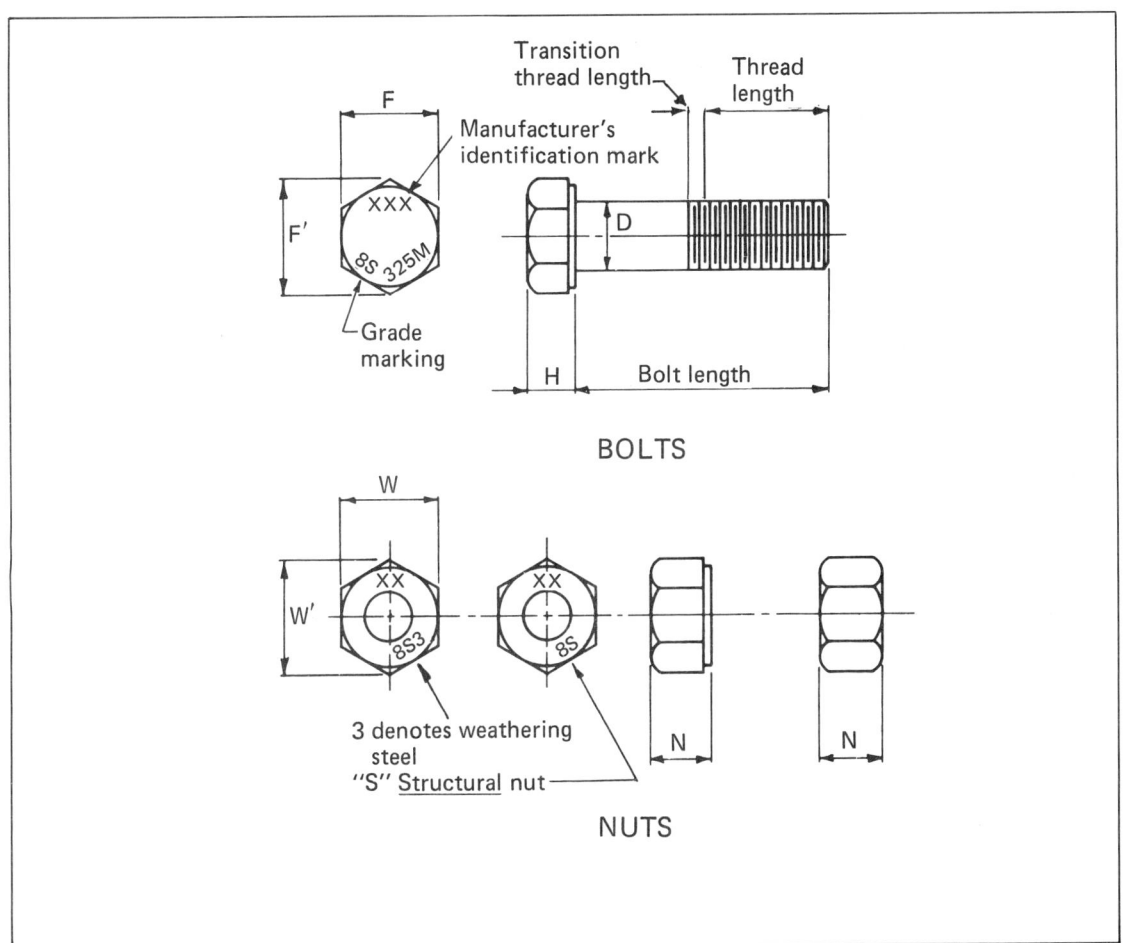

BOLTS

NUTS

DIMENSIONS

Nominal Bolt Size	Heavy Hex Bolt or Nut Dimension					Heavy Hex Structural Bolt				
	Across Flats F or W		Across Corners F' or W'		Heavy Hex Nut Max. Height N	Max Head Height H	Thread Length*		Max. Transition Thread Length
	Max.	Min.	Max.	Min.			Bolt Lengths ⩽100	Bolt Lengths >100	
mm	mm	mm	mm	mm	mm	mm	mm	mm	mm
M16 x 2	27.00	26.16	31.18	29.56	17.1	10.75	31	38	6.0
M20 x 2.5	34.00	33.00	39.26	37.29	20.7	13.40	36	43	7.5
M22 x 2.5	36.00	35.00	41.57	39.55	23.6	14.90	38	45	7.5
M24 x 3	41.00	40.00	47.34	45.20	24.2	15.90	41	48	9.0
M27 x 3	46.00	45.00	53.12	50.85	27.6	17.90	44	51	9.0
M30 x 3.5	50.00	49.00	57.74	55.37	30.7	19.75	49	56	10.5
M36 x 4	60.00	58.80	69.28	66.44	36.6	23.55	56	63	12.0

*Does not include transition thread length.

Bolt dimensions conform to those listed in ANSI B18.2.3.7M-1979 "Metric Heavy Hex Structural Bolts", and the nut dimensions conform to those listed in CSA Standard B18.2.4.6-M1980 "Metric Heavy Hex Nuts".

** Strength requirements are based on ASTM Specifications A325M-79 and A490M (tentative). See page 3—5.

WASHERS

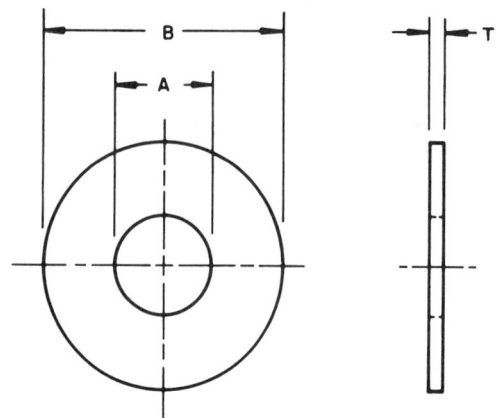

PLAIN CIRCULAR WASHERS

Metric Bolt Size	B		A		T	
	Outside Diameter		Hole Diameter		Thickness	
	Max	Min	Max	Min	Max	Min
M16 x 2	34.0	32.4	18.4	18.0	4.6	3.1
M20 x 2.5	41.0	39.4	22.5	22.0	4.6	3.1
M22 x 2.5	44.0	42.4	24.5	24.0	4.6	3.4
M24 x 3	50.0	48.4	26.5	26.0	4.6	3.4
M27 x 3	56.0	54.1	30.5	30.0	4.6	3.4
M30 x 3.5	60.0	58.1	33.5	33.0	4.6	3.4
M36 x 4	72.0	70.1	39.5	39.0	4.6	3.4

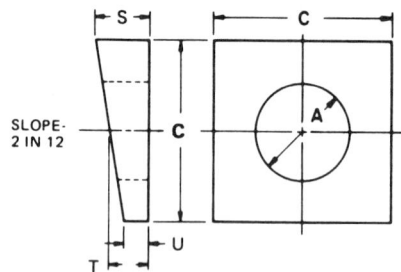

BEVELLED SQUARE WASHERS

Metric Bolt Size	C		A		S	T	U
	Width		Hole Diameter			Thickness	
					Thick Side ±0.5	Mean Nom.	Thin Side ±0.5
	Max	Min	Max	Min			
M16 x 2	45.0	43.0	18.4	18.0	11.7	8	4.3
M20 x 2.5	45.0	43.0	22.5	22.0	11.7	8	4.3
M22 x 2.5	45.0	43.0	24.5	24.0	11.7	8	4.3
M24 x 3	45.0	43.0	26.5	26.0	11.7	8	4.3
M27 x3	59.0	57.0	30.5	30.0	12.8	8	3.2
M30 x 3.5	59.0	57.0	33.5	33.0	12.8	8	3.2
M36 x 4	59.0	57.0	39.5	39.0	12.8	8	3.2

ASTM A325M BOLTS, NUTS AND WASHERS

APPROXIMATE MASS* OF 1000 UNITS (kg)

Bolt Length	Bolt Size (number following the letter M is the nominal bolt diameter in millimetres)						
mm	M16	M20	M22	M24	M27	M30	M36
40	170						
45	177	321	396				
50	184	331	409	539	744		
55	191	342	423	554	764		
60	198	353	436	570	784	1000	
65	204	364	449	586	804	1030	
70	211	375	462	601	824	1050	1710
75	218	386	476	617	845	1000	1750
80	225	397	489	632	865	1100	1780
85	232	407	502	648	885	1120	1820
90	239	418	515	664	905	1150	1850
95	246	429	529	679	925	1170	1890
100	253	440	542	695	945	1200	1920
110	267	462	569	726	985	1250	2000
120	281	483	595	757	1020	1300	2070
130	295	505	622	788	1070	1350	2140
140	309	527	648	820	1110	1400	2210
150	322	548	675	851	1150	1440	2280
160	336	570	701	882	1190	1490	2350
170	350	592	728	913	1230	1540	2420
180	364	613	754	945	1270	1590	2490
190	378	635	781	976	1310	1640	2570
Extra per 10 mm	13.9	21.7	26.5	31.2	40.1	49.2	71.3
Mass of Nuts	61.0	118	145	201	286	371	635
Mass of Plain Washers	4.75	6.91	7.88	10.7	13.0	14.7	21.6
Mass of Bevel Washers	105	97.2	92.6	87.6	166	157	135

*Computed theoretical mass using a steel density of 7 850 kg/m^3.

MINIMUM AND MAXIMUM GRIPS FOR METRIC HEAVY HEX. STRUCTURAL BOLTS, IN MILLIMETRES

Nominal Bolt Size	M16		M20		M22		M24		M27		M30		M36	
L Nominal Length (mm)	Min. Grip	Max. Grip	Min. Grip	Max. Grip	Min. Grip	Max. Grip	Min. Grip	Max. Grip	Min. Grip	Max. Grip	Min. Grip	Max. Grip	Min. Grip	Max. Grip
45	14	26		23		20								
50	19	31	14	28		25		24						
55	24	36	19	32	17	29		29		25				
60	29	41	24	37	22	34	19	34		30		27		
65	34	46	29	42	27	39	24	39	21	35		32		
70	39	51	34	47	32	44	29	44	26	40	21	37		31
75	44	56	39	52	37	49	34	49	31	45	26	42		36
80	49	61	44	57	42	54	39	54	36	50	31	47	24	41
85	54	66	49	62	47	59	44	59	41	55	36	52	29	46
90	59	71	54	67	52	64	49	64	46	60	41	57	34	51
95	64	76	59	72	57	69	54	69	51	65	46	62	39	56
100	69	81	64	77	62	74	59	74	56	70	51	67	44	61
110	72	91	67	87	65	84	62	84	59	80	54	77	47	71
120	82	101	77	97	75	94	72	94	69	90	64	87	57	81
130	92	110	87	107	85	104	82	103	79	100	74	97	67	91
140	102	120	97	117	95	114	92	113	89	110	84	107	77	101
150	112	130	107	127	105	124	102	123	99	120	94	117	87	111
160	122	138	117	135	115	132	112	131	109	128	104	125	97	119
170	132	148	127	145	125	142	122	141	119	138	114	135	107	129
180	142	158	137	155	135	152	132	151	129	148	124	145	117	139
190	152	168	147	165	145	162	142	161	139	158	134	155	127	149
200	162	178	157	175	155	172	152	171	149	168	144	165	137	159
210	172	188	167	185	165	182	162	181	159	178	154	175	147	169
220	182	198	177	195	175	192	172	191	169	188	164	185	157	179
230	192	208	187	205	185	202	182	201	179	198	174	195	167	189
240	202	218	197	215	195	212	192	211	189	208	184	205	177	199
250	212	228	207	225	205	222	202	221	199	218	194	215	187	209
260	222	238	217	235	215	232	212	231	209	228	204	225	197	219
270	232	248	227	245	225	242	222	241	219	238	214	235	207	229
280	242	258	237	255	235	252	232	251	229	248	224	245	217	239
290	252	268	247	265	245	262	242	261	239	258	234	255	227	249
300	262	278	257	275	255	272	252	271	249	268	244	265	237	259

1. This table is based on ANSI B18.2.3.7M-1979.
2. Bolts with lengths above the heavy solid line are threaded full length.

ASTM A325 AND ASTM A490 HIGH STRENGTH BOLTS
Bolt Lengths in inches for Various Grips in millimetres

Grip, mm	Bolt Diam, in. ½	⅝	¾	⅞	1	1⅛	1¼	1⅜	1½
20 / 22	1½	1¾		2			2½		2¾
24 / 26 / 28	1¾	2	2	2¼	2½		2¾	2¾	3
30 / 32 / 34	2	2¼	2¼	2½	2¾	3	3		3¼
36 / 38 / 40	2¼	2½	2½	2¾	3	3¼	3¼		3½
42 / 44 / 46	2½	2¾	2¾	3	3¼	3½	3½		3¾
48 / 50 / 52	2¾	3	3	3¼	3½	3¾	3¾		4
54 / 56 / 58	3	3¼	3¼	3½	3¾	4	4		4¼
60 / 62 / 64	3¼	3½	3½	3¾	4	4¼	4¼		4½
66 / 68 / 70	3½	3¾	3¾	4	4¼	4½	4½		4¾
72 / 74 / 76	3¾	4	4	4¼	4½	4¾	4¾		5

Grip, mm	Bolt Diam, in. ½	⅝	¾	⅞	1	1⅛	1¼	1⅜	1½
(76)	4			4¼			4¾		5
78 / 80 / 82 / 84	4	4¼	4¼	4½	4¾		5	5	5¼
86 / 88 / 90	4¼	4½	4½	4¾	5	5¼	5¼		5½
92 / 94 / 96	4½	4¾	4¾	5	5¼	5½	5½		5¾
98 / 100 / 102	4¾	5	5	5¼	5½	5¾	5¾		6
104 / 106 / 108	5	5¼	5¼	5½	5¾	6	6		6¼
110 / 112 / 114	5¼	5½	5½	5¾	6	6¼	6¼		6½
116 / 118 / 120 / 122	5½	5¾	5¾	6	6¼	6½	6½		6¾
124 / 126 / 128	5¾	6	6	6¼	6½	6¾	6¾		7
130 / 132 / 134	6	6¼	6¼	6½	6¾	7	7		7¼

*Grip is thickness of material to be connected *exclusive of washers*.

For each flat washer used, add 5 mm to grip.

For each beveled washer used, add 8 mm to grip.

ASTM A307 BOLTS AND NUTS
DIMENSIONS IN IMPERIAL UNITS

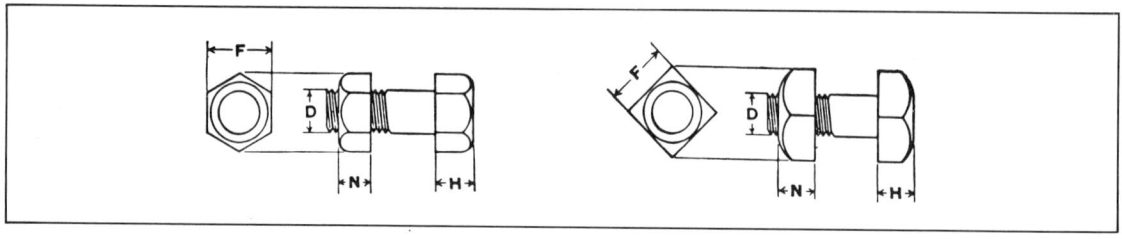

Nominal Diameter of Bolt	Regular Square Bolts		Finished Hex Bolts		Minimum Thread Lengths		Regular Square Nuts		Finished Hex Nuts	
	Nominal Width F	Nominal Height H	Basic Width F	Basic Height H	Length Under Head		Nominal Width F	Nominal Height N	Basic Width F	Basic Height N
					6 In. and Under	Over 6 In.				
Inches	Inches	Inches	Inches	Inches	Inches	Inches	Inches	Inches	Inches	Inches
1/4	3/8	11/64	7/16	5/32	¾	1	7/16	7/32	7/16	7/32
3/8	9/16	1/4	9/16	15/64	1	1¼	5/8	21/64	9/16	21/64
1/2	3/4	21/64	3/4	5/16	1¼	1½	13/16	7/16	3/4	7/16
5/8	15/16	27/64	15/16	25/64	1½	1¾	1	35/64	15/16	35/64
3/4	1 1/8	1/2	1 1/8	15/32	1¾	2	1 1/8	21/32	1 1/8	41/64
7/8	1 5/16	19/32	1 5/16	35/64	2	2¼	1 5/16	49/64	1 5/16	3/4
1	1 1/2	21/32	1 1/2	39/64	2¼	2½	1 1/2	7/8	1 1/2	55/64
1 1/8	1 11/16	3/4	1 11/16	11/16	2½	2¾	1 11/16	1	1 11/16	31/32
1 1/4	1 7/8	27/32	1 7/8	25/32	2¾	3	1 7/8	1 3/32	1 7/8	1 1/16

The dimensions for Regular Square Bolts conform to those for Square Head Bolts, Regular Series listed in CSA Standard B33.1-1961, "Square and Hexagon Bolts and Nuts, Studs and Wrench Openings", and to those for Square Bolts listed in ANSI Standard B18.2.1-1965, "Square and Hex Bolts and Screws".

The dimensions for Finished Hexagon Bolts (Hex Cap Screws) conform to those for Hexagon Head Bolts, Finished Grade, Regular Series listed in CSA Standard B33.1-1961, and to those for Hex Cap Screws (Finished Hex Bolts) listed in ANSI Standard B18.2.1-1965.

The minimum thread lengths are in agreement with the requirements of CSA Standard B33.1-1961 and with ANSI Standard B18.2.1-1965. In general, these requirements are as follows:

Bolts 6 inches or less in length — twice diameter plus ¼-inch.
Bolts longer than 6 inches — twice diameter plus ½-inch.
Bolts too short for the above thread lengths shall be threaded as close to the head as practicable.

The dimensions for Regular Square Nuts conform to those for Square Nuts, Regular Series listed in CSA Standard B33.1-1961, and to those for Square Nuts listed in ANSI Standard B18.2.2-1965, "Square and Hex Nuts".

The dimensions for Finished Hexagon Nuts conform to those for Hexagon Nuts, Finished Grade, Regular Series listed in CSA Standard B33.1-1961 and to those for Hex Nuts listed in ANSI Standard B18.2.2-1965.

Note: Square head bolts are used with either square or hexagon nuts. However, the use of Finished Hexagon Bolts and Finished Hexagon Nuts is gradually replacing the use of square head bolts and nuts in sizes up to one inch in diameter and six inches in length.
A307 bolts and nuts are manufactured in Imperial dimensions only.

THREAD DATA

Diameter Pitch Combinations

Nominal dia. (mm)	Thread pitch (mm)	Nominal dia. (mm)	Thread pitch (mm)
1.6	0.35	20	2.5
2	0.4	22	2.5
2.5	0.45	24	3
3	0.5	27	3
3.5	0.6	30	3.5
4	0.7	36	4
5	0.8	42	4.5
6.0	1.0	48	5
8	1.25	56	5.5
10	1.5	64	6
12	1.75	72	6
14	2	80	6
16	2	90	6
		100	6

Basic Metric Thread designation: Metric screw threads are designated by the letter "M" followed by the nominal size (basic major diameter) in millimetres and the pitch in millimetres separated by the symbol "X".

M12	X	**1.75**	**−6g**
Size (mm)		Thread (pitch in mm)	Standard class of fit

Note: In the metric system, the pitch of the thread is given in mm instead of threads per inch — thus a M12 × 1.75 thread has a nominal diameter of 12 mm and the pitch of the thread is 1.75 mm.

PRODUCT DESIGNATION

Metric Bolt designation: The standard method of designating a metric bolt is by specifying (in sequence) the product name, nominal diameter and thread pitch, nominal length, type, steel property class, and protective coating (if required).

Heavy Hex Structural Bolt, M22 × 2.5 × 160, Type 2, ASTM A325M-79, Zinc Galvanized

Metric Nut designation: The standard method of designating a metric nut is by specifying (in sequence) the product name, nominal diameter and pitch, steel property class or material identification, and protective coating (if required).

Heavy Hex Nut, M30 × 3.5, ASTM A563M class 105, hot dipped galvanized

Note: It is common practice to omit the thread pitch from the product designation.

SLOT DIMENSIONS

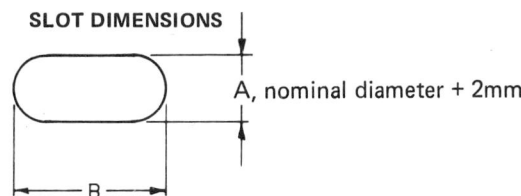

A, nominal diameter + 2mm

SHORT SLOT DIMENSIONS*

Nominal Bolt Diameter	Slot Dimensions	
	Width, A	Length, B
mm	mm	mm
16	18	22
20	22	26
22	24	28
24	26	32
27	29	37
30	32	40
36	38	46

LONG SLOT DIMENSIONS*

Nominal Bolt Diameter	Slot Dimensions	
	Width, A	Length, B
mm	mm	mm
16	18	40
20	22	50
22	24	55
24	26	60
27	29	67.5
30	32	75
36	38	90

*See S16.1-M78 Clause 22.3.2 for use provisions.

STAGGERED FASTENERS

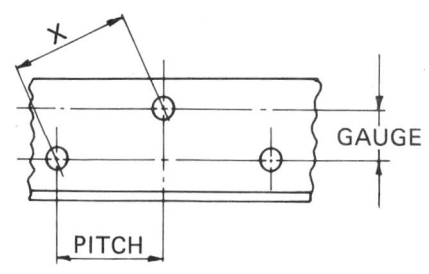

Pitch mm	GAUGE, mm																	
	25	30	35	40	45	50	55	60	65	70	75	80	85	90	95	100	105	110
5	25	30	35	40	45	50	55	60	65	70	75	80	85	90	95	100	105	110
10	27	32	36	41	46	51	56	61	66	71	76	81	86	91	96	100	105	110
15	29	34	38	43	47	52	57	62	67	72	76	81	86	91	96	101	106	111
20	32	36	40	45	49	54	59	63	68	73	78	82	87	92	97	102	107	112
25	35	39	43	47	51	56	60	65	70	74	79	84	89	93	98	103	108	113
30	39	42	46	50	54	58	63	67	72	76	81	85	90	95	100	104	109	114
35	43	46	49	53	57	61	65	69	74	78	83	87	92	97	101	106	111	115
40	47	50	53	57	60	64	68	72	76	81	85	89	94	98	103	108	112	117
45	51	54	57	60	64	67	71	75	79	83	87	92	96	101	105	110	114	119
50	56	58	61	64	67	71	74	78	82	86	90	94	99	103	107	112	116	121
55	60	63	65	68	71	74	78	81	85	89	93	97	101	105	110	114	119	123
60	65	67	69	72	75	78	81	85	88	92	96	100	104	108	112	117	121	125
65	70	72	74	76	79	82	85	88	92	96	99	103	107	111	115	119	123	128
70	74	76	78	81	83	86	89	92	96	99	103	106	110	114	118	122	126	130
75	79	81	83	85	87	90	93	96	99	103	106	110	113	117	121	125	129	133
80	84	85	87	89	92	94	97	100	103	106	110	113	117	120	124	128	132	136
85	89	90	92	94	99	99	101	104	107	110	113	117	120	124	127	131	135	139
90	93	95	97	98	101	103	105	108	111	114	117	120	124	127	131	135	138	142

BOLT LENGTH TOLERANCES

Nominal Length	Nominal Bolt Dia
	M16 thru M36
to 50 mm	± 1.2
over 50 to 80 mm	± 1.5
over 80 to 120 mm	± 1.8
over 120 to 150 mm	± 2.0
over 150 mm	± 4.0

MINIMUM EDGE DISTANCE FOR BOLT HOLES

Bolt Diameter mm	At sheared Edge mm	At Rolled or Gas Cut Edge † mm
16	28	22
20	34	26
22	38	28
24	42	30
27	48	34
30	52	38
36	64	46
over 36	1¾ x Diameter	1¼ x Diameter

†Gas cut edges shall be smooth and free from notches. Edge distance in this column may be decreased 3 mm when hole is at a point where computed stress under factored loads is not more than 0.3 of the yield stress.

USUAL GAUGES for W, M, S and C Shapes, Millimetres

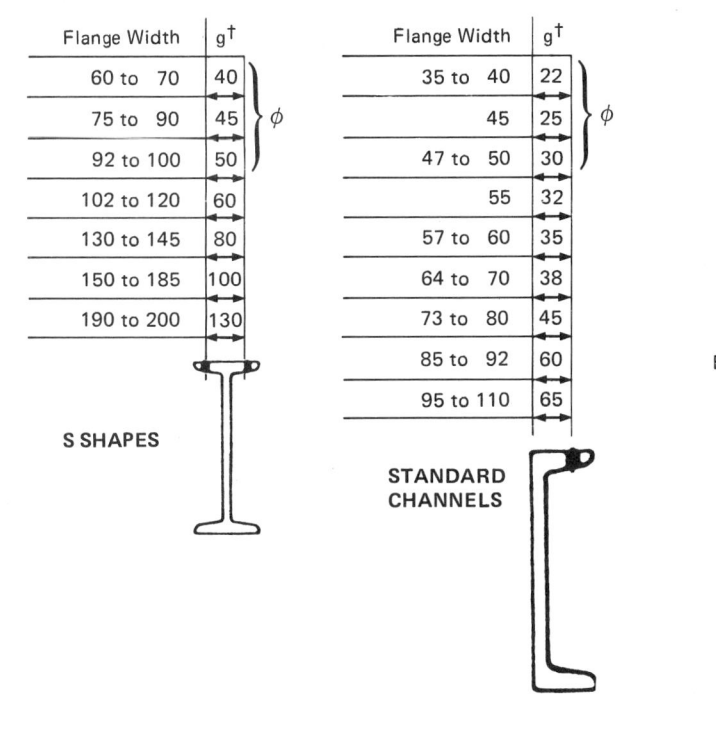

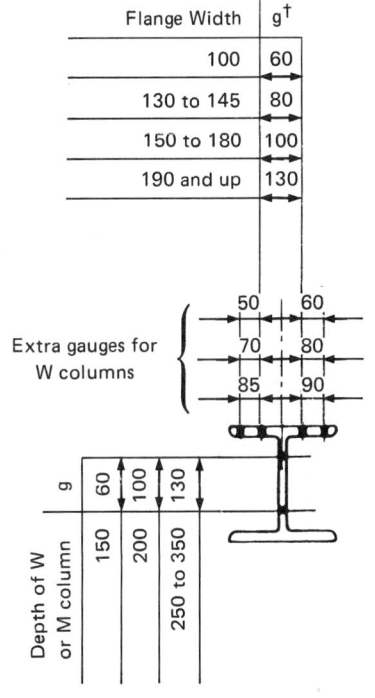

Flange Width	g†
60 to 70	40
75 to 90	45
92 to 100	50
102 to 120	60
130 to 145	80
150 to 185	100
190 to 200	130

φ

S SHAPES

Flange Width	g†
35 to 40	22
45	25
47 to 50	30
55	32
57 to 60	35
64 to 70	38
73 to 80	45
85 to 92	60
95 to 110	65

φ

STANDARD CHANNELS

Flange Width	g†
100	60
130 to 145	80
150 to 180	100
190 and up	130

Extra gauges for W columns

Depth of W or M column	g
150	60
200	100
250 to 350	130

W AND M SHAPES

φ Holes usually drilled due to size of punch die block.

† Dependent on edge distance — see page 6-124.

USUAL GAUGES for Angles, millimetres

Notes:
Those values shown above the dashed line allow for full socket wrench clearance requirements.

The bolt sizes shown in italics to the left of g and g_1 are the maximum bolt sizes permissible for the dimensions shown.

$g_2 \geqslant$ 2-2/3 bolt diameters.

Gauge Leg	g		g_1		g_2
200	M36	115	M30	80	80
150	M36	90	M24	55	65
125	M30	80	M20	45	54
100	M27	65			
90	M24	60			
80	M24	50			
75	M24	45			
65	M24	35			
60	M24	30			
55	M22	27			
50	M16	30			
45	M16	23			
35	M12	17			

BOLTS
Erection Clearances for Impact Wrenches

METRIC	IMPERIAL

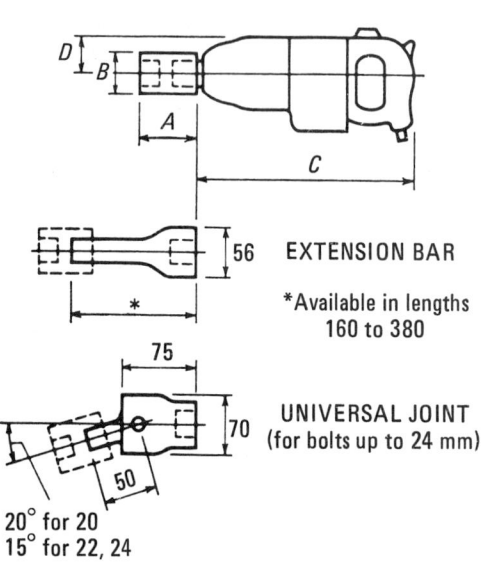

56 EXTENSION BAR

*Available in lengths
160 to 380

75

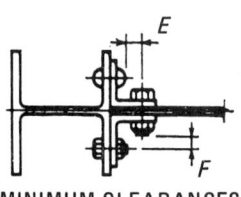

70 UNIVERSAL JOINT
(for bolts up to 24 mm)

50

20° for 20
15° for 22, 24

MINIMUM CLEARANCES

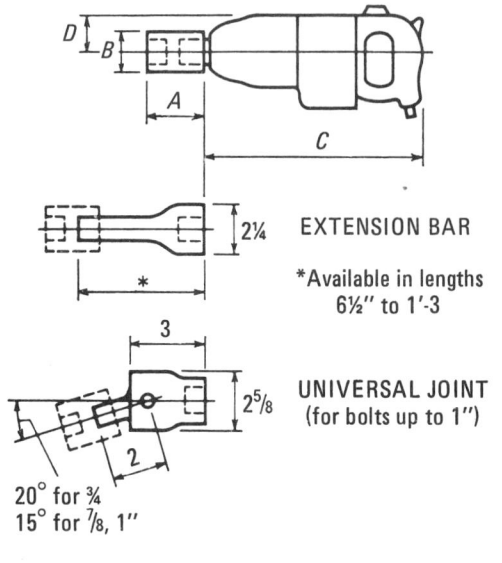

2¼ EXTENSION BAR

*Available in lengths
6½" to 1'-3

3

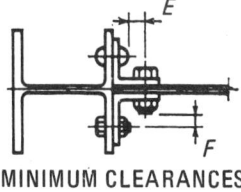

2⁵⁄₈ UNIVERSAL JOINT
(for bolts up to 1")

2

20° for ¾
15° for ⅞, 1"

MINIMUM CLEARANCES

	Size	C	D
Light Wrenches	16 to 24	337 to 356	54
Heavy Wrenches	24 to 36	375 to 438	64

	Size	C	D
Light Wrenches	5/8 to 1	1-1¼ to 1-2	2¹⁄₈
Heavy Wrenches	1 to 1½	1-2¾ to 1-5¼	2½

Bolt Size	Sockets		Min. Clear.	
	A	B	E	F
16	80	45	25	28
20	85	54	30	34
22	90	57	32	36
24	95	60	34	38
27	100	70	38	42
30	110	75	41	45
36	130	90	48	52

Bolt Size	Sockets		Min. Clear.	
	A	B	E	F
5/8	2-5/8	1-3/4	1-1/8	1-1/4
3/4	3	2-1/4	1-1/4	1-3/8
7/8	3-1/4	2-1/2	1-5/16	1-7/16
1	3-1/2	2-5/8	1-7/16	1-9/16
1-1/8	3-3/4	2-7/8	1-9/16	1-11/16
1-1/4	4	3-1/8	1-5/8	1-3/4
1-3/8	4-1/4	3-1/4	2-1/8	2-1/4
1-1/2	4-3/8	4-1/4		

WELDING

The welding of steel shapes and plates for structural purposes is governed by CAN3-S16.1-M78, Steel Structures for Buildings — Limit States Design and CSA Standard W59-77, Welded Steel Construction (Metal-Arc Welding).

While both standards provide design information on the strength of welds, CSA Standard W59 extensively covers workmanship, inspection and acceptance criteria for welded joints in both statically and dynamically loaded structures.

Welding is a process used to join two or more pieces of material together. Arc welding is a process which produces coalescence of metals by heating them with an arc, with or without the application of pressure, and with or without the use of filler metal.

Welding processes used primarily for structural steel work are:

Manual Shielded Metal Arc Welding	SMAW
Flux Cored Arc Welding	FCAW
Gas Metal Arc Welding	GMAW
Submerged Arc Welding	SAW
Electroslag Welding	EW
Stud Welding	SW

Welding Definitions

Arc Cutting: means a group of cutting processes which melts the metal to be cut with the heat of an arc between an electrode and the base metal.

Arc Spot Weld: means a weld made by arc welding between or upon overlapping members in which coalescence may start and occur on the faying surfaces or may proceed from the surface of one member.

Base Metal: means the metal to be welded or cut.

Bevel Angle: means the angle formed between the prepared edge of a member and a plane perpendicular to the surface of the member.

Chain Intermittent Welds: means intermittent welds on both sides of a joint in which the weld increments on one side are approximately opposite those on the other side.

Coalescence: means the growing together or growth into one body of the material being welded.

Complete Joint Penetration: means when the weld metal completely fills the groove and is fused to the base metal throughout its total thickness.

Edge Joint: means a joint between the edge of two or more parallel or nearly parallel members.

Effective Weld Length: means the length of weld throughout which the correctly proportioned cross section exists. In a curved weld, it is measured along the axis of the weld.

Effective Throat: means the minimum distance from the root of a weld to its face less any reinforcement.

End Return (Boxing): means the continuation of a fillet weld around a corner of a member as an extension of the principal weld.

Face of Weld: means the exposed surface of a weld on the side from which the welding was done.

Fillet Weld: means a weld of approximately triangular cross section joining two surfaces approximately at right angles to each other in a lap joint, T-joint, or corner joint.

Groove Weld: means a weld made in a groove between two members to be joined.

Intermittent Weld: means a weld in which the continuity is broken by recurring unwelded spaces.

Joint Design: means the joint geometry together with the required dimensions of the welded joint.

Joint Penetration: means the minimum depth a groove weld extends from its face into a joint, exclusive of reinforcement, but including, if present, root penetration.

Leg of a Fillet Weld: is the distance from the root of the joint to the toe of the fillet weld.

Partial Joint Penetration: means a joint penetration which is less than complete.

Procedure Qualification: means a demonstration that welds made by a specific procedure can meet prescribed standards.

Root of Joint: means that portion of a joint to be welded where the members approach closest to each other. In cross section, the root of the joint may be either a point, a line or an area.

Root of Weld: means the points, as shown in cross section, at which the back of the weld intersects the base metal surfaces.

Root Penetration: means the depth that a weld extends into the root of a joint measured on the centreline of the root cross section.

Size of Weld:

Groove Weld: means the joint penetration (depth of bevel plus the root penetration when specified). The size of a groove weld and its effective throat are one and the same.

Fillet Weld:

For equal leg fillet welds, the leg lengths of the largest isosceles right triangle which can be inscribed within the fillet weld cross section.

For unequal leg fillet welds, the leg lengths of the largest right triangle which can be inscribed within the fillet weld cross section.

Note: When one member makes an angle with the other member greater than 105 degrees, the leg length (size) is of less significance than the effective throat which is the controlling factor for the strength of a weld.

Tack Weld: means a weld made to hold parts of a weldment in proper alignment until the final welds are made.

Throat of a Fillet Weld.

Theoretical Throat: means the distance from the beginning of the root of the joint perpendicular to the hypotenuse of the largest right triangle that can be inscribed within the fillet weld cross section. This dimension is based on the assumption that the root opening is equal to zero.

Actual Throat: means the shortest distance from the root of weld to its face.

Effective Throat: means the minimum distance minus any reinforcement from the root of weld to its face.

WELDING PRACTICE*

Fillet Welds

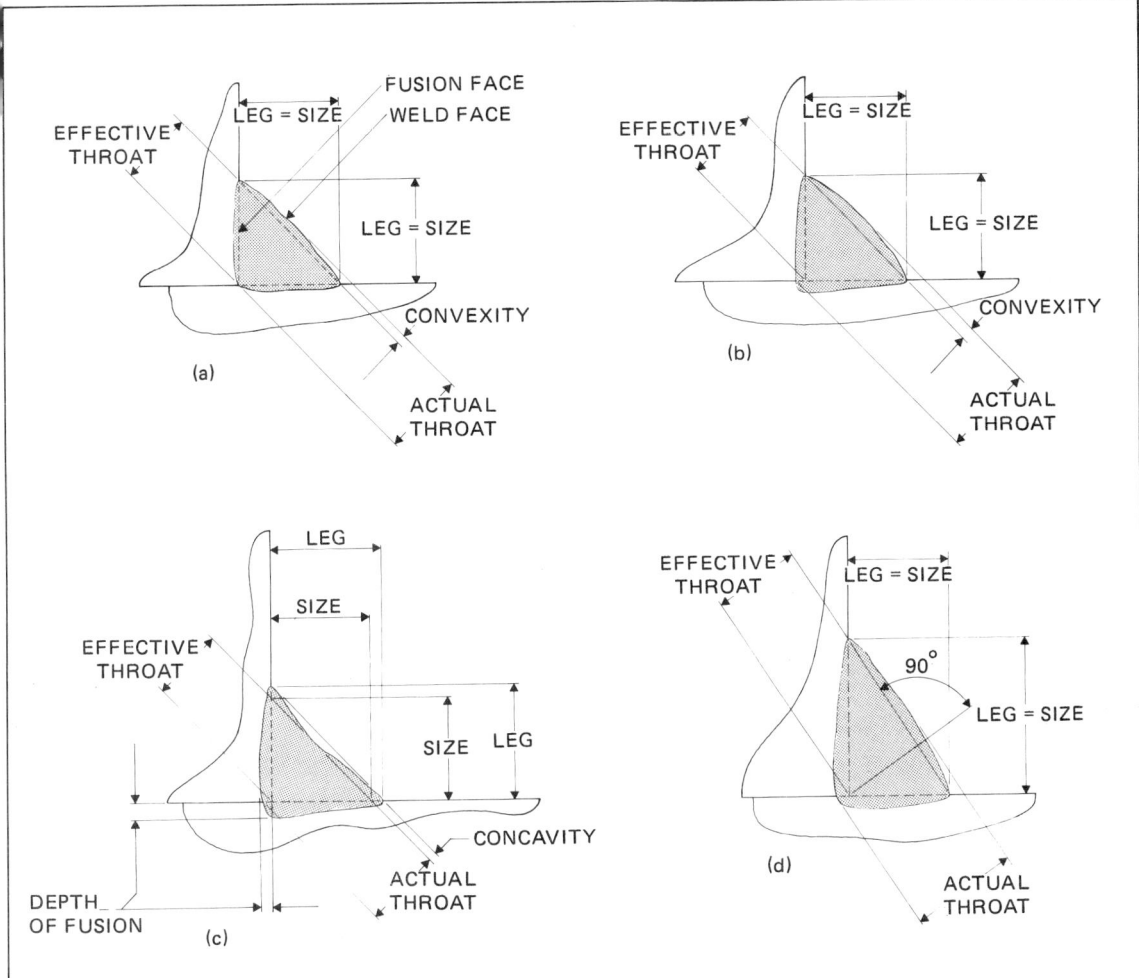

Minimum Size

- The minimum size of a fillet weld as measured should not be less than the values shown on the right, except that it need not exceed the thickness of the thinner part.

  When welding attachments to non-load carrying members the values on the right need not apply.

Material thickness of thicker part joined	Minimum Size of fillet weld, mm
to 12 mm incl.	5
over 12 mm to 20	6
over 20	8

- The minimum effective length of a fillet weld should be 40 mm or 4 times the size of the fillet, whichever is larger.

Maximum Size of Weld

- The maximum fillet weld size, D_{max}, recommended by good practice along a sheared edge is:

$$D_{max} \leqslant t \qquad \text{when } t \leqslant 6 \text{ mm}$$
$$D_{max} = t-2 \qquad \text{when } t > 6 \text{ mm}$$

*Based upon metric draft of CSA Standard W59.

- Material with rolled edges:

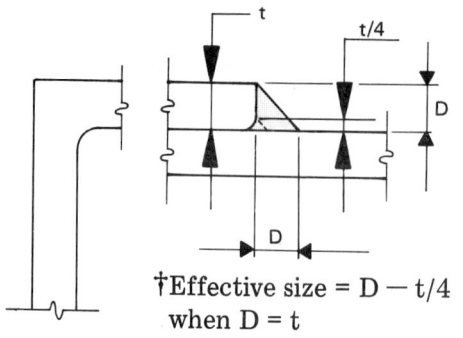 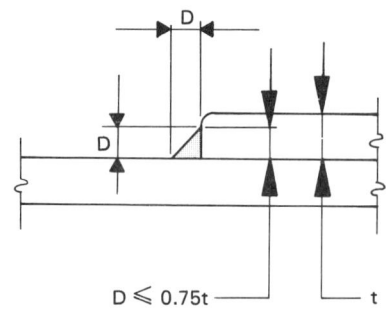

†Effective size = $D - t/4$
when $D = t$

$D \leqslant 0.75t$

- When fillet welds are used in holes or slots, the diameter of the hole or the width of the slot should not be less than the thickness of the member containing it plus 8 mm.

Lap Joints

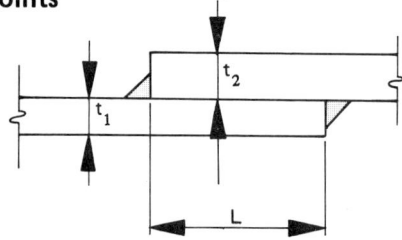

$$L_{min} = 5t_1 \geqslant 25 \text{ mm when } t_1 \leqslant t_2$$
$$L_{min} = 5t_2 \geqslant 25 \text{ mm} \qquad t_2 < t_1$$

†This detail is not part of W59, but rather is a detail often used by the steel fabricating industry.

Partial Penetration Groove Welds

Minimum Groove Depth for Partial Joint Penetration Groove Welds†

Thickness of Thicker Part Joined	Minimum Groove Depth*, mm	
	Groove Angle, α, at Root	Groove Angle, α, at Root
(Millimetres)	$45° \leqslant \alpha < 60°$ (V-, Bevel Grooves)	$\alpha \geqslant 60°$ (V-, Bevel, J-, U- Grooves)
Total 12 incl.	8	5
Over 12 – 20	10	6
Over 20 – 40	11	8
Over 40 – 60	12	10
Over 60	16	12

†Not combined with fillet welds.
*See Notes 2a and 2b of diagram on next page.

Flare Bevel and Flare V-Welds

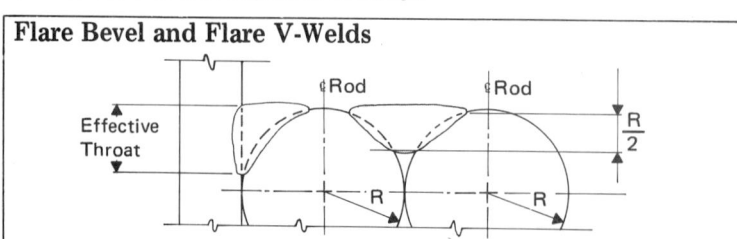

The effective throat thickness for flare groove welds on solid bars, when filled flush to the surface of the solid section of the bar is 5/16 R for Flare Bevel Groove welds and 1/2 R for Flare Vee Groove welds.

Note: Based upon metric draft of CSA Standard W59.

GROOVE WELDS

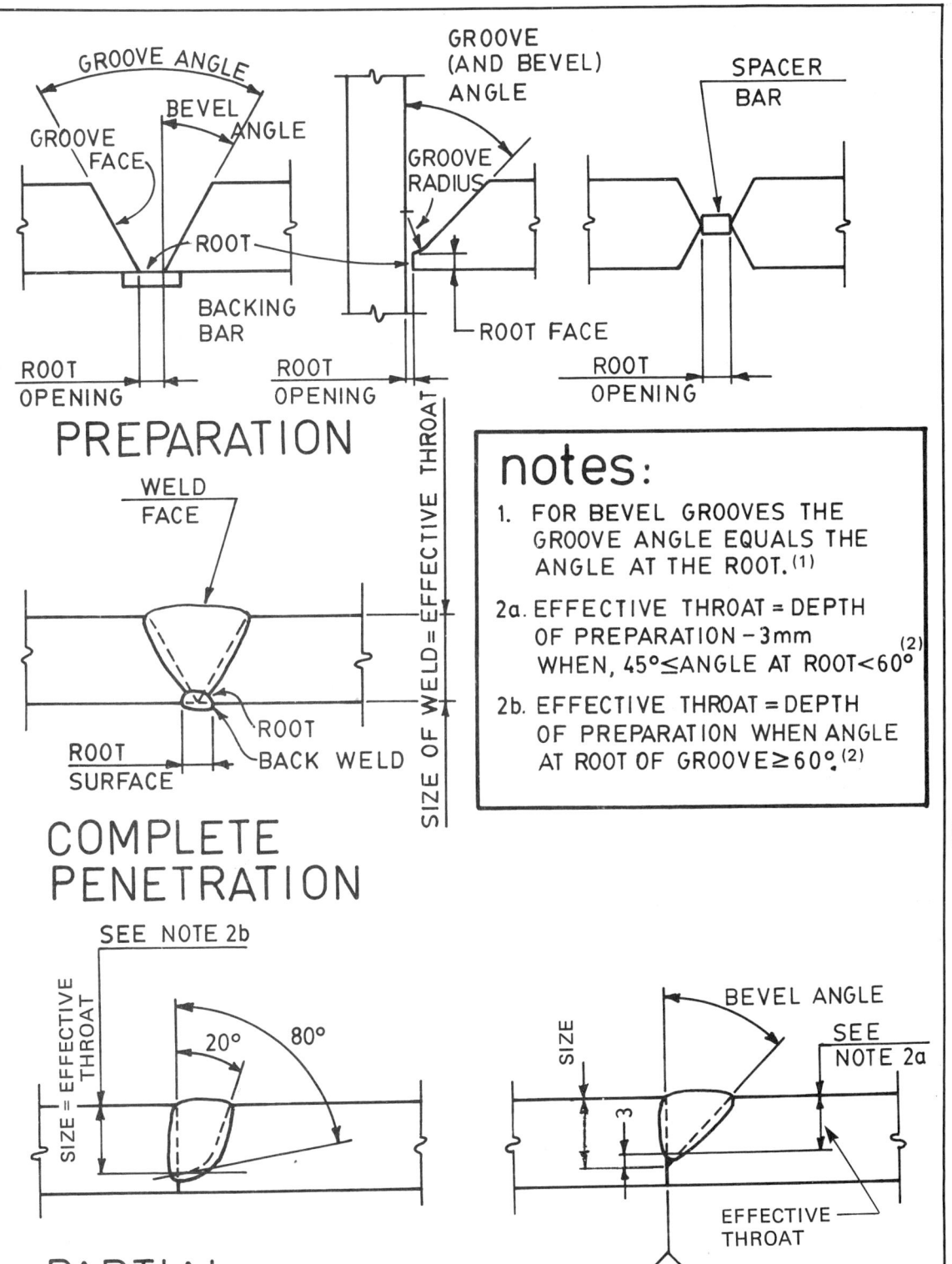

PREPARATION

COMPLETE PENETRATION

PARTIAL PENETRATION

notes:

1. FOR BEVEL GROOVES THE GROOVE ANGLE EQUALS THE ANGLE AT THE ROOT.[1]

2a. EFFECTIVE THROAT = DEPTH OF PREPARATION – 3mm WHEN, 45° ≤ ANGLE AT ROOT < 60° [2]

2b. EFFECTIVE THROAT = DEPTH OF PREPARATION WHEN ANGLE AT ROOT OF GROOVE ≥ 60°. [2]

(1) Not for J and U grooves.
(2) Applies only to PJPG welds.

WELDED JOINTS
Standard Symbols

			BASIC WELD SYMBOLS							
			GROOVE OR BUTT							
BACK	FILLET	PLUG OR SLOT	SQUARE	V	BEVEL	U	J	FLARE V	FLARE BEVEL

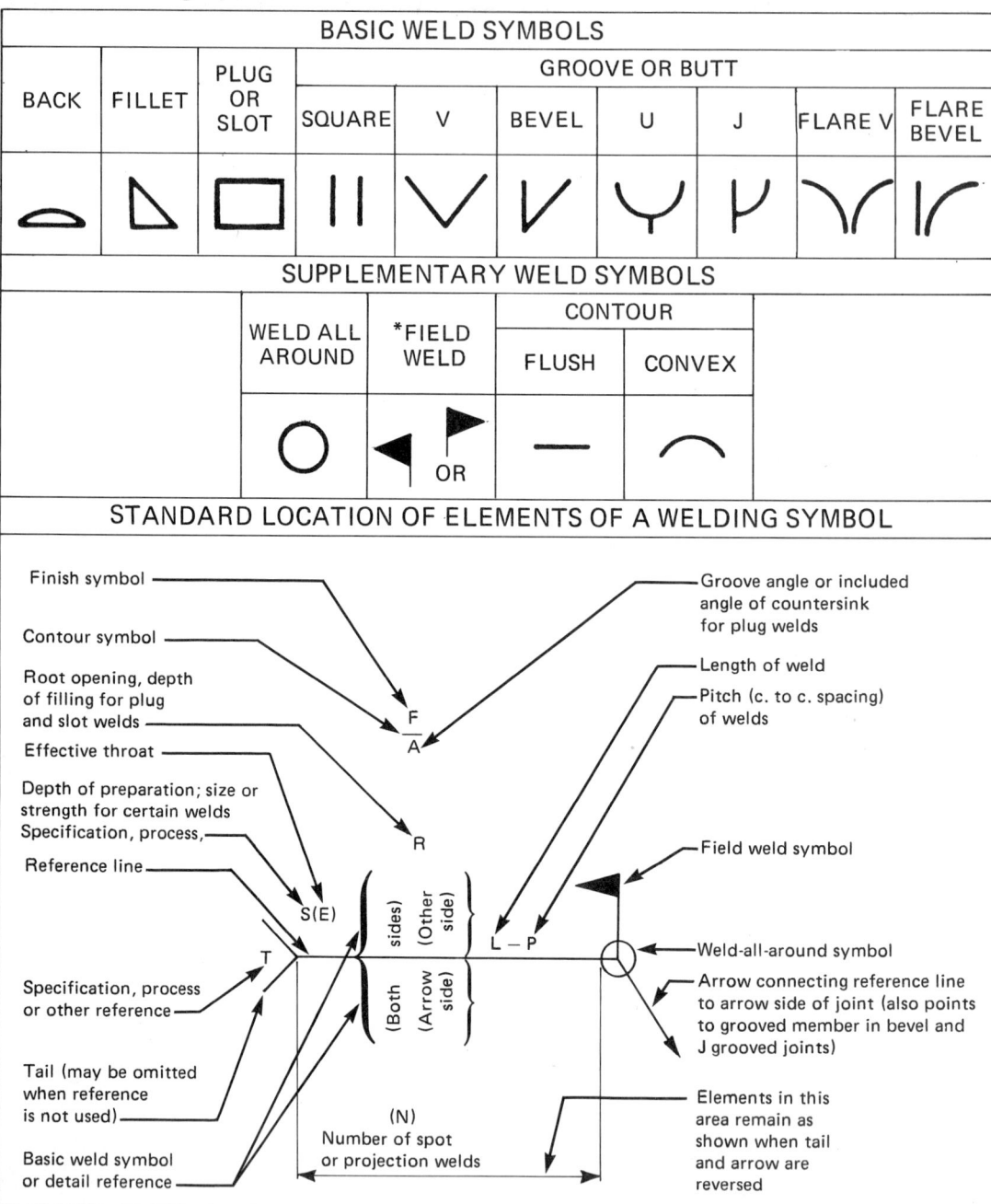

		WELD ALL AROUND	*FIELD WELD	CONTOUR		
				FLUSH	CONVEX	
			OR			

SUPPLEMENTARY WELD SYMBOLS

STANDARD LOCATION OF ELEMENTS OF A WELDING SYMBOL

Finish symbol

Contour symbol

Root opening, depth of filling for plug and slot welds

Effective throat

Depth of preparation; size or strength for certain welds

Specification, process,

Reference line

Specification, process or other reference

Tail (may be omitted when reference is not used)

Basic weld symbol or detail reference

Groove angle or included angle of countersink for plug welds

Length of weld

Pitch (c. to c. spacing) of welds

Field weld symbol

Weld-all-around symbol

Arrow connecting reference line to arrow side of joint (also points to grooved member in bevel and J grooved joints)

Elements in this area remain as shown when tail and arrow are reversed

F / A

R

S(E)

T

L — P

(Both) (Arrow side)

(sides) (Other side)

(N) Number of spot or projection welds

Note:

Size, weld symbol, length of weld and spacing must read in that order from left to right along the reference line. Neither orientation of reference line nor location of the arrow alter this rule.

The perpendicular leg of ⊿, V, Ƿ, Ʋ weld symbols must be at left.

Arrow and Other Side welds are of the same size unless otherwise shown.

Symbols apply between abrupt changes in direction of welding unless governed by the "all around" symbol or otherwise dimensioned.

These symbols do not explicitly provide for the case that frequently occurs in structural work, where duplicate material (such as stiffeners) occurs on the far side of a web or gusset plate. The fabricating industry has adopted this convention; that when the billing of the detail material discloses the identity of far side with near side, the welding shown for the near side shall also be duplicated on the far side.

*Pennant points away from arrow.

WELDING SYMBOLS

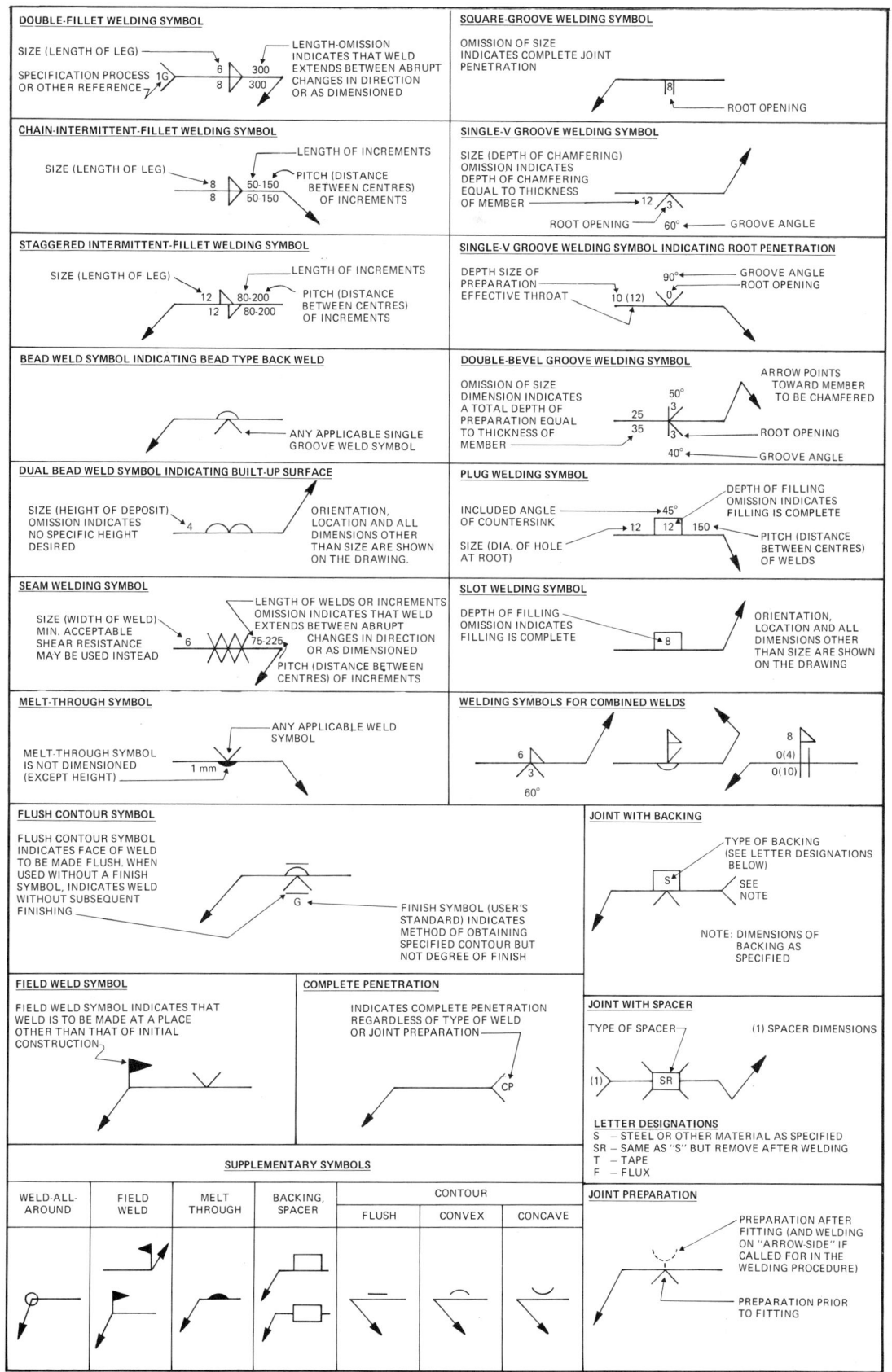

DOUBLE-FILLET WELDING SYMBOL

SIZE (LENGTH OF LEG)

SPECIFICATION PROCESS OR OTHER REFERENCE

1G

6 300
8 300

LENGTH-OMISSION INDICATES THAT WELD EXTENDS BETWEEN ABRUPT CHANGES IN DIRECTION OR AS DIMENSIONED

CHAIN-INTERMITTENT-FILLET WELDING SYMBOL

SIZE (LENGTH OF LEG)

8 50-150
8 50-150

LENGTH OF INCREMENTS

PITCH (DISTANCE BETWEEN CENTRES) OF INCREMENTS

STAGGERED INTERMITTENT-FILLET WELDING SYMBOL

SIZE (LENGTH OF LEG)

12 80-200
12 80-200

LENGTH OF INCREMENTS

PITCH (DISTANCE BETWEEN CENTRES) OF INCREMENTS

BEAD WELD SYMBOL INDICATING BEAD TYPE BACK WELD

ANY APPLICABLE SINGLE GROOVE WELD SYMBOL

DUAL BEAD WELD SYMBOL INDICATING BUILT-UP SURFACE

SIZE (HEIGHT OF DEPOSIT) OMISSION INDICATES NO SPECIFIC HEIGHT DESIRED

4

ORIENTATION, LOCATION AND ALL DIMENSIONS OTHER THAN SIZE ARE SHOWN ON THE DRAWING.

SEAM WELDING SYMBOL

SIZE (WIDTH OF WELD) MIN. ACCEPTABLE SHEAR RESISTANCE MAY BE USED INSTEAD

6 75-225

LENGTH OF WELDS OR INCREMENTS OMISSION INDICATES THAT WELD EXTENDS BETWEEN ABRUPT CHANGES IN DIRECTION OR AS DIMENSIONED

PITCH (DISTANCE BETWEEN CENTRES) OF INCREMENTS

MELT-THROUGH SYMBOL

MELT-THROUGH SYMBOL IS NOT DIMENSIONED (EXCEPT HEIGHT)

1 mm

ANY APPLICABLE WELD SYMBOL

SQUARE-GROOVE WELDING SYMBOL

OMISSION OF SIZE INDICATES COMPLETE JOINT PENETRATION

8

ROOT OPENING

SINGLE-V GROOVE WELDING SYMBOL

SIZE (DEPTH OF CHAMFERING) OMISSION INDICATES DEPTH OF CHAMFERING EQUAL TO THICKNESS OF MEMBER

12 3

ROOT OPENING   60°   GROOVE ANGLE

SINGLE-V GROOVE WELDING SYMBOL INDICATING ROOT PENETRATION

DEPTH SIZE OF PREPARATION EFFECTIVE THROAT

10 (12)

90°   GROOVE ANGLE
0   ROOT OPENING

DOUBLE-BEVEL GROOVE WELDING SYMBOL

OMISSION OF SIZE DIMENSION INDICATES A TOTAL DEPTH OF PREPARATION EQUAL TO THICKNESS OF MEMBER

25 3
35 3

50°
40°

ARROW POINTS TOWARD MEMBER TO BE CHAMFERED

ROOT OPENING

GROOVE ANGLE

PLUG WELDING SYMBOL

INCLUDED ANGLE OF COUNTERSINK

SIZE (DIA. OF HOLE AT ROOT)

12 12 150

45°

DEPTH OF FILLING OMISSION INDICATES FILLING IS COMPLETE

PITCH (DISTANCE BETWEEN CENTRES) OF WELDS

SLOT WELDING SYMBOL

DEPTH OF FILLING OMISSION INDICATES FILLING IS COMPLETE

8

ORIENTATION, LOCATION AND ALL DIMENSIONS OTHER THAN SIZE ARE SHOWN ON THE DRAWING

WELDING SYMBOLS FOR COMBINED WELDS

6
3
60°

0(4)
0(10)

8

FLUSH CONTOUR SYMBOL

FLUSH CONTOUR SYMBOL INDICATES FACE OF WELD TO BE MADE FLUSH. WHEN USED WITHOUT A FINISH SYMBOL, INDICATES WELD WITHOUT SUBSEQUENT FINISHING

G

FINISH SYMBOL (USER'S STANDARD) INDICATES METHOD OF OBTAINING SPECIFIED CONTOUR BUT NOT DEGREE OF FINISH

JOINT WITH BACKING

S

TYPE OF BACKING (SEE LETTER DESIGNATIONS BELOW)

SEE NOTE

NOTE: DIMENSIONS OF BACKING AS SPECIFIED

FIELD WELD SYMBOL

FIELD WELD SYMBOL INDICATES THAT WELD IS TO BE MADE AT A PLACE OTHER THAN THAT OF INITIAL CONSTRUCTION

COMPLETE PENETRATION

INDICATES COMPLETE PENETRATION REGARDLESS OF TYPE OF WELD OR JOINT PREPARATION

CP

JOINT WITH SPACER

TYPE OF SPACER

(1)

SR

(1) SPACER DIMENSIONS

LETTER DESIGNATIONS
S – STEEL OR OTHER MATERIAL AS SPECIFIED
SR – SAME AS "S" BUT REMOVE AFTER WELDING
T – TAPE
F – FLUX

SUPPLEMENTARY SYMBOLS

WELD-ALL-AROUND	FIELD WELD	MELT THROUGH	BACKING, SPACER	CONTOUR		
				FLUSH	CONVEX	CONCAVE

JOINT PREPARATION

PREPARATION AFTER FITTING (AND WELDING ON "ARROW-SIDE" IF CALLED FOR IN THE WELDING PROCEDURE)

PREPARATION PRIOR TO FITTING

PART SEVEN
MISCELLANEOUS

CISC Code of Standard Practice .... 7—3

Structural Sheet Steel Products................................. 7—25

Mass and Forces for Materials .... 7—28

M/D Ratios .... 7—30

Coefficients of Thermal Expansion .... 7—33

Electronic Aids .... 7—34

Properties of Geometric Sections .... 7—38

Properties of Geometric Sections and Structural Shapes .... 7—45

Properties of the Circle .... 7—49

Properties of Parabola and Ellipse .... 7—50

Properties of Solids .... 7—51

Trigonometric Formulae...................................... 7—53

Bracing Formulae .... 7—54

Length of Circular Arcs...................................... 7—55

SI Summary .... 7—56

Millimetre Equivalents....................................... 7—61

Miscellaneous Conversion Factors.............................. 7—62

CISC
CODE OF STANDARD PRACTICE
for
Structural Steel

Published by the

CANADIAN INSTITUTE OF STEEL CONSTRUCTION

201 Consumers Road ● Willowdale ● Ontario

TABLE OF CONTENTS

1. General Provisions 5

1.1 — Scope 5

1.2 — Definitions 5

1.3 — Governing Technical Standards 6

1.4 — Responsiblity for Design 6

1.5 — Responsibility for Erection Procedure 7

1.6 — Patented Devices 7

1.7 — Scheduling 7

2. Classification of Material 7

2.1 — Structural Steel 7

2.2 — Field Connection Material 8

2.3 — Items Supplied by Others 8

3. Contracts 9

3.1 — Standard Form of Contract 9

3.2 — Types of Contracts 9

3.3 — Revisions to Contract Documents 9

3.4 — Computation of Mass 9

3.5 — Contract Price Adjustments 11

3.6 — Scheduling 11

4. Contract Documents 11

4.1 — Tender Drawings and Tender Specifications 11

4.2 — Architectural, Electrical and Mechanical Drawings 12

4.3 — Construction Drawings and Construction Specifications 12

5. Erection Diagrams and Shop Details 12

5.1 — Erection Diagrams 12

5.2 — Shop Details 13

5.3 — Approvals 13

5.4 — Additions, Deletions or Changes 13

5.5 — Shop Details Furnished by the Client 13

6. Material, Fabrication, Inspection, Painting and Delivery 14

6.1 — Stock Material 14

6.2 — Identification 14

6.3 — Preparation of Material 14

6.4 — Filling and Fastening 14

6.5 — Dimensional Tolerances 14

6.6 — Inspection of Steelwork 14

6.7 — Painting Preparation 14

6.8 — Liability for Deterioration of Paint 14
6.9 — Marking and Shipping 14
6.10 — Delivery of Materials 15

7. Erection 15
7.1 — Method of Erection 15
7.2 — Site Conditions 15
7.3 — Foundations 16
7.4 — Building Lines and Bench Marks 16
7.5 — Installation of Anchor Bolts and Embedded Items 16
7.6 — Bearing Devices 16
7.7 — Examination by Erector 17
7.8 — Adjustable Shelf Angles and Sash Angles 17
7.9 — Loose Lintels and Wall Bearing Members 17
7.10 — Tolerances 17
7.11 — Checking Erected Steelwork 17
7.12 — Removal of Temporary Erection Bracing 17
7.13 — Correction of Errors when Material is Not Erected by the Fabricator 17
7.14 — Field Assembly 17
7.15 — Accommodation of Other Trades 17
7.16 — Temporary Floors and Access Stairs 17
7.17 — Touch-Up of Shop Paint 17
7.18 — Field Painting 17
7.19 — Final Clean-Up 17

Appendix A — Structural Steel in Buildings 18
Appendix B — A Suggested Format for Accommodating
             Contract Price Adjustments 19
Appendix C — A Suggested Format for Price Per Unit of Mass or Price Per Item
             Contracts 20
Appendix D — Tolerances on Anchor Bolt Placement 21
Appendix E — Conversion of SI Units to Imperial Units 22

CISC CODE OF STANDARD PRACTICE
FOR STRUCTURAL STEEL
PREFACE

The CISC Code of Standard Practice for Structural Steel is a compilation of usual industry practices relating to the design, fabrication and erection of structural steel. These practices evolve over a period of time and are subject to change as improved methods replace those of an earlier period. The Code is revised whenever a sufficient number of changes have occurred to warrant a new edition.

The first edition of the Code was adopted and published in November 1958. A second edition incorporating minor revisions was published in October 1962. The third edition, published in September 1967 and revised in May 1970, incorporated minor changes throughout with principal changes in Section 2 — Definition of Structural Steel and Section 3 — Computation of Weights for Unit Price Bids.

This fourth edition is revised extensively throughout. The scope has been broadened to include bridges as well as other structures. A related document, the CISC "Guide to Tendering Procedures" has been incorporated in the Code in Section 3 — Contracts, and Appendices B and C. New terms which are being used in the trade have been defined. The Code uses SI (metric) units but, to facilitate use of the Code with contract documents using Imperial units, Appendix E provides Imperial units and conversion factors. The procedure for submission and approval of erection diagrams and, if required, shop details has been clarified. Other minor revisions have been made also.

By documenting standard practices the Code aims to promote a clear understanding between the Canadian structural steel fabricating industry and its clients. It is hoped that the Code will be useful in the preparation of specifications and contracts.

Canadian Institute of Steel Construction
Adopted June 4, 1980

Revised Second Printing December, 1980

CISC CODE OF STANDARD PRACTICE FOR STRUCTURAL STEEL

1. General Provisions

1.1 Scope. This Code covers standard industry practice with respect to the furnishing of structural steel. In the absence of provisions to the contrary contained in contracts to which members of the Canadian Institute of Steel Construction are contracting parties, members will abide by the practices described herein. Additional information on standard industry practice with respect to open web steel joists is contained in the CISC publication "Steel Joist Facts".

1.2 Definitions.

Architect	As defined under the appropriate Architect's Act.
Client	A person, corporation, or authority with whom the fabricator has contracted.
Construction Drawings	Drawings used to govern the construction of the works.
Construction Specifications	Specifications used to govern the construction of the works.
Contract	The agreement between the fabricator and/or erector, and the client.
Contract Documents	The documents which define the responsibilities of the parties involved in tendering, purchasing, supplying, fabricating and erecting structural steel, including tender drawings and tender specifications and applicable revisions in effect and agreed to at the time of contract award.
Cost Plus a Fee Contract	An agreement whereby the fabricator and/or erector agrees to fulfill the contract for a consideration which is calculated on the basis of the fabricator's costs plus a specified fee as defined in the contract.
Engineer	As defined under the appropriate Engineer's Act.
Erection Diagrams	Drawings showing the dimensioned layout of the steel structure, from which shop details are made, and which correlate the fabricator's piece markings with the location in the structure.
Erector	Means the party responsible for erection of the structural steelwork.
Fabricator	Means the party responsible for fabrication of the structural steelwork, having on staff a full time professional engineer. Where the contract documents so stipulate, the fabricator may also be responsible for erection.
General Contractor, Constructor or Construction Manager	The person or corporation who constructs or supervises the construction of the work.
General Terminology, e.g. Beams, Joists, Columns, etc.	These terms have the meanings stated or implied in CSA Standard CAN3-S16.1-M, CSA Standard CAN3-S6-M and Appendix A of this Code.
Lump Sum Price Contract	Also called Stipulated Price Contract. An agreement whereby the fabricator and/or erector contracts to fulfill the contract terms for a lump sum (stipulated price) consideration.

Others	Means a party or parties other than the fabricator and/or erector.
Owner	Means the owner of a structure and shall include his authorized agent and any person taking possession of a structure on the owner's behalf. Depending on the circumstances an authorized agent may be the architect, engineer, general contractor, construction manager, public authority or other designated representative of the owner.
Price Per Item Contract	An agreement whereby the fabricator and/or erector agrees to fulfill the contract terms for a consideration which is calculated on a "per item" basis, where the term "item" is defined in the contract.
Price Per Unit of Mass Contract	Also called Unit Price Contract. An agreement whereby the fabricator and/or erector contracts to fulfill the contract terms for a consideration which is based on the mass of steel calculated in accordance with the CISC Code of Standard Practice.
Release	The release by the client permitting the fabricator to commence work under the contract, including ordering material and the preparation of shop details and erection diagrams.
Revision	A change in the contract documents.
Shop Details	Documents showing all necessary information required to fabricate the structural steel. Shop details may be in the form of drawings, computer print-outs, numerical control tapes or other control documents required for fabrication.
Stipulated Price Contract	See Lump Sum Price Contract.
Sturctural Steel	Those items listed under clause 2.1
Structural Drawings	The tender drawings showing the structural steel required.
Structural Steel Specifications	The portion of the tender specifications containing the requirements for the fabrication and erection of the structural steel.
Tender Drawings	Drawings used as the basis for preparing a tender.
Tender Specifications	Specifications used as the basis for preparing a tender.
Unit Price Contract	See Price Per Unit of Mass Contract.

1.3 Governing Technical Standards. The provisions of the latest edition of CSA Standard CAN3-S16.1-M "Steel Structures for Buildings — Limit States Design", of the Canadian Standards Association, shall govern the design, fabrication and erection of structural steel for buildings. The provisions of the latest edition of CSA Standard CAN3-S6-M "Design of Highway Bridges", "The Ontario Highway Bridge Design Code" (in Ontario) or the American Railway Engineering Association's "Specifications for Steel Railway Bridges" shall govern the design, fabrication and erection of structural steel for bridges. The provisions of the latest edition of CSA Standard W59 "Welded Steel Construction (Metal-Arc Welding)" shall govern arc welding design and practice. The provisions of other standards shall be applicable if called for in the tender drawings and tender specifications.

1.4 Responsibility for Design. When the client provides the structural drawings and specifications, the fabricator and the erector shall not be responsible for determining the adequacy of the design nor liable for the loss or damage resulting from an inadequate design. Should the client desire the fabricator to assume any responsibility for design beyond that of suitable connections and details, and, when required, components, members, or assemblies standardized by the fabricator, the client shall state clearly his requirements in the invitation to tender or in the accompanying tender drawings and tender specifications. (See also Clause 5.3).

1.5 Responsibility for Erection Procedure. When the erection of the structural steel is not part of his contract, the fabricator shall not be responsible for determining the erection procedure, for checking the adequacy of the connections for the uncompleted structure, for providing temporary bracing or temporary connection details not included in the contract documents, nor shall he be liable for loss or damage resulting from faulty erection. (See also Clause 5.3).

1.6 Patented Devices. Except when the contract documents call for the design to be furnished by the fabricator or erector, the fabricator and erector assume that all necessary patent rights have been obtained by the client and that the fabricator and erector will be fully protected by the client in the use of patented designs, devices or parts required by the contract documents.

1.7 Scheduling. The client should provide a construction schedule in the tender documents. In the absence of such a schedule, one should be mutually agreed upon between the contracting parties.

2. Classification of Material

2.1 Structural Steel. Unless otherwise specified in the invitation to tender or in the tender drawings and tender specifications, a contract to supply, fabricate and deliver structural steel shall include only those items from the following list which are clearly indicated as being required by the structural drawings and tender specifications.

Anchors for structural steel.
Base plates and bearings for structural steel members.
Beams, purlins, girts.
Bearing plates and bearings of structural steel members and steel deck including corner support angles.
Bins and hoppers for 6 mm plate or heavier, if attached to the structural steel frame.
Bracing for steel members, trusses or frames.
Brackets attached to the structural steel.
Bridge bearings, grating and railings, if connected to the structural steel members.
Cables for permanent bracing or suspension systems.
Canopy framing.
Columns.
Conveyor galleries and supporting bents (exclusive of conveyor stringers, deck plate and supporting posts which are normally part of the conveyor assembly).
Crane rails and stops.
Curb angles and plates if attached to the structural steel frame.
Diaphragms for bridges.
Door frames if attached to the structural steel frame.
Expansion joints connected to the structural steel frame (excluding expansion joints for bridges).
Floor plates, roof plates (raised pattern or plain) and steel grating connected to the structural steel frame.
Girders.
Grillage beams of structural steel.
Hangers supporting structural steel framing.
Jacking girders.
Lintels shown on the structural drawings.
Mechanical support framing.

Monorail beams of standard structural steel shapes.

Open-web steel joists, including anchors, bridging, headers and trimmers; also, when specified to be included, in the structural steel contract documents, light-gauge forms and temperature reinforcement.

Sash angles attached to the structural steel frame.

Separators, angles, tees, clips and other detail fittings essential to the structural steel frame.

Shear connectors when shop installed.

Shelf angles attached to the structural steel frame.

Shop fasteners or welds, and fasteners required to assemble parts for shipment.

Steel tubes or cores for composite columns.

Steel stairs, walkways, ladders and handrails forming part of the structural steel-work and so noted on the structural drawings.

Steel window sills attached to the structural steel frame.

Struts.

Suspended ceiling supports of structural steel shapes at least 75 mm in depth.

Tie, hanger and sag rods forming part of the structural steel frame.

Trusses.

2.2 Field Connection Material. When the fabricator erects the structural steel, he shall supply all material required for temporary and for permanent connection of the component parts of the structural steel.

When the erection of the structural steel is not part of the fabricator's contract, unless otherwise specified, the fabricator shall furnish appropriate quality bolts and nuts (plus washers, if required) or special fasteners, of suitable size and in sufficient quantity for all field connections of steel to steel which are specified to be thus permanently connected, plus an over-allowance of two per cent of each size to cover waste.

Unless otherwise specified in the tender specifications, welding electrodes, temporary shims, levelling plates, fitting-up bolts and drift pins required for the structural steel shall not be furnished by the fabricator when the erection of the structural steel is not part of the fabricator's contract.

2.3 Items Supplied by Others. Unless otherwise specified in the tender drawings and tender specifications, the following steel or other items shall not be supplied by the fabricator.

Bolts for wood lagging.

Bins and hoppers not covered in clause 2.1 of this Code.

Catch basin frames.

Connection material for other trades (e.g. precast concrete).

Conveyor stringers, deck plate and supporting posts.

Door and corner guards.

Door frames not covered in clause 2.1 of this Code.

Drilling of holes into masonry or concrete.

Embedded steel parts in precast or cast-in-place concrete.

Flagpoles and supports.

Floor plates, roof plates and grating not covered in clause 2.1 of this Code.

Grout.

Hose and tire brackets.

Lag bolts, machine bolts and shields or inserts for attaching shelf angles, trimmer angles and channels to masonry or concrete.

Lintels over wall recesses.

Lintels which are an integral part of door frames not attached to the structural steel frame.

Machine bases, rollers and pulleys.

Metal-clad doors and frames.

Shear connectors field installed.

Sheet steel cladding.

Sheet steel deck.

Sheet steel flashing.

Shelf angles not covered in clause 2.1 of this Code.

Small hoppers and chutes.

Steel doors.

Steel sash.

Steel stacks.

Steel stairs, landings, walkways, ladders and handrails not covered in clause 2.1 of this Code.

Steel tanks and pressure vessels.

Steel window sills not covered in clause 2.1 of this Code.

Trench covers.

Trim angles, eave angles or fascia plates not directly attached to the structural steel frame.

3. Contracts

3.1 Standard Form of Contract. Unless otherwise agreed upon, a contract to fabricate, deliver and/or erect structural steel shall be based on the appropriate Standard Construction Documents approved by the Canadian Construction Documents Committee, or the Canadian Construction Association.

3.2 Types of Contracts.

3.2.1 For contracts stipulating a "lump sum price", the work required to be performed by the fabricator and/or erector must be completely defined by the contract documents.

3.2.2 For contracts stipulating a "price per unit of mass", the scope of the work, type of materials, character of fabrication, and conditions of erection are based upon the contract documents which must be representative of the work to be performed. See Appendix C of this Code.

3.2.3 For contracts stipulating "price per item", the work required to be performed by the fabricator and/or erector is based upon the quantity and character of the items described in the contract documents. See Appendix C of this Code.

3.2.4 For contracts stipulating "cost plus fee", the work required to be performed by the fabricator and/or erector is indefinite in nature at the time the contract documents are prepared. Consequently the contract documents should define the method of measurement of work performed, and the fee to be paid in addition to the fabricator's costs.

3.3 Revisions to Contract Documents.

3.3.1 Revisions to the contract shall be made by the issuance of new documents or the reissuance of existing (revised) documents. In either case, all revisions must be clearly indicated and the documents dated.

3.3.2 Revisions to the requirements of the contract documents shall be made by change orders, extra work orders, or notations on the shop details and erection drawings returned after approval by the client or client's designated representative.

3.3.3 Unless specifically stated to the contrary, the issuance of a revision is authorization by the client to release these documents for construction.

3.4 Computation of Mass

3.4.1 Unless another method is specified and fully described at the time tenders are requested, the computed mass of steel required for the structure shall be determined by the method of computation described herein. (Although the method of computation described does not result in the actual mass of fabricated structural steel and other items its relative simplicity results in low computational cost and it is based on quantities which can be readily computed by all parties involved. Any greater degree of precision is seldom warranted provided that the parties involved are each cognizant of the mass to which the tender specifications apply).

(a) *Mass Density.* The mass density of steel is assumed to be 7850 kilograms per cubic metre.

(b) *Shapes, Bars and Hollow Structural Sections.* The mass of shapes, bars and hollow structural sections is computed using the finished dimensions shown on shop details. No deductions shall be made for holes created by cutting, punching or drilling, for material removed by coping or clipping, or for material removed by weld joint preparation. No cutting, milling or planing allowance shall be added to the finished dimensions. The mass per metre of length for shapes and hollow structural sections is the published mass. The mass per metre of length for bars is the published mass, or if no mass is published, the mass computed from the specified cross-sectional area.

(c) *Plates and Slabs.* The mass of plates and slabs is computed using the theoretical rectangular dimensions of plates or slabs from which the finished plate or slab pieces shown on the shop details can be cut. No burning, cutting, trimming or planing allowance shall be added. When it is practical and economical to do so, several irregularly-shaped pieces may be cut from the same plate or slab. In this case, the mass shall be computed using the theoretical rectangular dimensions of the plate or slab from which the pieces can be cut. No cutting or trimming allowance shall be added. In all cases, the specified plate or slab thickness is to be used to compute the mass. The mass of raised-pattern rolled plate is that published by the manufacturer.

(d) *Bolts.* The mass of shop and field bolts, nuts and washers is computed on the basis of the shop details and the nominal published mass of the applicable types and sizes of fastener.

(e) *Welds.* The mass of shop welds, and the field welds in work erected by the fabricator, is computed on the basis of the shop details and/or erection diagrams and the gross mass of electrode required to lay the weld. For all fillet welds (continuous or intermittent) and all groove welds, the gross mass of the electrode is computed by adding 100 per cent to the mass based on the net theoretical weld cross-section and length. The computations are as follows:

   i)   for equal leg fillet welds:
        mass per millimetre of length (kg/mm) = leg size (mm) x leg size (mm) x mass density of steel (kg/m^3) x 10^{-9};

   ii) for unequal leg fillet welds:
        mass per millimetre of length (kg/mm) = long leg size (mm) x short leg size (mm) x mass density of steel (kg/m^3) x 10^{-9} ;

   iii) for groove welds;
        mass per millimetre of length (kg/mm) = theoretical cross-section area of groove weld (mm^2) x 2 x mass density of steel (kg/m^3) x 10^{-9} .
        For square groove welds with zero root opening use a theoretical cross-section area based on a root opening of 1 mm.

(f) *Studs.* If not included in the contract on a "price per item basis", the mass of studs is computed on the basis of the shop details and/or erection diagrams and the published mass of the studs.

(g) *Grating.* If not included in the contract on the basis of a price per square metre, the mass of grating is computed on the basis of the shop details and/or erection diagrams and the published mass of the grating.

(h) *Painting, Galvanizing and Metallizing.* When painting, galvanizing or metallizing is specified as part of the fabrication contract, the cost shall be included in the price per unit of mass submitted for fabrication. Unless otherwise specified a price per unit of mass which includes painting, galvanizing or metallizing shall apply only to the material required to be so protected and shall be assessed on the computed mass of this material plus the following percentages of this computed mass which are added to approximate the mass of the protective coating:

for each shop coat of paint . . . . ½ percent
for galvanizing or metallizing . . . . 4 percent.

(i) Where supplied, such items as shims, levelling plates, temporary connection material, and certain field "consumables" shall be considered as part of the structural steel whether or not indicated specifically in the contract documents. Such items then will be added to, and become a part of, the computed mass of steel for the structure.

3.5 Contract Price Adjustments

3.5.1 When the responsibilities of the fabricator and/or erector are changed from those previously established by the contract documents, an appropriate modification of the contract price shall be made. In computing the contract price adjustment, the fabricator and/or erector shall consider the quantity of work added or deleted, modifications in the character of the work, and the timeliness of the change with respect to the status of material ordering, detailing, fabrication and erection operations.

3.5.2 Requests for contract price adjustments shall be presented by the fabricator and/or erector and shall be accompanied by a description of the change in sufficient detail to permit evaluation and prompt approval by the client.

3.5.3 Price Per Unit of Mass and Price Per Item Contracts generally provide for minor revisions to the quantity of work prior to the time work is released for construction. Changes to the character of the work or the mix of the work, at any time, or changes to the quantity of the work after the work is released for construction, may require a contract price adjustment.

3.5.4 A suggested format for accommodating contract price adjustments is contained in Appendix B.

3.6 Scheduling

3.6.1 The contract documents should specify the schedule for the performance of the work. This schedule should state when the released for construction drawings will be issued and when the job site, foundations, piers and abutments will be ready, free from obstructions and accessible to the erector, so that erection can start at the designated time and continue without interference or delay caused by the client or other trades.

3.6.2 The fabricator and/or erector has the responsibility to advise the client of the effect any revision may have on the contract schedule.

3.6.3 If the fabrication and erection schedule is significantly delayed due to revisions, or for other reasons which are the client's responsiblity, the fabricator and erector shall be compensated for additional costs incurred.

4. Contract Documents

4.1 Tender Drawings and Tender Specifications

4.1.1 At the time tenders are called, the steel fabricator shall receive a complete set of structural drawings and a complete set of tender specifications. In order to ensure adequate and complete tenders for Lump Sum Price Contracts*, these documents shall

---

*For other types of contract, it is desirable for the contract documents to be as complete as possible.

include complete structural drawings, conforming to the requirements for design drawings of the governing technical standard. The drawings should show clearly the work to be performed and should give the size, section, material grade and the location of all members, floor levels, column centres, offsets, and camber of members, with sufficient dimensions to convey accurately the quantity and nature of the structural steel to be furnished. Structural steel specifications should include any special requirements controlling the fabrication and erection of the structural steel and should indicate the extent of non-destructive examination, if any, to be carried out.

4.1.2 Wind bracing, connections, column stiffeners, bearing stiffeners on beams and girders, web reinforcement, openings for other trades, and other special details where required shall be shown in sufficient detail so that they may be readily understood.

4.1.3 Drawings shall include sufficient data concerning design loads, shears, moments and axial forces to be resisted by members and their connections, as may be required for the development of connection details on the shop details and for the erection of the structure.

4.1.4 Where connections are not shown, the connections shall be assumed to be in accordance with the requirements of the governing technical standard (see clause 1.3).

4.2 Architectural, Electrical and Mechanical Drawings. Architectural, electrical and mechanical drawings may be used as a supplement to the structural drawings to define detail configurations and construction information, provided all requirements for the structural steel are noted on the structural drawings.

4.3 Construction Drawings and Construction Specifications

4.3.1 As soon as possible following award of the contract, the client shall furnish the fabricator with a plot plan of the construction site, and a set of complete drawings and specifications released for construction consistent with the tender drawings and tender specifications. These construction drawings and specifications are required by the fabricator for ordering the mill material and for the preparation and completion of erection diagrams and shop details. The released for contruction drawings shall show:

    (a) all changes or revisions to the tender drawings, clearly indicated on the construction drawings,

    (b) the design of the structural steelwork with all the building openings, mechanical support framing, floor levels, etc., definitely located;

    (c) all materials to be furnished by the fabricator, together with sufficient information to prepare complete erection diagrams and shop details.

The fabricator shall receive a complete set of the tender drawings and tender specifications.

5. Erection Diagrams and Shop Details

Note: The term "shop drawings", frequently used in the construction industry, is replaced in this Code of Practice by the terms "erection diagrams" and "shop details". These terms more correctly describe the separate and distinct documents that are prepared by a fabricator. See also Clause 1.2 for definitions of erection diagrams and shop details.

5.1 Erection Diagrams. Unless provided by the client, the fabricator will prepare erection diagrams from the approved construction drawings and will submit these erection diagrams to the client for approval. In this regard the fabricator may request reproducible copies of the structural drawings which may be altered for use as erection diagrams. The erection diagrams prepared or altered will state types of connection under the heading of General Notes and show typical special types of details such as moment connections, eccentric connections, etc., on the appropriate erection diagram to be used in preparing the shop details. Only one reproducible copy of each diagram will be submitted for approval.

5.2 Shop Details. Unless provided by the client, the fabricator will prepare shop details from the information on the client's approved construction drawings and from the erection diagrams approved by the client. Shop details will not be submitted for approval unless required by the client as part of the tender specifications. When shop details are required to be submitted for approval, only one reproducible copy of each shop detail will be submitted, unless a larger number of copies is required by the client as part of the tender specifications.

5.3 Approvals. Approval by the client of erection diagrams and, if required, shop details, prepared or altered by the fabricator and/or erector indicates that the fabricator has interpreted correctly the contract requirements. Approval by the client, if required, of shop details prepared by the fabricator does not relieve the fabricator of the responsibility for accuracy of the detail dimensions on shop details, nor of the general fit-up of parts to be assembled.

The preparation of erection diagrams and shop details is governed by the following procedures.

(a) The fabricator must receive from the client sufficient information on the contruction drawings to prepare the necessary erection diagrams and shop details. This information is stipulated in Clauses 4.1 and 4.3 of this Code.

(b) The erection diagrams and shop details are prepared by skilled technicians using industry and company standards, and represent the fabricator's interpretation of the intent of the contract documents, particularly as described by the construction drawings.

(c) The erection diagrams, including sketches of special connections, are issued to the client for approval.

(d) It is assumed by the fabricator that the erection diagrams and sketches are reviewed by the client for the accuracy of dimensions and interpretation of the contract requirements. It is assumed by the fabricator that connection details are reviewed by the client for structural adequacy and to ensure conformance with the loads, forces and special instructions contained in the contract documents.

(e) Shop details are prepared from the approved erection diagrams and sketches.

If the client does not wish to review and approve the fabricator's erection diagrams and sketches of special connections, the basis for interpreting the contract requirements, as well as the adequacy of connection details, is limited to the information contained in the structural steel specifications and shown on the structural drawings. This information shall be sufficient, as indicated in Clause 4.1, to permit proper execution of the work.

5.4 Additions, Deletions or Changes. Additions, deletions or changes, when approved, will be considered as contract revisions and constitute the client's authorization to release the additions, deletions or revisions for construction.

5.5 Shop Details Furnished by the Client. When the shop details are furnished by the client he shall deliver them in time to permit fabrication to proceed in an orderly manner according to the time schedule agreed upon. The client shall prepare these shop details, in so far as practicable, in accordance with the detailing standard of the fabricator. The client shall be responsible for the completeness and accuracy of shop details so prepared.

6. Material, Fabrication, Inspection, Painting and Delivery

6.1 Stock Material. Materials taken from stock by the fabricator for structural use shall conform to structural steel material standards of the Canadian Standards Association, or the American Society for Testing and Materials, or to other published material specifications, in accordance with the requirements of the construction drawings and construction specifications.

6.2 Identification

6.2.1 The method of identification stipulated in CSA Standard CAN3-S16.1-M shall form the basis for a fabricator's identification of stock material. Stock control and identification procedures may differ to some extent from fabricator to fabricator.

6.3 Preparation of Material

6.3.1 Flame cutting of structural steel may be by hand or mechanically guided means.

6.3.2 Surfaces noted as "finished" on the drawings are defined as having a roughness height rating not exceeding 500 (12.5 μm) as defined in CSA Standard B95, Surface Texture (Roughness, Waviness and Lay), unless otherwise specified. Any fabricating technique such as friction sawing, cold sawing, milling, etc., that produces such a finish may be used.

6.4 Filling and Fastening

6.4.1 Projecting elements of connection attachments need not be straightened in the connecting plane if it can be demonstrated that installation of the connectors or fitting aids will provide contact between faying surfaces.

6.4.2 When runoff tabs are used, the fabricator or erector need not remove them unless specified in the contract documents or governing technical standard. When their removal is required, they may be hand flame-cut close to the edge of the finished member with no more finishing required, unless other finishing is specifically called for in the contract documents or governing technical standard.

6.5 Dimensional Tolerances. Tolerances on fabricated members shall be those prescribed in the applicable governing technical standard. Tolerances on steel material supplied from the mills or from fabricator's stock shall meet those prescribed in Canadian Standards Association Standard G40.20-M.

6.6 Inspection of Steelwork. Should the client wish to have an independent inspection of the steelwork, he shall reserve the right to do so in the tender specifications. Arrangements should be made with the fabricator for inspection of steelwork at the fabrication shop by the client's inspectors.

6.7 Painting Preparation. If paint is specified, the fabricator shall clean all steel surfaces to be painted of loose rust, loose mill scale, prominent spatter, slag or flux deposit, oil, dirt, and other foreign matter by hand powered tools or other means. Unless specified, the fabricator shall not be obliged to blast-clean, pickle or perform any specific surface preparation operation aimed at total or near-total removal of tight mill scale, rust or non-deleterious matter.

6.8 Liability for Deterioration of Paint. When structural steel is specified to receive a shop coat of paint, the fabricator shall be responsible only to the extent of performing the surface preparation and painting in the specified manner. Unless otherwise agreed upon as part of the contract documents the fabricator shall not be responsible for the deterioration of the paint that may result from exposure to the weather for more than ninety days after completion of the painting.

6.9 Marking and Shipping

6.9.1. Erection marks shall be painted or otherwise legibly marked on the members. Preferably, members which are heavy enough to require special erection equipment shall be marked also so as to indicate the computed or scale mass.

6.9.2 Bolts and rivets of the same length and diameter, and loose nuts and washers of each size shall be packaged separately. Pins, bolts, nuts, washers and other small parts shall be shipped in boxes, crates, kegs or barrels, none of which exceed 135 kg gross mass. A list and description of material contained therein shall be marked plainly on the outside of each container.

6.9.3 When requested by the erector, long girders shall be loaded and marked so that they will arrive at the job site in position for handling without turning. Instructions for such delivery shall be given to the carrying agency when required.

6.9.4 For each shipment, the fabricator, if requested, shall furnish a shipping bill listing the items in the shipment. Such bill shall show the erection mark, the approximate length, the description (whether beam, column, angle, etc.) of each item. Such bill shall be signed by the receiver and returned to the fabricator within 48 hours of receipt of the shipment with a note regarding shortages or damages, if any, and the bill shall act as a receipt for the shipment. When the shipments are made by truck transport, the bills should accompany the shipment. When shipments are made by rail or water, the bills shall be mailed to the receiver on the day of shipment.

6.10 Delivery of Materials

6.10.1 Fabricated structural steel shall be delivered in such sequence as will permit the most efficient and economical performance of shop fabrication and erection. If the client contracts separately for delivery and erection he must coordinate planning between the fabricator, erector and general contractor.

6.10.2 Anchor bolts, washers and other anchorages, grillages, or materials to be built into masonry or concrete should be shipped so that they will be on hand when needed. The client must give the fabricator sufficient notice to permit fabrication and shipping of materials before they are needed.

6.10.3 The quantities of material shown by the shipping bill are customarily accepted by the client, fabricator and erector as correct. If any shortage or damage is claimed, the client or erector should, within 48 hours, notify the carrier and the fabricator in order that the claim may be investigated.

6.10.4 The size and mass of structural steel assemblies may be limited by the shop capabilities, the permissible mass and clearance dimensions of available transportation or government regulations and the job site conditions. The fabricator limits the number of field splices to those consistent with economy.

7. Erection

7.1 Method of Erection. Unless otherwise specified or agreed upon, the erector shall proceed according to the most efficient and economical method available to him consistent with the drawings and specifications.

7.2 Site Conditions. The client shall provide and maintain adequate access roads cleared of snow and ice into and through the site for the safe delivery of derricks, cranes, other necessary equipment, and the material to be erected. The client shall provide for the erector a firm, properly graded, drained, convenient and adequate space at the site for the operation of his equipment and shall remove at the client's cost all overhead obstructions such as power lines, telephone lines, etc., in order to provide a safe working area for erection of the steelwork. The erector shall provide and install the safety protection required for his own operations or for his work forces to meet the safety requirements of applicable Acts or Codes. The general contractor shall install protective covers to all protruding rebar, machinery anchor bolts, etc., which are a hazard to workers. Any protection for pedestrians, property, other trades, etc., not essential to the steel erection activity is the responsibility of the client. When the structure does not occupy the full available site, the client shall provide adequate storage space to enable the fabricator and erector to operate at maximum practicable speed.

7.3 Foundations. The tender specifications preferably shall specify the time that foundations will be ready, free from obstruction and accessible to the erector. Unless otherwise agreed upon, the work of erection shall be tendered on the basis that it will start at a time designated in the tender specifications without interference or delay caused by others.

Neither the fabricator nor the erector shall be responsible for the accurate location, strength and suitability of foundations. The finished tops of all footings shall be at a specified level to predetermine the amount of shimming that may be required.

7.4 Building Lines and Bench Marks. The erector shall be provided with a plot plan accurately locating building lines and bench marks at the site of the structure.

7.5 Installation of Anchor Bolts and Embedded Items

7.5.1 Anchor bolts and foundation bolts shall be set by the client in accordance with the erection diagrams. They must not vary from the dimensions shown on the erection diagrams by more than the following (see also Appendix D):

(a) 3 mm centre to centre of any two bolts within an anchor bolt group, where an anchor bolt group is defined as the set of anchor bolts which receives a single fabricated steel shipping piece;

(b) 6 mm centre-to-centre of adjacent anchor bolt groups;

(c) Maximum accumulation of 6 mm per 30 000 mm along the established column line of multiple anchor bolt groups, but not to exceed a total of 25 mm. The established column line is the actual field line most representative of the centres of the as-built anchor bolt groups along a line of columns;

(d) 6 mm from the centre of any anchor bolt group to the established column line through that group.

The tolerances of paragraphs b, c and d apply to offset dimensions, shown on the construction drawings, measured parallel and perpendicular to the nearest established column line for individual columns shown on the drawings to be offset from established column lines.

7.5.2 Unless shown otherwise, anchor bolts shall be set perpendicular to the theoretical bearing surface, threads shall be protected and free of concrete and nuts should run freely on the threads.

7.5.3 Other embedded items or connection materials between the structural steel and the work of others shall be located and set by the client in accordance with approved erection diagrams. Accuracy of these items must satisfy the erection tolerance requirements of Section 7.10.

7.5.4 All work performed by the client shall be completed so as not to delay or interfere with the erection of the structural steel.

7.6 Bearing Devices. The client shall set to line and grade all levelling plates and loose bearing plates which can be handled without a derrick or crane. All other bearing devices supporting structural steel shall be set and wedged, shimmed or adjusted with levelling screws by the erector to lines and grades established by the client. The fabricator and/or erector shall provide the wedges, shims or levelling screws that are required, and shall describe clearly the bearing devices with working lines to facilitate proper alignment. Promptly after the setting of any bearing devices, the client shall check lines and grades, and grout as required. The final location and proper grouting of bearing devices are the responsibility of the client.

When steel columns, girders or beams which will be supported on concrete or masonry have base plates or bearing plates fabricated as an integral part of the member, the bearing area of the support shall be suitably prepared by others so as to be at exact grade and level to receive the steelwork.

7.7 Examination by Erector. Prior to field erection, the erector shall examine the work of all others on which his work is in any way dependent and shall report to the client any errors or discrepancies that may affect erection of structural steel.

7.8 Adjustable Shelf Angles and Sash Angles. The erector shall position at time of erection all adjustable shelf angles and sash angles attached to the steel frame true and level within the tolerances permitted by the governing technical standard. Any subsequent adjustment that may be necessary to accommodate the work of others shall be performed by others.

7.9 Loose Lintels and Wall Bearing Members. Unless otherwise specified, loose lintels, shelf angles, wall bearing members and other pieces not attached to the structural steel frame shall be received and set by others.

7.10 Tolerances. Unless otherwise specified, tolerances on erected structural steel shall be those prescribed in the applicable governing technical standard.

7.11 Checking Erected Steelwork. The erector shall check the steelwork as it is erected into final position. Upon completion of the steel structure, or of a reasonable part of it, and within a reasonable time prior to removal of erection equipment, the client or his designated field inspector shall check as to whether the work is plumb, aligned and level, and whether all members are in the proper location, bolts torqued, welds tested, and generally whether the work meets the requirements of the contract documents.

7.12 Removal of Temporary Erection Bracing. Temporary guys, braces and falsework or cribbing supplied by the erector shall remain the property of the erector. He shall remove them when the steel structure is otherwise adequately braced unless other arrangements are made. Guys and braces temporarily left in place under such other arrangements shall be removed by others and returned to the erector in good condition.

7.13 Correction of Errors when Material is Not Erected by the Fabricator. Correction of minor misfits and a moderate amount of cutting and reaming shall be considered a part of the erection. Any error in shop work which will prevent the proper assembling and fitting of parts by the moderate use of drifts pins, or a moderate amount of reaming, chipping or cutting, shall be immediately reported to the fabricator so that the fabricator may either correct the error or approve the method of correction that is to be used.

7.14 Field Assembly. Unless otherwise specified, the fabricator shall provide for suitable field connections that will, in his opinion, afford the greatest overall economy.

7.15 Accommodation of Other Trades. Neither the fabricator nor the erector shall cut, drill or otherwise alter the work of others or his own work to accommodate other trades unless such work is clearly defined in the tender drawings and tender specifications and unless detailed information is provided before the erection diagrams are approved. Any subsequent cutting, drilling or other alteration of the structural steel performed by the fabricator or the erector for the accommodation of other trades, shall be specifically agreed upon and authorized by the client before such work is commenced.

7.16 Temporary Floors and Access Stairs. Unless otherwise required by law, all temporary access stairs shall be provided by others, except for the floor upon which erecting equipment is located. On this floor the erector shall provide such temporary flooring as he requires, moving his planking, etc., as the work progresses.

7.17 Touch-Up of Shop Paint. Unless so specified, the erector will not spot-paint field fasteners and field welds nor touch-up abrasions to the shop paint.

7.18 Field Painting. Unless so specified, the erector will not be responsible for cleaning the steel after erection in preparation for field painting, nor for any general field painting that may be required.

7.19 Final Clean-Up. Except as provided in clause 7.12, upon completion of erection and before final acceptance, the erector shall remove all falsework, rubbish and temporary buildings furnished by him.

STRUCTURAL STEEL IN BUILDINGS

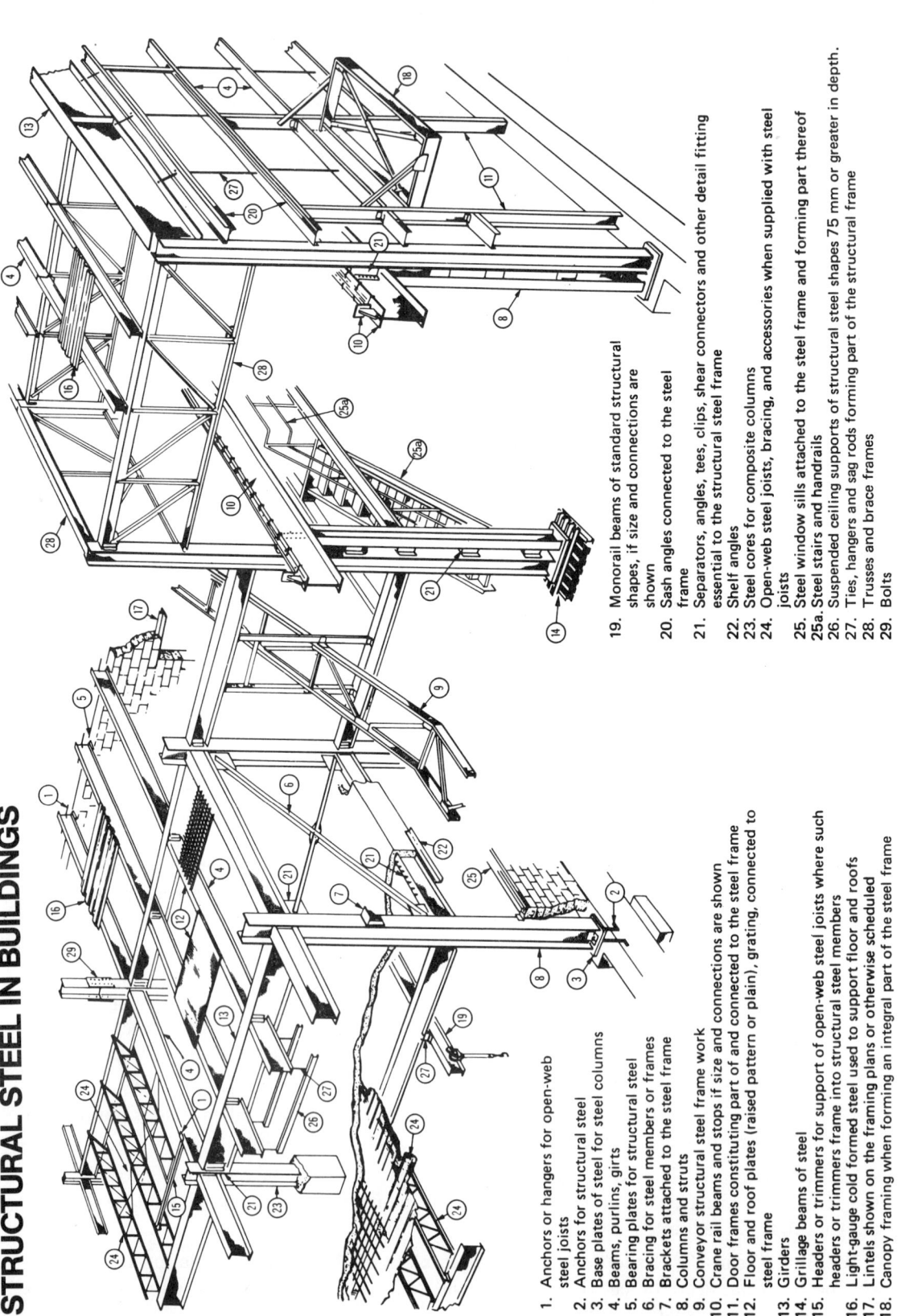

1. Anchors or hangers for open-web steel joists
2. Anchors for structural steel
3. Base plates of steel for steel columns
4. Beams, purlins, girts
5. Bearing plates for structural steel
6. Bracing for steel members or frames
7. Brackets attached to the steel frame
8. Columns and struts
9. Conveyor structural steel frame work
10. Crane rail beams and stops if size and connections are shown
11. Door frames constituting part of and connected to the steel frame
12. Floor and roof plates (raised pattern or plain), grating, connected to steel frame
13. Girders
14. Grillage beams of steel
15. Headers or trimmers for support of open-web steel joists where such headers or trimmers frame into structural steel members
16. Light-gauge cold formed steel used to support floor and roofs
17. Lintels shown on the framing plans or otherwise scheduled
18. Canopy framing when forming an integral part of the steel frame
19. Monorail beams of standard structural shapes, if size and connections are shown
20. Sash angles connected to the steel frame
21. Separators, angles, tees, clips, shear connectors and other detail fitting essential to the structural steel frame
22. Shelf angles
23. Steel cores for composite columns
24. Open-web steel joists, bracing, and accessories when supplied with steel joists
25. Steel window sills attached to the steel frame and forming part thereof
25a. Steel stairs and handrails
26. Suspended ceiling supports of structural steel shapes 75 mm or greater in depth.
27. Ties, hangers and sag rods forming part of the structural frame
28. Trusses and brace frames
29. Bolts

Appendix B

A Suggested Format For Accommodating Contract Price Adjustments

The cost of revisions SHOULD BE NEGOTIATED

The total value of revisions should not exceed 10% of the value of the original contract, and if exceeded the contract is subject to re-negotiation.

Negotiation of revisions shall be based on the following pricing conditions.

1. Revisions shall be negotiated on a lump sum basis, a unit price basis, or a cost plus basis.

2. A negotiated price revision shall only be made after the degree of complexity, type of member, and material specifications involved in the change are known.

3. If revisions affect the fabricator's and erector's labour force, the cost of such revisions will be based on the following labour rates, including overheads and profit but not including overtime premiums:

   Drawing Office Labour — $ /labour hour

   Shop Labour — $ /labour hour

   Field Labour — $ /labour hour

   Equipment used for revisions will be charged at negotiated rental rates, according to Canadian Construction Association standard practice.

4. Revisions involving the use of grades of steel, sources of supply, or types of sections, other than specified, will be subject to price adjustments.

5. Masses will be computed in accordance with clause 3.4 of the CISC Code of Standard Practice for Structural Steel.

Appendix C

A Suggested Format For Price Per Unit Of Mass Or Price Per Item Contracts

The following is a list of suggested categories for which unit prices could be asked, *such categories being selected or added to*, depending upon the nature of the project.

Suggested Categories*

1. Primary Steel

(a) Main structural steel columns, floor and roof framing of rolled sections, including column base plates.

(b) When welded wide flange, hollow structural sections and cold formed sections are used, the above categories should be amplified.

(c) Building skin components including girts, sag rods, channel door frames, trim angles, framing for openings, fascias and other wall framing.

(d) Crane runways, rails, accessories and monorail beams.

(e) Shop welded plate girders.

(f) Built up sections fabricated with rolled sections including cover plates, stiffeners, etc.

(g) Trusses, sway frames, and bracing.

(h) Standardized open web joists.

(i) Joist accessories.

(j) Conveyor galleries and bents.

2. Secondary Steel

(a) Miscellaneous steel framing for walkways, equipment supports, etc.

(b) Steel stairs, including treads and landings.

(c) Handrail for platforms, walkways, and stairs.

(d) Steel floor plate (raised pattern or plain);

(e) Grating.

(f) Ladders and cages.

(g) Loose lintels, wall bearing beams, wall plates, curb and shelf angles, delivered only.

(h) Anchor bolts for structural steel levelling plates for columns delivered only, to be set by others.

The following items should be carefully considered when price per unit of mass or price per item contracts are being contemplated: mix, scope, complexity, material specification, coating, quality control standard, work performed out of sequence, site access, etc.

*For payment purposes, the connection material required to connect an individual member to its supporting member is assumed to be part of the member to which it is attached for shipping purposes.

Appendix D

Tolerances on Anchor Bolt Placement (Clause 7.5.1)

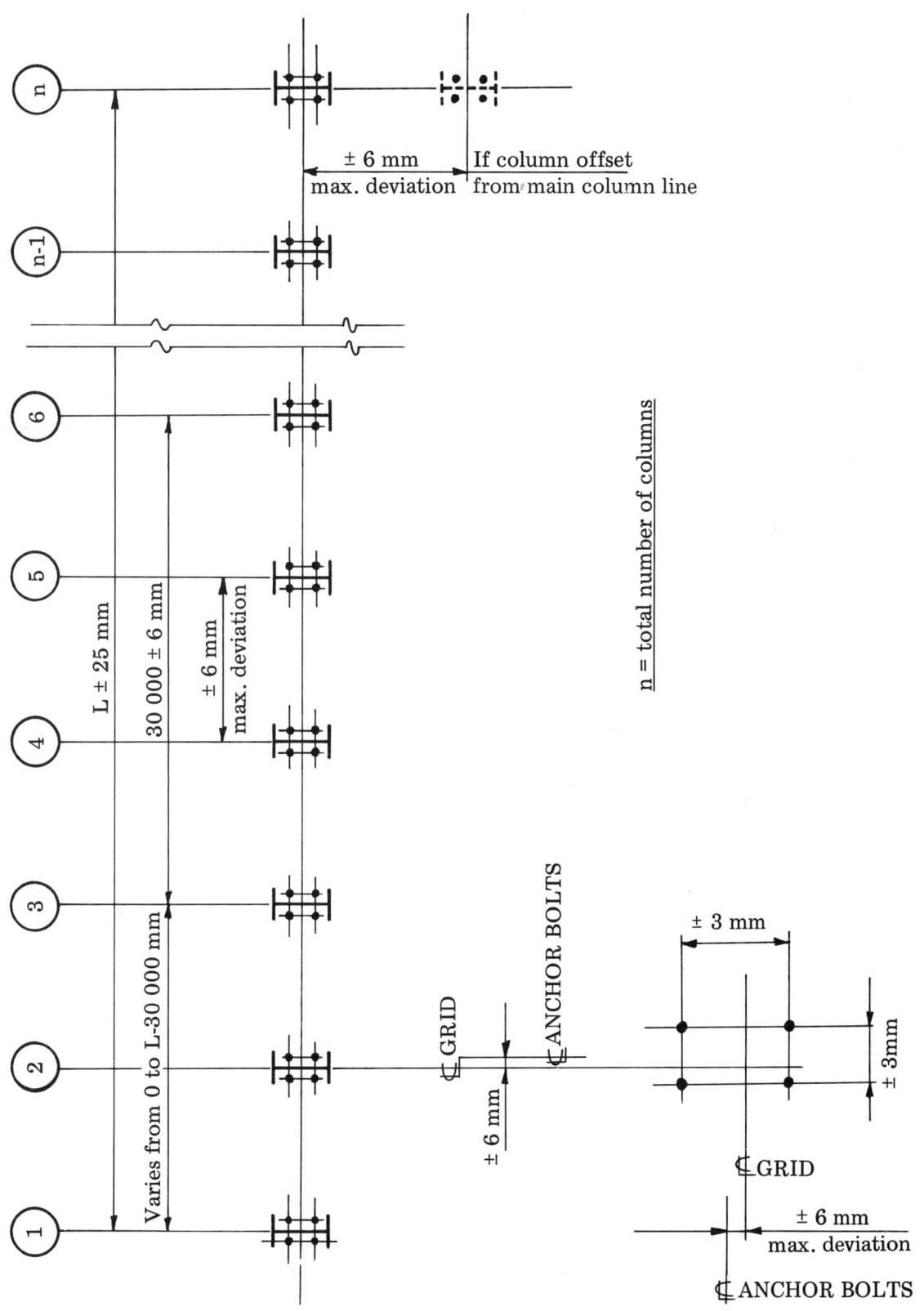

n = total number of columns

Appendix E

Conversion of SI Units to Imperial Units

When Imperial units are used in contract documents, unless otherwise stipulated, the SI units used in the CISC Code of Standard Practice for Structural Steel shall be replaced by the Imperial units shown, for the clause as noted.

Clause 3.2(a). Unit Weight. The unit weight of steel is assumed to be 0.2833 pounds per cubic inch.

Clause 3.2(e) Welds. The weight of shop welds, and the field welds in work erected by the fabricator, is computed on the basis of the shop details and/or erection diagrams and the gross weight of electrode required to lay the weld. For all fillet welds (continuous or intermittent) and all groove welds, the weight of the electrode is computed by adding 100 per cent to the weight based on the net theoretical weld cross-section and length. The computations are as follows:

i)   for equal leg fillet welds:

weight per inch of length (lb/in) = leg size (in) x leg size (in) x weight of steel (lb/in^3);

ii) for unequal leg fillet welds:

weight per inch of length (lb/in) = long leg size (in) x short leg size (in) x unit weight of steel (lb/in^3);

iii) for groove welds:

weight per inch of length (lb/in) = theoretical cross-section area of groove weld (in^2) x 2 x unit weight of steel (lb/in^3).

For other clauses, the standard conversion factors (for length, mass, etc.) stipulated in CISC handbooks should be used.

STRUCTURAL SHEET STEEL PRODUCTS

General

Structural sheet steel products such as roof deck, floor deck and cladding complement the structural steel frame of a building. These large-surface elements often perform both structural and non-structural functions, thereby enhancing the overall economy of the design.

Many of the sheet steel products used in Canada are supplied by members of the Canadian Sheet Steel Building Institute, a national association of steel producers, zinc producers, coil coaters, insulation manufacturers and fabricators of steel building products, steel building systems and steel farm buildings. The Institute promotes the use of sheet steel in building construction by encouraging good design, pleasing form and greater economy.

TYPICAL PRODUCTS

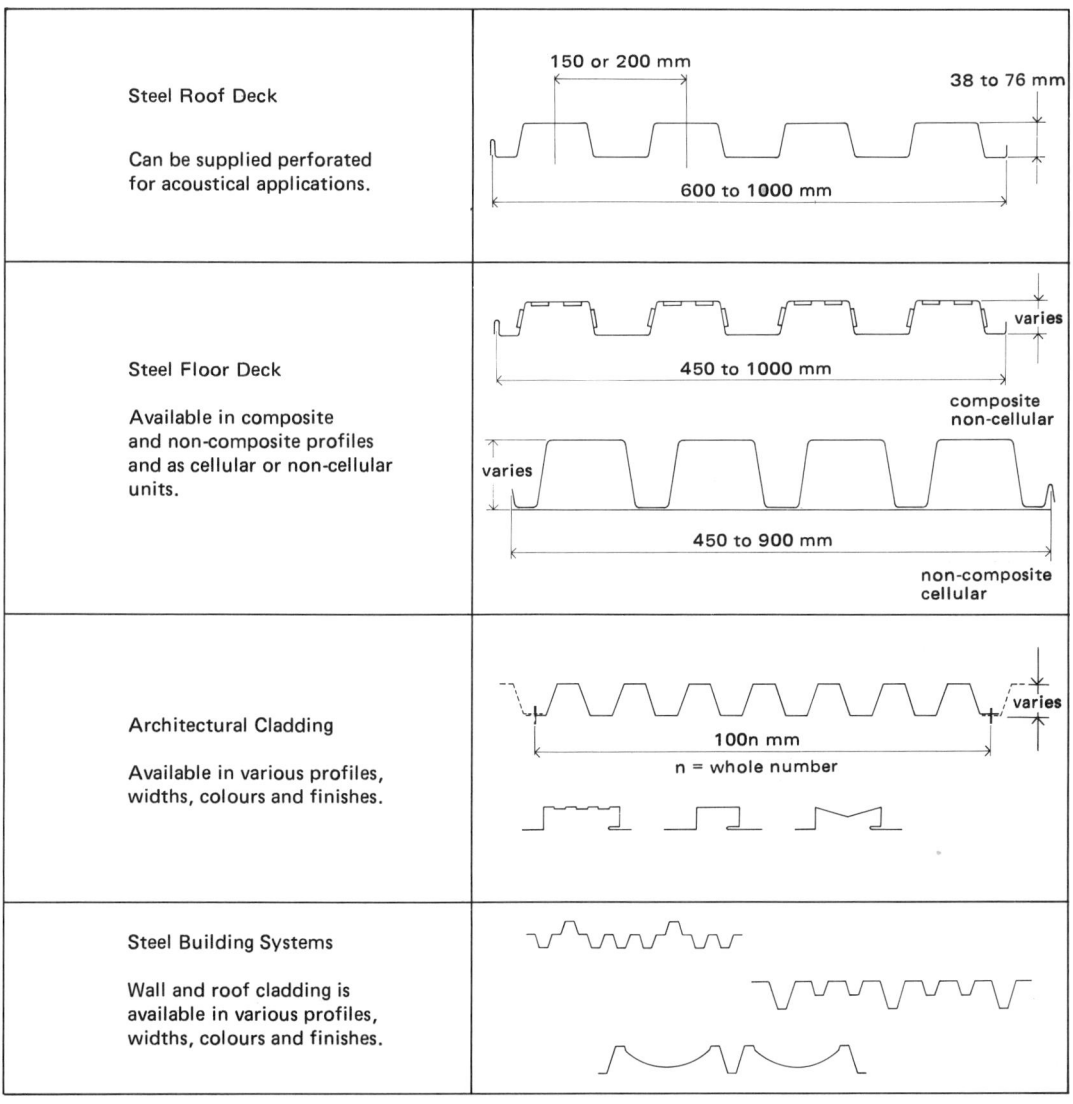

Steel Roof Deck Can be supplied perforated for acoustical applications.	150 or 200 mm · 38 to 76 mm · 600 to 1000 mm
Steel Floor Deck Available in composite and non-composite profiles and as cellular or non-cellular units.	450 to 1000 mm · varies · composite non-cellular varies · 450 to 900 mm · non-composite cellular
Architectural Cladding Available in various profiles, widths, colours and finishes.	100n mm · n = whole number · varies
Steel Building Systems Wall and roof cladding is available in various profiles, widths, colours and finishes.	

Sheet steel materials include zinc coated, prefinished, weathering and stainless steel sheet. Consult fabricators' catalogues for details of available products, profiles, widths, lengths, thicknesses, load capacities and other characteristics. The table below relates base steel thickness increments with the corresponding overall zinc coated thickness for various zinc coating designations applicable to structural quality sheets. For structural design calculations the base steel thickness is used.

METRIC THICKNESS DIMENSIONS FOR ZINC COATED STRUCTURAL QUALITY STEEL SHEET

Base Steel Nominal Thickness (1) (mm)	Overall Zinc Coated Nominal Thickness (mm)					
	Zinc Coating Designation (2)					
	(3) ZF075	Z275	Z350	Z450	Z600	Z700
2.67	2.67	2.71	2.72	2.74	2.76	2.77
1.91	1.91	1.95	1.96	1.98	2.00 (4)	2.01
1.52	1.52	1.56	1.57	1.59	1.61	1.62
1.22	1.22	1.26	1.27	1.29	1.31	1.32
0.91	0.91	0.95	0.96	0.98	1.00	1.01
0.76	0.76	0.80	0.81	0.83	0.85	0.86
0.61	0.61	0.65	0.66	0.68	0.70	0.71
0.46	0.46	0.50	0.51	0.53	0.55 (5)	0.56

Notes:
(1) Base steel nominal thickness is used to establish section properties and for structural design calculations.
(2) The listed zinc coating designations apply to metric material from Canadian producers.
(3) The small thickness increment for ZF075 (wiped coat) is disregarded.
(4) Enquire as to delivery date, if time is critical.
(5) Enquire as to availability.

CSSBI PUBLICATIONS

CSSBI publications include industry product standards, technical bulletins, and information bulletins as well as non-technical promotional material. A selection of current publications is listed below.

CSSBI Standards

Steel Roof Deck — covers design, fabrication and erection of steel roof deck with flutes not more than 8 inch (200 mm) on centre and a nominal 3 inch (75 mm) maximum profile depth, intended for use with built-up roofing or other suitable weather-resistant cover on top of the deck. (Pub. No. 38.36)

Steel Floor Deck — covers design, fabrication and erection of cellular and non-cellular steel floor deck with a nominal 3 inch (75 mm) maximum profile depth, intended for use with a concrete cover slab on top of the deck. (Pub. No. 38.12)

Metric Sheet Steel Cladding — covers design, fabrication and erection of weather-tight wall and roof cladding made from zinc coated, prefinished, stainless or weathering steel sheet for use on buildings with low internal humidity. (Pub. No. 38.6)

Steel Building Systems — covers the design, fabrication, and erection of steel building systems (SBS). Includes definitions, classification of SBS by type, checklist of items normally furnished, criteria for loads and load combinations, design standards, and certification by a registered engineer. (Pub. No. 38.4)

Steel Farm Buildings — covers minimum requirements for live loads, materials, design, fabrication and erection. (Pub. No. 38.120-80)

Technical Bulletins

No. 6 — **Metric Zinc Coated Sheet Steel for Structural Building Products** — contains technical requirements pertaining to zinc coated (galvanized) sheet steel for structural building products such as roof deck, cladding, insulated panels, and components of steel building systems. (Pub. No. 40.6-79)

No. 7 — **Prefinished and Post-Painted Galvanized Sheet Steel for Exterior Building Products** — contains quality and performance standards for prefinished and post-painted material used for exterior building products. Lists eleven proprietary paint systems which meet the specified criteria. (Pub. No. 40.7-79)

Information Bulletins

No. 3 — **Diaphragm Action of Cellular Steel Floor and Roof Deck Construction** — offers a simple and practical approach to the design of steel deck diaphragms supported by horizontal steel framing (Pub. No. 18.8)

No. 4 — **Snow Load Design Criteria for Steel Building Systems** — illustrates the roof snow load magnitudes, distributions and special accumulations for which Steel Building Systems should be designed. (Pub. No. 18.38)

No. 5 — **Metric Practice Guide: Steel Deck and Cladding** — a guide for designers, specifiers and users of steel deck and cladding products during the period of metric conversion. (Pub. No. 18.26)

Contact CSSBI at the address below for complete listing of publications, copies of publications, or other information concerning sheet steel in construction.

Canadian Sheet Steel Building Institute
201 Consumers Road, Suite 305
Willowdale, Ontario M2J 4G8
(416) 493-8780

MASS AND FORCES FOR MATERIALS

MATERIAL	Mass (kg/m³)	Force (kN/m³)	MATERIAL	Mass (kg/m³)	Force (kN/m³)
METALS, ALLOYS, ORES			**TIMBER, AIR-DRY**		
Aluminum	2 640	25.9	Birch	689	6.76
Brass	8 550	83.8	Cedar	352	3.45
Bronze, 7.9-14% tin	8 150	79.9	Fir, Douglas, seasoned	545	5.34
Bronze, aluminum	7 700	75.5	Fir, Douglas, unseasoned	641	6.29
Copper	8 910	87.4	Fir, Douglas, wet	801	7.86
Copper ore, pyrites	4 200	41.2	Fir, Douglas, glue laminated	545	5.34
Gold	19 300	189	Hemlock	481	4.72
Iron, cast, pig	7 210	70.7	Larch, tamarack	561	5.50
Iron, wrought	7 770	76.2	Larch, western	609	5.97
Iron, spiegel-eisen	7 500	73.5	Maple	737	7.23
Iron, ferro-silicon	7 000	68.6	Oak, red	689	6.76
Iron ore, hematite	5 210	51.1	Oak, white	753	7.38
Iron ore, hematite in bank	2 560-2 880	25.1-28.2	Pine, jack	481	4.72
Iron ore, hematite, loose	2 080-2 560	20.4-25.1	Pine, ponderosa	513	5.03
Iron ore, limonite	3 800	37.3	Pine, red	449	4.40
Iron ore, magnetite	5 050	49.5	Pine, white	416	4.08
Iron slag	2 760	27.1	Poplar	481	4.72
Lead	11 400	112	Spruce	449	4.40
Lead ore, galena	7 450	73.1	For pressure treated timber		
Magnesium	1 790	17.6	add retention to mass of		
Manganese	7 610	74.6	air-dry material.		
Manganese ore	4 150	40.7			
Mercury	13 600	133	**LIQUIDS**		
Monel	8 910	87.4	Alcohol, pure	785	7.70
Nickel	9 050	88.8	Gasoline	673	6.60
Platinum	21 300	209	Oils	929	9.11
Silver	10 500	103	Water, fresh at 4°C (max.		
Steel, rolled	7 850	77.0	density)	1 000	9.81
Tin	7 350	72.1	Water, fresh at 100°C	961	9.42
Tin ore, cassiterite	6 700	65.7	Water, salt	1 030	10.1
Zinc	7 050	69.1			
Zinc ore, blende	4 050	39.7	**EARTH, ETC. EXCAVATED**		
			Earth, wet	1 600	15.7
MASONRY			Earth, dry	1 200	11.8
Ashlar	2 240-2 560	22.0-25.1	Sand and gravel, wet	1 920	18.8
Brick, soft	1 760	17.3	Sand and gravel, dry	1 680	16.5
Brick, common	2 000	19.6			
Brick, pressed	2 240	22.0	**VARIOUS BUILDING**		
Clay tile, average	961	9.42	**MATERIALS**		
Rubble	2 080-2 480	20.4-24.3	Cement, portland, loose	1 510	14.8
Concrete, cinder, haydite	1 600-1 760	15.7-17.3	Cement, portland, set	2 930	28.7
Concrete, slag	2 080	20.4	Lime, gypsum, loose	849-1 030	8.33-10.1
Concrete, stone	2 310	22.7	Mortar, cement-lime, set	1 650	16.2
Concrete, stone, reinforced	2 400	23.5	Quarry stone, piled	1 440-1 760	14.1-17.3
SOLID FUELS			**MISCELLANEOUS**		
Coal, anthracite, piled	753-929	7.38-9.11	Asphaltum	1 300	12.7
Coal, bituminous, piled	641-865	6.29-8.48	Tar, bituminous	1 200	11.8
Coke, piled	368-513	3.61-5.03	Glass, common	2 500	24.5
Charcoal, piled	160-224	1.57-2.20	Glass, plate or crown	2 580	25.3
Peat, piled	320-416	3.14-4.08	Glass, crystal	2 950	28.9
			Paper	929	9.11
ICE AND SNOW					
Ice	897	8.80			
Snow, dry, fresh fallen	128	1.26			
Snow, dry, packed	192-400	1.88-3.92			
Snow, wet	432-641	4.24-6.29			

MATERIAL	Mass (kg/m²)	Force ($kPa = kN/m^2$)	MATERIAL	Mass (kg/m²)	Force ($kPa = kN/m^2$)
DECKS AND SLABS			**CLADDING (continued)**		
Roof deck, 38 mm x 0.76 mm	9.86	0.096 7	*Insulation, per 100 mm*		
Roof deck, 38 mm x 0.91 mm	11.7	0.115	Glass fibre, batts	4.88	0.047 9
Roof deck, wide rib, 51 x 0.76	10.6	0.104	Glass fibre, blown	4.00	0.039 2
Roof deck, wide rib, 51 x 0.91	12.7	0.124	Glass fibre, rigid	7.20	0.070 6
Roof deck, wide rib, 76 x 0.76	12.2	0.120	Urea Formaldehyde (foam)	0.80	0.007 84
Roof deck, wide rib, 76 x 0.91	14.6	0.144	Urethane, rigid	3.00	0.029 4
Floor deck, fluted, std. rib, 38 x 0.76	9.28	0.091 0	*Roofing*		
Floor deck, fluted, std. rib, 38 x 0.91	11.2	0.110	3-ply asphalt, no gravel (15 mm)	16.8	0.165
Floor deck, fluted, std. rib, 38 x 1.22	14.6	0.144	4-ply asphalt, no gravel (20 mm)	22.4	0.220
Floor deck, fluted, wide rib, 51 x 0.76	7.32	0.071 8	Crushed stone surfacing per 10 mm	14.9	0.146
			Asphalt shingles	31.7	0.311
Floor deck, fluted, wide rib, 51 x 0.91	8.30	0.081 4	*Windows*		
Floor deck, fluted, wide rib, 51 x 1.22	10.7	0.105	Steel frame, non-thermal break, single glazed	15.0	0.147
Floor deck, fluted, wide rib, 76 x 0.76	10.7	0.105	Aluminum frame, thermal break, double glazed	28.0	0.257
Floor deck, fluted, wide rib, 76 x 0.91	13.2	0.129	**FINISHES**		
Floor deck, fluted, wide rib, 76 x 1.22	17.6	0.172	*Floors*		
			Vinyl Asbestos tile, 3 mm	7.20	0.070 6
Floor deck, cellular, std. rib, 38 x 0.76	15.3	0.150	Parquet Flooring, per 10 mm	7.30	0.071 6
38 x 0.91	19.8	0.194	Carpet	6.00-13.5	0.0588-0.132
38 x 1.22	25.9	0.254	Terrazzo, per 10 mm	24.0	0.236
Floor deck, cellular, wide rib,			*Walls*		
51 x 0.76	13.3	0.130	16 mm Gypsum wallboard on furring channels	11.1	0.109
51 x 0.91	16.3	0.159	*Ceilings*		
51 x 1.22	20.3	0.199	Gypsum Wallboard, no channels, per 10 mm	8.0	0.078 5
76 x 0.76	16.7	0.163	Lay-in acoustic (excl'd fixtures)	13.6	0.133
76 x 0.91	20.3	0.200	Coffered acoustic ceiling including fixtures & fittings, avg.	7.0	0.068 6
76 x 1.22	27.2	0.267			
Concrete, std. wt., per 10 mm	24.0	0.235	**PARTITIONS**		
Concrete, semi-light wt., per 10 mm	17.5	0.172	100 mm std. block, plus mortar	240	2.35
Hollow core precast, avg. 150 mm	200	1.96	100 mm clay brick, plus mortar	192	1.88
Hollow core precast, avg. 200 mm	225	2.20	38 mm x 89 mm wood studs @ 400 o.c.	3.93	0.038 5
Wood Joists, 38 x 184	7.85	0.077 0	63 mm steel studs @ 400 o.c.	2.85	0.027 9
@ 400 c.c. 38 x 235	10.0	0.098 3	89 mm steel studs @ 400 o.c.	3.50	0.034 3
38 x 286	12.2	0.120	13 mm gypsum wallboard	10.4	0.102
Plywood, 11 mm	6.34	0.062 2	16 mm gypsum wallboard	12.8	0.126
Plywood, 14 mm	8.07	0.079 2			
Plywood, 19 mm	11.0	0.107			
Chipboard, 12.7 mm	7.62	0.074 7			
Chipboard, 15.9 mm	9.54	0.093 6			
Chipboard, 19.0 mm	11.40	0.112			
CLADDING					
Exterior Walls					
Brick, 100 mm thk., burnt clay	192	1.883			
Brick, 100 mm thk., concrete	240	2.35			
Precast concrete plus glazing	244-390	2.39-3.83			
Metal curtain wall plus glazing	75-150	0.735-1.47			
Steel siding plus mullions & girts	50-100	0.490-0.980			

M/D RATIOS

Designation	SI (kg/m)/m Beam[1]	SI (kg/m)/m Column[2]	Imperial (lb./ft.)/in. Beam[1]	Imperial (lb./ft.)/in. Column[2]	Designation	SI (kg/m)/m Beam[1]	SI (kg/m)/m Column[2]	Imperial (lb./ft.)/in. Beam[1]	Imperial (lb./ft.)/in. Column[2]
WWF1200					**WWF450**				
X487	121		2.07		X503		191		3.25
X403	100		1.71		X409		154		2.62
X364	94.1		1.61		X342		129		2.19
X302	84.6		1.44		X308		116		1.98
X263	80.4		1.37		X274		103		1.76
WWF1100					X248		92.9		1.59
X458	120		2.05		X228		85.4		1.46
X388	106		1.80		X201		75.3		1.28
X335	91.3		1.56		X177		66.0		1.13
X291	86.4		1.47		**WWF400**				
X255	75.7		1.29		X444		190		3.24
X220	71.7		1.22		X362		153		2.62
WWF1000					X303		128		2.19
X447	123		2.11		X273		116		1.97
X377	109		1.85		X243		103		1.76
X324	93.4		1.59		X220		92.8		1.58
X280	88.3		1.51		X202		85.2		1.45
X244	77.0		1.31		X178		75.1		1.28
X200	69.7		1.19		X157		66.0		1.13
WWF900					**WWF350**				
X417	122		2.08		X385		189		3.22
X347	106		1.81		X315		153		2.61
X293	89.3		1.52		X263		128		2.18
X249	83.6		1.43		X238		116		1.97
X213	71.5		1.22		X212		103		1.76
X192	71.6		1.22		X192		92.8		1.58
X169	63.1		1.08		X176		85.0		1.45
WWF800					X155		74.9		1.28
X332	108		1.84		X137		65.9		1.12
X279	90.6		1.55		**WWF300**				
X235	84.5		1.44		X446	144		2.47	
X198	71.2		1.22		X417	135		2.31	
X164	66.1		1.13		X387	126		2.16	
X154	62.1		1.06		X365	120		2.04	
WWF700					X342	112		1.92	
X222	86.0		1.47		**W920**				
X203	78.7		1.34		X313	114		1.94	
X185	71.7		1.22		X289	105		1.80	
X164	71.9		1.23		X271	99.2		1.69	
X151	66.2		1.13		X253	92.9		1.59	
X141	61.8		1.06		X238	87.7		1.50	
WWF550					X223	82.4		1.41	
X721		227		3.87	X201	74.8		1.28	
X620		191		3.27	**W840**				
X503		154		2.63	X359	123		2.11	
X420		129		2.20	X329	114		1.94	
X217		66.2		1.13	X299	104		1.78	
WWF500					**W840**				
X651		226		3.86	X226	88.4		1.51	
X561		191		3.26	X210	82.8		1.41	
X456		154		2.63	X193	76.3		1.30	
X381		129		2.20	X176	69.9		1.19	
X343		116		1.98	**W760**				
X306		103		1.76	X314	117		2.00	
X276		92.9		1.59	X284	106		1.82	
X254		85.5		1.46	X257	96.7		1.65	
X223		75.1		1.28					
X197		66.1		1.13					

[1] M/D = mass/(surface area—top of top flange)

[2] M/D = mass/surface area

Designation	SI (kg/m)/m Beam[1]	SI (kg/m)/m Column[2]	Imperial (lb./ft.)/in. Beam[1]	Imperial (lb./ft.)/in. Column[2]	Designation	SI (kg/m)/m Beam[1]	SI (kg/m)/m Column[2]	Imperial (lb./ft.)/in. Beam[1]	Imperial (lb./ft.)/in. Column[2]
W760					**W460**				
X196	84.8		1.45		X68	49.8		0.850	
X185	80.3		1.37		X60	44.2		0.755	
X173	75.4		1.29		X52	38.9		0.663	
X161	70.5		1.20		**W410**				
X147	64.6		1.10		X149	91.7		1.57	
W690					X132	81.6		1.39	
X265	108		1.84		X114	71.3		1.22	
X240	98.6		1.68		X100	62.9		1.07	
X217	89.5		1.53		**W410**				
W690					X85	62.5		1.07	
X170	80.0		1.37		X74	54.8		0.936	
X152	71.8		1.23		X67	50.0		0.853	
X140	66.5		1.13		X60	45.0		0.769	
X125	59.9		1.02		X54	40.8		0.697	
W610					**W410**				
X241	109		1.85		X46	38.0		0.649	
X217	98.5		1.68		X39	32.2		0.550	
X195	88.9		1.52		**W360**				
X174	80.0		1.37		X1086		388		6.62
X155	71.6		1.22		X990		360		6.14
W610					X900		333		5.69
X140	73.7		1.26		X818		309		5.27
X125	66.1		1.13		X744		285		4.87
X113	60.0		1.02		X677		262		4.48
X101	54.0		0.921		**W360**				
W610					X634		249		4.24
X92	53.5		0.912		X592		235		4.01
X82	47.9		0.818		X551		220		3.76
W530					X509		205		3.50
X219	107		1.83		X463		189		3.23
X196	96.8		1.65		X421		174		2.97
X182	90.3		1.54		X382		159		2.72
X165	82.2		1.40		X347		146		2.49
X150	75.1		1.28		X314		134		2.28
W530					X287		123		2.09
X138	80.9		1.38		X262		113		1.93
X123	72.4		1.24		X237		103		1.76
X109	64.5		1.10		X216		94.3		1.61
X101	60.1		1.03		**W360**				
X92	55.1		0.940		X196		88.7		1.51
X82	49.4		0.843		X179		81.4		1.39
W530					X162	89.1	74.0	1.52	1.26
X85	55.1		0.940		X147	81.2	67.4	1.39	1.15
X74	48.2		0.823		X134	74.4	61.8	1.27	1.05
X66	43.3		0.739		**W360**				
W460					X122	82.8	70.5	1.41	1.20
X177	99.2		1.69		X110	75.1	64.0	1.28	1.09
X158	89.0		1.52		X101	69.4	59.1	1.18	1.01
X144	81.5		1.39		X91	62.9	53.5	1.07	0.914
X128	72.8		1.24		**W360**				
X113	64.9		1.11		X79	60.5	52.3	1.03	0.893
W460					X72	55.6	48.0	0.948	0.819
X106	70.9		1.21		X64	49.7	43.0	0.849	0.733
X97	65.2		1.11		**W360**				
X89	60.2		1.03		X57	46.8		0.799	
X82	55.8		0.953		X51	42.2		0.720	
X74	50.3		0.859		X45	37.5		0.641	
X67	45.9		0.783		**W360**				
X61	42.0		0.718		X39	36.4		0.621	
					X33	31.0		0.530	

[1] M/D = mass/(surface area—top of top flange)
[2] M/D = mass/surface area

M/D RATIOS

Designation	SI (kg/m)/m Beam[1]	SI (kg/m)/m Column[2]	Imperial (lb./ft.)/in. Beam[1]	Imperial (lb./ft.)/in. Column[2]
W310				
X500		236		4.03
X454		217		3.71
X415		201		3.44
X375		185		3.15
X342		170		2.90
X313		157		2.68
W310				
X283		144		2.46
X253		130		2.23
X226		118		2.01
X202		106		1.81
X179		95.2		1.63
X158		84.9		1.45
X143		77.3		1.32
X129	84.2	70.1	1.44	1.20
X118	77.5	64.5	1.32	1.10
X107	70.7	58.8	1.21	1.00
X97	64.0	53.3	1.09	0.910
W310				
X86	63.0	53.1	1.07	0.906
X79	58.3	49.1	0.994	0.838
W310				
X74	60.9	52.1	1.04	0.889
X67	55.6	47.5	0.948	0.811
X60	50.1	42.9	0.856	0.731
W310				
X52	46.3		0.790	
X45	40.4		0.689	
X39	35.3		0.602	
W310				
X33	35.9		0.614	
X28	30.8		0.526	
X24	26.7		0.456	
X21	23.4		0.399	
W250				
X167		104		1.78
X149		94.3		1.61
X131		84.0		1.43
X115		74.2		1.27
X101	79.3	66.0	1.35	1.13
X89	70.4	58.6	1.20	0.999
X80	63.7	53.0	1.09	0.904
X73	58.6	48.7	1.00	0.831
W250				
X67	60.6	51.1	1.03	0.873
X58	52.9	44.6	0.902	0.761
X49	45.0	38.0	0.769	0.648
W250				
X45	46.8		0.798	
X39	40.9		0.698	
X33	35.0		0.597	
W250				
X28	34.2		0.584	
X25	30.9		0.528	
X22	27.6		0.471	
X18	22.5		0.385	
W200				
X100	94.3	78.7	1.61	1.34
X86	82.6	68.8	1.41	1.17
X71	68.7	57.3	1.17	0.977
X59	58.1	48.4	0.992	0.825
X52	51.7	43.0	0.882	0.734
X46	46.1	38.3	0.787	0.654

Designation	SI (kg/m)/m Beam[1]	SI (kg/m)/m Column[2]	Imperial (lb./ft.)/in. Beam[1]	Imperial (lb./ft.)/in. Column[2]
W200				
X42	47.0	39.6	0.802	0.676
X36	40.7	34.3	0.694	0.585
W200				
X31	38.5	33.0	0.656	0.563
X27	33.9	29.0	0.578	0.496
W200				
X22	31.1		0.530	
X19	27.2		0.465	
X15	21.7		0.371	
W150				
X37	48.3	40.2	0.824	0.686
X30	39.6	33.0	0.676	0.563
X22	29.4	24.4	0.502	0.417
W150				
X24	39.5	33.8	0.674	0.577
X18	30.1	25.7	0.514	0.439
X14	23.7	20.3	0.405	0.346
W130				
X28		36.8		0.629
X24		32.0		0.546
W100				
X19		31.1		0.532
S610				
X180	99.1		1.69	
X158	87.3		1.49	
S610				
X149	85.8		1.46	
X134	77.5		1.32	
X119	68.7		1.17	
S510				
X143	93.0		1.59	
X128	83.6		1.43	
S510				
X112	76.3		1.30	
X98	66.6		1.14	
S460				
X104	77.0		1.31	
X81.4	60.4		1.03	
S380				
X74	63.4		1.08	
X64	55.2		0.942	
S310				
X74	74.7		1.27	
S310				
X60.7	61.5		1.05	
S310				
X52	53.6		0.914	
X47	48.3		0.824	
S250				
X52	60.9		1.04	
X38	45.1		0.770	
S200				
X34	48.3		0.824	
X27	38.7		0.660	
S180				
X30	47.5		0.810	
X22.8	36.4		0.621	
S150				
X26	47.4		0.808	
X19	34.9		0.595	
M100				
X19		32.1		0.550

[1] M/D = mass (surface area—top of top flange)

[2] M/D = mass/surface area

COEFFICIENTS OF THERMAL EXPANSION

(Linear, per degree x 10^{-6})

METALS	c per °C	c per °F	NON-METALS	c per °C	c per °F
Aluminum	23	13	Cement, Portland	13	7
Brass	19	10.4	Concrete, Stone	10	5.7
Bronze	18	10.1	Glass	7	4
Copper	16.7	9.3	Granite	8.3	4.6
Iron, Gray Cast	11	5.9	Limestone	7.9	4.4
Iron, Wrought	12.0	6.7	Marble	9	5
Lead	28.7	15.9	Masonry, Ashlar	6.3	3.5
Magnesium	28.8	16	Masonry, Brick	6.1	3.4
Nickel	12.6	7	Masonry, Rubble	6.3	3.5
Steel, Cast	11.3	6.3	Plaster	16	9
Steel, Stainless	17.8	9.9	Sandstone	11	6
Steel, Structural	11.7	6.5	Slate	10	5.8
Zinc, Rolled	31	17.3	Fir (parallel to fibre)	3.8	2.1
			Fir (perpendicular to fibre)	58	32

NOTE: *Coefficients of thermal expansion indicated are average values from various sources. Minor variations may be expected in metals. Large variations may be expected in concrete and masonry due to the many combinations of constituents possible.*

Coefficients apply in general to a temperature range from 0 to 100 degrees Celsius.

The coefficient of linear thermal expansion (c) is the change in length per unit of length for a change of one degree of temperature. The coefficient for surface expansion is approximately two times, and the coefficient of volume expansion is approximately three times, the linear coefficient.

Change in length = cL x change in temperature, if member is free to elongate or contract.

Change in unit stress = cE x change in temperature, if member is not permitted to elongate or contract.

ELECTRONIC AIDS

General

Electronic aids now range from the simple pocket calculator, through the desk top and mini computers, to the powerful main frame large core computer in datacentres. An increasing number of reasonably priced but powerful computers are available to designers which can be programmed for steel design. In various parts of this book, for example, Built Up Sections in Part 6, expressions or flow charts are provided for rapid use on a calculator or to assist in the preparation of programs.

The CISC together with the Canadian Steel Construction Council (CSCC) have developed computer programs on calculators (HP97), desk top computers (HP9845) and large scale computers (FORTRAN language) for a broad range of steel design situations. Further information on current programs for steel design may be obtained from the CISC.

Electronic Calculators and Metric

Converting to, and using SI has been made easier by the availability of a broad range of electronic calculators. Although even an inexpensive model will be of some help, a more sophisticated model will be more effective in dealing with engineering problems.

Handling All Those Zeros

Both Hewlett-Packard (HP) and Texas Instruments (TI) market calculators that offer display format control in what is called "engineering notation". The display value in this format consists of a mantissa (the significant digits) and an exponent (power of ten) that have been adjusted so that exponent is a multiple of three (10^9, 10^{-6}, etc.) and the mantissa has 1, 2, or 3 digits to the left of the decimal point. Some models also allow the user to control the number of digits in the mantissa, that is, the number of significant digits displayed may be limited.

Since the properties of steel shapes in this book are organized so that the exponents are also in multiples of three, stress calculations are simplified by being able to use the number (mantissa and exponent) as tabulated.

This exploits a basic feature of the SI system. For example, to determine the extreme fibre stress of a W250 X 33 beam subject to 60 kN·m moment the following operations are performed:

Operation	Display	
1. Enter 60 kN·m	60.0	00
2. Multiply by 1 000 once to bring m to mm and again to bring kN to N	60.0	06
3. Obtain S_x for W250 X 33 beam (See p. 6—50), 379 x 10³ mm³	379.0	03
4. Divide to obtain stress in MPa ($N/mm^2 \equiv MN/m^2 \equiv MPa$)	158.3	00

Data Storage

A calculator with at least 6 data storage registers is very convenient in that it can be used to hold a number of conversion factors which pertain to structural design, such as the number of kN per kip, kN·m per ft-kip, MPa per ksi etc. Thus, easy comparisons between systems of units can be made, if required. Calculators with preprogrammed conversions are generally of marginal value as they are designed for the US household, not the engineering market, and they convert US Customary units instead of Imperial units.

Programmable vs. Non-programmable

Although price may determine the choice, the programmable models do offer some unique advantages when dealing with metric conversion. One such application is the manipulation of the display to show values of linear measure in the Imperial system in feet, inches and sixteenth of an inch, as shown

$$
\begin{array}{c}
\text{feet} \\
\overbrace{\quad}\;\;\overbrace{\quad}\;1/16\;\text{inches} \\
\boxed{14.0613}\;\longleftarrow\text{---Input/Output Display} \\
\underbrace{\text{inches}}
\end{array}
$$

and have them converted to metric or vice versa. Subsequent measurements can then be added to or subtracted from a previous value.

Of course, any repetitive calculation is greatly simplified with the programmable models.

Aids

The following expressions are provided in addition to those found in other Parts of this book.

1. Mass of Any Cross-Section in kilograms per metre

$$7\,850 \times 10^{-6} \times A \ (mm^2)$$

2. Force Due to Gravity on Any Cross-Section in kilonewtons per metre

$$77 \times 10^{-6} \times A \ (mm^2)$$

3. Factored Moment Resistance of Composite Beam

The following expressions are structured for easy programming on a programmable calculator. The majority of the symbols used are defined in Part One, CAN3-S16.1-M78 or in Composite Beams, Part Five of this book.

a) Plastic Neutral Axis in the Slab

When $\phi\,A_s\,F_y \leqslant 0.85\,\phi_c\,b_1 t_c\,F_c'$

$$M_{rc} = \phi\,A_s\,F_y\left(\frac{d}{2} + t_d + t_c - \frac{\phi\,A_s\,F_y}{1.7\phi_c b_1 F_c'}\right)$$

b) Plastic Neutral Axis in the Steel Flange

When $\phi\,A_s\,F_y > 0.85\,\phi_c\,b_1\,t_c\,F_c'$ and

$$(\phi\,A_s\,F_y - 0.85\,\phi_c\,b_1\,t_c\,F_c')/2 \leqslant \phi\,b\,t\,F_y$$

$$M_{rc} = \phi\,b\,t_1\,F_y\left[d + \frac{A_s(t_1 - d) + 2\,t_1\,b\,(d - t_1)}{2\,(A_s - b\,t_1)}\right] +$$

$$0.85\,\phi_c b_1 t_c F_c'\left[d + t_d + \frac{t_c}{2} - \frac{A_s d - bt_1\,(2d - t_1)}{2(A_s - bt_1)}\right]$$

Where $t_1 = \dfrac{\phi\, A_s\, F_y - 0.85\, \phi_c\, b_1\, t_c\, F'_c}{2\,\phi\, F_y\, b}$

c) Plastic Neutral Axis in the Steel Web

When $\phi\, A_s\, F_y > 0.85\, \phi_c\, b_1\, t_c\, F'_c$ and

$$(\phi A_s\, F_y - 0.85\, \phi_c\, b_1\, t_c\, F'_c)/2 > \phi\, b\, t\, F_y$$

$$M_{rc} = \phi\, F_y (bt + d_1 w)\left[d - \frac{bt^2 + 2d_1 tw + d_1{}^2 w}{2(bt + d_1 w)} - d_2 \right] +$$

$$0.85\, \phi_c\, b_1\, t_c\, F'_c \left[d + t_d + \frac{t_c}{2} - d_2 \right]$$

Where $d_1 = \dfrac{\left[\dfrac{\phi A_s\, F_y - 0.85\, \phi_c\, b_1\, t_c\, F'_c}{2\,\phi\, F_y} \right] - b\, t}{w}$;

and, $d_2 = \dfrac{\dfrac{A_s d}{2} - (b\, t + d_1 w)\left[d - \dfrac{bt^2 + 2d_1 tw + d_1{}^2 w}{2(b\, t + d_1 w)} \right]}{A_s - (b\, t + d_1 w)}$

For partial shear connection the above expressions are applicable when the following substitutions are made

t_d = Deck thickness + Slab thickness − t_c

$t_c = nq_r/\phi_{sc}/(0.85 b_1\, F'_c)$

NOTES

PROPERTIES OF GEOMETRIC SECTIONS
Definitions

Neutral Axis

The line, in any given section of a member subject to bending, on which there is neither tension nor compression.

For pure elastic bending of a straight beam, the neutral axis at any cross-section is coincident with the centroidal axis of the cross-section.

In the case of fully plastic bending, the neutral axis divides the sectional area equally. Therefore, the neutral axis for elastic and plastic bending coincide only in the case of sections symmetrical about the neutral axis.

Moment of Inertia I

The sum of the products obtained by multiplying each of the elementary areas, of which the section is composed, by the square of its perpendicular distance from the axis about which the moment of inertia is being calculated.

Elastic Section Modulus S

The moment of inertia divided by the perpendicular distance from the axis about which the moment of inertia has been calculated to the most remote part of the section.

The elastic section modulus is used to determine the bending stress in the extreme fibre of a section by dividing the bending moment by the section modulus, referred to the neutral axis perpendicular to the plane of bending, both values being expressed in like units of measure.

Radius of Gyration r

The perpendicular distance from a neutral axis to the centre of gyration (i.e., the point where the entire area is considered to be concentrated so as to have the same moment of inertia as the actual area). The square of the radius of gyration of a section is equal to the moment of inertia (referred to the appropriate axis) divided by the area.

The radius of gyration of a section is used to ascertain the load this section will sustain when used in compression as a strut or column. The ratio of the effective unsupported length of the section divided by the least radius of gyration applicable to this length is called the slenderness ratio.

Plastic Modulus Z

The modulus of resistance to bending of a completely yielded cross-section, calculated by taking the combined statical moment, about the neutral axis, of the cross-sectional areas above and below that axis.

In general, the plastic modulus is calculated by simple statics and has been included for only a few of the shapes listed.

PROPERTIES OF GEOMETRIC SECTIONS

SQUARE

Axis of moments through center

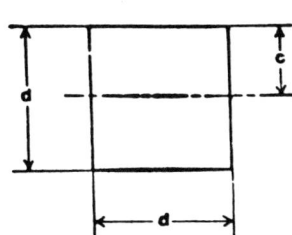

$$A = d^2$$

$$c = \frac{d}{2}$$

$$I = \frac{d^4}{12}$$

$$S = \frac{d^3}{6}$$

$$r = \frac{d}{\sqrt{12}}$$

$$Z = \frac{d^3}{4}$$

SQUARE

Axis of moments on base

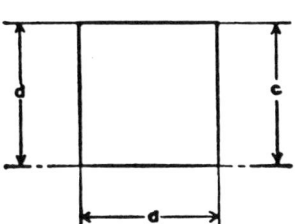

$$A = d^2$$

$$c = d$$

$$I = \frac{d^4}{3}$$

$$S = \frac{d^3}{3}$$

$$r = \frac{d}{\sqrt{3}}$$

SQUARE

Axis of moments on diagonal

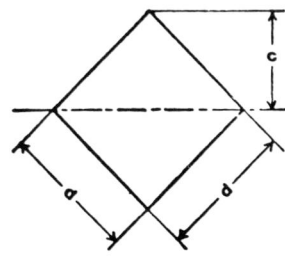

$$A = d^2$$

$$c = \frac{d}{\sqrt{2}}$$

$$I = \frac{d^4}{12}$$

$$S = \frac{d^3}{6\sqrt{2}}$$

$$r = \frac{d}{\sqrt{12}}$$

$$Z = \frac{2c^3}{3} = \frac{d^3}{3\sqrt{2}}$$

RECTANGLE

Axis of moments through center

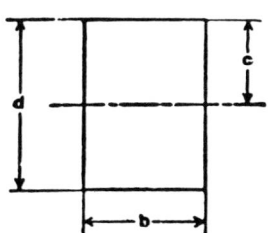

$$A = bd$$

$$c = \frac{d}{2}$$

$$I = \frac{bd^3}{12}$$

$$S = \frac{bd^2}{6}$$

$$r = \frac{d}{\sqrt{12}}$$

$$Z = \frac{bd^2}{4}$$

PROPERTIES OF GEOMETRIC SECTIONS

RECTANGLE

Axis of moments on base

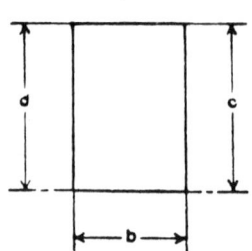

$$A = bd$$

$$c = d$$

$$I = \frac{bd^3}{3}$$

$$S = \frac{bd^2}{3}$$

$$r = \frac{d}{\sqrt{3}}$$

RECTANGLE

Axis of moments on diagonal

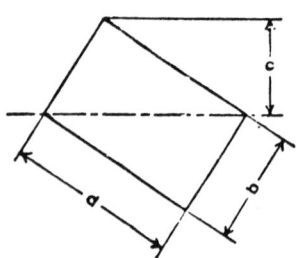

$$A = bd$$

$$c = \frac{bd}{\sqrt{b^2 + d^2}}$$

$$I = \frac{b^3 d^3}{6\,(b^2 + d^2)}$$

$$S = \frac{b^2 d^2}{6\sqrt{b^2 + d^2}}$$

$$r = \frac{bd}{\sqrt{6\,(b^2 + d^2)}}$$

RECTANGLE

Axis of moments any line
through center of gravity

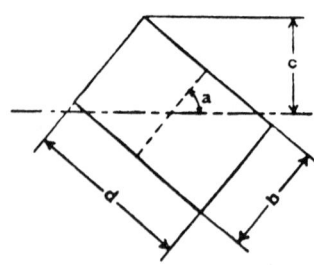

$$A = bd$$

$$c = \frac{b \sin a + d \cos a}{2}$$

$$I = \frac{bd\,(b^2 \sin^2 a + d^2 \cos^2 a)}{12}$$

$$S = \frac{bd\,(b^2 \sin^2 a + d^2 \cos^2 a)}{6\,(b \sin a + d \cos a)}$$

$$r = \sqrt{\frac{b^2 \sin^2 a + d^2 \cos^2 a}{12}}$$

HOLLOW RECTANGLE

Axis of moments through center

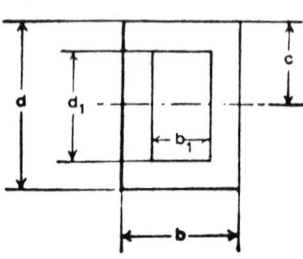

$$A = bd - b_1 d_1$$

$$c = \frac{d}{2}$$

$$I = \frac{bd^3 - b_1 d_1^3}{12}$$

$$S = \frac{bd^3 - b_1 d_1^3}{6d}$$

$$r = \sqrt{\frac{bd^3 - b_1 d_1^3}{12A}}$$

$$Z = \frac{1}{4}(bd^2 - b_1 d_1^2)$$

EQUAL RECTANGLES

Axis of moments through center of gravity

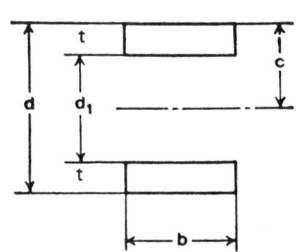

$$A = b(d - d_1)$$

$$c = \frac{d}{2}$$

$$I = \frac{b(d^3 - d_1{}^3)}{12}$$

$$S = \frac{b(d^3 - d_1{}^3)}{6d}$$

$$r = \sqrt{\frac{d^3 - d_1{}^3}{12(d - d_1)}}$$

$$Z = \frac{b}{4}(d^2 - d_1^2) = bt(d - t)$$

UNEQUAL RECTANGLES

Axis of moments through center of gravity

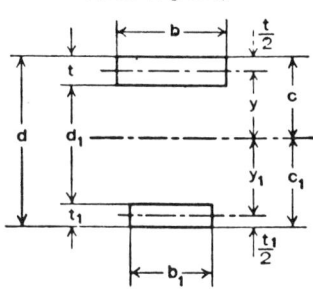

$$A = bt + b_1 t_1$$

$$c = \frac{\frac{1}{2} bt^2 + b_1 t_1 (d - \frac{1}{2} t_1)}{A}$$

$$I = \frac{bt^3}{12} + bty^2 + \frac{b_1 t_1{}^3}{12} + b_1 t_1 y_1{}^2$$

$$S = \frac{I}{c} \qquad S_1 = \frac{I}{c_1}$$

$$r = \sqrt{\frac{I}{A}}$$

TRIANGLE

Axis of moments through center of gravity

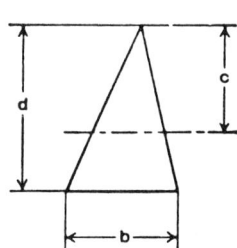

$$A = \frac{bd}{2}$$

$$c = \frac{2d}{3}$$

$$I = \frac{bd^3}{36}$$

$$S = \frac{bd^2}{24}$$

$$r = \frac{d}{\sqrt{18}}$$

TRIANGLE

Axis of moments on base

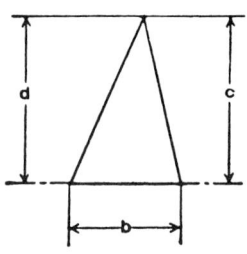

$$A = \frac{bd}{2}$$

$$c = d$$

$$I = \frac{bd^3}{12}$$

$$S = \frac{bd^2}{12}$$

$$r = \frac{d}{\sqrt{6}}$$

PROPERTIES OF GEOMETRIC SECTIONS

TRAPEZOID

Axis of moments through center of gravity

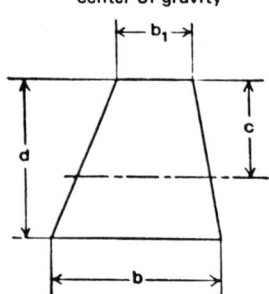

$$A = \frac{d(b + b_1)}{2}$$

$$c = \frac{d(2b + b_1)}{3(b + b_1)}$$

$$I = \frac{d^3(b^2 + 4bb_1 + b_1{}^2)}{36(b + b_1)}$$

$$S = \frac{d^2(b^2 + 4bb_1 + b_1{}^2)}{12(2b + b_1)}$$

$$r = \frac{d}{6(b + b_1)}\sqrt{2(b^2 + 4bb_1 + b_1{}^2)}$$

CIRCLE

Axis of moments through center

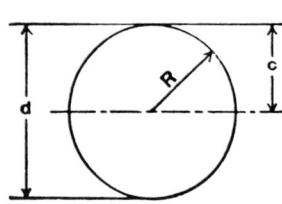

$$A = \frac{\pi d^2}{4} = \pi R^2$$

$$c = \frac{d}{2} = R$$

$$I = \frac{\pi d^4}{64} = \frac{\pi R^4}{4}$$

$$S = \frac{\pi d^3}{32} = \frac{\pi R^3}{4}$$

$$r = \frac{d}{4} = \frac{R}{2}$$

$$Z = \frac{d^3}{6}$$

HOLLOW CIRCLE

Axis of moments through center

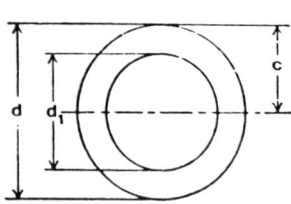

$$A = \frac{\pi(d^2 - d_1{}^2)}{4}$$

$$c = \frac{d}{2}$$

$$I = \frac{\pi(d^4 - d_1{}^4)}{64}$$

$$S = \frac{\pi(d^4 - d_1{}^4)}{32d}$$

$$r = \frac{\sqrt{d^2 + d_1{}^2}}{4}$$

$$Z = \frac{1}{6}(d^3 - d_1{}^3)$$

HALF CIRCLE

Axis of moments through center of gravity

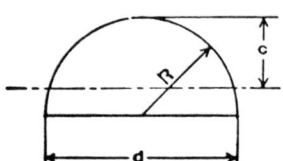

$$A = \frac{\pi R^2}{2}$$

$$c = R\left(1 - \frac{4}{3\pi}\right)$$

$$I = R^4\left(\frac{\pi}{8} - \frac{8}{9\pi}\right)$$

$$S = \frac{R^3(9\pi^2 - 64)}{24(3\pi - 4)}$$

$$r = R\frac{\sqrt{9\pi^2 - 64}}{6\pi}$$

PARABOLA

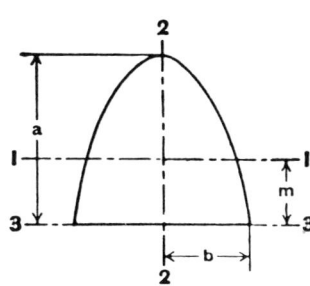

$$A = \frac{4}{3}ab$$

$$m = \frac{2}{5}a$$

$$I_1 = \frac{16}{175}a^3 L$$

$$I_2 = \frac{4}{15}ab^3$$

$$I_3 = \frac{32}{105}a^3 b$$

HALF PARABOLA

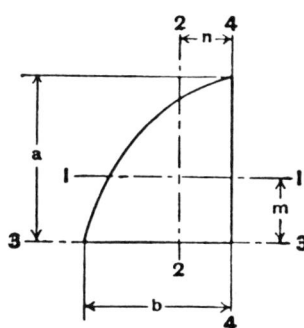

$$A = \frac{2}{3}ab$$

$$m = \frac{2}{5}a$$

$$n = \frac{3}{8}b$$

$$I_1 = \frac{8}{175}a^3 b$$

$$I_2 = \frac{19}{480}ab^3$$

$$I_3 = \frac{16}{105}a^3 b$$

$$I_4 = \frac{2}{15}ab^3$$

COMPLEMENT OF HALF PARABOLA

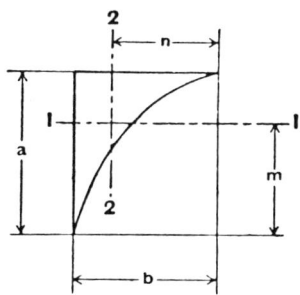

$$A = \frac{1}{3}ab$$

$$m = \frac{7}{10}a$$

$$n = \frac{3}{4}b$$

$$I_1 = \frac{37}{2100}a^3 b$$

$$I_2 = \frac{1}{80}ab^3$$

PARABOLIC FILLET IN RIGHT ANGLE

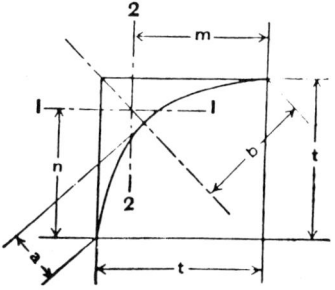

$$a = \frac{t}{2\sqrt{2}}$$

$$b = \frac{t}{\sqrt{2}}$$

$$A = \frac{1}{6}t^2$$

$$m = n = \frac{4}{5}t$$

$$I_1 = I_2 = \frac{11}{2100}t^4$$

PROPERTIES OF GEOMETRIC SECTIONS

* HALF ELLIPSE

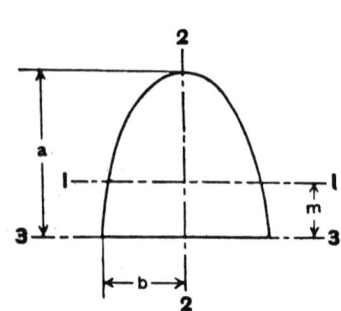

$$A = \frac{1}{2}\pi ab$$

$$m = \frac{4a}{3\pi}$$

$$I_1 = a^3 b\left(\frac{\pi}{8} - \frac{8}{9\pi}\right)$$

$$I_2 = \frac{1}{8}\pi ab^3$$

$$I_3 = \frac{1}{8}\pi a^3 b$$

* QUARTER ELLIPSE

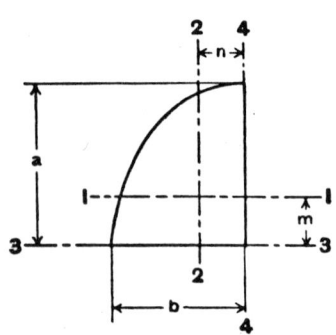

$$A = \frac{1}{4}\pi ab$$

$$m = \frac{4a}{3\pi}$$

$$n = \frac{4b}{3\pi}$$

$$I_1 = a^3 b\left(\frac{\pi}{16} - \frac{4}{9\pi}\right)$$

$$I_2 = ab^3\left(\frac{\pi}{16} - \frac{4}{9\pi}\right)$$

$$I_3 = \frac{1}{16}\pi a^3 b$$

$$I_4 = \frac{1}{16}\pi ab^3$$

* ELLIPTIC COMPLEMENT

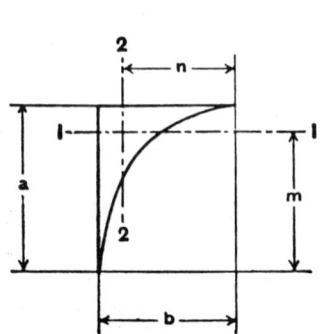

$$A = ab\left(1 - \frac{\pi}{4}\right)$$

$$m = \frac{a}{6\left(1 - \frac{\pi}{4}\right)}$$

$$n = \frac{b}{6\left(1 - \frac{\pi}{4}\right)}$$

$$I_1 = a^3 b\left(\frac{1}{3} - \frac{\pi}{16} - \frac{1}{36\left(1 - \frac{\pi}{4}\right)}\right)$$

$$I_2 = ab^3\left(\frac{1}{3} - \frac{\pi}{16} - \frac{1}{36\left(1 - \frac{\pi}{4}\right)}\right)$$

* To obtain properties of half circle, quarter circle and circular complement substitute a = b = R.

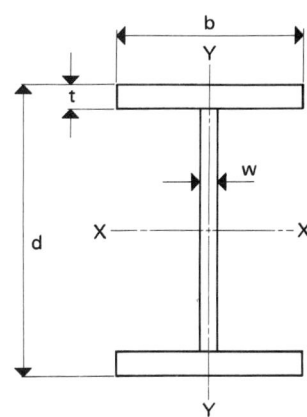

$$A = 2bt + (d - 2t)\,w$$

$$I = \frac{1}{12}\left[bd^3 - (b - w)(d - 2t)^3\right]$$

$$S = \frac{1}{6d}\left[bd^3 - (b - w)(d - 2t)^3\right]$$

$$r = \sqrt{\frac{I}{A}}$$

$$Z = \frac{1}{4}\left[bd^2 - (b - w)(d - 2t)^2\right]$$

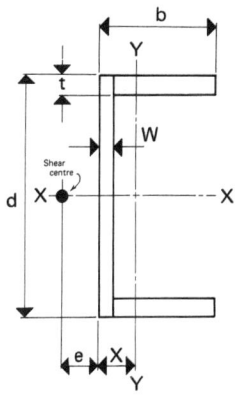

$$A = dw + 2\,(b - w)\,t$$

$$I = \frac{1}{12}\left[bd^3 - (b - w)(d - 2t)^3\right]$$

$$S = \frac{1}{6d}\left[bd^3 - (b - w)(d - 2t)^3\right]$$

$$r = \sqrt{\frac{I}{A}}$$

$$e = \frac{b^2 d^2 t}{4I} - \frac{w}{2}$$

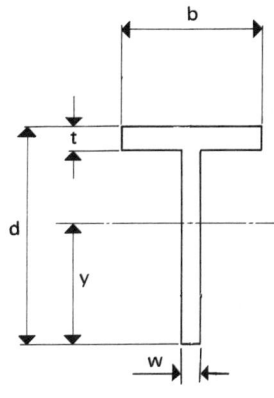

$$A = bt + w\,(d - t)$$

$$y = \frac{1}{2}\left(\frac{bdt}{A} + d - t\right)$$

$$I = \frac{1}{12}\left[bt^3 + w\,(d - t)^3 + \frac{3\,bwtd^2\,(d - t)}{A}\right]$$

$$S_1 = \frac{I}{y}$$

$$S_2 = \frac{I}{d - y}$$

$$r = \sqrt{\frac{I}{A}}$$

PROPERTIES OF GEOMETRIC SECTIONS
AND STRUCTURAL SHAPES

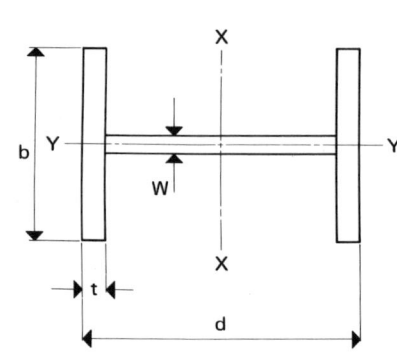

$$A = 2bt + w(d - 2t)$$

$$I = \frac{1}{12}\left[2tb^3 + (d - 2t)w^3\right]$$

$$S = \frac{1}{6b}\left[2tb^3 + (d - 2t)w^3\right]$$

$$r = \sqrt{\frac{I}{A}}$$

$$Z = \frac{1}{4}\left[2t\,(b^2 - w^2) + d\,w^2\right]$$

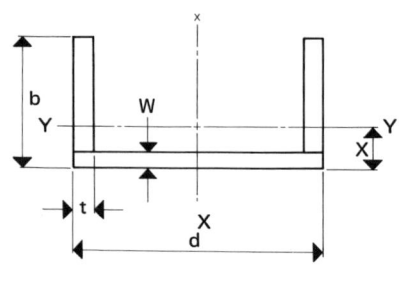

$$A = dw + 2(b - w)t$$

$$x = \frac{1}{2A}\left[(d - 2t)\,w^2 + 2tb^2\right]$$

$$I = \frac{1}{3}\left[dx^3 + 2t\,(b-x)^3 - (d-2t)\,(x-w)^3\right]$$

$$S_1 = \frac{I}{b - x} \;;\; S_2 = \frac{I}{x}$$

$$r = \sqrt{\frac{I}{A}}$$

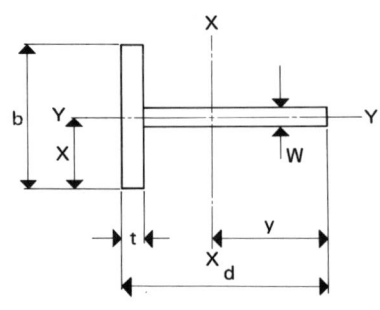

$$A = bt + (d - t)w$$

$$x = b/2$$

$$I = \frac{1}{12}\left[tb^3 + (d - 2t)\,w^3\right]$$

$$S = \frac{2I}{b}$$

$$r = \sqrt{\frac{I}{A}}$$

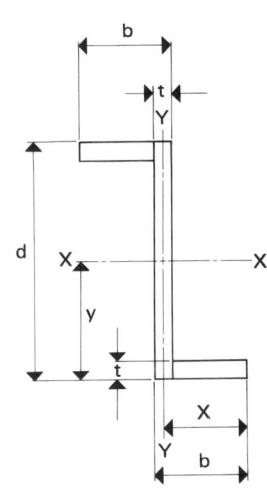

$$A = t\left[d + 2(b - t)\right]$$

$$y = d/2$$

$$I = \frac{bd^3 - (b - t)(d - 2t)^3}{12}$$

$$S = \frac{I}{y}$$

$$r = \sqrt{\frac{bd^3 - (b - t)(d - 2t)^3}{12t\left[d + 2(b - t)\right]}}$$

ANGLE

Axis of moments through center of gravity

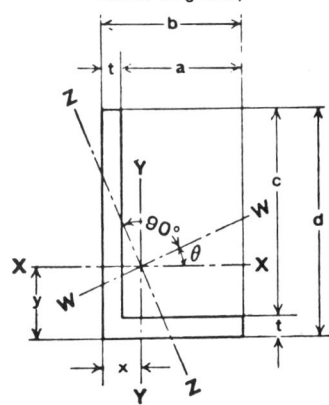

Z-Z is axis of minimum I

$$\tan 2\theta = \frac{2K}{I_y - I_x}$$

$$A = t(b + c) \qquad x = \frac{b^2 + ct}{2(b + c)} \qquad y = \frac{d^2 + at}{2(b + c)}$$

$$K = \text{Product of Inertia about X-X \& Y-Y}$$

$$= \mp\frac{abcdt}{4(b + c)}$$

$$I_x = \frac{1}{3}\left(t(d - y)^3 + by^3 - a(y - t)^3\right)$$

$$I_y = \frac{1}{3}\left(t(b - x)^3 + dx^3 - c(x - t)^3\right)$$

$$I_z = I_x \sin^2\theta + I_y \cos^2\theta + K \sin2\theta$$

$$I_w = I_x \cos^2\theta + I_y \sin^2\theta - K \sin2\theta$$

K is negative when heel of angle, with respect to c. g., is in 1st or 3rd quadrant, positive when in 2nd or 4th quadrant.

BEAMS AND CHANNELS

Transverse force oblique through center of gravity

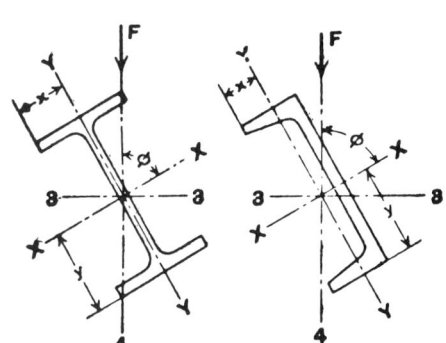

$$I_3 = I_x \sin^2\phi + I_y \cos^2\phi$$

$$I_4 = I_x \cos^2\phi + I_y \sin^2\phi$$

$$f = M\left(\frac{y}{I_x}\sin\phi + \frac{x}{I_y}\cos\phi\right)$$

where M is bending moment due to force F.

PROPERTIES OF GEOMETRIC SECTIONS
AND STRUCTURAL SHAPES

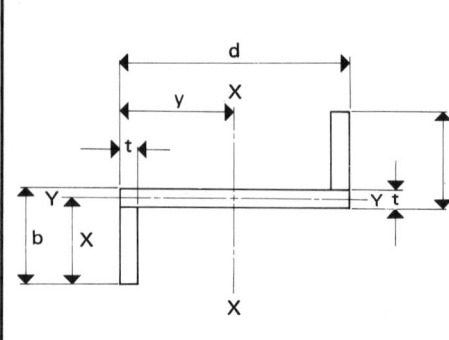

$$A = t \, [d + 2(b - t)]$$

$$x = b - t/2$$

$$I = \frac{1}{12} \left[2tb^3 + \frac{(d-2t)t^3}{12} \right]$$

$$S = \frac{I}{x}$$

$$r = \sqrt{\frac{I}{A}}$$

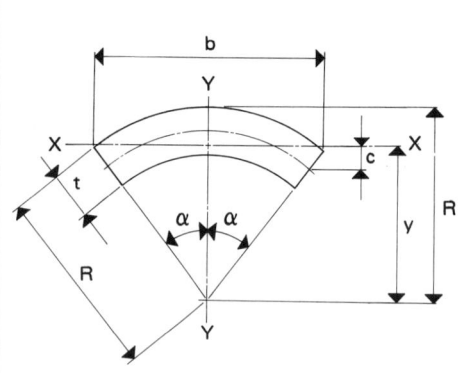

$$A = \frac{\pi \alpha t}{180} (2R - t)$$

$$c = \left(\frac{180 \sin \alpha}{\pi \alpha} - \cos \alpha \right) (R - \frac{t}{2})$$

$$n = (R - \frac{t}{2}) \sin \alpha$$

$$I_x = \left(\frac{\pi \alpha}{180} + \sin \alpha \cos \alpha - \frac{360 \sin^2 \alpha}{\pi \alpha} \right) \left(R - \frac{t}{2} \right)^3 t$$

$$I_y = \left(\frac{\pi \alpha}{180} - \sin \alpha \cos \alpha \right) R^3 \, t$$

$$y = \frac{180 \sin \alpha}{\pi \alpha} (R - \frac{t}{2})$$

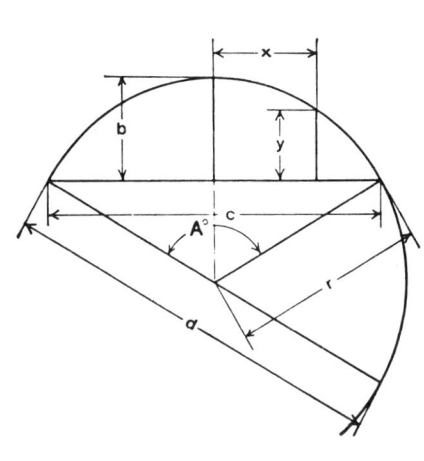

Circumference = 6.28318 r = 3.14159 d

Diameter = 0.31831 circumference

Area = 3.14159 r^2

Arc $a = \dfrac{\pi r A^\circ}{180^\circ} = 0.017453\, r\, A^\circ$

Angle $A^\circ = \dfrac{180^\circ a}{\pi r} = 57.29578 \dfrac{a}{r}$

Radius $r = \dfrac{4 b^2 + c^2}{8 b}$

Chord $c = 2\sqrt{2\,br - b^2} = 2\,r \sin \dfrac{A}{2}$

Rise $b = r - \tfrac{1}{2}\sqrt{4\,r^2 - c^2} = \dfrac{c}{2}\tan\dfrac{A}{4}$

$= 2\,r \sin^2 \dfrac{A}{4} = r + y - \sqrt{r^2 - x^2}$

$y = b - r + \sqrt{r^2 - x^2}$

$x = \sqrt{r^2 - (r + y - b)^2}$

Diameter of circle of equal periphery as square = 1.27324 side of square

Side of square of equal periphery as circle = 0.78540 diameter of circle

Diameter of circle circumscribed about square = 1.41421 side of square

Side of square inscribed in circle = 0.70711 diameter of circle

---

CIRCULAR SECTOR

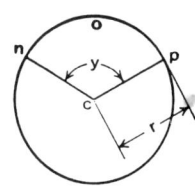

r = radius of circle   y = angle ncp in degrees

Area of Sector ncpo = ½ (length of arc nop X r)

$= \text{Area of Circle} \times \dfrac{y}{360}$

$= 0.0087266 \times r^2 \times y$

CIRCULAR SEGMENT

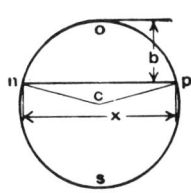

r = radius of circle   x = chord   b = rise

Area of Segment nop = Area of Sector ncpo − Area of triangle ncp

$= \dfrac{(\text{Length of arc nop} \times r) - x\,(r - b)}{2}$

Area of Segment nsp = Area of Circle − Area of Segment nop

VALUES FOR FUNCTIONS OF π

$\pi = 3.14159265359, \quad \log = 0.4971499$

$\pi^2 = 9.8696044, \log = 0.9942997 \qquad \dfrac{1}{\pi} = 0.3183099, \log = 1.5028501 \qquad \sqrt{\dfrac{1}{\pi}} = 0.5641896, \log = \overline{1}.7514251$

$\pi^3 = 31.0062767, \log = 1.4914496 \qquad \dfrac{1}{\pi^2} = 0.1013212, \log = 1.0057003 \qquad \dfrac{\pi}{180} = 0.0174533, \log = 2.2418774$

$\sqrt{\pi} = 1.7724539, \log = 0.2485749 \qquad \dfrac{1}{\pi^3} = 0.0322515, \log = 2.5085500 \qquad \dfrac{180}{\pi} = 57.2957795, \log = 1.7581226$

Note: Logs of fractions such as $\overline{1}.5028501$ and $\overline{2}.5085500$ may also be written 9.5028501 − 10 and 8.5085500 − 10 respectively.

PROPERTIES OF PARABOLA AND ELLIPSE

PARABOLA	ELLIPSE

PARABOLA

When $H \div B = 0.1$ or less, approximate ½ perimeter $= \sqrt{B^2 + 4/3H^2}$ or use formulas for circular arcs

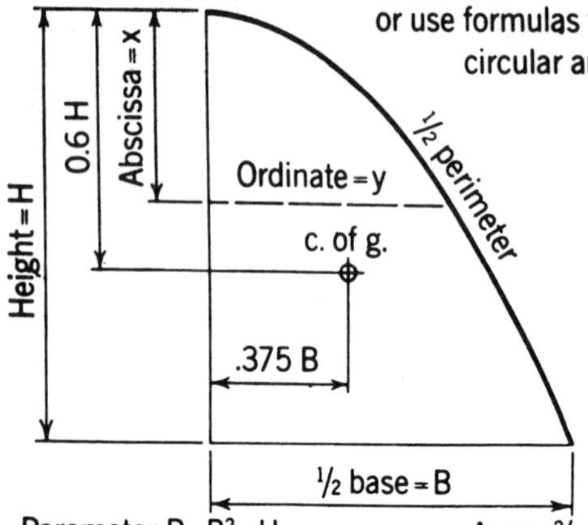

Apex

Abscissa = x

0.6 H

Ordinate = y

c. of g.

.375 B

Height = H

½ perimeter

½ base = B

Parameter $P = B^2 \div H$

$x = y^2 \div P$

$y = \sqrt{xP}$

Area $= \frac{2}{3} HB$

Construction

a b c d e

H

B

1 2 3 4 5

Construction

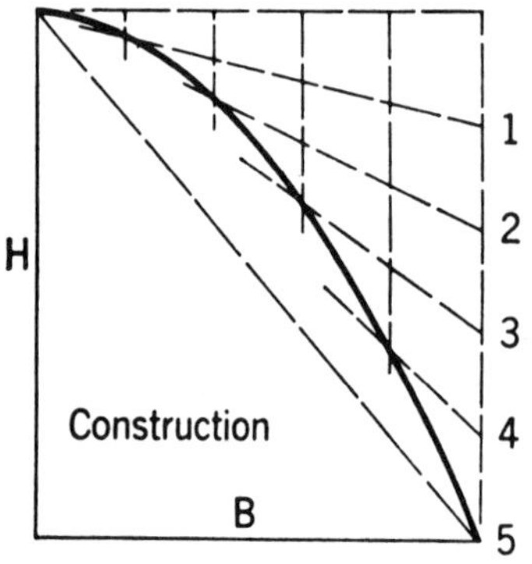

ELLIPSE

$(x^2 \div H^2) + (y^2 \div B^2) = 1$

$x = (H \div B)\sqrt{B^2 - y^2}$

$y = (B \div H)\sqrt{H^2 - x^2}$

Approximate ¼ perimeter $=$ $\frac{\pi}{4}\sqrt{2(H^2 + B^2)}$

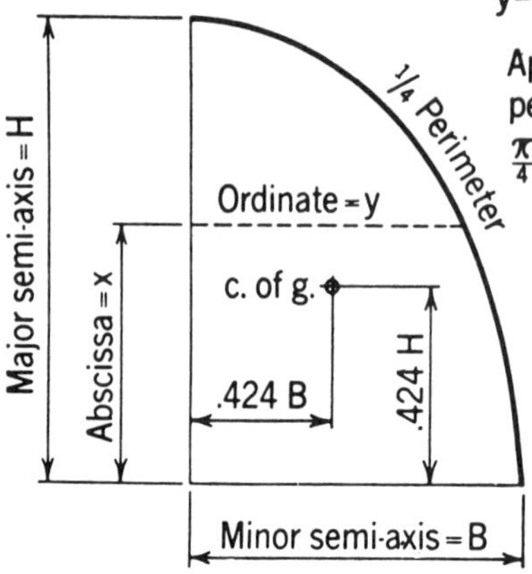

Major semi-axis = H

Abscissa = x

¼ Perimeter

Ordinate = y

c. of g.

.424 B

.424 H

Minor semi-axis = B

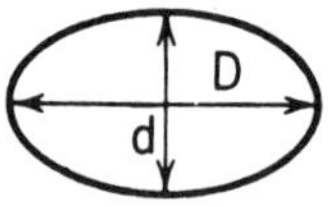

Area $= .7854\, Dd$

D

d

Construction

a

b

c

e

H

B

1 2 3 4

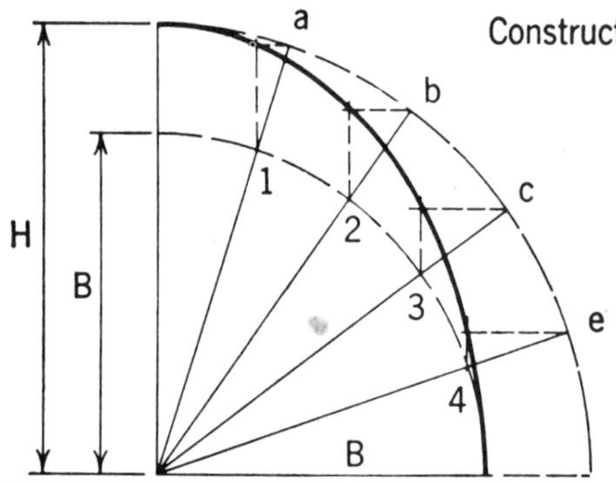

AREA BETWEEN PARABOLIC CURVE AND SECANT

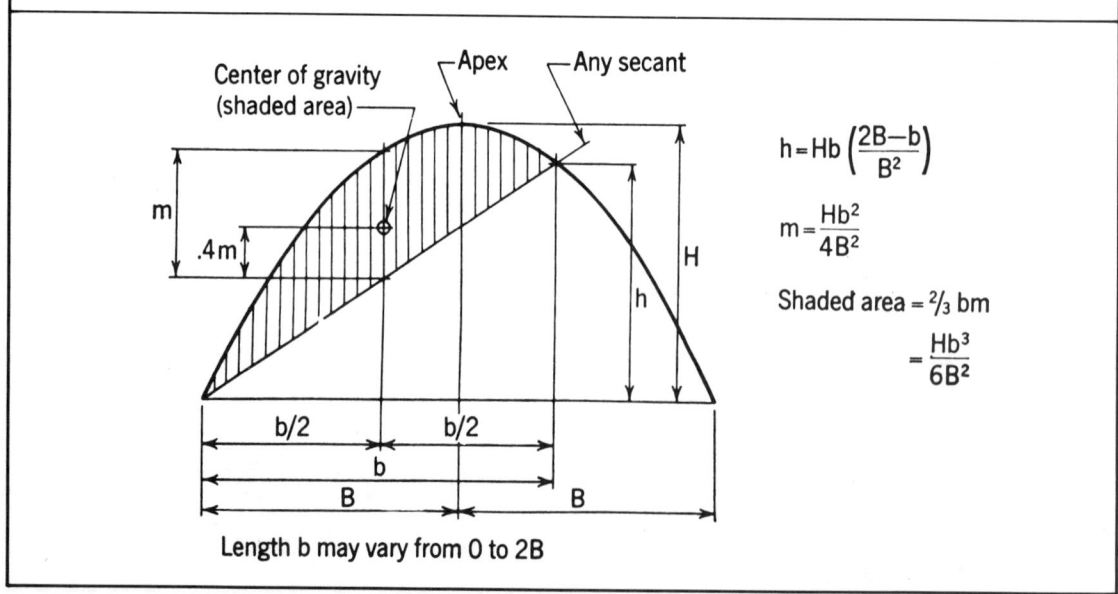

Center of gravity (shaded area)

Apex

Any secant

m

.4m

b/2   b/2

b

B   B

H

h

$h = Hb\left(\dfrac{2B - b}{B^2}\right)$

$m = \dfrac{Hb^2}{4B^2}$

Shaded area $= \frac{2}{3}\, bm$

$= \dfrac{Hb^3}{6B^2}$

Length b may vary from 0 to 2B

RECTANGULAR PARALLELEPIPED

Volume = *abc*

Surface area = 2(*ab* + *ac* + *bc*)

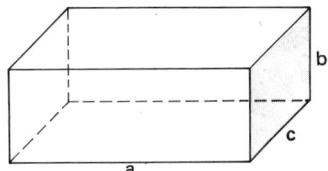

PARALLELEPIPED

Volume = *Ah* = *abc* sin θ

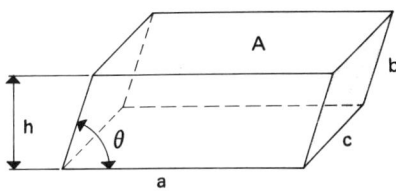

PYRAMID

Volume = $\frac{1}{3}$ *Ah*

The centroid of a pyramid is located y-distance from the base on the line joining the centre of gravity of area A and the apex.

$$y = \frac{h}{4}$$

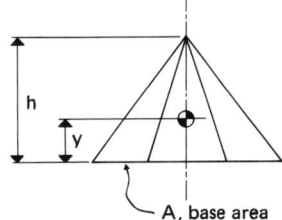

FRUSTUM OF PYRAMID

$$V = \frac{h}{3}(A_1 + A_2 + \sqrt{A_1 A_2})$$

The centroid is located y-distance up from area A_2 on the line joining the centres of gravity of areas A_1 and A_2

$$y = \frac{h(A_1 + 2\sqrt{A_1 A_2} + 3A_2)}{4(A_1 + \sqrt{A_1 A_2} + A_2)}$$

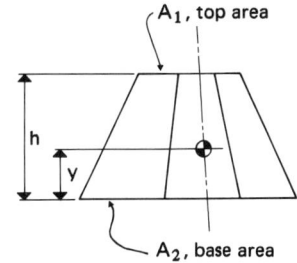

WEDGE

$$V = \frac{(2a + c)\,bh}{6}$$

The centroid is located y-distance from the base on the line joining the centre of gravity of the base area and the mid point of edge, c.

$$y = \frac{h(a + c)}{2(2a + c)}$$

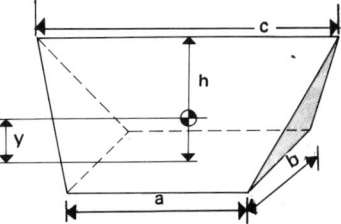

PROPERTIES OF SOLIDS

RIGHT CIRCULAR CYLINDER

Volume = $\pi r^2 h$

Lateral surface area = $2\pi rh$

$$y = \frac{h}{2}$$

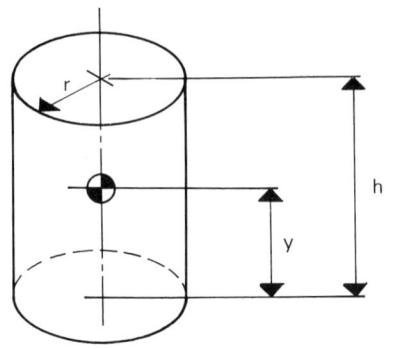

RIGHT CIRCULAR CONE

Volume = $\frac{1}{3}\pi r^2 h$

Lateral surface area = $\pi r \sqrt{r^2 + h^2} = \pi rl$

$$y = \frac{h}{4}$$

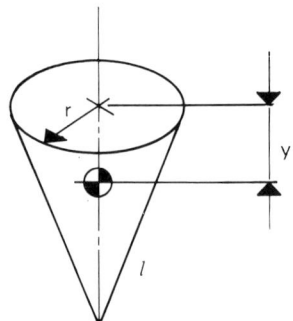

FRUSTRUM OF RIGHT CIRCULAR CONE

Volume = $\frac{1}{3}\pi h(a^2 + ab + b^2)$

Lateral surface area = $\pi(a + b)\sqrt{h^2 + (b-a)^2}$

$$= \pi(a + b)l$$
$$y = \frac{h}{4}\frac{(b^2 + 2ab + 3a^2)}{(b^2 + ab + a^2)}$$

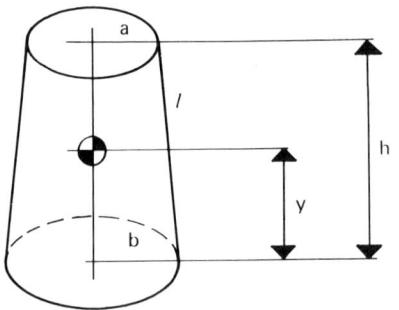

SPHERE

Volume = $\frac{4}{3}\pi r^3$

Surface area = $4\pi r^2$

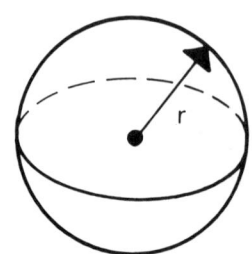

TRIGONOMETRIC FUNCTIONS

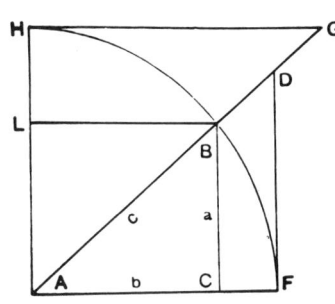

$Radius\ AF = 1$
$= \sin^2 A + \cos^2 A = \sin A \csc A$
$= \cos A \sec A = \tan A \cot A$

Sine A $= \dfrac{\cos A}{\cot A} = \dfrac{1}{\csc A} = \cos A \tan A = \sqrt{1-\cos^2 A} = BC$

Cosine A $= \dfrac{\sin A}{\tan A} = \dfrac{1}{\sec A} = \sin A \cot A = \sqrt{1-\sin^2 A} = AC$

Tangent A $= \dfrac{\sin A}{\cos A} = \dfrac{1}{\cot A} = \sin A \sec A \qquad = FD$

Cotangent A $= \dfrac{\cos A}{\sin A} = \dfrac{1}{\tan A} = \cos A \csc A \qquad = HG$

Secant A $= \dfrac{\tan A}{\sin A} = \dfrac{1}{\cos A} \qquad = AD$

Cosecant A $= \dfrac{\cot A}{\cos A} = \dfrac{1}{\sin A} \qquad = AG$

RIGHT ANGLED TRIANGLES

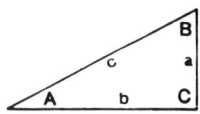

$a^2 = c^2 - b^2$
$b^2 = c^2 - a^2$
$c^2 = a^2 + b^2$

Known	Required					
	A	B	a	b	c	Area
a, b	$\tan A = \dfrac{a}{b}$	$\tan B = \dfrac{b}{a}$			$\sqrt{a^2 + b^2}$	$\dfrac{ab}{2}$
a, c	$\sin A = \dfrac{a}{c}$	$\cos B = \dfrac{a}{c}$		$\sqrt{c^2 - a^2}$		$\dfrac{a\sqrt{c^2 - a^2}}{2}$
A, a		$90° - A$		$a \cot A$	$\dfrac{a}{\sin A}$	$\dfrac{a^2 \cot A}{2}$
A, b		$90° - A$	$b \tan A$		$\dfrac{b}{\cos A}$	$\dfrac{b^2 \tan A}{2}$
A, c		$90° - A$	$c \sin A$	$c \cos A$		$\dfrac{c^2 \sin 2A}{4}$

OBLIQUE ANGLED TRIANGLES

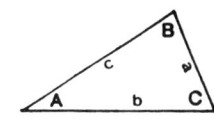

$s = \dfrac{a + b + c}{2}$

$K = \sqrt{\dfrac{(s-a)(s-b)(s-c)}{s}}$

$a^2 = b^2 + c^2 - 2bc \cos A$
$b^2 = a^2 + c^2 - 2ac \cos B$
$c^2 = a^2 + b^2 - 2ab \cos C$

Known	Required					
	A	B	C	b	c	Area
a, b, c	$\tan \tfrac{1}{2} A = \dfrac{K}{s-a}$	$\tan \tfrac{1}{2} B = \dfrac{K}{s-b}$	$\tan \tfrac{1}{2} C = \dfrac{K}{s-c}$			$\sqrt{s(s-a)(s-b)(s-c)}$
a, A, B			$180° - (A+B)$	$\dfrac{a \sin B}{\sin A}$	$\dfrac{a \sin C}{\sin A}$	
a, b, A		$\sin B = \dfrac{b \sin A}{a}$			$\dfrac{b \sin C}{\sin B}$	
a, b, C	$\tan A = \dfrac{a \sin C}{b - a \cos C}$				$\sqrt{a^2 + b^2 - 2ab \cos C}$	$\dfrac{ab \sin C}{2}$

BRACING FORMULAE

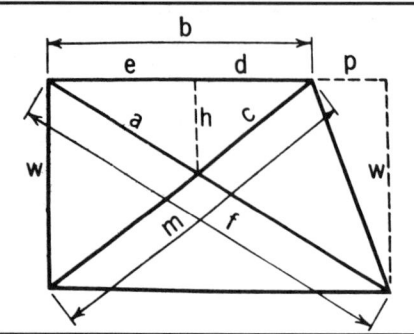

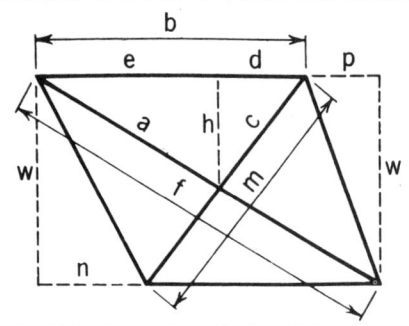

Given	To Find	Formula
bpw	f	$\sqrt{(b + p)^2 + w^2}$
bw	m	$\sqrt{b^2 + w^2}$
bp	d	$b^2 \div (2b + p)$
bp	e	$b(b + p) \div (2b + p)$
bfp	a	$bf \div (2b + p)$
bmp	c	$bm \div (2b + p)$
bpw	h	$bw \div (2b + p)$
afw	h	$aw \div f$
cmw	h	$cw \div m$

Given	To Find	Formula
bpw	f	$\sqrt{(b + p)^2 + w^2}$
bnw	m	$\sqrt{(b - n)^2 + w^2}$
bnp	d	$b(b - n) \div (2b + p - n)$
bnp	e	$b(b + p) \div (2b + p - n)$
bfnp	a	$bf \div (2b + p - n)$
bmnp	c	$bm \div (2b + p - n)$
bnpw	h	$bw \div (2b + p - n)$
afw	h	$aw \div f$
cmw	h	$cw \div m$

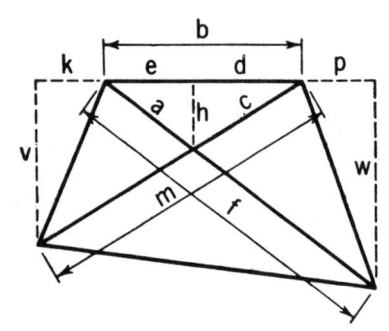

Given	To Find	Formula
bpw	f	$\sqrt{(b + p)^2 + w^2}$
bkv	m	$\sqrt{(b + k)^2 + v^2}$
bkpvw	d	$bw(b + k) \div [v(b + p) + w(b + k)]$
bkpvw	e	$bv(b + p) \div [v(b + p) + w(b + k)]$
bfkpvw	a	$fbv \div [v(b + p) + w(b + k)]$
bkmpvw	c	$bmw \div [v(b + p) + w(b + k)]$
bkpvw	h	$bvw \div [v(b + p) + w(b + k)]$
afw	h	$aw \div f$
cmv	h	$cv \div m$

PARALLEL BRACING

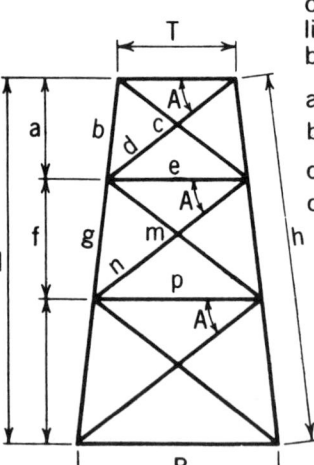

$k = (\log B - \log T) \div$ no. of panels. Constant k plus the logarithm of any line equals the log of the corresponding line in the next panel below.

$a = TH \div (T + e + p)$

$b = Th \div (T + e + p)$

$c = \sqrt{(\tfrac{1}{2} T + \tfrac{1}{2} e)^2 + a^2}$

$d = ce \div (T + e)$

$\log e = k + \log T$
$\log f = k + \log a$
$\log g = k + \log b$
$\log m = k + \log c$
$\log n = k + \log d$
$\log p = k + \log e$

The above method can be used for any number of panels.
In the formulas for "a" and "b" the sum in parenthesis, which in the case shown is (T + e + p), is always composed of all the horizontal distances except the base.

LENGTH OF CIRCULAR ARCS FOR UNIT RADIUS

By the use of this table, the length of any arc may be found if the length of the radius and the angle of the segment are known.

Example: Required the length of arc of segment 32° 15′ 27″ with radius of 8 000 mm.

From table: Length of arc (Radius 1) for 32° = .5585054
15′ = .0043633
27″ = .0001309
.5629996

.5629996 X 8 000 (length of radius) = 4504 mm

For the same arc but with the radius expressed as 24 feet 3 inches, the length of arc would be 0.5629996 X 24.25 = 13.65 feet

DEGREES							MINUTES		SECONDS	
1	.017 4533	61	1.064 6508	121	2.111 8484	1	.000 2909	1	.000 0048
2	.034 9066	62	1.082 1041	122	2.129 3017	2	.000 5818	2	.000 0097
3	.052 3599	63	1.099 5574	123	2.146 7550	3	.000 8727	3	.000 0145
4	.069 8132	64	1.117 0107	124	2.164 2083	4	.001 1636	4	.000 0194
5	.087 2665	65	1.134 4640	125	2.181 6616	5	.001 4544	5	.000 0242
6	.104 7198	66	1.151 9173	126	2.199 1149	6	.001 7453	6	.000 0291
7	.122 1730	67	1.169 3706	127	2.216 5682	7	.002 0362	7	.000 0339
8	.139 6263	68	1.186 8239	128	2.234 0214	8	.002 3271	8	.000 0388
9	.157 0796	69	1.204 2772	129	2.251 4747	9	.002 6180	9	.000 0436
10	.174 5329	70	1.221 7305	130	2.268 9280	10	.002 9089	10	.000 0485
11	.191 9862	71	1.239 1838	131	2.286 3813	11	.003 1998	11	.000 0533
12	.209 4395	72	1.256 6371	132	2.303 8346	12	.003 4907	12	.000 0582
13	.226 8928	73	1.274 0904	133	2.321 2879	13	.003 7815	13	.000 0630
14	.244 3461	74	1.291 5436	134	2.338 7412	14	.004 0724	14	.000 0679
15	.261 7994	75	1.308 9969	135	2.356 1945	15	.004 3633	15	.000 0727
16	.279 2527	76	1.326 4502	136	2.373 6478	16	.004 6542	16	.000 0776
17	.296 7060	77	1.343 9035	137	2.391 1011	17	.004 9451	17	.000 0824
18	.314 1593	78	1.361 3568	138	2.408 5544	18	.005 2360	18	.000 0873
19	.331 6126	79	1.378 8101	139	2.426 0077	19	.005 5269	19	.000 0921
20	.349 0659	80	1.396 2634	140	2.443 4610	20	.005 8178	20	.000 0970
21	.366 5191	81	1.413 7167	141	2.460 9142	21	.006 1087	21	.000 1018
22	.383 9724	82	1.431 1700	142	2.478 3675	22	.006 3995	22	.000 1067
23	.401 4257	83	1.448 6233	143	2.495 8208	23	.006 6904	23	.000 1115
24	.418 8790	84	1.466 0766	144	2.513 2741	24	.006 9813	24	.000 1164
25	.436 3323	85	1.483 5299	145	2.530 7274	25	.007 2722	25	.000 1212
26	.453 7856	86	1.500 9832	146	2.548 1807	26	.007 5631	26	.000 1261
27	.471 2389	87	1.518 4364	147	2.565 6340	27	.007 8540	27	.000 1309
28	.488 6922	88	1.535 8897	148	2.583 0873	28	.008 1449	28	.000 1357
29	.506 1455	89	1.553 3430	149	2.600 5406	29	.008 4358	29	.000 1406
30	.523 5988	90	1.570 7963	150	2.617 9939	30	.008 7266	30	.000 1454
31	.541 0521	91	1.588 2496	151	2.635 4472	31	.009 0175	31	.000 1503
32	.558 5054	92	1.605 7029	152	2.652 9005	32	.009 3084	32	.000 1551
33	.575 9587	93	1.623 1562	153	2.670 3538	33	.009 5993	33	.000 1600
34	.593 4119	94	1.640 6095	154	2.687 8070	34	.009 8902	34	.000 1648
35	.610 8652	95	1.658 0628	155	2.705 2603	35	.010 1811	35	.000 1697
36	.628 3185	96	1.675 5161	156	2.722 7136	36	.010 4720	36	.000 1745
37	.645 7718	97	1.692 9694	157	2.740 1669	37	.010 7629	37	.000 1794
38	.663 2251	98	1.710 4227	158	2.757 6202	38	.011 0538	38	.000 1842
39	.680 6784	99	1.727 8760	159	2.775 0735	39	.011 3446	39	.000 1891
40	.698 1317	100	1.745 3293	160	2.792 5268	40	.011 6355	40	.000 1939
41	.715 5850	101	1.762 7825	161	2.809 9801	41	.011 9264	41	.000 1988
42	.733 0383	102	1.780 2358	162	2.827 4334	42	.012 2173	42	.000 2036
43	.750 4916	103	1.797 6891	163	2.844 8867	43	.012 5082	43	.000 2085
44	.767 9449	104	1.815 1424	164	2.862 3400	44	.012 7991	44	.000 2133
45	.785 3982	105	1.832 5957	165	2.879 7933	45	.013 0900	45	.000 2182
46	.802 8515	106	1.850 0490	166	2.897 2466	46	.013 3809	46	.000 2230
47	.820 3047	107	1.867 5023	167	2.914 6999	47	.013 6717	47	.000 2279
48	.837 7580	108	1.884 9556	168	2.932 1531	48	.013 9626	48	.000 2327
49	.855 2113	109	1.902 4089	169	2.949 6064	49	.014 2535	49	.000 2376
50	.872 6646	110	1.919 8622	170	2.967 0597	50	.014 5444	50	.000 2424
51	.890 1179	111	1.937 3155	171	2.984 5130	51	.014 8353	51	.000 2473
52	.907 5712	112	1.954 7688	172	3.001 9663	52	.015 1262	52	.000 2521
53	.925 0245	113	1.972 2221	173	3.019 4196	53	.015 4171	53	.000 2570
54	.942 4778	114	1.989 6753	174	3.036 8729	54	.015 7080	54	.000 2618
55	.959 9311	115	2.007 1286	175	3.054 3262	55	.015 9989	55	.000 2666
56	.977 3844	116	2.024 5819	176	3.071 7795	56	.016 2897	56	.000 2715
57	.994 8377	117	2.042 0352	177	3.089 2328	57	.016 5806	57	.000 2763
58	1.012 2910	118	2.059 4885	178	3.106 6861	58	.016 8715	58	.000 2812
59	1.029 7443	119	2.076 9418	179	3.124 1394	59	.017 1624	59	.000 2860
60	1.047 1976	120	2.094 3951	180	3.141 5927	60	.017 4533	60	.000 2909

SI SUMMARY

General

The following information on SI units is provided to assist those involved in the planning, design, fabrication and erection of steel structures prepared in SI units. Information related to the metric system in general is to be found in CAN3-Z234.1-79, "Canadian Metric Practice Guide" and for terms related to the steel industry in the "Industry Practice Guide for SI Metric Units in the Canadian Iron and Steel Industry". The latter is available from the Task Force for Metric Conversion in the Canadian Iron and Steel Industry, P.O. Box 4248, Station "D", Hamilton, Ontario, L8V 4L6.

The eleventh General Conference of Weights and Measures, in 1960, adopted the name International System of Units for a coherent system which includes the metre as the base unit of length and the kilogram as the base unit of mass. The international abbreviation of the name of this system, in all languages, is SI.

Canada is a signatory to the General Conference on Weights and Measures, and in 1970, the Canadian government stated that the eventual conversion to the metric system is an objective of Canadian policy. Since that time, metric conversion activity in Canada has developed to the point where material and design standards, building codes and technical literature are available in SI units.

The SI system is based on the seven base units listed in Table 7—1. Decimal multiples and sub-multiples of the SI base units are formed by the addition of the prefixes given in Table 7-2.

SI BASE UNITS
Table 7-1

Quantity	Name	Symbol
length	metre	m
mass	kilogram	kg
time	second	s
electric current	ampere	A
thermodynamic temperature	kelvin	K
amount of substance	mole	mol
luminous intensity	candela	cd

SI PREFIXES
Table 7-2

Multiplying Factor	Prefix	Symbol
$1\,000\,000\,000\,000 = 10^{12}$	tera	T
$1\,000\,000\,000 = 10^{9}$	giga	G
$1\,000\,000 = 10^{6}$	mega	M
$1\,000 = 10^{3}$	kilo	k
$100 = 10^{2}$	hecto	h
$10 = 10^{1}$	deca	da
$0.1 = 10^{-1}$	deci	d
$0.01 = 10^{-2}$	centi	c
$0.001 = 10^{-3}$	milli	m
$0.000\,001 = 10^{-6}$	micro	μ
$0.000\,000\,001 = 10^{-9}$	nano	n
$0.000\,000\,000\,001 = 10^{-12}$	pico	p
$0.000\,000\,000\,000\,001 = 10^{-15}$	femto	f
$0.000\,000\,000\,000\,000\,001 = 10^{-18}$	atto	a

In choosing the appropriate decimal multiple or sub-multiple, the Canadian Metric Practice Guide recommends the use of prefixes representing 10 raised to a power that is a multiple of 3, a ternary power. Thus, common structural steel design units would be:

Force — newton (N), kilonewton (kN)
Stress — pascal (Pa), kilopascal (kPa), megapascal (MPa)
Length — millimetre (mm), metre (m)
Mass — kilogram (kg), megagram (Mg)

The tonne is a special unit, equal to 1 000 kg (or 1 Mg) that will be used in the basic steel industry, but should not be used in structural design calculations.

Designers using SI units must transform loads given in mass (kilograms) to forces, using the relationship force = mass times acceleration. In the design of structures on earth, acceleration is the acceleration due to gravity, designated by "g" and established as 9.806 65 metres per second per second at the third General Conference on Weights and Measures in 1901.

The unit of force to be used in design is the newton (N) (or multiples thereof) where a newton is defined as the force that, when applied to a body having a mass of one kilogram (kg), gives the body an acceleration of one metre (m) per second squared (s^2). The unit of stress is the pascal (Pa), which is one newton per square metre (m^2). Since this is a very small unit, designers of steel structures will generally use megapascals (MPa), where one megapascal is one million pascals and equals one newton per square millimetre (N/mm^2). See also "Structural Loads, Mass and Force".

Properties and dimensions of steel sections are given, in this book, in millimetre units, tabulated to an appropriate ternary power of 10, and millimetres should be used for dimensioning steel structures. Some relationships and values of interest to steel designers are shown below:

SI PREFIXES
Table 7-3

Density of Steel		7 850	kg/m^3
Modulus of Elasticity	E	200 000	MPa
Shear Modulus of Steel	G	77 000	MPa
Coefficient of Thermal Expansion		11.7×10^{-6}	/°C
Acceleration due to Earth's Gravity	g	9.806 65	m/s^2

For a more complete description of SI, the Canadian Metric Practice Guide should be consulted; however, Table 7—4 provides a convenient summary listing selected SI units, the quantity represented, the unit name and typical application.

Structural Loads, Mass and Force

Since most civil engineers have been accustomed to designing structures on earth to withstand loads more variable than the acceleration due to gravity, the pound-force and the kilogram-force have been used as standard units of force. These units were assumed to be numerically equal to their mass counter-parts, the pound-mass and the kilogram-mass respectively.

In SI, the units of mass and force, the kilogram and the newton respectively, are distinctly different both in name and in value. The two are related through the famous Newtonian equation, force = mass times acceleration, or

F = ma.

Thus a newton (N) is defined as the force required to give one kilogram (kg) mass an acceleration of one metre (m) per second (s) squared, or

$1 \text{ N} = 1 \text{ kg} \cdot m/s^2$.

The standard international value of acceleration due to gravity is 9.806 65 m/s^2.

However, for hand calculations in Canada a value of

$g = 9.81 \text{ m/s}^2$

may be more acceptable as it retains three significant figures (adequate for most structural design) and produces a numerical value of force distinctly different from the value of mass. Thus, whether or not the mass has been converted to a force will be readily apparent, and errors will tend to be reduced.

SELECTED SI UNITS
Table 7-4

Quantity	Preferred Units	Unit Name	Typical Applications	Remarks
Area	mm^2	square millimetre	Area of cross section for structural sections	Avoid cm^2
	m^2	square metre	Areas in general	
Bending Moment	kN·m	kilonewton metre	Bending moment in structural sections	
Coating mass	g/m^2	gram per square metre	Mass of zinc coating on steel deck	
Coefficient of Thermal Expansion	$1/^\circ C*$	reciprocal (of) degree Celsius	Expansion of materials subject to temperature change (generally expressed as a ratio per degree Celsius)	$11.7 \times 10^{-6}/^\circ C$ for steel
Density, mass	kg/m^3	kilogram per cubic metre	Density of materials in general; mass per unit volume	$7\ 850\ kg/m^3$ for steel
Force	N	newton	Unit of force used in structural calculations	$1N = 1\ kg·m/s^2$
	kN	kilonewton	Force in structural elements such as columns; concentrated forces; axial forces; reactions; shear force; gravitational force	
Force per Unit Length	N/m	newton per metre	Unit for use in calculations	$1\ kg/m \times 9.81\ m/s^2$ $= (9.81\ kg·m/s^2) \times \dfrac{1}{m}$ $= 9.81\ N/m$
	kN/m	kilonewton per metre	Transverse force per unit length on a beam, column etc.; dead load of a beam for stress calculations	$(1\ kg/m \times 9.81\ m/s^2) \times \dfrac{1\ 000}{1\ 000}$ $= (9.81\ kg·m/s^2) \times \dfrac{1}{m} \times \dfrac{1\ 000}{1\ 000}$ $= (9.81\ N/m) \times \dfrac{1\ 000}{1\ 000}$ $= 9.81\ kN/m \times 1/1\ 000$ $= 0.009\ 81\ kN/m$
Force per Unit Area (See Pressure)				
Frequency	Hz	hertz	Frequency of vibration	$1\ Hz = 1/s = s^{-1}$ replaces cycle per second (cps)
Impact energy	J	joule	Charpy V-notch test	
Length	mm	millimetre	Dimensions on all drawings; dimensions of sections, spans, deflection, elongations, eccentricity	
	m	metre	Overall dimensions; in calculations; contours; surveys	
	km	kilometre	Distances for transportation purposes	
	μm	micrometre	Thickness of coatings (paint)	
Mass	kg	kilogram	Mass of materials, structural elements and machinery	A metric tonne, t $1t = 10^3\ kg = 1Mg = 1\ 000\ kg$
Mass per Unit Length	kg/m	kilogram per metre	Mass per unit length of section, bar, or similar items of uniform cross section.	Also known as "linear density"
Mass per Unit Area	kg/m^2	kilogram per square metre	Mass per unit area of plates, slabs, or similar items of uniform thickness; rating for load-carrying capacities on floors (display on notices only)	DO NOT USE IN STRESS CALCULATION
Mass Density	kg/m^3	kilogram per cubic metre	Density of materials in general; mass per unit volume	$7\ 850\ kg/m^3$ for steel
Modulus of Elasticity (Young's)	MPa	megapascal	Modulus of elasticity; Young's modulus	$200\ 000$ MPa for carbon, high-strength low alloy and low-alloy wrought steels
Modulus, Shear	MPa	megapascal	Shear Modulus	$77\ 000$ MPa assumed for steel
Modulus, Section	mm^3	millimetre to third power	First moment of area of cross section of structural section, such as plastic section modulus, elastic section modulus	

* The preferred unit is 1/K, however $1/^\circ C$ is an acceptable unit for the construction industry.

SELECTED SI UNITS
Table 7-4

Quantity	Preferred Units	Unit Name	Typical Applications	Remarks
Moment of Inertia	mm^4	millimetre to fourth power	Second moment of area; moment of inertia of a section; torsional constant of cross section	
Moment of Force	$kN \cdot m$	kilonewton metre	Bending moment (in structural sections); overturning moment	
	$N \cdot m$	newton metre		
Pressure (see also Stress)	Pa	pascal	Unit used in calculation	$1\ Pa = 1\ N/m^2$
	kPa	kilopascal	Uniformly distributed loads on floors; soil pressure; wind loads; snow loads; dead loads; live loads.	$1\ kPa = 1\ kN/m^2$
Section Modulus (see Modulus)				
Stress	MPa	megapascal	Stress (yield, ultimate, permitted, calculated) in structural steel	$1\ MPa = 1\ MN/m^2$ $= 1\ N/mm^2$
Structural Load (see Force)				
Temperature	$^\circ C$	degree Celsius	Ambient temperature	$0^\circ C \simeq 273.15K$ However, for temperature intervals $1^\circ C = 1K$
Thickness	mm	millimetre	Thickness of web, flange, plate, etc.	
	μm	micrometre	Thickness of paint	
Torque	$kN \cdot m$	kilonewton metre	Torsional moment on a cross section; inspection torque for high strength bolts.	
Volume	m^3	cubic metre	Volume; volume of earthworks, excavation, concrete, sand, all bulk materials.	$1\ m^3 = 1\ 000\ L$ The cubic metre is the preferred unit of volume for engineering purposes
	L	litre	Volume of fluids and containers for fluids	
Work, Energy	J	joule	Energy absorbed in impact testing of materials; energy in general	$1\ kWh = 3.6\ MJ$ where kWh is a kilowatt hour.

There are two common areas where the designer of a structure must be alert to the distinction between mass and force:

1. dead loads due to the mass of the structural elements, permanent equipment etc.,

2. superimposed, or live loads due to storage of materials.

In these, and other cases where mass is well known since it is the unit of commerce, the designer must convert mass to force by multiplying by g.

COMMON CONVERSION FACTORS
Table 7-5

Item	Imperial — SI	SI — Imperial
Acceleration	1 ft./s^2 = 0.304 8 m/s^2	1 m/s^2 = 3.2808 ft./s^2
Area	1 acre = 0.404 685 6 ha 1 ft.^{2} = 0.092 903 04 m^2 1 in.^{2} = 645.16 mm^2 1 mi.^{2} = 2.589 988 km^2 1 yd.^{2} = 0.836 127 4 m^2	1 ha = 2.471 acres 1 m^2 = 10.764 ft.^{2} 1 mm^2 = 1.55x10^{-3} in.^{2} 1 km^2 = 0.3861 mi.^{2} 1 m^2 = 1.20 yd.^{2}
Capacity (Canadian Legal Units)	1 oz. = 28.413 062 mL 1 gal. = 4.546 090 L 1 pt. = 0.568 261 L 1 qt. = 1.136 522 L	1 mL = 35.2x10^{-3} oz. 1 L = 0.220 gal. 1 L = 1.76 pt. 1 L = 0.880 qt.
Density, Mass	1 lb./ft. = 1.488 16 kg/m 1 lb./yd. = 0.496 055 kg/m 1 oz./ft.^{2} = 305.152 g/m^2 1 lb./ft.^{2} = 4.882 43 kg/m^2 1 lb./in.^{2} = 703.069 6 kg/m^2 1 lb./ft.^{3} = 16.018 46 kg/m^3 1 lb./in.^{3} = 27.679 90 Mg/m^3	1 kg/m = 0.672 lb./ft. 1 kg/m = 2.016 lb./yd. 1 g/m^2 = 3.277x10^{-3} oz./ft.^{2} 1 kg/m^2 = 0.205 lb./ft.^{2} 1 kg/m^2 = 1.42x10^{-3} lb./in.^{2} 1 kg/m^3 = 62.4x10^{-3} lb./ft.^{3} 1 Mg/m^3 = 0.0361 lb./in.^{3}
Force	1 kip = 4.448 222 kN	1 kN = 0.225 kip
Length	1 ft. = 0.304 8 m = 304.8 mm 1 in. = 25.4 mm 1 mile = 1.609 344 km 1 yd. = 0.914 4 m	1 m = 3.28 ft. 1 mm = 0.0394 in. 1 km = 0.622 mi. 1 m = 1.09 yd.
Mass	1 pd. (av.) = 0.453 592 37 kg 1 ton (2000 lb.) = 0.907 184 74 Mg	1 kg = 2.20 lb. 1 Mg = 1.10 ton = 2200 lb.
Mass per Unit Area	1 lb./ft.^{2} = 4.882 43 kg/m^2	1 kg/m^2 = 0.205 lb./ft.^{2}
Mass per Unit Length	1 lb./ft. = 1.488 16 kg/m	1 kg/m = 0.672 lb./ft.
Moment of Inertia a) Second Moment of Area b) Section Modulus	 1 in.^{4} = 416 231.4 mm^4 1 in.^{3} = 16 387.064 mm^3	 1 mm^4 = 2.4x10^{-6} in.^{4} 1 mm^3 = 0.061x10^{-3} in.^{3}
Pressure or Stress	1 ksi = 6.894 757 MPa 1 psf = 47.880 26 Pa 1 psi = 6.894 757 kPa	1 MPa = 0.145 ksi 1 Pa = 0.0209 psf 1 kPa = 0.145 psi
Torque or Moment of Force	1 ft.•kipf = 1.355 818 kN•m	1 kN•m = 0.738 ft.•kipf
Volume	1 in.^{3} = 16 387.064 mm^3 1 ft.^{3} = 28.316 85 dm^3 1 yd.^{3} = 0.764 555 m^3	1 mm^3 = 0.061x10^{-3} in.^{3} 1 dm^3 = 0.0353 ft.^{3} 1 m^3 = 1.308 yd.^{3}
Costs	1 \$/ft. = 3.28 \$/m 1 \$/ft.^{2} = 10.764 \$/m^2 1 \$/yd.^{2} = 1.20 \$/m^2 1 \$/ft.^{3} = 35.34 \$/m^3 1 \$/yd.^{3} = 1.307 \$/m^3	1 \$/m = 0.305 \$/ft. 1 \$/m^2 = 0.0929 \$/ft.^{2} 1 \$/m^2 = 0.836 \$/yd.^{2} 1 \$/m^3 = 0.0283 \$/ft.^{3} 1 \$/m^3 = 0.765 \$/yd.^{3}

MILLIMETRE EQUIVALENTS
DECIMALS AND EACH 64TH OF AN INCH

FRACTIONS		INCHES—mm			FRACTIONS		INCHES—mm
1/64		.015625 —— .397					.51181 —— **13**
	1/32	.03125 —— .794			33/64		.515625 – 13.097
		.03937 —— ①				17/32	.53125 —— 13.494
3/64		.046875 —— 1.191			35/64		.546875 – 13.891
	1/16	.0625 —— 1.588					.55118 —— **14**
5/64		.078125 —— 1.984				9/16	.5625 —— 14.288
		.07874 —— ②			37/64		.578125 – 14.684
	3/32	.09375 —— 2.381					.59055 —— ⑮
7/64		.109375 —— 2.778				19/32	.59375 —— 15.081
		.11811 —— ③			39/64		.609375 – 15.478
	1/8	.125 —— 3.175				5/8	.625 —— 15.875
9/64		.140625 —— 3.572					.62992 —— **16**
	5/32	.15625 —— 3.969			41/64		.640625 – 16.272
		.15748 —— ④				21/32	.65625 —— 16.669
11/64		.171875 —— 4.366					.66929 —— **17**
	3/16	.1875 —— 4.763			43/64		.671875 – 17.066
		.19685 —— ⑤				11/16	.6875 —— 17.463
13/64		.203125 —— 5.159			45/64		.703125 – 17.859
	7/32	.21875 —— 5.556					.70866 —— **18**
15/64		.234375 —— 5.953				23/32	.71875 —— 18.256
		.23622 —— **6**			47/64		.734375 – 18.653
¼		.25 —— 6.350					.74893 —— **19**
17/64		.265625 —— 6.747			¾		.75 —— 19.050
		.27559 —— **7**			49/64		.765625 – 19.447
	9/32	.28125 —— 7.144				25/32	.781250 – 19.844
19/64		.296875 —— 7.541					.7874 —— ⑳
	5/16	.3125 —— 7.938			51/64		.796875 – 20.241
		.31496 —— **8**				13/16	.8125 —— 20.638
21/64		.328125 —— 8.334					.82677 —— **21**
	11/32	.34375 —— 8.731			53/64		.828125 – 21.034
		.35433 —— **9**				27/32	.84375 —— 21.431
23/64		.359375 —— 9.128			55/64		.859375 – 21.828
	3/8	.375 —— 9.525					.86614 —— **22**
25/64		.390625 —— 9.922				7/8	.875 —— 22.225
		.3937 —— ⑩			57/64		.890625 – 22.622
	13/32	.40625 —— 10.319					.90551 —— **23**
27/64		.421875 – 10.716				29/32	.90625 —— 23.019
		.43307 —— **11**			59/64		.921875 – 23.416
	7/16	.4375 —— 11.113				15/16	.9375 —— 23.813
29/64		.453125 – 11.509					.94488 —— **24**
	15/32	.46875 —— 11.906			61/64		.953125 – 24.209
		.47244 —— **12**				31/32	.96875 —— 24.606
31/64		.484375 – 12.303					.98425 —— ㉕
½		.5 —— 12.700			63/64		.984375 – 25.003
					①		1.000 —— 25.4

MISCELLANEOUS CONVERSION FACTORS

Multiply	by	to obtain
acres	.404686	hectares
"	4.04686×10^{-3}	square kilometres
board feet	144 sq. in X 1 in.	cubic inches
" "	.0833	cubic feet
centimetres	3.28083×10^{-2}	feet
"	.3937	inches
cubic centimetres	3.53145×10^{-5}	cubic feet
" "	6.102×10^{-2}	cubic inches
cubic feet	2.8317×10^{-4}	cubic centimetres
" "	2.8317×10^{-2}	cubic metres
" "	6.22905	gallons, British Imperial
" "	28.3170	litres
" "	2.38095×10^{-2}	tons, British Shipping
" "	.025	tons, U.S. Shipping
cubic inches	16.38716	cubic centimetres
cubic metres	35.3145	cubic feet
" "	1.30794	cubic yards
cubic yards	.764559	cubic metres
degrees, angular	.0174533	radians
degrees, Fahrenheit (less 32 F.)	.5556	degress, Celsius
" Celsius	1.8	degrees, Fahrenheit (less 32F.)
foot pounds	1.3558	newton metre
feet	30.48	centimetres
"	.3048	metres
"	304.8	millimetres
"	1.64468×10^{-4}	miles, nautical
gallons, Canadian	.160538	cubic feet
" "	1.20091	gallons, U.S.
" "	4.546090	cubic decimetres
gallons, U.S.	.832702	gallons, Canadian
" "	.13368	cubic feet
" "	231.	cubic inches
" "	3.785412	cubic decimetres
grams, metric	2.20462×10^{-3}	pounds, avoirdupois
hectares	2.47104	acres
"	1.076387×10^{-5}	square feet
"	3.86101×10^{-3}	square miles
horse-power (metric, cheval vapeur) . .	735.499	watts
horse-power (550 ft. lbf/s)	745.6999	watts
inches	2.54	centimetres
"	0.0254	metres
"	25.4	millimetres
kilograms	2.20462	pounds
"	9.84206×10^{-4}	long tons (2240 lb.)
"	1.10231×10^{-3}	short tons (2000 lb.)
Newton metre	0.73756	foot pounds
kilograms per metre	.67197	pounds per foot
kilograms per square centimetre	14.2234	pounds per square inch
kilograms per square metre	.204817	pounds per square foot
" " " "	9.14362×10^{-5}	long tons per square foot
kilograms per square millimetre	1422.34	pounds per square inch
" " " "	.634973	long tons per square inch
kilograms per cubic metre	6.24283×10^{-2}	pounds per cubic foot
kilometres	.62137	miles, statute
"	.53959	miles, nautical

MISCELLANEOUS CONVERSION FACTORS

Multiply	by	to obtain
cubic decimetre	.219969	gallons, Canadian
" "	.26417	gallons, U.S.
" "	3.53145×10^{-2}	cubic feet
metres	3.28084	feet
"	39.37	inches
"	1.09361	yards
miles, statute	1.60935	kilometres
" "	.8684	miles, nautical
miles, nautical	6080.204	feet
" "	1.85325	kilometres
" "	1.1516	miles, statute
millimetres	3.28084×10^{-3}	feet
"	3.937×10^{-2}	inches
pounds, avoirdupois	453.592	grams, metric
" "	.453592	kilograms
" "	4.464×10^{-4}	tons, long
" "	4.53592×10^{-4}	tons, metric
pounds per foot	1.48816	kilograms per metre
pounds per square foot	4.88241	kilograms per square metre
pounds per square inch	7.031×10^{-2}	kilograms per square centimetre
" " " "	7.031×10^{-4}	kilograms per square millimetre
pounds per cubic foot	16.0184	kilograms per cubic metre
radians	57.29578	degrees, angular
square centimetres	.1550	square inches
square feet	9.29034×10^{-6}	hectares
" "	.0929034	square metres
square inches	6.45163	square centimetres
" "	645.163	square millimetres
square kilometres	247.104	acres
" "	.3861	square miles
square metres	10.7639	square feet
" "	1.19599	square yards
square miles	259.0	hectares
" "	2.590	square kilometres
square millimetres	1.550×10^{-3}	square inches
square yards	.83613	square metres
tons, long	1016.05	kilograms
" "	2240.	pounds
" "	1.01605	tons, metric
" "	1.120	tons, short
tons, long, per square foot	1.09366×10^{-4}	kilograms per square metre
tons, long, per square inch	1.57494	kilograms per square millimetre
tons, metric	2204.62	pounds
" "	.98421	tons, long
" "	1.10231	tons, short
tons, short	907.185	kilograms
" "	.892857	tons, long
" "	.907185	tons, metric
tons, British Shipping	42.00	cubic feet
" "	.952381	tons, U.S. Shipping
tons, U.S. Shipping	40.00	cubic feet
" " "	1.050	tons, British Shipping
yards	.914402	metres

PART EIGHT
PROPERTIES AND DIMENSIONS IN IMPERIAL UNITS

General Information 8-3
WWF Shapes 8-4
W Shapes. 8-8
HP Shapes 8-22
M Shapes. 8-24
S Shapes 8-26
Standard Channels (C). 8-30
Miscellaneous Channels (MC) 8-32
Equal Leg Angles (L). 8-36
Unequal Leg Angles (L). 8-38
Double Angles. 8-40
HSS. 8-46

GENERAL INFORMATION

Pages 8—4 to 8—51 inclusive list the properties and dimensions of WWF, W, HP, M, S, C and MC shapes, angles and HSS in Imperial units for those still dealing with plans prepared in Imperial units.

The designation given in the tables is the metric designation (mm × kg/m) and is the one preferred for use in Canada (see also Designations, page vii). The Comparison Tables, pages 6—22 to 6—32, provide a means of determining the older designation in Imperial terms (inches × lb./ft.) of a comparable section.

The basic theoretical dimensions used in the computation of the properties and dimensions of the rolled shapes are taken from ASTM Standard A6 or from the manufacturers for those sections not listed in ASTM A6. For a further description of the properties and dimensions and the method of calculation refer to Part 6.

Shapes not rolled in Canada are identified in the tables with the note "not available from Canadian mills".

WELDED WIDE FLANGE SHAPES
WWF1200 – WWF700

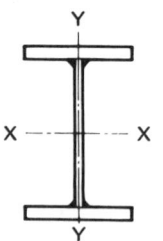

PROPERTIES

Designation[‡]	Nominal Mass	Total Area	Axis X-X				Axis Y-Y				Torsional Constant	Warping Constant
			I_x	S_x	r_x	Z_x	I_y	S_y	r_y	Z_y	J	C_W
	Lb./Ft.	In.²	In.⁴	In.³	In.	In.³	In.⁴	In.³	In.	In.³	In.⁴	In.⁶
WWF1200												
X487	326	96.2	40200	1700	20.4	1870	2670	247	5.27	374	60.1	1390000
X403	270	79.6	32000	1350	20.1	1500	2000	185	5.01	281	27.5	1060000
X364	244	72.0	28000	1190	19.7	1330	1400	142	4.41	218	21.3	745000
X302	203	59.7	21600	914	19.0	1040	642	81.5	3.28	127	13.8	343000
X263	176	52.0	17400	737	18.3	865	271	45.9	2.28	73.2	11.3	145000
WWF1100												
X458	307	90.5	32800	1510	19.0	1650	2670	247	5.43	372	58.6	1160000
X388	260	76.8	27000	1250	18.8	1370	1750	178	4.77	270	36.6	769000
X335	225	66.3	22600	1040	18.5	1150	1400	142	4.60	217	19.9	623000
X291	195	57.6	18700	864	18.0	969	718	91.2	3.53	140	16.4	320000
X255	171	50.4	15700	725	17.6	821	564	71.6	3.35	111	9.14	254000
X220	147	43.6	12600	582	17.0	676	238	40.3	2.34	63.6	7.44	107000
WWF1000												
X447	300	88.4	26600	1350	17.3	1470	2670	247	5.50	372	58.4	954000
X377	253	74.6	21900	1110	17.1	1220	1750	178	4.84	270	36.4	631000
X324	217	64.1	18300	930	16.9	1020	1400	142	4.67	216	19.7	513000
X280	188	55.4	15100	767	16.5	858	718	91.2	3.60	140	16.1	263000
X244	163	48.2	12600	640	16.2	724	564	71.6	3.42	110	8.92	209000
X200	134	39.6	9470	481	15.5	559	217	36.7	2.34	57.9	5.95	80800
WWF900												
X417	279	82.4	20800	1170	15.9	1270	2670	247	5.69	371	57.3	765000
X347	233	68.6	17000	960	15.7	1040	1750	178	5.05	269	35.2	507000
X293	197	58.0	14200	802	15.7	868	1400	142	4.91	215	18.5	413000
X249	167	49.3	11600	655	15.3	719	718	91.2	3.82	138	15.0	212000
X213	142	42.1	9590	541	15.1	598	564	71.6	3.66	109	7.73	168000
X192	128	37.9	8310	469	14.8	525	271	45.9	2.67	70.3	8.41	80400
X169	113	33.5	7040	397	14.5	450	216	36.6	2.54	56.6	4.76	64800
WWF800												
X332	223	65.8	13100	832	14.1	901	1750	178	5.16	268	34.9	397000
X279	187	55.1	10900	692	14.1	747	1400	142	5.04	215	18.2	323000
X235	157	46.4	8890	565	13.8	615	718	91.2	3.93	138	14.7	166000
X198	133	39.2	7310	464	13.7	508	564	71.6	3.79	109	7.43	132000
X164	109	32.4	5710	363	13.3	403	238	40.3	2.71	61.6	5.72	55800
X154	103	30.6	5310	337	13.2	377	216	36.6	2.66	56.1	4.45	50900
WWF700												
X222	149	43.9	6590	478	12.3	519	718	91.2	4.04	138	14.4	126000
X203	136	40.3	6000	435	12.2	472	641	81.4	3.99	123	10.4	113000
X185	124	36.6	5400	392	12.1	426	564	71.6	3.93	108	7.20	100000
X164	110	32.5	4630	336	11.9	369	270	45.7	2.88	69.5	7.89	47700
X151	101	29.8	4190	304	11.9	335	238	40.3	2.83	61.3	5.50	42400
X141	95	28.0	3880	282	11.8	311	216	36.6	2.78	55.8	4.23	38700

[‡]Nominal depth in millimetres and mass in kilograms per metre.

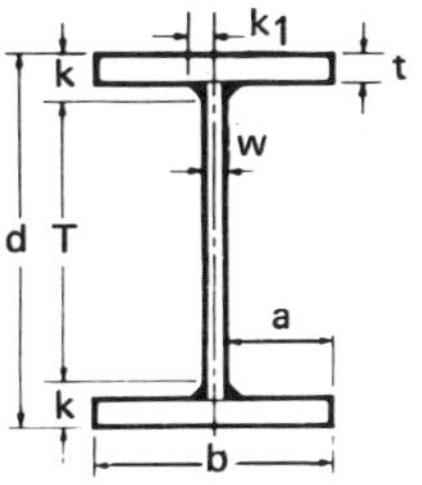

WELDED WIDE FLANGE SHAPES WWF1200 – WWF700

DIMENSIONS AND SURFACE AREAS

Nominal Mass	Depth d		Flange Width b		Flange Thickness t		Web Thickness w		Distances a	Distances T	Distances k	Distances k_1	Distances d-2t	Surface Area (Ft.[2]) per foot of length: Total	Surface Area (Ft.[2]) per foot of length: Minus Top of Top Flange
kg/m	In.	In.	In.	In.	In.	In.	In.	In.	In.	In.	In.	In.	In.		
487	47.24	47 1/4	21.65	21 5/8	1.57	1 9/16	.630	5/8	10 1/2	43 1/4	2	11/16	44 1/8	15.1	13.3
403	47.24	47 1/4	21.65	21 5/8	1.18	1 3/16	.630	5/8	10 1/2	44 1/8	1 9/16	11/16	44 7/8	15.0	13.2
364	47.24	47 1/4	19.69	19 5/8	1.10	1 1/8	.630	5/8	9 1/2	44 1/4	1 1/2	11/16	45	14.3	12.7
302	47.24	47 1/4	15.75	15 3/4	.984	1	.630	5/8	7 1/2	44 1/2	1 3/8	11/16	45 1/4	13.0	11.6
263	47.24	47 1/4	11.81	11 3/4	.984	1	.630	5/8	5 5/8	44 1/2	1 3/8	11/16	45 1/4	11.6	10.7
458	43.31	43 1/4	21.65	21 5/8	1.57	1 9/16	.551	9/16	10 1/2	39 3/8	1 15/16	5/8	40 1/8	14.5	12.7
388	43.31	43 1/4	19.69	19 5/8	1.38	1 3/8	.551	9/16	9 5/8	39 3/4	1 3/4	5/8	40 1/2	13.8	12.1
335	43.31	43 1/4	19.69	19 5/8	1.10	1 1/8	.551	9/16	9 5/8	40 1/4	1 1/2	5/8	41	13.7	12.0
291	43.31	43 1/4	15.75	15 3/4	1.10	1 1/8	.551	9/16	7 5/8	40 1/4	1 1/2	5/8	41	12.4	11.0
255	43.31	43 1/4	15.75	15 3/4	.866	7/8	.551	9/16	7 5/8	40 3/4	1 1/4	5/8	41 1/2	12.3	11.0
220	43.31	43 1/4	11.81	11 3/4	.866	7/8	.551	9/16	5 5/8	40 3/4	1 1/4	5/8	41 1/2	11.0	9.98
447	39.37	39 3/8	21.65	21 5/8	1.57	1 9/16	.551	9/16	10 1/2	35 3/8	2	5/8	36 1/4	13.8	12.0
377	39.37	39 3/8	19.69	19 5/8	1.38	1 3/8	.551	9/16	9 5/8	35 3/4	1 13/16	5/8	36 5/8	13.1	11.5
324	39.37	39 3/8	19.69	19 5/8	1.10	1 1/8	.551	9/16	9 5/8	36 3/8	1 1/2	5/8	37 1/8	13.0	11.4
280	39.37	39 3/8	15.75	15 3/4	1.10	1 1/8	.551	9/16	7 5/8	36 3/8	1 1/2	5/8	37 1/8	11.7	10.4
244	39.37	39 3/8	15.75	15 3/4	.866	7/8	.551	9/16	7 5/8	36 7/8	1 1/4	5/8	37 5/8	11.6	10.3
200	39.37	39 3/8	11.81	11 3/4	.787	13/16	.551	9/16	5 5/8	37	1 3/16	5/8	37 3/4	10.3	9.31
417	35.43	35 3/8	21.65	21 5/8	1.57	1 9/16	.433	7/16	10 5/8	31 1/2	1 15/16	9/16	32 1/4	13.2	11.4
347	35.43	35 3/8	19.69	19 5/8	1.38	1 3/8	.433	7/16	9 5/8	31 7/8	1 3/4	9/16	32 5/8	12.5	10.8
293	35.43	35 3/8	19.69	19 5/8	1.10	1 1/8	.433	7/16	9 5/8	32 3/8	1 1/2	9/16	33 1/8	12.4	10.8
249	35.43	35 3/8	15.75	15 3/4	1.10	1 1/8	.433	7/16	7 5/8	32 3/8	1 1/2	9/16	33 1/8	11.1	9.77
213	35.43	35 3/8	15.75	15 3/4	.866	7/8	.433	7/16	7 5/8	32 7/8	1 1/4	9/16	33 5/8	11.0	9.69
192	35.43	35 3/8	11.81	11 3/4	.984	1	.433	7/16	5 3/4	32 5/8	1 3/8	9/16	33 3/8	9.73	8.74
169	35.43	35 3/8	11.81	11 3/4	.787	13/16	.433	7/16	5 3/4	33	1 3/16	9/16	33 3/4	9.66	8.68
332	31.50	31 1/2	19.69	19 5/8	1.38	1 3/8	.394	3/8	9 5/8	27 7/8	1 13/16	9/16	28 3/4	11.9	10.2
279	31.50	31 1/2	19.69	19 5/8	1.10	1 1/8	.394	3/8	9 5/8	28 1/2	1 1/2	9/16	29 1/4	11.8	10.1
235	31.50	31 1/2	15.75	15 3/4	1.10	1 1/8	.394	3/8	7 5/8	28 1/2	1 1/2	9/16	29 1/4	10.5	9.15
198	31.50	31 1/2	15.75	15 3/4	.866	7/8	.394	3/8	7 5/8	29	1 1/4	9/16	29 3/4	10.4	9.07
164	31.50	31 1/2	11.81	11 3/4	.866	7/8	.394	3/8	5 3/4	29	1 1/4	9/16	29 3/4	9.07	8.09
154	31.50	31 1/2	11.81	11 3/4	.787	13/16	.394	3/8	5 3/4	29 1/8	1 3/16	9/16	29 7/8	9.04	8.06
222	27.56	27 1/2	15.75	15 3/4	1.10	1 1/8	.354	3/8	7 3/4	24 1/2	1 1/2	1/2	25 1/4	9.84	8.53
203	27.56	27 1/2	15.75	15 3/4	.984	1	.354	3/8	7 3/4	24 3/4	1 3/8	1/2	25 1/2	9.80	8.49
185	27.56	27 1/2	15.75	15 3/4	.866	7/8	.354	3/8	7 3/4	25	1 1/4	1/2	25 3/4	9.76	8.45
164	27.56	27 1/2	11.81	11 3/4	.984	1	.354	3/8	5 3/4	24 3/4	1 3/8	1/2	25 1/2	8.49	7.50
151	27.56	27 1/2	11.81	11 3/4	.866	7/8	.354	3/8	5 3/4	25	1 1/4	1/2	25 3/4	8.45	7.46
141	27.56	27 1/2	11.81	11 3/4	.787	13/16	.354	3/8	5 3/4	25 1/8	1 3/16	1/2	25 7/8	8.42	7.44

IMP

WELDED WIDE FLANGE SHAPES
WWF550 – WWF350

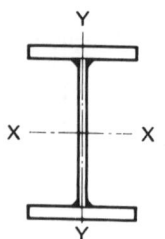

PROPERTIES

Designation[‡]	Nominal Mass	Total Area	Axis X-X				Axis Y-Y				Torsional Constant	Warping Constant
			I_x	S_x	r_x	Z_x	I_y	S_y	r_y	Z_y	J	C_W
	Lb./Ft.	In.^{2}	In.^{4}	In.^{3}	In.	In.^{3}	In.^{4}	In.^{3}	In.	In.^{3}	In.^{4}	In.^{6}
WWF550												
X721**	484	143	10500	970	8.57	1160	4020	371	5.30	578	265	374000
X620**	416	123	10100	933	9.06	1070	4000	369	5.70	560	200	372000
X503	338	99.5	8670	801	9.33	903	3330	308	5.79	464	113	323000
X420	282	83.1	7330	677	9.39	755	2670	247	5.67	372	59.4	269000
X217	146	43.0	4020	371	9.67	401	1330	123	5.56	186	7.59	145000
WWF500												
X651**	437	129	7690	781	7.72	940	3020	307	4.84	479	239	227000
X561**	377	111	7360	748	8.14	874	3010	306	5.21	463	181	226000
X456	306	90.2	6380	648	8.41	738	2500	254	5.26	384	103	196000
X381	256	75.3	5410	550	8.48	618	2000	203	5.15	308	53.9	164000
X343	230	67.9	4890	497	8.49	555	1750	178	5.08	270	37.1	147000
X306	205	60.4	4350	442	8.49	492	1500	152	4.98	232	24.4	128000
X276	185	54.6	4050	411	8.61	453	1400	142	5.06	215	19.0	121000
X254	170	50.1	3700	376	8.59	413	1250	127	5.00	193	14.0	109000
X223	150	44.2	3300	335	8.64	367	1100	112	4.99	169	9.53	97400
X197	132	39.0	3000	305	8.77	330	1000	102	5.06	153	6.90	89300
WWF450												
X503**	337	99.3	5200	587	7.24	694	2190	247	4.70	375	163	129000
X409	275	80.9	4530	511	7.48	588	1830	207	4.76	311	92.3	113000
X342	229	67.6	3860	436	7.56	494	1460	165	4.65	250	48.5	95100
X308	207	60.9	3500	395	7.58	445	1280	144	4.58	219	33.3	85400
X274	184	54.2	3120	352	7.59	395	1100	124	4.51	188	22.0	75200
X248	166	49.0	2910	329	7.71	364	1020	115	4.56	175	17.1	70400
X228	152	45.0	2660	300	7.69	332	913	103	4.50	156	12.6	63900
X201	134	39.7	2380	269	7.74	295	803	90.6	4.50	137	8.57	57000
X177	119	35.1	2160	244	7.84	266	730	82.4	4.56	124	6.20	52300
WWF400												
X444**	298	87.7	3510	446	6.33	535	1540	196	4.19	297	144	69000
X362	243	71.6	3080	391	6.56	456	1280	163	4.23	246	82.0	60800
X303	203	59.8	2640	335	6.64	384	1030	131	4.15	197	43.1	51700
X273	183	53.9	2400	305	6.67	347	898	114	4.08	173	29.6	46400
X243	163	48.0	2150	273	6.69	308	769	97.7	4.00	149	19.5	40800
X220	147	43.4	2000	254	6.79	284	718	91.2	4.07	138	15.2	38500
X202	135	39.9	1840	234	6.79	260	641	81.4	4.01	123	11.2	34900
X178	119	35.2	1650	210	6.85	231	564	71.6	4.00	109	7.60	31200
X157	105	31.1	1500	190	6.94	209	513	65.2	4.06	98.4	5.51	28700
WWF350												
X385**	258	76.1	2230	324	5.41	397	1030	149	3.68	228	126	33600
X315	211	62.3	1980	287	5.64	341	859	125	3.71	189	71.7	30000
X263	177	52.1	1710	248	5.73	289	687	99.7	3.63	151	37.6	25600
X238	159	46.9	1560	226	5.77	261	601	87.2	3.58	133	25.8	23100
X212	142	41.8	1400	203	5.79	232	516	74.9	3.51	114	17.0	20500
X192	128	37.9	1310	190	5.88	215	481	69.8	3.56	106	13.3	19300
X176	118	34.8	1210	176	5.90	197	429	62.3	3.51	94.7	9.74	17600
X155	104	30.7	1080	157	5.93	175	378	54.9	3.51	83.2	6.64	15800
X137	92	27.2	989	144	6.03	158	343	49.8	3.55	75.4	4.82	14500

[‡]Nominal depth in millimetres and mass in kilograms per metre.
**Welding does not fully develop the web strength for these sections.

DIMENSIONS AND SURFACE AREAS

Nominal Mass	Depth d		Flange Width b		Flange Thickness t		Web Thickness w		Distances a	T	k	k1	d-2t	Surface Area (Ft.²) per foot of length Total	Minus Top of Top Flange
kg/m	In.	In.	In.	In.	In.	In.	In.	In.	In.	In.	In.	In.	In.		
721	21.65	21 5/8	21.65	21 5/8	2.36	2 3/8	2.36	2 3/8	9 5/8	16	2 13/16	1 5/8	16 7/8	10.6	8.81
620	21.65	21 5/8	21.65	21 5/8	2.36	2 3/8	1.18	1 3/16	10 1/4	16	2 13/16	1	16 7/8	10.8	9.01
503	21.65	21 5/8	21.65	21 5/8	1.97	1 15/16	.787	13/16	10 3/8	16 3/4	2 7/16	13/16	17 3/4	10.7	8.94
420	21.65	21 5/8	21.65	21 5/8	1.57	1 9/16	.787	13/16	10 3/8	17 1/2	2 1/16	13/16	18 1/2	10.6	8.81
217	21.65	21 5/8	21.65	21 5/8	.787	13/16	.433	7/16	10 5/8	19 1/4	1 3/16	9/16	20	10.4	8.61
651	19.69	19 5/8	19.69	19 5/8	2.36	2 3/8	2.36	2 3/8	8 5/8	14	2 13/16	1 5/8	14 7/8	9.75	8.11
561	19.69	19 5/8	19.69	19 5/8	2.36	2 3/8	1.18	1 3/16	9 1/4	14	2 13/16	1	14 7/8	9.95	8.31
456	19.69	19 5/8	19.69	19 5/8	1.97	1 15/16	.787	13/16	9 1/2	14 3/4	2 7/16	13/16	15 3/4	9.88	8.24
381	19.69	19 5/8	19.69	19 5/8	1.57	1 9/16	.787	13/16	9 1/2	15 1/2	2 1/16	13/16	16 1/2	9.75	8.11
343	19.69	19 5/8	19.69	19 5/8	1.38	1 3/8	.787	13/16	9 1/2	16	1 13/16	13/16	16 7/8	9.69	8.04
306	19.69	19 5/8	19.69	19 5/8	1.18	1 3/16	.787	13/16	9 1/2	16 3/8	1 5/8	13/16	17 1/4	9.62	7.98
276	19.69	19 5/8	19.69	19 5/8	1.10	1 1/8	.630	5/8	9 1/2	16 5/8	1 1/2	11/16	17 3/4	9.62	7.98
254	19.69	19 5/8	19.69	19 5/8	.984	1	.630	5/8	9 1/2	16 7/8	1 3/8	11/16	17 5/8	9.58	7.94
223	19.69	19 5/8	19.69	19 5/8	.866	7/8	.551	9/16	9 5/8	17 1/8	1 1/4	5/8	17 7/8	9.55	7.91
197	19.69	19 5/8	19.69	19 5/8	.787	13/16	.433	7/16	9 5/8	17 1/4	1 3/16	9/16	18	9.55	7.91
503	17.72	17 3/4	17.72	17 3/4	2.36	2 3/8	1.18	1 3/16	8 1/4	12	2 7/8	1	13	9.00	7.52
409	17.72	17 3/4	17.72	17 3/4	1.97	1 15/16	.787	13/16	8 1/2	12 3/4	2 1/2	13/16	13 7/8	8.93	7.45
342	17.72	17 3/4	17.72	17 3/4	1.57	1 9/16	.787	13/16	8 1/2	13 5/8	2 1/16	13/16	14 5/8	8.80	7.32
308	17.72	17 3/4	17.72	17 3/4	1.38	1 3/8	.787	13/16	8 1/2	14	1 7/8	13/16	15	8.73	7.26
274	17.72	17 3/4	17.72	17 3/4	1.18	1 3/16	.787	13/16	8 1/2	14 3/8	1 11/16	13/16	15 3/8	8.67	7.19
248	17.72	17 3/4	17.72	17 3/4	1.10	1 1/8	.630	5/8	8 1/2	14 3/4	1 1/2	11/16	15 1/2	8.67	7.19
228	17.72	17 3/4	17.72	17 3/4	.984	1	.630	5/8	8 1/2	14 7/8	1 7/16	11/16	15 3/4	8.63	7.15
201	17.72	17 3/4	17.72	17 3/4	.866	7/8	.551	9/16	8 5/8	15 1/8	1 5/16	5/8	16	8.60	7.13
177	17.72	17 3/4	17.72	17 3/4	.787	13/16	.433	7/16	8 5/8	15 3/8	1 3/16	9/16	16 1/8	8.60	7.12
444	15.75	15 3/4	15.75	15 3/4	2.36	2 3/8	1.18	1 3/16	7 1/4	10	2 7/8	1	11	8.01	6.70
362	15.75	15 3/4	15.75	15 3/4	1.97	1 15/16	.787	13/16	7 1/2	10 7/8	2 7/16	13/16	11 7/8	7.95	6.63
303	15.75	15 3/4	15.75	15 3/4	1.57	1 9/16	.787	13/16	7 1/2	11 5/8	2 1/16	13/16	12 5/8	7.82	6.50
273	15.75	15 3/4	15.75	15 3/4	1.38	1 3/8	.787	13/16	7 1/2	12	1 7/8	13/16	13	7.75	6.44
243	15.75	15 3/4	15.75	15 3/4	1.18	1 3/16	.787	13/16	7 1/2	12 3/8	1 11/16	13/16	13 3/8	7.68	6.37
220	15.75	15 3/4	15.75	15 3/4	1.10	1 1/8	.630	5/8	7 1/2	12 3/4	1 1/2	11/16	13 1/2	7.68	6.37
202	15.75	15 3/4	15.75	15 3/4	.984	1	.630	5/8	7 1/2	13	1 3/8	11/16	13 3/4	7.65	6.33
178	15.75	15 3/4	15.75	15 3/4	.866	7/8	.551	9/16	7 5/8	13 1/4	1 1/4	5/8	14	7.62	6.31
157	15.75	15 3/4	15.75	15 3/4	.787	13/16	.433	7/16	7 5/8	13 3/8	1 3/16	9/16	14 1/8	7.61	6.30
385	13.78	13 3/4	13.78	13 3/4	2.36	2 3/8	1.18	1 3/16	6 1/4	8 1/8	2 13/16	1	9	7.03	5.88
315	13.78	13 3/4	13.78	13 3/4	1.97	1 15/16	.787	13/16	6 1/2	8 7/8	2 7/16	13/16	9 7/8	6.96	5.81
263	13.78	13 3/4	13.78	13 3/4	1.57	1 9/16	.787	13/16	6 1/2	9 5/8	2 1/16	13/16	10 5/8	6.83	5.68
238	13.78	13 3/4	13.78	13 3/4	1.38	1 3/8	.787	13/16	6 1/2	10	1 7/8	13/16	11	6.77	5.62
212	13.78	13 3/4	13.78	13 3/4	1.18	1 3/16	.787	13/16	6 1/2	10 1/2	1 5/8	13/16	11 3/8	6.70	5.55
192	13.78	13 3/4	13.78	13 3/4	1.10	1 1/8	.630	5/8	6 5/8	10 3/4	1 1/2	11/16	11 1/2	6.70	5.55
176	13.78	13 3/4	13.78	13 3/4	.984	1	.630	5/8	6 5/8	11	1 3/8	11/16	11 3/4	6.66	5.51
155	13.78	13 3/4	13.78	13 3/4	.866	7/8	.551	9/16	6 5/8	11 1/4	1 1/4	5/8	12	6.63	5.49
137	13.78	13 3/4	13.78	13 3/4	.787	13/16	.433	7/16	6 5/8	11 3/8	1 3/16	9/16	12 1/8	6.63	5.48

W SHAPES
W920 – W690

PROPERTIES

Designation‡	Nominal Mass	Total Area	Axis X-X				Axis Y-Y				Torsional Constant	Warping Constant
			I_x	S_x	r_x	Z_x	I_y	S_y	r_y	Z_y	J	C_W
	Lb./Ft.	In.^{2}	In.^{4}	In.^{3}	In.	In.^{3}	In.^{4}	In.^{3}	In.	In.^{3}	In.^{4}	In.^{6}
W920												
X446*	300	88.3	20300	1110	15.2	1260	1300	156	3.84	241	64.2	399000
X417*	280	82.4	18900	1040	15.1	1170	1200	145	3.82	223	52.6	366000
X387*	260	76.5	17300	954	15.0	1080	1090	132	3.77	204	41.5	330000
X365*	245	72.1	16100	892	14.9	1010	1010	122	3.74	190	34.6	305000
X342*	230	67.6	15000	836	14.9	943	940	114	3.73	176	28.6	282000
W920												
X313*	210	61.8	13200	720	14.6	833	411	67.5	2.58	107	28.0	128000
X289*	194	57.0	12100	663	14.6	767	375	61.9	2.56	97.8	22.2	116000
X271*	182	53.6	11300	622	14.5	718	347	57.5	2.54	90.7	18.4	107000
X253*	170	50.0	10500	581	14.5	668	320	53.2	2.53	83.8	15.1	98400
X238*	160	47.0	9750	542	14.4	624	295	49.2	2.51	77.3	12.4	90300
X223*	150	44.2	9040	504	14.3	581	270	45.1	2.47	70.9	10.1	82300
X201*	135	39.7	7800	439	14.0	509	225	37.7	2.38	59.7	6.99	68000
W840												
X359*	241	70.9	14200	831	14.2	939	932	118	3.63	182	35.8	250000
X329*	221	65.0	12800	754	14.0	855	840	106	3.59	164	27.5	224000
X299*	201	59.1	11500	683	13.9	772	749	95.1	3.56	147	20.5	198000
W840												
X226*	152	44.7	8160	487	13.5	559	273	47.2	2.47	73.9	12.4	71800
X210*	141	41.6	7450	447	13.4	514	246	42.7	2.43	66.9	9.70	64300
X193*	130	38.3	6710	406	13.2	467	218	37.9	2.39	59.5	7.37	56600
X176*	118	34.7	5900	359	13.0	415	187	32.6	2.32	51.3	5.30	48200
W760												
X314*	211	62.0	10300	666	12.9	749	757	100	3.49	154	27.9	166000
X284*	191	56.1	9170	598	12.8	673	673	89.5	3.46	138	20.6	146000
X257*	173	50.8	8200	539	12.7	605	598	79.8	3.43	123	15.3	129000
W760												
X196*	132	38.9	5770	381	12.2	437	196	37.2	2.24	58.4	9.72	42100
X185*	124	36.5	5360	355	12.1	408	181	34.4	2.23	54.0	7.99	38700
X173*	116	34.2	4930	329	12.0	378	164	31.3	2.19	49.2	6.43	34900
X161*	108	31.7	4470	300	11.9	346	146	27.9	2.15	43.9	4.99	30800
X147*	99	29.1	3990	269	11.7	312	128	24.5	2.10	38.6	3.77	26900
W690												
X265*	178	52.3	6990	503	11.6	567	555	78.8	3.26	122	19.5	98300
X240*	161	47.4	6280	455	11.5	512	497	70.9	3.24	109	14.7	87300
X217*	146	42.9	5630	411	11.5	461	443	63.4	3.21	97.5	10.9	77200
W690												
X170*	114	33.5	4090	300	11.0	343	159	31.6	2.18	49.3	7.33	27600
X152*	102	30.0	3620	267	11.0	305	139	27.8	2.15	43.4	5.29	24000
X140*	94	27.7	3270	243	10.9	278	124	24.8	2.12	38.8	4.03	21200
X125*	84	24.8	2850	213	10.7	244	106	21.3	2.07	33.2	2.81	18000

‡Nominal depth in millimetres and mass in kilograms per metre.
*Not available from Canadian mills.

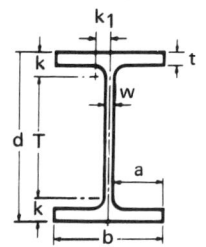

DIMENSIONS AND SURFACE AREAS

Nominal Mass	Depth d		Flange Width b		Flange Thickness t		Web Thickness w		Distances a	T	k	k₁	d-2t	Surface Area (Ft.²) per foot of length Total	Minus Top of Top Flange
kg/m	In.	In.	In.	In.	In.	In.	In.	In.	In.	In.	In.	In.	In.		
446	36.74	36¾	16.65	16⅝	1.68	1¹¹/₁₆	.945	¹⁵/₁₆	7⅞	31⅛	2¹³/₁₆	1½	33⅜	11.5	10.1
417	36.52	36½	16.60	16⅝	1.57	1⁹/₁₆	.885	⅞	7⅞	31⅛	2¹¹/₁₆	1½	33⅜	11.5	10.1
387	36.26	36¼	16.55	16½	1.44	1⁷/₁₆	.840	¹³/₁₆	7⅞	31⅛	2⁹/₁₆	1½	33⅜	11.4	10.0
365	36.08	36⅛	16.51	16½	1.35	1⅜	.800	¹³/₁₆	7⅞	31⅛	2½	1⁷/₁₆	33⅜	11.4	10.0
342	35.90	35⅞	16.47	16½	1.26	1¼	.760	¾	7⅞	31⅛	2⅜	1⁷/₁₆	33⅜	11.3	9.97
313	36.69	36¾	12.18	12⅛	1.36	1⅜	.830	¹³/₁₆	5⅝	32⅛	2⁵/₁₆	1¼	34	10.0	9.02
289	36.49	36½	12.12	12⅛	1.26	1¼	.765	¾	5⅝	32⅛	2³/₁₆	1³/₁₆	34	9.99	8.98
271	36.33	36⅜	12.07	12⅛	1.18	1³/₁₆	.725	¾	5⅝	32⅛	2⅛	1³/₁₆	34	9.96	8.95
253	36.17	36⅛	12.03	12	1.10	1⅛	.680	¹¹/₁₆	5⅝	32⅛	2	1³/₁₆	34	9.92	8.92
238	36.01	36	12.00	12	1.02	1	.650	⅝	5⅝	32⅛	1¹⁵/₁₆	1⅛	34	9.89	8.89
223	35.85	35⅞	11.98	12	.940	¹⁵/₁₆	.625	⅝	5⅝	32⅛	1⅞	1⅛	34	9.86	8.86
201	35.55	35½	11.95	12	.790	¹³/₁₆	.600	⅝	5⅝	32⅛	1¹¹/₁₆	1⅛	34	9.81	8.81
359	34.18	34⅛	15.86	15⅞	1.40	1⅜	.830	¹³/₁₆	7½	29¾	2³/₁₆	1³/₁₆	31⅜	10.8	9.52
329	33.93	33⅞	15.81	15¾	1.27	1¼	.775	¾	7½	29¾	2¹/₁₆	1³/₁₆	31⅜	10.8	9.48
299	33.68	33⅝	15.74	15¾	1.15	1⅛	.715	¹¹/₁₆	7½	29¾	1¹⁵/₁₆	1⅛	31⅜	10.7	9.43
226	33.49	33½	11.56	11⅝	1.06	1¹/₁₆	.635	⅝	5½	29¾	1⅞	1⅛	31⅜	9.33	8.37
210	33.30	33¼	11.53	11½	.960	¹⁵/₁₆	.605	⅝	5½	29¾	1¾	1¹/₁₆	31⅜	9.29	8.33
193	33.09	33⅛	11.51	11½	.855	⅞	.580	⁹/₁₆	5½	29¾	1¹¹/₁₆	1¹/₁₆	31⅜	9.25	8.30
176	32.86	32⅞	11.48	11½	.740	¾	.550	⁹/₁₆	5½	29¾	1⁹/₁₆	1¹/₁₆	31⅜	9.21	8.25
314	30.94	31	15.10	15⅛	1.31	1⁵/₁₆	.775	¾	7⅛	26¾	2⅛	1⅛	28¼	10.1	8.80
284	30.68	30⅝	15.04	15	1.19	1³/₁₆	.710	¹¹/₁₆	7⅛	26¾	1¹⁵/₁₆	1¹/₁₆	28¼	10.0	8.75
257	30.44	30½	14.98	15	1.06	1¹/₁₆	.655	⅝	7⅛	26¾	1⅞	1¹/₁₆	28¼	9.96	8.71
196	30.31	30¼	10.55	10½	1.00	1	.615	⅝	5	26¾	1¾	1¹/₁₆	28¼	8.46	7.59
185	30.17	30⅛	10.52	10½	.930	¹⁵/₁₆	.585	⁹/₁₆	5	26¾	1¹¹/₁₆	1	28¼	8.44	7.56
173	30.01	30	10.49	10½	.850	⅞	.565	⁹/₁₆	5	26¾	1⅝	1	28¼	8.41	7.53
161	29.83	29⅞	10.48	10½	.760	¾	.545	⁹/₁₆	5	26¾	1⁹/₁₆	1	28¼	8.37	7.50
147	29.65	29⅝	10.45	10½	.670	¹¹/₁₆	.520	½	5	26¾	1⁷/₁₆	1	28¼	8.34	7.47
265	27.81	27¾	14.09	14⅛	1.19	1³/₁₆	.725	¾	6⅝	24	1⅞	1¹/₁₆	25⅜	9.21	8.04
240	27.59	27⅝	14.02	14	1.08	1¹/₁₆	.660	¹¹/₁₆	6⅝	24	1¹³/₁₆	1	25⅜	9.16	7.99
217	27.38	27⅜	13.97	14	.975	1	.605	⅝	6⅝	24	1¹¹/₁₆	1	25⅜	9.12	7.95
170	27.29	27¼	10.07	10⅛	.930	¹⁵/₁₆	.570	⁹/₁₆	4¾	24	1⅝	¹⁵/₁₆	25⅜	7.81	6.97
152	27.09	27⅛	10.02	10	.830	¹³/₁₆	.515	½	4¾	24	1⁹/₁₆	¹⁵/₁₆	25⅜	7.77	6.93
140	26.92	26⅞	9.99	10	.745	¾	.490	½	4¾	24	1⁷/₁₆	¹⁵/₁₆	25⅜	7.73	6.90
125	26.71	26¾	9.96	10	.640	⅝	.460	⁷/₁₆	4¾	24	1⅜	¹⁵/₁₆	25⅜	7.69	6.86

W SHAPES
W610 – W530

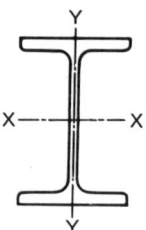

PROPERTIES

Designation[‡]	Nominal Mass	Total Area	Axis X-X				Axis Y-Y				Torsional Constant	Warping Constant
			I_x	S_x	r_x	Z_x	I_y	S_y	r_y	Z_y	J	C_w
	Lb./Ft.	In.^{2}	In.^{4}	In.^{3}	In.	In.^{3}	In.^{4}	In.^{3}	In.	In.^{3}	In.^{4}	In.^{6}
W610												
X241	162	47.7	5170	414	10.4	468	443	68.4	3.05	105	18.5	62600
X217	146	43.0	4580	370	10.3	418	391	60.6	3.02	93.2	13.4	54700
X195	131	38.5	4020	328	10.2	370	340	52.9	2.97	81.5	9.50	47000
X174	117	34.4	3540	292	10.1	327	297	46.4	2.94	71.4	6.72	40700
X155	104	30.6	3100	258	10.1	289	259	40.6	2.91	62.4	4.72	35200
W610												
X140	94	27.7	2700	222	9.87	254	109	24.1	1.98	37.5	5.26	15000
X125	84	24.7	2370	197	9.80	224	94.4	20.9	1.95	32.6	3.70	12800
X113	76	22.4	2100	176	9.68	200	82.5	18.4	1.92	28.6	2.68	11100
X101	68	20.1	1830	154	9.54	177	70.4	15.7	1.87	24.5	1.87	9430
W610												
X92*	62	18.2	1550	131	9.23	153	34.5	9.80	1.38	15.7	1.71	4620
X82*	55	16.2	1350	115	9.13	134	29.1	8.31	1.34	13.3	1.18	3870
W530												
X219*	147	43.2	3630	329	9.17	373	376	60.1	2.95	92.6	15.4	41100
X196*	132	38.8	3220	295	9.11	333	333	53.5	2.93	82.3	11.3	36000
X182*	122	35.9	2960	273	9.08	307	305	49.2	2.91	75.6	8.98	32700
X165*	111	32.7	2670	248	9.04	279	274	44.4	2.89	68.2	6.83	29200
X150*	101	29.8	2420	227	9.01	253	248	40.4	2.88	61.7	5.21	26200
W530												
X138	93	27.3	2070	191	8.71	221	92.9	22.1	1.84	34.7	6.03	9940
X123	83	24.3	1830	171	8.68	196	81.4	19.5	1.83	30.5	4.34	8630
X109	73	21.5	1600	151	8.63	172	70.6	17.0	1.81	26.6	3.02	7420
X101	68	20.0	1480	140	8.60	160	64.7	15.6	1.80	24.4	2.45	6760
X92	62	18.3	1330	127	8.53	144	57.5	14.0	1.77	21.7	1.83	5970
X82	55	16.3	1150	111	8.40	126	48.3	11.8	1.72	18.4	1.27	4970
W530												
X85*	57	16.7	1170	111	8.37	129	30.6	9.33	1.35	14.8	1.77	3190
X74*72	50	14.7	984	94.5	8.18	110	24.9	7.63	1.30	12.2	1.14	2560
X66*	44	13.0	843	81.6	8.05	95.4	20.7	6.37	1.26	10.2	.770	2110

[‡]Nominal depth in millimetres and mass in kilograms per metre.
*Not available from Canadian mills.

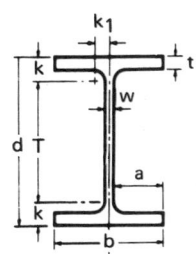

DIMENSIONS AND SURFACE AREAS

Nominal Mass	Depth d		Flange				Web Thickness w		Distances					Surface Area (Ft.²) per foot of length	
			Width b		Thickness t				a	T	k	k_1	d-2t	Total	Minus Top of Top Flange
kg/m	In.	In.	In.	In.	In.	In.	In.	In.	In.	In.	In.	In.	In.		
241	25.00	25	12.95	13	1.22	1¼	.705	¹¹/₁₆	6⅛	21	2	1¹/₁₆	22½	8.37	7.29
217	24.74	24¾	12.90	12⅞	1.09	1¹/₁₆	.650	⅝	6⅛	21	1⅞	1¹/₁₆	22½	8.31	7.24
195	24.48	24½	12.85	12⅞	.960	¹⁵/₁₆	.605	⅝	6⅛	21	1¾	1¹/₁₆	22½	8.26	7.19
174	24.26	24¼	12.80	12¾	.850	⅞	.550	⁹/₁₆	6⅛	21	1⅝	1	22½	8.22	7.15
155	24.06	24	12.75	12¾	.750	¾	.500	½	6⅛	21	1½	1	22½	8.18	7.11
140	24.31	24¼	9.06	9⅛	.875	⅞	.515	½	4¼	21	1⅝	1	22½	6.99	6.23
125	24.10	24⅛	9.02	9	.770	¾	.470	½	4¼	21	1⁹/₁₆	¹⁵/₁₆	22½	6.94	6.19
113	23.92	23⅞	8.99	9	.680	¹¹/₁₆	.440	⁷/₁₆	4¼	21	1⁷/₁₆	¹⁵/₁₆	22½	6.91	6.16
101	23.73	23¾	8.97	9	.585	⁹/₁₆	.415	⁷/₁₆	4¼	21	1⅜	¹⁵/₁₆	22½	6.87	6.13
92	23.74	23¾	7.04	7	.590	⁹/₁₆	.430	⁷/₁₆	3¼	21	1⅜	¹⁵/₁₆	22½	6.23	5.64
82	23.57	23⅝	7.01	7	.505	½	.395	⅜	3¼	21	1⁵/₁₆	¹⁵/₁₆	22½	6.20	5.61
219	22.06	22	12.51	12½	1.15	1⅛	.720	¾	5⅞	18¼	1⅞	1¹/₁₆	19¾	7.73	6.68
196	21.83	21⅞	12.44	12½	1.03	1¹/₁₆	.650	⅝	5⅞	18¼	1¹³/₁₆	1	19¾	7.68	6.64
182	21.68	21⅝	12.39	12⅜	.960	¹⁵/₁₆	.600	⅝	5⅞	18¼	1¹¹/₁₆	1	19¾	7.64	6.61
165	21.51	21½	12.34	12⅜	.875	⅞	.550	⁹/₁₆	5⅞	18¼	1⅝	¹⁵/₁₆	19¾	7.61	6.58
150	21.36	21⅜	12.29	12¼	.800	¹³/₁₆	.500	½	5⅞	18¼	1⁹/₁₆	¹⁵/₁₆	19¾	7.57	6.55
138	21.62	21⅝	8.42	8⅜	.930	¹⁵/₁₆	.580	⁹/₁₆	3⅞	18¼	1¹¹/₁₆	1	19¾	6.31	5.61
123	21.43	21⅜	8.35	8⅜	.835	¹³/₁₆	.515	½	3⅞	18¼	1⁹/₁₆	¹⁵/₁₆	19¾	6.27	5.57
109	21.24	21¼	8.30	8¼	.740	¾	.455	⁷/₁₆	3⅞	18¼	1½	¹⁵/₁₆	19¾	6.23	5.54
101	21.13	21⅛	8.27	8¼	.685	¹¹/₁₆	.430	⁷/₁₆	3⅞	18¼	1⁷/₁₆	⅞	19¾	6.21	5.52
92	20.99	21	8.24	8¼	.615	⅝	.400	⅜	3⅞	18¼	1⅜	⅞	19¾	6.18	5.49
82	20.80	20¾	8.22	8¼	.522	½	.375	⅜	3⅞	18¼	1¼	⅞	19¾	6.14	5.46
85	21.06	21	6.56	6½	.650	⅝	.405	⅜	3⅛	18¼	1⅜	⅞	19¾	5.63	5.08
74	20.83	20⅞	6.53	6½	.535	⁹/₁₆	.380	⅜	3⅛	18¼	1⁵/₁₆	⅞	19¾	5.58	5.04
66	20.66	20⅝	6.50	6½	.450	⁷/₁₆	.350	⅜	3⅛	18¼	1³/₁₆	⅞	19¾	5.55	5.01

W SHAPES
W460 – W410

PROPERTIES

Designation #	Nominal Mass	Total Area	Axis X-X				Axis Y-Y				Torsional Constant	Warping Constant
			I_x	S_x	r_x	Z_x	I_y	S_y	r_y	Z_y	J	C_w
	Lb./Ft.	In.^{2}	In.^{4}	In.^{3}	In.	In.^{3}	In.^{4}	In.^{3}	In.	In.^{3}	In.^{4}	In.^{6}
W460												
X177*	119	35.1	2190	231	7.90	261	253	44.9	2.68	69.1	10.6	20300
X158*	106	31.1	1910	204	7.84	230	220	39.3	2.66	60.5	7.48	17400
X144*	97	28.5	1750	188	7.84	211	201	36.1	2.66	55.3	5.86	15800
X128*	86	25.3	1530	166	7.78	186	175	31.6	2.63	48.4	4.10	13600
X113*	76	22.3	1330	146	7.72	163	152	27.6	2.61	42.2	2.83	11700
W460												
X106	71	20.8	1170	127	7.50	145	60.3	15.8	1.70	24.7	3.48	4700
X97	65	19.1	1070	117	7.48	133	54.8	14.4	1.69	22.5	2.73	4240
X89	60	17.6	984	108	7.48	123	50.1	13.3	1.69	20.6	2.17	3860
X82	55	16.2	890	98.3	7.41	112	44.9	11.9	1.66	18.5	1.66	3430
X74	50	14.7	800	88.9	7.38	101	40.1	10.7	1.65	16.6	1.24	3040
X67	45	13.4	719	80.5	7.33	91.3	34.8	9.31	1.61	14.5	.986	2620
X61	41	12.1	623	70.4	7.18	80.1	29.3	7.87	1.56	12.3	.696	2190
W460												
X68*	46	13.5	712	78.8	7.26	90.7	22.5	7.43	1.29	11.7	1.22	1710
X60*	40	11.8	612	68.4	7.20	78.4	19.1	6.35	1.27	9.95	.809	1440
X52*	35	10.3	510	57.6	7.04	66.5	15.3	5.10	1.22	8.06	.505	1140
W410												
X149*	100	29.4	1490	176	7.12	198	186	35.7	2.52	54.9	7.73	11900
X132*	89	26.2	1300	155	7.04	175	163	31.5	2.49	48.1	5.45	10300
X114*	77	22.6	1110	134	7.01	150	138	26.8	2.47	41.1	3.57	8570
X100*	67	19.7	954	117	6.96	130	119	23.3	2.46	35.5	2.39	7300
W410												
X85	57	16.8	758	92.3	6.72	105	43.1	12.1	1.60	18.9	2.22	2660
X74	50	14.7	659	81.1	6.70	92.0	37.2	10.5	1.59	16.3	1.52	2270
X67	45	13.3	586	72.7	6.64	82.3	32.8	9.33	1.57	14.5	1.11	1990
X60	40	11.8	518	64.7	6.63	72.9	28.9	8.26	1.56	12.7	.793	1740
X54	36	10.6	448	56.5	6.50	64.0	24.5	7.02	1.52	10.8	.544	1460
W410												
X46	31	9.12	375	47.2	6.41	54.0	12.4	4.49	1.17	7.03	.460	739
X39	26	7.68	301	38.4	6.26	44.2	9.59	3.49	1.12	5.48	.261	565

Nominal depth in millimetres and mass in kilograms per metre.
*Not available from Canadian mills.

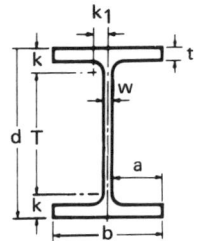

DIMENSIONS AND SURFACE AREAS

Nominal Mass	Depth d		Flange				Web Thickness w		Distances					Surface Area (Ft.²) per foot of length	
			Width b		Thickness t				a	T	k	k₁	d-2t	Total	Minus Top of Top Flange
kg/m	In.	In.	In.	In.	In.	In.	In.	In.	In.	In.	In.	In.	In.		
177	18.97	19	11.27	11¼	1.06	1¹/₁₆	.655	⅝	5¼	15½	1¾	¹⁵/₁₆	16⅞	6.81	5.87
158	18.73	18¾	11.20	11¼	.940	¹⁵/₁₆	.590	⁹/₁₆	5¼	15½	1⅝	¹⁵/₁₆	16⅞	6.76	5.82
144	18.59	18⅝	11.15	11⅛	.870	⅞	.535	⁹/₁₆	5¼	15½	1⁹/₁₆	⅞	16⅞	6.72	5.80
128	18.39	18⅜	11.09	11⅛	.770	¾	.480	½	5¼	15½	1⁷/₁₆	⅞	16⅞	6.68	5.76
113	18.21	18¼	11.03	11	.680	¹¹/₁₆	.425	⁷/₁₆	5¼	15½	1⅜	¹³/₁₆	16⅞	6.64	5.72
106	18.47	18½	7.64	7⅝	.810	¹³/₁₆	.495	½	3⅝	15⅜	1⁹/₁₆	⅞	16⅞	5.54	4.90
97	18.35	18⅜	7.59	7⅝	.750	¾	.450	⁷/₁₆	3⅝	15⅜	1½	⅞	16⅞	5.51	4.88
89	18.24	18¼	7.56	7½	.695	¹¹/₁₆	.415	⁷/₁₆	3⅝	15⅜	1⁷/₁₆	⅞	16⅞	5.49	4.86
82	18.11	18⅛	7.53	7½	.630	⅝	.390	⅜	3⅝	15⅜	1⅜	⅞	16⅞	5.46	4.84
74	17.99	18	7.49	7½	.570	⁹/₁₆	.355	⅜	3⅝	15⅜	1⁵/₁₆	¹³/₁₆	16⅞	5.44	4.81
67	17.86	17⅞	7.48	7½	.499	½	.335	⁵/₁₆	3⅝	15⅜	1¼	¹³/₁₆	16⅞	5.41	4.79
61	17.70	17¾	7.45	7½	.425	⁷/₁₆	.320	⁵/₁₆	3⅝	15⅜	1³/₁₆	¹³/₁₆	16⅞	5.38	4.76
68	18.06	18	6.06	6	.605	⅝	.360	⅜	2⅞	15½	1¼	¹³/₁₆	16⅞	4.97	4.46
60	17.90	17⅞	6.02	6	.525	½	.315	⁵/₁₆	2⅞	15½	1³/₁₆	¹³/₁₆	16⅞	4.94	4.43
52	17.70	17¾	6.00	6	.425	⁷/₁₆	.300	⁵/₁₆	2⅞	15½	1⅛	¾	16⅞	4.90	4.40
149	16.97	17	10.43	10⅜	.985	1	.585	⁹/₁₆	4⅞	13⅝	1¹¹/₁₆	¹⁵/₁₆	15	6.21	5.34
132	16.75	16¾	10.36	10⅜	.875	⅞	.525	½	4⅞	13⅝	1⁹/₁₆	⅞	15	6.16	5.30
114	16.52	16½	10.30	10¼	.760	¾	.455	⁷/₁₆	4⅞	13⅝	1⁷/₁₆	⅞	15	6.11	5.25
100	16.33	16⅜	10.23	10¼	.665	¹¹/₁₆	.395	⅜	4⅞	13⅝	1⅜	¹³/₁₆	15	6.07	5.21
85	16.43	16⅜	7.12	7⅛	.715	¹¹/₁₆	.430	⁷/₁₆	3⅜	13⅝	1⅜	⅞	15	5.04	4.45
74	16.26	16¼	7.07	7⅛	.630	⅝	.380	⅜	3⅜	13⅝	1⁵/₁₆	¹³/₁₆	15	5.00	4.41
67	16.13	16⅛	7.03	7	.565	⁹/₁₆	.345	⅜	3⅜	13⅝	1¼	¹³/₁₆	15	4.98	4.39
60	16.01	16	6.99	7	.505	½	.305	⁵/₁₆	3⅜	13⅝	1³/₁₆	¹³/₁₆	15	4.95	4.37
54	15.86	15⅞	6.98	7	.430	⁷/₁₆	.295	⁵/₁₆	3⅜	13⅝	1⅛	¹³/₁₆	15	4.92	4.34
46	15.88	15⅞	5.52	5½	.440	⁷/₁₆	.275	¼	2⅝	13⅝	1⅛	¹³/₁₆	15	4.44	3.98
39	15.69	15¾	5.50	5½	.345	⅜	.250	¼	2⅝	13⅝	1¹/₁₆	¾	15	4.41	3.95

W SHAPES
W360

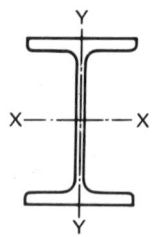

PROPERTIES

Designation ‡	Nominal Mass	Total Area	Axis X-X				Axis Y-Y				Torsional Constant	Warping Constant
			I_x	S_x	r_x	Z_x	I_y	S_y	r_y	Z_y	J	C_W
	Lb./Ft.	In.²	In.⁴	In.³	In.	In.³	In.⁴	In.³	In.	In.³	In.⁴	In.⁶
W360												
X1086*	730	215	14300	1280	8.16	1660	4720	528	4.69	816	1450	362000
X990*	665	196	12400	1150	7.95	1480	4170	473	4.61	730	1120	306000
X900*	605	178	10800	1030	7.79	1320	3680	423	4.55	652	870	258000
X818*	550	162	9430	932	7.63	1180	3250	378	4.48	583	670	219000
X744*	500	147	8210	838	7.47	1050	2880	339	4.43	522	514	187000
X677*	455	134	7190	756	7.33	936	2560	304	4.37	468	395	160000
W360												
X634*	426	125	6600	707	7.27	869	2360	283	4.35	434	331	144000
X592*	398	117	6000	656	7.16	801	2170	262	4.31	402	273	129000
X551*	370	109	5440	607	7.06	736	1990	242	4.27	370	222	116000
X509*	342	101	4900	559	6.97	672	1810	221	4.23	338	178	103000
X463*	311	91.4	4330	506	6.88	603	1610	198	4.20	304	136	88900
X421*	283	83.3	3840	459	6.79	542	1440	179	4.16	274	104	77500
X382*	257	75.6	3400	415	6.71	487	1290	161	4.13	246	79.1	67700
X347*	233	68.5	3010	375	6.63	436	1150	145	4.10	221	59.5	59000
X314*	211	62.0	2660	338	6.55	390	1030	130	4.08	198	44.6	51600
X287*	193	56.8	2400	310	6.50	355	931	119	4.05	180	34.8	45900
X262*	176	51.8	2140	281	6.43	320	838	107	4.02	163	26.5	40500
X237*	159	46.7	1900	254	6.38	287	748	96.1	4.00	146	19.8	35600
X216*	145	42.7	1710	231	6.33	260	677	87.4	3.98	133	15.2	31700
W360												
X196*	132	38.8	1530	209	6.28	234	548	74.4	3.76	113	12.3	25500
X179*	120	35.3	1380	191	6.25	212	495	67.5	3.74	102	9.37	22700
X162*	109	32.0	1240	173	6.22	192	447	61.2	3.74	92.7	7.12	20200
X147*	99	29.1	1110	157	6.18	173	402	55.2	3.72	83.6	5.37	18000
X134*	90	26.5	999	143	6.14	157	362	49.9	3.70	75.6	4.06	16000
W360												
X122*	82	24.1	882	123	6.05	139	148	29.2	2.48	44.8	5.08	6700
X110*	74	21.8	796	112	6.04	126	134	26.6	2.48	40.6	3.88	6000
X101*	68	20.0	723	103	6.01	115	121	24.1	2.46	36.9	3.02	5370
X91*	61	17.9	640	92.2	5.98	102	107	21.4	2.44	32.8	2.20	4690
W360												
X79	53	15.6	541	77.7	5.89	87.1	57.7	14.3	1.92	22.0	1.94	2540
X72	48	14.1	485	70.3	5.86	78.4	51.4	12.8	1.91	19.6	1.46	2240
X64	43	12.6	428	62.7	5.83	69.6	45.2	11.3	1.89	17.3	1.05	1950
W360												
X57	38	11.2	385	54.6	5.86	61.5	26.7	7.89	1.54	12.1	.798	1230
X51	34	10.0	340	48.6	5.83	54.6	23.3	6.91	1.53	10.6	.569	1070
X45	30	8.85	291	42.1	5.73	47.3	19.6	5.82	1.49	8.99	.380	887
W360												
X39	26	7.69	245	35.2	5.64	40.2	8.91	3.55	1.08	5.54	.358	405
X33	22	6.49	199	29.0	5.54	33.2	7.00	2.80	1.04	4.39	.208	314

‡Nominal depth in millimetres and mass in kilograms per metre.
*Not available from Canadian mills.

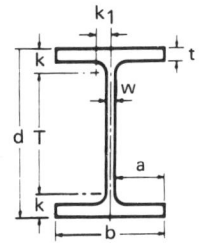

DIMENSIONS AND SURFACE AREAS

Nominal Mass	Depth d		Flange Width b		Flange Thickness t		Web Thickness w		Distances a	Distances T	Distances k	Distances k₁	Distances d-2t	Surface Area (Ft.²) per foot of length Total	Surface Area (Ft.²) per foot of length Minus Top of Top Flange
kg/m	In.	In.	In.	In.	In.	In.	In.	In.	In.	In.	In.	In.	In.		
1086	22.42	22 3/8	17.89	17 7/8	4.91	4 15/16	3.07	3 1/16	7 3/8	11 1/4	5 9/16	2 3/16	12 5/8	9.19	7.70
990	21.64	21 5/8	17.65	17 5/8	4.52	4 1/2	2.83	2 13/16	7 3/8	11 1/4	5 3/16	2 1/16	12 5/8	9.02	7.55
900	20.92	20 7/8	17.41	17 3/8	4.16	4 3/16	2.59	2 5/8	7 3/8	11 1/4	4 13/16	1 15/16	12 5/8	8.86	7.41
818	20.24	20 1/4	17.20	17 1/4	3.82	3 13/16	2.38	2 3/8	7 3/8	11 1/4	4 1/2	1 13/16	12 5/8	8.71	7.28
744	19.60	19 5/8	17.01	17	3.50	3 1/2	2.19	2 3/16	7 3/8	11 1/4	4 3/16	1 3/4	12 5/8	8.57	7.15
677	19.02	19	16.84	16 7/8	3.21	3 3/16	2.01	2	7 3/8	11 1/4	3 7/8	1 5/8	12 5/8	8.45	7.04
634	18.67	18 5/8	16.70	16 3/4	3.03	3 1/16	1.88	1 7/8	7 3/8	11 1/4	3 11/16	1 9/16	12 5/8	8.36	6.97
592	18.29	18 1/4	16.59	16 5/8	2.84	2 7/8	1.77	1 3/4	7 3/8	11 1/4	3 1/2	1 1/2	12 5/8	8.28	6.90
551	17.92	17 7/8	16.48	16 1/2	2.66	2 11/16	1.65	1 5/8	7 3/8	11 1/4	3 5/16	1 7/16	12 5/8	8.20	6.83
509	17.54	17 1/2	16.36	16 3/8	2.47	2 1/2	1.54	1 9/16	7 3/8	11 1/4	3 1/8	1 3/8	12 5/8	8.12	6.76
463	17.12	17 1/8	16.23	16 1/4	2.26	2 1/4	1.41	1 7/16	7 3/8	11 1/4	2 15/16	1 5/16	12 5/8	8.03	6.68
421	16.74	16 3/4	16.11	16 1/8	2.07	2 1/16	1.29	1 5/16	7 3/8	11 1/4	2 3/4	1 1/4	12 5/8	7.94	6.60
382	16.38	16 3/8	15.99	16	1.89	1 7/8	1.18	1 3/16	7 3/8	11 1/4	2 9/16	1 3/16	12 5/8	7.87	6.53
347	16.04	16	15.89	15 7/8	1.72	1 3/4	1.07	1 1/16	7 3/8	11 1/4	2 3/8	1 3/16	12 5/8	7.79	6.47
314	15.72	15 3/4	15.80	15 3/4	1.56	1 9/16	.980	1	7 3/8	11 1/4	2 1/4	1 1/8	12 5/8	7.72	6.41
287	15.48	15 1/2	15.71	15 3/4	1.44	1 7/16	.890	7/8	7 3/8	11 1/4	2 1/8	1 1/16	12 5/8	7.67	6.36
262	15.22	15 1/4	15.65	15 5/8	1.31	1 5/16	.830	13/16	7 3/8	11 1/4	2	1 1/16	12 5/8	7.61	6.31
237	14.98	15	15.56	15 5/8	1.19	1 3/16	.745	3/4	7 3/8	11 1/4	1 7/8	1	12 5/8	7.56	6.26
216	14.78	14 3/4	15.50	15 1/2	1.09	1 1/16	.680	11/16	7 3/8	11 1/4	1 3/4	1	12 5/8	7.52	6.22
196	14.66	14 5/8	14.73	14 3/4	1.03	1	.645	5/8	7	11 1/4	1 11/16	15/16	12 5/8	7.24	6.02
179	14.48	14 1/2	14.67	14 5/8	.940	15/16	.590	9/16	7	11 1/4	1 5/8	15/16	12 5/8	7.20	5.98
162	14.32	14 3/8	14.60	14 5/8	.860	7/8	.525	1/2	7	11 1/4	1 9/16	7/8	12 5/8	7.17	5.95
147	14.16	14 1/8	14.56	14 5/8	.780	3/4	.485	1/2	7	11 1/4	1 7/16	7/8	12 5/8	7.13	5.92
134	14.02	14	14.52	14 1/2	.710	11/16	.440	7/16	7	11 1/4	1 3/8	7/8	12 5/8	7.10	5.89
122	14.31	14 1/4	10.13	10 1/8	.855	7/8	.510	1/2	4 3/4	11	1 5/8	1	12 5/8	5.68	4.83
110	14.17	14 1/8	10.07	10 1/8	.785	13/16	.450	7/16	4 3/4	11	1 9/16	15/16	12 5/8	5.64	4.80
101	14.04	14	10.03	10	.720	3/4	.415	7/16	4 3/4	11	1 1/2	15/16	12 5/8	5.62	4.78
91	13.89	13 7/8	9.99	10	.645	5/8	.375	3/8	4 3/4	11	1 7/16	15/16	12 5/8	5.58	4.75
79	13.92	13 7/8	8.06	8	.660	11/16	.370	3/8	3 7/8	11	1 7/16	15/16	12 5/8	4.94	4.27
72	13.79	13 3/4	8.03	8	.595	5/8	.340	5/16	3 7/8	11	1 3/8	7/8	12 5/8	4.92	4.25
64	13.66	13 5/8	7.99	8	.530	1/2	.305	5/16	3 7/8	11	1 5/16	7/8	12 5/8	4.89	4.22
57	14.10	14 1/8	6.77	6 3/4	.515	1/2	.310	5/16	3 1/4	11 5/8	1 1/4	13/16	13 1/8	4.55	3.99
51	13.98	14	6.74	6 3/4	.455	7/16	.285	5/16	3 1/4	11 5/8	1 3/16	13/16	13 1/8	4.53	3.97
45	13.84	13 7/8	6.73	6 3/4	.385	3/8	.270	1/4	3 1/4	11 5/8	1 1/8	13/16	13 1/8	4.50	3.94
39	13.91	13 7/8	5.02	5	.420	7/16	.255	1/4	2 3/8	11 5/8	1 1/8	3/4	13 1/8	3.95	3.53
33	13.74	13 3/4	5.00	5	.335	5/16	.230	1/4	2 3/8	11 5/8	1 1/16	3/4	13 1/8	3.92	3.50

W SHAPES
W310

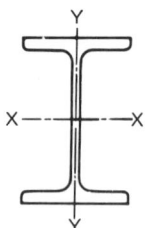

PROPERTIES

Designation[‡]	Nominal Mass	Total Area	Axis X-X				Axis Y-Y				Torsional Constant	Warping Constant
			I_x	S_x	r_x	Z_x	I_y	S_y	r_y	Z_y	J	C_W
	Lb./Ft.	In.^{2}	In.^{4}	In.^{3}	In.	In.^{3}	In.^{4}	In.^{3}	In.	In.^{3}	In.^{4}	In.^{6}
W310												
X500*	336	98.8	4060	483	6.41	603	1190	178	3.47	274	243	57200
X454*	305	89.6	3550	435	6.29	537	1050	159	3.42	244	185	48700
X415*	279	81.9	3110	392	6.16	481	937	143	3.38	220	143	41900
X375*	252	74.1	2720	353	6.06	428	828	127	3.34	196	108	35800
X342*	230	67.7	2420	322	5.98	386	742	115	3.31	177	83.8	31300
X313*	210	61.8	2140	291	5.88	348	664	104	3.28	159	64.7	27200
W310												
X283	190	55.8	1890	263	5.82	311	589	93.0	3.25	143	48.8	23500
X253	170	50.0	1650	235	5.74	275	517	82.3	3.22	126	35.6	20100
X226	152	44.7	1430	209	5.66	243	454	72.8	3.19	111	25.8	17200
X202	136	39.9	1240	185	5.57	214	398	64.2	3.16	98.0	18.5	14700
X179	120	35.3	1070	163	5.51	186	345	56.0	3.13	85.4	12.9	12500
X158	106	31.2	933	145	5.47	164	301	49.3	3.11	75.1	9.13	10700
X143	96	28.2	833	131	5.43	147	270	44.4	3.09	67.5	6.86	9410
X129	87	25.6	740	118	5.38	132	241	39.7	3.07	60.4	5.10	8280
X118	79	23.2	662	107	5.34	119	216	35.8	3.05	54.3	3.84	7320
X107	72	21.1	597	97.5	5.32	108	195	32.4	3.04	49.2	2.93	6540
X97	65	19.1	533	88.0	5.28	96.8	174	29.0	3.02	44.1	2.18	5770
W310												
X86	58	17.0	475	77.9	5.29	86.4	107	21.4	2.51	32.5	2.10	3570
X79	53	15.6	425	70.5	5.22	77.9	95.8	19.2	2.48	29.1	1.58	3160
W310												
X74	50	14.7	394	64.6	5.18	72.4	56.3	13.9	1.96	21.4	1.78	1880
X67	45	13.2	350	58.0	5.15	64.7	50.0	12.4	1.95	19.0	1.31	1650
X60	40	11.8	310	51.9	5.13	57.5	44.1	11.0	1.93	16.8	.953	1440
W310												
X52	35	10.3	285	45.6	5.26	51.2	24.5	7.47	1.54	11.5	.741	879
X45	30	8.79	238	38.6	5.20	43.1	20.3	6.23	1.52	9.56	.457	719
X39	26	7.65	204	33.4	5.16	37.2	17.3	5.33	1.50	8.17	.300	606
W310												
X33*	22	6.48	156	25.3	4.91	29.3	4.66	2.31	.848	3.66	.293	165
X28*	19	5.57	130	21.4	4.83	24.7	3.76	1.88	.822	2.98	.180	131
X24*	16	4.71	103	17.2	4.68	20.1	2.82	1.41	.774	2.26	.103	96.9
X21*	14	4.16	88.6	14.9	4.61	17.4	2.36	1.19	.753	1.90	.070	80.6

‡Nominal depth in millimetres and mass in kilograms per metre.
*Not available from Canadian mills.

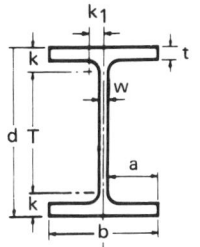

DIMENSIONS AND SURFACE AREAS

Nominal Mass	Depth d		Flange				Web Thickness w		Distances					Surface Area (Ft.^{2}) per foot of length	
			Width b		Thickness t				a	T	k	k_1	d-2t	Total	Minus Top of Top Flange
kg/m	In.	In.	In.	In.	In.	In.	In.	In.	In.	In.	In.	In.	In.		
500	16.82	16^7/$_8$	13.39	13^3/$_8$	2.95	2^{15}/$_{16}$	1.77	1^3/$_4$	5^3/$_4$	9^1/$_2$	3^{11}/$_{16}$	1^1/$_2$	10^7/$_8$	6.97	5.85
454	16.32	16^3/$_8$	13.23	13^1/$_4$	2.70	2^{11}/$_{16}$	1.62	1^5/$_8$	5^3/$_4$	9^1/$_2$	3^7/$_{16}$	1^7/$_{16}$	10^7/$_8$	6.86	5.76
415	15.85	15^7/$_8$	13.14	13^1/$_8$	2.47	2^1/$_2$	1.53	1^1/$_2$	5^3/$_4$	9^1/$_2$	3^3/$_{16}$	1^3/$_8$	10^7/$_8$	6.77	5.67
375	15.41	15^3/$_8$	13.01	13	2.25	2^1/$_4$	1.40	1^3/$_8$	5^3/$_4$	9^1/$_2$	2^{15}/$_{16}$	1^5/$_{16}$	10^7/$_8$	6.67	5.59
342	15.05	15	12.90	12^7/$_8$	2.07	2^1/$_{16}$	1.28	1^5/$_{16}$	5^3/$_4$	9^1/$_2$	2^3/$_4$	1^1/$_4$	10^7/$_8$	6.59	5.52
313	14.71	14^3/$_4$	12.79	12^3/$_4$	1.90	1^7/$_8$	1.18	1^3/$_{16}$	5^3/$_4$	9^1/$_2$	2^5/$_8$	1^1/$_4$	10^7/$_8$	6.52	5.45
283	14.38	14^3/$_8$	12.67	12^5/$_8$	1.73	1^3/$_4$	1.06	1^1/$_{16}$	5^3/$_4$	9^1/$_2$	2^7/$_{16}$	1^3/$_{16}$	10^7/$_8$	6.44	5.39
253	14.03	14	12.57	12^5/$_8$	1.56	1^9/$_{16}$	.960	^{15}/$_{16}$	5^3/$_4$	9^1/$_2$	2^1/$_4$	1^1/$_8$	10^7/$_8$	6.37	5.32
226	13.71	13^3/$_4$	12.48	12^1/$_2$	1.40	1^3/$_8$	.870	^{7}/$_8$	5^3/$_4$	9^1/$_2$	2^1/$_8$	1^1/$_{16}$	10^7/$_8$	6.30	5.26
202	13.41	13^3/$_8$	12.40	12^3/$_8$	1.25	1^1/$_4$	.790	^{13}/$_{16}$	5^3/$_4$	9^1/$_2$	1^{15}/$_{16}$	1^1/$_{16}$	10^7/$_8$	6.24	5.20
179	13.12	13^1/$_8$	12.32	12^3/$_8$	1.10	1^1/$_8$	.710	^{11}/$_{16}$	5^3/$_4$	9^1/$_2$	1^{13}/$_{16}$	1	10^7/$_8$	6.17	5.15
158	12.89	12^7/$_8$	12.22	12^1/$_4$	.990	1	.610	^{5}/$_8$	5^3/$_4$	9^1/$_2$	1^{11}/$_{16}$	^{15}/$_{16}$	10^7/$_8$	6.12	5.10
143	12.71	12^3/$_4$	12.16	12^1/$_8$	.900	^{7}/$_8$	.550	^{9}/$_{16}$	5^3/$_4$	9^1/$_2$	1^5/$_8$	^{15}/$_{16}$	10^7/$_8$	6.08	5.07
129	12.53	12^1/$_2$	12.13	12^1/$_8$	.810	^{13}/$_{16}$	.515	^{1}/$_2$	5^3/$_4$	9^1/$_2$	1^1/$_2$	^{15}/$_{16}$	10^7/$_8$	6.04	5.03
118	12.38	12^3/$_8$	12.08	12^1/$_8$	.735	^{3}/$_4$	.470	^{1}/$_2$	5^3/$_4$	9^1/$_2$	1^7/$_{16}$	^{7}/$_8$	10^7/$_8$	6.01	5.00
107	12.25	12^1/$_4$	12.04	12	.670	^{11}/$_{16}$	.430	^{7}/$_{16}$	5^3/$_4$	9^1/$_2$	1^3/$_8$	^{7}/$_8$	10^7/$_8$	5.98	4.98
97	12.12	12^1/$_8$	12.00	12	.605	^{5}/$_8$	.390	^{3}/$_8$	5^3/$_4$	9^1/$_2$	1^5/$_{16}$	^{7}/$_8$	10^7/$_8$	5.95	4.95
86	12.19	12^1/$_4$	10.01	10	.640	^{5}/$_8$	.360	^{3}/$_8$	4^7/$_8$	9^1/$_2$	1^3/$_8$	^{13}/$_{16}$	10^7/$_8$	5.31	4.47
79	12.06	12	9.99	10	.575	^{9}/$_{16}$	.345	^{3}/$_8$	4^7/$_8$	9^1/$_2$	1^1/$_4$	^{13}/$_{16}$	10^7/$_8$	5.28	4.45
74	12.19	12^1/$_4$	8.08	8^1/$_8$	.640	^{5}/$_8$	.370	^{3}/$_8$	3^7/$_8$	9^1/$_2$	1^3/$_8$	^{13}/$_{16}$	10^7/$_8$	4.66	3.99
67	12.06	12	8.05	8	.575	^{9}/$_{16}$	.335	^{5}/$_{16}$	3^7/$_8$	9^1/$_2$	1^1/$_4$	^{13}/$_{16}$	10^7/$_8$	4.64	3.97
60	11.94	12	8.01	8	.515	^{1}/$_2$	.295	^{5}/$_{16}$	3^7/$_8$	9^1/$_2$	1^1/$_4$	^{13}/$_{16}$	10^7/$_8$	4.61	3.94
52	12.50	12^1/$_2$	6.56	6^1/$_2$	.520	^{1}/$_2$	.300	^{5}/$_{16}$	3^1/$_8$	10	1^1/$_4$	^{13}/$_{16}$	11^1/$_2$	4.22	3.67
45	12.34	12^3/$_8$	6.52	6^1/$_2$	.440	^{7}/$_{16}$	.260	^{1}/$_4$	3^1/$_8$	10	1^3/$_{16}$	^{3}/$_4$	11^1/$_2$	4.19	3.64
39	12.22	12^1/$_4$	6.49	6^1/$_2$	.380	^{3}/$_8$	.230	^{1}/$_4$	3^1/$_8$	10	1^1/$_8$	^{3}/$_4$	11^1/$_2$	4.16	3.62
33	12.31	12^1/$_4$	4.03	4	.425	^{7}/$_{16}$	.260	^{1}/$_4$	1^7/$_8$	10^1/$_2$	^{7}/$_8$	^{1}/$_2$	11^1/$_2$	3.35	3.02
28	12.16	12^1/$_8$	4.01	4	.350	^{3}/$_8$	.235	^{1}/$_4$	1^7/$_8$	10^1/$_2$	^{13}/$_{16}$	^{1}/$_2$	11^1/$_2$	3.32	2.99
24	11.99	12	3.99	4	.265	^{1}/$_4$	.220	^{1}/$_4$	1^7/$_8$	10^1/$_2$	^{3}/$_4$	^{1}/$_2$	11^1/$_2$	3.29	2.96
21	11.91	11^7/$_8$	3.97	4	.225	^{1}/$_4$	.200	^{3}/$_{16}$	1^7/$_8$	10^1/$_2$	^{11}/$_{16}$	^{1}/$_2$	11^1/$_2$	3.27	2.94

W SHAPES
W250 – W200

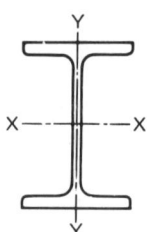

PROPERTIES

Designation[‡]	Nominal Mass	Total Area	Axis X-X				Axis Y-Y				Torsional Constant	Warping Constant
			I_x	S_x	r_x	Z_x	I_y	S_y	r_y	Z_y	J	C_w
	Lb./Ft.	In.²	In.⁴	In.³	In.	In.³	In.⁴	In.³	In.	In.³	In.⁴	In.⁶
W250												
X167	112	32.9	716	126	4.67	147	236	45.3	2.68	69.2	15.1	6030
X149	100	29.4	623	112	4.60	130	207	40.0	2.65	61.0	10.9	5150
X131	88	25.9	534	98.5	4.54	113	179	34.9	2.63	53.1	7.53	4340
X115	77	22.6	455	85.8	4.49	97.6	154	30.2	2.61	45.9	5.11	3640
X101	68	20.0	394	75.8	4.44	85.3	134	26.5	2.59	40.1	3.56	3110
X89	60	17.6	341	66.7	4.40	74.6	116	23.0	2.57	35.0	2.48	2640
X80	54	15.8	303	60.1	4.38	66.6	103	20.5	2.55	31.3	1.82	2310
X73	49	14.4	272	54.5	4.35	60.4	93.4	18.7	2.55	28.3	1.39	2070
W250												
X67	45	13.3	248	49.1	4.32	54.9	53.4	13.3	2.00	20.3	1.51	1200
X58	39	11.5	209	42.1	4.26	46.8	45.0	11.3	1.98	17.2	.976	992
X49	33	9.71	170	34.9	4.18	38.8	36.6	9.20	1.94	14.0	.583	791
W250												
X45	30	8.84	170	32.5	4.39	36.6	16.7	5.75	1.37	8.84	.622	414
X39	26	7.61	144	27.9	4.35	31.3	14.1	4.89	1.36	7.50	.402	345
X33	22	6.49	118	23.2	4.26	26.0	11.4	3.97	1.33	6.10	.239	274
W250												
X28*	19	5.62	96.3	18.8	4.14	21.6	4.29	2.13	.874	3.35	.233	104
X25*	17	4.99	81.9	16.2	4.05	18.7	3.56	1.78	.845	2.80	.156	85.1
X22*	15	4.41	68.9	13.8	3.95	16.0	2.89	1.44	.810	2.30	.104	68.3
X18*	12	3.54	53.8	10.9	3.90	12.6	2.18	1.10	.785	1.74	.055	50.9
W200												
X100	67	19.7	272	60.4	3.72	70.2	88.6	21.4	2.12	32.7	5.06	1440
X86	58	17.1	228	52.1	3.65	59.8	75.1	18.3	2.10	27.9	3.34	1180
X71	48	14.1	184	43.3	3.61	49.0	60.9	15.0	2.08	22.9	1.96	930
X59	40	11.7	146	35.4	3.53	39.8	49.1	12.2	2.05	18.5	1.12	726
X52	35	10.3	127	31.3	3.51	34.7	42.6	10.6	2.03	16.1	.771	619
X46	31	9.13	110	27.5	3.47	30.4	37.1	9.28	2.02	14.1	.538	531
W200												
X42	28	8.25	98.0	24.3	3.45	27.2	21.7	6.64	1.62	10.1	.538	313
X36	24	7.08	82.8	20.9	3.42	23.2	18.3	5.64	1.61	8.57	.347	259
W200												
X31	21	6.16	75.3	18.2	3.50	20.4	9.77	3.71	1.26	5.69	.282	152
X27	18	5.26	61.9	15.2	3.43	17.0	7.97	3.04	1.23	4.66	.172	122
W200												
X22*	15	4.44	48.0	11.8	3.29	13.6	3.41	1.70	.876	2.67	.137	51.8
X19*	13	3.84	39.6	9.91	3.21	11.4	2.73	1.36	.843	2.15	.087	40.8
X15*	10	2.96	30.8	7.81	3.23	8.87	2.09	1.06	.840	1.66	.043	30.9

[‡]Nominal depth in millimetres and mass in kilograms per metre.
*Not available from Canadian mills.

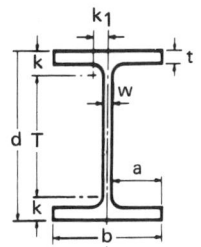

DIMENSIONS AND SURFACE AREAS

Nominal Mass	Depth d		Flange				Web Thickness w		Distances					Surface Area (Ft.²) per foot of length	
			Width b		Thickness t				a	T	k	k_1	d-2t	Total	Minus Top of Top Flange
kg/m	In.	In.	In.	In.	In.	In.	In.	In.	In.	In.	In.	In.	In.		
167	11.36	11³⁄₈	10.41	10³⁄₈	1.25	1¹⁄₄	.755	³⁄₄	4⁷⁄₈	7³⁄₈	2	1	8⁷⁄₈	5.24	4.37
149	11.10	11¹⁄₈	10.34	10³⁄₈	1.12	1¹⁄₈	.680	¹¹⁄₁₆	4⁷⁄₈	7³⁄₈	1⁷⁄₈	1	8⁷⁄₈	5.18	4.32
131	10.84	10⁷⁄₈	10.27	10¹⁄₄	.990	1	.605	⁵⁄₈	4⁷⁄₈	7³⁄₈	1³⁄₄	¹⁵⁄₁₆	8⁷⁄₈	5.13	4.27
115	10.60	10⁵⁄₈	10.19	10¹⁄₄	.870	⁷⁄₈	.530	¹⁄₂	4⁷⁄₈	7³⁄₈	1⁵⁄₈	¹⁵⁄₁₆	8⁷⁄₈	5.07	4.23
101	10.40	10³⁄₈	10.13	10¹⁄₈	.770	³⁄₄	.470	¹⁄₂	4⁷⁄₈	7³⁄₈	1¹⁄₂	⁷⁄₈	8⁷⁄₈	5.03	4.19
89	10.22	10¹⁄₄	10.08	10¹⁄₈	.680	¹¹⁄₁₆	.420	⁷⁄₁₆	4⁷⁄₈	7³⁄₈	1⁷⁄₁₆	⁷⁄₈	8⁷⁄₈	4.99	4.15
80	10.09	10¹⁄₈	10.03	10	.615	⁵⁄₈	.370	³⁄₈	4⁷⁄₈	7³⁄₈	1³⁄₈	¹³⁄₁₆	8⁷⁄₈	4.96	4.13
73	9.98	10	10.00	10	.560	⁹⁄₁₆	.340	⁵⁄₁₆	4⁷⁄₈	7³⁄₈	1⁵⁄₁₆	¹³⁄₁₆	8⁷⁄₈	4.94	4.11
67	10.10	10¹⁄₈	8.02	8	.620	⁵⁄₈	.350	³⁄₈	3⁷⁄₈	7³⁄₈	1³⁄₈	¹³⁄₁₆	8⁷⁄₈	4.30	3.63
58	9.92	9⁷⁄₈	7.98	8	.530	¹⁄₂	.315	⁵⁄₁₆	3⁷⁄₈	7³⁄₈	1¹⁄₄	¹³⁄₁₆	8⁷⁄₈	4.26	3.60
49	9.73	9³⁄₄	7.96	8	.435	⁷⁄₁₆	.290	⁵⁄₁₆	3⁷⁄₈	7³⁄₈	1³⁄₁₆	¹³⁄₁₆	8⁷⁄₈	4.23	3.56
45	10.47	10¹⁄₂	5.81	5³⁄₄	.510	¹⁄₂	.300	⁵⁄₁₆	2³⁄₄	8⁵⁄₈	¹⁵⁄₁₆	¹⁄₂	9¹⁄₂	3.63	3.15
39	10.33	10³⁄₈	5.77	5³⁄₄	.440	⁷⁄₁₆	.260	¹⁄₄	2³⁄₄	8⁵⁄₈	⁷⁄₈	¹⁄₂	9¹⁄₂	3.60	3.12
33	10.17	10¹⁄₈	5.75	5³⁄₄	.360	³⁄₈	.240	¹⁄₄	2³⁄₄	8⁵⁄₈	³⁄₄	¹⁄₂	9¹⁄₂	3.57	3.09
28	10.24	10¹⁄₄	4.02	4	.395	³⁄₈	.250	¹⁄₄	1⁷⁄₈	8⁵⁄₈	¹³⁄₁₆	¹⁄₂	9¹⁄₂	3.00	2.67
25	10.11	10¹⁄₈	4.01	4	.330	⁵⁄₁₆	.240	¹⁄₄	1⁷⁄₈	8⁵⁄₈	³⁄₄	¹⁄₂	9¹⁄₂	2.98	2.65
22	9.99	10	4.00	4	.270	¹⁄₄	.230	¹⁄₄	1⁷⁄₈	8⁵⁄₈	¹¹⁄₁₆	⁷⁄₁₆	9¹⁄₂	2.96	2.63
18	9.87	9⁷⁄₈	3.96	4	.210	³⁄₁₆	.190	³⁄₁₆	1⁷⁄₈	8⁵⁄₈	⁵⁄₈	⁷⁄₁₆	9¹⁄₂	2.93	2.60
100	9.00	9	8.28	8¹⁄₄	.935	¹⁵⁄₁₆	.570	⁹⁄₁₆	3⁷⁄₈	6¹⁄₈	1⁷⁄₁₆	³⁄₄	7¹⁄₈	4.16	3.47
86	8.75	8³⁄₄	8.22	8¹⁄₄	.810	¹³⁄₁₆	.510	¹⁄₂	3⁷⁄₈	6¹⁄₈	1⁵⁄₁₆	³⁄₄	7¹⁄₈	4.11	3.43
71	8.50	8¹⁄₂	8.11	8¹⁄₈	.685	¹¹⁄₁₆	.400	³⁄₈	3⁷⁄₈	6¹⁄₈	1³⁄₁₆	¹¹⁄₁₆	7¹⁄₈	4.05	3.38
59	8.25	8¹⁄₄	8.07	8¹⁄₈	.560	⁹⁄₁₆	.360	³⁄₈	3⁷⁄₈	6¹⁄₈	1¹⁄₁₆	⁵⁄₈	7¹⁄₈	4.00	3.33
52	8.12	8¹⁄₈	8.02	8	.495	¹⁄₂	.310	⁵⁄₁₆	3⁷⁄₈	6¹⁄₈	1	⁵⁄₈	7¹⁄₈	3.97	3.31
46	8.00	8	7.99	8	.435	⁷⁄₁₆	.285	⁵⁄₁₆	3⁷⁄₈	6¹⁄₈	¹⁵⁄₁₆	⁵⁄₈	7¹⁄₈	3.95	3.28
42	8.06	8	6.53	6¹⁄₂	.465	⁷⁄₁₆	.285	⁵⁄₁₆	3¹⁄₈	6¹⁄₈	¹⁵⁄₁₆	⁵⁄₈	7¹⁄₈	3.47	2.93
36	7.93	7⁷⁄₈	6.49	6¹⁄₂	.400	³⁄₈	.245	¹⁄₄	3¹⁄₈	6¹⁄₈	⁷⁄₈	⁹⁄₁₆	7¹⁄₈	3.45	2.90
31	8.28	8¹⁄₄	5.27	5¹⁄₄	.400	³⁄₈	.250	¹⁄₄	2¹⁄₂	6⁵⁄₈	¹³⁄₁₆	¹⁄₂	7¹⁄₂	3.09	2.66
27	8.14	8¹⁄₈	5.25	5¹⁄₄	.330	⁵⁄₁₆	.230	¹⁄₄	2¹⁄₂	6⁵⁄₈	³⁄₄	⁷⁄₁₆	7¹⁄₂	3.07	2.63
22	8.11	8¹⁄₈	4.02	4	.315	⁵⁄₁₆	.245	¹⁄₄	1⁷⁄₈	6⁵⁄₈	³⁄₄	¹⁄₂	7¹⁄₂	2.65	2.31
19	7.99	8	4.00	4	.255	¹⁄₄	.230	¹⁄₄	1⁷⁄₈	6⁵⁄₈	¹¹⁄₁₆	⁷⁄₁₆	7¹⁄₂	2.63	2.29
15	7.89	7⁷⁄₈	3.94	4	.205	³⁄₁₆	.170	³⁄₁₆	1⁷⁄₈	6⁵⁄₈	⁵⁄₈	⁷⁄₁₆	7¹⁄₂	2.60	2.27

W SHAPES
W150 – W100

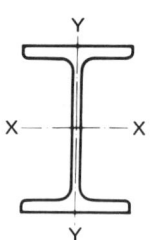

PROPERTIES

Designation[‡]	Nominal Mass	Total Area	Axis X-X				Axis Y-Y				Torsional Constant	Warping Constant
			I_x	S_x	r_x	Z_x	I_y	S_y	r_y	Z_y	J	C_w
	Lb./Ft.	In.^{2}	In.^{4}	In.^{3}	In.	In.^{3}	In.^{4}	In.^{3}	In.	In.^{3}	In.^{4}	In.^{6}
W150												
X37	25	7.34	53.4	16.7	2.70	18.9	17.1	5.62	1.53	8.56	.461	150
X30	20	5.87	41.4	13.4	2.66	14.9	13.3	4.42	1.51	6.72	.240	113
X22	15	4.43	29.1	9.72	2.56	10.8	9.32	3.11	1.45	4.75	.101	76.5
W150												
X24*	16	4.74	32.1	10.2	2.60	11.7	4.43	2.20	.967	3.39	.223	38.2
X18*	12	3.55	22.1	7.33	2.50	8.30	2.99	1.49	.918	2.32	.090	24.7
X14*	9	2.68	16.4	5.56	2.47	6.23	2.19	1.11	.904	1.72	.040	17.7
W130												
X28*	19	5.54	26.2	10.2	2.17	11.6	9.13	3.63	1.28	5.53	.308	50.9
X24*	16	4.68	21.3	8.50	2.13	9.59	7.51	3.00	1.27	4.57	.187	40.6
W100												
X19*	13	3.83	11.3	5.43	1.72	6.28	3.86	1.90	1.00	2.92	.151	14.0

[‡]Nominal depth in millimetres and mass in kilograms per metre.
*Not available from Canadian mills.

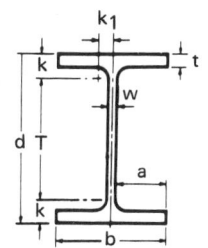

DIMENSIONS AND SURFACE AREAS

Nominal Mass	Depth d		Flange				Web Thickness w		Distances					Surface Area (Ft.²) per foot of length	
			Width b		Thickness t				a	T	k	k_1	d-2t	Total	Minus Top of Top Flange
kg/m	In.	In.	In.	In.	In.	In.	In.	In.	In.	In.	In.	In.	In.		
37	6.38	6⅜	6.08	6⅛	.455	⁷⁄₁₆	.320	⁵⁄₁₆	2⅞	4¾	¹³⁄₁₆	⁷⁄₁₆	5½	3.04	2.53
30	6.20	6¼	6.02	6	.365	⅜	.260	¼	2⅞	4¾	¾	⁷⁄₁₆	5½	3.00	2.49
22	5.99	6	5.99	6	.260	¼	.230	¼	2⅞	4¾	⅝	⅜	5½	2.96	2.46
24	6.28	6¼	4.03	4	.405	⅜	.260	¼	1⅞	4¾	¾	⁷⁄₁₆	5½	2.35	2.01
18	6.03	6	4.00	4	.280	¼	.230	¼	1⅞	4¾	⅝	⅜	5½	2.30	1.97
14	5.90	5⅞	3.94	4	.215	³⁄₁₆	.170	³⁄₁₆	1⅞	4¾	⁹⁄₁₆	⅜	5½	2.27	1.94
28	5.15	5⅛	5.03	5	.430	⁷⁄₁₆	.270	¼	2⅜	3⅝	¾	⁷⁄₁₆	4¼	2.49	2.07
24	5.01	5	5.00	5	.360	⅜	.240	¼	2⅜	3⅝	¹¹⁄₁₆	⅜	4¼	2.46	2.04
19	4.16	4⅛	4.06	4	.345	⅜	.280	¼	1⅞	2¾	¹¹⁄₁₆	⁷⁄₁₆	3½	2.00	1.66

HP SHAPES

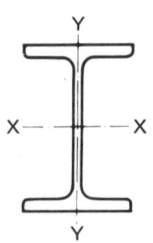

PROPERTIES

Designation‡	Nominal Mass	Total Area	Axis X-X				Axis Y-Y				Torsional Constant	Warping Constant
			I_x	S_x	r_x	Z_x	I_y	S_y	r_y	Z_y	J	C_w
	Lb./Ft.	In.^{2}	In.^{4}	In.^{3}	In.	In.^{3}	In.^{4}	In.^{3}	In.	In.^{3}	In.^{4}	In.^{6}
HP360												
X174*	117	34.4	1220	172	5.96	194	443	59.5	3.59	91.4	8.02	19900
X152*	102	30.0	1050	150	5.92	169	380	51.4	3.56	78.8	5.40	16800
X132*	89	26.1	904	131	5.89	146	326	44.4	3.53	67.7	3.60	14200
X108*	73	21.4	729	107	5.84	118	261	35.8	3.49	54.6	2.01	11200
HP330												
X149*	100	29.4	886	135	5.49	153	294	44.5	3.16	68.6	6.25	11300
X129*	87	25.5	755	117	5.44	131	250	38.2	3.13	58.5	4.12	9430
X109*	73	21.6	630	98.8	5.40	110	207	31.8	3.10	48.8	2.54	7680
X89*	60	17.5	503	80.2	5.36	89.0	165	25.6	3.07	39.0	1.39	6020
HP310												
X174[1]	117	34.4	950	149	5.26	171	331	51.4	3.10	79.6	10.8	11600
X152[1]	102	30.0	811	129	5.20	147	275	43.6	3.03	67.3	7.33	9460
X132[1]	89	25.9	688	1.11	5.15	126	225	36.5	2.95	56.3	4.92	7610
X125*	84	24.6	650	106	5.14	120	213	34.6	2.94	53.2	4.24	7160
X110	74	21.8	569	93.8	5.11	105	186	30.5	2.92	46.6	2.98	6170
X94	63	18.4	472	79.1	5.06	88.3	153	25.2	2.88	38.7	1.83	4990
X79	53	15.5	393	66.7	5.04	74.0	127	21.1	2.86	32.2	1.12	4090
HP250												
X85	57	16.8	294	58.9	4.18	66.5	101	19.8	2.45	30.3	1.97	2240
X62	42	12.4	210	43.3	4.12	48.3	71.7	14.2	2.40	21.8	.813	1540
HP200												
X54	36	10.6	119	29.7	3.35	33.6	40.3	9.88	1.95	15.2	.770	578

‡Nominal depth in millimetres and mass in kilograms per metre.
*Not available from Canadian mills.

[1] Produced exclusively by Algoma Steel.

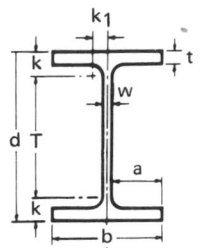

Nominal Mass	Depth d		Flange Width b		Flange Thickness t		Web Thickness w		Distances					Surface Area (Ft.²) per foot of length	
									a	T	k	k_1	d-2t	Total	Minus Top of Top Flange
kg/m	In.	In.	In.	In.	In.	In.	In.	In.	In.	In.	In.	In.	In.		
174	14.21	$14\frac{1}{4}$	14.89	$14\frac{7}{8}$	.805	$^{13}/_{16}$	.805	$^{13}/_{16}$	7	$11\frac{1}{4}$	$1\frac{1}{2}$	$1\frac{1}{16}$	$12\frac{5}{8}$	7.20	5.96
152	14.01	14	14.78	$14\frac{3}{4}$	.705	$^{11}/_{16}$	.705	$^{11}/_{16}$	7	$11\frac{1}{4}$	$1\frac{3}{8}$	1	$12\frac{5}{8}$	7.15	5.91
132	13.83	$13\frac{7}{8}$	14.69	$14\frac{3}{4}$	.615	$\frac{5}{8}$	.615	$\frac{5}{8}$	7	$11\frac{1}{4}$	$1\frac{5}{16}$	$^{15}/_{16}$	$12\frac{5}{8}$	7.10	5.88
108	13.61	$13\frac{5}{8}$	14.59	$14\frac{5}{8}$	.505	$\frac{1}{2}$	.505	$\frac{1}{2}$	7	$11\frac{1}{4}$	$1\frac{3}{16}$	$\frac{7}{8}$	$12\frac{5}{8}$	7.05	5.83
149	13.15	$13\frac{1}{8}$	13.20	$13\frac{1}{4}$	.765	$\frac{3}{4}$	.765	$\frac{3}{4}$	$6\frac{1}{4}$	$10\frac{1}{4}$	$1\frac{7}{16}$	$1\frac{1}{16}$	$11\frac{5}{8}$	6.47	5.37
129	12.95	13	13.10	$13\frac{1}{8}$	.665	$^{11}/_{16}$	.665	$^{11}/_{16}$	$6\frac{1}{4}$	$10\frac{1}{4}$	$1\frac{3}{8}$	1	$11\frac{5}{8}$	6.42	5.32
109	12.75	$12\frac{3}{4}$	13.01	13	.565	$\frac{9}{16}$	.565	$\frac{9}{16}$	$6\frac{1}{4}$	$10\frac{1}{4}$	$1\frac{1}{4}$	$^{15}/_{16}$	$11\frac{5}{8}$	6.37	5.28
89	12.54	$12\frac{1}{2}$	12.90	$12\frac{7}{8}$	.460	$\frac{7}{16}$	.460	$\frac{7}{16}$	$6\frac{1}{4}$	$10\frac{1}{4}$	$1\frac{1}{8}$	$\frac{7}{8}$	$11\frac{5}{8}$	6.31	5.24
174	12.77	$12\frac{3}{4}$	12.87	$12\frac{7}{8}$	.930	$^{15}/_{16}$	.930	$^{15}/_{16}$	6	$9\frac{1}{2}$	$1\frac{5}{8}$	$1\frac{1}{8}$	$10\frac{7}{8}$	6.26	5.19
152	12.55	$12\frac{1}{2}$	12.62	$12\frac{5}{8}$	.820	$^{13}/_{16}$	.820	$^{13}/_{16}$	$5\frac{7}{8}$	$9\frac{1}{2}$	$1\frac{1}{2}$	$1\frac{1}{16}$	$10\frac{7}{8}$	6.16	5.11
132	12.35	$12\frac{3}{8}$	12.33	$12\frac{3}{8}$	.720	$\frac{3}{4}$	.720	$\frac{3}{4}$	$5\frac{3}{4}$	$9\frac{1}{2}$	$1\frac{7}{16}$	1	$10\frac{7}{8}$	6.05	5.02
125	12.28	$12\frac{1}{4}$	12.30	$12\frac{1}{4}$	.685	$^{11}/_{16}$	.685	$^{11}/_{16}$	$5\frac{3}{4}$	$9\frac{1}{2}$	$1\frac{3}{8}$	1	$10\frac{7}{8}$	6.03	5.01
110	12.13	$12\frac{1}{8}$	12.22	$12\frac{1}{4}$	.605	$\frac{5}{8}$	.605	$\frac{5}{8}$	$5\frac{3}{4}$	$9\frac{1}{2}$	$1\frac{5}{16}$	$^{15}/_{16}$	$10\frac{7}{8}$	5.99	4.97
94	11.94	12	12.13	$12\frac{1}{8}$	.515	$\frac{1}{2}$	.515	$\frac{1}{2}$	$5\frac{3}{4}$	$9\frac{1}{2}$	$1\frac{1}{4}$	$^{15}/_{16}$	$10\frac{7}{8}$	5.95	4.94
79	11.78	$11\frac{3}{4}$	12.05	12	.435	$\frac{7}{16}$	.435	$\frac{7}{16}$	$5\frac{3}{4}$	$9\frac{1}{2}$	$1\frac{1}{8}$	$\frac{7}{8}$	$10\frac{7}{8}$	5.91	4.90
85	9.99	10	10.23	$10\frac{1}{4}$	.565	$\frac{9}{16}$	.565	$\frac{9}{16}$	$4\frac{7}{8}$	$7\frac{7}{8}$	$1\frac{5}{16}$	$^{15}/_{16}$	$8\frac{7}{8}$	4.98	4.13
62	9.70	$9\frac{3}{4}$	10.07	$10\frac{1}{8}$	.420	$\frac{7}{16}$	.415	$\frac{7}{16}$	$4\frac{7}{8}$	$7\frac{7}{8}$	$1\frac{3}{16}$	$\frac{7}{8}$	$8\frac{7}{8}$	4.91	4.07
54	8.02	8	8.15	$8\frac{1}{8}$	.445	$\frac{7}{16}$	.445	$\frac{7}{16}$	$3\frac{7}{8}$	$6\frac{1}{8}$	$^{15}/_{16}$	$^{11}/_{16}$	$7\frac{1}{8}$	3.98	3.30

IMP

M SHAPES

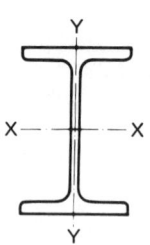

PROPERTIES

Designation#	Nominal Mass	Total Area	Axis X-X				Axis Y-Y				Torsional Constant	Warping Constant
			I_x	S_x	r_x	Z_x	I_y	S_y	r_y	Z_y	J	C_W
	Lb./Ft.	In.^{2}	In.^{4}	In.^{3}	In.	In.^{3}	In.^{4}	In.^{3}	In.	In.^{3}	In.^{4}	In.^{6}
M310 X17.6*	11.8	3.47	71.9	12.0	4.55	14.3	.979	.639	.531	1.08	.053	33.9
M250 X13.4*	9	2.65	38.8	7.76	3.83	9.19	.608	.452	.479	.760	.033	14.6
M200 X9.7*	6.5	1.91	18.5	4.62	3.11	5.42	.343	.301	.424	.499	.019	5.23
M150 X29.8*	20	5.88	38.9	13.0	2.57	14.5	11.7	3.94	1.41	6.26	.291	92.4
M150 X6.5*	4.4	1.29	7.2	2.40	2.36	2.79	.166	.180	.359	.295	.010	1.41
M130 X28.1*	18.9	5.55	24.1	9.64	2.08	11.0	7.95	3.18	1.20	5.03	.339	41.8
M100 X19	13	3.82	10.5	5.25	1.66	6.07	3.40	1.72	.943	2.74	.189	11.2

#For sections available from Canadian mills, the nominal mass has been rounded to the nearest kg/m.
Designation consists of nominal depth in millimetres by nominal mass in kilograms per metre.
* Not available from Canadian mills.

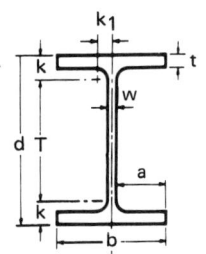

M SHAPES

Nominal Mass	Depth d		Flange				Web Thickness w		Distances				Surface Area (Ft.^{2}) per foot of length	
			Width b		Thickness t				a	T	k	k_1	Total	Minus Top of Top Flange
kg/m	In.	In.	In.	In.	In.	In.	In.	In.	In.	In.	In.	In.		
17.6	12.00	12	3.06	3 1/8	.225	1/4	.177	3/16	1 1/2	10 7/8	9/16	5/16	2.99	2.74
13.4	10.00	10	2.69	2 3/4	.206	3/16	.157	3/16	1 1/4	9	1/2	5/16	2.54	2.31
9.7	8.00	8	2.28	2 1/4	.189	3/16	.135	1/8	1 1/8	7 1/8	7/16	1/4	2.07	1.88
29.8	6.00	6	5.94	6	.379	3/8	.250	1/4	2 7/8	4 3/8	13/16	7/16	2.94	2.44
6.5	6.00	6	1.84	1 7/8	.171	3/16	.114	1/8	7/8	5 1/4	3/8	3/16	1.60	1.44
28.1	5.00	5	5.00	5	.416	7/16	.316	5/16	2 3/8	3 1/4	7/8	7/16	2.45	2.03
19	4.00	4	3.94	4	.371	3/8	.254	1/4	1 7/8	2 3/8	13/16	7/16	1.94	1.61

IMP

S SHAPES
S610 – S180

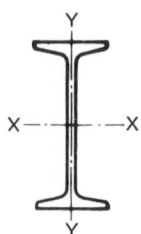

PROPERTIES

Designation#	Nominal Mass	Total Area	Axis X-X				Axis Y-Y				Torsional Constant	Warping Constant
			I_x	S_x	r_x	Z_x	I_y	S_y	r_y	Z_y	J	C_w
	Lb./Ft.	In.^{2}	In.^{4}	In.^{3}	In.	In.^{3}	In.^{4}	In.^{3}	In.	In.^{3}	In.^{4}	In.^{6}
S610												
X180*	121	35.6	3160	258	9.42	307	83.9	20.9	1.54	36.2	12.8	11500
X158*	106	31.2	2940	240	9.71	280	77.7	19.7	1.58	33.2	10.1	10600
S610												
X149*	100	29.4	2390	199	9.02	240	48.2	13.3	1.28	23.9	7.58	6450
X134*	90	26.5	2250	188	9.21	223	45.4	12.8	1.31	22.3	6.04	6070
X119*	80	23.5	2110	176	9.48	205	42.8	12.2	1.35	20.7	4.88	5720
S510												
X143*	96	28.3	1680	166	7.70	199	50.6	14.1	1.34	24.9	8.56	4750
X128*	86	25.4	1580	156	7.89	184	47.3	13.4	1.36	23.0	6.78	4440
S510												
X112*	75	22.0	1280	128	7.63	153	30.2	9.46	1.17	16.7	4.59	2780
X98*	66	19.4	1190	119	7.83	140	28.1	8.99	1.20	15.4	3.58	2590
S460												
X104*	70	20.6	928	103	6.71	125	24.5	7.83	1.09	14.4	4.15	1840
X81.4*	54.7	16.1	807	89.7	7.08	105	21.2	7.05	1.15	12.1	2.37	1590
S380												
X74*	50	14.7	487	64.9	5.76	77.3	15.9	5.65	1.04	9.98	2.12	822
X64*	42.9	12.6	448	59.7	5.96	69.5	14.6	5.31	1.08	9.04	1.54	755
S310												
X74*	50	14.7	306	51.0	4.56	61.3	15.9	5.82	1.04	10.3	2.82	511
X60.7*	40.8	12.0	273	45.5	4.77	53.2	13.8	5.25	1.07	8.85	1.75	444
S310												
X52	35	10.3	230	38.3	4.73	44.9	10.0	3.94	.985	6.79	1.08	328
X47	31.8	9.37	219	36.5	4.83	42.1	9.49	3.79	1.01	6.41	.900	311
S250												
X52	35	10.3	147	29.4	3.78	35.5	8.45	3.42	.906	6.20	1.29	191
X38	25.4	7.47	124	24.8	4.07	28.4	6.88	2.95	.960	4.96	.603	156
S200												
X34	23	6.77	64.9	16.2	3.10	19.3	4.35	2.09	.802	3.67	.550	62.4
X27	18.4	5.41	57.7	14.4	3.27	16.6	3.77	1.89	.835	3.16	.335	54.1
S180												
X30*	20	5.89	42.5	12.1	2.69	14.5	3.20	1.66	.737	2.95	.451	34.9
X22.8*	15.3	4.50	36.8	10.5	2.86	12.1	2.67	1.46	.770	2.44	.241	29.1

#For sections available from Canadian mills, the nominal mass has been rounded to the nearest kg/m.
 Designation consists of nominal depth in millimetres by nominal mass in kilograms per metre.
*Not available from Canadian mills.

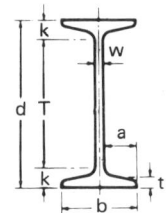

DIMENSIONS AND SURFACE AREAS

Nominal Mass	Depth d		Flange				Web Thickness w		Distances					Surface Area (Ft.²) per foot of length	
			Width b		Thickness t							a	T	k	Total	Minus Top of Top Flange
kg/m	In.	In.	In.	In.	In.	In.	In.	In.			In.	In.	In.		
180	24.50	24½	8.05	8	1.09	1¹/₁₆	.800	¹³/₁₆			3⅝	20⅝	1¹⁵/₁₆	6.63	5.96
158	24.50	24½	7.87	7⅞	1.09	1¹/₁₆	.620	⅝			3⅝	20⅝	1¹⁵/₁₆	6.60	5.95
149	24.00	24	7.24	7¼	.870	⅞	.745	¾			3¼	20⅝	1¹¹/₁₆	6.29	5.69
134	24.00	24	7.13	7⅛	.870	⅞	.625	⅝			3¼	20⅝	1¹¹/₁₆	6.27	5.68
119	24.00	24	7.00	7	.870	⅞	.500	½			3¼	20⅝	1¹¹/₁₆	6.25	5.67
143	20.30	20¼	7.20	7¼	.920	¹⁵/₁₆	.800	¹³/₁₆			3¼	16⅝	1¹³/₁₆	5.65	5.05
128	20.30	20¼	7.06	7	.920	¹⁵/₁₆	.660	¹¹/₁₆			3¼	16⅝	1¹³/₁₆	5.63	5.04
112	20.00	20	6.39	6⅜	.795	¹³/₁₆	.635	⅝			2⅞	16¾	1⅝	5.36	4.82
98	20.00	20	6.26	6¼	.795	¹³/₁₆	.505	½			2⅞	16¾	1⅝	5.33	4.81
104	18.00	18	6.25	6¼	.691	¹¹/₁₆	.711	¹¹/₁₆			2¾	15⅛	1⁷/₁₆	4.97	4.44
81.4	18.00	18	6.00	6	.691	¹¹/₁₆	.461	⁷/₁₆			2¾	15⅛	1⁷/₁₆	4.92	4.42
74	15.00	15	5.64	5⅝	.622	⅝	.550	⁹/₁₆			2½	12⅜	1⁵/₁₆	4.29	3.82
64	15.00	15	5.50	5½	.622	⅝	.411	⁷/₁₆			2½	12⅜	1⁵/₁₆	4.27	3.81
74	12.00	12	5.48	5½	.659	¹¹/₁₆	.687	¹¹/₁₆			2⅜	9¼	1⅜	3.71	3.25
60.7	12.00	12	5.25	5¼	.659	¹¹/₁₆	.462	⁷/₁₆			2⅜	9¼	1⅜	3.67	3.24
52	12.00	12	5.08	5⅛	.544	⁹/₁₆	.428	⁷/₁₆			2⅜	9⅝	1³/₁₆	3.62	3.20
47	12.00	12	5.00	5	.544	⁹/₁₆	.350	⅜			2⅜	9⅝	1³/₁₆	3.61	3.19
52	10.00	10	4.94	5	.491	½	.594	⅝			2⅛	7⅞	1¹/₁₆	3.22	2.80
38	10.00	10	4.66	4⅝	.491	½	.311	⁵/₁₆			2⅛	7⅞	1¹/₁₆	3.17	2.78
34	8.00	8	4.17	4⅛	.425	⁷/₁₆	.441	⁷/₁₆			1⅞	6⅛	¹⁵/₁₆	2.65	2.30
27	8.00	8	4.00	4	.425	⁷/₁₆	.271	¼			1⅞	6⅛	¹⁵/₁₆	2.62	2.29
30	7.00	7	3.86	3⅞	.392	⅜	.450	⁷/₁₆			1¾	5¼	⅞	2.38	2.06
22.8	7.00	7	3.66	3⅝	.392	⅜	.252	¼			1¾	5¼	⅞	2.35	2.04

S SHAPES
S150 – S75

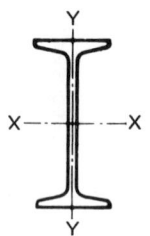

PROPERTIES

Designation #	Nominal Mass	Total Area	Axis X-X				Axis Y-Y				Torsional Constant	Warping Constant
			I_x	S_x	r_x	Z_x	I_y	S_y	r_y	Z_y	J	C_w
	Lb./Ft.	In.^{2}	In.^{4}	In.^{3}	In.	In.^{3}	In.^{4}	In.^{3}	In.	In.^{3}	In.^{4}	In.^{6}
S150												
X26	17.25	5.07	26.4	8.80	2.28	10.6	2.33	1.31	.678	2.35	.374	18.5
X19	12.5	3.67	22.2	7.40	2.46	8.49	1.85	1.11	.710	1.85	.168	14.7
S130												
X22	14.75	4.34	15.2	6.08	1.87	7.43	1.68	1.02	.622	1.86	.323	9.18
X15	10	2.94	12.3	4.92	2.05	5.68	1.23	.819	.647	1.36	.114	6.72
S100												
X14.1*	9.5	2.80	6.8	3.40	1.56	4.05	.911	.651	.570	1.12	.120	3.13
X11	7.7	2.26	6.1	3.04	1.64	3.51	.772	.580	.584	.961	.073	2.65
S75												
X11	7.5	2.21	2.9	1.95	1.15	2.36	.591	.471	.517	.817	.091	1.11
X8	5.7	1.67	2.5	1.69	1.23	1.96	.460	.395	.525	.649	.044	.863

For sections available from Canadian mills, the nominal mass has been rounded to the nearest kg/m.
 Designation consists of nominal depth in millimetres by nominal mass in kilograms per metre.
* Not available from Canadian mills.

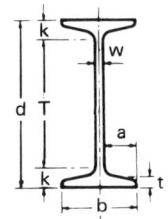

DIMENSIONS AND SURFACE AREAS

Nominal Mass	Depth d		Flange				Web Thickness w		Distances				Surface Area (Ft.^{2}) per foot of length	
			Width b		Thickness t				a	T	k			Minus Top of Top Flange
kg/m	In.	In.	In.	In.	In.	In.	In.	In.	In.	In.	In.		Total	
26	6.00	6	3.56	3⅝	.359	⅜	.465	⁷/₁₆	1½	4⅜	¹³/₁₆		2.11	1.81
19	6.00	6	3.33	3⅜	.359	⅜	.232	¼	1½	4⅜	¹³/₁₆		2.07	1.79
22	5.00	5	3.28	3¼	.326	⁵/₁₆	.494	½	1⅜	3½	¾		1.85	1.57
15	5.00	5	3.00	3	.326	⁵/₁₆	.214	³/₁₆	1⅜	3½	¾		1.80	1.55
14.1	4.00	4	2.80	2¾	.293	⁵/₁₆	.326	⁵/₁₆	1¼	2⅝	¹¹/₁₆		1.54	1.31
11	4.00	4	2.66	2⅝	.293	⁵/₁₆	.193	³/₁₆	1¼	2⅝	¹¹/₁₆		1.52	1.30
11	3.00	3	2.51	2½	.260	¼	.349	⅜	1⅛	1¾	⅝		1.28	1.07
8	3.00	3	2.33	2⅜	.260	¼	.170	³/₁₆	1⅛	1¾	⅝		1.25	1.05

STANDARD CHANNELS (C SHAPES)

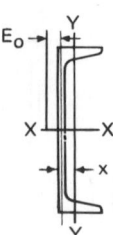

PROPERTIES

Designation#	Nominal Mass	Total Area	Axis X-X			Axis Y-Y				Shear Centre	Torsional Constant	Warping Constant
			I_x	S_x	r_x	I_y	S_y	r_y	x	E_o	J	C_W
	Lb./Ft.	In.^{2}	In.^{4}	In.^{3}	In.	In.^{4}	In.^{3}	In.	In.	In.	In.^{4}	In.^{6}
C380												
X74	50	14.7	404	53.9	5.24	11.2	3.84	.873	.802	.941	2.67	492
X60	40	11.8	349	46.5	5.44	9.35	3.41	.890	.782	1.03	1.46	411
X50	33.9	9.97	315	42.0	5.62	8.24	3.16	.909	.792	1.10	1.02	358
C310												
X45	30	8.82	162	27.0	4.29	5.18	2.08	.766	.676	.873	.870	151
X37	25	7.35	144	24.0	4.43	4.51	1.90	.783	.676	.939	.544	130
X31	20.7	6.09	129	21.5	4.60	3.92	1.75	.802	.700	1.01	.372	112
C250												
X45*	30	8.82	103	20.6	3.42	3.97	1.67	.671	.650	.705	1.23	79.3
X37	25	7.35	91.2	18.2	3.52	3.38	1.49	.678	.619	.757	.694	68.4
X30	20	5.88	79.0	15.8	3.67	2.83	1.33	.694	.608	.826	.372	57.0
X23	15.3	4.49	67.4	13.5	3.87	2.30	1.17	.716	.636	.916	.211	45.6
C230												
X30	20	5.88	61.0	13.6	3.22	2.44	1.18	.644	.584	.739	.431	39.5
X22	15	4.41	51.1	11.4	3.40	1.94	1.03	.663	.589	.824	.210	31.1
X20	13.4	3.94	47.9	10.6	3.49	1.78	.972	.672	.603	.859	.170	28.2
C200												
X28	18.75	5.51	44.0	11.0	2.83	2.00	1.02	.602	.567	.674	.439	25.1
X21	13.75	4.04	36.2	9.05	2.99	1.54	.863	.617	.556	.756	.188	19.3
X17	11.5	3.38	32.6	8.15	3.11	1.33	.790	.627	.574	.807	.131	16.5
C180												
X22*	14.75	4.33	27.3	7.80	2.51	1.39	.787	.567	.533	.651	.270	13.2
X18	12.25	3.60	24.3	6.94	2.60	1.18	.710	.573	.527	.695	.162	11.2
X15	9.8	2.87	21.3	6.09	2.72	.978	.632	.584	.543	.752	.101	9.18
C150												
X19	13	3.83	17.4	5.80	2.13	1.06	.648	.526	.516	.598	.243	7.22
X16	10.5	3.09	15.2	5.07	2.22	.874	.570	.532	.501	.643	.132	5.95
X12	8.2	2.40	13.1	4.37	2.34	.700	.498	.540	.514	.699	.076	4.72
C130												
X17	11.5	3.38	10.4	4.16	1.75	.815	.535	.491	.506	.547	.233	3.69
X13	9	2.65	8.9	3.56	1.83	.639	.455	.491	.480	.590	.111	2.94
X10	6.7	1.97	7.5	3.00	1.95	.484	.383	.496	.486	.647	.056	2.23
C100												
X11	7.25	2.13	4.6	2.29	1.47	.437	.347	.453	.461	.546	.083	1.24
X9	6.25	1.84	4.2	2.10	1.51	.377	.316	.453	.456	.571	.056	1.08
X8	5.4	1.59	3.9	1.93	1.56	.323	.287	.451	.460	.593	.040	.925
C75												
X9	6	1.76	2.1	1.39	1.09	.309	.271	.419	.457	.500	.074	.464
X7	5	1.47	1.9	1.24	1.12	.250	.236	.412	.440	.521	.043	.382
X6	4.1	1.21	1.7	1.11	1.17	.199	.205	.406	.439	.546	.027	.309

#For sections available from Canadian mills, the nominal mass has been rounded to the nearest kg/m.
  Designation consists of nominal depth in millimetres by nominal mass in kilograms per metre.
* Not available from Canadian mills.

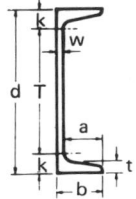

STANDARD CHANNELS (C SHAPES)

DIMENSIONS AND SURFACE AREAS

Nominal Mass	Depth d		Flange Width b		Flange Thickness t		Web Thickness w		Distances a	T	k	Surface Area (Ft.²) per foot of length Total	Minus Top of Top Flange
kg/m	In.	In.	In.	In.	In.	In.	In.	In.	In.	In.	In.		
74	15.00	15	3.72	3¾	.650	⅝	.716	¹¹/₁₆	3	12¼	1⅜	3.62	3.31
60	15.00	15	3.52	3½	.650	⅝	.520	½	3	12¼	1⅜	3.59	3.29
50	15.00	15	3.40	3⅜	.650	⅝	.400	⅜	3	12¼	1⅜	3.57	3.28
45	12.00	12	3.17	3⅛	.501	½	.510	½	2⅝	9¾	1⅛	2.97	2.71
37	12.00	12	3.05	3	.501	½	.387	⅜	2⅝	9¾	1⅛	2.95	2.70
31	12.00	12	2.94	3	.501	½	.282	⁵/₁₆	2⅝	9¾	1⅛	2.93	2.69
45	10.00	10	3.03	3	.436	⁷/₁₆	.673	¹¹/₁₆	2⅜	8	1	2.57	2.31
37	10.00	10	2.89	2⅞	.436	⁷/₁₆	.526	½	2⅜	8	1	2.54	2.30
30	10.00	10	2.74	2¾	.436	⁷/₁₆	.379	⅜	2⅜	8	1	2.52	2.29
23	10.00	10	2.60	2⅝	.436	⁷/₁₆	.240	¼	2⅜	8	1	2.49	2.28
30	9.00	9	2.65	2⅝	.413	⁷/₁₆	.448	⁷/₁₆	2¼	7⅛	¹⁵/₁₆	2.31	2.09
22	9.00	9	2.48	2½	.413	⁷/₁₆	.285	⁵/₁₆	2¼	7⅛	¹⁵/₁₆	2.28	2.07
20	9.00	9	2.43	2⅜	.413	⁷/₁₆	.233	¼	2¼	7⅛	¹⁵/₁₆	2.27	2.07
28	8.00	8	2.53	2½	.390	⅜	.487	½	2	6¼	⅞	2.09	1.88
21	8.00	8	2.34	2⅜	.390	⅜	.303	⁵/₁₆	2	6¼	⅞	2.06	1.87
17	8.00	8	2.26	2¼	.390	⅜	.220	¼	2	6¼	⅞	2.05	1.86
22	7.00	7	2.30	2¼	.366	⅜	.419	⁷/₁₆	1⅞	5⅜	¹³/₁₆	1.86	1.67
18	7.00	7	2.19	2¼	.366	⅜	.314	⁵/₁₆	1⅞	5⅜	¹³/₁₆	1.85	1.66
15	7.00	7	2.09	2⅛	.366	⅜	.210	³/₁₆	1⅞	5⅜	¹³/₁₆	1.83	1.65
19	6.00	6	2.16	2⅛	.343	⁵/₁₆	.437	⁷/₁₆	1¾	4⅜	¹³/₁₆	1.65	1.47
16	6.00	6	2.03	2	.343	⁵/₁₆	.314	⁵/₁₆	1¾	4⅜	¹³/₁₆	1.63	1.46
12	6.00	6	1.92	1⅞	.343	⁵/₁₆	.200	³/₁₆	1¾	4⅜	¹³/₁₆	1.61	1.45
17	5.00	5	2.03	2	.320	⁵/₁₆	.472	½	1½	3½	¾	1.43	1.26
13	5.00	5	1.89	1⅞	.320	⁵/₁₆	.325	⁵/₁₆	1½	3½	¾	1.41	1.25
10	5.00	5	1.75	1¾	.320	⁵/₁₆	.190	³/₁₆	1½	3½	¾	1.38	1.24
11	4.00	4	1.72	1¾	.296	⁵/₁₆	.321	⁵/₁₆	1⅜	2⅝	¹¹/₁₆	1.19	1.04
9	4.00	4	1.65	1⅝	.296	⁵/₁₆	.247	¼	1⅜	2⅝	¹¹/₁₆	1.18	1.04
8	4.00	4	1.58	1⅝	.296	⁵/₁₆	.184	³/₁₆	1⅜	2⅝	¹¹/₁₆	1.16	1.03
9	3.00	3	1.60	1⅝	.273	¼	.356	⅜	1¼	1⅝	¹¹/₁₆	.97	.84
7	3.00	3	1.50	1½	.273	¼	.258	¼	1¼	1⅝	¹¹/₁₆	.96	.83
6	3.00	3	1.41	1⅜	.273	¼	.170	³/₁₆	1¼	1⅝	¹¹/₁₆	.94	.82

MISCELLANEOUS CHANNELS
MC460 – MC200

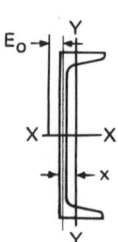

PROPERTIES

Designation #	Nominal Mass	Total Area	Axis X-X			Axis Y-Y				Shear Centre	Torsional Constant	Warping Constant
			I_x	S_x	r_x	I_y	S_y	r_y	x	E_o	J	C_W
	Lb./Ft.	In.²	In.⁴	In.³	In.	In.⁴	In.³	In.	In.	In.	In.⁴	In.⁶
MC460												
X86*	58	17.1	679	75.4	6.30	17.7	5.31	1.02	.861	1.04	2.86	1070
X77.2*	51.9	15.3	631	70.1	6.42	16.4	5.06	1.04	.857	1.10	2.07	990
X68.2*	45.8	13.5	582	64.7	6.57	15.1	4.81	1.06	.864	1.16	1.49	903
X63.5*	42.7	12.6	558	62.0	6.65	14.4	4.68	1.07	.874	1.19	1.26	858
MC330												
X74*	50	14.7	315	48.5	4.63	16.6	4.85	1.06	.978	1.21	2.98	559
X60*	40	11.8	273	42.0	4.81	13.9	4.31	1.09	.968	1.31	1.57	463
X52*	35	10.3	253	38.9	4.96	12.5	4.04	1.10	.985	1.38	1.14	414
X47.3*	31.8	9.36	239	36.8	5.05	11.6	3.86	1.11	1.01	1.43	.944	380
MC310												
X74*	50	14.7	270	45.0	4.29	17.4	5.64	1.09	1.05	1.16	3.27	412
X67*	45	13.2	252	42.0	4.37	15.8	5.30	1.09	1.03	1.20	2.36	374
X60*	40	11.8	235	39.2	4.46	14.2	4.99	1.10	1.03	1.25	1.72	337
X52*	35	10.3	217	36.2	4.59	12.6	4.65	1.11	1.05	1.30	1.26	298
X46*	31	9.15	203	33.8	4.71	11.3	4.38	1.11	1.08	1.36	1.02	268
MC310												
X15.8*	10.6	3.11	55.5	9.25	4.22	.388	.316	.353	.271	.379	.060	11.7
MC250												
X61.2*	41.1	12.1	159	31.8	3.62	16.1	4.98	1.15	1.09	1.26	2.29	271
X50*	33.6	9.93	140	28.0	3.75	13.4	4.47	1.16	1.09	1.35	1.22	226
X42.4*	28.5	8.43	128	25.6	3.90	11.6	4.11	1.17	1.12	1.43	.807	196
MC250												
X37*	25	7.37	111	22.2	3.88	7.40	3.02	1.00	.953	1.22	.642	126
X33*	22	6.47	103	20.6	3.99	6.55	2.82	1.01	.990	1.27	.513	111
MC250												
X12.5*	8.4	2.46	32.1	6.42	3.61	.335	.276	.369	.286	.417	.042	7.03
MC250												
X9.7*	6.5	1.92	22.2	4.44	3.40	.110	.116	.239	.178	.242	.019	2.46
MC230												
X37.8*	25.4	7.51	88.7	19.7	3.44	7.66	3.02	1.01	.967	1.21	.715	105
X35.6*	23.9	7.06	85.7	19.0	3.48	7.23	2.93	1.01	.977	1.24	.620	99.3
MC200												
X33.9*	22.8	6.74	64.4	16.1	3.09	7.08	2.84	1.02	1.01	1.26	.591	76.2
X31.8*	21.4	6.33	62.1	15.5	3.13	6.65	2.74	1.02	1.02	1.28	.512	71.7
MC200												
X29.8*	20	5.91	55.0	13.7	3.05	4.50	2.06	.873	.840	1.04	.455	48.5
X27.8*	18.7	5.54	53.0	13.2	3.09	4.23	1.99	.874	.849	1.07	.393	45.6
MC200												
X12.6*	8.5	2.50	23.3	5.82	3.05	.636	.441	.504	.431	.631	.059	8.22

#For sections available from Canadian mills, the nominal mass has been rounded to the nearest kg/m.
 Designation consists of nominal depth in millimetres by nominal mass in kilograms per metre.
* Not available from Canadian mills.

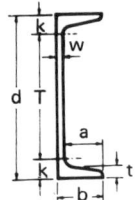

DIMENSIONS AND SURFACE AREAS

Nominal Mass	Depth d		Flange Width b		Flange Thickness t		Web Thickness w		Distances a	Distances T	Distances k	Surface Area (Ft.²) per foot of length Total	Surface Area (Ft.²) per foot of length Minus Top of Top Flange
kg/m	In.	In.	In.	In.	In.	In.	In.	In.	In.	In.	In.		
86	18.00	18	4.20	4¼	.625	⅝	.700	¹¹/₁₆	3½	15¼	1⅜	4.28	3.93
77.2	18.00	18	4.10	4⅛	.625	⅝	.600	⅝	3½	15¼	1⅜	4.27	3.92
68.2	18.00	18	4.00	4	.625	⅝	.500	½	3½	15¼	1⅜	4.25	3.92
63.5	18.00	18	3.95	4	.625	⅝	.450	⁷/₁₆	3½	15¼	1⅜	4.24	3.91
74	13.00	13	4.41	4⅜	.610	⅝	.787	¹³/₁₆	3⅝	10¼	1⅜	3.51	3.14
60	13.00	13	4.19	4⅛	.610	⅝	.560	⁹/₁₆	3⅝	10¼	1⅜	3.47	3.12
52	13.00	13	4.07	4⅛	.610	⅝	.447	⁷/₁₆	3⅝	10¼	1⅜	3.45	3.11
47.3	13.00	13	4.00	4	.610	⅝	.375	⅜	3⅝	10¼	1⅜	3.44	3.10
74	12.00	12	4.14	4⅛	.700	¹¹/₁₆	.835	¹³/₁₆	3¼	9⅜	1⁵/₁₆	3.24	2.89
67	12.00	12	4.01	4	.700	¹¹/₁₆	.710	¹¹/₁₆	3¼	9⅜	1⁵/₁₆	3.22	2.88
60	12.00	12	3.89	3⅞	.700	¹¹/₁₆	.590	⁹/₁₆	3¼	9⅜	1⁵/₁₆	3.20	2.87
52	12.00	12	3.77	3¾	.700	¹¹/₁₆	.465	⁷/₁₆	3¼	9⅜	1⁵/₁₆	3.18	2.86
46	12.00	12	3.67	3⅝	.700	¹¹/₁₆	.370	⅜	3¼	9⅜	1⁵/₁₆	3.16	2.86
15.8	12.00	12	1.50	1½	.309	⁵/₁₆	.190	³/₁₆	1¼	10⅝	¹¹/₁₆	2.47	2.34
61.2	10.00	10	4.32	4⅜	.575	⁹/₁₆	.796	¹³/₁₆	3½	7½	1¼	2.97	2.61
50	10.00	10	4.10	4⅛	.575	⁹/₁₆	.575	⁹/₁₆	3½	7½	1¼	2.94	2.60
42.4	10.00	10	3.95	4	.575	⁹/₁₆	.425	⁷/₁₆	3½	7½	1¼	2.91	2.58
37	10.00	10	3.40	3⅜	.575	⁹/₁₆	.380	⅜	3	7⅝	1³/₁₆	2.74	2.45
33	10.00	10	3.31	3⅜	.575	⁹/₁₆	.290	⁵/₁₆	3	7⅝	1³/₁₆	2.72	2.45
12.5	10.00	10	1.50	1½	.280	¼	.170	³/₁₆	1⅜	8⅝	¹¹/₁₆	2.14	2.01
9.7	10.00	10	1.13	1⅛	.202	³/₁₆	.152	⅛	1	9⅛	⁷/₁₆	2.02	1.92
37.8	9.00	9	3.50	3½	.550	⁹/₁₆	.450	⁷/₁₆	3	6½	1¼	2.59	2.30
35.6	9.00	9	3.45	3½	.550	⁹/₁₆	.400	⅜	3	6½	1¼	2.58	2.30
33.9	8.00	8	3.50	3½	.525	½	.427	⁷/₁₆	3⅛	5⅝	1³/₁₆	2.43	2.14
31.8	8.00	8	3.45	3½	.525	½	.375	⅜	3⅛	5⅝	1³/₁₆	2.42	2.13
29.8	8.00	8	3.02	3	.500	½	.400	⅜	2⅝	5¾	1⅛	2.27	2.02
27.8	8.00	8	2.98	3	.500	½	.353	⅜	2⅝	5¾	1⅛	2.27	2.02
12.6	8.00	8	1.87	1⅞	.311	⁵/₁₆	.179	³/₁₆	1¾	6½	¾	1.93	1.77

MISCELLANEOUS CHANNELS
MC180 – MC150

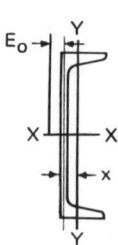

PROPERTIES

Designation #	Nominal Mass	Total Area	Axis X-X			Axis Y-Y				Shear Centre	Torsional Constant	Warping Constant
			I_x	S_x	r_x	I_y	S_y	r_y	x	E_o	J	C_w
	Lb./Ft.	In.^{2}	In.^{4}	In.^{3}	In.	In.^{4}	In.^{3}	In.	In.	In.	In.^{4}	In.^{6}
MC180												
X33.8*	22.7	6.71	47.8	13.7	2.67	7.24	2.82	1.04	1.04	1.26	.649	59.0
X28.4*	19.1	5.65	43.5	12.4	2.77	6.08	2.55	1.04	1.07	1.33	.424	50.0
MC180												
X26.2*	17.6	5.20	37.9	10.8	2.70	4.02	1.89	.879	.871	1.08	.366	32.8
MC150												
X26.8*	18	5.33	30.0	10.0	2.37	6.02	2.52	1.06	1.12	1.36	.388	35.2
X22.8*	15.3	4.53	25.6	8.53	2.38	5.01	2.05	1.05	1.05	1.33	.229	30.5
MC150												
X24.3*	16.3	4.83	26.2	8.73	2.33	3.83	1.84	.890	.924	1.12	.349	22.4
X22.5*	15.1	4.47	25.2	8.40	2.37	3.52	1.76	.887	.935	1.14	.296	20.8
MC150												
X17.9*	12	3.55	18.9	6.30	2.31	1.87	1.04	.726	.700	.880	.160	11.4

For sections available from Canadian mills, the nominal mass has been rounded to the nearest kg/m.
  Designation consists of nominal depth in millimetres by nominal mass in kilograms per metre.
* Not available from Canadian mills.

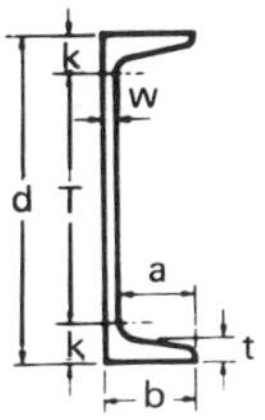

DIMENSIONS AND SURFACE AREAS

Nominal Mass	Depth d		Flange Width b		Flange Thickness t		Web Thickness w		Distances a	Distances T	Distances k	Surface Area (Ft.²) per foot of length Total	Surface Area (Ft.²) per foot of length Minus Top of Top Flange
kg/m	In.	In.	In.	In.	In.	In.	In.	In.	In.	In.	In.	In.	In.
33.8	7.00	7	3.60	3⅝	.500	½	.503	½	3⅛	4¾	1⅛	2.28	1.98
28.4	7.00	7	3.45	3½	.500	½	.352	⅜	3⅛	4¾	1⅛	2.26	1.97
26.2	7.00	7	3.00	3	.475	½	.375	⅜	2⅝	4⅞	1¹⁄₁₆	2.10	1.85
26.8	6.00	6	3.50	3½	.475	½	.379	⅜	3⅛	3⅞	1¹⁄₁₆	2.10	1.81
22.8	6.00	6	3.50	3½	.385	⅜	.340	⁵⁄₁₆	3⅛	4¼	⅞	2.11	1.82
24.3	6.00	6	3.00	3	.475	½	.375	⅜	2⅝	3⅞	1¹⁄₁₆	1.94	1.69
22.5	6.00	6	2.94	3	.475	½	.316	⁵⁄₁₆	2⅝	3⅞	1¹⁄₁₆	1.93	1.68
17.9	6.00	6	2.50	2½	.375	⅜	.310	⁵⁄₁₆	2⅛	4¼	⅞	1.78	1.57

ANGLES
Equal Legs

PROPERTIES AND DIMENSIONS

Size mm x mm (In. x In.)	Thickness t mm	Thickness t In.	Mass Lb./Ft.	Area In.²	Axis X-X and Axis Y-Y I In.⁴	Axis X-X and Axis Y-Y S In.³	Axis X-X and Axis Y-Y r In.	Axis X-X and Axis Y-Y x or y In.	Axis Z-Z r In.
200X200 (7.87X7.87)	30	1.18	58.5	17.2	96.8	17.7	2.37	2.40	1.53
	25	.984	49.4	14.5	83.5	15.1	2.40	2.33	1.54
	20	.787	40.1	11.8	69.2	12.3	2.42	2.26	1.55
	16	.630	32.4	9.52	57.0	10.0	2.45	2.20	1.56
	13	.512	26.5	7.80	47.3	8.27	2.46	2.16	1.56
	10	.394	20.6	6.05	37.2	6.46	2.48	2.11	1.57
150X150 (5.91X5.91)	20	.787	29.5	8.68	27.9	6.73	1.79	1.76	1.15
	16	.630	24.0	7.04	23.1	5.51	1.81	1.71	1.16
	13	.512	19.7	5.78	19.3	4.56	1.83	1.67	1.16
	10	.394	15.3	4.50	15.3	3.57	1.85	1.62	1.17
125X125 (4.92X4.92)	16	.630	19.7	5.80	13.0	3.76	1.50	1.46	.962
	13	.512	16.3	4.78	10.9	3.12	1.51	1.42	.967
	10	.394	12.7	3.72	8.69	2.45	1.53	1.38	.973
	8	.315	10.2	3.00	7.12	1.99	1.54	1.35	.978
100X100 (3.94X3.94)	16	.630	15.5	4.56	6.37	2.34	1.18	1.21	.767
	13	.512	12.8	3.77	5.39	1.95	1.20	1.17	.769
	10	.394	10.0	2.95	4.32	1.54	1.21	1.13	.774
	8	.315	8.10	2.38	3.56	1.26	1.22	1.10	.778
	6	.236	6.14	1.80	2.75	.959	1.23	1.07	.783
90X90 (3.54X3.54)	13	.512	11.5	3.37	3.85	1.56	1.07	1.07	.691
	10	.394	8.97	2.64	3.10	1.24	1.09	1.03	.695
	8	.315	7.26	2.13	2.56	1.01	1.10	1.00	.699
	6	.236	5.51	1.62	1.98	.772	1.11	.973	.703
75X75 (2.95X2.95)	13	.512	9.39	2.76	2.14	1.06	.881	.924	.575
	10	.394	7.38	2.17	1.74	.841	.896	.882	.577
	8	.315	5.99	1.76	1.45	.689	.906	.854	.580
	6	.236	4.56	1.34	1.13	.529	.917	.826	.584
	5	.197	3.82	1.12	.957	.447	.923	.811	.586

Notes: 1. The dimensions in brackets listed below the metric sizes are the soft converted Imperial dimensions in inches.
2. The properties of angles currently produced by cold forming are up to 7 percent less than the properties shown in the above tables. Check manufacturers' catalogue for the exact properties and dimensions. See also page 6-19.

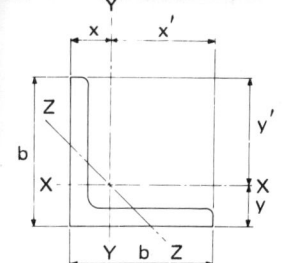

PROPERTIES AND DIMENSIONS

Size mm x mm (In. x In.)	Thickness t		Mass	Area	Axis X-X and Axis Y-Y				Axis Z-Z
					I	S	r	x or y	r
	mm	In.	Lb./Ft.	In.^{2}	In.^{4}	In.^{3}	In.	In.	In.
65X65 (2.56X2.56)	10	.394	6.33	1.86	1.10	.621	.770	.783	.499
	8	.315	5.15	1.51	.920	.510	.780	.755	.501
	6	.236	3.92	1.15	.720	.393	.790	.727	.504
	5	.197	3.30	.969	.614	.332	.796	.713	.506
55X55 (2.17X2.17)	10	.394	5.27	1.55	.643	.434	.644	.684	.421
	8	.315	4.30	1.26	.540	.358	.654	.656	.422
	6	.236	3.29	.967	.426	.277	.664	.628	.425
	5	.197	2.77	.814	.364	.235	.669	.614	.427
	4	.157	2.24	.657	.299	.191	.675	.600	.429
	3	.118	1.69	.498	.230	.146	.681	.585	.432
45X45 (1.77X1.77)	8	.315	3.46	1.02	.283	.233	.528	.557	.345
	6	.236	2.66	.781	.226	.182	.537	.529	.346
	5	.197	2.24	.659	.194	.154	.543	.515	.347
	4	.157	1.81	.533	.160	.126	.548	.501	.349
	3	.118	1.38	.405	.124	.096	.554	.487	.352
35X35 (1.38X1.38)	6	.236	2.03	.595	.101	.106	.412	.430	.268
	5	.197	1.71	.504	.087	.091	.416	.416	.269
	4	.157	1.39	.409	.073	.074	.421	.402	.270
	3	.118	1.06	.312	.057	.057	.427	.388	.272
25X25 (0.98X0.98)	5	.197	1.19	.349	.029	.044	.291	.317	.192
	4	.157	.97	.285	.025	.036	.295	.303	.192
	3	.118	.74	.219	.020	.028	.300	.289	.193

ANGLES
Unequal Legs

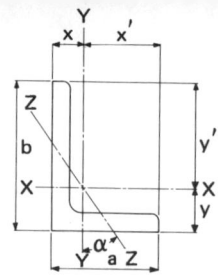

PROPERTIES AND DIMENSIONS

Size mm x mm (In. x In.)	Thickness t mm	Thickness t In.	Mass Lb./Ft.	Area In.^{2}	Axis X-X I_x In.^{4}	Axis X-X S_x In.^{3}	Axis X-X r_x In.	Axis X-X y In.	Axis Y-Y I_y In.^{4}	Axis Y-Y S_y In.^{3}	Axis Y-Y r_y In.	Axis Y-Y x In.	Axis Z-Z r_z In.	Axis Z-Z Tan α
200X150* (7.87X5.91)	25	.984	42.9	12.6	75.8	14.4	2.45	2.61	36.4	8.51	1.70	1.63	1.26	.543
	20	.787	34.8	10.2	62.9	11.8	2.48	2.54	30.4	6.99	1.72	1.56	1.27	.549
	16	.630	28.2	8.28	51.8	9.62	2.50	2.48	25.2	5.72	1.74	1.50	1.27	.554
	13	.512	23.1	6.79	43.1	7.93	2.52	2.44	21.1	4.73	1.76	1.46	1.28	.557
200X100* (7.87X3.94)	20	.787	29.5	8.68	54.4	11.0	2.50	2.92	9.23	3.10	1.03	.956	.837	.256
	16	.630	24.0	7.04	44.9	8.97	2.53	2.87	7.75	2.55	1.05	.897	.843	.262
	13	.512	19.7	5.78	37.4	7.40	2.54	2.82	6.54	2.12	1.06	.853	.850	.266
	10	.394	15.3	4.50	29.5	5.79	2.56	2.78	5.23	1.67	1.08	.808	.858	.271
150X100 (5.91X3.94)	16	.630	19.7	5.80	20.2	5.17	1.86	2.01	7.20	2.47	1.11	1.02	.850	.434
	13	.512	16.3	4.78	16.9	4.28	1.88	1.96	6.08	2.05	1.13	.979	.855	.440
	10	.394	12.7	3.72	13.4	3.36	1.90	1.92	4.87	1.62	1.14	.935	.862	.445
	8	.315	10.2	3.00	10.9	2.72	1.91	1.89	4.00	1.32	1.15	.906	.868	.448
125X90 (4.92X3.54)	16	.630	16.8	4.94	11.6	3.57	1.53	1.66	5.02	1.95	1.01	.974	.758	.499
	13	.512	13.9	4.07	9.78	2.96	1.55	1.62	4.26	1.63	1.02	.931	.762	.505
	10	.394	10.8	3.18	7.80	2.33	1.57	1.58	3.42	1.29	1.04	.888	.768	.511
	8	.315	8.73	2.57	6.39	1.90	1.58	1.55	2.82	1.05	1.05	.859	.773	.515
125X75 (4.92X2.95)	13	.512	12.8	3.77	9.17	2.87	1.56	1.73	2.50	1.13	.814	.745	.637	.356
	10	.394	10.0	2.95	7.32	2.26	1.58	1.69	2.02	.897	.828	.702	.642	.363
	8	.315	8.10	2.38	6.00	1.84	1.59	1.66	1.67	.734	.838	.673	.647	.367
	6	.236	6.14	1.80	4.62	1.40	1.60	1.63	1.30	.563	.849	.643	.653	.372
100X90 (3.94X3.54)	13	.512	12.1	3.57	5.21	1.92	1.21	1.22	3.98	1.58	1.06	1.03	.723	.796
	10	.394	9.49	2.79	4.18	1.52	1.22	1.18	3.21	1.25	1.07	.984	.728	.800
	8	.315	7.68	2.26	3.44	1.24	1.24	1.15	2.65	1.02	1.08	.956	.732	.802
	6	.236	5.82	1.71	2.66	.945	1.25	1.12	2.05	.783	1.09	.927	.737	.805

* Not available from Canadian mills.

Notes: 1. The dimensions in brackets listed below the metric sizes are the soft converted Imperial dimensions in inches.

2. The properties of angles currently produced by cold forming are up to 7 percent less than the properties shown in the above tables. Check manufacturers' catalogue for the exact properties and dimensions. See also page 6-19.

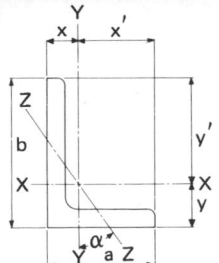

PROPERTIES AND DIMENSIONS

Size mm x mm (In. x In.)	Thickness t		Mass	Area	Axis X-X				Axis Y-Y				Axis Z-Z	
	mm	In.	Lb./Ft.	In.²	I_x In.⁴	S_x In.³	r_x In.	y In.	I_y In.⁴	S_y In.³	r_y In.	x In.	r_z In.	Tan α
100X75 (3.94X2.95)	13	.512	11.1	3.26	4.89	1.86	1.22	1.31	2.35	1.10	.848	.821	.629	.541
	10	.394	8.70	2.56	3.93	1.47	1.24	1.27	1.90	.874	.862	.778	.633	.549
	8	.315	7.05	2.07	3.24	1.20	1.25	1.24	1.58	.716	.872	.750	.637	.554
	6	.236	5.35	1.57	2.50	.919	1.26	1.21	1.23	.550	.883	.721	.642	.559
90X75 (3.54X2.95)	13	.512	10.4	3.06	3.02	1.52	1.09	1.15	2.27	1.08	.861	.858	.615	.672
	10	.394	8.18	2.40	2.92	1.20	1.10	1.11	1.84	.862	.876	.816	.619	.679
	8	.315	6.62	1.95	2.42	.982	1.11	1.08	1.53	.706	.886	.788	.622	.683
	6	.236	5.03	1.48	1.87	.752	1.13	1.05	1.19	.543	.897	.759	.627	.687
	5	.197	4.22	1.24	1.59	.633	1.13	1.04	1.01	.458	.903	.744	.630	.689
90X65 (3.54X2.56)	10	.394	7.65	2.25	2.78	1.17	1.11	1.17	1.22	.649	.736	.682	.549	.506
	8	.315	6.20	1.82	2.30	.960	1.12	1.15	1.01	.532	.746	.654	.553	.512
	6	.236	4.72	1.39	1.78	.735	1.13	1.12	.793	.410	.757	.625	.557	.518
	5	.197	3.96	1.16	1.51	.620	1.14	1.10	.675	.346	.762	.610	.560	.520
80X60 (3.15X2.36)	10	.394	6.86	2.02	1.94	.922	.981	1.04	.932	.544	.680	.651	.503	.543
	8	.315	5.57	1.64	1.61	.755	.992	1.02	.779	.448	.690	.623	.506	.549
	6	.236	4.24	1.25	1.25	.580	1.00	.988	.611	.345	.700	.594	.510	.555
	5	.197	3.56	1.05	1.06	.489	1.01	.973	.521	.292	.706	.580	.513	.558
75X50 (2.95X1.97)	8	.315	4.94	1.45	1.26	.647	.932	1.00	.450	.309	.557	.511	.425	.434
	6	.236	3.77	1.11	.984	.498	.943	.974	.355	.239	.567	.482	.429	.441
	5	.197	3.16	.930	.837	.420	.949	.960	.304	.203	.572	.468	.431	.445
65X50 (2.56X1.97)	8	.315	4.51	1.33	.842	.490	.797	.839	.432	.303	.570	.544	.418	.572
	6	.236	3.45	1.01	.661	.378	.807	.811	.342	.235	.580	.515	.421	.580
	5	.197	2.90	.853	.564	.320	.813	.796	.292	.199	.586	.501	.423	.583
	4	.157	2.34	.688	.461	.260	.819	.782	.241	.162	.591	.487	.426	.587
55X35 (2.17X1.38)	6	.236	2.66	.781	.365	.258	.684	.750	.116	.113	.385	.356	.297	.396
	5	.197	2.24	.659	.313	.219	.689	.735	.100	.096	.389	.342	.299	.401
	4	.157	1.81	.533	.258	.178	.695	.721	.083	.079	.394	.327	.301	.406
	3	.118	1.38	.405	.199	.136	.701	.706	.065	.061	.400	.312	.304	.411
45X30 (1.77X1.18)	6	.236	2.18	.642	.196	.170	.553	.619	.069	.081	.329	.324	.253	.426
	5	.197	1.85	.543	.169	.145	.558	.605	.060	.069	.333	.309	.255	.433
	4	.157	1.50	.440	.140	.118	.564	.590	.050	.057	.338	.295	.256	.439
	3	.118	1.14	.335	.109	.091	.569	.576	.039	.044	.343	.281	.259	.445

TWO ANGLES EQUAL LEGS
Back to Back

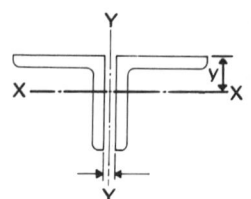

PROPERTIES OF SECTIONS

Size mm x mm (In. x In.)	Thickness t mm	Thickness t In.	Mass Lb./Ft.	Area of 2 Angles In.²	Axis X-X I In.⁴	Axis X-X S In.³	Axis X-X r In.	Axis X-X y In.	Radii of Gyration about Axis Y-Y back to back of angles, inches 0	1/4	3/8	1/2	5/8	3/4
200X200 (7.87X7.87)	30	1.18	117	34.4	194	35.4	2.37	2.40	3.37	3.46	3.51	3.56	3.60	3.65
	25	.984	98.9	29.1	167	30.1	2.40	2.33	3.34	3.43	3.48	3.52	3.57	3.61
	20	.787	80.2	23.6	138	24.6	2.42	2.26	3.31	3.40	3.44	3.49	3.53	3.58
	16	.630	64.8	19.0	114	20.1	2.45	2.20	3.29	3.38	3.42	3.46	3.51	3.55
	13	.512	53.1	15.6	94.6	16.5	2.46	2.16	3.27	3.36	3.40	3.44	3.49	3.53
	10	.394	41.1	12.1	74.4	12.9	2.48	2.11	3.26	3.34	3.38	3.43	3.47	3.51
150X150 (5.91X5.91)	20	.787	59.1	17.4	55.7	13.5	1.79	1.76	2.51	2.60	2.65	2.70	2.74	2.79
	16	.630	47.9	14.1	46.3	11.0	1.81	1.71	2.49	2.58	2.62	2.67	2.71	2.76
	13	.512	39.4	11.6	38.7	9.12	1.83	1.67	2.47	2.56	2.60	2.65	2.69	2.74
	10	.394	30.6	8.99	30.6	7.15	1.85	1.62	2.46	2.54	2.58	2.63	2.67	2.72
125X125 (4.92X4.92)	16	.630	39.5	11.6	26.0	7.51	1.50	1.46	2.09	2.18	2.23	2.27	2.32	2.37
	13	.512	32.5	9.55	21.8	6.23	1.51	1.42	2.07	2.16	2.21	2.25	2.30	2.35
	10	.394	25.3	7.44	17.4	4.90	1.53	1.38	2.06	2.14	2.19	2.23	2.28	2.32
	8	.315	20.4	6.00	14.2	3.98	1.54	1.35	2.05	2.13	2.17	2.22	2.26	2.31
100X100 (3.94X3.94)	16	.630	31.1	9.13	12.7	4.68	1.18	1.21	1.69	1.79	1.83	1.88	1.93	1.98
	13	.512	25.6	7.54	10.8	3.90	1.20	1.17	1.67	1.76	1.81	1.86	1.91	1.96
	10	.394	20.0	5.89	8.65	3.08	1.21	1.13	1.66	1.74	1.79	1.84	1.88	1.93
	8	.315	16.2	4.76	7.12	2.51	1.22	1.10	1.65	1.73	1.78	1.82	1.87	1.92
	6	.236	12.3	3.61	5.50	1.92	1.23	1.07	1.63	1.72	1.76	1.81	1.85	1.90
90X90 (3.54X3.54)	13	.512	22.9	6.73	7.70	3.12	1.07	1.07	1.52	1.61	1.65	1.70	1.75	1.80
	10	.394	17.9	5.27	6.21	2.47	1.09	1.03	1.50	1.59	1.63	1.68	1.73	1.78
	8	.315	14.5	4.27	5.12	2.02	1.10	1.00	1.49	1.57	1.62	1.66	1.71	1.76
	6	.236	11.0	3.24	3.97	1.54	1.11	.973	1.47	1.56	1.60	1.65	1.70	1.74
75X75 (2.95X2.95)	13	.512	18.8	5.52	4.29	2.11	.881	.924	1.28	1.37	1.42	1.47	1.52	1.57
	10	.394	14.8	4.34	3.48	1.68	.896	.882	1.26	1.35	1.40	1.44	1.49	1.54
	8	.315	12.0	3.52	2.89	1.38	.906	.854	1.25	1.33	1.38	1.43	1.48	1.53
	6	.236	9.11	2.68	2.25	1.06	.917	.826	1.23	1.32	1.37	1.41	1.46	1.51
	5	.197	7.65	2.25	1.91	.894	.923	.811	1.23	1.31	1.36	1.41	1.45	1.50

Notes: 1. The dimensions in brackets listed below the metric sizes are the soft converted Imperial dimensions in inches.
2. The properties of angles currently produced by cold forming are up to 7 percent less than the properties shown in the above tables. Check manufacturers' catalogue for the exact properties and dimensions. See also page 6-19.

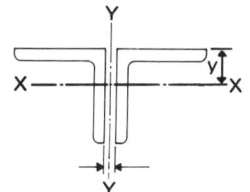

PROPERTIES OF SECTIONS

Size mm x mm (In. x In.)	Thickness t		Mass	Area of 2 Angles	Axis X-X				Radii of Gyration about Axis Y-Y					
					I	S	r	y	back to back of angles, inches					
	mm	In.	Lb./Ft.	In.^{2}	In.^{4}	In.^{3}	In.	In.	0	1/4	3/8	1/2	5/8	3/4
65X65 (2.56X2.56)	10	.394	12.7	3.72	2.20	1.24	.770	.783	1.10	1.19	1.24	1.29	1.34	1.39
	8	.315	10.3	3.03	1.84	1.02	.780	.755	1.09	1.18	1.22	1.27	1.32	1.37
	6	.236	7.85	2.31	1.44	.786	.790	.727	1.07	1.16	1.21	1.26	1.31	1.36
	5	.197	6.59	1.94	1.23	.665	.796	.713	1.07	1.16	1.20	1.25	1.30	1.35
55X55 (2.17X2.17)	10	.394	10.5	3.10	1.29	.868	.644	.684	.940	1.03	1.08	1.13	1.19	1.24
	8	.315	8.61	2.53	1.08	.716	.654	.656	.926	1.02	1.07	1.12	1.17	1.22
	6	.236	6.58	1.93	.852	.555	.664	.628	.914	1.00	1.05	1.10	1.15	1.20
	5	.197	5.54	1.63	.729	.470	.669	.614	.908	.997	1.04	1.09	1.14	1.19
	4	.157	4.47	1.31	.599	.382	.675	.600	.903	.990	1.04	1.09	1.13	1.19
	3	.118	3.39	.995	.461	.292	.681	.585	.898	.984	1.03	1.08	1.13	1.18
45X45 (1.77X1.77)	8	.315	6.92	2.03	.567	.467	.528	.557	.768	.863	.913	.964	1.02	1.07
	6	.236	5.32	1.56	.451	.363	.537	.529	.754	.847	.896	.947	.999	1.05
	5	.197	4.48	1.32	.388	.309	.543	.515	.748	.839	.888	.938	.990	1.04
	4	.157	3.63	1.07	.320	.252	.548	.501	.743	.832	.880	.930	.981	1.03
	3	.118	2.75	.809	.248	.193	.554	.487	.737	.825	.872	.922	.972	1.02
35X35 (1.38X1.38)	6	.236	4.05	1.19	.202	.213	.412	.430	.595	.691	.742	.795	.849	.904
	5	.197	3.43	1.01	.175	.182	.416	.416	.589	.683	.734	.786	.839	.894
	4	.157	2.78	.818	.145	.149	.421	.402	.583	.675	.725	.777	.830	.884
	3	.118	2.12	.623	.114	.115	.427	.388	.577	.667	.717	.768	.820	.874
25X25 (0.98X0.98)	5	.197	2.37	.698	.059	.088	.291	.317	.430	.529	.582	.637	.694	.751
	4	.157	1.94	.570	.050	.073	.295	.303	.423	.520	.573	.627	.683	.740
	3	.118	1.49	.437	.039	.057	.300	.289	.417	.512	.564	.617	.673	.729

Notes: 1. The dimensions in brackets listed below the metric sizes are the soft converted Imperial dimensions in inches.
2. The properties of angles currently produced by cold forming are up to 7 percent less than the properties shown in the above tables. Check manufacturers' catalogue for the exact properties and dimensions. See also page 6-19.

TWO ANGLES UNEQUAL LEGS
Long Legs Back to Back

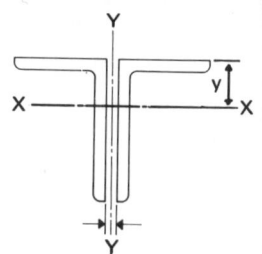

PROPERTIES OF SECTIONS

Size mm x mm (In. x In.)	Thickness t		Mass	Area of 2 Angles	Axis X-X				Radii of Gyration about Axis Y-Y					
					I	S	r	y	back to back of angles, inches					
	mm	In.	Lb./Ft.	In.²	In.⁴	In.³	In.	In.	0	1/4	3/8	1/2	5/8	3/4
200X150 (7.87X5.91)	25	.984	85.7	25.2	152	28.8	2.45	2.61	2.35	2.44	2.49	2.53	2.58	2.63
	20	.787	69.6	20.5	126	23.6	2.48	2.54	2.32	2.41	2.45	2.50	2.54	2.59
	16	.630	56.4	16.6	104	19.2	2.50	2.48	2.30	2.38	2.43	2.47	2.52	2.56
	13	.512	46.2	13.6	86.2	15.9	2.52	2.44	2.29	2.37	2.41	2.45	2.50	2.54
200X100 (7.87X3.94)	20	.787	59.1	17.4	109	22.0	2.50	2.92	1.41	1.49	1.54	1.59	1.64	1.68
	16	.630	47.9	14.1	89.9	17.9	2.53	2.87	1.38	1.46	1.51	1.55	1.60	1.65
	13	.512	39.4	11.6	74.8	14.8	2.54	2.82	1.36	1.44	1.49	1.53	1.58	1.62
	10	.394	30.6	8.99	59.0	11.6	2.56	2.78	1.35	1.43	1.47	1.51	1.55	1.60
150X100 (5.91X3.94)	16	.630	39.5	11.6	40.3	10.3	1.86	2.01	1.51	1.60	1.64	1.69	1.74	1.79
	13	.512	32.5	9.55	33.8	8.57	1.88	1.96	1.49	1.58	1.62	1.67	1.71	1.76
	10	.394	25.3	7.44	26.8	6.72	1.90	1.92	1.48	1.56	1.60	1.65	1.69	1.74
	8	.315	20.4	6.00	21.9	5.45	1.91	1.89	1.47	1.55	1.59	1.63	1.68	1.72
125X 90 (4.92X3.54)	16	.630	33.6	9.87	23.2	7.13	1.53	1.66	1.40	1.49	1.54	1.59	1.63	1.68
	13	.512	27.7	8.14	19.6	5.93	1.55	1.62	1.38	1.47	1.52	1.56	1.61	1.66
	10	.394	21.6	6.36	15.6	4.67	1.57	1.58	1.37	1.45	1.49	1.54	1.59	1.63
	8	.315	17.5	5.13	12.8	3.79	1.58	1.55	1.36	1.44	1.48	1.53	1.57	1 62
125X 75 (4.92X2.95)	13	.512	25.6	7.54	18.3	5.75	1.56	1.73	1.10	1.19	1.24	1.29	1.33	1.38
	10	.394	20.0	5.89	14.6	4.53	1.58	1.69	1.09	1.17	1.22	1.26	1.31	1.36
	8	.315	16.2	4.76	12.0	3.68	1.59	1.66	1.07	1.16	1.20	1.25	1.29	1.34
	6	.236	12.3	3.61	9.24	2.80	1.60	1.63	1.07	1.15	1.19	1.23	1.28	1.33
100X 90 (3.94X3.54)	13	.512	24.3	7.13	10.4	3.84	1.21	1.22	1.47	1.56	1.61	1.66	1.71	1.76
	10	.394	19.0	5.58	8.36	3.03	1.22	1.18	1.46	1.54	1.59	1.63	1.68	1.73
	8	.315	15.4	4.51	6.88	2.47	1.24	1.15	1.44	1.53	1.57	1.62	1.67	1.72
	6	.236	11.6	3.42	5.32	1.89	1.25	1.12	1.43	1.52	1.56	1.61	1.65	1.70

* Not available from Canadian mills.

Notes: 1. The dimensions in brackets listed below the metric sizes are the soft converted Imperial dimensions in inches.

2. The properties of angles currently produced by cold forming are up to 7 percent less than the properties shown in the above tables. Check manufacturers' catalogue for the exact properties and dimensions. See also page 6-19.

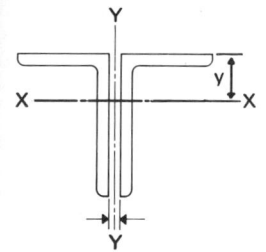

PROPERTIES OF SECTIONS

Size mm x mm (In. x In.)	Thickness t		Mass	Area of 2 Angles	Axis X-X				Radii of Gyration about Axis Y-Y					
									back to back of angles, inches					
	mm	In.	Lb./Ft.	In.²	I In.⁴	S In.³	r In.	y In.	0	1/4	3/8	1/2	5/8	3/4
100X75 (3.94X2.95)	13	.512	22.2	6.53	9.78	3.73	1.22	1.31	1.18	1.27	1.32	1.37	1.42	1.47
	10	.394	17.4	5.12	7.86	2.95	1.24	1.27	1.16	1.25	1.29	1.34	1.39	1.44
	8	.315	14.1	4.14	6.48	2.40	1.25	1.24	1.15	1.24	1.28	1.33	1.37	1.42
	6	.236	10.7	3.14	5.01	1.84	1.26	1.21	1.14	1.22	1.27	1.31	1.36	1.41
90X75 (3.54X2.95)	13	.512	20.8	6.13	7.25	3.03	1.09	1.15	1.22	1.31	1.35	1.40	1.45	1.50
	10	.394	16.4	4.81	5.85	2.40	1.10	1.11	1.20	1.29	1.33	1.38	1.43	1.48
	8	.315	13.2	3.89	4.83	1.96	1.11	1.08	1.19	1.27	1.32	1.36	1.41	1.46
	6	.236	10.1	2.96	3.74	1.50	1.13	1.05	1.18	1.26	1.30	1.35	1.40	1.45
	5	.197	8.44	2.48	3.17	1.27	1.13	1.04	1.17	1.25	1.30	1.34	1.39	1.44
90X65 (3.54X2.56)	10	.394	15.3	4.50	5.57	2.35	1.11	1.17	1.00	1.09	1.14	1.19	1.24	1.29
	8	.315	12.4	3.65	4.60	1.92	1.12	1.15	.992	1.08	1.12	1.17	1.22	1.27
	6	.236	9.43	2.77	3.57	1.47	1.13	1.12	.981	1.07	1.11	1.16	1.20	1.25
	5	.197	7.91	2.33	3.02	1.24	1.14	1.10	.976	1.06	1.10	1.15	1.20	1.25
80X60 (3.15X2.36)	10	.394	13.7	4.03	3.88	1.84	.981	1.04	.941	1.03	1.08	1.13	1.18	1.23
	8	.315	11.1	3.27	3.22	1.51	.992	1.02	.929	1.02	1.06	1.11	1.16	1.21
	6	.236	8.48	2.49	2.51	1.16	1.00	.988	.918	1.00	1.05	1.10	1.15	1.20
	5	.197	7.12	2.09	2.13	.978	1.01	.973	.913	.997	1.04	1.09	1.14	1.19
75X50 (2.95X1.97)	8	.315	9.87	2.90	2.52	1.29	.932	1.00	.756	.845	.893	.943	.994	1.05
	6	.236	7.53	2.21	1.97	.995	.943	.974	.744	.830	.877	.926	.976	1.03
	5	.197	6.33	1.86	1.67	.840	.949	.960	.739	.824	.870	.918	.967	1.02
65X50 (2.56X1.97)	8	.315	9.03	2.65	1.68	.980	.797	.839	.788	.879	.928	.978	1.03	1.08
	6	.236	6.90	2.03	1.32	.756	.807	.811	.776	.864	.912	.961	1.01	1.06
	5	.197	5.80	1.71	1.13	.639	.813	.796	.771	.857	.904	.952	1.00	1.05
	4	.157	4.68	1.38	.923	.519	.819	.782	.766	.851	.897	.945	.994	1.04
55X35 (2.17X1.38)	6	.236	5.32	1.56	.731	.516	.684	.750	.524	.616	.666	.718	.771	.826
	5	.197	4.48	1.32	.626	.438	.689	.735	.518	.608	.657	.708	.761	.815
	4	.157	3.63	1.07	.515	.357	.695	.721	.512	.600	.648	.699	.751	.805
	3	.118	2.75	.809	.397	.272	.701	.706	.507	.593	.640	.690	.742	.795
45X30 (1.77X1.18)	6	.236	4.37	1.28	.393	.341	.553	.619	.461	.556	.608	.661	.716	.772
	5	.197	3.69	1.09	.338	.290	.558	.605	.455	.547	.598	.651	.705	.761
	4	.157	3.00	.880	.280	.237	.564	.590	.449	.539	.589	.641	.695	.750
	3	.118	2.28	.670	.217	.181	.569	.576	.443	.531	.580	.632	.685	.740

Notes: 1. The dimensions in brackets listed below the metric sizes are the soft converted Imperial dimensions in inches.
2. The properties of angles currently produced by cold forming are up to 7 percent less than the properties shown in the above tables. Check manufacturers' catalogue for the exact properties and dimensions. See also page 6-19.

TWO ANGLES UNEQUAL LEGS
Short Legs Back to Back

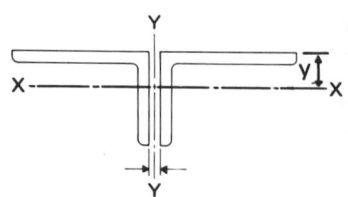

PROPERTIES OF SECTIONS

Size mm x mm (In. x In.)	Thickness t		Mass	Area of 2 Angles	Axis X-X				Radii of Gyration about Axis Y-Y back to back of angles, inches					
	mm	In.	Lb./Ft.	In.^{2}	I In.^{4}	S In.^{3}	r In.	y In.	0	1/4	3/8	1/2	5/8	3/4
200X150* (7.87X5.91)	25	.984	85.7	25.2	72.8	17.0	1.70	1.63	3.58	3.68	3.72	3.77	3.82	3.87
	20	.787	69.6	20.5	60.8	14.0	1.72	1.56	3.55	3.64	3.69	3.73	3.78	3.83
	16	.630	56.4	16.6	50.4	11.4	1.74	1.50	3.53	3.61	3.66	3.71	3.75	3.80
	13	.512	46.2	13.6	42.1	9.47	1.76	1.46	3.51	3.60	3.64	3.69	3.73	3.78
200X100* (7.87X3.94)	20	.787	59.1	17.4	18.5	6.20	1.03	.956	3.85	3.95	3.99	4.04	4.09	4.14
	16	.630	47.9	14.1	15.5	5.10	1.05	.897	3.82	3.91	3.96	4.01	4.06	4.11
	13	.512	39.4	11.6	13.1	4.24	1.06	.853	3.80	3.89	3.94	3.99	4.04	4.08
	10	.394	30.6	8.99	10.5	3.34	1.08	.808	3.78	3.87	3.92	3.96	4.01	4.06
150X100 (5.91X3.94)	16	.630	39.5	11.6	14.4	4.94	1.11	1.02	2.74	2.83	2.88	2.93	2.98	3.02
	13	.512	32.5	9.55	12.2	4.11	1.13	.979	2.72	2.81	2.86	2.90	2.95	3.00
	10	.394	25.3	7.44	9.74	3.24	1.14	.935	2.70	2.79	2.84	2.88	2.93	2.98
	8	.315	20.4	6.00	8.01	2.64	1.15	.906	2.69	2.78	2.82	2.87	2.91	2.96
125X90 (4.92X3.54)	16	.630	33.6	9.87	10.0	3.91	1.01	.974	2.26	2.36	2.40	2.45	2.50	2.55
	13	.512	27.7	8.14	8.51	3.26	1.02	.931	2.24	2.33	2.38	2.43	2.48	2.53
	10	.394	21.6	6.36	6.85	2.58	1.04	.888	2.22	2.31	2.36	2.41	2.45	2.50
	8	.315	17.5	5.13	5.65	2.10	1.05	.859	2.21	2.30	2.35	2.39	2.44	2.49
125X75 (4.92X2.95)	13	.512	25.6	7.54	4.99	2.26	.814	.745	2.33	2.42	2.47	2.52	2.57	2.62
	10	.394	20.0	5.89	4.04	1.79	.828	.702	2.31	2.40	2.45	2.50	2.55	2.60
	8	.315	16.2	4.76	3.35	1.47	.838	.673	2.30	2.39	2.43	2.48	2.53	2.58
	6	.236	12.3	3.61	2.60	1.13	.849	.643	2.28	2.37	2.42	2.47	2.51	2.56
100X90 (3.94X3.54)	13	.512	24.3	7.13	7.97	3.17	1.06	1.03	1.72	1.81	1.86	1.91	1.95	2.00
	10	.394	19.0	5.58	6.41	2.51	1.07	.984	1.70	1.79	1.84	1.88	1.93	1.98
	8	.315	15.4	4.51	5.29	2.05	1.08	.956	1.69	1.78	1.82	1.87	1.92	1.96
	6	.236	11.6	3.42	4.10	1.57	1.09	.927	1.68	1.76	1.81	1.85	1.90	1.95

*Not available from Canadian mills.
Notes: 1. The dimensions in brackets listed below the metric sizes are the soft converted Imperial dimensions in inches.
2. The properties of angles currently produced by cold forming are up to 7 percent less than the properties shown in the above tables. Check manufacturers' catalogue for the exact properties and dimensions. See also page 6-19.

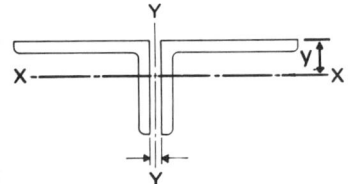

TWO ANGLES UNEQUAL LEGS
Short Legs Back to Back

PROPERTIES OF SECTIONS

Size mm x mm (In. x In.)	Thickness t		Mass	Area of 2 Angles	Axis X-X				Radii of Gyration about Axis Y-Y					
					I	S	r	y	back to back of angles, inches					
	mm	In.	Lb./Ft.	In.²	In.⁴	In.³	In.	In.	0	1/4	3/8	1/2	5/8	3/4
100X75 (3.94X2.95)	13	.512	22.2	6.53	4.69	2.20	.848	.821	1.80	1.89	1.94	1.99	2.03	2.09
	10	.394	17.4	5.12	3.80	1.75	.862	.778	1.78	1.87	1.91	1.96	2.01	2.06
	8	.315	14.1	4.14	3.15	1.43	.872	.750	1.76	1.85	1.90	1.95	2.00	2.04
	6	.236	10.7	3.14	2.45	1.10	.883	.721	1.75	1.84	1.89	1.93	1.98	2.03
90X75 (3.54X2.95)	13	.512	20.8	6.13	4.54	2.17	.861	.858	1.59	1.68	1.73	1.78	1.83	1.88
	10	.394	16.4	4.81	3.69	1.72	.876	.816	1.57	1.66	1.70	1.75	1.80	1.85
	8	.315	13.2	3.89	3.06	1.41	.886	.788	1.55	1.64	1.69	1.74	1.79	1.83
	6	.236	10.1	2.96	2.38	1.09	.897	.759	1.54	1.63	1.68	1.72	1.77	1.82
	5	.197	8.44	2.48	2.02	.915	.903	.744	1.54	1.62	1.67	1.72	1.76	1.81
90X65 (3.54X2.56)	10	.394	15.3	4.50	2.43	1.30	.736	.682	1.62	1.71	1.76	1.81	1.86	1.91
	8	.315	12.4	3.65	2.03	1.06	.746	.654	1.60	1.70	1.74	1.79	1.84	1.89
	6	.236	9.43	2.77	1.59	.820	.757	.625	1.59	1.68	1.73	1.78	1.83	1.87
	5	.197	7.91	2.33	1.35	.693	.762	.610	1.59	1.68	1.72	1.77	1.82	1.87
80X60 (3.15X2.36)	10	.394	13.7	4.03	1.86	1.09	.680	.651	1.43	1.53	1.58	1.62	1.67	1.73
	8	.315	11.1	3.27	1.56	.895	.690	.623	1.42	1.51	1.56	1.61	1.66	1.71
	6	.236	8.48	2.49	1.22	.691	.700	.594	1.41	1.50	1.55	1.59	1.64	1.69
	5	.197	7.12	2.09	1.04	.584	.706	.580	1.40	1.49	1.54	1.59	1.63	1.68
75X50 (2.95X1.97)	8	.315	9.87	2.90	.900	.617	.557	.511	1.37	1.46	1.51	1.56	1.61	1.66
	6	.236	7.53	2.21	.711	.478	.567	.482	1.36	1.45	1.50	1.55	1.60	1.65
	5	.197	6.33	1.86	.609	.405	.572	.468	1.35	1.44	1.49	1.54	1.59	1.64
65X50 (2.56X1.97)	8	.315	9.03	2.65	.864	.606	.570	.544	1.16	1.25	1.30	1.35	1.40	1.45
	6	.236	6.90	2.03	.683	.470	.580	.515	1.14	1.24	1.28	1.33	1.38	1.43
	5	.197	5.80	1.71	.585	.399	.586	.501	1.14	1.23	1.28	1.33	1.37	1.43
	4	.157	4.68	1.38	.481	.325	.591	.487	1.13	1.22	1.27	1.32	1.37	1.42
55X35 (2.17X1.38)	6	.236	5.32	1.56	.231	.226	.385	.356	1.01	1.11	1.16	1.21	1.26	1.32
	5	.197	4.48	1.32	.200	.193	.389	.342	1.01	1.10	1.15	1.20	1.25	1.31
	4	.157	3.63	1.07	.166	.158	.394	.327	1.00	1.09	1.14	1.19	1.25	1.30
	3	.118	2.75	.809	.129	.121	.400	.312	.995	1.09	1.14	1.19	1.24	1.29
45X30 (1.77X1.18)	6	.236	4.37	1.28	.139	.162	.329	.324	.830	.927	.978	1.03	1.08	1.14
	5	.197	3.69	1.09	.120	.138	.333	.309	.823	.919	.969	1.02	1.07	1.13
	4	.157	3.00	.880	.101	.113	.338	.295	.816	.911	.961	1.01	1.06	1.12
	3	.118	2.28	.670	.079	.088	.343	.281	.810	.903	.952	1.00	1.06	1.11

HOLLOW STRUCTURAL SECTIONS
Rectangular

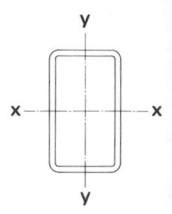

PROPERTIES AND DIMENSIONS

Outside Dimensions mm x mm (In. x In.)	Wall Thickness		Mass	Area	Axis X-X				Axis Y-Y				Torsional Constant J	Shear Constant C_{rt}
					I_x	S_x	r_x	Z_x	I_y	S_y	r_y	Z_y		
	mm	In.	Lb./Ft.	In.²	In.⁴	In.³	In.	In.³	In.⁴	In.³	In.	In.³	In.⁴	In.²
304.8X203.2 (12X8)	12.70	.500	62.5	18.4	353	58.8	4.39	72.4	188	46.9	3.20	54.7	402	10.0
	11.13	.438	55.3	16.3	318	52.9	4.42	64.7	169	42.3	3.23	48.9	359	8.98
	9.53	.375	47.9	14.1	279	46.5	4.45	56.5	149	37.3	3.25	42.7	313	7.88
	7.95	.313	40.4	11.9	239	39.8	4.49	48.0	128	32.0	3.28	36.4	266	6.73
	6.35	.250	32.6	9.59	196	32.6	4.52	39.1	105	26.3	3.31	29.6	216	5.50
254.0X152.4 (10X6)	12.70	.500	48.9	14.4	181	36.1	3.55	45.6	80.7	26.9	2.37	31.8	188	8.00
	11.13	.438	43.4	12.8	164	32.7	3.58	40.9	73.5	24.5	2.40	28.7	169	7.23
	9.53	.375	37.7	11.1	145	29.0	3.62	35.9	65.4	21.8	2.43	25.2	148	6.38
	7.95	.313	31.9	9.37	125	25.0	3.65	30.7	56.6	18.9	2.46	21.6	126	5.48
	6.35	.250	25.8	7.59	103	20.6	3.69	25.1	46.9	15.6	2.49	17.7	103	4.50
203.2X152.4 (8X6)	12.70	.500	42.0	12.4	103	25.8	2.89	32.2	65.6	21.9	2.30	26.3	136	6.00
	11.13	.438	37.5	11.0	94.0	23.5	2.92	29.0	59.9	20.0	2.33	23.8	122	5.47
	9.53	.375	32.6	9.58	83.7	20.9	2.96	25.6	53.5	17.8	2.36	21.0	107	4.88
	7.95	.313	27.6	8.12	72.5	18.1	2.99	21.9	46.4	15.5	2.39	18.0	91.7	4.22
	6.35	.250	22.4	6.59	60.1	15.0	3.02	18.0	38.6	12.9	2.42	14.8	75.1	3.50
	4.78	.188	17.1	5.04	46.9	11.7	3.05	13.9	30.2	10.1	2.45	11.5	57.9	2.73
203.2X101.6 (8X4)	12.70	.500	35.2	10.4	75.0	18.8	2.69	24.7	24.5	12.3	1.54	15.0	65.0	6.00
	11.13	.438	31.5	9.25	68.9	17.2	2.73	22.4	22.7	11.4	1.57	13.6	59.2	5.47
	9.53	.375	27.5	8.08	61.9	15.5	2.77	19.9	20.6	10.3	1.60	12.1	52.6	4.88
	7.95	.313	23.4	6.87	54.0	13.5	2.80	17.1	18.1	9.05	1.62	10.5	45.4	4.22
	6.35	.250	19.0	5.59	45.1	11.3	2.84	14.1	15.3	7.63	1.65	8.71	37.6	3.50
	4.78	.188	14.6	4.28	35.4	8.86	2.88	11.0	12.1	6.04	1.68	6.79	29.2	2.73
177.8X127.0†† (7X5)	12.70	.500	35.2	10.4	63.4	18.1	2.47	23.0	37.1	14.8	1.89	18.2	80.8	5.00
	11.13	.438	31.5	9.25	58.2	16.6	2.51	20.9	34.2	13.7	1.92	16.5	73.1	4.60
	9.53	.375	27.5	8.08	52.2	14.9	2.54	18.5	30.8	12.3	1.95	14.6	64.6	4.13
	7.95	.313	23.4	6.87	45.5	13.0	2.57	15.9	27.0	10.8	1.98	12.6	55.6	3.60
	6.35	.250	19.0	5.59	38.0	10.9	2.61	13.2	22.6	9.03	2.01	10.4	45.8	3.00
	4.78	.188	14.6	4.28	29.9	8.53	2.64	10.2	17.8	7.12	2.04	8.12	35.4	2.35
152.4X101.6 (6X4)	11.13	.438	25.5	7.50	32.7	10.9	2.09	14.0	17.1	8.57	1.51	10.5	39.2	3.72
	9.53	.375	22.4	6.58	29.7	9.90	2.12	12.5	15.6	7.81	1.54	9.42	34.9	3.38
	7.95	.313	19.1	5.62	26.2	8.72	2.16	10.9	13.8	6.92	1.57	8.21	30.3	2.97
	6.35	.250	15.6	4.59	22.1	7.36	2.19	9.05	11.7	5.87	1.60	6.84	25.1	2.50
	4.78	.188	12.0	3.53	17.5	5.83	2.23	7.08	9.35	4.67	1.63	5.36	19.6	1.97

†† Check with manufacturer for current availability.

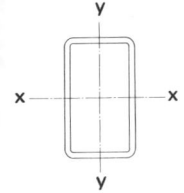

HOLLOW STRUCTURAL SECTIONS
Rectangular

Outside Dimensions mm x mm (In. x In.)	Wall Thickness		Mass	Area	Axis X-X				Axis Y-Y				Torsional Constant J	Shear Constant C_{rt}
	mm	In.	Lb./Ft.	In.^{2}	I_x In.^{4}	S_x In.^{3}	r_x In.	Z_x In.^{3}	I_y In.^{4}	S_y In.^{3}	r_y In.	Z_y In.^{3}	In.^{4}	In.^{2}
127.0X76.2 (5X3)	9.53	.375	17.3	5.08	14.7	5.88	1.70	7.70	6.46	4.30	1.13	5.34	15.9	2.63
	7.95	.313	14.8	4.36	13.2	5.27	1.74	6.77	5.84	3.89	1.16	4.71	14.0	2.35
	6.35	.250	12.2	3.59	11.3	4.52	1.77	5.69	5.05	3.36	1.19	3.98	11.7	2.00
	4.78	.188	9.45	2.78	9.08	3.63	1.81	4.50	4.09	2.73	1.21	3.16	9.27	1.60
127.0X63.5 (5X2½)	9.53	.375	16.0	4.70	12.7	5.08	1.64	6.83	4.09	3.27	.932	4.12	11.2	2.63
	7.95	.313	13.8	4.05	11.5	4.58	1.68	6.04	3.74	2.99	.961	3.66	9.92	2.35
	6.35	.250	11.4	3.34	9.88	3.95	1.72	5.10	3.27	2.62	.990	3.11	8.43	2.00
	4.78	.188	8.81	2.59	7.99	3.20	1.76	4.05	2.68	2.15	1.02	2.49	6.72	1.60
127.0X50.8 (5X2)	9.53	.375	14.7	4.33	10.7	4.27	1.57	5.96	2.31	2.31	.730	2.99	7.03	2.63
	7.95	.313	12.7	3.74	9.74	3.90	1.61	5.30	2.15	2.15	.759	2.69	6.37	2.35
	6.35	.250	10.5	3.09	8.47	3.39	1.66	4.51	1.92	1.92	.788	2.31	5.50	2.00
	4.78	.188	8.17	2.40	6.90	2.76	1.70	3.60	1.60	1.60	.816	1.86	4.44	1.60
101.6X76.2 (4X3)	9.53	.375	14.7	4.33	8.20	4.10	1.38	5.34	5.16	3.44	1.09	4.35	11.3	1.88
	7.95	.313	12.7	3.74	7.44	3.72	1.41	4.74	4.70	3.14	1.12	3.87	10.0	1.72
	6.35	.250	10.5	3.09	6.45	3.22	1.44	4.02	4.10	2.73	1.15	3.29	8.47	1.50
	4.78	.188	8.17	2.40	5.24	2.62	1.48	3.21	3.35	2.23	1.18	2.63	6.72	1.22
101.6X50.8 (4X2)	7.95	.313	10.6	3.11	5.31	2.65	1.31	3.59	1.70	1.70	.740	2.16	4.68	1.72
	6.35	.250	8.81	2.59	4.69	2.34	1.35	3.09	1.53	1.53	.769	1.87	4.06	1.50
	4.78	.188	6.89	2.03	3.88	1.94	1.38	2.49	1.29	1.29	.797	1.52	3.29	1.22
	3.81	.150	5.62	1.65	3.27	1.63	1.41	2.07	1.10	1.10	.815	1.27	2.74	1.02
	3.18	.125	4.76	1.40	2.82	1.41	1.42	1.77	.954	.954	.826	1.09	2.35	.876
88.9X63.5 (3½X2½)	7.95	.313	10.6	3.11	4.49	2.57	1.20	3.35	2.61	2.09	.916	2.63	5.89	1.41
	6.35	.250	8.81	2.59	3.96	2.26	1.24	2.88	2.32	1.86	.947	2.27	5.05	1.25
	4.78	.188	6.89	2.03	3.27	1.87	1.27	2.32	1.93	1.54	.976	1.83	4.05	1.03
	3.81	.150	5.62	1.65	2.75	1.57	1.29	1.92	1.63	1.30	.994	1.52	3.35	.870
	3.18	.125	4.76	1.40	2.38	1.36	1.30	1.65	1.41	1.13	1.01	1.31	2.86	.751
76.2X50.8 (3X2)	7.95	.313	8.46	2.49	2.43	1.62	.990	2.19	1.25	1.25	.710	1.63	3.06	1.09
	6.35	.250	7.11	2.09	2.20	1.47	1.03	1.92	1.15	1.15	.741	1.44	2.68	1.00
	4.78	.188	5.61	1.65	1.86	1.24	1.06	1.57	.978	.978	.770	1.18	2.19	.846
	3.81	.150	4.60	1.35	1.59	1.06	1.08	1.32	.839	.839	.788	.992	1.83	.720
50.8X25.4 (2X1)	3.18	.125	2.21	.648	.293	.293	.673	.386	.096	.192	.385	.234	.254	.375
	2.54	.100	1.82	.534	.253	.253	.688	.326	.084	.168	.396	.199	.216	.320

HOLLOW STRUCTRUAL SECTIONS
Square

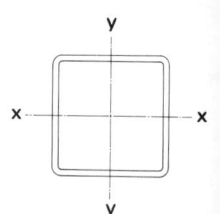

PROPERTIES AND DIMENSIONS

Outside Dimensions mm x mm (In. x In.)	Wall Thickness		Mass	Area	I	S	r	Z	Torsional Constant J	Surface Area	Shear Constant C_{rt}
	mm	In.	Lb./Ft.	In.^{2}	In.^{4}	In.^{3}	In.	In.^{3}	In.^{4}	Ft.^{2}/Ft.	In.^{2}
304.8X304.8 (12X12)	12.70	.500	76.1	22.4	485	80.9	4.66	95.4	778	3.86	10.0
	11.13	.438	67.3	19.8	435	72.5	4.69	85.0	692	3.87	8.98
	9.53	.375	58.1	17.1	381	63.4	4.72	73.9	600	3.89	7.88
	7.95	.313	48.9	14.4	324	54.1	4.75	62.6	507	3.91	6.73
	6.35	.250	39.4	11.6	265	44.1	4.78	50.8	411	3.93	5.50
254.0X254.0 (10X10)	12.70	.500	62.5	18.4	271	54.2	3.84	64.6	441	3.19	8.00
	11.13	.438	55.3	16.3	244	48.8	3.87	57.7	393	3.21	7.23
	9.53	.375	47.9	14.1	215	42.9	3.90	50.4	342	3.23	6.38
	7.95	.313	40.4	11.9	184	36.7	3.93	42.8	290	3.24	5.48
	6.35	.250	32.6	9.59	151	30.1	3.96	34.9	235	3.26	4.50
203.2X203.2 (8X8)	12.70	.500	48.9	14.4	131	32.8	3.02	39.7	218	2.52	6.00
	11.13	.438	43.4	12.8	119	29.8	3.06	35.7	195	2.54	5.47
	9.53	.375	37.7	11.1	106	26.4	3.09	31.3	171	2.56	4.88
	7.95	.313	31.9	9.37	91.0	22.8	3.12	26.8	145	2.58	4.22
	6.35	.250	25.8	7.59	75.1	18.8	3.15	21.9	119	2.60	3.50
177.8X177.8 (7X7)	12.70	.500	42.0	12.4	84.5	24.2	2.62	29.5	142	2.19	5.00
	11.13	.438	37.5	11.0	77.1	22.0	2.65	26.6	128	2.21	4.60
	9.53	.375	32.6	9.58	68.7	19.6	2.68	23.5	112	2.23	4.13
	7.95	.313	27.6	8.12	59.5	17.0	2.71	20.1	95.9	2.24	3.60
	6.35	.250	22.4	6.59	49.4	14.1	2.74	16.5	78.5	2.26	3.00
	4.78	.188	17.1	5.04	38.6	11.0	2.77	12.8	60.4	2.28	2.35
152.4X152.4 (6X6)	12.70	.500	35.2	10.4	50.4	16.8	2.21	20.8	86.4	1.86	4.00
	11.13	.438	31.5	9.25	46.3	15.4	2.24	18.9	78.1	1.87	3.72
	9.53	.375	27.5	8.08	41.6	13.9	2.27	16.8	69.0	1.89	3.38
	7.95	.313	23.4	6.87	36.3	12.1	2.30	14.4	59.2	1.91	2.97
	6.35	.250	19.0	5.59	30.3	10.1	2.33	11.9	48.7	1.93	2.50
	4.78	.188	14.6	4.28	23.9	7.95	2.36	9.27	37.6	1.95	1.97
127.0X127.0 (5X5)	11.13	.438	25.5	7.50	25.1	10.0	1.83	12.5	43.3	1.54	2.85
	9.53	.375	22.4	6.58	22.7	9.10	1.86	11.2	38.5	1.56	2.63
	7.95	.313	19.1	5.62	20.1	8.03	1.89	9.70	33.3	1.58	2.35
	6.35	.250	15.6	4.59	16.9	6.78	1.92	8.07	27.5	1.60	2.00
	4.78	.188	12.0	3.53	13.4	5.38	1.95	6.31	21.4	1.61	1.60

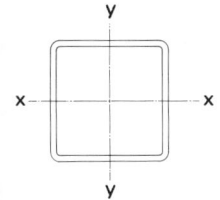

PROPERTIES AND DIMENSIONS

Outside Dimensions mm x mm (In. x In.)	Wall Thickness		Mass	Area	I	S	r	Z	Torsional Constant J	Surface Area	Shear Constant C_{rt}
	mm	In.	Lb./Ft.	In.^{2}	In.^{4}	In.^{3}	In.	In.^{3}	In.^{4}	Ft.^{2}/Ft.	In.^{2}
101.6 X 101.6 (4X4)	9.53	.375	17.3	5.08	10.7	5.34	1.45	6.70	18.6	1.23	1.88
	7.95	.313	14.8	4.36	9.57	4.79	1.48	5.90	16.3	1.24	1.72
	6.35	.250	12.2	3.59	8.21	4.11	1.51	4.96	13.6	1.26	1.50
	4.78	.188	9.45	2.78	6.61	3.31	1.54	3.92	10.7	1.28	1.22
88.9 X 88.9 (3½X3½)	9.53	.375	14.7	4.33	6.70	3.83	1.24	4.90	11.9	1.06	1.50
	7.95	.313	12.7	3.74	6.09	3.48	1.28	4.35	10.5	1.08	1.41
	6.35	.250	10.5	3.09	5.28	3.02	1.31	3.69	8.89	1.10	1.25
	4.78	.188	8.17	2.40	4.30	2.46	1.34	2.94	7.04	1.11	1.03
76.2 X 76.2 (3X3)	7.95	.313	10.6	3.11	3.57	2.38	1.07	3.03	6.33	.910	1.09
	6.35	.250	8.81	2.59	3.15	2.10	1.10	2.60	5.40	.928	1.00
	4.78	.188	6.89	2.03	2.60	1.74	1.13	2.10	4.32	.946	.846
63.5 X 63.5 (2½X2½)	6.35	.250	7.11	2.09	1.68	1.35	.898	1.71	2.97	.762	.750
	4.78	.188	5.61	1.65	1.42	1.14	.929	1.40	2.41	.779	.658
	3.81	.150	4.60	1.35	1.22	.973	.948	1.17	2.01	.790	.570
	3.18	.125	3.91	1.15	1.06	.848	.961	1.01	1.72	.798	.501
50.8 X 50.8 (2X2)	6.35	.250	5.41	1.59	.761	.761	.692	.998	1.39	.595	.500
	4.78	.188	4.33	1.27	.668	.668	.725	.840	1.17	.613	.469
	3.81	.150	3.58	1.05	.582	.582	.744	.714	.985	.624	.420
	3.18	.125	3.06	.899	.514	.514	.756	.621	.852	.631	.375
	2.79	.110	2.72	.799	.466	.466	.764	.558	.764	.635	.343
38.1 X 38.1 (1½X1½)	4.78	.188	3.05	.896	.241	.322	.519	.422	.442	.446	.281
	3.81	.150	2.56	.752	.218	.291	.539	.369	.384	.457	.270
	3.18	.125	2.21	.648	.197	.263	.551	.326	.338	.464	.250
	2.54	.100	1.82	.534	.170	.227	.564	.275	.284	.471	.220
31.8 X 31.8 (1¼X1¼)	3.81	.150	2.05	.603	.115	.184	.437	.239	.209	.374	.196
	3.18	.125	1.78	.524	.106	.169	.450	.214	.187	.381	.188
	2.54	.100	1.48	.435	.093	.149	.463	.184	.159	.389	.170
25.4 X 25.4 (1X1)	3.18	.125	1.35	.398	.048	.095	.346	.125	.087	.298	.125
	2.54	.100	1.14	.334	.043	.086	.359	.109	.076	.305	.120

HOLLOW STRUCTURAL SECTIONS
Round

PROPERTIES AND DIMENSIONS

Outside Diameter mm (In.)	Wall Thickness		Mass	Area	I	S	r	Z	J	Surface Area	Shear Constant C_{rt}
	mm	In.	Lb./Ft.	In.^{2}	In.^{4}	In.^{3}	In.	In.^{3}	In.^{4}	Ft.^{2}/Ft.	In.^{2}
406.4 (16.00)	12.70	.500	82.8	24.3	732	91.5	5.48	120	1460	4.19	12.2
	11.13	.438	72.9	21.4	649	81.1	5.50	106	1300	4.19	10.7
	9.53	.375	62.7	18.4	562	70.3	5.53	91.6	1120	4.19	9.21
	7.95	.313	52.5	15.4	475	59.3	5.55	77.0	949	4.19	7.71
	6.35	.250	42.1	12.4	384	48.0	5.57	62.0	767	4.19	6.18
355.6 (14.00)	12.70	.500	72.2	21.2	484	69.1	4.78	91.2	968	3.67	10.6
	11.13	.438	63.5	18.7	430	61.4	4.80	80.6	859	3.67	9.34
	9.53	.375	54.6	16.1	373	53.3	4.82	69.7	746	3.67	8.03
	7.95	.313	45.8	13.5	315	45.0	4.84	58.6	631	3.67	6.73
	6.35	.250	36.7	10.8	255	36.5	4.86	47.3	511	3.67	5.40
323.9 (12.75)	12.70	.500	65.5	19.2	362	56.7	4.34	75.1	723	3.34	9.63
	11.13	.438	57.7	17.0	322	50.5	4.36	66.5	643	3.34	8.48
	9.53	.375	49.6	14.6	280	43.9	4.38	57.5	559	3.34	7.30
	7.95	.313	41.6	12.2	237	37.1	4.40	48.4	473	3.34	6.12
	6.35	.250	33.4	9.82	192	30.1	4.42	39.1	384	3.34	4.91
273.1 (10.75)	12.70	.500	54.8	16.1	212	39.4	3.63	52.6	424	2.81	8.07
	11.13	.438	48.3	14.2	189	35.2	3.65	46.6	378	2.81	7.11
	9.53	.375	41.6	12.2	165	30.7	3.67	40.4	330	2.81	6.12
	7.95	.313	34.9	10.3	140	26.0	3.69	34.1	280	2.81	5.13
	6.35	.250	28.1	8.25	114	21.2	3.71	27.6	228	2.81	4.12
219.1 (8.625)	12.70	.500	43.4	12.8	106	24.5	2.88	33.1	212	2.26	6.40
	11.13	.438	38.4	11.3	94.7	22.0	2.90	29.4	189	2.26	5.65
	9.53	.375	33.1	9.73	82.9	19.2	2.92	25.6	166	2.26	4.87
	7.95	.313	27.8	8.17	70.7	16.4	2.94	21.6	141	2.26	4.09
	6.35	.250	22.4	6.58	57.7	13.4	2.96	17.5	115	2.26	3.29
	4.78	.188	17.0	4.99	44.4	10.3	2.98	13.4	88.8	2.26	2.49
168.3 (6.625)	9.53	.375	25.1	7.37	36.1	10.9	2.21	14.7	72.2	1.73	3.70
	7.95	.313	21.1	6.21	31.0	9.36	2.23	12.5	62.0	1.73	3.11
	6.35	.250	17.0	5.01	25.5	7.69	2.26	10.2	51.0	1.73	2.51
	4.78	.188	13.0	3.81	19.7	5.96	2.28	7.80	39.5	1.73	1.90
141.3 (5.562)	9.53	.375	20.8	6.11	20.7	7.43	1.84	10.1	41.4	1.46	3.07
	7.95	.313	17.6	5.16	17.8	6.42	1.86	8.64	35.7	1.46	2.59
	6.35	.250	14.2	4.17	14.8	5.31	1.88	7.06	29.5	1.46	2.09
	4.78	.188	10.8	3.18	11.5	4.13	1.90	5.44	23.0	1.46	1.59

HOLLOW STRUCTURAL SECTIONS
Round

PROPERTIES AND DIMENSIONS

Outside Diameter mm (In.)	Wall Thickness		Mass	Area	I	S	r	Z	J	Surface Area	Shear Constant C_{rt}
	mm	In.	Lb./Ft.	In.^{2}	In.^{4}	In.^{3}	In.	In.^{3}	In.^{4}	Ft.^{2}/Ft.	In.^{2}
114.3 (4.50)	7.95	.313	14.0	4.12	9.07	4.03	1.48	5.50	18.1	1.18	2.07
	6.35	.250	11.4	3.34	7.56	3.36	1.51	4.52	15.1	1.18	1.67
	4.78	.188	8.67	2.55	5.94	2.64	1.53	3.50	11.9	1.18	1.28
101.6 (4.00)	7.95	.313	12.3	3.63	6.20	3.10	1.31	4.27	12.4	1.05	1.82
	6.35	.250	10.0	2.95	5.20	2.60	1.33	3.52	10.4	1.05	1.48
	4.78	.188	7.67	2.25	4.10	2.05	1.35	2.74	8.21	1.05	1.13
	3.81	.150	6.17	1.81	3.37	1.68	1.36	2.22	6.73	1.05	.908
88.9 (3.50)	7.95	.313	10.7	3.13	4.02	2.30	1.13	3.19	8.03	.916	1.58
	6.35	.250	8.69	2.55	3.39	1.94	1.15	2.65	6.78	.916	1.28
	4.78	.188	6.66	1.96	2.69	1.54	1.17	2.07	5.39	.916	.982
	3.81	.150	5.37	1.58	2.22	1.27	1.19	1.68	4.44	.916	.790
73.0 (2.875)	6.35	.250	7.01	2.06	1.79	1.25	.932	1.73	3.58	.752	1.04
	4.78	.188	5.40	1.59	1.44	1.00	.952	1.36	2.88	.752	.797
	3.81	.150	4.37	1.28	1.19	.831	.965	1.11	2.39	.752	.643
	3.18	.125	3.68	1.08	1.02	.712	.973	.947	2.05	.752	.541
60.3 (2.375)	6.35	.250	5.68	1.67	.954	.804	.756	1.13	1.91	.622	.845
	4.78	.188	4.40	1.29	.778	.655	.776	.901	1.56	.622	.651
	3.81	.150	3.57	1.05	.651	.548	.788	.743	1.30	.622	.526
	3.18	.125	3.01	.885	.561	.473	.796	.634	1.12	.622	.443
48.3 (1.90)	4.78	.188	3.45	1.01	.376	.396	.609	.555	.752	.498	.512
	3.81	.150	2.81	.825	.319	.335	.622	.461	.638	.498	.415
	3.18	.125	2.38	.699	.277	.291	.630	.396	.554	.498	.351
	2.79	.110	2.10	.618	.249	.262	.635	.353	.498	.498	.310
42.2 (1.66)	3.18	.125	2.06	.604	.179	.216	.545	.296	.359	.435	.304
	2.54	.100	1.67	.491	.150	.181	.553	.244	.300	.435	.246
33.4 (1.315)	3.18	.125	1.59	.468	.084	.127	.423	.178	.167	.344	.236
	2.54	.100	1.30	.382	.071	.108	.431	.148	.142	.344	.192
26.7 (1.05)	3.18	.125	1.24	.364	.040	.076	.330	.108	.079	.275	.185
	2.54	.100	1.02	.299	.034	.065	.338	.091	.068	.275	.151

PART NINE
LIMIT STATES DESIGN TABLES IN IMPERIAL UNITS

General Information   9-3

Bolts
      Bolt Data.   9-5
      Bolts in Bearing-Type Connections   9-5
      Bolts in Slip-Resistant Connections.   9-8

Weld Data   9-9

Unit Factored Compressive Resistances For Compression Members   9-11

C_e/A — Euler Buckling Load per Unit of Area   9-17

Factored Axial Compressive Resistances of Columns
      WWF, W and M Shapes—CSA G40.21 — 44W   9-19
      HSS — Class C—CSA G40.21 — 50W   9-31
      HSS — Class H—CSA G40.21 — 50W   9-56

Composite Beam Trial Selection Tables.   9-81
      5″ Solid Slab   9-82
      1-1/2″ Deck + 2-1/2″ Slab   9-92
      2″ deck + 2-1/2″ Slab   9-102
      3″ deck + 2-1/2″ Slab   9-112
      2″ deck + 3-1/4″ Slab   9-122
      3″ deck + 3-1/4″ Slab   9-132

Beam Selection Table   9-143

GENERAL INFORMATION

Bolts

Tables 9—1 to 9—8 list basic bolt data and resistances for metric bolts M16 to M36 and for 1/2-inch to 1-1/2-inch diameter Imperial bolts for bearing-type and slip-resistant connections.

Bolt Data

Table 9—1 on page 9—5 lists in Imperial units the nominal diameter, nominal area, A_b, and values of the quantity $A_b F_u$ for A325M, A490M, A325, A490 and A307 bolts.

Bolts in Bearing-Type Connections

Table 9—3 on page 9—6 lists the specified minimum tensile strength, F_u, the unit factored shear resistance for threads excluded and threads intercepted and the unit factored tensile resistance of A325M and A490M metric series bolts and of A325, A490 and A307 Imperial series bolts.

Table 9—4 on page 9—6 lists the nominal area, the factored single shear resistance for threads excluded and threads intercepted and the factored tensile resistance for M16 to M36 A325M and A490M bolts and 1/2-inch to 1-1/2-inch A325 and A490 bolts and 5/8, 3/4 and 7/8-inch A307 bolts.

Table 9—6 on page 9—7 lists the factored bearing resistance, B_r, for CSA G40.21 grades 44W, 44WT and 50W steels for material thicknesses from 1/8 inch to 1-1/4 inches and end distances from 3/4 inch to 4 inches.

Bolts in Slip-Resistant Connections

Table 9—7 on page 9—8, lists the unit slip resistance for 5% probability of slip for six surface treatments for A325M, A490M, A325 and A490 bolts.

Table 9—8 on page 9—8 lists the slip resistance for single shear for M16 to M36 A325M and A490M bolts and 1/2-inch to 1-1/2-inch A325 and A490 bolts for two surface treatments.

Weld Data

Tables 9—9 to 9—11 on page 9—9 list the factored shear resistances for partial joint penetration groove (PJPG) welds and fillet welds on the effective throat and on the weld leg size for fillet welds.

Unit Factored Compressive Resistance for Compression Members — See page 9—11.

C_e/A — Euler Buckling Load per Unit of Area

Table 9—14 on page 9—17 lists the values of C_e/A for KL/r ratios varying from 1 to 200. The values of C_e/A have been computed in accordance with the definition in Clause 3.2, CSA S16.1-1974.

Factored Axial Compressive Resistances of Columns — See page 9—19.

Composite Beam Trial Selection Tables — See page 9—81.

Beam Selection Table — See page 9—143.

NOTES

Bolt Size		Nominal Diameter of Bolt (in.)	Nominal Area (A_b) (in.^{2})	$A_b F_u{}^{\ddagger}$ (kips)				
Metric*	Imperial			A325M	A490M	A325	A490	A307
	1/2	0.500	.1963			23.6	29.4	11.8
	5/8	0.625	.3068			36.8	46.0	18.4
M16		0.630	.3116	37.4	47.1			
	3/4	0.750	.4418			53.0	66.3	26.5
M20		0.787	.4869	58.4	73.5			
M22		0.866	.5892	70.7	89.0			
	7/8	0.875	.6013			72.2	90.2	36.1
M24		0.945	.7012	84.1	106			
	1	1.000	.7854			94.2	118	47.1
M27		1.063	.8875	106	134			
	1-1/8	1.125	.9940			104	149	59.6
M30		1.181	1.096	131	165			
	1-1/4	1.250	1.227			129	184	73.6
M36		1.417	1.578	189	238			
	1-1/2	1.500	1.767			186	265	106

*The number following the letter M is the nominal bolt diameter in millimetres.
$\ddagger$See Table 9—3 page 9—6 for specified minimum tensile strengths, F_u.

Table 9-2
CSA S16.1 – 1974 SUMMARY
Bearing-Type Connections

Bolt Situation in Joint	Factored Resistance	Unit Factored Resistance $(n = m = A_b = 1)$	Clause Reference
BOLTS IN SHEAR			13.11.1
Shear on bolts with threads excluded from shear plane.	$V_r = 0.60\,\phi\,n\,m\,A_b\,F_u$	$V_r = 0.40\,F_u$	13.11.1 (b)
Shear on bolts with threads intercepted by shear plane.	$V_r = 0.42\,\phi\,n\,m\,A_b\,F_u$	$V_r = 0.28\,F_u$	
For joints longer than 50 in.	Shear $= 0.80\,V_r$		
Bearing on main material.	$B_r = \phi\,t\,n\,e\,F_u$ $\leqslant 3\phi\,t\,d\,n\,F_u$	$B_r = 0.67\,t\,e\,F_u$ $\leqslant 2.0\,t\,d\,F_u$	13.10 (c)
BOLTS IN TENSION	$T_r = 0.75\,\phi\,n\,A_b F_u$	$T_r = 0.50\,F_u$	13.11.2

Notes:

1. Oversize holes are not permitted in bearing-type connections (see Clause 22.3.2(a) of CSA S16.1-1974 or CAN3-S16.1-M78).

2. See Clause 22.3.2(b), (c) of CSA S16.1-1974 or CAN3-S16.1-M78 re use of slotted holes in bearing-type connections.

3. See Clause 23.3.2(d) of CAN3-S16.1-M78 for hole diameters permitted with M20 or 3/4-inch diameter, M22 or 7/8-inch diameter and M24 or 1 inch diameter bolts.

BOLTS IN BEARING-TYPE CONNECTIONS

UNIT FACTORED SHEAR AND TENSILE RESISTANCES, $\phi = 0.67$

Table 9-3

Bolt Grade	Specified Minimum Tensile Strength, F_u (ksi)	Unit Factored Shear Resistance[†]		Unit Factored Tensile Resistance[†] 0.50 F_u (ksi)
		Threads Excluded 0.40 F_u (ksi)	Threads Intercepted 0.28 F_u (ksi)	
A325M**	120	48	34	60
A490M**	151	61	42	76
A325(d≤1")	120	48	34	60
A325(d≥1-1/8")	105	42	30	53
A490	150	60	42	75
A307*	60	24	17	30

† Rounded to the nearest ksi.

* Use of A307 bolts in connections is covered in Clause 20.12.2 of CSA S16.1-1974 and CAN3-S16.1-M78.

** Values for metric series bolts are based on ASTM specifications A325M and the draft of A490M soft converted to Imperial units.

FACTORED SHEAR AND TENSILE RESISTANCES (Kips per bolt)

Table 9-4

Bolt Size		Nominal Area (A_b) (in.²)	Factored Shear Resistance[†] — Single Shear** (kips/bolt)						Factored Tensile Resistance, T_r (kips/bolt)		
			Threads Excluded			Threads Intercepted[†‡]					
Metric*	Imperial		A325 A325M	A490 A490M	A307	A325 A325M	A490 A490M	A307	A325 A325M	A490 A490M	A307
	1/2	.1963	9.47	11.8		6.63	8.29		11.8	14.8	
	5/8	.3068	14.8	18.5	7.40	10.4	12.9	5.18	18.5	23.1	9.25
M16		.3116	15.0	18.9		10.5	13.2		18.8	23.6	
	3/4	.4418	21.3	26.6	10.7	14.9	18.6	7.46	26.6	33.3	13.3
M20		.4869	23.5	29.6		16.6	20.7		29.4	36.9	
M22		.5892	28.4	35.8		20.0	25.0		35.5	44.7	
	7/8	.6013	29.0	36.3	14.5	20.3	25.4	10.2	36.3	45.3	18.1
M24		.7012	33.8	42.6		23.8	29.8		42.3	53.2	
	1	.7854	37.9	47.4		26.5	33.2		47.4	59.2	
M27		.8875	42.8	53.9		30.2	37.7		53.5	67.3	
	1-1/8	.9940	42.0	59.9		29.4	41.9		52.4	74.9	
M30		1.096	52.9	66.5		37.3	46.6		66.1	83.2	
	1-1/4	1.227	51.8	74.0		36.3	51.8		64.7	92.5	
M36		1.578	76.1	95.8		53.6	67.1		95.2	120	
	1-1/2	1.767	74.8	107		52.3	74.6		93.5	133	

* The number following the letter M is the nominal bolt diameter in millimetres.

† For joints longer than 50 inches use 80% of the factored shear resistance.

** For double shear multiply tabulated values by 2.0.

†‡ Threads assumed to be intercepted when thickness of part adjacent to nut < 3/8 inch unless special precautions are taken.

BOLTS IN BEARING-TYPE CONNECTIONS

Table 9-5   UNIT FACTORED BEARING RESISTANCES

	Material Standard Grade	Specified Minimum Tensile Strength, F_u (ksi)	0.67 F_u (ksi)	Maximum 2.0 F_u (ksi)
CSA G40.21	33 G	55	36.9	110
	38W, 38WT 44W for HSS only	60	40.2	120
	44W, 44WT, 50W	65	43.6	130
	50G, 50WT, 50R, 50A, 50AT 55W and 55WT for HSS only	70	46.9	140
	60W, 60WT, 60A, 60AT	75	50.3	150
	70W, 70WT, 70A, 70AT	85	57.0	170
ASTM	A36	58	38.9	116
	A572 Grade 42	60	40.2	120
	Grade 50	65	43.6	130
	A441 F_y = 42	63	42.2	126
	F_y = 46	67	44.9	134
	F_y = 50	70	46.9	140

FACTORED BEARING RESISTANCE, B_r, (Kips/Bolt)
Table 9-6   G40.21 – 44W, 44WT, 50W*

Material Thickness t (inches)	End Distance**, e (inches)												
	3/4	7/8	1	1-1/4	1-1/2	1-3/4	2	2-1/4	2-1/2	2-3/4	3	3-1/2	4
1/8	4.08	4.76	5.44	6.80	8.17	9.53	10.9	12.2	13.6	15.0	16.3	19.1	21.8
3/16	6.12	7.14	8.17	10.2	12.2	14.3	16.3	18.4	20.4	22.5	24.5	28.6	32.7
1/4	8.17	9.53	10.9	13.6	16.3	19.1	21.8	24.5	27.2	29.9	32.7	38.1	43.6
5/16	10.2	11.9	13.6	17.0	20.4	23.8	27.2	30.6	34.0	37.4	40.8	47.6	54.4
3/8	12.2	14.3	16.3	20.4	24.5	28.6	32.7	36.7	40.8	44.9	49.0	57.2	65.3
7/16	14.3	16.7	19.1	23.8	28.6	33.3	38.1	42.9	47.6	52.4	57.2	66.7	76.2
1/2	16.3	19.1	21.8	27.2	32.7	38.1	43.6	49.0	54.4	59.9	65.3	76.2	87.1
9/16	18.4	21.4	24.5	30.6	36.7	42.9	49.0	55.1	61.2	67.4	73.5	85.7	98.0
5/8	20.4	23.8	27.2	34.0	40.8	47.6	54.4	61.2	68.0	74.9	81.7	95.3	109
11/16	22.5	26.2	29.9	37.4	44.9	52.4	59.9	67.4	74.9	82.3	89.8	105	120
3/4	24.5	28.6	32.7	40.8	49.0	57.2	65.3	73.5	81.7	89.8	98.0	114	131
13/16	26.5	31.0	35.4	44.2	53.1	61.9	70.8	79.6	88.5	97.3	106	124	142
7/8	28.6	33.3	38.1	47.6	57.2	66.7	76.2	85.7	95.3	105	114	133	152
15/16	30.6	35.7	40.8	51.0	61.2	71.4	81.7	91.9	102	112	122	143	163
1	32.7	38.1	43.6	54.4	65.3	76.2	87.1	98.0	109	120	131	152	174
1-1/16	34.7	40.5	46.3	57.8	69.4	81.0	92.5	104	116	127	139	162	185
1-1/8	36.7	42.9	49.0	61.2	73.5	85.7	98.0	110	122	135	147	171	196
1-3/16	38.8	45.3	51.7	64.6	77.6	90.5	103	116	129	142	155	181	207
1-1/4	40.8	47.6	54.4	68.0	81.7	95.3	109	122	136	150	163	191	218

Approx. Range of B_r for bolt diameters, d: 1/2, 5/8, 3/4, 7/8, 1, 1-1/8, 1-1/4, 1-1/2

Approx. e = 3d line

Approx. end distance line (Clause 21.8)

* B_r = 0.67 t e F_u, where F_u = 65 ksi for CSA G40.21 grades 44W, 44WT and 50W.
** When e exceeds 3 times bolt diameter, use B_r for e equal to 3d.

Note: Bolt shear governs if less than bearing. See Table 9-4.

BOLTS IN SLIP-RESISTANT CONNECTIONS

UNIT SLIP RESISTANCES, 0.26 μ F$_u$ (KSI)
For 5% Probability of Slip, μ

Table 9-7

Steel Surface Treatment	Bolt Grade**									
	A325M		A490M		A325 d ≤ 1″		A325 d ≥ 1-1/8″		A490	
	F$_u$ = 120 ksi		F$_u$ = 151 ksi		F$_u$ = 120 ksi		F$_u$ = 105 ksi		F$_u$ = 150 ksi	
	0.26μ F$_u$ (ksi)	μ	0.26μ F$_u$ (ksi)	μ	0.26μ F$_u$ (ksi)	μ	0.26μ F$_u$ (ksi)	μ	0.26μ F$_u$ (ksi)	μ
Tight clean mill scale except quenched and tempered steels	18.4	0.59	20.0	0.51	18.4	0.59	16.1	0.59	19.9	0.51
Blast-cleaned carbon and low-alloy steels	30.9	0.99	34.2	0.87	30.9	0.99	27.0	0.99	33.9	0.87
Blast-cleaned quenched and tempered steel	21.5	0.69	23.6	0.60	21.5	0.69	18.8	0.69	23.4	0.60
Hot-dip galvanized	9.7	0.31	10.6	0.27	9.7	0.31	8.5	0.31	10.5	0.27
Hot-dip galvanized and roughened	23.7	0.76	25.9	0.66	23.7	0.76	20.7	0.76	25.7	0.66
Vinyl treated	19.3	0.62	21.2	0.54	19.3	0.62	16.9	0.62	21.1	0.54

** Values for metric series bolts are based on ASTM specifications A325M and the draft of A490M soft converted to Imperial units.

SLIP RESISTANCES, V$_S$, (Kips/Bolt)**
For Single Shear† (m = 1)

Table 9-8

Bolt Size		Nominal Area A$_b$ (in.²)	Tight Clean Mill Scale Except Q & QT		Blast-Cleaned Carbon and low-alloy steels	
Metric*	Imperial		A325M A325	A490M A490	A325M A325	A490M A490
	1/2	.1963	3.61	3.90	6.06	6.66
	5/8	.3068	5.65	6.10	9.48	10.2
M16		.3116	5.74	6.24	9.62	10.6
	3/4	.4418	8.13	8.78	13.6	15.0
M20		.4869	8.96	9.75	15.0	16.6
M22		.5892	10.8	11.8	18.2	20.1
	7/8	.6013	11.1	12.0	18.6	21.0
M24		.7012	12.9	14.0	21.7	24.0
	1	.7854	14.5	15.6	24.3	26.6
M27		.8875	16.3	17.8	27.4	30.3
	1-1/8	.9940	16.0	19.8	26.9	33.7
M30		1.096	20.2	21.9	33.9	37.4
	1-1/4	1.227	19.8	24.4	33.2	41.6
M36		1.578	29.0	31.6	48.7	53.9
	1-1/2	1.767	28.5	35.1	47.9	59.9

** These resistances are for use with specified loads in accordance with Clause 13.12 of CSA S16.1-1974.

* The number following the letter M is the nominal bolt diameter in millimetres.

† For double shear (m = 2) multiply tabulated values by 2.0.

IMP

WELD DATA
UNIT FACTORED SHEAR RESISTANCE OF WELD METAL, $\phi = 0.90$

Table 9-9

Electrode Classification	Groove Welds and Fillet Welds Unit Factored Shear Resistance on Effective Throat A_W, $(0.50\,\phi\,X_u)$ (ksi)	Fillet Welds Unit Factored Shear Resistance per 1/16-inch of Fillet Size per inch of length
E60XX	27.0	1.19
E70XX	31.5	1.39
E80XX	36.0	1.59
E90XX	40.5	1.79
E100XX	45.0	1.99
E110XX	49.5	2.19
E120XX	54.0	2.39

FACTORED SHEAR RESISTANCE ON EFFECTIVE THROAT PER INCH OF WELD LENGTH (Kips)

Table 9-10

Electrode Classification	Unit Shear Resistance (kips)	Effective Throat Thickness (inch)												
		3/16	1/4	5/16	3/8	7/16	1/2	9/16	5/8	11/16	3/4	13/16	7/8	15/16
E60XX	27.0	5.06	6.75	8.44	10.1	11.8	13.5	15.2	16.9	18.6	20.3	21.9	23.6	25.3
E70XX	31.5	5.91	7.88	9.84	11.8	13.8	15.8	17.7	19.7	21.7	23.6	25.6	27.6	29.5
E80XX	36.0	6.75	9.00	11.6	13.5	15.8	18.0	20.3	22.5	24.8	27.0	29.3	31.5	33.8
E90XX	40.5	7.59	10.1	12.7	15.2	17.7	20.3	22.8	25.3	27.8	30.4	32.9	35.4	38.0
E100XX	45.0	8.44	11.3	14.1	16.9	19.7	22.5	25.3	28.1	30.9	33.8	36.6	39.4	42.2
E110XX	49.5	9.28	12.4	15.5	18.6	21.7	24.8	27.8	30.9	34.0	37.1	40.2	43.3	46.4
E120XX	54.0	10.1	13.5	16.9	20.3	23.6	27.0	30.4	33.8	37.1	40.5	43.9	47.3	50.6

FACTORED SHEAR RESISTANCE OF FILLET WELDS PER INCH OF WELD LENGTH (Kips)

Table 9-11

Electrode Classification	Unit Shear Resistance	Fillet Weld Size D (inch)									
		3/16	1/4	5/16	3/8	7/16	1/2	9/16	5/8	11/16	3/4
E60XX	1.19	3.58	4.77	5.97	7.16	8.35	9.55	10.7	11.9	13.1	14.3
E70XX	1.39	4.18	5.57	6.96	8.35	9.74	11.1	12.5	13.9	15.3	16.7
E80XX	1.59	4.77	6.36	7.95	9.55	11.1	12.7	14.3	15.9	17.5	19.1
E90XX	1.79	5.37	7.16	8.95	10.7	12.5	14.3	16.1	17.9	19.7	21.5
E100XX	1.99	5.97	7.95	9.94	11.9	13.9	15.9	17.9	19.9	21.9	23.9
E110XX	2.19	6.56	8.75	10.9	13.1	15.3	17.5	19.7	21.9	24.1	26.2
E120XX	2.39	7.16	9.55	11.9	14.3	16.7	19.1	21.5	23.9	26.2	28.6

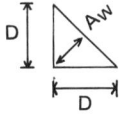

$A_W = D/\sqrt{2}$

\# Factored resistance of 1 inch of fillet weld leg size per inch of length.

NOTES

UNIT FACTORED COMPRESSIVE RESISTANCES FOR COMPRESSION MEMBERS, C_r/A

General

Table 9—12 on pages 9—12 to 9—15 lists the unit factored compressive resistance, C_r/A, in ksi, for compression members for steels with specified minimum yield points varying from 36 ksi to 100 ksi. The values for F_y = 44 are printed in bold faced type. The unit factored compressive resistances have been calculated in accordance with the requirements of Clause 13.3.1, CSA Standard S16.1-1974, "Steel Structures for Buildings — Limit States Design", for values of KL/r from 1 to 200.

Table 9—13 on page 9—16 lists the unit factored compressive resistance, C_r/A, for compression members consisting of hollow structural sections (HSS) manufactured according to CSA Standard G40.20, Class H for steel with a specified minimum yield point of 50 ksi. The unit factored compressive resistances have been calculated in accordance with the requirements of Clause 13.3.2 of CSA Standard S16.1-1974 for values of KL/r from 1 to 200.

For examples on the use of similar tables in SI units refer to page 4—8.

Notes:

1. Tables of C_r, factored axial compressive resistance, for columns in CSA G40.21 — 44W steel are given on pages 9—20 to 9—30.

2. Tables of C_r for HSS Class C columns in CSA G40.21 — 50W steel are given on pages 9—32 to 9—55.

3. Tables of C_r for HSS Class H columns in CSA G40.21 — 50W steel are given on pages 9—56 to 9—79.

Note:

CSA Standard S16.1-1974 has been revised to be consistant with CAN3-S16.1-M78 as reprinted in Part 1 of this Handbook. Clause references to CSA S16.1-1974 in Part 9 of this Handbook refer to this latest revision. The revision to CSA Standard S16.1-1974 is to be printed by CSA in Supplement No. 2 during 1981.

UNIT FACTORED COMPRESSIVE RESISTANCES, C_r/A (KSI)* FOR COMPRESSION MEMBERS

Table 9-12

$\emptyset = 0.90$

$\dfrac{KL}{r}$	F_y (ksi)									
	36	38	40	42	44	50	55	60	70	100
1	32.4	34.2	36.0	37.8	**39.6**	45.0	49.5	54.0	63.0	90.0
2	32.4	34.2	36.0	37.8	**39.6**	45.0	49.5	54.0	63.0	90.0
3	32.4	34.2	36.0	37.8	**39.6**	45.0	49.5	54.0	63.0	90.0
4	32.4	34.2	36.0	37.8	**39.6**	45.0	49.5	54.0	63.0	90.0
5	32.4	34.2	36.0	37.8	**39.6**	45.0	49.5	54.0	63.0	90.0
6	32.4	34.2	36.0	37.8	**39.6**	45.0	49.5	54.0	63.0	90.0
7	32.4	34.2	36.0	37.8	**39.6**	45.0	49.5	54.0	63.0	90.0
8	32.4	34.2	36.0	37.8	**39.6**	45.0	49.5	54.0	63.0	90.0
9	32.4	34.2	36.0	37.8	**39.6**	45.0	49.5	54.0	63.0	89.5
10	32.4	34.2	36.0	37.8	**39.6**	45.0	49.5	54.0	62.9	89.1
11	32.4	34.2	36.0	37.8	**39.6**	45.0	49.5	53.8	62.6	88.6
12	32.4	34.2	36.0	37.8	**39.6**	44.9	49.3	53.6	62.3	88.1
13	32.4	34.2	36.0	37.7	**39.5**	44.7	49.1	53.4	62.0	87.6
14	32.3	34.1	35.8	37.6	**39.3**	44.6	48.9	53.2	61.7	87.0
15	32.2	34.0	35.7	37.5	**39.2**	44.4	48.7	53.0	61.5	86.5
16	32.1	33.9	35.6	37.3	**39.1**	44.2	48.5	52.7	61.1	85.9
17	32.0	33.8	35.5	37.2	**38.9**	44.0	48.3	52.5	60.8	85.4
18	31.9	33.6	35.4	37.1	**38.8**	43.8	48.1	52.2	60.5	84.8
19	31.8	33.5	35.2	36.9	**38.6**	43.7	47.8	52.0	60.2	84.2
20	31.7	33.4	35.1	36.8	**38.5**	43.5	47.6	51.7	59.9	83.6
21	31.6	33.3	35.0	36.6	**38.3**	43.3	47.4	51.5	59.5	82.9
22	31.5	33.2	34.8	36.5	**38.1**	43.1	47.2	51.2	59.2	82.3
23	31.4	33.0	34.7	36.3	**38.0**	42.9	46.9	50.9	58.8	81.6
24	31.3	32.9	34.6	36.2	**37.8**	42.7	46.7	50.7	58.5	81.0
25	31.1	32.8	34.4	36.0	**37.7**	42.5	46.4	50.4	58.1	80.3
26	31.0	32.6	34.3	35.9	**37.5**	42.3	46.2	50.1	57.7	79.6
27	30.9	32.5	34.1	35.7	**37.3**	42.1	46.0	49.8	57.3	78.9
28	30.8	32.4	34.0	35.6	**37.1**	41.8	45.7	49.5	57.0	78.2
29	30.6	32.2	33.8	35.4	**37.0**	41.6	45.4	49.2	56.6	77.4
30	30.5	32.1	33.7	35.2	**36.8**	41.4	45.2	48.9	56.2	76.7
31	30.4	32.0	33.5	35.1	**36.6**	41.2	44.9	48.6	55.7	75.9
32	30.3	31.8	33.4	34.9	**36.4**	40.9	44.6	48.3	55.3	75.1
33	30.1	31.7	33.2	34.7	**36.2**	40.7	44.4	47.9	54.9	74.3
34	30.0	31.5	33.0	34.6	**36.1**	40.5	44.1	47.6	54.5	73.5
35	29.9	31.4	32.9	34.4	**35.9**	40.2	43.8	47.3	54.0	72.7
36	29.7	31.2	32.7	34.2	**35.7**	40.0	43.5	46.9	53.6	71.9
37	29.6	31.1	32.6	34.0	**35.5**	39.7	43.2	46.6	53.2	71.0
38	29.4	30.9	32.4	33.8	**35.3**	39.5	42.9	46.3	52.7	70.2
39	29.3	30.8	32.2	33.6	**35.1**	39.2	42.6	45.9	52.2	69.3
40	29.2	30.6	32.0	33.5	**34.9**	39.0	42.3	45.6	51.8	68.4
41	29.0	30.4	31.9	33.3	**34.6**	38.7	42.0	45.2	51.3	67.5
42	28.9	30.3	31.7	33.1	**34.4**	38.5	41.7	44.8	50.8	66.6
43	28.7	30.1	31.5	32.9	**34.2**	38.2	41.4	44.5	50.3	65.6
44	28.6	29.9	31.3	32.7	**34.0**	37.9	41.0	44.1	49.8	64.7
45	28.4	29.8	31.1	32.5	**33.8**	37.6	40.7	43.7	49.3	63.7
46	28.2	29.6	30.9	32.3	**33.6**	37.4	40.4	43.3	48.8	62.7
47	28.1	29.4	30.8	32.1	**33.3**	37.1	40.1	42.9	48.3	61.8
48	27.9	29.3	30.6	31.8	**33.1**	36.8	39.7	42.5	47.8	60.8
49	27.8	29.1	30.4	31.6	**32.9**	36.5	39.4	42.1	47.2	59.7
50	27.6	28.9	30.2	31.4	**32.6**	36.2	39.0	41.7	46.7	58.7

*Calculated in accordance with Clause 13.3.1 of CSA S16.1-1974.
For Class H hollow structural sections, see Table 9-13, page 9-16.

UNIT FACTORED COMPRESSIVE RESISTANCES, C$_r$/A (KSI)* FOR COMPRESSION MEMBERS
$\phi = 0.90$

$$\frac{KL}{r} = 51 \text{ to } 100$$

Table 9-13

$\frac{KL}{r}$	F$_y$ (ksi)									
	36	38	40	42	44	50	55	60	70	100
51	27.4	28.7	30.0	31.2	32.4	35.9	38.7	41.3	46.2	57.7
52	27.3	28.5	29.8	31.0	32.2	35.6	38.3	40.9	45.6	56.6
53	27.1	28.3	29.6	30.8	31.9	35.3	38.0	40.5	45.0	55.5
54	26.9	28.2	29.4	30.5	31.7	35.0	37.6	40.0	44.5	54.4
55	26.8	28.0	29.2	30.3	31.4	34.7	37.2	39.6	43.9	53.1
56	26.6	27.8	28.9	30.1	31.2	34.4	36.8	39.2	43.3	51.8
57	26.4	27.6	28.7	29.8	30.9	34.1	36.5	38.7	42.7	50.6
58	26.2	27.4	28.5	29.6	30.7	33.7	36.1	38.3	42.2	49.5
59	26.1	27.2	28.3	29.4	30.4	33.4	35.7	37.8	41.6	48.4
60	25.9	27.0	28.1	29.1	30.2	33.1	35.3	37.4	40.9	47.3
61	25.7	26.8	27.9	28.9	29.9	32.8	34.9	36.9	40.3	46.2
62	25.5	26.6	27.6	28.7	29.6	32.4	34.5	36.4	39.7	45.2
63	25.3	26.4	27.4	28.4	29.4	32.1	34.1	36.0	39.1	44.3
64	25.1	26.2	27.2	28.2	29.1	31.7	33.7	35.5	38.5	43.3
65	24.9	26.0	27.0	27.9	28.8	31.4	33.3	35.0	37.7	42.4
66	24.7	25.8	26.7	27.7	28.6	31.0	32.9	34.5	37.0	41.6
67	24.6	25.5	26.5	27.4	28.3	30.7	32.5	34.0	36.2	40.7
68	24.4	25.3	26.2	27.1	28.0	30.3	32.0	33.5	35.5	39.9
69	24.2	25.1	26.0	26.9	27.7	30.0	31.6	33.0	34.8	39.1
70	24.0	24.9	25.8	26.6	27.4	29.6	31.2	32.5	34.2	38.3
71	23.8	24.7	25.5	26.3	27.1	29.2	30.7	31.9	33.5	37.6
72	23.6	24.4	25.3	26.1	26.8	28.9	30.3	31.3	32.9	36.9
73	23.4	24.2	25.0	25.8	26.5	28.5	29.8	30.7	32.3	36.2
74	23.1	24.0	24.8	25.5	26.2	28.1	29.3	30.2	31.7	35.5
75	22.9	23.8	24.5	25.3	25.9	27.7	28.8	29.6	31.2	34.8
76	22.7	23.5	24.3	25.0	25.6	27.4	28.3	29.1	30.6	34.2
77	22.5	23.3	24.0	24.7	25.3	26.9	27.8	28.6	30.1	33.6
78	22.3	23.1	23.8	24.4	25.0	26.4	27.3	28.1	29.5	33.0
79	22.1	22.8	23.5	24.1	24.7	26.0	26.8	27.6	29.0	32.4
80	21.9	22.6	23.2	23.8	24.4	25.6	26.4	27.2	28.5	31.8
81	21.7	22.3	23.0	23.6	24.1	25.2	26.0	26.7	28.1	31.2
82	21.4	22.1	22.7	23.3	23.7	24.7	25.5	26.3	27.6	30.7
83	21.2	21.8	22.4	23.0	23.3	24.3	25.1	25.8	27.1	30.2
84	21.0	21.6	22.2	22.6	23.0	24.0	24.7	25.4	26.7	29.6
85	20.8	21.3	21.9	22.3	22.6	23.6	24.3	25.0	26.3	29.1
86	20.5	21.1	21.6	21.9	22.3	23.2	23.9	24.6	25.8	28.6
87	20.3	20.9	21.2	21.6	21.9	22.9	23.6	24.2	25.4	28.2
88	20.1	20.5	20.9	21.3	21.6	22.5	23.2	23.9	25.0	27.7
89	19.8	20.2	20.6	20.9	21.3	22.2	22.9	23.5	24.6	27.2
90	19.6	19.9	20.3	20.6	20.9	21.8	22.5	23.1	24.2	26.8
91	19.3	19.7	20.0	20.3	20.6	21.5	22.2	22.8	23.9	26.4
92	19.0	19.4	19.7	20.0	20.3	21.2	21.8	22.4	23.5	25.9
93	18.8	19.1	19.4	19.7	20.0	20.9	21.5	22.1	23.1	25.5
94	18.5	18.8	19.1	19.5	19.8	20.6	21.2	21.8	22.8	25.1
95	18.2	18.6	18.9	19.2	19.5	20.3	20.9	21.5	22.5	24.7
96	18.0	18.3	18.6	18.9	19.2	20.0	20.6	21.1	22.1	24.3
97	17.7	18.0	18.4	18.6	18.9	19.7	20.3	20.8	21.8	24.0
98	17.5	17.8	18.1	18.4	18.7	19.4	20.0	20.5	21.5	23.6
99	17.2	17.6	17.9	18.1	18.4	19.2	19.7	20.3	21.2	23.2
100	17.0	17.3	17.6	17.9	18.2	18.9	19.5	20.0	20.9	22.9

*Calculated in accordance with Clause 13.3.1 of CSA S16.1-1974.
For Class H hollow structural sections, see Table 9-13, page 9-16.

UNIT FACTORED COMPRESSIVE RESISTANCES, C_r/A (KSI)* FOR COMPRESSION MEMBERS

Table 9-12

$\phi = 0.90$

$\dfrac{KL}{r}$	F_y (ksi)									
	36	38	40	42	44	50	55	60	70	100
101	16.8	17.1	17.4	17.7	**17.9**	18.6	19.2	19.7	20.6	22.5
102	16.6	16.9	17.1	17.4	**17.7**	18.4	18.9	19.4	20.3	22.2
103	16.4	16.6	16.9	17.2	**17.4**	18.1	18.7	19.1	20.0	21.9
104	16.1	16.4	16.7	17.0	**17.2**	17.9	18.4	18.9	19.7	21.5
105	15.9	16.2	16.5	16.7	**17.0**	17.7	18.2	18.6	19.4	21.2
106	15.7	16.0	16.3	16.5	**16.8**	17.4	17.9	18.4	19.2	20.9
107	15.5	15.8	16.1	16.3	**16.5**	17.2	17.7	18.1	18.9	20.5
108	15.3	15.6	15.9	16.1	**16.3**	17.0	17.5	17.9	18.7	20.2
109	15.1	15.4	15.7	15.9	**16.1**	16.8	17.2	17.7	18.4	19.8
110	15.0	15.2	15.5	15.7	**15.9**	16.5	17.0	17.4	18.2	19.5
111	14.8	15.0	15.3	15.5	**15.7**	16.3	16.8	17.2	17.9	19.1
112	14.6	14.8	15.1	15.3	**15.5**	16.1	16.6	17.0	17.7	18.8
113	14.4	14.7	14.9	15.1	**15.3**	15.9	16.4	16.8	17.4	18.5
114	14.2	14.5	14.7	14.9	**15.1**	15.7	16.2	16.5	17.2	18.2
115	14.1	14.3	14.5	14.8	**15.0**	15.5	15.9	16.3	17.0	17.9
116	13.9	14.1	14.4	14.6	**14.8**	15.3	15.7	16.1	16.8	17.6
117	13.7	14.0	14.2	14.4	**14.6**	15.1	15.6	15.9	16.5	17.3
118	13.6	13.8	14.0	14.2	**14.4**	15.0	15.4	15.7	16.3	17.0
119	13.4	13.6	13.9	14.1	**14.3**	14.8	15.2	15.5	16.1	16.8
120	13.3	13.5	13.7	13.9	**14.1**	14.6	15.0	15.3	15.9	16.5
121	13.1	13.3	13.5	13.7	**13.9**	14.4	14.8	15.1	15.7	16.2
122	13.0	13.2	13.4	13.6	**13.8**	14.3	14.6	15.0	15.5	16.0
123	12.8	13.0	13.2	13.4	**13.6**	14.1	14.5	14.8	15.3	15.7
124	12.7	12.9	13.1	13.3	**13.4**	13.9	14.3	14.6	15.1	15.5
125	12.5	12.7	12.9	13.1	**13.3**	13.8	14.1	14.4	14.9	15.3
126	12.4	12.6	12.8	13.0	**13.1**	13.6	13.9	14.2	14.8	15.0
127	12.3	12.5	12.6	12.8	**13.0**	13.4	13.8	14.1	14.6	14.8
128	12.1	12.3	12.5	12.7	**12.8**	13.3	13.6	13.9	14.4	14.6
129	12.0	12.2	12.4	12.5	**12.7**	13.1	13.5	13.7	14.1	14.4
130	11.9	12.1	12.2	12.4	**12.6**	13.0	13.3	13.6	13.9	14.2
131	11.7	11.9	12.1	12.3	**12.4**	12.8	13.1	13.4	13.7	14.0
132	11.6	11.8	12.0	12.1	**12.3**	12.7	13.0	13.3	13.5	13.8
133	11.5	11.7	11.8	12.0	**12.1**	12.6	12.8	13.1	13.3	13.6
134	11.4	11.5	11.7	11.9	**12.0**	12.4	12.7	13.0	13.1	13.4
135	11.2	11.4	11.6	11.7	**11.9**	12.3	12.6	12.8	13.0	13.2
136	11.1	11.3	11.5	11.6	**11.8**	12.1	12.4	12.7	12.8	13.0
137	11.0	11.2	11.3	11.5	**11.6**	12.0	12.3	12.5	12.6	12.8
138	10.9	11.1	11.2	11.4	**11.5**	11.9	12.1	12.4	12.4	12.7
139	10.8	10.9	11.1	11.2	**11.4**	11.7	12.0	12.2	12.3	12.5
140	10.7	10.8	11.0	11.1	**11.3**	11.6	11.9	12.0	12.1	12.3
141	10.6	10.7	10.9	11.0	**11.1**	11.5	11.7	11.8	11.9	12.2
142	10.5	10.6	10.8	10.9	**11.0**	11.4	11.6	11.7	11.8	12.0
143	10.3	10.5	10.6	10.8	**10.9**	11.2	11.5	11.5	11.6	11.9
144	10.2	10.4	10.5	10.7	**10.8**	11.1	11.4	11.4	11.5	11.7
145	10.1	10.3	10.4	10.6	**10.7**	11.0	11.2	11.2	11.3	11.6
146	10.0	10.2	10.3	10.4	**10.6**	10.9	11.0	11.1	11.2	11.4
147	9.94	10.1	10.2	10.3	**10.5**	10.8	10.9	10.9	11.0	11.3
148	9.84	9.98	10.1	10.2	**10.4**	10.7	10.8	10.8	10.9	11.1
149	9.74	9.88	10.0	10.1	**10.2**	10.5	10.6	10.7	10.7	11.0
150	9.65	9.78	9.91	10.0	**10.1**	10.4	10.5	10.5	10.6	10.9

*Calculated in accordance with Clause 13.3.1 of CSA S16.1-1974.
For Class H hollow structural sections, see Table 9-13, page 9-16.

$\dfrac{KL}{r}$	F_y (ksi)									
	36	38	40	42	44	50	55	60	70	100
151	9.55	9.69	9.81	9.93	**10.0**	10.3	10.4	10.4	10.5	10.7
152	9.46	9.59	9.72	9.83	**9.94**	10.2	10.2	10.3	10.3	10.6
153	9.37	9.50	9.62	9.73	**9.84**	10.1	10.1	10.1	10.2	10.5
154	9.28	9.41	9.53	9.64	**9.74**	9.93	9.97	10.0	10.1	10.3
155	9.19	9.32	9.43	9.54	**9.64**	9.81	9.85	9.89	9.97	10.2
156	9.10	9.23	9.34	9.45	**9.55**	9.69	9.73	9.77	9.85	10.1
157	9.02	9.14	9.25	9.35	**9.45**	9.57	9.61	9.65	9.73	9.98
158	8.93	9.05	9.16	9.26	**9.36**	9.45	9.50	9.54	9.62	9.86
159	8.85	8.96	9.07	9.17	**9.27**	9.34	9.38	9.42	9.50	9.75
160	8.76	8.88	8.98	9.08	**9.18**	9.23	9.27	9.31	9.39	9.63
161	8.68	8.79	8.90	9.00	**9.09**	9.12	9.16	9.20	9.28	9.53
162	8.60	8.71	8.81	8.91	**8.96**	9.01	9.05	9.09	9.18	9.42
163	8.52	8.63	8.73	8.82	**8.86**	8.91	8.95	8.99	9.07	9.31
164	8.44	8.55	8.65	8.74	**8.76**	8.80	8.84	8.89	8.97	9.21
165	8.36	8.47	8.57	8.66	**8.65**	8.70	8.74	8.78	8.86	9.11
166	8.29	8.39	8.48	8.54	**8.55**	8.60	8.64	8.68	8.77	9.01
167	8.21	8.31	8.41	8.44	**8.46**	8.51	8.55	8.59	8.67	8.91
168	8.13	8.23	8.33	8.34	**8.36**	8.41	8.45	8.49	8.57	8.81
169	8.06	8.16	8.25	8.25	**8.27**	8.31	8.36	8.40	8.48	8.72
170	7.99	8.08	8.14	8.16	**8.17**	8.22	8.26	8.30	8.38	8.63
171	7.91	8.01	8.05	8.07	**8.08**	8.13	8.17	8.21	8.29	8.54
172	7.84	7.94	7.96	7.98	**7.99**	8.04	8.08	8.12	8.20	8.45
173	7.77	7.86	7.87	7.89	**7.90**	7.95	7.99	8.03	8.12	8.36
174	7.70	7.77	7.79	7.80	**7.82**	7.87	7.91	7.95	8.03	8.27
175	7.63	7.68	7.70	7.72	**7.73**	7.78	7.82	7.86	7.94	8.19
176	7.57	7.60	7.62	7.63	**7.65**	7.70	7.74	7.78	7.86	8.10
177	7.50	7.52	7.53	7.55	**7.57**	7.62	7.66	7.70	7.78	8.02
178	7.43	7.44	7.45	7.47	**7.49**	7.54	7.58	7.62	7.70	7.94
179	7.34	7.36	7.37	7.39	**7.41**	7.46	7.50	7.54	7.62	7.86
180	7.26	7.28	7.30	7.31	**7.33**	7.38	7.42	7.46	7.54	7.78
181	7.19	7.20	7.22	7.24	**7.25**	7.30	7.34	7.38	7.46	7.71
182	7.11	7.13	7.14	7.16	**7.18**	7.23	7.27	7.31	7.39	7.63
183	7.04	7.05	7.07	7.09	**7.10**	7.15	7.19	7.23	7.31	7.56
184	6.96	6.98	7.00	7.01	**7.03**	7.08	7.12	7.16	7.24	7.48
185	6.89	6.91	6.92	6.94	**6.96**	7.01	7.05	7.09	7.17	7.41
186	6.82	6.84	6.85	6.87	**6.89**	6.94	6.98	7.02	7.10	7.34
187	6.75	6.77	6.78	6.80	**6.82**	6.87	6.91	6.95	7.03	7.27
188	6.68	6.70	6.72	6.73	**6.75**	6.80	6.84	6.88	6.96	7.20
189	6.62	6.63	6.65	6.66	**6.68**	6.73	6.77	6.81	6.89	7.13
190	6.55	6.57	6.58	6.60	**6.61**	6.66	6.70	6.74	6.82	7.07
191	6.48	6.50	6.52	6.53	**6.55**	6.60	6.64	6.68	6.76	7.00
192	6.42	6.44	6.45	6.47	**6.48**	6.53	6.57	6.61	6.70	6.94
193	6.36	6.37	6.39	6.41	**6.42**	6.47	6.51	6.55	6.63	6.92
194	6.29	6.31	6.33	6.34	**6.36**	6.41	6.45	6.49	6.57	6.84
195	6.23	6.25	6.27	6.28	**6.30**	6.35	6.39	6.43	6.51	6.77
196	6.17	6.19	6.20	6.22	**6.24**	6.29	6.33	6.37	6.45	6.71
197	6.11	6.13	6.15	6.16	**6.18**	6.23	6.27	6.31	6.39	6.64
198	6.05	6.07	6.09	6.10	**6.12**	6.17	6.21	6.25	6.33	6.57
199	6.00	6.01	6.03	6.04	**6.06**	6.11	6.15	6.19	6.27	6.50
200	5.94	5.96	5.97	5.99	**6.00**	6.05	6.09	6.13	6.21	6.44

*Calculated in accordance with Clause 13.3.1 of CSA S16.1-1974.
 For Class H hollow structural sections, see Table 9-13, page 9-16.

HSS CLASS H
Fy = 50 KSI

UNIT FACTORED COMPRESSIVE
RESISTANCES, C$_r$/A (KSI)*
FOR CLASS H HOLLOW STRUCTURAL SECTIONS

Table 9-13

$\emptyset = 0.90$

$\dfrac{KL}{r}$	$\dfrac{C_r}{A}$ (ksi)	$\dfrac{KL}{r}$	$\dfrac{C_r}{A}$ (ksi)	$\dfrac{KL}{r}$	$\dfrac{C_r}{A}$ (ksi)	$\dfrac{KL}{r}$	$\dfrac{C_r}{A}$ (ksi)	$\dfrac{KL}{r}$	$\dfrac{C_r}{A}$ (ksi)
1	45.0	41	42.7	81	31.5	121	16.4	161	9.72
2	45.0	42	42.5	82	31.1	122	16.2	162	9.61
3	45.0	43	42.3	83	30.7	123	15.9	163	9.49
4	45.0	44	42.2	84	30.3	124	15.7	164	9.38
5	45.0	45	42.0	85	29.9	125	15.5	165	9.27
6	45.0	46	41.8	86	29.5	126	15.3	166	9.17
7	45.0	47	41.6	87	29.0	127	15.1	167	9.06
8	45.0	48	41.4	88	28.6	128	14.9	168	8.96
9	45.0	49	41.2	89	28.2	129	14.7	169	8.86
10	45.0	50	41.0	90	27.7	130	14.5	170	8.76
11	45.0	51	40.7	91	27.2	131	14.3	171	8.66
12	45.0	52	40.5	92	26.7	132	14.1	172	8.56
13	45.0	53	40.3	93	26.2	133	14.0	173	8.47
14	45.0	54	40.1	94	25.6	134	13.8	174	8.37
15	45.0	55	39.8	95	25.2	135	13.6	175	8.28
16	45.0	56	39.6	96	24.7	136	13.5	176	8.19
17	44.9	57	39.3	97	24.2	137	13.3	177	8.11
18	44.9	58	39.1	98	23.8	138	13.1	178	8.02
19	44.9	59	38.8	99	23.3	139	12.9	179	7.93
20	44.8	60	38.5	100	22.9	140	12.7	180	7.85
21	44.8	61	38.2	101	22.5	141	12.6	181	7.77
22	44.7	62	38.0	102	22.1	142	12.4	182	7.69
23	44.7	63	37.7	103	21.7	143	12.2	183	7.61
24	44.6	64	37.4	104	21.4	144	12.1	184	7.53
25	44.6	65	37.1	105	21.0	145	11.9	185	7.45
26	44.5	66	36.8	106	20.7	146	11.7	186	7.37
27	44.4	67	36.5	107	20.3	147	11.6	187	7.30
28	44.3	68	36.1	108	20.0	148	11.4	188	7.23
29	44.2	69	35.8	109	19.7	149	11.3	189	7.15
30	44.1	70	35.5	110	19.3	150	11.1	190	7.08
31	44.0	71	35.2	111	19.0	151	11.0	191	7.01
32	43.9	72	34.8	112	18.7	152	10.9	192	6.94
33	43.8	73	34.5	113	18.5	153	10.7	193	6.87
34	43.7	74	34.1	114	18.2	154	10.6	194	6.81
35	43.6	75	33.8	115	17.9	155	10.5	195	6.74
36	43.4	76	33.4	116	17.6	156	10.3	196	6.68
37	43.3	77	33.0	117	17.4	157	10.2	197	6.61
38	43.1	78	32.7	118	17.1	158	10.1	198	6.55
39	43.0	79	32.3	119	16.9	159	9.96	199	6.49
40	42.8	80	31.9	120	16.6	160	9.84	200	6.43

*Calculated in accordance with Clause 13.3.2 of CSA S16.1-1974.
 For Class C HSS use Table 9-12, pages 9-12 to 9-15.

$\frac{KL}{r}$	$\frac{C_e}{A}$ (ksi)	$\frac{KL}{r}$	$\frac{C_e}{A}$ (ksi)	$\frac{KL}{r}$	$\frac{C_e}{A}$ (ksi)	$\frac{KL}{r}$	$\frac{C_e}{A}$ (ksi)	$\frac{KL}{r}$	$\frac{C_e}{A}$ (ksi)
1	286000	41	170	81	43.6	121	19.5	161	11.0
2	71500	42	162	82	42.5	122	19.2	162	10.9
3	31778	43	155	83	41.5	123	18.9	163	10.8
4	17875	44	148	84	40.5	124	18.6	164	10.6
5	11440	45	141	85	39.6	125	18.3	165	10.5
6	7944	46	135	86	38.7	126	18.0	166	10.4
7	5837	47	129	87	37.8	127	17.7	167	10.3
8	4469	48	124	88	36.9	128	17.5	168	10.1
9	3531	49	119	89	36.1	129	17.2	169	10.0
10	2860	50	114	90	35.3	130	16.9	170	9.90
11	2364	51	110	91	34.5	131	16.7	171	9.78
12	1986	52	106	92	33.8	132	16.4	172	9.67
13	1692	53	102	93	33.1	133	16.2	173	9.56
14	1459	54	98.1	94	32.4	134	15.9	174	9.45
15	1271	55	94.5	95	31.7	135	15.7	175	9.34
16	1117	56	91.2	96	31.0	136	15.5	176	9.23
17	990	57	88.0	97	30.4	137	15.2	177	9.13
18	883	58	85.0	98	29.8	138	15.0	178	9.03
19	792	59	82.2	99	29.2	139	14.8	179	8.93
20	715	60	79.4	100	28.6	140	14.6	180	8.83
21	649	61	76.9	101	28.0	141	14.4	181	8.73
22	591	62	74.4	102	27.5	142	14.2	182	8.63
23	541	63	72.1	103	27.0	143	14.0	183	8.54
24	497	64	69.8	104	26.4	144	13.8	184	8.45
25	458	65	67.7	105	25.9	145	13.6	185	8.36
26	423	66	65.7	106	25.5	146	13.4	186	8.27
27	392	67	63.7	107	25.0	147	13.2	187	8.18
28	365	68	61.9	108	24.5	148	13.1	188	8.09
29	340	69	60.1	109	24.1	149	12.9	189	8.01
30	318	70	58.4	110	23.6	150	12.7	190	7.92
31	298	71	56.7	111	23.2	151	12.5	191	7.84
32	279	72	55.2	112	22.8	152	12.4	192	7.76
33	263	73	53.7	113	22.4	153	12.2	193	7.68
34	247	74	52.2	114	22.0	154	12.1	194	7.60
35	233	75	50.8	115	21.6	155	11.9	195	7.52
36	221	76	49.5	116	21.3	156	11.8	196	7.44
37	209	77	48.2	117	20.9	157	11.6	197	7.37
38	198	78	47.0	118	20.5	158	11.5	198	7.30
39	188	79	45.8	119	20.2	159	11.3	199	7.22
40	179	80	44.7	120	19.9	160	11.2	200	7.15

To obtain C_e in kips, multiply tabular value by the cross sectional area A_x, in.^{2}. Divide C_e into the factored compressive load, C_f, to obtain C_f/C_e; then enter Table 4–9 to determine the amplification factor, U.

NOTES

FACTORED AXIAL COMPRESSIVE RESISTANCES OF COLUMNS

Tables

The tables on pages 9—20 to 9—55 inclusive list the factored axial compressive resistances, C_r, in kips, for WWF and W shapes, the M100 × 19 and Class C HSS. The factored axial compressive resistances have been computed, for effective lengths with respect to the least radius of gyration varying from 0 feet to a maximum of 40 feet, in accordance with the requirements of Clauses 13.3.1 and 13.3.3 CSA Standard S16.1-1974, "Steel Structures for Buildings — Limit States Design".

The tables on pages 9—56 to 9—79 inclusive list the factored axial compressive resistances, C_r, in kips, for Class H HSS computed in accordance with the requirements of Clauses 13.3.2 and 13.3.3 of CSA S16.1-1974.

The factored axial compressive resistances for Class 4 sections have been computed in accordance with the requirements of Clause 13.3.3 of S16.1-1974 and are so identified in the tables.

At the top of each table is listed the applicable steel grade. The metric designation of each shape is given at the top of the columns while the equivalent Imperial size and mass are listed at the bottom.

Symbols

Area = Total cross-sectional area, in.^{2}

Z_x = Plastic section modulus for bending about X—X axis, in.^{3}

S_x = Elastic section modulus for bending about X—X axis, in.^{3}

r_x = Radius of gyration about the strong, X—X, axis, in.

Z_y = Plastic section modulus for bending about Y—Y axis, in.^{3}

S_y = Elastic section modulus for bending about Y—Y axis, in.^{3}

r_y = Radius of gyration about the weak, Y—Y, axis, in.

r_x/r_y = Ratio of radius of gyration of X—X axis to that for Y—Y axis.

M_{rx} = Factored moment resistance for bending about the X—X axis, computed considering $L < L_u$, using the Class of the section considering bending about the X—X axis only and the value of F_y shown, for Class 1 and 2 sections, $\phi\, Z_x F_y/12$; for Class 3 sections, $\phi\, S_x F_y/12$; and for Class 4 sections Clause 13.5.3 of CSA S16.1-1974, ft-kips.

M_{ry} = Factored moment resistance for bending about the Y—Y axis computed using the Class of the section considering bending about the Y—Y axis only and the value of F_y shown, for Class 1 and 2 section, $\phi\, Z_y F_y/12$; for Class 3 sections, $\phi\, S_y F_y/12$; and for Class 4 sections, Clause 13.5.3 of CSA S16.1-1974, ft-kips.

J = St. Venant torsional constant, in.^{4}

C_w = Warping torsional constant, 10^2 in.^{6}

L_u = Maximum unsupported length of compression flange for which no reduction in M_r is required, ft.

F_y = Specified minimum yield strength, ksi.

For further information and examples on the use of similar tables in SI, refer to page 4—33.

WWF COLUMNS
Factored Axial Compressive Resistances, C_r, in Kips

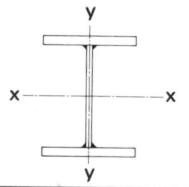

G40.21-44W
$\emptyset = 0.90$

Designation		WWF550			WWF550		WWF500		
Mass (kg/m)		**721	**620	503	420	†217*	**651	**561	456
Effective length (KL) in feet with respect to least radius of gyration	0	5405	4649	3761	3291	1421	4876	4196	3410
	6	5382	4644	3759	3283	1412	4834	4175	3394
	7	5341	4612	3733	3259	1406	4792	4142	3367
	8	5297	4578	3706	3234	1395	4748	4107	3340
	9	5252	4542	3678	3208	1384	4702	4071	3311
	10	5205	4505	3649	3181	1372	4653	4034	3281
	11	5156	4467	3619	3153	1360	4603	3995	3250
	12	5105	4428	3588	3124	1347	4551	3954	3217
	13	5053	4387	3556	3094	1333	4497	3913	3184
	14	4998	4345	3523	3063	1320	4441	3869	3149
	15	4942	4302	3488	3031	1305	4383	3825	3113
	16	4884	4257	3453	2998	1291	4324	3779	3076
	17	4825	4211	3416	2964	1276	4262	3731	3038
	18	4763	4164	3379	2929	1260	4198	3682	2999
	19	4700	4115	3340	2893	1244	4132	3632	2959
	20	4635	4065	3301	2856	1228	4065	3580	2917
	21	4568	4013	3260	2818	1211	3995	3526	2874
	22	4499	3960	3218	2779	1193	3923	3471	2830
	23	4428	3906	3176	2739	1176	3850	3415	2785
	24	4356	3851	3132	2698	1157	3774	3357	2739
	25	4282	3794	3087	2655	1139	3697	3298	2692
	26	4206	3736	3041	2612	1120	3618	3238	2643
	27	4128	3676	2994	2568	1100	3536	3176	2594
	28	4048	3615	2946	2523	1080	3453	3112	2543
	29	3967	3553	2897	2477	1059	3368	3047	2491
	30	3884	3489	2847	2430	1038	3281	2981	2438
	32	3712	3358	2743	2333	995	3100	2843	2328
	34	3533	3222	2636	2231	950	2903	2700	2213
	36	3347	3080	2524	2126	903	2690	2553	2094
	38	3131	2933	2408	2017	853	2502	2376	1955
	40	2924	2771	2289	1889	797	2334	2218	1826

PROPERTIES AND DESIGN DATA

	**721	**620	503	420	†217*	**651	**561	456
Area (in.^{2})	143	123	99.5	83.1	43.0	129	111	90.2
Z_x (in.^{3})	1160	1070	903	755	401	940	874	738
S_x (in.^{3})	970	933	801	677	371	781	748	648
r_x (in.)	8.57	9.06	9.33	9.39	9.67	7.72	8.14	8.41
Z_y (in.^{3})	578	560	464	372	186	479	463	384
S_y (in.^{3})	371	369	308	247	123	307	306	254
r_y (in.)	5.30	5.70	5.79	5.67	5.56	4.84	5.21	5.26
r_x/r_y	1.62	1.59	1.61	1.66	1.74	1.60	1.56	1.60
M_{rx} (ft.-kips)($L < L_u$)	3650	3370	2840	2490	1220	2960	2750	2320
M_{ry} (ft.-kips)	1820	1760	1460	1230	406	1510	1460	1210
J (in.^{4})	265	200	113	59.4	7.59	239	181	103
C_W (10^2 in.^{6})	3740	3720	3230	2690	1450	2270	2260	1960
L_u (feet)	48.6	46.6	40.4	34.1	29.7	48.5	46.1	39.4
F_y (ksi)	42	42	42	44	44	42	42	42

IMPERIAL SIZE AND MASS

Mass (lb./ft.)	484	416	338	282	146	437	377	306
Nominal Depth and Width (in.)	22 x 22			22 x 22		20 x 20		

* Resistance for this column calculated according to CSA-S16.1-1974 Clause 13.3.3.
† Class 3 in bending.
** Welding does not fully develop web strength for this section.

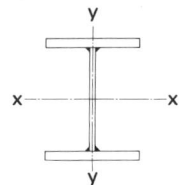

Designation		WWF500						
Mass (kg/m)		381	343	306	276	†254	†223	†197*
Effective length (KL) in feet with respect to least radius of gyration	0	2982	2689	2392	2162	1984	1750	1369
	6	2962	2669	2372	2146	1968	1736	1358
	7	2937	2647	2351	2128	1951	1721	1347
	8	2912	2623	2330	2109	1933	1705	1335
	9	2885	2598	2307	2089	1914	1689	1322
	10	2857	2573	2284	2068	1895	1672	1309
	11	2828	2546	2259	2046	1875	1654	1296
	12	2798	2518	2234	2024	1854	1635	1281
	13	2767	2490	2208	2001	1832	1616	1267
	14	2734	2460	2181	1977	1810	1596	1252
	15	2701	2429	2152	1952	1787	1576	1236
	16	2666	2397	2123	1926	1763	1554	1219
	17	2631	2365	2093	1900	1738	1533	1203
	18	2594	2331	2062	1872	1712	1510	1185
	19	2556	2296	2030	1844	1686	1487	1168
	20	2517	2260	1997	1815	1659	1463	1149
	21	2477	2223	1963	1785	1631	1438	1130
	22	2436	2185	1929	1754	1602	1412	1111
	23	2394	2146	1893	1723	1573	1386	1091
	24	2350	2106	1856	1691	1543	1360	1070
	25	2306	2065	1818	1657	1512	1332	1049
	26	2260	2023	1780	1623	1480	1304	1028
	27	2214	1980	1740	1589	1447	1275	1006
	28	2166	1936	1700	1553	1414	1246	983
	29	2117	1891	1658	1516	1380	1215	960
	30	2067	1845	1616	1479	1345	1184	936
	32	1964	1750	1528	1402	1272	1120	888
	34	1856	1650	1434	1321	1196	1052	837
	36	1732	1534	1329	1227	1108	975	777
	38	1612	1427	1236	1141	1031	907	723
	40	1504	1332	1153	1065	962	846	674

PROPERTIES AND DESIGN DATA

	381	343	306	276	254	223	197
Area (in.²)	75.3	67.9	60.4	54.6	50.1	44.2	39.0
Z_x (in.³)	618	555	492	453	413	367	330
S_x (in.³)	550	497	442	411	376	335	305
r_x (in.)	8.48	8.49	8.49	8.61	8.59	8.64	8.77
Z_y (in.³)	308	270	232	215	193	169	153
S_y (in.³)	203	178	152	142	127	112	102
r_y (in.)	5.15	5.08	4.98	5.06	5.00	4.99	5.06
r_x/r_y	1.65	1.67	1.70	1.70	1.72	1.73	1.73
M_{rx} (ft.-kips)(L < L_u)	2040	1830	1620	1490	1240	1110	1010
M_{ry} (ft.-kips)	1020	891	766	709	419	370	337
J (in.⁴)	53.9	37.1	24.4	19.0	14.0	9.53	6.90
C_w (10^2 in.⁶)	1640	1470	1280	1210	1090	974	893
L_u (feet)	32.4	30.3	28.4	28.0	28.7	27.8	27.4
F_y (ksi)	44	44	44	44	44	44	44

IMPERIAL SIZE AND MASS

	381	343	306	276	254	223	197
Mass (lb./ft.)	256	230	205	185	170	150	132
Nominal Depth and Width (in.)	20 x 20						

† Class 3 in bending.

* Resistance for this column calculated according to CSA-S16.1-1974 Clause 13.3.3.

WWF COLUMNS
Factored Axial Compressive Resistance, C_r, in Kips

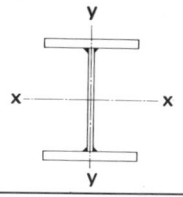

Designation	WWF450		WWF450						
Mass (kg/m)	**503	409	342	308	274	248	228	†201	†177
0	3754	3058	2677	2412	2146	1940	1782	1568	1390
6	3716	3029	2645	2381	2117	1915	1757	1547	1372
7	3682	3002	2620	2358	2096	1896	1740	1531	1358
8	3646	2974	2593	2333	2074	1877	1721	1515	1344
9	3609	2944	2566	2308	2051	1856	1702	1498	1330
10	3571	2913	2537	2281	2027	1835	1682	1480	1314
11	3531	2881	2507	2254	2001	1812	1661	1462	1298
12	3489	2848	2475	2225	1975	1789	1639	1443	1281
13	3445	2813	2443	2195	1948	1765	1617	1423	1264
14	3400	2777	2409	2164	1920	1739	1593	1402	1246
15	3354	2740	2374	2132	1890	1713	1569	1380	1227
16	3306	2701	2338	2098	1860	1686	1543	1358	1208
17	3256	2661	2301	2064	1828	1658	1517	1335	1188
18	3205	2620	2262	2028	1796	1630	1490	1311	1167
19	3152	2578	2222	1991	1762	1600	1462	1287	1146
20	3097	2535	2181	1954	1728	1569	1433	1261	1124
21	3041	2490	2139	1915	1692	1538	1404	1235	1101
22	2983	2444	2096	1874	1656	1505	1373	1208	1078
23	2924	2396	2051	1833	1618	1472	1342	1181	1054
24	2863	2348	2005	1791	1579	1437	1310	1152	1030
25	2800	2298	1958	1747	1540	1402	1277	1123	1004
26	2736	2247	1910	1703	1499	1366	1243	1093	978
27	2671	2194	1860	1657	1457	1329	1208	1063	952
28	2603	2140	1809	1610	1414	1291	1172	1031	925
29	2534	2086	1757	1562	1371	1252	1136	999	897
30	2464	2029	1704	1513	1326	1212	1098	966	868
32	2318	1913	1588	1402	1222	1121	1012	890	803
34	2149	1780	1465	1293	1127	1034	933	821	741
36	1991	1650	1356	1197	1044	958	864	760	686
38	1851	1534	1261	1112	969	890	802	706	637
40	1726	1431	1175	1037	903	829	748	658	594

Effective length (KL) in feet with respect to least radius of gyration

PROPERTIES AND DESIGN DATA

Area (in.^{2})	99.3	80.9	67.6	60.9	54.2	49.0	45.0	39.7	35.1
Z_x (in.^{3})	694	588	494	445	395	364	332	295	266
S_x (in.^{3})	587	511	436	395	352	329	300	269	244
r_x (in.)	7.24	7.48	7.56	7.58	7.59	7.71	7.69	7.74	7.84
Z_y (in.^{3})	375	311	250	219	188	175	156	137	124
S_y (in.^{3})	247	207	165	144	124	115	103	90.6	82.4
r_y (in.)	4.70	4.76	4.65	4.58	4.51	4.56	4.50	4.50	4.56
r_x/r_y	1.54	1.57	1.63	1.66	1.68	1.69	1.71	1.72	1.72
M_{rx} (ft.-kips)($L < L_u$)	2190	1850	1630	1470	1300	1200	1100	888	805
M_{ry} (ft.-kips)	1180	980	822	723	620	577	515	299	272
J (in.^{4})	163	92.3	48.5	33.3	22.0	17.1	12.6	8.57	6.20
C_w (10^2 in.^{6})	1290	1130	951	854	752	704	639	570	523
L_u (feet)	46.1	38.8	31.2	28.7	26.7	26.0	25.1	25.7	25.2
F_y (ksi)	42	42	44	44	44	44	44	44	44

IMPERIAL SIZE AND MASS

Mass (lb./ft.)	337	275	229	207	184	166	152	134	119
Nominal Depth and Width (in.)	18 x 18		18 x 18						

† Class 3 in bending.

** Welding does not fully develop web strength for this section.

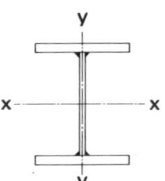

Designation		WWF400		WWF400						
Mass (kg/m)		**444	362	303	273	243	220	202	178	†157
	0	3315	2706	2368	2134	1901	1719	1580	1394	1232
	6	3260	2663	2324	2092	1861	1684	1547	1364	1207
	7	3225	2635	2298	2068	1839	1665	1529	1348	1193
	8	3189	2605	2271	2043	1816	1645	1510	1332	1178
	9	3150	2575	2242	2017	1791	1623	1490	1314	1163
	10	3110	2542	2212	1989	1766	1601	1469	1295	1147
	11	3068	2509	2181	1960	1740	1577	1447	1276	1130
	12	3025	2474	2148	1930	1712	1553	1424	1255	1112
	13	2979	2437	2114	1898	1683	1528	1400	1234	1094
	14	2932	2399	2078	1866	1653	1501	1375	1212	1075
	15	2883	2360	2042	1832	1622	1474	1349	1189	1055
	16	2833	2319	2004	1796	1589	1445	1322	1166	1035
	17	2780	2277	1964	1760	1556	1416	1294	1141	1014
	18	2726	2233	1923	1722	1521	1385	1266	1115	992
	19	2670	2188	1881	1683	1485	1354	1236	1089	969
	20	2612	2142	1838	1643	1448	1321	1205	1062	945
	21	2553	2094	1793	1601	1410	1287	1174	1034	921
	22	2491	2044	1747	1558	1371	1253	1141	1005	896
	23	2428	1994	1699	1514	1330	1217	1108	975	871
	24	2363	1942	1650	1469	1288	1181	1073	945	844
	25	2297	1888	1600	1422	1245	1143	1037	913	817
	26	2228	1833	1548	1374	1201	1104	1001	881	789
	27	2158	1777	1495	1325	1157	1064	965	848	761
	28	2086	1719	1442	1271	1102	1020	919	808	728
	29	2013	1660	1376	1213	1052	973	877	771	695
	30	1924	1591	1316	1159	1005	930	838	737	664
	32	1765	1460	1206	1063	921	853	768	676	609
	34	1627	1345	1111	979	848	785	708	622	561
	36	1505	1245	1028	905	784	726	654	575	519
	38	1397	1156	954	839	727	674	606	533	481
	40	1301	1076	888	781	676	627	564	496	448

Effective length (KL) in feet with respect to least radius of gyration

PROPERTIES AND DESIGN DATA

	444	362	303	273	243	220	202	178	157
Area (in.^{2})	87.7	71.6	59.8	53.9	48.0	43.4	39.9	35.2	31.1
Z_x (in.^{3})	535	456	384	347	308	284	260	231	209
S_x (in.^{3})	446	391	335	305	273	254	234	210	190
r_x (in.)	6.33	6.56	6.64	6.67	6.69	6.79	6.79	6.85	6.94
Z_y (in.^{3})	297	246	197	173	149	138	123	109	98.4
S_y (in.^{3})	196	163	131	114	97.7	91.2	81.4	71.6	65.2
r_y (in.)	4.19	4.23	4.15	4.08	4.00	4.07	4.01	4.00	4.06
r_x/r_y	1.51	1.55	1.60	1.63	1.67	1.67	1.69	1.71	1.71
M_{rx} (ft.-kips)($L < L_u$)	1690	1440	1270	1150	1020	937	858	762	627
M_{ry} (ft.-kips)	936	775	650	571	492	455	406	356	215
J (in.^{4})	144	82.0	43.1	29.6	19.5	15.2	11.2	7.60	5.51
C_w (10^2 in.^{6})	690	608	517	464	408	385	349	312	287
L_u (feet)	46.6	38.5	30.2	27.3	25.0	24.3	23.1	22.2	23.0
F_y (ksi)	42	42	44	44	44	44	44	44	44

IMPERIAL SIZE AND MASS

	298	243	203	183	163	147	135	119	105
Mass (lb./ft.)	298	243	203	183	163	147	135	119	105
Nominal Depth and Width (in.)	16 x 16		16 x 16						

† Class 3 in bending.

** Welding does not fully develop web strength for this section.

WWF COLUMNS
Factored Axial Compressive Resistances, C_r, in Kips

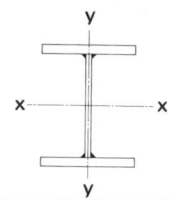

G40.21-44W
$\varnothing = 0.90$

Designation		WWF350		WWF350						
Mass (kg/m)		**385	315	263	238	212	192	176	155	137
	0	2877	2355	2063	1857	1655	1501	1378	1216	1077
	6	2804	2297	2005	1803	1604	1456	1336	1178	1045
	7	2768	2268	1978	1778	1582	1436	1317	1162	1030
	8	2730	2237	1949	1752	1558	1415	1297	1144	1015
	9	2690	2205	1919	1724	1532	1392	1276	1125	999
	10	2648	2171	1888	1695	1505	1368	1253	1106	982
	11	2604	2135	1854	1665	1477	1344	1230	1085	964
	12	2558	2098	1820	1633	1448	1318	1206	1064	945
	13	2510	2059	1783	1599	1417	1290	1180	1041	925
	14	2461	2019	1745	1564	1385	1262	1153	1017	905
	15	2409	1977	1706	1528	1352	1232	1126	993	884
	16	2355	1934	1665	1490	1317	1202	1097	968	861
	17	2299	1889	1623	1451	1281	1170	1067	941	838
	18	2241	1842	1579	1411	1244	1137	1036	914	815
	19	2181	1793	1533	1369	1206	1103	1004	885	790
	20	2120	1744	1486	1326	1166	1067	970	856	764
	21	2056	1692	1437	1281	1124	1031	936	826	738
	22	1990	1639	1387	1235	1082	993	901	795	711
	23	1922	1584	1335	1187	1038	954	864	762	683
	24	1852	1528	1282	1138	990	915	824	727	654
	25	1781	1470	1222	1080	938	867	781	689	620
	26	1699	1406	1160	1025	890	822	741	654	588
	27	1616	1337	1103	975	846	782	704	621	559
	28	1539	1274	1051	928	805	744	671	592	532
	29	1468	1215	1002	885	768	710	639	564	508
	30	1403	1161	957	845	733	678	610	538	485
	32	1285	1063	876	773	671	620	558	493	443
	34	1182	978	805	711	616	570	513	452	407
	36	1091	903	743	656	568	526	473	417	376
	38	1011	837	687	607	525	486	437	386	348
	40	939	778	638	563	487	451	406	358	322

Effective length (KL) in feet with respect to least radius of gyration

PROPERTIES AND DESIGN DATA

	**385	315	263	238	212	192	176	155	137
Area (in.^{2})	76.1	62.3	52.1	46.9	41.8	37.9	34.8	30.7	27.2
Z_x (in.^{3})	397	341	289	261	232	215	197	175	158
S_x (in.^{3})	324	287	248	226	203	190	176	157	144
r_x (in.)	5.41	5.64	5.73	5.77	5.79	5.88	5.90	5.93	6.03
Z_y (in.^{3})	228	189	151	133	114	106	94.7	83.2	75.4
S_y (in.^{3})	149	125	99.7	87.2	74.9	69.8	62.3	54.9	49.8
r_y (in.)	3.68	3.71	3.63	3.58	3.51	3.56	3.51	3.51	3.55
r_x/r_y	1.47	1.52	1.58	1.61	1.65	1.65	1.68	1.69	1.70
M_{rx} (ft.-kips)(L $<$ L_u)	1250	1070	954	861	766	709	650	577	521
M_{ry} (ft.-kips)	715	592	498	439	376	350	312	274	248
J (in.^{4})	126	71.7	37.6	25.8	17.0	13.3	9.74	6.64	4.82
C_w (10^2 in.^{6})	336	300	256	231	205	193	176	158	145
L_u (feet)	47.6	38.7	29.4	26.2	23.6	22.6	21.3	20.3	19.7
F_y (ksi)	42	42	44	44	44	44	44	44	44

IMPERIAL SIZE AND MASS

	**385	315	263	238	212	192	176	155	137
Mass (lb./ft.)	258	211	177	159	142	128	118	104	92
Nominal Depth and Width (in.)	14 x 14		14 x 14						

** Welding does not fully develop web strength for this section.

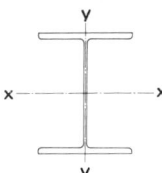

Designation		W360			W310				
Mass (kg/m)		79	72	64*	283	253	226	202	179
Effective length (KL) in feet with respect to least radius of gyration	0	618	558	499	2109	1890	1690	1508	1334
	6	552	498	444	2035	1822	1627	1451	1283
	7	531	480	427	2004	1794	1602	1428	1262
	8	509	459	409	1971	1764	1575	1404	1240
	9	486	438	389	1936	1732	1546	1377	1217
	10	460	415	368	1899	1698	1515	1350	1192
	11	433	390	346	1860	1663	1483	1321	1166
	12	405	364	322	1819	1626	1450	1291	1139
	13	374	336	296	1777	1588	1415	1259	1110
	14	339	304	268	1733	1547	1378	1226	1081
	15	309	278	244	1686	1505	1340	1191	1050
	16	283	254	224	1638	1461	1301	1155	1017
	17	261	234	206	1588	1416	1259	1118	984
	18	241	216	190	1537	1369	1216	1079	949
	19	223	200	176	1483	1320	1172	1039	913
	20	207	186	164	1427	1269	1126	997	875
	21	193	173	152	1370	1217	1079	954	836
	22	180	162	139	1310	1163	1031	909	794
	23	169	151	127	1243	1100	972	856	748
	24	158	142	116	1175	1040	918	809	707
	25	149	133	107	1112	984	869	766	669
	26	139	124	99	1055	934	824	726	634
	27	129	116	92	1003	887	783	690	602
	28	121	108	86	954	844	745	656	573
	29	113	101	80	909	804	710	625	546
	30	106	95	75	868	767	677	597	521
	32				793	701	619	545	475
	34				727	643	567	500	436
	36				670	592	522	460	401
	38				619	547	482	424	370
	40				573	506	446	393	342

PROPERTIES AND DESIGN DATA

	79	72	64*	283	253	226	202	179
Area (in.^{2})	15.6	14.1	12.6	55.8	50.0	44.7	39.9	35.3
Z$_x$ (in.^{3})	87.1	78.4	69.6	311	275	243	214	186
S$_x$ (in.^{3})	77.7	70.3	62.7	263	235	209	185	163
r$_x$ (in.)	5.89	5.86	5.83	5.82	5.74	5.66	5.57	5.51
Z$_y$ (in.^{3})	22.0	19.6	17.3	143	126	111	98.0	85.4
S$_y$ (in.^{3})	14.3	12.8	11.3	93.0	82.3	72.8	64.2	56.0
r$_y$ (in.)	1.92	1.91	1.89	3.25	3.22	3.19	3.16	3.13
r$_x$/r$_y$	3.07	3.07	3.08	1.79	1.78	1.77	1.76	1.76
M$_{rx}$ (ft.-kips)(L < L$_u$)	287	259	230	980	866	765	674	586
M$_{ry}$ (ft.-kips)	72.6	64.7	57.1	450	397	350	309	269
J (in.^{4})	1.94	1.46	1.05	48.8	35.6	25.8	18.5	12.9
C$_w$ (10^2 in.^{6})	25.4	22.4	19.5	235	201	172	147	125
L$_u$ (feet)	10.6	10.4	10.1	29.6	27.3	25.2	23.4	21.8
F$_y$ (ksi)	44	44	44	42	42	42	42	42

IMPERIAL SIZE AND MASS

Mass (lb./ft.)	53	48	43	190	170	152	136	120
Nominal Depth and Width (in.)		14 x 8				12 x 12		

* Resistance for this column calculated according to CSA-S16.1-1974 Clause 13.3.3.

W COLUMNS
Factored Axial Compressive Resistances, C_r, in Kips

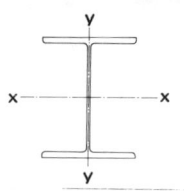

G40.21-44W
$\phi = 0.90$

Designation	W310						W310	
Mass (kg/m)	158	143	129	118	107	97†	86	79
0	1236	1117	1014	919	836	756	673	618
6	1185	1070	971	879	799	723	629	577
7	1164	1052	954	864	785	710	615	563
8	1143	1032	936	847	770	697	599	548
9	1120	1011	917	830	754	682	582	532
10	1097	990	897	812	738	667	564	515
11	1071	967	876	793	720	651	545	497
12	1045	943	854	772	702	634	524	478
13	1017	917	831	751	682	616	503	459
14	989	891	807	729	662	598	481	438
15	958	864	781	706	641	578	458	416
16	927	835	755	682	619	558	433	393
17	894	805	728	657	596	537	408	368
18	860	774	699	631	572	515	378	341
19	825	742	670	604	547	493	352	317
20	789	709	639	576	522	469	328	296
21	752	673	606	545	493	442	307	277
22	706	633	570	512	464	416	288	260
23	666	597	537	482	437	392	271	244
24	629	563	507	455	412	370	255	230
25	595	533	480	431	390	350	241	217
26	564	505	455	408	370	332	228	205
27	536	480	432	388	351	315	216	194
28	509	456	410	369	334	299	204	184
29	485	435	391	351	318	285	194	175
30	463	414	373	335	303	272	185	166
32	422	378	340	305	276	248	167	151
34	387	346	311	279	253	227	151	136
36	355	318	286	257	232	208	136	122
38	328	293	264	236	214	192	122	110
40	303	271	244	218	198	177	111	100

Effective length (KL) in feet with respect to least radius of gyration

PROPERTIES AND DESIGN DATA

Area (in.^{2})	31.2	28.2	25.6	23.2	21.1	19.1	17.0	15.6
Z_x (in.^{3})	164	147	132	119	108	96.8	86.4	77.9
S_x (in.^{3})	145	131	118	107	97.5	88.0	77.9	70.5
r_x (in.)	5.47	5.43	5.38	5.34	5.32	5.28	5.29	5.22
Z_y (in.^{3})	75.1	67.5	60.4	54.3	49.2	44.1	32.5	29.1
S_y (in.^{3})	49.3	44.4	39.7	35.8	32.4	29.0	21.4	19.2
r_y (in.)	3.11	3.09	3.07	3.05	3.04	3.02	2.51	2.48
r_x/r_y	1.76	1.76	1.75	1.75	1.75	1.75	2.11	2.10
M_{rx} (ft.-kips)($L < L_u$)	541	485	436	393	356	290	285	257
M_{ry} (ft.-kips)	248	223	199	179	162	95.7	107	96.0
J (in.^{4})	9.13	6.86	5.10	3.84	2.93	2.18	2.10	1.58
C_W (10^2 in.^{6})	107	94.1	82.8	73.2	65.4	57.7	35.7	31.6
L_u (feet)	19.7	18.9	18.1	17.5	17.0	17.6	13.9	13.5
F_y (ksi)	44	44	44	44	44	44	44	44

IMPERIAL SIZE AND MASS

Mass (lb./ft.)	106	96	87	79	72	65	58	53
Nominal Depth and Width (in.)	12 x 12						12 x 10	

† Class 3 in bending.

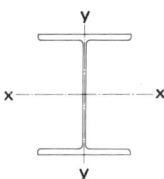

Designation		W310			W250				
Mass (kg/m)		74	67	60	167	149	131	115	101
Effective length (KL) in feet with respect to least radius of gyration	0	582	523	467	1303	1164	1026	895	792
	6	522	468	418	1229	1096	965	841	744
	7	504	452	402	1202	1073	944	823	727
	8	483	433	386	1175	1047	921	803	709
	9	462	414	368	1145	1020	897	781	690
	10	439	393	349	1113	991	871	759	670
	11	414	371	329	1080	961	844	735	648
	12	388	347	308	1045	929	816	710	626
	13	361	322	285	1008	896	786	683	602
	14	329	293	258	969	860	755	655	577
	15	300	267	236	929	824	722	626	551
	16	275	245	216	886	785	687	596	524
	17	253	225	199	842	745	652	564	496
	18	233	208	183	797	703	613	529	464
	19	216	193	170	743	654	570	493	431
	20	201	179	158	694	611	532	460	403
	21	188	167	147	650	572	498	430	377
	22	175	156	137	610	537	468	404	354
	23	164	146	129	574	505	440	380	333
	24	154	137	121	541	476	415	358	314
	25	145	129	113	511	450	392	338	296
	26	136	121	106	484	426	371	320	280
	27	127	113	99	459	403	351	303	265
	28	118	105	92	435	383	334	288	252
	29	111	98	86	414	364	317	273	239
	30	104	92	81	394	346	301	260	228
	32	92	82	72	358	314	274	236	206
	34				326	286	249	215	188
	36				298	260	226	194	170
	38				268	235	204	175	153
	40				243	213	185	159	139

PROPERTIES AND DESIGN DATA

	74	67	60	167	149	131	115	101
Area (in.^{2})	14.7	13.2	11.8	32.9	29.4	25.9	22.6	20.0
Z_x (in.^{3})	72.4	64.7	57.5	147	130	113	97.6	85.3
S_x (in.^{3})	64.6	58.0	51.9	126	112	98.5	85.8	75.8
r_x (in.)	5.18	5.15	5.13	4.67	4.60	4.54	4.49	4.44
Z_y (in.^{3})	21.4	19.0	16.8	69.2	61.0	53.1	45.9	40.1
S_y (in.^{3})	13.9	12.4	11.0	45.3	40.0	34.9	30.2	26.5
r_y (in.)	1.96	1.95	1.93	2.68	2.65	2.63	2.61	2.59
r_x/r_y	2.64	2.64	2.66	1.74	1.74	1.73	1.72	1.71
M_{rx} (ft.-kips)($L < L_u$)	239	214	190	485	429	373	322	281
M_{ry} (ft.-kips)	70.6	62.7	55.4	228	201	175	151	132
J (in.^{4})	1.78	1.31	.953	15.1	10.9	7.53	5.11	3.56
C_W (10^2 in.^{6})	18.8	16.5	14.4	60.3	51.5	43.4	36.4	31.1
L_u (feet)	11.0	10.7	10.4	21.6	19.9	18.4	17.1	16.1
F_y (ksi)	44	44	44	44	44	44	44	44

IMPERIAL SIZE AND MASS

	74	67	60	167	149	131	115	101
Mass (lb./ft.)	50	45	40	112	100	88	77	68
Nominal Depth and Width (in.)		12 x 8				10 x 10			

W COLUMNS
Factored Axial Compressive Resistances, C_r, in Kips

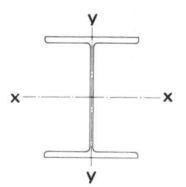

Designation		W250			W250		
Mass (kg/m)		89	80	73	67	58	49
Effective length (KL) in feet with respect to least radius of gyration	0	697	626	570	527	455	385
	6	654	586	534	474	409	344
	7	639	573	522	458	395	332
	8	623	558	509	440	380	318
	9	606	543	495	421	363	304
	10	588	527	480	401	345	288
	11	569	509	464	380	326	272
	12	549	491	447	357	306	254
	13	528	472	430	333	285	236
	14	506	452	412	305	261	214
	15	482	431	392	279	238	195
	16	458	409	372	255	218	179
	17	433	386	351	235	200	165
	18	404	359	327	217	185	152
	19	376	334	304	201	172	141
	20	351	312	284	187	160	131
	21	328	292	266	175	149	122
	22	308	274	249	163	139	114
	23	290	257	235	153	130	107
	24	273	242	221	144	122	100
	25	258	229	209	135	115	94
	26	244	217	197	127	108	88
	27	231	205	187	119	101	82
	28	219	195	177	111	94	77
	29	208	185	168	104	88	72
	30	198	176	160	97	83	67
	32	180	159	145	86	73	59
	34	163	145	132			
	36	147	130	118			
	38	133	117	107			
	40	120	106	97			

PROPERTIES AND DESIGN DATA

	89	80	73	67	58	49
Area (in.^{2})	17.6	15.8	14.4	13.3	11.5	9.71
Z_x (in.^{3})	74.6	66.6	60.4	54.9	46.8	38.8
S_x (in.^{3})	66.7	60.1	54.5	49.1	42.1	34.9
r_x (in.)	4.40	4.38	4.35	4.32	4.26	4.18
Z_y (in.^{3})	35.0	31.3	28.3	20.3	17.2	14.0
S_y (in.^{3})	23.0	20.5	18.7	13.3	11.3	9.20
r_y (in.)	2.57	2.55	2.55	2.00	1.98	1.94
r_x/r_y	1.71	1.72	1.71	2.16	2.15	2.15
M_{rx} (ft.-kips)($L < L_u$)	246	220	199	181	154	128
M_{ry} (ft.-kips)	115	103	93.4	67.0	56.8	46.2
J (in.^{4})	2.48	1.82	1.39	1.51	.976	.583
C_w (10^2 in.^{6})	26.4	23.1	20.7	12.0	9.92	7.91
L_u (feet)	15.2	14.6	14.2	11.6	11.1	10.5
F_y (ksi)	44	44	44	44	44	44

IMPERIAL SIZE AND MASS

		89	80	73	67	58	49
Mass (lb./ft.)		60	54	49	45	39	33
Nominal Depth and Width (in.)		10 x 10			10 x 8		

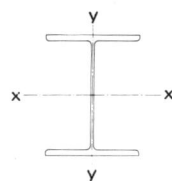
Designation		W200						W200	
Mass (kg/m)		100	86	71	59	52	46	42	36
Effective length (KL) in feet with respect to least radius of gyration	0	780	677	558	463	408	362	327	280
	6	710	616	507	419	368	326	280	240
	7	688	596	490	405	356	315	266	227
	8	664	575	473	391	343	303	250	214
	9	639	553	454	375	328	291	234	200
	10	612	528	434	357	313	277	216	185
	11	583	503	412	339	297	262	197	168
	12	552	476	390	320	280	247	176	150
	13	519	447	366	300	261	231	158	134
	14	485	417	341	278	241	212	143	121
	15	446	382	311	253	220	194	130	110
	16	409	351	285	232	202	178	118	101
	17	377	323	263	214	186	164	108	92
	18	349	299	243	198	172	151	100	85
	19	324	277	226	183	159	140	92	78
	20	301	258	210	171	148	130	85	72
	21	281	241	196	159	138	122	79	67
	22	263	225	183	149	129	114	73	62
	23	247	211	172	140	121	107	67	57
	24	232	198	161	131	114	100	62	53
	25	218	187	152	123	107	94	57	49
	26	206	176	143	116	101	89	53	45
	27	194	166	135	109	95	83		
	28	183	157	127	103	89	78		
	29	172	147	119	96	83	73		
	30	161	138	111	90	78	68		
	32	143	122	98	80	69	60		
	34	127	108	88	71				
	36								
	38								
	40								

PROPERTIES AND DESIGN DATA

	100	86	71	59	52	46	42	36
Area (in.^{2})	19.7	17.1	14.1	11.7	10.3	9.13	8.25	7.08
Z_x (in.^{3})	70.2	59.8	49.0	39.8	34.7	30.4	27.2	23.2
S_x (in.^{3})	60.4	52.1	43.3	35.4	31.3	27.5	24.3	20.9
r_x (in.)	3.72	3.65	3.61	3.53	3.51	3.47	3.45	3.42
Z_y (in.^{3})	32.7	27.9	22.9	18.5	16.1	14.1	10.1	8.57
S_y (in.^{3})	21.4	18.3	15.0	12.2	10.6	9.28	6.64	5.64
r_y (in.)	2.12	2.10	2.08	2.05	2.03	2.02	1.62	1.61
r_x/r_y	1.75	1.74	1.74	1.72	1.73	1.72	2.13	2.12
M_{rx} (ft.-kips)($L < L_u$)	232	197	162	131	115	100	89.8	76.6
M_{ry} (ft.-kips)	108	92.1	75.6	61.0	53.1	46.5	33.3	28.3
J (in.^{4})	5.06	3.34	1.96	1.12	.771	.538	.538	.347
C_w (10^2 in.^{6})	14.4	11.8	9.30	7.26	6.19	5.31	3.13	2.59
L_u (feet)	16.3	14.9	13.4	12.3	11.7	11.3	9.27	8.86
F_y (ksi)	44	44	44	44	44	44	44	44

IMPERIAL SIZE AND MASS

	100	86	71	59	52	46	42	36
Mass (lb./ft.)	67	58	48	40	35	31	28	24
Nominal Depth and Width (in.)	8 x 8						8 x 6½	

W and M COLUMNS
Factored Axial Compressive Resistances, C_r, in Kips

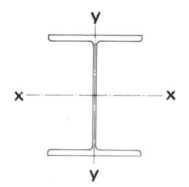

G40.21-44W
$\varnothing = 0.90$

Designation	W200		W150			M100
Mass (kg/m)	31	27	37	30	22†	19
Effective length (KL) in feet with respect to least radius of gyration						
0	244	208	291	232	175	151
6	190	161	245	195	145	98
7	175	147	231	184	136	81
8	158	132	216	172	126	68
9	138	114	200	158	116	57
10	120	99	183	144	104	49
11	105	87	163	128	91	43
12	93	77	145	114	81	38
13	83	68	130	102	73	33
14	75	61	117	92	66	29
15	67	55	106	83	59	25
16	61	50	97	76	54	
17	55	45	89	70	50	
18	50	40	82	64	45	
19	45	36	75	59	42	
20	41	33	69	54	38	
21			64	50	35	
22			58	45	32	
23			54	42	29	
24			49	39	27	
25			46	36		
26						
27						
28						
29						
30						
32						
34						
36						
38						
40						

PROPERTIES AND DESIGN DATA

Area (in.^{2})	6.16	5.26	7.34	5.87	4.43	3.82
Z_x (in.^{3})	20.4	17.0	18.9	14.9	10.8	6.07
S_x (in.^{3})	18.2	15.2	16.7	13.4	9.72	5.25
r_x (in.)	3.50	3.43	2.70	2.66	2.56	1.66
Z_y (in.^{3})	5.69	4.66	8.56	6.72	4.75	2.74
S_y (in.^{3})	3.71	3.04	5.62	4.42	3.11	1.73
r_y (in.)	1.26	1.23	1.53	1.51	1.45	.943
r_x/r_y	2.78	2.79	1.76	1.76	1.77	1.76
M_{rx} (ft.-kips)($L < L_u$)	67.3	56.1	62.4	49.2	32.1	20.0
M_{ry} (ft.-kips)	18.8	15.4	28.2	22.2	10.3	9.04
J (in.^{4})	.282	.172	.461	.240	.101	.052
C_w (10^2 in.^{6})	1.52	1.22	1.50	1.13	.765	.112
L_u (feet)	6.98	6.70	9.46	8.67	8.44	5.30
F_y (ksi)	44	44	44	44	44	44

IMPERIAL SIZE AND MASS

Mass (lb./ft.)	21	18	25	20	15	13
Nominal Depth and Width (in.)	8 x 5¼		6 x 6			M4 x 4

† Class 3 in bending.

FACTORED AXIAL COMPRESSIVE RESISTANCES
Hollow Structural Sections

Class C

For rectangular hollow sections, see page 9—32.
For square hollow sections, see page 9—40.
For round hollow sections, see page 9—48.

Class H

For rectangular hollow sections, see page 9—56.
For square hollow sections, see page 9—64.
For round hollow sections, see page 9—72.

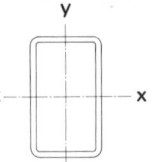

G40.21-50W
$\phi = 0.90$

Size (mm)	304.8 x 203.2					254.0 x 152.4		
Thickness (mm)	12.7	11.13	9.53	††7.95	6.35‡	12.7	11.13	9.53
Mass (kg/m)	93.0	82.4	71.3	60.1	48.6	72.7	64.6	56.1
0	828	733	634	535	405	648	576	499
3	828	733	634	535	402	639	568	493
4	817	724	626	529	400	625	556	483
5	804	713	617	521	394	611	544	472
6	791	701	607	513	388	595	530	460
7	777	689	596	504	381	578	515	448
8	762	676	585	495	374	559	499	434
9	746	662	573	485	367	540	482	419
10	729	647	561	474	359	519	463	404
11	711	632	547	463	351	496	444	387
12	692	615	533	451	342	473	423	370
13	673	598	519	439	333	448	402	352
14	652	580	503	427	323	422	379	332
15	631	562	487	413	314	395	355	312
16	609	542	471	399	303	362	327	289
17	586	522	453	385	293	334	302	266
18	561	501	435	370	281	309	279	246
19	536	479	417	355	270	287	260	229
20	511	457	397	338	258	267	242	213
21	481	431	376	321	246	250	226	199
22	452	405	353	302	231	234	212	187
23	425	382	333	284	218	220	199	175
24	402	360	314	269	205	207	187	165
25	380	341	297	254	194	195	176	156
26	360	323	282	241	184	184	166	147
27	342	307	268	229	175	173	157	139
28	325	292	254	218	166	164	149	131
29	309	278	242	207	158	155	141	125
30	295	265	231	197	151	147	134	118
31	281	253	220	188	144	138	126	111
32	269	241	211	180	138	130	118	105
33	257	231	201	172	132	122	111	99
34	246	221	193	165	126	116	105	93
35	236	212	185	158	121	109	100	88

Left axis: Effective length (KL) in feet with respect to least radius of gyration

PROPERTIES AND DESIGN DATA								
Area (in.^{2})	18.4	16.3	14.1	11.9	9.59	14.4	12.8	11.1
Z_x (in.^{3})	72.4	64.7	56.5	48.0	39.1	45.6	40.9	35.9
S_x (in.^{3})	58.8	52.9	46.5	39.8	32.6	36.1	32.7	29.0
r_x (in.)	4.39	4.42	4.45	4.49	4.52	3.55	3.58	3.62
Z_y (in.^{3})	54.7	48.9	42.7	36.4	29.6	31.8	28.7	25.2
S_y (in.^{3})	46.9	42.3	37.3	32.0	26.3	26.9	24.5	21.8
r_y (in.)	3.20	3.23	3.25	3.28	3.31	2.37	2.40	2.43
r_x/r_y	1.37	1.37	1.37	1.37	1.36	1.50	1.49	1.49
M_{rx} (ft.-kips)	271	243	212	180	147	171	153	135
M_{ry} (ft.-kips)	205	183	160	120	89.1	119	108	94.5

IMPERIAL SIZE AND MASS								
Mass (lb./ft.)	62.5	55.4	47.9	40.4	32.6	48.9	43.4	37.7
Thickness (in.)	.500	.438	.375	.313	.250	.500	.438	.375
Size (in.)	12 x 8					10 x 6		

†† Class 3 in bending about Y-Y axis.

‡ Class 4 in bending about Y-Y axis and resistance for this column calculated according to CSA-S16.1-1974 Clause 13.3.3.

G40.21-50W
$\phi = 0.90$

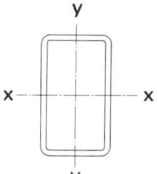

Size (mm)	254.0 x 152.4		203.2 x 152.4					
Thickness (mm)	7.95	††6.35	12.7	11.13	9.53	7.95	6.35	4.78‡
Mass (kg/m)	47.5	38.4	62.6	55.7	48.5	41.1	33.4	25.5
0	422	342	558	495	431	365	297	227
3	416	338	549	487	425	360	293	224
4	408	331	537	477	416	353	287	219
5	399	324	524	466	406	345	280	215
6	389	316	510	453	396	336	273	209
7	379	308	494	440	384	326	266	204
8	368	299	478	425	372	316	257	198
9	355	289	460	410	359	305	249	191
10	343	279	441	393	344	293	239	184
11	329	268	421	376	330	281	230	177
12	314	256	399	357	314	268	219	169
13	299	244	377	338	297	254	208	161
14	283	232	353	317	280	240	197	152
15	266	218	327	295	261	224	184	143
16	248	204	300	270	240	207	170	132
17	228	188	276	249	221	190	157	122
18	212	174	255	231	204	176	145	113
19	197	162	237	214	190	164	135	105
20	183	151	221	200	177	153	126	98
21	171	141	206	186	165	143	118	92
22	160	132	193	174	155	134	110	86
23	151	124	181	164	145	125	104	81
24	142	117	170	154	137	118	97	76
25	134	110	160	145	129	111	92	71
26	126	104	151	137	121	105	87	67
27	119	98	143	129	115	99	82	62
28	113	93	135	122	108	94	78	58
29	107	88	128	116	103	89	73	54
30	102	84	119	109	97	84	70	50
31	97	80	112	102	91	79	66	47
32	91	75	106	96	86	74	62	44
33	85	71	100	90	81	70	58	41
34	81	67	94	85	76	66	55	39
35	76	63	89	81	72	63	52	37

Left axis label: Effective length (KL) in feet with respect to least radius of gyration

PROPERTIES AND DESIGN DATA

Area (in.^{2})	9.37	7.59	12.4	11.0	9.58	8.12	6.59	5.04
Z_x (in.^{3})	30.7	25.1	32.2	29.0	25.6	21.9	18.0	13.9
S_x (in.^{3})	25.0	20.6	25.8	23.5	20.9	18.1	15.0	11.7
r_x (in.)	3.65	3.69	2.89	2.92	2.96	2.99	3.02	3.05
Z_y (in.^{3})	21.6	17.7	26.3	23.8	21.0	18.0	14.8	11.5
S_y (in.^{3})	18.9	15.6	21.9	20.0	17.8	15.5	12.9	10.1
r_y (in.)	2.46	2.49	2.30	2.33	2.36	2.39	2.42	2.45
r_x/r_y	1.49	1.48	1.25	1.25	1.25	1.25	1.25	1.25
M_{rx} (ft.-kips)	115	94.1	121	109	96.0	82.1	67.5	52.1
M_{ry} (ft.-kips)	81.0	58.5	98.6	89.2	78.7	67.5	55.5	36.8

IMPERIAL SIZE AND MASS

Mass (lb./ft.)	31.9	25.8	42.1	37.5	32.6	27.6	22.4	17.1
Thickness (in.)	.313	.250	.500	.438	.375	.313	.250	.188
Size (in.)	10 x 6		8 x 6					

†† Class 3 in bending about Y-Y axis.

‡ Class 4 in bending about Y-Y axis and resistance for this column calculated according to CSA-S16.1-1974 Clause 13.3.3.

RECTANGULAR HOLLOW SECTIONS
Factored Axial Compressive
Resistances, C_r, in Kips

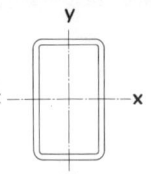

G40.21-50W
Ø = 0.90

Size (mm)	203.2 x 101.6						177.8 x 127.0 #		
Thickness (mm)	12.7	11.13	9.53	7.95	6.35	4.78 ‡	12.7	11.13	9.53
Mass (kg/m)	52.4	46.9	40.9	34.8	28.3	21.7	52.4	46.9	40.9
Effective length (KL) in feet with respect to least radius of gyration									
0	468	416	364	309	252	193	468	416	364
3	445	397	347	296	241	185	454	404	354
4	428	382	335	285	233	179	441	393	344
5	408	365	320	273	223	171	426	380	333
6	386	346	304	260	212	164	410	366	321
7	362	325	286	245	201	155	393	351	308
8	336	303	267	229	188	146	374	335	294
9	307	278	247	212	175	135	354	317	279
10	275	251	224	193	160	125	332	298	263
11	243	221	198	171	143	112	309	278	246
12	216	197	176	153	127	100	284	257	228
13	193	176	158	137	114	90	255	232	207
14	174	159	143	123	103	81	231	210	187
15	158	144	129	112	94	73	210	191	170
16	144	131	118	102	85	67	192	175	156
17	131	120	108	94	78	61	177	161	143
18	120	110	99	86	72	56	163	148	132
19	111	102	91	79	66	50	151	137	123
20	101	93	84	73	61	45	140	127	114
21	92	85	77	67	56	41	130	118	106
22	84	78	70	61	52	37	121	110	99
23	77	71	65	56	47	34	113	103	92
24	71	66	60	52	44	31	105	97	86
25	66	61	55	48	40	29	97	89	80
26		57	51	45	38	27	90	83	75
27					35	25	84	77	69
28							79	72	65
29							74	67	61
30							69	63	57
31							65	59	53
32									50
33									
34									
35									

PROPERTIES AND DESIGN DATA

Area (in.^{2})	10.4	9.25	8.08	6.87	5.59	4.28	10.4	9.25	8.08
Z_x (in.^{3})	24.7	22.4	19.9	17.1	14.1	11.0	23.0	20.9	18.5
S_x (in.^{3})	18.8	17.2	15.5	13.5	11.3	8.86	18.1	16.6	14.9
r_x (in.)	2.69	2.73	2.77	2.80	2.84	2.88	2.47	2.51	2.54
Z_y (in.^{3})	15.0	13.6	12.1	10.5	8.71	6.79	18.2	16.5	14.6
S_y (in.^{3})	12.3	11.4	10.3	9.05	7.63	6.04	14.8	13.7	12.3
r_y (in.)	1.54	1.57	1.60	1.62	1.65	1.68	1.89	1.92	1.95
r_x/r_y	1.75	1.74	1.73	1.73	1.72	1.71	1.31	1.30	1.30
M_{rx} (ft.-kips)	92.6	84.0	74.6	64.1	52.9	41.2	86.2	78.4	69.4
M_{ry} (ft.-kips)	56.2	51.0	45.4	39.4	32.7	22.0	68.2	61.9	54.7

IMPERIAL SIZE AND MASS

Mass (lb./ft.)	35.2	31.5	27.5	23.4	19.0	14.6	35.2	31.5	27.5
Thickness (in.)	.500	.438	.375	.313	.250	.188	.500	.438	.375
Size (in.)	8 x 4						7 x 5		

‡ Class 4 in bending about Y-Y axis and resistance for this column calculated according to CSA-S16.1-1974 Clause 13.3.3.
# Check manufacturer for current availability.

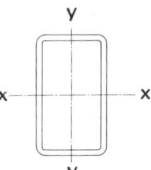

RECTANGULAR HOLLOW SECTIONS
Factored Axial Compressive Resistances, C_r, in Kips

Size (mm)	177.8 x 127.0#			152.4 x 101.6				
Thickness (mm)	7.95	6.35	††4.78	11.13	9.53	7.95	6.35	4.78
Mass (kg/m)	34.8	28.3	21.7	38.0	33.3	28.4	23.2	17.9
0	309	252	193	337	296	253	207	159
3	301	245	188	320	282	241	197	152
4	293	239	183	307	271	232	190	147
5	284	232	178	293	258	222	182	140
6	274	224	172	277	244	210	173	134
7	263	215	166	259	229	198	163	126
8	252	206	159	239	213	184	152	118
9	239	196	151	218	195	169	140	109
10	226	185	143	194	174	153	127	100
11	212	174	135	170	153	134	113	89
12	197	162	126	151	136	120	100	79
13	179	149	116	135	122	107	90	71
14	162	135	105	122	110	97	81	64
15	148	123	96	111	100	88	74	58
16	135	113	88	101	91	80	67	53
17	125	104	81	92	83	73	61	48
18	115	96	75	84	76	67	56	45
19	106	89	69	77	70	62	52	41
20	99	82	64	70	64	57	48	38
21	92	77	60	64	58	52	44	35
22	86	71	56	58	53	47	40	32
23	80	67	52	54	49	43	37	29
24	75	63	49	50	45	40	34	27
25	70	59	46	46	42	37	31	25
26	65	55	43			34	29	23
27	61	51	40					22
28	57	47	37					
29	53	44	35					
30	50	42	33					
31	47	39	31					
32	44	37	29					
33		35	27					
34								
35								

Effective length (KL) in feet with respect to least radius of gyration

PROPERTIES AND DESIGN DATA

Area (in.²)	6.87	5.59	4.28	7.50	6.58	5.62	4.59	3.53
Z_x (in.³)	15.9	13.2	10.2	14.0	12.5	10.9	9.05	7.08
S_x (in.³)	13.0	10.9	8.53	10.9	9.90	8.72	7.36	5.83
r_x (in.)	2.57	2.61	2.64	2.09	2.12	2.16	2.19	2.23
Z_y (in.³)	12.6	10.4	8.12	10.5	9.42	8.21	6.84	5.36
S_y (in.³)	10.8	9.03	7.12	8.57	7.81	6.92	5.87	4.67
r_y (in.)	1.98	2.01	2.04	1.51	1.54	1.57	1.60	1.63
r_x/r_y	1.30	1.30	1.29	1.38	1.38	1.38	1.37	1.37
M_{rx} (ft.-kips)	59.6	49.5	38.2	52.5	46.9	40.9	33.9	26.5
M_{ry} (ft.-kips)	47.2	39.0	26.7	39.4	35.3	30.8	25.6	20.1

IMPERIAL SIZE AND MASS

Mass (lb./ft.)	23.4	19.0	14.6	25.5	22.4	19.1	15.6	12.0
Thickness (in.)	.313	.250	.188	.438	.375	.313	.250	.188
Size (in.)	7 x 5			6 x 4				

†† Class 3 in bending about Y-Y axis.
#Check manufacturer for current availability.

RECTANGULAR HOLLOW SECTIONS
Factored Axial Compressive Resistances, C_r, in Kips

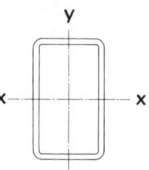

G40.21-50W
$\emptyset = 0.90$

Size (mm)	127.0 x 76.2				127.0 x 63.5			
Thickness (mm)	9.53	7.95	6.35	4.78	9.53	7.95	6.35	4.78
Mass (kg/m)	25.7	22.1	18.2	14.1	23.8	20.5	16.9	13.1
0	229	196	162	125	211	182	150	117
3	208	179	148	115	185	160	133	104
4	195	168	140	109	168	147	122	96
5	179	156	130	101	149	131	110	87
6	162	141	118	92	126	112	96	76
7	142	125	106	83	102	92	79	64
8	120	107	91	72	85	77	66	53
9	102	91	77	61	72	65	56	45
10	88	79	67	53	62	56	48	39
11	77	69	59	47	54	48	42	34
12	68	61	52	41	46	42	37	30
13	60	54	46	37	40	36	32	26
14	54	48	41	33	35	32	28	23
15	47	43	37	29	30	28	24	20
16	42	38	33	26		25	21	18
17	37	34	29	23				
18	33	30	26	21				
19		27	24	19				
20				17				
21								
22								
23								
24								
25								
26								
27								
28								
29								
30								
31								
32								
33								
34								
35								

Row label (left vertical axis): Effective length (KL) in feet with respect to least radius of gyration

PROPERTIES AND DESIGN DATA

Area (in.^{2})	5.08	4.36	3.59	2.78	4.70	4.05	3.34	2.59
Z_x (in.^{3})	7.70	6.77	5.69	4.50	6.83	6.04	5.10	4.05
S_x (in.^{3})	5.88	5.27	4.52	3.63	5.08	4.58	3.95	3.20
r_x (in.)	1.70	1.74	1.77	1.81	1.64	1.68	1.72	1.76
Z_y (in.^{3})	5.34	4.71	3.98	3.16	4.12	3.66	3.11	2.49
S_y (in.^{3})	4.30	3.89	3.36	2.73	3.27	2.99	2.62	2.15
r_y (in.)	1.13	1.16	1.19	1.21	.932	.961	.990	1.02
r_x/r_y	1.51	1.50	1.50	1.49	1.76	1.75	1.74	1.73
M_{rx} (ft.-kips)	28.9	25.4	21.3	16.9	25.6	22.6	19.1	15.2
M_{ry} (ft.-kips)	20.0	17.7	14.9	11.8	15.4	13.7	11.7	9.34

IMPERIAL SIZE AND MASS

Mass (lb./ft.)	17.3	14.9	12.2	9.45	16.0	13.8	11.4	8.81
Thickness (in.)	.375	.313	.250	.188	.375	.313	.250	.188
Size (in.)	5 x 3				5 x 2½			

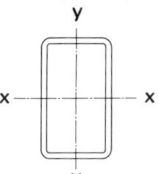
Size (mm)	127.0 x 50.8				101.6 x 76.2			
Thickness (mm)	9.53	7.95	6.35	4.78	9.53	7.95	6.35	4.78
Mass (kg/m)	21.9	18.9	15.6	12.2	21.9	18.9	15.6	12.2
0	195	168	139	108	195	168	139	108
3	158	138	116	91	176	153	127	99
4	135	120	101	80	164	143	119	93
5	107	97	84	68	150	131	110	86
6	83	76	66	54	134	118	100	79
7	67	61	53	44	116	104	88	70
8	55	51	44	36	97	87	75	60
9	46	42	37	30	83	74	64	51
10	38	35	31	26	72	64	55	44
11	32	29	26	22	62	56	48	39
12	27	25	22	18	55	49	42	34
13			19	16	49	44	38	30
14					43	39	34	27
15					38	34	30	24
16					33	30	26	21
17					30	27	23	19
18					27	24	21	17
19							19	15
20								
21								
22								
23								
24								
25								
26								
27								
28								
29								
30								
31								
32								
33								
34								
35								

Effective length (KL) in feet with respect to least radius of gyration

IMP

PROPERTIES AND DESIGN DATA

Area (in.^{2})	4.33	3.74	3.09	2.40	4.33	3.74	3.09	2.40
Z_x (in.^{3})	5.96	5.30	4.51	3.60	5.34	4.74	4.02	3.21
S_x (in.^{3})	4.27	3.90	3.39	2.76	4.10	3.72	3.22	2.62
r_x (in.)	1.57	1.61	1.66	1.70	1.38	1.41	1.44	1.48
Z_y (in.^{3})	2.99	2.69	2.31	1.86	4.35	3.87	3.29	2.63
S_y (in.^{3})	2.31	2.15	1.92	1.60	3.44	3.14	2.73	2.23
r_y (in.)	.730	.759	.788	.816	1.09	1.12	1.15	1.18
r_x/r_y	2.15	2.13	2.10	2.08	1.26	1.26	1.25	1.25
M_{rx} (ft.-kips)	22.3	19.9	16.9	13.5	20.0	17.8	15.1	12.0
M_{ry} (ft.-kips)	11.2	10.1	8.66	6.97	16.3	14.5	12.3	9.86

IMPERIAL SIZE AND MASS

Mass (lb./ft.)	14.7	12.7	10.5	8.17	14.7	12.7	10.5	8.17
Thickness (in.)	.375	.313	.250	.188	.375	.313	.250	.188
Size (in.)	5 x 2				4 x 3			

RECTANGULAR HOLLOW SECTIONS
Factored Axial Compressive
Resistances, C_r, in Kips

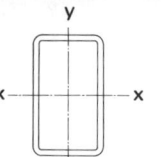

G40.21-50W
$\phi = 0.90$

Size (mm)	101.6 x 50.8					88.9 x 63.5		
Thickness (mm)	7.95	6.35	4.78	3.81	3.18	7.95	6.35	4.78
Mass (kg/m)	15.8	13.1	10.3	8.37	7.09	15.8	13.1	10.3
Effective length (KL) in feet with respect to least radius of gyration 0	140	117	91	74	63	140	117	91
3	114	96	76	62	53	122	102	81
4	98	84	67	55	47	110	93	74
5	78	68	56	47	40	97	83	66
6	61	54	44	37	32	81	71	57
7	49	43	36	30	26	66	58	47
8	41	36	29	25	21	55	48	39
9	34	30	25	21	18	47	41	33
10	28	25	21	18	15	40	35	29
11	23	21	18	15	13	35	30	25
12	20	18	15	13	11	30	26	22
13			13	11	9	25	23	19
14						22	20	16
15						19	17	14
16								13
17								
18								
19								
20								
21								
22								
23								
24								
25								
26								
27								
28								
29								
30								
31								
32								
33								
34								
35								

PROPERTIES AND DESIGN DATA

Area (in.^{2})	3.11	2.59	2.03	1.65	1.40	3.11	2.59	2.03
Z_x (in.^{3})	3.59	3.09	2.49	2.07	1.77	3.35	2.88	2.32
S_x (in.^{3})	2.65	2.34	1.94	1.63	1.41	2.57	2.26	1.87
r_x (in.)	1.31	1.35	1.38	1.41	1.42	1.20	1.24	1.27
Z_y (in.^{3})	2.16	1.87	1.52	1.27	1.09	2.63	2.27	1.83
S_y (in.^{3})	1.70	1.53	1.29	1.10	.954	2.09	1.86	1.54
r_y (in.)	.740	.769	.797	.815	.826	.916	.947	.976
r_x/r_y	1.77	1.75	1.73	1.73	1.72	1.31	1.31	1.30
M_{rx} (ft.-kips)	13.5	11.6	9.34	7.76	6.64	12.6	10.8	8.70
M_{ry} (ft.-kips)	8.10	7.01	5.70	4.76	4.09	9.86	8.51	6.86

IMPERIAL SIZE AND MASS

Mass (lb./ft.)	10.6	8.81	6.89	5.62	4.76	10.6	8.81	6.89
Thickness (in.)	.313	.250	.188	.150	.125	.313	.250	.188
Size (in.)	4 x 2					3½ x 2½		

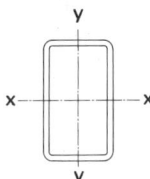

G40.21-50W
$\phi = 0.90$

RECTANGULAR HOLLOW SECTIONS
Factored Axial Compressive Resistances, C_r, in Kips

Size (mm)	88.9 x 63.5		76.2 x 50.8				50.8 x 25.4	
Thickness (mm)	3.81	3.18	7.95	6.35	4.78	3.81	3.18	2.54
Mass (kg/m)	8.37	7.09	12.6	10.6	8.35	6.85	3.28	2.71
0	74	63	112	94	74	61	29	24
3	66	56	90	77	61	51	13	12
4	61	52	76	66	53	44	9	8
5	54	47	59	53	44	37	6	5
6	47	41	46	41	34	29	4	4
7	39	34	37	33	28	23		
8	33	28	30	27	23	19		
9	28	24	25	23	19	16		
10	24	21	21	19	16	14		
11	21	18	17	16	13	11		
12	18	16		13	11	10		
13	16	14				8		
14	14	12						
15	12	11						
16	11	9						
17								
18								
19								
20								
21								
22								
23								
24								
25								
26								
27								
28								
29								
30								
31								
32								
33								
34								
35								

Effective length (KL) in feet with respect to least radius of gyration

PROPERTIES AND DESIGN DATA

Area (in.^{2})	1.65	1.40	2.49	2.09	1.65	1.35	.648	.534
Z_x (in.^{3})	1.92	1.65	2.19	1.92	1.57	1.32	.386	.326
S_x (in.^{3})	1.57	1.36	1.62	1.47	1.24	1.06	.293	.253
r_x (in.)	1.29	1.30	.990	1.03	1.06	1.08	.673	.688
Z_y (in.^{3})	1.52	1.31	1.63	1.44	1.18	.992	.234	.199
S_y (in.^{3})	1.30	1.13	1.25	1.15	.978	.839	.192	.168
r_y (in.)	.994	1.01	.710	.741	.770	.788	.385	.396
r_x/r_y	1.30	1.30	1.39	1.39	1.38	1.37	1.75	1.74
M_{rx} (ft.-kips)	7.20	6.19	8.21	7.20	5.89	4.95	1.45	1.22
M_{ry} (ft.-kips)	5.70	4.91	6.11	5.40	4.42	3.72	.877	.746

IMPERIAL SIZE AND MASS

Mass (lb./ft.)	5.62	4.76	8.46	7.11	5.61	4.60	2.21	1.82
Thickness (in.)	.150	.125	.313	.250	.188	.150	.125	.100
Size (in.)	3½ x 2½		3 x 2				2 x 1	

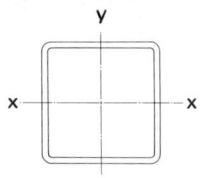

SQUARE HOLLOW SECTIONS
Factored Axial Compressive Resistances, C_r, in Kips

G40.21-50W
$\emptyset = 0.90$

Size (mm)		304.8 x 304.8					254.0 x 254.0		
Thickness (mm)		12.70	11.13	9.53	††7.95	‡6.35	12.70	11.13	9.53
Mass (kg/m)		113	100	86.5	72.8	58.7	93.0	82.4	71.3
Effective length (KL) in feet with respect to least radius of gyration	0	1010	891	769	648	468	828	733	634
	3	1010	891	769	648	467	828	733	634
	4	1010	891	769	648	466	824	731	632
	5	1000	886	765	645	465	815	722	625
	6	992	878	758	639	461	804	713	617
	7	982	868	750	632	457	793	703	609
	8	971	859	742	625	452	782	693	600
	9	960	849	734	618	447	769	682	591
	10	948	839	725	611	442	757	671	581
	11	936	828	716	603	436	743	659	571
	12	923	817	706	595	430	729	647	561
	13	909	805	696	587	424	714	634	550
	14	895	793	686	578	418	699	621	538
	15	881	780	675	569	412	683	607	526
	16	866	767	663	560	405	666	592	514
	17	851	753	652	550	398	649	577	501
	18	835	739	640	540	391	631	561	487
	19	818	725	628	530	384	613	545	474
	20	801	710	615	519	376	593	528	459
	21	783	695	602	508	368	574	511	445
	22	765	679	588	497	360	553	493	429
	23	747	663	574	485	352	532	475	414
	24	728	646	560	473	343	511	456	397
	25	708	629	545	461	334	486	435	380
	26	688	611	530	449	326	461	413	361
	27	667	593	515	436	316	438	392	343
	28	646	574	499	423	307	417	374	327
	29	624	555	483	409	297	398	356	311
	30	600	535	466	396	287	380	340	297
	31	574	512	446	379	276	363	325	284
	32	551	491	428	363	265	348	311	272
	33	528	471	410	349	254	333	298	261
	34	508	453	394	335	244	320	286	250
	35	488	435	379	322	235	307	275	240

PROPERTIES AND DESIGN DATA

	12.70	11.13	9.53	7.95	6.35	12.70	11.13	9.53
Area (in.^{2})	22.4	19.8	17.1	14.4	11.6	18.4	16.3	14.1
Z (in.^{3})	95.4	85.0	73.9	62.6	50.8	64.6	57.7	50.4
S (in.^{3})	80.9	72.5	63.4	54.1	44.1	54.2	48.8	42.9
r (in.)	4.66	4.69	4.72	4.75	4.78	3.84	3.87	3.90
M_r (ft.-kips)	358	319	277	203	149	242	216	189

IMPERIAL SIZE AND MASS

	12.70	11.13	9.53	7.95	6.35	12.70	11.13	9.53
Mass (lb./ft.)	76.1	67.3	58.1	48.9	39.4	62.5	55.4	47.9
Thickness (in.)	.500	.438	.375	.313	.250	.500	.438	.375
Size (in.)	12 x 12					10 x 10		

†† Class 3 in bending.
‡ Class 4 in bending and resistance for this column calculated according to CSA-S16.1-1974 Clause 13.3.3.

Size (mm)	254.0 x 254.0		203.2 x 203.2				
Thickness (mm)	7.95	‡6.35	12.70	11.13	9.53	7.95	6.35
Mass (kg/m)	60.1	48.6	72.7	64.6	56.1	47.5	38.4
0	535	432	648	576	499	422	342
3	535	432	646	575	499	421	341
4	534	430	637	567	492	415	337
5	528	425	626	557	484	409	331
6	521	420	615	548	475	402	326
7	514	415	603	537	466	394	320
8	507	409	590	526	457	386	313
9	499	403	577	514	447	378	307
10	491	396	562	501	436	369	300
11	483	390	547	488	425	360	292
12	474	383	531	474	413	350	284
13	465	375	514	460	400	339	276
14	455	368	497	444	387	328	267
15	445	360	478	428	374	317	258
16	435	351	459	412	359	305	249
17	424	343	439	394	345	293	239
18	413	334	418	376	329	280	229
19	401	325	397	358	313	267	218
20	389	315	372	336	295	252	207
21	377	306	348	315	277	237	194
22	364	295	327	296	260	222	182
23	351	285	308	279	245	209	172
24	338	274	291	263	231	198	162
25	324	264	275	249	219	187	153
26	307	250	260	235	207	177	145
27	292	238	247	223	196	168	138
28	278	227	234	212	187	160	131
29	266	216	223	202	178	152	125
30	254	207	212	192	169	145	119
31	243	198	202	183	161	138	113
32	232	189	193	175	154	132	108
33	223	181	185	167	147	126	104
34	214	174	177	160	141	121	99
35	205	167	169	153	135	116	95

Effective length (KL) in feet with respect to least radius of gyration

PROPERTIES AND DESIGN DATA							
Area (in.²)	11.9	9.59	14.4	12.8	11.1	9.37	7.59
Z (in.³)	42.8	34.9	39.7	35.7	31.3	26.8	21.9
S (in.³)	36.7	30.1	32.8	29.8	26.4	22.8	18.8
r (in.)	3.93	3.96	3.02	3.06	3.09	3.12	3.15
M_r (ft.-kips)	160	113	149	134	117	100	82.1

IMPERIAL SIZE AND MASS							
Mass (lb./ft.)	40.4	32.6	48.9	43.4	37.7	31.9	25.8
Thickness (in.)	.313	.250	.500	.438	.375	.313	.250
Size (in.)	10 x 10		8 x 8				

‡ Class 4 in bending and resistance for this column calculated according to CSA-S16.1-1974 Clause 13.3.3.

SQUARE HOLLOW SECTIONS
Factored Axial Compressive Resistances, C_r, in Kips

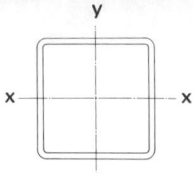

G40.21-50W
$\emptyset = 0.90$

Size (mm)	177.8 x 177.8						152.4 x 152.4		
Thickness (mm)	12.70	11.13	9.53	7.95	6.35	††4.78	12.70	11.13	9.53
Mass (kg/m)	62.6	55.7	48.5	41.1	33.4	25.5	52.4	46.9	40.9
0	558	495	431	365	297	227	468	416	364
3	553	491	428	363	295	225	459	409	357
4	543	482	420	356	290	222	449	400	349
5	532	473	412	350	284	217	437	389	341
6	520	462	403	342	278	213	424	378	331
7	508	451	394	334	272	208	411	366	321
8	494	439	384	326	265	203	396	354	310
9	479	427	373	317	258	198	380	340	298
10	464	413	361	307	250	192	363	325	286
11	448	399	349	297	242	186	345	309	272
12	430	384	336	286	234	179	326	293	258
13	412	368	323	275	225	173	306	275	243
14	393	351	308	263	215	166	285	257	227
15	373	334	293	251	205	158	260	235	209
16	352	316	278	238	195	151	238	216	192
17	329	296	262	224	184	142	219	199	177
18	305	274	243	209	172	133	203	184	164
19	283	255	226	194	160	124	188	171	152
20	264	238	211	181	149	116	175	159	141
21	247	223	197	170	140	108	163	148	132
22	232	209	185	159	131	102	153	139	123
23	218	196	174	150	123	96	143	130	116
24	205	185	164	141	116	90	135	122	109
25	194	175	155	133	110	85	127	115	102
26	183	165	146	126	104	81	119	108	97
27	173	156	138	119	98	76	113	102	91
28	164	148	131	113	93	72	106	97	86
29	156	141	125	107	89	69	99	90	81
30	148	134	118	102	84	65	93	85	76
31	141	127	113	97	80	62	87	80	71
32	134	121	107	93	76	59	82	75	67
33	128	115	102	88	73	57	77	71	63
34	121	109	97	84	70	54	73	67	60
35	114	103	92	80	66	52	69	63	57

Leftmost axis label: Effective length (KL) in feet with respect to least radius of gyration

PROPERTIES AND DESIGN DATA									
Area (in.²)	12.4	11.0	9.58	8.12	6.59	5.04	10.4	9.25	8.08
Z (in.³)	29.5	26.6	23.5	20.1	16.5	12.8	20.8	18.9	16.8
S (in.³)	24.2	22.0	19.6	17.0	14.1	11.0	16.8	15.4	13.9
r (in.)	2.62	2.65	2.68	2.71	2.74	2.77	2.21	2.24	2.27
M_r (ft.-kips)	111	99.7	88.1	75.4	61.9	41.2	78.0	70.9	63.0

IMPERIAL SIZE AND MASS									
Mass (lb./ft.)	42.1	37.5	32.6	27.6	22.4	17.1	35.2	31.5	27.5
Thickness (in.)	.500	.438	.375	.313	.250	.188	.500	.438	.375
Size (in.)	7 x 7						6 x 6		

†† Class 3 in bending.

G40.21-50W
$\phi = 0.90$

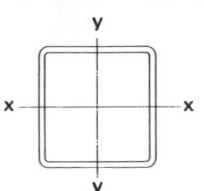

SQUARE HOLLOW SECTIONS
Factored Axial Compressive Resistances, C_r, in Kips

Size (mm)	152.4 x 152.4			127.0 x 127.0				
Thickness (mm)	7.95	6.35	4.78	11.13	9.53	7.95	6.35	4.78
Mass (kg/m)	34.8	28.3	21.7	38.0	33.3	28.4	23.2	17.9
0	309	252	193	337	296	253	207	159
3	304	248	190	327	287	245	201	154
4	298	242	186	317	278	238	195	150
5	290	237	181	306	269	230	189	146
6	282	230	177	294	259	222	182	140
7	274	223	172	280	247	212	174	135
8	265	216	166	266	235	202	166	129
9	255	208	160	251	222	191	157	122
10	244	200	154	234	208	179	148	115
11	233	191	147	216	193	167	138	107
12	221	182	140	196	176	153	127	99
13	209	172	133	176	158	138	115	90
14	196	161	125	159	143	125	104	82
15	181	150	117	145	130	114	95	74
16	166	137	107	133	119	104	87	68
17	153	127	99	122	109	95	80	63
18	142	117	91	112	101	88	74	58
19	131	109	85	104	93	81	68	54
20	122	101	79	96	86	76	63	50
21	114	95	74	89	80	70	59	46
22	107	89	69	83	75	66	55	43
23	100	83	65	78	70	61	51	40
24	94	78	61	71	65	57	48	38
25	89	74	57	66	60	53	44	35
26	84	69	54	61	55	49	41	33
27	79	66	51	57	52	45	38	30
28	75	62	48	53	48	42	36	28
29	71	59	46	50	45	40	33	26
30	66	55	43	47	42	37	31	25
31	62	52	41			35	29	23
32	58	49	38					22
33	55	46	36					
34	52	43	34					
35	49	41	32					

Effective length (KL) in feet with respect to least radius of gyration

PROPERTIES AND DESIGN DATA

	152.4 x 152.4			127.0 x 127.0				
Area (in.^{2})	6.87	5.59	4.28	7.50	6.58	5.62	4.59	3.53
Z (in.^{3})	14.4	11.9	9.27	12.5	11.2	9.70	8.07	6.31
S (in.^{3})	12.1	10.1	7.95	10.0	9.10	8.03	6.78	5.38
r (in.)	2.30	2.33	2.36	1.83	1.86	1.89	1.92	1.95
M_r (ft.-kips)	54.0	44.6	34.8	46.9	42.0	36.4	30.3	23.7

IMPERIAL SIZE AND MASS

	152.4 x 152.4			127.0 x 127.0				
Mass (lb./ft.)	23.4	19.0	14.6	25.5	22.4	19.1	15.6	12.0
Thickness (in.)	.313	.250	.188	.438	.375	.313	.250	.188
Size (in.)	6 x 6			5 x 5				

SQUARE HOLLOW SECTIONS
Factored Axial Compressive
Resistances, C_r, in Kips

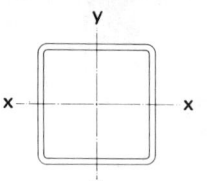

G40.21-50W
$\phi = 0.90$

Size (mm)	101.6 x 101.6				88.9 x 88.9			
Thickness (mm)	9.53	7.95	6.35	4.78	9.53	7.95	6.35	4.78
Mass (kg/m)	25.7	22.1	18.2	14.1	21.9	18.9	15.6	12.2
0	229	196	162	125	195	168	139	108
3	216	186	153	119	180	156	130	101
4	207	178	147	114	170	148	123	96
5	196	169	140	109	159	139	116	90
6	184	160	132	103	146	128	107	84
7	171	149	124	97	132	117	98	77
8	157	137	114	90	116	104	88	70
9	142	124	104	82	99	89	76	61
10	124	110	93	74	86	77	66	53
11	109	96	82	65	75	68	58	46
12	97	86	72	58	66	60	51	41
13	87	77	65	52	59	53	46	37
14	78	69	58	47	53	48	41	33
15	71	62	53	42	48	43	37	30
16	64	57	48	38	43	39	33	27
17	59	52	44	35	38	35	30	24
18	54	47	40	32	34	31	27	22
19	48	43	37	30	31	28	24	20
20	44	39	34	27	28	26	22	18
21	40	36	31	25		23	20	16
22	37	33	28	22				15
23	34	30	26	21				
24	31	28	24	19				
25			22	18				
26								
27								
28								
29								
30								
31								
32								
33								
34								
35								

Effective length (KL) in feet with respect to least radius of gyration

PROPERTIES AND DESIGN DATA

Area (in.²)	5.08	4.36	3.59	2.78	4.33	3.74	3.09	2.40
Z (in.³)	6.70	5.90	4.96	3.92	4.90	4.35	3.69	2.94
S (in.³)	5.34	4.79	4.11	3.31	3.83	3.48	3.02	2.46
r (in.)	1.45	1.48	1.51	1.54	1.24	1.28	1.31	1.34
M_r (ft.-kips)	25.1	22.1	18.6	14.7	18.4	16.3	13.8	11.0

IMPERIAL SIZE AND MASS

Mass (lb./ft.)	17.3	14.9	12.2	9.45	14.7	12.7	10.5	8.17
Thickness (in.)	.375	.313	.250	.188	.375	.313	.250	.188
Size (in.)	4 x 4				3½ x 3½			

G40.21-50W
$\phi = 0.90$

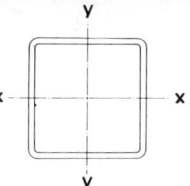

SQUARE HOLLOW SECTIONS
Factored Axial Compressive Resistances, C_r, in Kips

Size (mm)	76.2 x 76.2			63.5 x 63.5			
Thickness (mm)	7.95	6.35	4.78	6.35	4.78	3.81	3.18
Mass (kg/m)	15.8	13.1	10.3	10.6	8.35	6.85	5.82
0	140	117	91	94	74	61	52
3	126	106	83	81	65	53	46
4	117	98	78	73	59	49	42
5	107	90	72	64	52	43	37
6	95	81	65	53	44	37	32
7	82	70	57	43	36	30	26
8	68	59	48	36	30	25	22
9	58	50	41	30	25	21	18
10	50	43	35	26	22	18	16
11	44	38	31	23	19	16	14
12	38	33	27	19	16	14	12
13	34	29	24	16	14	12	10
14	30	26	21	14	12	10	9
15	26	23	19		11	9	8
16	23	20	17				7
17	21	18	15				
18		16	13				
19							
20							
21							
22							
23							
24							
25							
26							
27							
28							
29							
30							
31							
32							
33							
34							
35							

Effective length (KL) in feet with respect to least radius of gyration

PROPERTIES AND DESIGN DATA							
Area (in.^{2})	3.11	2.59	2.03	2.09	1.65	1.35	1.15
Z (in.^{3})	3.03	2.60	2.10	1.71	1.40	1.17	1.01
S (in.^{3})	2.38	2.10	1.74	1.35	1.14	.973	.848
r (in.)	1.07	1.10	1.13	.898	.929	.948	.961
M_r (ft.-kips)	11.4	9.75	7.87	6.41	5.25	4.39	3.79

IMPERIAL SIZE AND MASS							
Mass (lb./ft.)	10.6	8.81	6.89	7.11	5.61	4.60	3.91
Thickness (in.)	.313	.250	.188	.250	.188	.150	.125
Size (in.)	3 x 3			2½ x 2½			

SQUARE HOLLOW SECTIONS
Factored Axial Compressive Resistances, C_r, in Kips

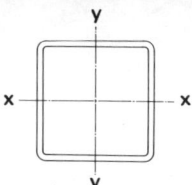

Size (mm)	50.8 x 50.8					38.1 x 38.1			
Thickness (mm)	6.35	4.78	3.81	3.18	2.79	4.78	3.81	3.18	2.54
Mass (kg/m)	8.05	6.45	5.33	4.55	4.05	4.54	3.81	3.28	2.71
0	72	57	47	40	36	40	34	29	24
3	57	46	39	33	30	27	23	20	17
4	47	39	33	29	26	19	17	15	13
5	37	31	27	23	21	14	12	11	9
6	28	24	21	18	16	11	9	8	7
7	23	20	17	15	13	8	7	7	6
8	19	16	14	12	11	6	6	5	4
9	15	13	12	10	9			4	4
10	13	11	10	8	8				
11	11	9	8	7	6				
12		8	7	6	5				
13									
14									
15									
16									
17									
18									
19									
20									
21									
22									
23									
24									
25									
26									
27									
28									
29									
30									
31									
32									
33									
34									
35									

(Left axis label: Effective length (KL) in feet with respect to least radius of gyration)

PROPERTIES AND DESIGN DATA

Area (in.^{2})	1.59	1.27	1.05	.899	.799	.896	.752	.648	.534
Z (in.^{3})	.998	.840	.714	.621	.558	.422	.369	.326	.275
S (in.^{3})	.761	.668	.582	.514	.466	.322	.291	.263	.227
r (in.)	.692	.725	.744	.756	.764	.519	.539	.551	.564
M_r (ft.-kips)	3.74	3.15	2.68	2.33	2.09	1.58	1.38	1.22	1.03

IMPERIAL SIZE AND MASS

Mass (lb./ft.)	5.41	4.33	3.58	3.06	2.72	3.05	2.56	2.21	1.82
Thickness (in.)	.250	.188	.150	.125	.110	.188	.150	.125	.100
Size (in.)	2 x 2					1½ x 1½			

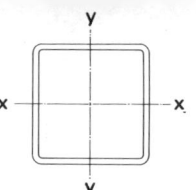

SQUARE HOLLOW SECTIONS
Factored Axial Compressive
Resistances, C_r, in Kips

Size (mm)	31.8 x 31.8			25.4 x 25.4	
Thickness (mm)	3.81	3.18	2.54	3.18	2.54
Mass (kg/m)	3.06	2.65	2.20	2.01	1.69
0	27	24	20	18	15
3	15	13	12	7	6
4	10	9	8	5	4
5	7	7	6	3	3
6	5	5	4		
7	4	4	3		
8					
9					
10					
11					
12					
13					
14					
15					
16					
17					
18					
19					
20					
21					
22					
23					
24					
25					
26					
27					
28					
29					
30					
31					
32					
33					
34					
35					

Effective length (KL) in feet with respect to least radius of gyration

PROPERTIES AND DESIGN DATA

Area (in.^{2})	.603	.524	.435	.398	.334
Z (in.^{3})	.239	.214	.184	.125	.109
S (in.^{3})	.184	.169	.149	.095	.086
r (in.)	.437	.450	.463	.346	.359
M_r (ft.-kips)	.896	.802	.690	.469	.409

IMPERIAL SIZE AND MASS

Mass (lb./ft.)	2.05	1.78	1.48	1.35	1.14
Thickness (in.)	.150	.125	.100	.125	.100
Size (in.)	1¼ x 1¼			1 x 1	

ROUND HOLLOW SECTIONS
Factored Axial Compressive Resistances, C_r, in Kips

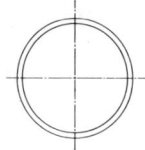

G40.21-50W
$\emptyset = 0.90$

Size (mm)	406.4 OD					355.6 OD		
Thickness (mm)	12.7	11.1	9.53	7.95	6.35	12.7	11.1	9.53
Mass (kg/m)	123	108	93.3	78.1	62.6	107	94.6	81.3
0	1090	963	828	693	558	954	841	724
3	1090	963	828	693	558	954	841	724
4	1090	963	828	693	558	954	841	724
5	1090	963	828	693	558	950	838	721
6	1090	957	823	689	555	941	830	715
7	1080	949	816	683	550	931	822	708
8	1070	940	809	677	545	921	813	700
9	1060	932	802	671	541	911	804	692
10	1050	923	794	665	535	900	794	684
11	1040	913	786	658	530	889	784	676
12	1030	904	778	651	525	877	774	667
13	1010	894	769	644	519	865	763	658
14	1000	883	760	637	513	852	752	648
15	990	873	751	629	507	839	741	638
16	977	861	742	621	500	825	729	628
17	964	850	732	613	494	811	717	618
18	951	838	722	605	487	797	704	607
19	937	826	711	596	480	782	691	595
20	923	813	701	587	473	766	677	584
21	908	800	690	578	466	750	663	572
22	893	787	678	568	458	734	649	560
23	877	774	667	559	451	717	634	547
24	861	760	655	549	443	700	619	534
25	845	745	643	539	435	682	603	521
26	828	731	630	528	426	664	587	507
27	811	716	617	518	418	645	571	493
28	793	700	604	507	409	626	554	478
29	775	685	591	496	400	606	537	464
30	757	668	577	484	391	586	519	449
31	738	652	563	472	382	562	499	432
32	719	635	549	461	372	539	478	414
33	699	618	534	448	362	517	459	397
34	679	600	519	436	352	497	441	382
35	658	582	504	424	342	478	424	367

Effective length (KL) in feet with respect to least radius of gyration

PROPERTIES AND DESIGN DATA								
Area (in.^{2})	24.3	21.4	18.4	15.4	12.4	21.2	18.7	16.1
Z (in.^{3})	120	106	91.6	77.0	62.0	91.2	80.6	69.7
S (in.^{3})	91.5	81.1	70.3	59.3	48.0	69.1	61.4	53.3
r (in.)	5.48	5.50	5.53	5.55	5.57	4.78	4.80	4.82
M_r (ft.-kips)	450	397	343	289	180	342	302	261

IMPERIAL SIZE AND MASS								
Mass (lb./ft.)	82.9	72.9	62.7	52.5	42.1	72.2	63.5	54.7
Thickness (in.)	.500	.438	.375	.313	.250	.500	.438	.375
Size (in.)	16 OD					14 OD		

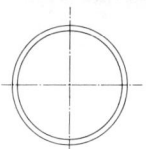

Size (mm)		355.6 OD		323.9 OD				
Thickness (mm)		7.95	6.35	12.7	11.1	9.53	7.95	6.35
Mass (kg/m)		68.2	54.7	97.5	85.9	73.9	61.9	49.7
	0	607	486	864	765	657	549	442
	3	607	486	864	765	657	549	442
	4	607	486	864	765	657	549	442
	5	605	484	856	758	651	544	438
	6	599	480	847	750	644	539	434
	7	594	475	837	741	637	532	429
	8	587	470	827	732	629	526	424
	9	581	465	816	723	621	519	418
	10	574	459	805	713	613	512	413
	11	567	454	793	703	604	505	407
	12	560	448	781	692	595	497	401
	13	552	442	768	681	585	489	394
	14	544	436	755	669	575	481	388
	15	536	429	741	657	565	473	381
	16	527	422	727	644	554	464	374
	17	519	415	712	631	543	454	366
	18	509	408	696	618	532	445	359
	19	500	401	681	604	520	435	351
	20	490	393	664	589	507	425	343
	21	480	385	647	575	495	414	334
	22	470	377	630	559	482	404	326
	23	460	369	612	544	468	392	317
	24	449	360	594	527	454	381	308
	25	438	351	575	511	440	369	298
	26	426	342	555	494	426	357	289
	27	415	333	535	476	411	345	279
	28	403	323	513	457	395	332	269
	29	390	313	490	436	377	317	257
	30	378	303	468	417	360	303	245
	31	364	293	448	399	345	290	235
	32	349	281	429	382	330	278	225
	33	335	270	411	367	317	266	216
	34	322	259	395	352	304	256	207
	35	310	249	380	338	292	246	199

Effective length (KL) in feet with respect to least radius of gyration

PROPERTIES AND DESIGN DATA								
Area (in.^{2})		13.5	10.8	19.2	17.0	14.6	12.2	9.82
Z (in.^{3})		58.6	47.3	75.1	66.5	57.5	48.4	39.1
S (in.^{3})		45.0	36.5	56.7	50.5	43.9	37.1	30.1
r (in.)		4.84	4.86	4.34	4.36	4.38	4.40	4.42
M_r (ft.-kips)		220	137	282	249	216	181	147

IMPERIAL SIZE AND MASS								
Mass (lb./ft.)		45.8	36.8	65.5	57.7	49.6	41.6	33.4
Thickness (in.)		.313	.250	.500	.438	.375	.313	.250
Size (in.)		14 OD		12.75 OD				

ROUND HOLLOW SECTIONS
Factored Axial Compressive
Resistances, C$_r$, in Kips

G40.21-50W
$\phi = 0.90$

Size (mm)		273.1 OD					219.1 OD		
Thickness (mm)		12.7	11.1	9.53	7.95	6.35	12.7	11.1	9.53
Mass (kg/m)		81.6	71.9	61.9	52.0	41.8	64.6	57.1	49.3
	0	724	639	549	463	371	576	508	438
	3	724	639	549	463	371	573	506	436
	4	719	635	545	461	369	564	498	429
	5	710	627	539	455	364	554	490	422
	6	700	618	531	449	360	544	480	414
	7	690	609	524	442	354	532	470	405
	8	679	599	515	435	349	520	460	396
	9	667	589	507	428	343	507	448	387
	10	655	578	498	420	337	493	436	376
	11	642	567	488	412	331	479	424	366
	12	629	555	478	404	324	463	410	354
	13	615	543	467	395	317	447	396	342
	14	600	530	457	386	310	430	381	330
	15	585	517	445	377	302	413	366	317
	16	569	503	433	367	294	394	350	303
	17	552	489	421	356	286	375	333	289
	18	535	474	408	346	278	355	316	274
	19	518	458	395	335	269	332	296	257
	20	499	442	381	323	260	310	276	240
	21	480	425	367	311	250	290	259	225
	22	461	408	353	299	241	273	243	211
	23	441	391	338	287	231	257	229	199
	24	416	370	320	272	220	242	216	187
	25	394	350	303	258	208	229	204	177
	26	374	332	288	245	197	216	193	168
	27	355	316	273	233	188	205	183	159
	28	338	301	260	221	179	195	174	151
	29	322	287	248	211	170	185	165	144
	30	308	274	237	201	163	176	157	137
	31	294	261	226	192	155	168	150	130
	32	281	250	217	184	149	160	143	124
	33	269	240	207	176	142	153	136	119
	34	258	230	199	169	137	146	130	113
	35	248	220	191	162	131	140	125	108

Left axis label: Effective length (KL) in feet with respect to least radius of gyration

PROPERTIES AND DESIGN DATA									
Area (in.^{2})		16.1	14.2	12.2	10.3	8.25	12.8	11.3	9.73
Z (in.^{3})		52.6	46.6	40.4	34.1	27.6	33.1	29.4	25.6
S (in.^{3})		39.4	35.2	30.7	26.0	21.2	24.5	22.0	19.2
r (in.)		3.63	3.65	3.67	3.69	3.71	2.88	2.90	2.92
M$_r$ (ft.-kips)		197	175	151	128	103	124	110	96.0

IMPERIAL SIZE AND MASS									
Mass (lb./ft.)		54.8	48.3	41.6	34.9	28.1	43.4	38.4	33.1
Thickness (in.)		.500	.438	.375	.313	.250	.500	.438	.375
Size (in.)		10.75 OD					8.625 OD		

G40.21-50W
∅ = 0.90

ROUND HOLLOW SECTIONS
Factored Axial Compressive
Resistances, C_r, in Kips

Size (mm)		219.1 OD			168.3 OD			
Thickness (mm)		7.95	6.35	4.78	9.53	7.95	6.35	4.78
Mass (kg/m)		41.4	33.3	25.3	37.3	31.4	25.4	19.3
Effective length (KL) in feet with respect to least radius of gyration	0	368	296	225	332	279	225	171
	3	366	295	224	325	274	222	169
	4	361	291	220	318	268	217	165
	5	355	286	217	310	261	211	161
	6	348	280	213	301	254	205	156
	7	341	275	209	291	246	199	152
	8	333	269	204	281	237	192	146
	9	325	262	199	269	228	185	141
	10	317	256	194	257	218	177	135
	11	308	248	189	244	207	168	129
	12	298	241	183	231	196	159	122
	13	288	233	177	217	184	150	115
	14	278	225	171	202	172	140	108
	15	267	216	164	184	157	129	99
	16	256	207	158	169	144	118	91
	17	244	197	151	155	133	109	84
	18	231	188	143	144	123	101	78
	19	218	177	135	133	114	94	72
	20	203	165	126	124	106	87	67
	21	191	155	118	116	99	81	63
	22	179	145	111	108	92	76	59
	23	168	137	105	102	87	71	55
	24	159	129	99	95	81	67	52
	25	150	122	93	90	77	63	49
	26	142	116	88	85	72	59	46
	27	135	110	84	80	68	56	43
	28	128	104	80	75	64	53	41
	29	122	99	76	70	60	50	38
	30	116	94	72	66	56	47	36
	31	110	90	69	62	53	44	34
	32	105	86	66	58	50	41	32
	33	101	82	63	55	47	39	30
	34	96	78	60	52	44	37	28
	35	92	75	57	49	42	35	27
PROPERTIES AND DESIGN DATA								
Area (in.^{2})		8.17	6.58	4.99	7.37	6.21	5.01	3.81
Z (in.^{3})		21.6	17.5	13.4	14.7	12.5	10.2	7.80
S (in.^{3})		16.4	13.4	10.3	10.9	9.36	7.69	5.96
r (in.)		2.94	2.96	2.98	2.21	2.23	2.26	2.28
M_r (ft.-kips)		81.0	65.6	50.2	55.1	46.9	38.2	29.2
IMPERIAL SIZE AND MASS								
Mass (lb./ft.)		27.8	22.4	17.0	25.1	21.1	17.0	13.0
Thickness (in.)		.313	.250	.188	.375	.313	.250	.188
Size (in.)			8.625 OD			6.625 OD		

ROUND HOLLOW SECTIONS
Factored Axial Compressive Resistances, C_r, in Kips

G40.21-50W
$\phi = 0.90$

Size (mm)	141.3 OD				114.3 OD		
Thickness (mm)	9.53	7.95	6.35	4.78	7.95	6.35	4.78
Mass (kg/m)	31.0	26.1	21.1	16.1	20.9	16.9	12.9
0	275	232	188	143	185	150	115
3	266	225	182	139	176	143	109
4	258	218	177	135	168	137	105
5	249	211	171	131	160	130	100
6	240	203	164	126	151	123	94
7	229	194	157	120	141	115	89
8	217	184	150	115	130	106	82
9	205	174	141	108	117	97	75
10	191	163	133	102	103	86	67
11	177	151	123	95	91	76	59
12	161	138	113	87	81	67	52
13	145	124	102	79	72	60	47
14	131	112	92	71	65	54	42
15	119	102	84	65	59	49	38
16	109	93	77	59	54	45	35
17	100	86	70	54	49	41	32
18	92	79	65	50	45	38	29
19	85	73	60	46	41	34	27
20	79	68	56	43	37	31	24
21	73	63	52	40	34	28	22
22	68	59	48	37	31	26	20
23	64	55	45	35	28	24	19
24	59	51	42	33	26	22	17
25	54	47	39	30		20	16
26	50	44	36	28			
27	47	41	33	26			
28	44	38	31	24			
29	41	35	29	23			
30	39	33	27	21			
31			26	20			
32							
33							
34							
35							

Effective length (KL) in feet with respect to least radius of gyration

PROPERTIES AND DESIGN DATA							
Area (in.^{2})	6.11	5.16	4.17	3.18	4.12	3.34	2.55
Z (in.^{3})	10.1	8.64	7.06	5.44	5.50	4.52	3.50
S (in.^{3})	7.43	6.42	5.31	4.13	4.03	3.36	2.64
r (in.)	1.84	1.86	1.88	1.90	1.48	1.51	1.53
M_r (ft.-kips)	37.9	32.4	26.5	20.4	20.6	16.9	13.1

IMPERIAL SIZE AND MASS							
Mass (lb./ft.)	20.8	17.6	14.2	10.8	14.0	11.4	8.68
Thickness (in.)	.375	.313	.250	.188	.313	.250	.188
Size (in.)	5.562 OD				4.5 OD		

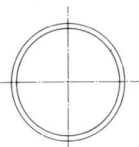

Size (mm)		101.6 OD				88.9 OD			
Thickness (mm)		7.95	6.35	4.78	3.81	7.95	6.35	4.78	3.81
Mass (kg/m)		18.4	14.9	11.4	9.19	15.9	12.9	9.92	8.00
Effective length (KL) in feet with respect to least radius of gyration	0	163	133	101	81	141	115	88	71
	1	163	133	101	81	141	115	88	71
	2	159	129	99	79	135	110	85	69
	3	152	124	95	76	128	105	81	65
	4	145	118	90	73	120	98	76	61
	5	136	111	85	69	110	91	70	57
	6	126	103	79	64	100	82	64	52
	7	115	94	73	59	88	73	57	46
	8	103	85	66	53	74	62	48	40
	9	89	74	58	47	63	53	41	34
	10	77	64	50	41	54	45	36	30
	11	68	56	44	36	48	40	31	26
	12	60	50	39	32	42	35	28	23
	13	54	45	35	28	37	31	25	20
	14	48	40	31	25	33	28	22	18
	15	43	36	28	23	29	25	20	16
	16	39	33	26	21	26	22	17	14
	17	35	30	23	19	23	19	15	13
	18	32	26	21	17	21	17	14	11
	19	29	24	19	15		16	12	10
	20	26	22	17	14				
	21	24	20	15	13				
	22		18	14	12				
	23								
	24								
	25								
	26								
	27								
	28								
	29								
	30								
	31								
	32								
	33								
PROPERTIES AND DESIGN DATA									
Area (in.^{2})		3.63	2.95	2.25	1.81	3.13	2.55	1.96	1.58
Z (in.^{3})		4.27	3.52	2.74	2.22	3.19	2.65	2.07	1.68
S (in.^{3})		3.10	2.60	2.05	1.68	2.30	1.94	1.54	1.27
r (in.)		1.31	1.33	1.35	1.36	1.13	1.15	1.17	1.19
M_r (ft.-kips)		16.0	13.2	10.3	8.32	12.0	9.94	7.76	6.30
IMPERIAL SIZE AND MASS									
Mass (lb./ft.)		12.3	10.0	7.67	6.17	10.7	8.69	6.66	5.37
Thickness (in.)		.313	.250	.188	.150	.313	.250	.188	.150
Size (in.)		4.OD				3.5 OD			

ROUND HOLLOW SECTIONS
Factored Axial Compressive Resistances, C_r, in Kips

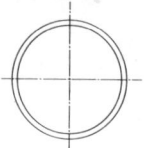

G40.21-50W
$\emptyset = 0.90$

Size (mm)		73.0 OD				60.3 OD			
Thickness (mm)		6.35	4.78	3.81	3.18	6.35	4.78	3.81	3.18
Mass (kg/m)		10.4	8.04	6.50	5.48	8.45	6.54	5.31	4.48
	0	93	72	58	49	75	58	47	40
	1	92	71	57	48	74	57	47	39
	2	87	67	54	46	68	53	43	37
	3	81	63	51	43	62	48	39	33
	4	74	57	46	39	53	42	34	29
	5	65	51	41	35	43	35	29	24
	6	55	44	36	30	34	27	22	19
	7	45	36	29	25	27	22	18	16
	8	37	30	24	21	22	18	15	13
	9	32	25	21	18	19	15	13	11
	10	27	22	18	15	16	13	11	9
	11	24	19	15	13	13	11	9	8
	12	20	16	13	12	11	9	8	6
	13	17	14	12	10			6	6
	14	15	12	10	9				
	15	13	11	9	8				
	16			8	7				
	17								
	18								
	19								
	20								
	21								
	22								
	23								
	24								
	25								
	26								
	27								
	28								
	29								
	30								
	31								
	32								
	33								

Effective length (KL) in feet with respect to least radius of gyration

IMP

PROPERTIES AND DESIGN DATA

Area (in.^{2})	2.06	1.59	1.28	1.08	1.67	1.29	1.05	.885
Z (in.^{3})	1.73	1.36	1.11	.947	1.13	.901	.743	.634
S (in.^{3})	1.25	1.00	.831	.712	.804	.655	.548	.473
r (in.)	.932	.952	.965	.973	.756	.776	.788	.796
M_r (ft.-kips)	6.49	5.10	4.16	3.55	4.24	3.38	2.79	2.38

IMPERIAL SIZE AND MASS

Mass (lb./ft.)	7.01	5.40	4.37	3.68	5.68	4.40	3.57	3.01
Thickness (in.)	.250	.188	.150	.125	.250	.188	.150	.125
Size (in.)	2.875 OD				2.375 OD			

G40.21-50W
$\emptyset = 0.90$

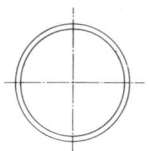

Size (mm)		48.3 OD				42.2 OD		33.4 OD		26.7 OD	
Thickness (mm)		4.78	3.81	3.18	2.79	3.18	2.54	3.18	2.54	3.18	2.54
Mass (kg/m)		5.13	4.18	3.54	3.13	3.06	2.48	2.37	1.93	1.84	1.51
	0	45	37	31	28	27	22	21	17	16	13
	1	44	36	31	27	26	21	20	16	15	12
	2	40	32	28	24	23	19	16	13	10	9
	3	34	28	24	21	19	15	11	9	6	5
	4	26	22	19	17	14	11	7	6	4	3
	5	19	16	14	13	10	8	5	4	3	2
	6	15	13	11	10	8	6	4	3		
	7	12	10	9	8	6	5	3	2		
	8	10	8	7	6	5	4				
	9	8	7	6	5	4	3				
	10	6	5	5	4						
	11										
	12										
	13										
	14										
	15										
	16										
	17										
	18										
	19										
	20										
	21										
	22										
	23										
	24										
	25										
	26										
	27										
	28										
	29										
	30										
	31										
	32										
	33										

Effective length (KL) in feet with respect to least radius of gyration

PROPERTIES AND DESIGN DATA

	48.3 OD				42.2 OD		33.4 OD		26.7 OD	
Area (in.^{2})	1.01	.825	.699	.618	.604	.491	.468	.382	.364	.299
Z (in.^{3})	.555	.461	.396	.353	.296	.244	.178	.148	.108	.091
S (in.^{3})	.396	.335	.291	.262	.216	.181	.127	.108	.076	.065
r (in.)	.609	.622	.630	.635	.545	.553	.423	.431	.330	.338
M_r (ft.-kips)	2.08	1.73	1.48	1.32	1.11	.915	.667	.555	.405	.340

IMPERIAL SIZE AND MASS

	48.3 OD				42.2 OD		33.4 OD		26.7 OD	
Mass (lb./ft.)	3.45	2.81	2.38	2.10	2.06	1.67	1.59	1.30	1.24	1.02
Thickness (in.)	1.88	.150	.125	.110	.125	.100	.125	.100	.125	.100
Size (in.)		1.9 OD			1.66 OD		1.315 OD		1.05 OD	

RECTANGULAR HOLLOW SECTIONS
Factored Axial Compressive
Resistances, C$_r$, in Kips

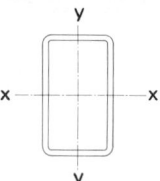

G40.21-50W
CLASS H
$\varnothing = 0.90$

Size (mm)	304.8 x 203.2					254.0 x 152.4		
Thickness (mm)	12.7	11.13	9.53	††7.95	6.35‡	12.7	11.13	9.53
Mass (kg/m)	93.0	82.4	71.3	60.1	48.6	72.7	64.6	56.1
0	828	733	634	535	405	648	576	499
3	828	733	634	535	402	648	576	499
4	828	733	634	535	400	646	574	498
5	826	732	633	534	398	641	570	495
6	823	729	631	533	395	635	565	490
7	818	725	627	530	392	626	558	484
8	812	720	623	526	388	616	548	476
9	804	713	617	521	383	603	537	467
10	795	705	610	516	378	588	524	456
11	784	696	603	509	373	571	510	444
12	772	685	594	502	367	552	493	430
13	759	674	584	494	360	530	475	414
14	743	660	572	484	353	507	454	397
15	727	646	560	474	346	481	432	378
16	709	630	547	463	338	454	408	358
17	689	613	532	451	329	424	382	336
18	668	595	516	438	320	391	355	313
19	645	575	500	424	310	354	322	286
20	621	554	482	410	300	323	293	260
21	596	532	463	394	289	296	269	238
22	569	509	443	377	278	273	248	220
23	540	484	422	360	266	252	229	203
24	510	458	399	341	254	234	213	189
25	474	427	374	321	241	218	198	176
26	442	398	348	299	228	204	186	164
27	413	372	325	279	214	192	174	154
28	387	348	305	261	200	179	163	145
29	363	327	286	245	186	167	152	135
30	342	308	269	231	174	157	143	127
31	323	291	254	218	163	147	134	119
32	306	275	241	206	153	138	126	112
33	290	261	228	196	144	130	119	105
34	276	248	217	186	135	123	112	100
35	263	236	207	177	128	116	106	94

Effective length (KL) in feet with respect to least radius of gyration

PROPERTIES AND DESIGN DATA								
Area (in.²)	18.4	16.3	14.1	11.9	9.59	14.4	12.8	11.1
Z$_x$ (in.³)	72.4	64.7	56.5	48.0	39.1	45.6	40.9	35.9
S$_x$ (in.³)	58.8	52.9	46.5	39.8	32.6	36.1	32.7	29.0
r$_x$ (in.)	4.39	4.42	4.45	4.49	4.52	3.55	3.58	3.62
Z$_y$ (in.³)	54.7	48.9	42.7	36.4	29.6	31.8	28.7	25.2
S$_y$ (in.³)	46.9	42.3	37.3	32.0	26.3	26.9	24.5	21.8
r$_y$ (in.)	3.20	3.23	3.25	3.28	3.31	2.37	2.40	2.43
r$_x$/r$_y$	1.37	1.37	1.37	1.37	1.36	1.50	1.49	1.49
M$_{rx}$ (ft. kips)	271	243	212	180	147	171	153	135
M$_{ry}$ (ft. kips)	205	183	160	120	89.1	119	108	94.5

IMPERIAL SIZE AND MASS								
Mass (lb./ft.)	62.5	55.4	47.9	40.4	32.6	48.9	43.4	37.7
Thickness (in.)	.500	.438	.375	.313	.250	.500	.438	.375
Size (in.)	12 x 8					10 x 6		

††Class 3 in bending about Y—Y axis.

‡Class 4 in bending about Y—Y axis and resistance for this column calculated according CSA S16.1- 1974 Clause 13.3.3.

G40.21-50W
CLASS H
$\emptyset = 0.90$

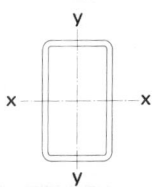

RECTANGULAR HOLLOW SECTIONS
Factored Axial Compressive
Resistances, C_r, in Kips

Size (mm)		254.0 x 152.4		203.2 x 152.4					
Thickness (mm)		7.95	††6.35	12.7	11.13	9.53	7.95	6.35	4.78‡
Mass (kg/m)		47.5	38.4	62.6	55.7	48.5	41.1	33.4	25.5
	0	422	342	558	495	431	365	297	227
	3	422	342	558	495	431	365	296	224
	4	420	341	556	493	429	364	296	222
	5	418	339	552	490	427	362	294	220
	6	414	336	546	484	422	358	291	217
	7	409	332	538	478	417	354	287	213
	8	403	327	528	469	409	348	283	209
	9	395	321	516	459	401	341	277	204
	10	386	314	502	447	391	332	271	198
	11	376	306	486	433	379	323	263	192
	12	365	297	469	418	366	312	255	186
	13	352	287	449	401	352	300	245	179
	14	338	276	427	383	336	287	235	171
	15	322	264	404	362	319	273	224	163
	16	306	250	378	340	300	258	212	154
	17	288	236	351	317	280	241	199	144
	18	269	221	319	289	258	224	185	134
	19	247	204	289	262	234	203	168	124
	20	225	186	263	239	213	185	153	113
	21	206	170	242	219	195	169	141	102
	22	189	157	223	202	180	156	129	93
	23	175	145	206	187	167	144	120	85
	24	163	134	192	174	155	134	111	78
	25	152	125	179	162	144	125	104	72
	26	142	117	167	152	135	117	97	67
	27	133	110	156	142	127	110	91	62
	28	125	103	145	132	118	103	85	58
	29	117	97	136	124	110	96	80	54
	30	110	91	127	116	103	90	75	50
	31	103	85	119	109	97	84	70	47
	32	97	80	112	102	91	79	66	44
	33	91	76	106	96	86	75	62	41
	34	86	71	100	91	81	71	59	39
	35	81	67	95	86	77	67	55	37

Effective length (KL) in feet with respect to least radius of gyration

PROPERTIES AND DESIGN DATA

	254.0 x 152.4		203.2 x 152.4					
Area (in.²)	9.37	7.59	12.4	11.0	9.58	8.12	6.59	5.04
Z_x (in.³)	30.7	25.1	32.2	29.0	25.6	21.9	18.0	13.9
S_x (in.³)	25.0	20.6	25.8	23.5	20.9	18.1	15.0	11.7
r_x (in.)	3.65	3.69	2.89	2.92	2.96	2.99	3.02	3.05
Z_y (in.³)	21.6	17.7	26.3	23.8	21.0	18.0	14.8	11.5
S_y (in.³)	18.9	15.6	21.9	20.0	17.8	15.5	12.9	10.1
r_y (in.)	2.46	2.49	2.30	2.33	2.36	2.39	2.42	2.45
r_x/r_y	1.49	1.48	1.25	1.25	1.25	1.25	1.25	1.25
M_{rx} (ft. kips)	115	94.1	121	109	96.0	82.1	67.5	52.1
M_{ry} (ft. kips)	81.0	58.5	98.6	89.2	78.7	67.5	55.5	36.8

IMPERIAL SIZE AND MASS

	254.0 x 152.4		203.2 x 152.4					
Mass (lb./ft.)	31.9	25.8	42.1	37.5	32.6	27.6	22.4	17.1
Thickness (in.)	.313	.250	.500	.438	.375	.313	.250	.188
Size (in.)	10 x 6		8 x 6					

††Class 3 in bending about Y—Y axis.

‡Class 4 in bending about Y—Y axis and resistance for this column calculated according to CSA S16.1-1974 Clause 13.3.3.

RECTANGULAR HOLLOW SECTIONS
Factored Axial Compressive Resistances, C$_r$, in Kips

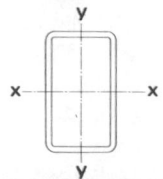

Size (mm)	203.2 x 101.6						177.8 x 127.0#		
Thickness (mm)	12.7	11.13	9.53	7.95	6.35	4.78‡	12.7	11.13	9.53
Mass (kg/m)	52.4	46.9	40.9	34.8	28.3	21.7	52.4	46.9	40.9
0	468	416	364	309	252	193	468	416	364
3	465	413	361	307	250	188	467	415	363
4	458	408	357	303	247	184	463	412	360
5	447	399	349	297	242	180	457	407	356
6	433	387	339	289	236	174	449	400	350
7	415	372	326	279	228	167	438	390	342
8	394	353	311	266	218	160	424	379	332
9	369	332	293	251	206	151	408	365	321
10	340	307	273	234	193	141	390	350	308
11	308	280	250	215	178	130	370	332	293
12	269	248	224	194	162	118	347	312	276
13	233	215	194	169	142	106	321	290	258
14	204	188	170	148	124	92	293	266	237
15	181	166	150	131	110	80	260	238	214
16	162	149	134	117	98	70	232	212	191
17	146	134	121	105	88	62	208	190	171
18	132	122	110	96	80	56	188	172	154
19	119	110	99	87	73	50	171	157	140
20	108	99	90	78	66	45	157	143	129
21	98	90	82	71	60	41	145	132	118
22	90	83	75	65	55	37	133	122	110
23	82	76	69	60	50	34	122	112	101
24	76	70	63	55	47	31	112	103	93
25	70	65	59	51	43	29	104	95	86
26		60	54	47	40	27	96	88	79
27					37	25	90	82	74
28							84	77	69
29							78	72	64
30							73	67	60
31							69	63	57
32									53
33									
34									
35									

(Left axis label: Effective length (KL) in feet with respect to least radius of gyration)

PROPERTIES AND DESIGN DATA

Area (in.²)	10.4	9.25	8.08	6.87	5.59	4.28	10.4	9.25	8.08
Z$_x$ (in.³)	24.7	22.4	19.9	17.1	14.1	11.0	23.0	20.9	18.5
S$_x$ (in.³)	18.8	17.2	15.5	13.5	11.3	8.86	18.1	16.6	14.9
r$_x$ (in.)	2.69	2.73	2.77	2.80	2.84	2.88	2.47	2.51	2.54
Z$_y$ (in.³)	15.0	13.6	12.1	10.5	8.71	6.79	18.2	16.5	14.6
S$_y$ (in.³)	12.3	11.4	10.3	9.05	7.63	6.04	14.8	13.7	12.3
r$_y$ (in.)	1.54	1.57	1.60	1.62	1.65	1.68	1.89	1.92	1.95
r$_x$/r$_y$	1.75	1.74	1.73	1.73	1.72	1.71	1.31	1.30	1.30
M$_{rx}$ (ft. kips)	92.6	84.0	74.6	64.1	52.9	41.2	86.2	78.4	69.4
M$_{ry}$ (ft. kips)	56.2	51.0	45.4	39.4	32.7	22.0	68.2	61.9	54.7

IMPERIAL SIZE AND MASS

Mass (lb./ft.)	35.2	31.5	27.5	23.4	19.0	14.6	35.2	31.5	27.5
Thickness (in.)	.500	.438	.375	.313	.250	.188	.500	.438	.375
Size (in.)	8 x 4						7 x 5		

‡Class 4 in bending about Y—Y axis and resistance for this column calculated according to CSA S16.1-1974 Clause 13.3.3.
#Check manufacturer for current availability.

G40.21-50W
CLASS H
∅ = 0.90

RECTANGULAR HOLLOW SECTIONS
Factored Axial Compressive
Resistances, C_r, in Kips

Size (mm)	177.8 x 127.0 #			152.4 x 101.6				
Thickness (mm)	7.95	6.35	††4.78	11.13	9.53	7.95	6.35	4.78
Mass (kg/m)	34.8	28.3	21.7	38.0	33.3	28.4	23.2	17.9
0	309	252	193	337	296	253	207	159
3	309	251	192	335	294	251	205	158
4	306	250	191	330	290	248	203	156
5	303	247	189	322	283	242	198	153
6	298	243	186	311	274	235	193	149
7	292	238	183	297	263	226	185	143
8	284	232	178	281	249	215	177	137
9	274	224	173	262	233	202	167	130
10	263	216	166	241	215	187	155	121
11	251	206	159	216	195	170	142	111
12	237	195	151	187	170	151	127	100
13	222	183	142	162	147	130	110	88
14	206	170	133	142	129	114	96	77
15	187	156	122	126	114	101	85	68
16	167	139	110	113	102	90	76	61
17	149	125	98	102	92	82	69	55
18	135	113	89	92	84	74	62	50
19	123	102	81	83	75	67	57	45
20	112	94	74	75	68	60	51	41
21	103	86	68	68	62	55	47	37
22	96	80	63	62	57	50	43	34
23	88	74	58	57	52	46	39	31
24	81	68	54	53	48	43	36	29
25	75	63	50	49	44	39	33	27
26	70	58	46			37	31	25
27	65	54	43					23
28	60	51	40					
29	56	47	37					
30	53	44	35					
31	50	42	33					
32	47	39	31					
33		37	29					
34								
35								

Effective length (KL) in feet with respect to least radius of gyration

PROPERTIES AND DESIGN DATA

Area (in.²)	6.87	5.59	4.28	7.50	6.58	5.62	4.59	3.53
Z_x (in.³)	15.9	13.2	10.2	14.0	12.5	10.9	9.05	7.08
S_x (in.³)	13.0	10.9	8.53	10.9	9.90	8.72	7.36	5.83
r_x (in.)	2.57	2.61	2.64	2.09	2.12	2.16	2.19	2.23
Z_y (in.³)	12.6	10.4	8.12	10.5	9.42	8.21	6.84	5.36
S_y (in.³)	10.8	9.03	7.12	8.57	7.81	6.92	5.87	4.67
r_y (in.)	1.98	2.01	2.04	1.51	1.54	1.57	1.60	1.63
r_x/r_y	1.30	1.30	1.29	1.38	1.38	1.38	1.37	1.37
M_{rx} (ft. kips)	59.6	49.5	38.2	52.5	46.9	40.9	33.9	26.5
M_{ry} (ft. kips)	47.2	39.0	26.7	39.4	35.3	30.8	25.6	20.1

IMPERIAL SIZE AND MASS

Mass (lb./ft.)	23.4	19.0	14.6	25.5	22.4	19.1	15.6	12.0
Thickness (in.)	.313	.250	.188	.438	.375	.313	.250	.188
Size (in.)	7 x 5			6 x 4				

††Class 3 in bending about Y—Y axis.
#Check manufacturer for current availability.

RECTANGULAR HOLLOW SECTIONS
Factored Axial Compressive Resistances, C_r, in Kips

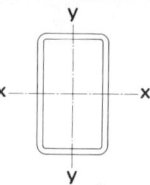

G40.21-50W
CLASS H
$\emptyset = 0.90$

Size (mm)	127.0 x 76.2				127.0 x 63.5			
Thickness (mm)	9.53	7.95	6.35	4.78	9.53	7.95	6.35	4.78
Mass (kg/m)	25.7	22.1	18.2	14.1	23.8	20.5	16.9	13.1
0	229	196	162	125	211	182	150	117
3	223	192	158	123	202	175	145	113
4	216	186	154	119	191	166	138	108
5	205	177	147	114	175	153	128	101
6	190	165	138	107	155	137	115	91
7	173	151	127	99	130	117	100	80
8	152	134	114	89	102	93	81	66
9	126	114	98	78	83	75	66	54
10	105	94	81	65	69	63	55	45
11	88	79	68	55	59	54	46	38
12	76	68	59	47	49	45	40	32
13	67	60	51	41	42	39	34	28
14	58	52	45	36	37	34	29	24
15	50	46	39	31	32	29	26	21
16	45	40	35	28		26	23	19
17	40	36	31	25				
18	36	32	28	22				
19		29	25	20				
20				18				
21								
22								
23								
24								
25								
26								
27								
28								
29								
30								
31								
32								
33								
34								
35								

Effective length (KL) in feet with respect to least radius of gyration

PROPERTIES AND DESIGN DATA

Area (in.^{2})	5.08	4.36	3.59	2.78	4.70	4.05	3.34	2.59
Z_x (in.^{3})	7.70	6.77	5.69	4.50	6.83	6.04	5.10	4.05
S_x (in.^{3})	5.88	5.27	4.52	3.63	5.08	4.58	3.95	3.20
r_x (in.)	1.70	1.74	1.77	1.81	1.64	1.68	1.72	1.76
Z_y (in.^{3})	5.34	4.71	3.98	3.16	4.12	3.66	3.11	2.49
S_y (in.^{3})	4.30	3.89	3.36	2.73	3.27	2.99	2.62	2.15
r_y (in.)	1.13	1.16	1.19	1.21	.932	.961	.990	1.02
r_x/r_y	1.51	1.50	1.50	1.49	1.76	1.75	1.74	1.73
M_{rx} (ft. kips)	28.9	25.4	21.3	16.9	25.6	22.6	19.1	15.2
M_{ry} (ft. kips)	20.0	17.7	14.9	11.8	15.4	13.7	11.7	9.34

IMPERIAL SIZE AND MASS

Mass (lb./ft.)	17.3	14.9	12.2	9.45	16.0	13.8	11.4	8.81
Thickness (in.)	.375	.313	.250	.188	.375	.313	.250	.188
Size (in.)	5 x 3				5 x 2½			

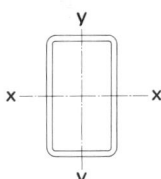

G40.21-50W
CLASS H
$\emptyset = 0.90$

RECTANGULAR HOLLOW SECTIONS
Factored Axial Compressive
Resistances, C_r, in Kips

Size (mm)	127.0 x 50.8				101.6 x 76.2			
Thickness (mm)	9.53	7.95	6.35	4.78	9.53	7.95	6.35	4.78
Mass (kg/m)	21.9	18.9	15.6	12.2	21.9	18.9	15.6	12.2
0	195	168	139	108	195	168	139	108
3	178	155	129	101	190	164	136	106
4	160	141	118	93	183	158	131	103
5	134	121	103	82	172	150	125	98
6	102	94	83	68	159	139	117	92
7	77	72	63	52	143	126	106	84
8	62	57	50	41	124	111	94	75
9	50	46	41	34	101	92	79	65
10	40	38	33	28	84	76	66	53
11	34	31	28	23	71	64	55	45
12	29	27	24	20	61	55	48	39
13			20	17	53	48	42	34
14					46	42	36	30
15					40	36	32	26
16					35	32	28	23
17					32	29	25	20
18					28	26	22	18
19							20	16
20								
21								
22								
23								
24								
25								
26								
27								
28								
29								
30								
31								
32								
33								
34								
35								

Effective length (KL) in feet with respect to least radius of gyration

PROPERTIES AND DESIGN DATA

Area (in.^{2})	4.33	3.74	3.09	2.40	4.33	3.74	3.09	2.40
Z_x (in.^{3})	5.96	5.30	4.51	3.60	5.34	4.74	4.02	3.21
S_x (in.^{3})	4.27	3.90	3.39	2.76	4.10	3.72	3.22	2.62
r_x (in.)	1.57	1.61	1.66	1.70	1.38	1.41	1.44	1.48
Z_y (in.^{3})	2.99	2.69	2.31	1.86	4.35	3.87	3.29	2.63
S_y (in.^{3})	2.31	2.15	1.92	1.60	3.44	3.14	2.73	2.23
r_y (in.)	.730	.759	.788	.816	1.09	1.12	1.15	1.18
r_x/r_y	2.15	2.13	2.10	2.08	1.26	1.26	1.25	1.25
M_{rx} (ft. kips)	22.3	19.9	16.9	13.5	20.0	17.8	15.1	12.0
M_{ry} (ft. kips)	11.2	10.1	8.66	6.97	16.3	14.5	12.3	9.86

IMPERIAL SIZE AND MASS

Mass (lb./ft.)	14.7	12.7	10.5	8.17	14.7	12.7	10.5	8.17
Thickness (in.)	.375	.313	.250	.188	.375	.313	.250	.188
Size (in.)	5 x 2				4 x 3			

RECTANGULAR HOLLOW SECTIONS
Factored Axial Compressive Resistances, C_r, in Kips

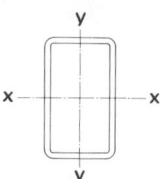

**G40.21-50W
CLASS H
$\emptyset = 0.90$**

Size (mm)		101.6 x 50.8					88.9 x 63.5		
Thickness (mm)		7.95	6.35	4.78	3.81	3.18	7.95	6.35	4.78
Mass (kg/m)		15.8	13.1	10.3	8.37	7.09	15.8	13.1	10.3
Effective length (KL) in feet with respect to least radius of gyration	0	140	117	91	74	63	140	117	91
	3	128	108	85	70	59	134	112	88
	4	115	98	78	64	55	126	106	84
	5	98	85	68	57	48	115	97	77
	6	75	67	56	47	41	101	86	69
	7	57	51	42	36	31	83	73	60
	8	45	40	34	28	25	66	58	48
	9	37	33	27	23	20	53	47	39
	10	30	27	22	19	17	45	39	32
	11	25	22	19	16	14	37	33	28
	12	21	19	16	13	12	32	28	23
	13			14	12	10	27	24	20
	14						24	21	17
	15						21	18	15
	16								13
	17								
	18								
	19								
	20								
	21								
	22								
	23								
	24								
	25								
	26								
	27								
	28								
	29								
	30								
	31								
	32								
	33								
	34								
	35								

PROPERTIES AND DESIGN DATA

Area (in.²)	3.11	2.59	2.03	1.65	1.40	3.11	2.59	2.03
Z_x (in.³)	3.59	3.09	2.49	2.07	1.77	3.35	2.88	2.32
S_x (in.³)	2.65	2.34	1.94	1.63	1.41	2.57	2.26	1.87
r_x (in.)	1.31	1.35	1.38	1.41	1.42	1.20	1.24	1.27
Z_y (in.³)	2.16	1.87	1.52	1.27	1.09	2.63	2.27	1.83
S_y (in.³)	1.70	1.53	1.29	1.10	.954	2.09	1.86	1.54
r_y (in.)	.740	.769	.797	.815	.826	.916	.947	.976
r_x/r_y	1.77	1.75	1.73	1.73	1.72	1.31	1.31	1.30
M_{rx} (ft. kips)	13.5	11.6	9.34	7.76	6.64	12.6	10.8	8.70
M_{ry} (ft. kips)	8.10	7.01	5.70	4.76	4.09	9.86	8.51	6.86

IMPERIAL SIZE AND MASS

Mass (lb./ft.)	10.6	8.81	6.89	5.62	4.76	10.6	8.81	6.89
Thickness (in.)	.313	.250	.188	.150	.125	.313	.250	.188
Size (in.)		4 x 2					3½ x 2½	

G40.21-50W
CLASS H
∅ = 0.90

RECTANGULAR HOLLOW SECTIONS
Factored Axial Compressive
Resistances, C_r, in Kips

Size (mm)	88.9 x 63.5		76.2 x 50.8				50.8 x 25.4	
Thickness (mm)	3.81	3.18	7.95	6.35	4.78	3.81	3.18	2.54
Mass (kg/m)	8.37	7.09	12.6	10.6	8.35	6.85	3.28	2.71
0	74	63	112	94	74	61	29	24
3	72	61	102	86	69	56	17	15
4	68	58	90	78	62	52	10	9
5	63	54	75	66	54	45	7	6
6	57	49	56	50	43	36	5	4
7	50	43	42	38	32	28		
8	40	35	34	30	26	22		
9	33	28	27	25	21	18		
10	27	24	22	20	17	15		
11	23	20	18	17	14	12		
12	20	17		14	12	10		
13	17	15				9		
14	15	13						
15	13	11						
16	11	10						
17								
18								
19								
20								
21								
22								
23								
24								
25								
26								
27								
28								
29								
30								
31								
32								
33								
34								
35								

Effective length (KL) in feet with respect to least radius of gyration

PROPERTIES AND DESIGN DATA

Area (in.²)	1.65	1.40	2.49	2.09	1.65	1.35	.648	.534
Z_x (in.³)	1.92	1.65	2.19	1.92	1.57	1.32	.386	.326
S_x (in.³)	1.57	1.36	1.62	1.47	1.24	1.06	.293	.253
r_x (in.)	1.29	1.30	.990	1.03	1.06	1.08	.673	.688
Z_y (in.³)	1.52	1.31	1.63	1.44	1.18	.992	.234	.199
S_y (in.³)	1.30	1.13	1.25	1.15	.978	.839	.192	.168
r_y (in.)	.994	1.01	.710	.741	.770	.788	.385	.396
r_x/r_y	1.30	1.30	1.39	1.39	1.38	1.37	1.75	1.74
M_{rx} (ft. kips)	7.20	6.19	8.21	7.20	5.89	4.95	1.45	1.22
M_{ry} (ft. kips)	5.70	4.91	6.11	5.40	4.42	3.72	.877	.746

IMPERIAL SIZE AND MASS

Mass (lb./ft.)	5.62	4.76	8.46	7.11	5.61	4.60	2.21	1.82
Thickness (in.)	.150	.125	.313	.250	.188	.150	.125	.100
Size (in.)	3½ x 2½		3 x 2				2 x 1	

SQUARE HOLLOW SECTIONS
Factored Axial Compressive
Resistances, C$_r$, in Kips

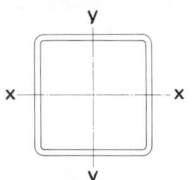

Size (mm)		304.8 x 304.8					254.0 x 254.0		
Thickness (mm)		12.70	11.13	9.53	††7.95	‡6.35	12.70	11.13	9.53
Mass (kg/m)		113	100	86.5	72.8	58.7	93.0	82.4	71.3
	0	1010	891	769	648	468	828	733	634
	3	1010	891	769	648	467	828	733	634
	4	1010	891	769	648	466	828	734	635
	5	1010	891	770	648	465	828	733	634
	6	1010	891	769	648	463	826	732	633
	7	1010	889	768	647	461	824	730	631
	8	1000	888	767	646	459	820	727	629
	9	1000	885	764	644	457	815	723	625
	10	997	881	761	641	454	810	718	621
	11	992	877	758	638	451	803	712	616
	12	986	872	754	635	448	795	705	610
	13	980	867	749	631	445	786	697	604
	14	973	860	743	627	441	777	689	597
	15	964	853	737	621	437	766	679	589
	16	955	845	731	616	433	754	669	580
	17	945	837	723	610	428	741	658	570
	18	934	827	715	603	423	727	646	560
	19	923	817	707	596	418	712	633	549
	20	910	806	697	588	413	696	619	537
	21	897	794	687	580	407	679	604	524
	22	883	782	677	571	401	661	588	511
	23	867	769	666	562	395	641	571	497
	24	852	755	654	552	388	621	554	482
	25	835	740	641	542	381	600	535	466
	26	817	725	628	531	374	578	516	450
	27	799	709	615	519	367	554	496	432
	28	779	692	600	508	359	530	474	414
	29	759	674	585	495	351	505	452	396
	30	738	656	569	482	343	474	426	374
	31	716	637	553	469	335	447	401	352
	32	693	617	536	454	326	422	379	332
	33	669	596	519	440	317	399	359	315
	34	645	575	500	425	308	379	340	298
	35	619	553	482	409	298	360	323	283

Effective length (KL) in feet with respect to least radius of gyration

PROPERTIES AND DESIGN DATA									
Area (in.²)		22.4	19.8	17.1	14.4	11.6	18.4	16.3	14.1
Z (in.³)		95.4	85.0	73.9	62.6	50.8	64.6	57.7	50.4
S (in.³)		80.9	72.5	63.4	54.1	44.1	54.2	48.8	42.9
r (in.)		4.66	4.69	4.72	4.75	4.78	3.84	3.87	3.90
M$_r$ (ft. kips)		358	319	277	203	149	242	216	189

IMPERIAL SIZE AND MASS									
Mass (lb./ft.)		76.1	67.3	58.1	48.9	39.4	62.5	55.4	47.9
Thickness (in.)		.500	.438	.375	.313	.250	.500	.438	.375
Size (in.)		12 x 12					10 x 10		

††Class 3 in bending.
‡Class 4 in bending and resistance for this column calculated according to CSA S16.1-1974 Clause 13.3.3.

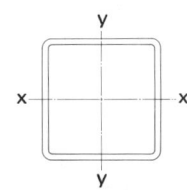

G40.21-50W
CLASS H
$\emptyset = 0.90$

SQUARE HOLLOW SECTIONS
Factored Axial Compressive
Resistances, C_r, in Kips

Size (mm)		254.0 x 254.0		203.2 x 203.2				
Thickness (mm)		7.95	‡6.35	12.70	11.13	9.53	7.95	6.35
Mass (kg/m)		60.1	48.6	72.7	64.6	56.1	47.5	38.4
	0	535	432	648	576	499	422	342
	3	535	432	648	576	500	422	342
	4	536	432	648	576	499	421	341
	5	535	431	646	574	498	421	341
	6	534	431	643	572	496	419	339
	7	533	430	638	568	493	416	337
	8	531	428	633	563	489	413	335
	9	528	426	626	557	484	409	331
	10	525	423	617	550	477	404	327
	11	520	420	608	542	470	398	323
	12	516	416	597	532	462	391	318
	13	510	412	585	522	454	384	312
	14	504	407	571	510	444	376	305
	15	498	402	556	497	433	367	298
	16	490	396	540	483	421	357	290
	17	482	390	523	468	408	346	282
	18	474	383	504	452	394	335	273
	19	465	376	484	434	380	323	263
	20	455	368	462	416	364	310	253
	21	444	359	439	396	347	296	242
	22	433	351	415	376	330	281	230
	23	421	341	389	354	311	266	218
	24	409	332	360	328	289	248	205
	25	396	321	334	304	268	231	190
	26	382	310	311	283	250	215	177
	27	368	299	291	265	234	201	165
	28	353	287	273	248	219	188	155
	29	337	275	257	234	206	177	146
	30	320	261	242	220	194	167	137
	31	301	246	229	208	183	158	130
	32	284	232	217	197	174	149	123
	33	269	220	206	187	165	142	117
	34	255	208	196	178	157	135	111
	35	242	198	186	169	149	128	106

Effective length (KL) in feet with respect to least radius of gyration

PROPERTIES AND DESIGN DATA

Area (in.²)	11.9	9.59	14.4	12.8	11.1	9.37	7.59
Z (in.³)	42.8	34.9	39.7	35.7	31.3	26.8	21.9
S (in.³)	36.7	30.1	32.8	29.8	26.4	22.8	18.8
r (in.)	3.93	3.96	3.02	3.06	3.09	3.12	3.15
M_r (ft. kips)	160	113	149	134	117	100	82.1

IMPERIAL SIZE AND MASS

Mass (lb./ft.)	40.4	32.6	48.9	43.4	37.7	31.9	25.8
Thickness (in.)	.313	.250	.500	.438	.375	.313	.250
Size (in.)	10 x 10		8 x 8				

‡Class 4 in bending and resistance for this column calculated according to CSA S16.1-1974 Clause 13.3.3.

SQUARE HOLLOW SECTIONS
Factored Axial Compressive Resistances, C_r, in Kips

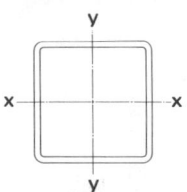

G40.21-50W
CLASS H
$\emptyset = 0.90$

Size (mm)	177.8 x 177.8						152.4 x 152.4		
Thickness (mm)	12.70	11.13	9.53	7.95	6.35	††4.78	12.70	11.13	9.53
Mass (kg/m)	62.6	55.7	48.5	41.1	33.4	25.5	52.4	46.9	40.9
0	558	495	431	365	297	227	468	416	364
3	558	495	431	365	297	227	468	416	363
4	557	494	430	365	296	227	466	414	362
5	554	492	428	363	295	226	462	411	359
6	550	488	426	361	293	224	456	406	355
7	544	483	421	358	290	222	449	400	350
8	537	477	416	353	287	220	439	392	343
9	529	470	410	348	283	217	429	382	335
10	519	461	403	342	278	213	416	371	326
11	507	451	394	335	272	209	401	359	315
12	494	440	384	327	266	204	385	345	303
13	479	427	374	318	259	199	367	329	290
14	463	413	362	308	251	193	347	312	276
15	445	398	349	298	243	187	326	294	260
16	426	381	335	286	234	180	302	274	243
17	406	363	320	273	224	173	276	251	224
18	383	344	303	260	213	165	249	226	203
19	360	324	286	245	202	156	225	205	184
20	333	302	267	230	190	147	206	187	168
21	305	276	246	212	176	137	189	172	154
22	280	254	226	195	162	126	174	159	142
23	259	234	208	180	149	116	161	147	131
24	240	217	193	167	138	108	150	137	122
25	224	202	180	155	129	100	140	128	114
26	209	189	168	145	120	94	130	119	107
27	196	177	157	136	112	88	121	111	99
28	184	166	148	128	106	82	113	103	92
29	173	157	139	120	99	77	106	96	86
30	164	148	132	114	94	73	99	90	81
31	154	139	124	107	89	69	93	85	76
32	145	131	117	101	84	65	87	80	71
33	136	123	110	95	79	62	82	75	67
34	129	117	104	90	74	58	78	71	64
35	122	110	98	85	70	55	74	67	60

Effective length (KL) in feet with respect to least radius of gyration

PROPERTIES AND DESIGN DATA

Area (in.²)	12.4	11.0	9.58	8.12	6.59	5.04	10.4	9.25	8.08
Z (in.³)	29.5	26.6	23.5	20.1	16.5	12.8	20.8	18.9	16.8
S (in.³)	24.2	22.0	19.6	17.0	14.1	11.0	16.8	15.4	13.9
r (in.)	2.62	2.65	2.68	2.71	2.74	2.77	2.21	2.24	2.27
M_r (ft. kips)	111	99.7	88.1	75.4	61.9	41.2	78.0	70.9	63.0

IMPERIAL SIZE AND MASS

Mass (lb./ft.)	42.1	37.5	32.6	27.6	22.4	17.1	35.2	31.5	27.5
Thickness (in.)	.500	.438	.375	.313	.250	.188	.500	.438	.375
Size (in.)	7 x 7						6 x 6		

†† Class 3 in bending.

G40.21-50W
CLASS H
∅ = 0.90

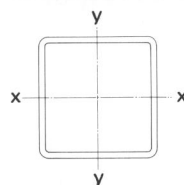

SQUARE HOLLOW SECTIONS
Factored Axial Compressive Resistances, C_r, in Kips

Size (mm)	152.4 x 152.4			127.0 x 127.0				
Thickness (mm)	7.95	6.35	4.78	11.13	9.53	7.95	6.35	4.78
Mass (kg/m)	34.8	28.3	21.7	38.0	33.3	28.4	23.2	17.9
0	309	252	193	337	296	253	207	159
3	309	251	193	336	295	252	206	159
4	308	251	192	334	293	250	205	157
5	306	249	191	329	289	247	202	156
6	302	246	189	322	283	242	198	153
7	298	243	186	314	276	236	194	149
8	292	238	183	303	267	229	188	145
9	286	233	179	291	257	221	181	140
10	278	227	175	277	245	211	174	134
11	269	220	169	261	231	200	165	128
12	260	213	164	243	216	187	155	121
13	249	204	157	223	200	174	144	113
14	237	194	150	201	181	159	132	104
15	224	184	143	177	160	141	118	94
16	210	173	134	158	143	125	105	83
17	194	161	125	142	128	112	94	75
18	176	147	115	128	116	102	85	67
19	160	133	104	117	105	93	78	61
20	146	122	95	107	97	85	71	56
21	134	111	87	99	89	78	66	52
22	123	103	80	90	82	72	61	48
23	114	95	74	83	75	66	56	44
24	106	88	69	76	69	61	51	41
25	99	82	64	70	64	56	47	37
26	93	77	60	65	59	52	44	35
27	86	72	57	61	55	48	41	32
28	81	67	53	57	51	45	38	30
29	75	63	49	53	48	42	36	28
30	71	59	46	50	45	40	33	26
31	66	55	43			37	31	25
32	62	52	41					23
33	59	49	38					
34	55	46	36					
35	52	44	34					

Effective length (KL) feet with respect to least radius of gyration

PROPERTIES AND DESIGN DATA

	152.4 x 152.4			127.0 x 127.0				
Area (in.²)	6.87	5.59	4.28	7.50	6.58	5.62	4.59	3.53
Z (in.³)	14.4	11.9	9.27	12.5	11.2	9.70	8.07	6.31
S (in.³)	12.1	10.1	7.95	10.0	9.10	8.03	6.78	5.38
r (in.)	2.30	2.33	2.36	1.83	1.86	1.89	1.92	1.95
M_r (ft. kips)	54.0	44.6	34.8	46.9	42.0	36.4	30.3	23.7

IMPERIAL SIZE AND MASS

	152.4 x 152.4			127.0 x 127.0				
Mass (lb./ft.)	23.4	19.0	14.6	25.5	22.4	19.1	15.6	12.0
Thickness (in.)	.313	.250	.188	.438	.375	.313	.250	.188
Size (in.)	6 x 6			5 x 5				

SQUARE HOLLOW SECTIONS
Factored Axial Compressive Resistances, C_r, in Kips

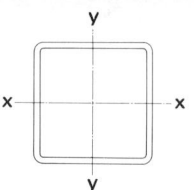

Size (mm)	101.6 x 101.6				88.9 x 88.9			
Thickness (mm)	9.53	7.95	6.35	4.78	9.53	7.95	6.35	4.78
Mass (kg/m)	25.7	22.1	18.2	14.1	21.9	18.9	15.6	12.2
0	229	196	162	125	195	168	139	108
3	226	194	160	124	191	166	137	107
4	222	191	158	122	186	162	134	104
5	216	186	154	120	179	156	129	101
6	208	180	149	116	169	148	123	96
7	198	172	142	111	157	138	115	91
8	186	162	135	105	142	126	106	84
9	172	150	126	99	126	113	96	76
10	156	137	115	91	105	96	83	67
11	138	122	104	82	89	81	70	57
12	118	105	90	72	76	70	60	48
13	102	91	78	62	66	61	52	42
14	90	80	68	55	59	53	46	37
15	80	71	60	48	51	47	41	33
16	71	63	54	43	45	42	36	29
17	64	57	49	39	40	37	32	26
18	57	51	44	35	36	33	29	23
19	52	46	40	32	33	30	26	21
20	47	42	36	29	30	27	23	19
21	43	38	33	26		25	21	17
22	39	35	30	24				16
23	36	32	27	22				
24	33	30	25	20				
25			23	19				
26								
27								
28								
29								
30								
31								
32								
33								
34								
35								

Effective length (KL) in feet with respect to least radius of gyration

PROPERTIES AND DESIGN DATA

Area (in.³)	5.08	4.36	3.59	2.78	4.33	3.74	3.09	2.40
Z (in.³)	6.70	5.90	4.96	3.92	4.90	4.35	3.69	2.94
S (in.³)	5.34	4.79	4.11	3.31	3.83	3.48	3.02	2.46
r (in.)	1.45	1.48	1.51	1.54	1.24	1.28	1.31	1.34
M_r (ft. kips)	25.1	22.1	18.6	14.7	18.4	16.3	13.8	11.0

IMPERIAL SIZE AND MASS

Mass (lb./ft.)	17.3	14.9	12.2	9.45	14.7	12.7	10.5	8.17
Thickness (in.)	.375	.313	.250	.188	.375	.313	.250	.188
Size (in.)	4 x 4				3½ x 3½			

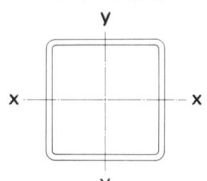

G40.21-50W CLASS H
$\varnothing = 0.90$

SQUARE HOLLOW SECTIONS
Factored Axial Compressive Resistances, C_r, in Kips

Size (mm)	76.2 x 76.2			63.5 x 63.5			
Thickness (mm)	7.95	6.35	4.78	6.35	4.78	3.81	3.18
Mass (kg/m)	15.8	13.1	10.3	10.6	8.35	6.85	5.82
Effective length (KL) in feet with respect to least radius of gyration							
0	140	117	91	94	74	61	52
3	136	114	89	89	71	58	50
4	131	109	86	84	67	55	47
5	123	103	82	76	61	51	44
6	113	96	76	67	54	45	39
7	101	86	69	54	45	38	33
8	87	75	61	43	36	30	26
9	70	61	51	35	29	25	21
10	58	51	42	29	24	20	18
11	49	43	35	24	20	17	15
12	43	37	30	20	17	15	13
13	37	32	27	18	15	13	11
14	32	28	23	15	13	11	10
15	28	24	20		11	10	8
16	25	22	18				7
17	22	19	16				
18		17	14				
19							
20							
21							
22							
23							
24							
25							
26							
27							
28							
29							
30							
31							
32							
33							
34							
35							

PROPERTIES AND DESIGN DATA

Area (in.²)	3.11	2.59	2.03	2.09	1.65	1.35	1.15
Z (in.³)	3.03	2.60	2.10	1.71	1.40	1.17	1.01
S (in.³)	2.38	2.10	1.74	1.35	1.14	.973	.848
r (in.)	1.07	1.10	1.13	.898	.929	.948	.961
M_r (ft. kips)	11.4	9.75	7.87	6.41	5.25	4.39	3.79

IMPERIAL SIZE AND MASS

Mass (lb./ft.)	10.6	8.81	6.89	7.11	5.61	4.60	3.91
Thickness (in.)	.313	.250	.188	.250	.188	.150	.125
Size (in.)	3 x 3			2½ x 2½			

SQUARE HOLLOW SECTIONS
Factored Axial Compressive Resistances, C_r, in Kips

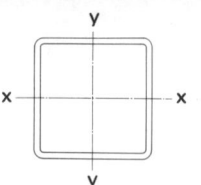

G40.21-50W
CLASS H
$\varnothing = 0.90$

Size (mm)		50.8 x 50.8					38.1 x 38.1			
Thickness (mm)		6.35	4.78	3.81	3.18	2.79	4.78	3.81	3.18	2.54
Mass (kg/m)		8.05	6.45	5.33	4.55	4.05	4.54	3.81	3.28	2.71
	0	72	57	47	40	36	40	34	29	24
	3	64	52	43	37	33	32	27	24	20
	4	57	47	39	34	30	24	21	19	16
	5	46	39	33	29	26	16	14	13	11
	6	34	29	26	23	20	12	10	9	8
	7	26	22	19	17	15	9	8	7	6
	8	21	18	15	14	12	7	6	5	5
	9	16	14	12	11	10			4	4
	10	13	12	10	9	8				
	11	11	10	8	7	7				
	12		8	7	6	6				
	13									
	14									
	15									
	16									
	17									
	18									
	19									
	20									
	21									
	22									
	23									
	24									
	25									
	26									
	27									
	28									
	29									
	30									
	31									
	32									
	33									
	34									
	35									

Effective length (KL) in feet with respect to least radius of gyration

PROPERTIES AND DESIGN DATA

Area (in.²)	1.59	1.27	1.05	.899	.799	.896	.752	.648	.534
Z (in.³)	.998	.840	.714	.621	.558	.422	.369	.326	.275
S (in.³)	.761	.668	.582	.514	.466	.322	.291	.263	.227
r (in.)	.692	.725	.744	.756	.764	.519	.539	.551	.564
M_r (ft. kips)	3.74	3.15	2.68	2.33	2.09	1.58	1.38	1.22	1.03

IMPERIAL SIZE AND MASS

Mass (lb./ft.)	5.41	4.33	3.58	3.06	2.72	3.05	2.56	2.21	1.82
Thickness (in.)	.250	.188	.150	.125	.110	.188	.150	.125	.100
Size (in.)	2 x 2					1½ x 1½			

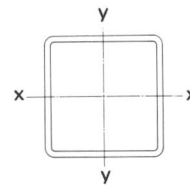

G40.21-50W
CLASS H
$\phi = 0.90$

SQUARE HOLLOW SECTIONS
Factored Axial Compressive
Resistances, C_r, in Kips

Size (mm)	31.8 x 31.8			25.4 x 25.4	
Thickness (mm)	3.81	3.18	2.54	3.18	2.54
Mass (kg/m)	3.06	2.65	2.20	2.01	1.69
0	27	24	20	18	15
3	19	17	14	8	8
4	12	11	9	5	5
5	8	7	6	3	3
6	6	5	5		
7	4	4	3		
8					
9					
10					
11					
12					
13					
14					
15					
16					
17					
18					
19					
20					
21					
22					
23					
24					
25					
26					
27					
28					
29					
30					
31					
32					
33					
34					
35					

Effective length (KL) in feet with respect to least radius of gyration

PROPERTIES AND DESIGN DATA

Area (in.^{2})	.603	.524	.435	.398	.334
Z (in.^{3})	.239	.214	.184	.125	.109
S (in.^{3})	.184	.169	.149	.095	.086
r (in.)	.437	.450	.463	.346	.359
M_r (ft. kips)	.896	.802	.690	.469	.409

IMPERIAL SIZE AND MASS

Mass (lb./ft.)	2.05	1.78	1.48	1.35	1.14
Thickness (in.)	.150	.125	.100	.125	.100
Size (in.)	1¼ x 1¼			1 x 1	

ROUND HOLLOW SECTIONS
Factored Axial Compressive Resistances, C_r, in Kips

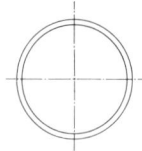

G40.21-50W
CLASS H
$\emptyset = 0.90$

Size (mm)		406.4 OD					355.6 OD		
Thickness (mm)		12.7	11.1	9.53	7.95	6.35	12.7	11.13	9.53
Mass (kg/m)		123	108	93.3	78.1	62.6	107	94.6	81.3
	0	1090	963	828	693	558	954	841	724
	3	1090	963	828	693	558	954	841	724
	4	1090	963	828	693	558	954	841	724
	5	1090	963	828	693	558	954	842	725
	6	1090	963	828	693	558	954	841	724
	7	1090	963	828	693	558	953	840	724
	8	1090	962	827	692	557	951	839	722
	9	1090	960	826	691	556	948	836	720
	10	1090	958	824	689	555	945	833	718
	11	1080	955	821	688	554	940	830	714
	12	1080	952	818	685	552	935	825	711
	13	1080	948	815	682	550	930	820	706
	14	1070	943	811	679	547	923	814	702
	15	1060	938	807	676	544	916	808	696
	16	1060	932	802	672	541	908	801	690
	17	1050	926	797	667	537	899	793	683
	18	1040	919	791	662	534	889	785	676
	19	1030	912	785	657	529	879	776	669
	20	1030	904	778	651	525	868	766	660
	21	1020	895	770	645	520	856	756	651
	22	1000	886	762	639	515	843	745	642
	23	994	876	754	632	509	829	733	632
	24	982	865	745	624	503	815	720	621
	25	969	854	736	617	497	800	707	610
	26	956	843	726	608	491	784	693	598
	27	942	831	716	600	484	768	679	586
	28	927	818	705	591	477	750	664	573
	29	912	804	694	581	469	732	648	559
	30	896	790	682	572	461	713	631	545
	31	879	776	669	561	453	694	614	531
	32	862	761	656	551	444	673	596	516
	33	844	745	643	540	436	652	578	500
	34	825	729	629	528	426	630	559	483
	35	806	712	615	516	417	607	539	466

Effective length (KL) in feet with respect to least radius of gyration

PROPERTIES AND DESIGN DATA

	406.4 OD					355.6 OD		
Area (in.²)	24.3	21.4	18.4	15.4	12.4	21.2	18.7	16.1
Z (in.³)	120	106	91.6	77.0	62.0	91.2	80.6	69.7
S (in.³)	91.5	81.1	70.3	59.3	48.0	69.1	61.4	53.3
r (in.)	5.48	5.50	5.53	5.55	5.57	4.78	4.80	4.82
M_r (ft.-kips)	450	397	343	289	180	342	302	261

IMPERIAL SIZE AND MASS

	406.4 OD					355.6 OD		
Mass (lb./ft.)	82.9	72.9	62.7	52.5	42.1	72.2	63.5	54.7
Thickness (in.)	.500	.438	.375	.313	.250	.500	.438	.375
Size (in.)	16 OD					14 OD		

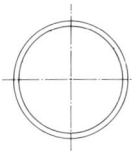

ROUND HOLLOW SECTIONS
Factored Axial Compressive
Resistances, C_r, in Kips

Size (mm)		.355.6 OD		323.9 OD				
Thickness (mm)		7.95	6.35	12.7	11.1	9.53	7.95	6.35
Mass (kg/m)		68.2	54.7	97.5	85.9	73.9	61.9	49.7
	0	607	486	864	765	657	549	442
	3	607	486	864	765	657	549	442
	4	607	486	864	765	657	549	442
	5	608	486	864	765	657	549	442
	6	607	486	863	764	656	549	442
	7	607	485	862	763	655	548	441
	8	606	484	859	761	653	546	440
	9	604	483	856	758	651	544	438
	10	602	481	852	754	648	541	436
	11	599	479	846	750	644	538	433
	12	596	477	841	745	640	535	431
	13	593	474	834	739	635	531	427
	14	589	471	826	732	629	526	424
	15	584	467	818	725	623	521	420
	16	579	463	809	717	616	515	415
	17	574	459	798	708	608	509	410
	18	568	454	787	698	600	502	405
	19	561	449	776	688	591	495	399
	20	554	444	763	677	582	487	393
	21	547	438	749	665	572	479	386
	22	539	432	735	652	561	470	379
	23	531	425	720	639	550	461	372
	24	522	418	704	625	538	451	364
	25	513	411	687	610	525	440	355
	26	503	403	669	594	512	429	347
	27	492	395	651	578	498	418	337
	28	482	386	631	561	484	406	328
	29	471	377	611	543	469	393	318
	30	459	368	590	525	453	380	308
	31	447	359	568	506	437	367	297
	32	434	349	545	486	420	353	286
	33	421	338	520	464	402	338	274
	34	407	327	492	440	381	321	260
	35	393	316	467	417	361	304	247

Effective length (KL) in feet with respect to least radius of gyration

PROPERTIES AND DESIGN DATA

Area (in.²)		13.5	10.8	19.2	17.0	14.6	12.2	9.82
Z (in.³)		58.6	47.3	75.1	66.5	57.5	48.4	39.1
S (in.³)		45.0	36.5	56.7	50.5	43.9	37.1	30.1
r (in.)		4.84	4.86	4.34	4.36	4.38	4.40	4.42
M_r (ft.-kips)		220	137	282	249	216	181	147

IMPERIAL SIZE AND MASS

Mass (lb./ft.)		45.8	36.8	65.5	57.7	49.6	41.6	33.4
Thickness (in.)		.313	.250	.500	.438	.375	.313	.250
Size (in.)		14 OD		12.75 OD				

ROUND HOLLOW SECTIONS
Factored Axial Compressive Resistances, C_r, in Kips

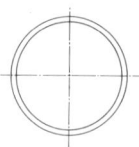

Size (mm)	273.1 OD					219.1 OD		
Thickness (mm)	12.7	11.13	9.53	7.95	6.35	12.7	11.13	9.53
Mass (kg/m)	81.6	71.9	61.9	52.0	41.8	64.6	57.1	49.3
0	724	639	549	463	371	576	508	438
3	724	639	549	463	371	576	509	438
4	725	639	549	464	371	575	508	437
5	724	638	549	463	371	574	506	436
6	722	637	547	462	370	570	504	434
7	719	635	545	460	369	566	500	431
8	716	631	543	458	367	560	495	426
9	711	627	539	455	365	553	489	421
10	705	622	535	452	362	545	482	415
11	698	616	530	448	359	535	473	408
12	691	609	524	443	355	524	464	400
13	682	602	518	437	351	512	453	391
14	672	593	510	431	346	499	442	381
15	661	584	502	425	341	484	429	370
16	649	573	493	417	335	468	415	359
17	636	562	484	409	328	451	400	346
18	622	550	474	401	322	432	384	332
19	607	537	463	392	314	412	366	317
20	591	523	451	382	307	391	348	302
21	575	508	438	371	298	369	328	285
22	557	493	425	360	290	344	307	268
23	538	476	411	349	280	317	283	247
24	518	459	396	336	271	293	262	229
25	497	441	381	323	260	273	244	213
26	475	421	364	310	250	254	227	198
27	451	401	347	295	238	238	213	185
28	425	378	328	280	227	223	200	174
29	398	355	308	263	212	210	188	164
30	375	334	290	247	200	198	177	154
31	353	315	273	233	188	188	168	146
32	334	297	258	220	178	178	159	138
33	316	282	244	208	168	169	151	131
34	300	267	232	197	160	159	143	124
35	285	254	220	188	152	151	135	118

Effective length (KL) in feet with respect to least radius of gyration

PROPERTIES AND DESIGN DATA

Area (in.²)	16.1	14.2	12.2	10.3	8.25	12.8	11.3	9.73
Z (in.³)	52.6	46.6	40.4	34.1	27.6	33.1	29.4	25.6
S (in.³)	39.4	35.2	30.7	26.0	21.2	24.5	22.0	19.2
r (in.)	3.63	3.65	3.67	3.69	3.71	2.88	2.90	2.92
M_r (ft.-kips)	197	175	151	128	103	124	110	96.0

IMPERIAL SIZE AND MASS

Mass (lb./ft.)	54.8	48.3	41.6	34.9	28.1	43.4	38.4	33.1
Thickness (in.)	.500	.438	.375	.313	.250	.500	.438	.375
Size (in.)	10.75 OD					8.625 OD		

G40.21-50W
CLASS H
Ø = 0.90

ROUND HOLLOW SECTIONS
Factored Axial Compressive
Resistances, C_r, in Kips

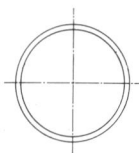

Size (mm)		219.1 OD			168.3 OD			
Thickness (mm)		7.95	6.35	4.78	9.53	7.95	6.35	4.78
Mass (kg/m)		41.4	33.3	25.3	37.3	31.4	25.4	19.3
Effective length (KL) in feet with respect to least radius of gyration	0	368	296	225	332	279	225	171
	3	368	296	225	331	279	225	171
	4	367	296	224	330	278	224	171
	5	366	295	224	327	276	223	169
	6	364	294	223	323	273	220	168
	7	362	291	221	318	268	217	165
	8	358	289	219	311	263	213	162
	9	354	285	217	304	256	208	158
	10	349	281	214	295	249	202	154
	11	343	277	210	284	241	195	149
	12	336	271	206	273	231	188	143
	13	329	266	202	260	221	179	137
	14	321	259	197	246	209	170	130
	15	312	252	192	231	196	160	123
	16	302	244	186	214	183	150	115
	17	292	236	180	195	167	138	106
	18	280	227	173	176	151	125	96
	19	268	217	166	160	137	113	87
	20	255	207	158	146	125	103	80
	21	242	196	150	134	115	95	73
	22	227	185	141	123	106	87	67
	23	210	171	131	114	98	81	62
	24	194	159	122	106	91	75	58
	25	181	147	113	99	85	70	54
	26	168	137	105	92	79	66	51
	27	158	128	99	86	74	61	47
	28	148	120	92	80	69	57	44
	29	139	113	87	75	64	53	41
	30	131	107	82	70	60	50	38
	31	124	101	78	66	56	47	36
	32	118	96	73	62	53	44	34
	33	112	91	70	58	50	41	32
	34	106	86	66	55	47	39	30
	35	100	82	63	52	45	37	29

PROPERTIES AND DESIGN DATA

	219.1 OD			168.3 OD			
Area (in.^{2})	8.17	6.58	4.99	7.37	6.21	5.01	3.81
Z (in.^{3})	21.6	17.5	13.4	14.7	12.5	10.2	7.80
S (in.^{3})	16.4	13.4	10.3	10.9	9.36	7.69	5.96
r (in.)	2.94	2.96	2.98	2.21	2.23	2.26	2.28
M_r (ft.-kips)	81.0	65.6	50.2	55.1	46.9	38.2	29.2

IMPERIAL SIZE AND MASS

	219.1 OD			168.3 OD			
Mass (lb./ft.)	27.8	22.4	17.0	25.1	21.1	17.0	13.0
Thickness (in.)	.313	.250	.188	.375	.313	.250	.188
Size (in.)	8.625 OD			6.625 OD			

ROUND HOLLOW SECTIONS
Factored Axial Compressive Resistances, C_r, in Kips

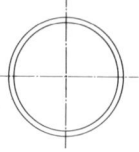

Size (mm)	141.3 OD				114.3 OD		
Thickness (mm)	9.53	7.95	6.35	4.78	7.95	6.35	4.78
Mass (kg/m)	31.0	26.1	21.1	16.1	20.9	16.9	12.9
0	275	232	188	143	185	150	115
3	274	232	187	143	184	149	114
4	272	230	186	142	181	147	112
5	268	226	183	140	176	143	110
6	263	222	180	137	170	138	106
7	256	216	175	134	162	132	102
8	247	210	170	130	153	125	96
9	237	201	163	125	142	117	90
10	226	192	156	120	130	107	83
11	213	181	148	113	116	96	75
12	199	170	138	106	99	83	65
13	183	157	128	99	86	72	56
14	165	142	117	90	75	63	49
15	146	126	103	80	67	56	44
16	130	112	92	72	60	50	39
17	117	100	83	64	54	45	35
18	106	91	75	58	48	41	32
19	96	83	68	53	44	37	29
20	88	76	62	48	40	33	26
21	81	70	57	45	36	30	24
22	74	64	53	41	33	28	22
23	68	59	48	38	30	25	20
24	63	54	45	35	28	23	18
25	58	50	41	32		22	17
26	54	46	38	30			
27	50	43	36	28			
28	47	40	33	26			
29	44	38	31	24			
30	41	35	29	23			
31			27	21			
32							
33							
34							
35							

Effective length (KL) in feet with respect to least radius of gyration

PROPERTIES AND DESIGN DATA

Area (in.^{2})	6.11	5.16	4.17	3.18	4.12	3.34	2.55
Z (in.^{3})	10.1	8.64	7.06	5.44	5.50	4.52	3.50
S (in.^{3})	7.43	6.42	5.31	4.13	4.03	3.36	2.64
r (in.)	1.84	1.86	1.88	1.90	1.48	1.51	1.53
M_r (ft.-kips)	37.9	32.4	26.5	20.4	20.6	16.9	13.1

IMPERIAL SIZE AND MASS

Mass (lb./ft.)	20.8	17.6	14.2	10.8	14.0	11.4	8.68
Thickness (in.)	.375	.313	.250	.188	.313	.250	.188
Size (in.)	5.562 OD				4.5 OD		

G40.21-50W
CLASS H
$\emptyset = 0.90$

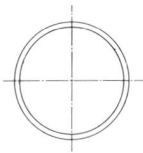

ROUND HOLLOW SECTIONS
Factored Axial Compressive Resistances, C_r, in Kips

Size (mm)		101.6 OD				88.9 OD			
Thickness (mm)		7.95	6.35	4.78	3.81	7.95	6.35	4.78	3.81
Mass (kg/m)		18.4	14.9	11.4	9.19	15.9	12.9	9.92	8.00
	0	163	133	101	81	141	115	88	71
	1	163	133	101	81	141	115	88	71
	2	163	133	101	81	140	114	88	71
	3	161	131	100	80	138	112	86	70
	4	157	128	98	79	133	109	84	68
	5	152	124	95	76	126	103	80	65
	6	145	118	90	73	117	96	75	61
	7	136	111	85	69	106	88	68	56
	8	125	103	79	64	94	78	61	50
	9	112	93	72	58	78	66	52	43
	10	98	81	63	52	64	54	43	36
	11	82	69	54	44	55	46	36	30
	12	70	59	46	37	47	39	31	26
	13	61	51	40	33	41	34	27	23
	14	54	45	35	29	35	30	24	20
	15	48	40	31	25	31	26	21	17
	16	42	35	28	23	27	23	18	15
	17	38	31	25	20	24	21	16	14
	18	34	28	22	18	22	18	15	12
	19	30	25	20	16		17	13	11
	20	28	23	18	15				
	21	25	21	16	13				
	22		19	15	12				
	23								
	24								
	25								
	26								
	27								
	28								
	29								
	30								
	31								
	32								
	33								

Effective length (KL) in feet with respect to least radius of gyration

PROPERTIES AND DESIGN DATA

		101.6 OD				88.9 OD			
Area (in.^{2})		3.63	2.95	2.25	1.81	3.13	2.55	1.96	1.58
Z (in.^{3})		4.27	3.52	2.74	2.22	3.19	2.65	2.07	1.68
S (in.^{3})		3.10	2.60	2.05	1.68	2.30	1.94	1.54	1.27
r (in.)		1.31	1.33	1.35	1.36	1.13	1.15	1.17	1.19
M_r (ft.-kips)		16.0	13.2	10.3	8.32	12.0	9.94	7.76	6.30

IMPERIAL SIZE AND MASS

		101.6 OD				88.9 OD			
Mass (lb./ft.)		12.3	10.0	7.67	6.17	10.7	8.69	6.66	5.37
Thickness (in.)		.313	.250	.188	.150	.313	.250	.188	.150
Size (in.)		4.OD				3.5 OD			

ROUND HOLLOW SECTIONS
Factored Axial Compressive
Resistances, C$_r$, in Kips

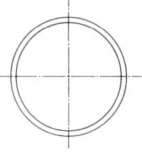

Size (mm)		73.0 OD				60.3 OD			
Thickness (mm)		6.35	4.78	3.81	3.18	6.35	4.78	3.81	3.18
Mass (kg/m)		10.4	8.04	6.50	5.48	8.45	6.54	5.31	4.48
	0	93	72	58	49	75	58	47	40
	1	93	72	58	49	75	58	47	40
	2	92	71	57	48	73	57	46	39
	3	89	69	55	47	69	54	44	37
	4	84	65	53	44	63	49	40	34
	5	77	60	49	41	54	42	35	30
	6	68	53	43	37	42	34	28	24
	7	57	45	37	32	32	26	21	18
	8	45	36	30	25	25	20	17	15
	9	36	29	24	21	20	17	14	12
	10	30	24	20	17	17	14	11	10
	11	26	21	17	15	14	11	9	8
	12	22	17	14	12	12	10	8	7
	13	19	15	12	11			7	6
	14	16	13	11	9				
	15	14	11	9	8				
	16			8	7				
	17								
	18								
	19								
	20								
	21								
	22								
	23								
	24								
	25								
	26								
	27								
	28								
	29								
	30								
	31								
	32								
	33								

Effective length (KL) in feet with respect to least radius of gyration

PROPERTIES AND DESIGN DATA									
Area (in.^{2})		2.06	1.59	1.28	1.08	1.67	1.29	1.05	.885
Z (in.^{3})		1.73	1.36	1.11	.947	1.13	.901	.743	.634
S (in.^{3})		1.25	1.00	.831	.712	.804	.655	.548	.473
r (in.)		.932	.952	.965	.973	.756	.776	.788	.796
M$_r$ (ft.-kips)		6.49	5.10	4.16	3.55	4.24	3.38	2.79	2.38

IMPERIAL SIZE AND MASS									
Mass (lb./ft.)		7.01	5.40	4.37	3.68	5.68	4.40	3.57	3.01
Thickness (in.)		.250	.188	.150	.125	.250	.188	.150	.125
Size (in.)		2.875 OD				2.375 OD			

G40.21-50W
CLASS H
$\emptyset = 0.90$

ROUND HOLLOW SECTIONS
Factored Axial Compressive
Resistances, C_r, in Kips

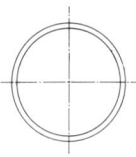

Size (mm)		48.3 OD				42.2 OD		33.4 OD		26.7 OD	
Thickness (mm)		4.78	3.81	3.18	2.79	3.18	2.54	3.18	2.54	3.18	2.54
Mass (kg/m)		5.13	4.18	3.54	3.13	3.06	2.48	2.37	1.93	1.84	1.51
	0	45	37	31	28	27	22	21	17	16	13
	1	45	37	31	28	27	22	21	17	16	13
	2	43	36	30	27	25	21	18	15	13	11
	3	39	32	27	24	22	18	14	12	7	6
	4	33	27	23	21	17	14	9	7	4	4
	5	24	20	18	16	12	10	6	5	3	2
	6	17	15	13	11	9	7	4	3		
	7	13	11	10	9	6	5	3	3		
	8	10	9	8	7	5	4				
	9	8	7	6	5	4	3				
	10	7	6	5	4						
	11										
	12										
	13										
	14										
	15										
	16										
	17										
	18										
	19										
	20										
	21										
	22										
	23										
	24										
	25										
	26										
	27										
	28										
	29										
	30										
	31										
	32										
	33										

Effective length (KL) in feet with respect to least radius of gyration

PROPERTIES AND DESIGN DATA											
Area (in.^{2})		1.01	.825	.699	.618	.604	.491	.468	.382	.364	.299
Z (in.^{3})		.555	.461	.396	.353	.296	.244	.178	.148	.108	.091
S (in.^{3})		.396	.335	.291	.262	.216	.181	.127	.108	.076	.065
r (in.)		.609	.622	.630	.635	.545	.553	.423	.431	.330	.338
M_r (ft.-kips)		2.08	1.73	1.48	1.32	1.11	.915	.667	.555	.405	.340

IMPERIAL SIZE AND MASS											
Mass (lb./ft.)		3.45	2.81	2.38	2.10	2.06	1.67	1.59	1.30	1.24	1.02
Thickness (in.)		1.88	.150	.125	.110	.125	.100	.125	.100	.125	.100
Size (in.)		1.9 OD				1.66 OD		1.315 OD		1.05 OD	

NOTES

COMPOSITE BEAM TRIAL SELECTION TABLES

Tables

The tables on pages 9—81 to 9—141 inclusive are based on the use of CSA G40.21-44W steel and list composite beams using W shapes manufactured in Canada from 8" to 24" nominal depth. Tables are provided for the following:

a) 5" solid slab with a 28-day specified concrete strength, f'_c, of 3 ksi.

b) 1-1/2", 2" and 3" cellular steel deck and 2-1/2" concrete cover slabs with f'_c of 3 ksi.

c) 2" and 3" cellular steel deck and 3-1/4" concrete cover slabs with f'_c of 4 ksi.

Symbols

b	=	Flange width of steel shape, in.
t	=	Flange thickness of steel shape, in.
b_1	=	Effective width of the concrete used in computing M_{rc}, Q_r, I_1 and S_{s1}, less than or equal to $b + 16t_s$ where t_s equals the overall slab thickness or overall cover slab plus cellular steel deck thickness (Clause 17.3.2 of CSA S16.1-1974), in.
M_{rc}	=	Factored moment resistance of the composite beam for percentages of shear connection from 50 to 100, ft.-kips.
$Q_{r100\%}$	=	Required sum of all the factored resistances of the shear connectors between points of maximum and zero moment for 100 percent shear connection; equal to either $\phi A_s F_y$ or $0.85 \phi_c btf'_c$, kips.
I_1	=	Moment of inertia of the composite section computed using a mass density of 145 lb./ft^3 for $f'_c = 3$ ksi and a mass density of 115 lb./ft^3 for $f'_c = 4$ ksi, in^4.
S_{s1}	=	Section modulus of the composite section related to the extreme fibre of the bottom flange of the steel beam based on the value of I_1, in^3.
M_r	=	Factored moment resistance of the steel beam alone, ft-kips.
V_r	=	Factored shear resistance of the steel beam alone, kips.
L_u	=	Maximum unsupported length of compression flange of the steel beam alone for which no reduction in M_r is required, ft.
I_x	=	Moment of inertia about the X—X axis of the steel beam alone, in^4.
S_x	=	Section modulus of the steel beam alone, in^3.

For more information on composite beams and similar tables in SI, refer to page 5—18.

COMPOSITE BEAMS
Trial Selection Tables

G40.21 – 44W
3 Ksi Concrete

5 Inch Slab
$\varnothing = 0.90$, $\varnothing_C = 0.67$, $\varnothing_{SC} = 0.80$

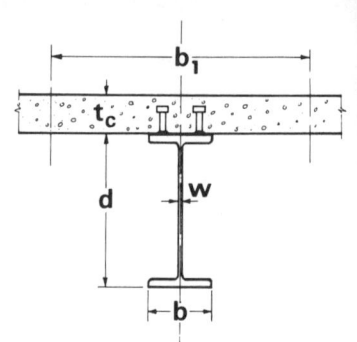

Steel Shape	b₁	M_{rc} in foot Kips for various percentages of shear connection						Q_r† for 100%	I₁	S_{s_1}	Steel Shape Data*	
	In.	100%	90%	80%	70%	60%	50%	Kips	In.⁴	In.³		
W610X241	93	2080	2080	2060	2040	2010	1960	794	10800	534	M$_r$	1540
W24X162	77	2040	2030	2010	1990	1950	1900	658	10300	527	V$_r$	461
b = 12.95	60	1990	1970	1940	1910	1880	1840	513	9600	516	L$_u$	16.9
t = 1.22	44	1900	1880	1860	1830	1800	1770	376	8810	503	I$_x$	5170
	28	1790	1780	1760	1740	1710	1690	239	7800	484	S$_x$	414
W610X217	93	1890	1880	1870	1850	1820	1780	794	9830	481	M$_r$	1380
W24X146	77	1850	1840	1830	1800	1770	1730	658	9360	475	V$_r$	420
b = 12.90	60	1800	1790	1760	1740	1700	1660	513	8750	466	L$_u$	16.5
t = 1.09	44	1730	1710	1690	1660	1630	1600	376	8030	454	I$_x$	4580
	28	1620	1610	1590	1570	1550	1520	239	7100	437	S$_x$	370
W610X195	93	1700	1690	1680	1670	1640	1610	794	8880	431	M$_r$	1220
W24X131	77	1660	1660	1650	1630	1600	1560	658	8470	425	V$_r$	387
b = 12.85	60	1620	1610	1590	1570	1540	1500	513	7930	417	L$_u$	16.1
t = .960	44	1550	1540	1520	1490	1470	1430	376	7280	407	I$_x$	4020
	28	1460	1440	1420	1410	1380	1360	239	6420	391	S$_x$	328
W610X174	93	1530	1520	1510	1500	1480	1450	794	8030	385	M$_r$	1080
W24X117	77	1490	1490	1480	1470	1440	1410	658	7670	380	V$_r$	349
b = 12.80	60	1450	1450	1430	1410	1390	1350	513	7190	374	L$_u$	15.7
t = .850	44	1400	1390	1370	1350	1320	1290	376	6610	365	I$_x$	3540
	28	1310	1300	1280	1260	1240	1220	239	5830	351	S$_x$	292
W610X155	93	1370	1370	1360	1350	1330	1310	794	7230	343	M$_r$	954
W24X104	77	1340	1330	1330	1320	1300	1270	658	6920	339	V$_r$	314
b = 12.75	60	1300	1300	1290	1270	1250	1220	513	6500	333	L$_u$	15.4
t = .750	44	1260	1250	1230	1210	1190	1160	376	5990	325	I$_x$	3100
	28	1180	1170	1150	1130	1110	1090	239	5280	313	S$_x$	258
W610X140	89	1260	1260	1250	1240	1220	1190	760	6590	307	M$_r$	838
W24X94	73	1230	1220	1220	1200	1180	1150	624	6290	302	V$_r$	327
b = 9.06	58	1190	1190	1180	1160	1130	1100	495	5930	297	L$_u$	10.8
t = .875	42	1140	1130	1110	1090	1070	1040	359	5440	290	I$_x$	2700
	27	1060	1050	1030	1010	993	971	231	4790	278	S$_x$	222
W610X125	89	1140	1130	1130	1110	1100	1080	760	5930	274	M$_r$	739
W24X84	73	1100	1100	1090	1080	1070	1040	624	5680	270	V$_r$	296
b = 9.02	58	1070	1070	1060	1050	1020	994	495	5370	266	L$_u$	10.6
t = .770	42	1030	1020	1000	986	963	935	359	4930	259	I$_x$	2370
	27	956	944	929	912	892	871	231	4350	249	S$_x$	197

†No. of studs/beam = 2 x Q$_r$ x percent shear connection/100/q$_r$ (per stud)
*Units — M$_r$ — Ft. Kips   L$_u$ — Ft.   b — In.
        V$_r$ — Kips   I$_x$ — In.⁴   t — In.
                S$_x$ — In.³

Note: The SI designation in bold face type is the one preferred for use in Canada.

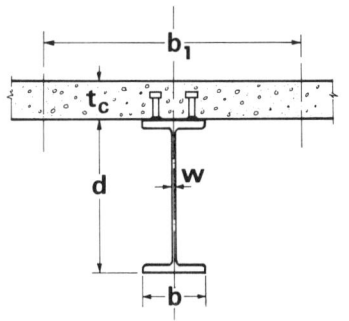

COMPOSITE BEAMS
Trial Selection Tables

G40.21 – 44W
3 Ksi Concrete

5 Inch Slab
$\varnothing = 0.90$, $\varnothing_C = 0.67$, $\varnothing_{SC} = 0.80$

Steel Shape	Composite Beam								Properties		Steel Shape Data*	
		Factored Resistances										
	b_1	M_{rc} in foot Kips for various percentages of shear connection						Q_r† for 100%	I_1	S_{s_1}		
	In.	100%	90%	80%	70%	60%	50%	Kips	In.⁴	In.³		
W610X113	89	1040	1040	1030	1020	1010	987	760	5400	247	M_r	660
W24X76	73	1010	1010	1000	990	977	953	624	5180	244	V_r	275
b = 8.99	58	978	975	969	957	938	910	495	4910	240	L_u	10.4
t = .680	42	940	932	920	902	880	854	359	4510	234	I_x	2100
	27	873	861	847	831	812	791	231	3990	225	S_x	176
W610X101	89	945	943	937	927	913	896	760	4860	221	M_r	584
W24X68	73	915	912	907	898	886	865	624	4670	218	V_r	257
b = 8.97	58	885	882	877	868	851	826	495	4430	215	L_u	10.1
t = .585	42	850	844	833	817	797	772	359	4080	209	I_x	1830
	27	789	778	765	749	731	711	231	3610	201	S_x	154
W530X138	88	1120	1120	1110	1100	1080	050	752	5250	272	M_r	729
W21X93	73	1090	1090	1080	1070	1050	020	624	5020	268	V_r	328
b = 8.42	57	1050	1050	1040	1020	996	966	487	4710	263	L_u	10.3
t = .930	42	1010	996	981	962	939	912	359	4320	256	I_x	2070
	27	932	920	905	889	871	851	231	3790	245	S_x	191
W530X123	88	1010	1010	1000	990	974	954	752	4740	244	M_r	647
W21X83	73	982	978	970	960	945	921	624	4550	240	V_r	288
b = 8.35	57	946	942	936	923	903	876	487	4270	236	L_u	10.1
t = .835	42	909	900	888	871	850	826	359	3930	230	I_x	1830
	27	843	832	818	803	786	767	231	3460	220	S_x	171
W530X109	88	909	907	900	889	875	857	752	4250	216	M_r	568
W21X73	73	880	877	870	861	848	829	624	4080	213	V_r	253
b = 8.30	57	847	843	837	829	813	790	487	3850	210	L_u	9.89
t = .740	42	813	808	798	785	766	743	359	3550	205	I_x	1600
	26	752	743	731	717	701	683	222	3100	196	S_x	151
W530X101	88	854	851	845	835	821	804	752	3990	202	M_r	528
W21X68	73	825	823	817	807	795	779	624	3830	199	V_r	237
b = 8.27	57	793	790	784	777	764	743	487	3620	196	L_u	9.74
t = .685	42	760	757	749	737	720	698	359	3350	191	I_x	1480
	26	706	697	686	673	657	640	222	2920	183	S_x	140
W530X92	88	790	787	781	771	757	740	725	3670	184	M_r	475
W21X62	73	763	761	755	747	735	720	624	3530	182	V_r	219
b = 8.24	57	732	729	724	717	706	687	487	3340	179	L_u	9.59
t = .615	42	700	697	692	681	665	645	359	3090	175	I_x	1330
	26	651	643	633	620	605	588	222	2710	167	S_x	127

†No. of studs/beam = 2 x Q_r x percent shear connection/100/q_r (per stud)

*Units — M_r — Ft. Kips L_u — Ft.   b — In.
     V_r — Kips I_x — In.⁴   t — In.
              S_x — In.³

Note: The SI designation in bold face type is the one preferred for use in Canada.

COMPOSITE BEAMS
Trial Selection Tables

G40.21 – 44W
3 Ksi Concrete

5 Inch Slab
$\varnothing = 0.90$, $\varnothing_C = 0.67$, $\varnothing_{SC} = 0.80$

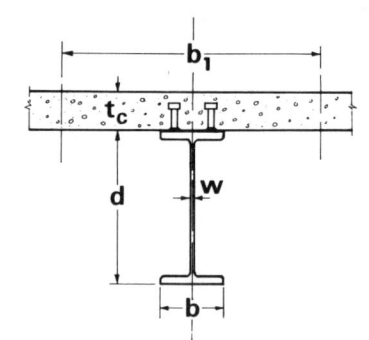

Steel Shape	Composite Beam											Steel Shape Data*	
		Factored Resistances							Properties				
	b_1	M_{rc} in foot Kips for various percentages of shear connection						Q_r† for 100%	I_1	S_{s_1}			
	In.	100%	90%	80%	70%	60%	50%	Kips	In.⁴	In.³		
W530X82	88	713	708	700	689	675	658	645	3270	163	M_r	416
W21X55	73	689	688	683	675	664	650	624	3160	161	V_r	204
b = 8.22	57	659	657	653	646	636	620	487	2990	159	L_u	9.31
t = .522	42	629	627	622	614	599	580	359	2780	155	I_x	1150
	26	585	578	568	556	542	525	222	2440	149	S_x	111
W460X106	88	790	787	781	770	756	738	752	3270	188	M_r	478
W18X71	72	759	756	749	740	727	711	615	3120	185	V_r	239
b = 7.64	57	728	724	718	710	698	679	487	2950	181	L_u	9.51
t = .810	42	694	691	684	673	657	638	359	2720	177	I_x	1170
	26	643	635	625	614	600	584	222	2360	169	S_x	127
W460X97	88	735	733	727	717	703	686	752	3030	173	M_r	439
W18X65	72	705	702	696	688	676	660	615	2900	170	V_r	216
b = 7.59	57	675	672	666	659	648	632	487	2750	167	L_u	9.35
t = .750	42	642	639	634	625	612	594	359	2540	163	I_x	1070
	26	597	590	582	571	558	543	222	2210	156	S_x	117
W460X89	88	685	682	675	664	650	633	697	2820	160	M_r	406
W18X60	72	657	655	650	641	630	615	615	2710	158	V_r	198
b = 7.56	57	628	625	620	613	603	590	487	2560	155	L_u	9.20
t = .695	42	596	594	590	583	571	555	359	2370	151	I_x	984
	26	556	550	543	533	520	506	222	2070	145	S_x	108
W460X82	88	637	632	624	613	599	582	642	2610	147	M_r	370
W18X55	72	612	610	606	598	587	572	615	2500	145	V_r	185
b = 7.53	57	584	582	577	570	561	548	487	2380	143	L_u	9.02
t = .630	42	553	551	547	541	531	516	359	2200	139	I_x	890
	26	516	511	504	494	482	468	222	1930	133	S_x	98.3
W460X74	87	584	577	569	557	544	528	582	2380	134	M_r	333
W18X50	72	564	561	556	548	537	523	582	2290	132	V_r	167
b = 7.49	57	537	535	531	525	516	504	487	2180	130	L_u	8.89
t = .570	42	508	506	502	497	489	475	359	2030	127	I_x	800
	26	473	469	463	455	444	431	222	1780	122	S_x	88.9
W460X67	87	537	530	520	509	496	481	531	2180	122	M_r	301
W18X45	72	521	516	510	501	490	477	531	2110	121	V_r	156
b = 7.48	57	496	495	491	485	476	465	487	2010	119	L_u	8.65
t = .499	42	468	466	462	457	450	438	359	1870	116	I_x	719
	26	434	431	426	418	407	394	222	1650	111	S_x	80.5

†No. of studs/beam = 2 x Q_r x percent shear connection/100/q_r (per stud)

*Units — M_r — Ft. Kips L_u — Ft.   b — In.
       V_r — Kips I_x — In.⁴   t — In.
                  S_x — In.³

Note: The SI designation in bold face type is the one preferred for use in Canada.

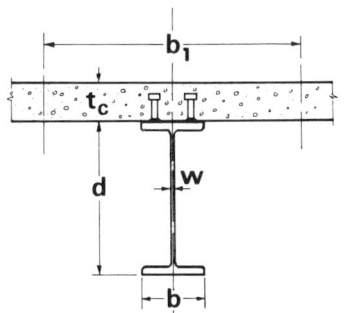

COMPOSITE BEAMS
Trial Selection Tables

G40.21 – 44W
3 Ksi Concrete

5 Inch Slab
$\phi = 0.90$, $\phi_C = 0.67$, $\phi_{SC} = 0.80$

Steel Shape		Composite Beam											Steel Shape Data*	
		Factored Resistances								Properties				
	b_1	M_{rc} in foot Kips for various percentages of shear connection						$Q_r^\dagger$ for 100%		I_1	S_{s_1}			
	In.	100%	90%	80%	70%	60%	50%	Kips		In.⁴	In.³			
W460X61	87	489	481	471	460	447	433	479		1960	110	M_r	264
W18X41	72	475	470	463	454	443	430	479		1900	108	V_r	148
b = 7.45	57	455	453	450	444	435	425	479		1810	106	L_u	8.40
t = .425	42	427	426	423	418	411	399	359		1690	104	I_x	623
	26	395	392	387	380	370	357	222		1490	99.7	S_x	70.4
W410X85	87	609	604	596	586	572	555	665		2280	141	M_r	346
W16X57	72	583	581	576	568	557	542	615		2190	139	V_r	185
b = 7.12	57	555	552	547	540	530	518	487		2070	137	L_u	8.91
t = .715	41	521	519	515	508	498	484	350		1900	133	I_x	758
	26	485	481	474	465	454	441	222		1670	127	S_x	92.3
W410X74	87	542	535	527	515	502	486	582		2030	125	M_r	304
W16X50	72	522	519	514	506	495	481	582		1950	123	V_r	161
b = 7.07	57	495	493	489	482	473	462	487		1850	121	L_u	8.67
t = .630	41	463	461	458	452	445	433	350		1710	117	I_x	659
	26	431	428	423	416	406	394	222		1500	113	S_x	81.1
W410X67	87	496	488	479	468	454	439	527		1840	113	M_r	272
W16X45	72	479	475	469	460	448	435	527		1780	111	V_r	145
b = 7.03	57	455	454	450	444	435	424	487		1690	109	L_u	8.50
t = .565	41	425	423	419	414	408	397	350		1560	106	I_x	586
	26	393	392	388	381	372	361	222		1380	102	S_x	72.7
W410X60	87	445	437	428	417	404	390	467		1660	101	M_r	241
W16X40	72	432	427	419	410	399	386	467		1600	99.5	V_r	128
b = 6.99	57	413	411	407	401	392	382	467		1530	97.7	L_u	8.38
t = .505	41	384	382	379	374	368	360	350		1420	95.2	I_x	518
	26	353	352	350	345	337	327	222		1260	91.6	S_x	64.7
W410X54	87	403	395	385	374	362	349	420		1490	90.3	M_r	211
W16X36	72	393	386	379	369	359	347	420		1440	89.0	V_r	122
b = 6.98	57	377	374	369	362	353	343	420		1370	87.4	L_u	8.14
t = .430	41	350	349	346	341	335	328	350		1280	85.1	I_x	448
	26	321	320	317	313	306	296	222		1140	81.8	S_x	56.5
W410X46	86	352	344	335	325	314	302	361		1300	77.8	M_r	178
W16X31	71	345	338	330	321	311	300	361		1260	76.7	V_r	114
b = 5.52	56	333	328	322	315	307	297	361		1200	75.3	L_u	6.31
t = .440	41	312	311	308	304	298	290	350		1130	73.4	I_x	375
	26	283	282	280	277	271	262	222		1010	70.6	S_x	47.2

†No. of studs/beam = 2 x Q_r x percent shear connection/100/q_r (per stud)
*Units — M_r — Ft. Kips L_u — Ft.   b — In.
        V_r — Kips I_x — In.⁴   t — In.
                 S_x — In.³

Note: The SI designation in bold face type is the one preferred for use in Canada.

COMPOSITE BEAMS
Trial Selection Tables

G40.21 – 44W
3 Ksi Concrete

5 Inch Slab
$\phi = 0.90$, $\phi_C = 0.67$, $\phi_{SC} = 0.80$

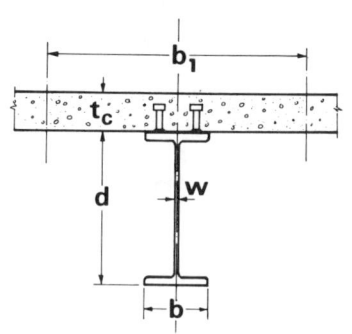

Steel Shape	b_1	Composite Beam									Steel Shape Data*	
		Factored Resistances							Properties			
		M_{rc} in foot Kips for various percentages of shear connection						$Q_r^\dagger$ for 100%	I_1	S_{s_1}		
	In.	100%	90%	80%	70%	60%	50%	Kips	In.^{4}	In.^{3}		
W410X39	86	299	292	283	274	264	253	304	1100	65.3	M_r	146
W16X26	71	294	287	280	271	262	252	304	1070	64.5	V_r	99.1
b = 5.50	56	285	280	274	267	259	250	304	1020	63.3	L_u	6.05
t = .345	41	271	268	265	260	254	246	304	959	61.7	I_x	301
	26	244	244	242	239	234	226	222	863	59.3	S_x	38.4
W360X79	88	510	504	496	484	471	454	618	1690	120	M_r	287
W14X53	73	488	486	482	474	463	449	618	1630	118	V_r	135
b = 8.06	57	459	457	452	446	437	425	487	1530	116	L_u	10.6
t = .660	42	429	427	423	418	411	401	359	1420	113	I_x	541
	26	394	393	390	384	376	366	222	1230	108	S_x	77.7
W360X72	88	467	460	451	440	426	410	558	1550	109	M_r	259
W14X48	73	449	446	439	431	420	406	558	1490	107	V_r	123
b = 8.03	57	422	420	416	410	401	390	487	1410	105	L_u	10.4
t = .595	42	393	391	388	383	376	367	359	1300	103	I_x	485
	26	360	358	356	351	345	335	222	1140	98.1	S_x	70.3
W360X64	88	423	415	405	394	381	367	499	1400	98.0	M_r	230
W14X43	73	409	404	396	387	376	363	499	1340	96.5	V_r	109
b = 7.99	57	385	384	381	375	366	356	487	1270	94.5	L_u	10.1
t = .530	42	357	356	353	348	341	333	359	1180	92.1	I_x	428
	26	325	324	322	318	313	304	222	1040	88.2	S_x	62.7
W360X57	87	390	382	373	362	349	335	444	1310	88.3	M_r	203
W14X38	72	379	373	365	356	345	332	444	1260	87.0	V_r	114
b = 6.77	56	360	357	353	347	338	328	444	1200	85.2	L_u	8.32
t = .515	41	333	332	329	324	318	310	350	1110	82.9	I_x	385
	26	303	302	299	296	290	282	222	985	79.5	S_x	54.6
W360X51	87	352	343	334	324	312	299	396	1180	79.2	M_r	180
W14X34	72	343	336	328	319	309	297	396	1140	78.1	V_r	104
b = 6.74	56	327	324	318	312	303	293	396	1080	76.5	L_u	8.16
t = .455	41	303	302	300	295	289	282	350	1010	74.5	I_x	340
	26	275	273	271	268	263	256	222	897	71.5	S_x	48.6
W360X45	87	314	306	296	287	276	264	350	1050	70.0	M_r	156
W14X30	72	307	300	292	283	273	262	350	1010	69.0	V_r	97.7
b = 6.73	56	295	290	284	277	269	259	350	963	67.7	L_u	7.93
t = .385	41	275	274	272	268	262	254	350	900	65.8	I_x	291
	26	247	246	244	241	237	230	222	804	63.2	S_x	42.1

†No. of studs/beam = 2 x Q_r x percent shear connection/100/q_r (per stud)

*Units — M_r — Ft. Kips L_u — Ft.   b — In.
         V_r — Kips I_x — In.^{4} t — In.
                   S_x — In.^{3}

Note: The SI designation in bold face type is the one preferred for use in Canada.

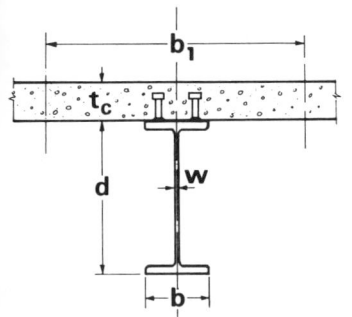

COMPOSITE BEAMS
Trial Selection Tables

G40.21 – 44W
3 Ksi Concrete

5 Inch Slab
$$\varnothing = 0.90, \varnothing_C = 0.67, \varnothing_{SC} = 0.80$$

Steel Shape	b_1	\multicolumn{6}{c}{Composite Beam — Factored Resistances M_{rc} in foot Kips for various percentages of shear connection}	$Q_r{}^\dagger$ for 100%	\multicolumn{2}{c}{Properties}	\multicolumn{2}{c}{Steel Shape Data*}
	In.	100%	90%	80%	70%	60%	50%	Kips	I_1 In.⁴	S_{s_1} In.³		
W360X39	85	277	269	261	251	241	231	305	925	60.8	M_r	133
W14X26	70	271	264	257	249	239	229	305	894	60.0	V_r	92.7
b = 5.02	55	262	257	251	244	236	227	305	854	58.9	L_u	5.83
t = .420	40	247	245	241	237	231	223	305	798	57.3	I_x	245
	26	222	221	219	216	212	206	222	720	55.0	S_x	35.2
W360X33	85	235	228	220	212	203	194	257	786	51.4	M_r	110
W14X22	70	231	225	218	210	202	193	257	761	50.7	V_r	82.6
b = 5.00	55	225	220	214	207	200	192	257	728	49.8	L_u	5.60
t = .335	40	214	211	207	202	196	189	257	683	48.5	I_x	199
	26	193	193	191	188	184	179	222	619	46.6	S_x	29.0
W310X129	92	691	687	680	669	654	635	786	2150	178	M_r	436
W12X87	76	659	655	649	639	626	610	649	2040	175	V_r	169
b = 12.13	60	625	622	616	608	597	584	513	1910	171	L_u	18.1
t = .810	44	590	587	582	576	568	556	376	1740	166	I_x	740
	28	553	551	546	539	530	519	239	1510	158	S_x	118
W310X118	92	637	634	627	617	603	585	786	1960	162	M_r	393
W12X79	76	606	603	597	588	575	560	649	1870	159	V_r	152
b = 12.08	60	574	571	565	557	547	535	513	1750	156	L_u	17.5
t = .735	44	539	537	532	526	519	509	376	1600	151	I_x	662
	28	504	502	498	492	484	474	239	1390	144	S_x	107
W310X107	92	590	588	582	572	558	541	786	1810	148	M_r	356
W12X72	76	560	558	552	543	531	517	649	1720	146	V_r	138
b = 12.04	60	529	526	521	514	504	492	513	1620	142	L_u	17.0
t = .670	44	496	493	489	483	476	467	376	1480	138	I_x	597
	28	461	459	456	451	444	434	239	1290	132	S_x	97.5
W310X97	92	545	543	536	526	512	495	756	1650	135	M_r	290
W12X65	76	517	515	509	501	490	475	649	1580	132	V_r	124
b = 12.00	60	486	484	479	472	463	451	513	1480	129	L_u	17.5
t = .605	44	454	452	448	443	435	427	376	1360	126	I_x	533
	28	420	418	416	412	405	397	239	1190	120	S_x	88.0
W310X86	90	500	495	487	476	462	446	673	1510	121	M_r	285
W12X58	74	474	472	467	459	448	434	632	1440	119	V_r	115
b = 10.01	59	445	443	439	432	423	411	504	1360	116	L_u	13.9
t = .640	43	414	412	408	402	395	387	367	1250	113	I_x	475
	27	380	378	376	372	366	358	231	1090	108	S_x	77.9

†No. of studs/beam = 2 x Q_r x percent shear connection/100/q_r (per stud)

*Units — M_r — Ft. Kips L_u — Ft.   b — In.
V_r — Kips I_x — In.⁴   t — In.
S_x — In.³

Note: The SI designation in bold face type is the one preferred for use in Canada.

COMPOSITE BEAMS
Trial Selection Tables

G40.21 – 44W
3 Ksi Concrete

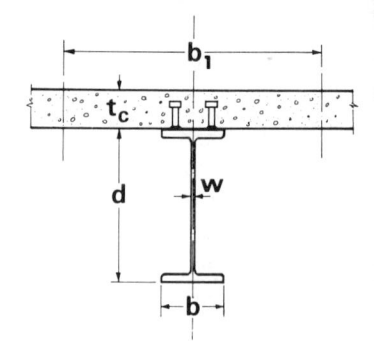

5 Inch Slab
$\emptyset = 0.90$, $\emptyset_C = 0.67$, $\emptyset_{SC} = 0.80$

Steel Shape	b_1	\multicolumn{6}{c}{M_{rc} in foot Kips for various percentages of shear connection}						$Q_r^\dagger$ for 100%	I_1	S_{s_1}	\multicolumn{2}{c}{Steel Shape Data*}
	In.	100%	90%	80%	70%	60%	50%	Kips	In.⁴	In.³		
W310X79	90	464	458	449	438	424	408	618	1390	111	M_r	257
W12X53	74	442	440	435	427	416	403	618	1330	109	V_r	109
b = 9.99	58	413	411	407	400	392	381	495	1250	107	L_u	13.5
t = .575	43	384	382	378	373	366	358	367	1150	104	I_x	425
	27	351	349	347	343	338	330	231	1010	99.0	S_x	70.5
W310X74	88	444	438	429	417	404	388	582	1320	104	M_r	239
W12X50	73	425	422	416	408	397	383	582	1270	103	V_r	118
b = 8.08	57	397	395	391	384	375	364	487	1200	100	L_u	11.0
t = .640	42	367	365	362	357	350	341	359	1100	97.3	I_x	394
	26	334	332	329	326	319	311	222	956	92.7	S_x	64.6
W310X67	88	405	397	388	376	363	348	523	1200	94.2	M_r	214
W12X45	73	389	385	378	369	358	344	523	1150	92.7	V_r	106
b = 8.05	57	364	363	359	353	344	334	487	1090	90.6	L_u	10.7
t = .575	42	336	334	331	326	319	311	359	1010	88.0	I_x	350
	26	303	302	299	296	291	283	222	876	83.9	S_x	58.0
W310X60	88	367	359	349	338	325	311	467	1090	84.7	M_r	190
W12X40	73	354	348	341	332	321	308	467	1040	83.4	V_r	92.1
b = 8.00	57	334	332	328	322	313	303	467	988	81.6	L_u	10.4
t = .515	42	306	305	302	297	291	283	359	916	79.3	I_x	310
	26	275	274	271	268	264	257	222	801	75.7	S_x	51.9
W310X52	87	336	327	318	307	295	282	408	1030	76.0	M_r	169
W12X35	71	325	319	311	302	292	280	408	987	74.8	V_r	98.0
b = 6.56	56	310	307	301	295	286	276	408	938	73.3	L_u	8.33
t = .520	41	285	284	281	277	271	263	350	871	71.2	I_x	285
	26	256	255	253	249	245	239	222	771	68.1	S_x	45.6
W310X45	87	290	282	273	263	252	241	348	888	65.2	M_r	142
W12X30	71	282	276	268	259	249	239	348	855	64.2	V_r	83.9
b = 6.52	56	271	267	261	254	245	236	348	814	63.0	L_u	8.09
t = .440	41	252	251	248	244	238	231	348	758	61.2	I_x	238
	26	224	223	221	218	214	209	222	675	58.6	S_x	38.6
W310X39	86	254	247	238	229	219	209	303	781	57.0	M_r	123
W12X26	71	249	242	235	226	217	208	303	754	56.2	V_r	73.5
b = 6.49	56	241	235	229	222	214	206	303	720	55.2	L_u	7.92
t = .380	41	226	224	220	215	209	202	303	673	53.7	I_x	204
	26	200	199	197	195	191	186	222	602	51.4	S_x	33.4

$\dagger$No. of studs/beam = 2 x Q_r x percent shear connection/100/q_r (per stud)

*Units — M_r — Ft. Kips L_u — Ft.   b — In.
        V_r — Kips I_x — In.⁴   t — In.
                 S_x — In.³

Note: The SI designation in bold face type is the one preferred for use in Canada.

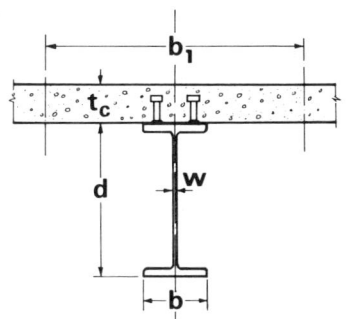

COMPOSITE BEAMS
Trial Selection Tables

G40.21 – 44W
3 Ksi Concrete

5 Inch Slab
$\phi = 0.90$, $\phi_C = 0.67$, $\phi_{SC} = 0.80$

Steel Shape	Composite Beam										Steel Shape Data*	
		Factored Resistances							Properties			
	b_1	M_{rc} in foot Kips for various percentages of shear connection						Q_r† for 100%	I_1	S_{s_1}		
	In.	100%	90%	80%	70%	60%	50%	Kips	In.⁴	In.³		
W250X101 W10X68 b = 10.13 t = .770	90 74 59 43 27	503 474 444 410 375	501 471 441 408 373	495 465 436 404 370	486 457 429 398 366	472 445 419 391 360	455 430 407 381 352	769 632 504 367 231	1340 1270 1190 1080 927	125 123 120 116 110	M_r V_r L_u I_x S_x	281 128 16.1 394 75.8
W250X89 W10X60 b = 10.08 t = .680	90 74 59 43 27	456 428 400 368 333	451 426 398 366 332	444 421 393 362 329	433 413 386 356 326	420 402 377 349 321	403 388 365 340 313	697 632 504 367 231	1190 1130 1070 971 835	111 109 106 103 97.4	M_r V_r L_u I_x S_x	246 112 15.2 341 66.7
W250X80 W10X54 b = 10.03 t = .615	90 74 59 43 27	418 395 367 336 303	412 393 365 334 301	403 388 361 331 299	392 380 355 326 295	378 370 346 319 291	362 356 334 310 285	626 626 504 367 231	1080 1030 973 889 767	101 98.6 96.3 93.1 88.4	M_r V_r L_u I_x S_x	220 97.6 14.6 303 60.1
W250X73 W10X49 b = 10.00 t = .560	90 74 59 43 27	387 368 342 311 279	379 364 340 310 278	370 358 336 307 275	359 349 330 302 272	345 338 322 295 268	330 325 311 287 262	570 570 504 367 231	996 951 897 821 711	92.0 90.3 88.2 85.3 81.0	M_r V_r L_u I_x S_x	199 88.7 14.2 272 54.5
W250X67 W10X45 b = 8.02 t = .620	88 73 57 42 26	364 348 323 295 262	357 344 322 293 260	347 337 318 290 258	336 328 312 285 255	323 317 303 278 250	308 304 292 270 244	527 527 487 359 222	939 898 843 775 668	85.1 83.6 81.6 78.9 74.7	M_r V_r L_u I_x S_x	181 92.4 11.6 248 49.1
W250X58 W10X39 b = 7.98 t = .530	88 73 57 42 26	321 309 289 262 231	312 303 287 261 230	303 295 283 258 228	292 286 276 254 224	279 275 268 247 220	265 262 258 239 215	455 455 455 359 222	820 786 740 682 591	74.0 72.8 71.0 68.8 65.2	M_r V_r L_u I_x S_x	154 81.7 11.1 209 42.1
W250X49 W10X33 b = 7.96 t = .435	88 73 57 42 26	275 267 253 231 200	267 260 249 230 199	257 252 243 227 197	247 243 236 223 195	236 233 228 217 191	223 221 218 209 186	385 385 385 359 222	700 672 635 587 512	62.7 61.7 60.3 58.5 55.4	M_r V_r L_u I_x S_x	128 73.7 10.5 170 34.9

†No. of studs/beam = 2 x Q_r x percent shear connection/100/q_r (per stud)
*Units — M_r — Ft. Kips L_u — Ft.   b — In.
          V_r — Kips I_x — In.⁴   t — In.
                                S_x — In.³

Note: The SI designation in bold face type is the one preferred for use in Canada.

COMPOSITE BEAMS
Trial Selection Tables

G40.21 – 44W
3 Ksi Concrete

5 Inch Slab
$\emptyset = 0.90$, $\emptyset_C = 0.67$, $\emptyset_{SC} = 0.80$

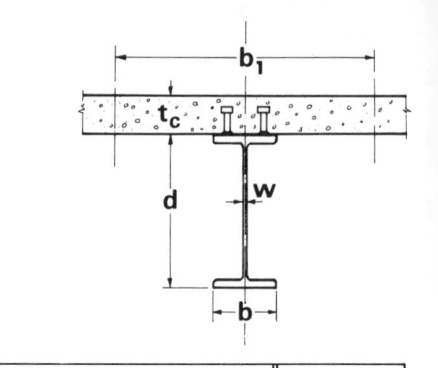

Steel Shape	b_1	M_{rc} in foot Kips for various percentages of shear connection						$Q_r^\dagger$ for 100%	I_1	S_{s_1}	Steel Shape Data*	
	In.	100%	90%	80%	70%	60%	50%	Kips	In.⁴	In.³		
W250X45	86	264	256	247	237	226	214	350	705	59.1	M_r	121
W10X30	71	256	250	242	233	223	212	350	677	58.2	V_r	82.1
b = 5.81	56	245	241	235	228	219	210	350	642	56.9	L_u	7.63
t = .510	41	226	225	222	218	212	205	350	595	55.2	I_x	170
	26	198	196	194	191	187	182	222	525	52.5	S_x	32.5
W250X39	86	230	222	213	204	194	184	301	615	51.2	M_r	103
W10X26	71	224	217	210	202	192	183	301	592	50.5	V_r	70.2
b = 5.77	56	216	211	205	197	189	181	301	563	49.5	L_u	7.38
t = .440	41	201	199	195	190	184	177	301	524	48.0	I_x	144
	26	175	175	173	170	166	161	222	464	45.7	S_x	27.9
W250X33	86	197	190	182	174	165	156	257	528	43.7	M_r	85.8
W10X22	71	193	187	180	172	164	155	257	509	43.1	V_r	63.8
b = 5.75	56	187	182	176	169	162	154	257	485	42.3	L_u	7.10
t = .360	41	177	173	169	164	158	151	257	453	41.1	I_x	118
	26	155	154	153	150	146	142	222	403	39.2	S_x	23.2
W200X100	88	449	447	441	431	417	400	752	1060	111	M_r	232
W8X67	73	421	418	412	403	391	376	624	1000	109	V_r	134
b = 8.28	57	389	386	380	373	363	350	487	927	106	L_u	16.3
t = .935	42	356	353	349	343	335	326	359	838	101	I_x	272
	26	319	317	314	310	304	296	222	705	94.9	S_x	60.4
W200X86	88	402	398	390	379	366	349	677	922	97.3	M_r	197
W8X58	73	377	375	370	361	350	336	624	876	95.2	V_r	117
b = 8.22	57	346	344	339	332	323	311	487	814	92.4	L_u	14.9
t = .810	42	315	313	309	303	296	287	359	738	88.8	I_x	228
	26	280	278	275	272	267	260	222	623	83.3	S_x	52.1
W200X71	88	344	337	328	316	303	287	558	777	81.3	M_r	162
W8X48	73	326	323	316	308	297	283	558	740	79.7	V_r	88.9
b = 8.11	57	299	297	293	287	278	267	487	690	77.5	L_u	13.4
t = .685	42	270	268	265	260	253	244	359	629	74.7	I_x	184
	26	237	235	233	229	225	219	222	535	70.1	S_x	43.3
W200X59	88	293	285	275	264	251	237	463	652	68.0	M_r	131
W8X40	73	281	275	267	258	247	234	463	622	66.7	V_r	77.6
b = 8.07	57	260	258	254	248	240	229	463	583	64.9	L_u	12.3
t = .560	42	233	232	229	224	218	210	359	533	62.6	I_x	146
	26	202	201	198	195	191	186	222	457	58.9	S_x	35.4

†No. of studs/beam = 2 x Q_r x percent shear connection/100/q_r (per stud)

*Units — M_r — Ft. Kips L_u — Ft.   b — In.
      V_r — Kips I_x — In.⁴   t — In.
                S_x — In.³

Note: The SI designation in bold face type is the one preferred for use in Canada.

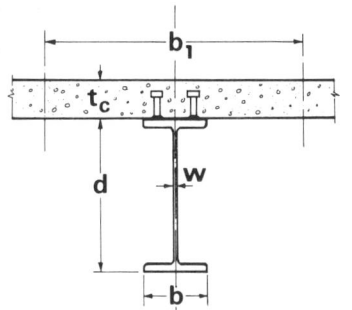

COMPOSITE BEAMS
Trial Selection Tables

G40.21 – 44W
3 Ksi Concrete

5 Inch Slab
$\varnothing = 0.90$, $\varnothing_C = 0.67$, $\varnothing_{SC} = 0.80$

Steel Shape	b₁	Composite Beam									Steel Shape Data*	
		Factored Resistances							Properties			
		M_{rc} in foot Kips for various percentages of shear connection						Q_r† for 100%	I_1	S_{s_1}		
		100%	90%	80%	70%	60%	50%	Kips	In.⁴	In.³		
	In.											
W200X52	88	262	253	244	233	222	209	408	582	60.3	M_r	115
W8X35	73	252	246	238	229	218	206	408	557	59.3	V_r	65.8
b = 8.02	57	237	233	228	221	213	202	408	523	57.8	L_u	11.7
t = .495	42	213	212	209	204	198	191	359	480	55.8	I_x	127
	26	182	181	179	176	172	167	222	413	52.6	S_x	31.3
W200X46	88	235	227	218	207	196	185	362	521	53.7	M_r	100
W8X31	73	227	221	213	204	194	183	362	500	52.8	V_r	59.6
b = 7.99	57	215	211	205	198	189	180	362	470	51.6	L_u	11.3
t = .435	42	195	194	192	188	182	174	359	433	49.9	I_x	110
	26	166	165	163	160	156	151	222	374	47.0	S_x	27.5
W200X42	87	216	208	199	190	179	168	327	482	48.8	M_r	89.8
W8X28	71	209	202	195	186	177	166	327	461	47.9	V_r	60.0
b = 6.53	56	199	194	189	181	173	164	327	435	46.8	L_u	9.27
t = .465	41	182	181	178	173	167	160	327	401	45.3	I_x	98.0
	26	155	154	152	149	146	141	222	350	42.9	S_x	24.3
W200X36	86	187	180	172	163	154	144	280	419	42.2	M_r	76.6
W8X24	71	182	176	169	161	152	143	280	402	41.5	V_r	50.8
b = 6.49	56	175	170	164	157	149	141	280	381	40.6	L_u	8.86
t = .400	41	163	160	156	151	145	138	280	353	39.4	I_x	82.8
	26	139	138	136	133	130	125	222	309	37.4	S_x	20.9
W200X31	85	169	162	154	146	138	129	244	390	37.6	M_r	67.3
W8X21	70	165	159	152	145	137	128	244	376	37.0	V_r	54.1
b = 5.27	55	159	154	148	142	135	127	244	357	36.2	L_u	6.98
t = .400	41	150	147	143	137	131	125	244	333	35.2	I_x	75.3
	26	130	130	128	125	122	117	222	294	33.5	S_x	18.2
W200X27	85	145	139	132	125	118	110	208	336	32.2	M_r	56.1
W8X18	70	142	136	130	124	117	109	208	324	31.7	V_r	48.9
b = 5.25	55	138	133	128	122	115	108	208	309	31.1	L_u	6.70
t = .330	40	131	127	123	118	113	106	208	287	30.2	I_x	61.9
	26	117	116	114	111	107	103	208	257	28.8	S_x	15.2

†No. of studs/beam = 2 x Q_r x percent shear connection/100/q_r (per stud)
*Units — M_r — Ft. Kips L_u — Ft.   b — In.
     V_r — Kips I_x — In.⁴   t — In.
                 S_x — In.³

Note: The SI designation in bold face type is the one preferred for use in Canada.

COMPOSITE BEAMS
Trial Selection Tables

G40.21 – 44W
3 Ksi Concrete

1½ Inch Deck with 2½ Inch Slab
$\emptyset = 0.90$, $\emptyset_C = 0.67$, $\emptyset_{SC} = 0.80$

Steel Shape	b₁	\multicolumn{6}{c}{Mrc in foot Kips for various percentages of shear connection}						Qr† for 100%	I₁	Ss₁	Steel Shape Data*	

Composite Beam / Factored Resistances / Properties / Steel Shape

Steel Shape	b₁ (In.)	100%	90%	80%	70%	60%	50%	Qr† for 100% (Kips)	I₁ (In.⁴)	Ss₁ (In.³)	\multicolumn{2}{c}{Steel Shape Data*}
W610X241	77	1880	1850	1830	1800	1770	1740	329	8570	499	Mr	1540
W24X162	63	1830	1810	1780	1760	1730	1700	269	8110	491	Vr	461
b = 12.95	50	1780	1760	1740	1720	1690	1670	214	7640	481	Lu	16.9
t = 1.22	37	1720	1700	1690	1670	1650	1640	158	7110	469	Ix	5170
	23	1650	1640	1630	1620	1610	1600	98.2	6460	453	Sx	414
W610X217	77	1700	1680	1650	1630	1600	1570	329	7810	451	Mr	1380
W24X146	63	1650	1630	1610	1590	1560	1530	269	7390	443	Vr	420
b = 12.90	50	1610	1590	1570	1550	1530	1500	214	6950	434	Lu	16.5
t = 1.09	37	1550	1540	1520	1500	1490	1470	158	6450	423	Ix	4580
	23	1490	1480	1470	1460	1440	1430	98.2	5830	408	Sx	370
W610X195	77	1530	1510	1490	1460	1430	1400	329	7080	404	Mr	1220
W24X131	63	1490	1470	1450	1420	1400	1370	269	6690	397	Vr	387
b = 12.85	50	1440	1420	1410	1390	1360	1340	214	6290	389	Lu	16.1
t = .960	37	1390	1370	1360	1340	1330	1310	158	5820	379	Ix	4020
	23	1330	1320	1310	1300	1290	1270	98.2	5230	365	Sx	328
W610X174	77	1380	1360	1340	1320	1290	1260	329	6430	362	Mr	1080
W24X117	63	1340	1320	1300	1280	1260	1230	269	6080	356	Vr	349
b = 12.80	50	1300	1280	1260	1240	1220	1200	214	5710	349	Lu	15.7
t = .850	36	1240	1230	1210	1200	1180	1170	154	5230	339	Ix	3540
	23	1190	1180	1170	1160	1140	1130	98.2	4720	327	Sx	292
W610X155	77	1240	1230	1210	1180	1160	1130	329	5830	323	Mr	954
W24X104	63	1210	1190	1170	1150	1130	1100	269	5510	318	Vr	314
b = 12.75	50	1160	1150	1130	1110	1090	1070	214	5160	312	Lu	15.4
t = .750	36	1110	1100	1090	1070	1060	1040	154	4730	303	Ix	3100
	23	1060	1050	1040	1030	1020	1010	98.2	4240	291	Sx	258
W610X140	73	1120	1110	1090	1060	1040	1010	312	5280	287	Mr	838
W24X94	60	1090	1070	1050	1030	1010	981	256	4990	282	Vr	327
b = 9.06	47	1040	1030	1010	991	971	951	201	4650	276	Lu	10.8
t = .875	35	995	982	968	953	938	922	149	4280	268	Ix	2700
	22	939	929	920	910	899	889	94.0	3800	256	Sx	222
W610X125	73	1010	998	980	959	935	908	312	4790	257	Mr	739
W24X84	60	979	964	946	926	904	881	256	4530	253	Vr	296
b = 9.02	47	938	923	907	890	872	852	201	4220	247	Lu	10.6
t = .770	35	894	882	868	854	839	823	149	3880	240	Ix	2370
	22	840	831	821	812	801	791	94.0	3430	230	Sx	197

†No. of studs/beam = 2 x Qr x percent shear connection/100/qr (per stud)

*Units — Mr — Ft. Kips   Lu — Ft.   b — In.
        Vr — Kips   Ix — In.⁴   t — In.
                    Sx — In.³

Note: The SI designation in bold face type is the one preferred for use in Canada.

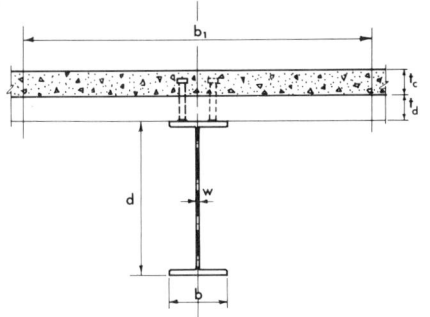

COMPOSITE BEAMS
Trial Selection Tables

G40.21 – 44W
3 Ksi Concrete

1½ Inch Deck with 2½ Inch Slab
$\phi = 0.90, \phi_C = 0.67, \phi_{SC} = 0.80$

Steel Shape		Composite Beam									Steel Shape Data*	
		Factored Resistances							Properties			
	b_1	M_{rc} in foot Kips for various percentages of shear connection						Q_r† for 100%	I_1	S_{s_1}		
	In.	100%	90%	80%	70%	60%	50%	Kips	In.⁴	In.³		
W610X113	73	927	913	896	876	853	827	312	4390	233	M_r	660
W24X76	60	895	880	864	845	824	801	256	4150	229	V_r	275
b = 8.99	47	856	842	827	810	792	772	201	3870	224	L_u	10.4
t = .680	35	814	801	788	774	760	744	149	3550	217	I_x	2100
	22	760	751	742	733	722	712	94.0	3130	207	S_x	176
W610X101	73	839	827	811	792	771	746	312	3970	208	M_r	584
W24X68	60	810	796	781	763	742	720	256	3760	204	V_r	257
b = 8.97	47	773	760	745	729	711	692	201	3510	200	L_u	10.1
t = .585	35	732	721	708	694	680	665	149	3220	194	I_x	1830
	22	680	672	663	653	643	633	94.0	2820	185	S_x	154
W530X138	72	987	971	953	932	909	884	308	4180	254	M_r	729
W21X93	60	955	939	922	903	882	860	256	3960	249	V_r	328
b = 8.42	47	914	900	885	869	851	832	201	3680	243	L_u	10.3
t = .930	34	868	857	844	831	818	803	145	3350	235	I_x	2070
	22	821	812	804	795	785	776	94.0	2980	225	S_x	191
W530X123	72	893	879	863	844	822	798	308	3810	228	M_r	647
W21X83	60	864	850	834	816	797	775	256	3610	224	V_r	288
b = 8.35	47	827	814	799	784	767	749	201	3360	219	L_u	10.1
t = .835	34	783	772	760	748	735	721	145	3050	211	I_x	1830
	22	737	729	721	712	703	693	94.0	2700	202	S_x	171
W530X109	72	802	790	776	759	740	717	308	3440	203	M_r	568
W21X73	60	777	765	750	734	716	695	256	3270	199	V_r	253
b = 8.30	47	743	731	718	703	687	669	201	3040	195	L_u	9.89
t = .740	34	702	692	681	669	656	642	145	2760	189	I_x	1600
	22	658	651	642	634	625	615	94.0	2440	180	S_x	151
W530X101	72	751	742	729	713	695	673	308	3240	189	M_r	528
W21X68	60	729	718	704	689	671	652	256	3080	186	V_r	237
b = 8.27	47	697	686	673	659	644	627	201	2870	182	L_u	9.74
t = .685	34	658	648	637	626	613	600	145	2610	176	I_x	1480
	22	616	608	600	592	583	573	94.0	2300	169	S_x	140
W530X92	72	693	685	673	659	641	620	308	3000	173	M_r	475
W21X62	60	673	663	650	636	619	599	256	2850	170	V_r	219
b = 8.24	47	643	633	620	607	592	575	201	2660	167	L_u	9.59
t = .615	34	606	596	585	574	562	548	145	2410	161	I_x	1330
	22	564	557	549	540	531	522	94.0	2120	154	S_x	127

†No. of studs/beam = 2 x Q_r x percent shear connection/100/q_r (per stud)
*Units — M_r — Ft. Kips L_u — Ft.   b — In.
       V_r — Kips I_x — In.⁴   t — In.
                   S_x — In.³

Note: The SI designation in bold face type is the one preferred for use in Canada.

COMPOSITE BEAMS
Trial Selection Tables

G40.21 – 44W
3 Ksi Concrete

1½ Inch Deck with 2½ Inch Slab
$\emptyset = 0.90$, $\emptyset_C = 0.67$, $\emptyset_{SC} = 0.80$

Steel Shape	b_1	\multicolumn{6}{c}{M_{rc} in foot Kips for various percentages of shear connection}	Q_r† for 100%	I_1	S_{s_1}	\multicolumn{2}{c}{Steel Shape Data*}
	In.	100%	90%	80%	70%	60%	50%	Kips	In.⁴	In.³		
W530X82	72	623	616	606	593	576	556	308	2700	154	M_r	416
W21X55	60	605	596	585	571	555	536	256	2570	151	V_r	204
b = 8.22	47	578	568	556	543	528	512	201	2400	148	L_u	9.31
t = .522	34	542	533	522	511	499	486	145	2180	143	I_x	1150
	22	501	494	486	478	469	460	94.0	1910	137	S_x	111
W460X106	72	685	676	665	651	634	614	308	2630	175	M_r	478
W18X71	59	663	652	640	626	611	593	252	2480	172	V_r	239
b = 7.64	47	636	625	614	601	587	572	201	2310	168	L_u	9.51
t = .810	34	600	591	581	571	560	548	145	2090	162	I_x	1170
	21	558	552	545	537	530	522	89.7	1820	154	S_x	127
W460X97	72	635	628	618	605	590	571	308	2460	161	M_r	439
W18X65	59	615	606	595	583	568	551	252	2320	159	V_r	216
b = 7.59	47	591	581	571	559	545	530	201	2170	155	L_u	9.35
t = .750	34	557	549	540	529	518	507	145	1960	150	I_x	1070
	21	517	510	504	497	489	481	89.7	1700	142	S_x	117
W460X89	72	590	584	576	564	550	533	308	2300	150	M_r	406
W18X60	59	573	565	555	544	530	514	252	2180	147	V_r	198
b = 7.56	47	551	542	532	521	508	494	201	2030	144	L_u	9.20
t = .695	34	520	512	503	493	482	471	145	1840	140	I_x	984
	21	481	475	468	461	454	446	89.7	1590	133	S_x	108
W460X82	72	547	541	534	524	511	495	308	2140	138	M_r	370
W18X55	59	531	524	516	505	491	476	252	2020	135	V_r	185
b = 7.53	46	509	501	492	481	469	455	196	1880	132	L_u	9.02
t = .630	34	482	474	465	456	445	434	145	1720	129	I_x	890
	21	444	438	431	424	417	409	89.7	1480	122	S_x	98.3
W460X74	71	500	495	489	481	469	454	303	1960	125	M_r	333
W18X50	59	486	481	474	464	452	438	252	1870	123	V_r	167
b = 7.49	46	468	461	452	442	431	418	196	1740	121	L_u	8.89
t = .570	34	442	435	427	418	408	397	145	1590	117	I_x	800
	21	406	400	394	387	380	373	89.7	1370	112	S_x	88.9
W460X67	71	461	456	450	442	431	417	303	1810	114	M_r	301
W18X45	59	447	443	436	427	415	401	252	1720	113	V_r	156
b = 7.48	46	430	423	415	406	394	381	196	1610	110	L_u	8.65
t = .499	34	406	399	391	382	372	361	145	1470	107	I_x	719
	21	370	364	358	351	344	337	89.7	1270	102	S_x	80.5

†No. of studs/beam = 2 x Q_r x percent shear connection/100/q_r (per stud)

*Units — M_r — Ft. Kips L_u — Ft.   b — In.
   V_r — Kips I_x — In.⁴   t — In.
   S_x — In.³

Note: The SI designation in bold face type is the one preferred for use in Canada.

1½ Inch Deck with 2½ Inch Slab
$\phi = 0.90$, $\phi_C = 0.67$, $\phi_{SC} = 0.80$

Steel Shape	b₁	Composite Beam — Factored Resistances — Mrc in foot Kips for various percentages of shear connection						Qr† for 100%	Properties I₁	Ss₁	Steel Shape Data*	
	In.	100%	90%	80%	70%	60%	50%	Kips	In.⁴	In.³		
W460X61	71	421	416	410	403	393	379	303	1630	102	Mr	264
W18X41	59	407	403	397	389	377	364	252	1560	101	Vr	148
b = 7.45	46	391	385	377	368	357	344	196	1460	98.8	Lu	8.40
t = .425	34	368	361	353	345	335	324	145	1330	96.1	Ix	623
	21	333	327	321	314	307	300	89.7	1150	91.3	Sx	70.4
W410X85	71	515	509	502	493	480	465	303	1850	131	Mr	346
W16X57	59	500	494	486	475	463	448	252	1750	129	Vr	185
b = 7.12	46	479	472	463	453	441	428	196	1630	126	Lu	8.91
t = .715	34	453	446	438	429	419	409	145	1480	122	Ix	758
	21	417	412	406	399	393	385	89.7	1270	116	Sx	92.3
W410X74	71	458	453	446	439	429	415	303	1660	116	Mr	304
W16X50	59	444	439	433	424	414	400	252	1580	114	Vr	161
b = 7.07	46	427	421	413	404	394	382	196	1470	112	Lu	8.67
t = .630	34	404	398	390	382	373	363	145	1340	108	Ix	659
	21	371	366	360	354	348	341	89.7	1150	103	Sx	81.1
W410X67	71	420	415	409	402	393	381	303	1520	105	Mr	272
W16X45	59	406	402	396	389	379	367	252	1450	103	Vr	145
b = 7.03	46	390	385	379	370	361	349	196	1350	101	Lu	8.50
t = .565	34	370	364	357	349	340	331	145	1230	98.3	Ix	586
	21	339	333	328	322	315	309	89.7	1060	93.4	Sx	72.7
W410X60	71	379	374	369	362	355	345	303	1380	93.7	Mr	241
W16X40	59	366	362	357	351	343	332	252	1310	92.4	Vr	128
b = 6.99	46	351	348	342	335	326	316	196	1230	90.6	Lu	8.38
t = .505	34	334	329	323	316	308	299	145	1120	88.2	Ix	518
	21	306	301	296	290	284	277	89.7	966	83.9	Sx	64.7
W410X54	71	346	341	336	329	322	313	303	1240	83.6	Mr	211
W16X36	59	333	329	324	319	311	301	252	1180	82.5	Vr	122
b = 6.98	46	319	315	310	304	295	285	196	1110	80.9	Lu	8.14
t = .430	34	303	298	292	285	277	268	145	1020	78.7	Ix	448
	21	275	271	265	260	254	247	89.7	874	74.9	Sx	56.5
W410X46	70	307	303	297	291	284	276	299	1090	71.8	Mr	178
W16X31	57	293	290	285	280	273	264	243	1040	70.8	Vr	114
b = 5.52	45	280	277	273	267	259	250	192	979	69.6	Lu	6.31
t = .440	33	265	261	256	249	242	233	141	897	67.7	Ix	375
	21	241	237	232	226	221	214	89.7	779	64.6	Sx	47.2

†No. of studs/beam = 2 x Qr x percent shear connection/100/qr (per stud)

*Units — Mr - Ft. Kips   Lu - Ft.   b - In.
      Vr - Kips   Ix - In.⁴   t - In.
            Sx - In.³

Note: The SI designation in bold face type is the one preferred for use in Canada.

COMPOSITE BEAMS
Trial Selection Tables

G40.21 – 44W
3 Ksi Concrete

1½ Inch Deck with 2½ Inch Slab
$\emptyset = 0.90$, $\emptyset_C = 0.67$, $\emptyset_{SC} = 0.80$

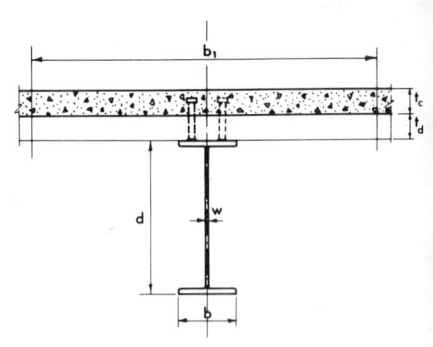

Steel Shape	b_1	Factored Resistances M_{rc} in foot Kips for various percentages of shear connection						$Q_r^†$ for 100%	Properties I_1	S_{S_1}	Steel Shape Data*	
		100%	90%	80%	70%	60%	50%	Kips				
	In.	100%	90%	80%	70%	60%	50%	Kips	In.⁴	In.³		
W410X39	70	267	263	258	252	246	239	299	925	60.1	M_r	146
W16X26	57	254	251	246	241	236	228	243	886	59.3	V_r	99.1
b = 5.50	45	242	239	235	230	224	215	192	837	58.3	L_u	6.05
t = .345	33	228	225	220	214	207	199	141	770	56.8	I_x	301
	21	207	203	198	193	187	181	89.7	672	54.3	S_x	38.4
W360X79	72	422	417	411	404	396	385	308	1370	111	M_r	287
W14X53	59	407	403	397	391	382	371	252	1300	109	V_r	135
b = 8.06	47	393	389	383	376	367	357	201	1210	107	L_u	10.6
t = .660	34	373	368	362	355	347	339	145	1090	103	I_x	541
	22	348	343	338	332	326	320	94.0	952	98.6	S_x	77.7
W360X72	72	387	382	376	369	362	352	308	1260	101	M_r	259
W14X48	59	372	368	363	357	350	340	252	1190	99.1	V_r	123
b = 8.03	47	358	355	350	344	336	326	201	1120	97.1	L_u	10.4
t = .595	34	341	337	331	325	317	309	145	1010	94.2	I_x	485
	22	317	313	308	303	297	291	94.0	879	90.0	S_x	70.3
W360X64	72	352	347	341	335	327	319	308	1140	90.2	M_r	230
W14X43	59	338	333	329	323	317	308	252	1080	88.9	V_r	109
b = 7.99	47	324	321	317	311	304	295	201	1020	87.3	L_u	10.1
t = .530	34	308	305	300	294	287	279	145	922	84.7	I_x	428
	22	287	283	278	273	267	261	94.0	804	81.0	S_x	62.7
W360X57	71	329	324	318	312	305	296	303	1080	81.2	M_r	203
W14X38	58	314	310	305	300	293	284	248	1020	80.0	V_r	114
b = 6.77	46	301	297	293	288	280	271	196	959	78.5	L_u	8.32
t = .515	34	286	282	277	271	264	256	145	876	76.3	I_x	385
	21	262	258	253	248	242	237	89.7	751	72.5	S_x	54.6
W360X51	71	299	295	289	283	276	269	303	975	72.7	M_r	180
W14X34	58	286	282	277	272	266	258	248	929	71.7	V_r	104
b = 6.74	46	273	269	266	261	254	246	196	874	70.4	L_u	8.16
t = .455	34	259	256	251	246	239	231	145	801	68.6	I_x	340
	21	237	233	229	224	219	213	89.7	688	65.3	S_x	48.6
W360X45	71	271	267	262	256	249	242	303	869	64.1	M_r	156
W14X30	58	258	254	250	245	239	232	248	829	63.2	V_r	97.7
b = 6.73	46	245	242	238	234	228	221	196	782	62.2	L_u	7.93
t = .385	34	232	229	225	220	214	207	145	719	60.6	I_x	291
	21	212	208	204	199	194	189	89.7	619	57.7	S_x	42.1

†No. of studs/beam = 2 x Q_r x percent shear connection/100/q_r (per stud)

*Units — M_r — Ft. Kips L_u — Ft.   b — In.
       V_r — Kips I_x — In.⁴   t — In.
                   S_x — In.³

Note: The SI designation in bold face type is the one preferred for use in Canada.

1½ Inch Deck with 2½ Inch Slab
$\varnothing = 0.90$, $\varnothing_C = 0.67$, $\varnothing_{SC} = 0.80$

Steel Shape		Composite Beam										Steel Shape Data*	
		Factored Resistances							Properties				
	b_1	M_{rc} in foot Kips for various percentages of shear connection						Q_r† for 100%	I_1	S_{s_1}			
	In.	100%	90%	80%	70%	60%	50%	Kips	In.⁴	In.³			
W360X39	69	244	240	235	229	223	215	295	769	55.5	M_r	133
W14X26	57	232	228	224	219	213	207	243	737	54.8	V_r	92.7
b = 5.02	45	219	216	213	208	203	196	192	696	53.9	L_u	5.83
t = .420	33	206	203	200	195	189	182	141	640	52.5	I_x	245
	21	188	184	180	176	171	165	89.7	557	50.2	S_x	35.2
W360X33	69	209	205	200	195	189	182	257	655	46.7	M_r	110
W14X22	57	203	199	195	191	185	179	243	630	46.2	V_r	82.6
b = 5.00	45	191	188	184	181	176	170	192	598	45.4	L_u	5.60
t = .335	33	178	176	173	169	163	157	141	552	44.3	I_x	199
	21	162	159	155	151	147	141	89.7	483	42.5	S_x	29.0
W310X129	76	583	577	570	562	551	538	325	1680	163	M_r	436
W12X87	63	567	561	555	547	536	524	269	1580	160	V_r	169
b = 12.13	49	548	543	536	527	517	506	209	1460	156	L_u	18.1
t = .810	36	526	520	513	506	497	488	154	1320	151	I_x	740
	23	497	492	487	481	475	469	98.2	1150	143	S_x	118
W310X118	76	533	527	520	512	503	492	325	1550	149	M_r	393
W12X79	63	517	512	506	499	490	478	269	1460	146	V_r	152
b = 12.08	49	500	495	489	481	472	461	209	1350	142	L_u	17.5
t = .735	36	480	474	468	461	453	444	154	1220	138	I_x	662
	23	452	448	443	437	431	425	98.2	1060	131	S_x	107
W310X107	76	489	484	477	469	461	451	325	1430	136	M_r	356
W12X72	63	474	469	463	457	449	438	269	1350	134	V_r	138
b = 12.04	49	457	453	448	441	433	423	209	1250	130	L_u	17.0
t = .670	36	439	434	429	422	414	406	154	1130	126	I_x	597
	23	414	409	405	399	394	388	98.2	980	120	S_x	97.5
W310X97	76	448	443	436	429	421	412	325	1310	124	M_r	290
W12X65	63	433	428	423	417	410	400	269	1240	122	V_r	124
b = 12.00	49	417	413	408	402	394	385	209	1150	119	L_u	17.5
t = .605	36	400	396	391	384	377	369	154	1040	115	I_x	533
	23	376	372	368	363	357	351	98.2	902	110	S_x	88.0
W310X86	74	408	402	396	389	381	372	316	1210	111	M_r	285
W12X58	61	393	388	383	377	370	361	261	1140	109	V_r	115
b = 10.01	48	377	374	369	364	357	348	205	1060	107	L_u	13.9
t = .640	35	361	358	353	347	340	332	149	957	103	I_x	475
	22	339	335	330	326	320	315	94.0	824	98.2	S_x	77.9

†No. of studs/beam = 2 x Q_r x percent shear connection/100/q_r (per stud)

*Units — M_r – Ft. Kips L_u – Ft.   b – In.
        V_r – Kips I_x – In.⁴   t – In.
                 S_x – In.³

Note: The SI designation in bold face type is the one preferred for use in Canada.

COMPOSITE BEAMS
Trial Selection Tables

G40.21 – 44W
3 Ksi Concrete

1½ Inch Deck with 2½ Inch Slab
$\phi = 0.90$, $\phi_C = 0.67$, $\phi_{SC} = 0.80$

Steel Shape	b_1 In.	Composite Beam — Factored Resistances — M_{rc} in foot Kips for various percentages of shear connection 100%	90%	80%	70%	60%	50%	Q_r† for 100% Kips	I_1 In.⁴	S_{s_1} In.³	Steel Shape Data*	
W310X79	74	378	373	367	360	352	344	316	1110	101	M_r	257
W12X53	61	363	359	354	348	341	333	261	1050	99.8	V_r	109
b = 9.99	48	348	345	341	335	329	320	205	980	97.7	L_u	13.5
t = .575	35	333	329	325	319	312	304	149	886	94.7	I_x	425
	22	311	307	302	298	292	287	94.0	762	90.0	S_x	70.5
W310X74	72	361	356	350	343	335	326	308	1060	95.2	M_r	239
W12X50	59	346	342	337	331	324	315	252	1000	93.6	V_r	118
b = 8.08	47	332	328	324	318	311	302	201	936	91.6	L_u	11.0
t = .640	34	316	311	306	300	293	286	145	843	88.6	I_x	394
	22	293	289	285	280	275	269	94.0	730	84.3	S_x	64.6
W310X67	72	330	325	319	313	305	297	308	968	85.9	M_r	214
W12X45	59	316	311	306	301	295	286	252	917	84.5	V_r	106
b = 8.05	47	302	298	294	289	283	275	201	857	82.8	L_u	10.7
t = .575	34	286	283	279	273	267	259	145	774	80.2	I_x	350
	22	266	263	259	254	249	243	94.0	671	76.5	S_x	58.0
W310X60	72	301	296	291	284	277	269	308	880	77.1	M_r	190
W12X40	59	287	283	278	273	267	260	252	835	76.0	V_r	92.1
b = 8.00	47	274	270	266	262	256	249	201	783	74.6	L_u	10.4
t = .515	34	259	256	252	247	242	235	145	709	72.3	I_x	310
	22	241	238	234	229	224	219	94.0	615	69.1	S_x	51.9
W310X52	71	281	276	271	265	258	250	303	839	69.2	M_r	169
W12X35	58	267	263	258	253	247	240	248	798	68.2	V_r	98.0
b = 6.56	46	254	251	247	242	237	230	196	749	67.0	L_u	8.33
t = .520	34	240	238	234	229	224	217	145	685	65.1	I_x	285
	21	221	218	214	210	205	200	89.7	586	61.9	S_x	45.6
W310X45	71	248	244	239	232	226	219	303	729	59.2	M_r	142
W12X30	58	235	231	227	222	216	210	248	695	58.4	V_r	83.9
b = 6.52	46	222	219	215	211	207	201	196	655	57.4	L_u	8.09
t = .440	33	208	205	203	199	194	188	141	596	55.8	I_x	238
	21	192	189	186	182	178	173	89.7	516	53.3	S_x	38.6
W310X39	70	223	219	214	208	202	194	299	642	51.7	M_r	123
W12X26	58	211	207	203	198	193	186	248	617	51.1	V_r	73.5
b = 6.49	46	198	195	192	188	183	178	196	583	50.2	L_u	7.92
t = .380	33	184	182	180	176	172	167	141	533	48.9	I_x	204
	21	170	168	165	161	157	153	89.7	464	46.9	S_x	33.4

†No. of studs/beam = 2 x Q_r x percent shear connection/100/q_r (per stud)
*Units — M_r — Ft. Kips L_u — Ft.   b — In.
   V_r — Kips I_x — In.⁴   t — In.
   S_x — In.³

Note: The SI designation in bold face type is the one preferred for use in Canada.

COMPOSITE BEAMS
Trial Selection Tables

G40.21 – 44W
3 Ksi Concrete

1½ Inch Deck with 2½ Inch Slab
$\phi = 0.90$, $\phi_C = 0.67$, $\phi_{SC} = 0.80$

Steel Shape	b_1	\multicolumn{6}{c}{M_{rc} in foot Kips for various percentages of shear connection}	Q_r† for 100%	I_1	S_{s_1}	\multicolumn{2}{c}{Steel Shape Data*}
	In.	100%	90%	80%	70%	60%	50%	Kips	In.⁴	In.³		
W250X101	74	404	398	391	384	376	366	316	1040	113	M_r	281
W10X68	61	388	383	378	371	364	355	261	976	111	V_r	128
b = 10.13	48	372	368	364	358	350	342	205	900	108	L_u	16.1
t = .770	35	355	351	346	341	334	327	149	807	104	I_x	394
	22	333	329	325	320	316	310	94.0	688	97.9	S_x	75.8
W250X89	74	362	356	350	343	335	326	316	932	100	M_r	246
W10X60	61	347	342	336	330	324	316	261	877	98.3	V_r	112
b = 10.08	48	331	327	323	318	312	304	205	811	95.9	L_u	15.2
t = .680	35	315	312	308	303	297	290	149	728	92.5	I_x	341
	22	295	292	288	284	279	274	94.0	620	87.3	S_x	66.7
W250X80	74	330	325	319	312	304	296	316	851	90.5	M_r	220
W10X54	61	316	311	306	300	294	287	261	803	88.9	V_r	97.6
b = 10.03	48	301	297	293	288	283	276	205	744	86.8	L_u	14.6
t = .615	35	285	283	279	275	269	263	149	669	83.9	I_x	303
	22	267	264	261	257	252	248	94.0	570	79.3	S_x	60.1
W250X73	74	306	301	295	288	281	273	316	785	82.7	M_r	199
W10X49	61	292	287	282	277	270	264	261	743	81.3	V_r	88.7
b = 10.00	48	277	274	269	265	260	254	205	689	79.5	L_u	14.2
t = .560	35	262	259	256	252	247	241	149	620	76.9	I_x	272
	22	245	242	239	235	231	226	94.0	528	72.8	S_x	54.5
W250X67	72	289	284	278	271	264	256	308	740	76.3	M_r	181
W10X45	59	274	270	265	260	253	246	252	699	75.0	V_r	92.4
b = 8.02	47	261	257	253	248	243	236	201	651	73.4	L_u	11.6
t = .620	34	245	243	239	235	230	223	145	585	70.9	I_x	248
	22	229	226	222	218	214	209	94.0	502	67.2	S_x	49.1
W250X58	72	257	252	247	240	233	225	308	650	66.2	M_r	154
W10X39	59	243	239	234	229	223	217	252	616	65.1	V_r	81.7
b = 7.98	47	230	227	223	218	213	208	201	576	63.8	L_u	11.1
t = .530	34	215	213	210	206	201	195	145	519	61.8	I_x	209
	22	200	197	194	191	186	182	94.0	446	58.7	S_x	42.1
W250X49	72	226	221	216	210	203	196	308	557	55.9	M_r	128
W10X33	59	212	209	204	199	193	187	252	529	55.1	V_r	73.7
b = 7.96	47	200	196	193	189	184	179	201	497	54.0	L_u	10.5
t = .435	34	185	183	180	177	173	167	145	450	52.4	I_x	170
	22	171	169	166	163	159	155	94.0	388	49.9	S_x	34.9

†No. of studs/beam = 2 x Q_r x percent shear connection/100/q_r (per stud)

*Units — M_r — Ft. Kips L_u — Ft.   b — In.
    V_r — Kips I_x — In.⁴   t — In.
    S_x — In.³

Note: The SI designation in bold face type is the one preferred for use in Canada.

COMPOSITE BEAMS
Trial Selection Tables

G40.21 – 44W
3 Ksi Concrete

1½ Inch Deck with 2½ Inch Slab
$\emptyset = 0.90$, $\emptyset_C = 0.67$, $\emptyset_{SC} = 0.80$

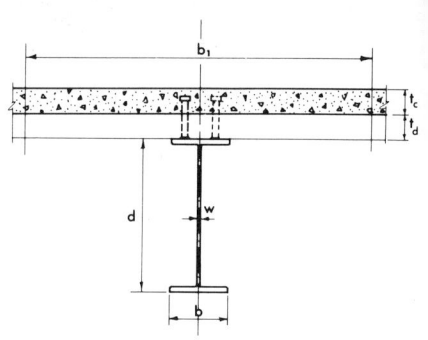

Steel Shape		Composite Beam								Properties		Steel Shape Data*	
			Factored Resistances										
	b_1	M_{rc} in foot Kips for various percentages of shear connection						Q_r† for 100%		I_1	S_{s_1}		
	In.	100%	90%	80%	70%	60%	50%	Kips		In.⁴	In.³		
W250X45	70	221	217	211	205	199	191	299		565	52.8	M_r	121
W10X30	58	209	205	200	195	189	183	248		539	52.1	V_r	82.1
b = 5.81	45	195	191	188	184	179	173	192		504	51.0	L_u	7.63
t = .510	33	181	179	176	172	168	162	141		459	49.5	I_x	170
	21	166	163	160	157	153	149	89.7		394	47.1	S_x	32.5
W250X39	70	198	194	189	183	177	170	299		495	45.7	M_r	103
W10X26	58	186	183	178	173	168	162	248		474	45.1	V_r	70.2
b = 5.77	45	173	170	166	162	158	153	192		444	44.2	L_u	7.38
t = .440	33	160	157	155	152	148	143	141		407	43.0	I_x	144
	21	146	144	141	138	135	130	89.7		351	41.1	S_x	27.9
W250X33	70	172	167	162	157	151	144	257		425	38.9	M_r	85.8
W10X22	58	166	162	158	153	148	142	248		409	38.4	V_r	63.8
b = 5.75	45	153	150	146	143	138	134	192		385	37.7	L_u	7.10
t = .360	33	140	138	135	132	129	124	141		354	36.7	I_x	118
	21	127	125	123	120	116	113	89.7		307	35.1	S_x	23.2
W200X100	72	349	343	336	328	320	311	308		798	98.4	M_r	232
W8X67	60	334	329	323	316	309	300	256		750	96.3	V_r	134
b = 8.28	47	317	313	308	303	296	288	201		686	93.3	L_u	16.3
t = .935	34	300	296	291	286	280	274	145		608	89.1	I_x	272
	22	280	276	273	268	264	259	94.0		516	83.4	S_x	60.4
W200X86	72	309	303	296	289	281	273	308		702	85.8	M_r	197
W8X58	60	294	289	284	278	271	263	256		660	84.1	V_r	117
b = 8.22	47	278	274	270	265	259	251	201		606	81.6	L_u	14.9
t = .810	34	262	259	255	250	244	238	145		538	78.2	I_x	228
	22	244	241	237	233	229	224	94.0		456	73.3	S_x	52.1
W200X71	72	264	259	253	246	239	230	308		596	71.6	M_r	162
W8X48	59	249	245	240	234	228	221	252		560	70.2	V_r	88.9
b = 8.11	47	235	232	228	223	218	212	201		519	68.5	L_u	13.4
t = .685	34	220	217	214	210	206	200	145		463	65.9	I_x	184
	22	205	202	199	196	192	188	94.0		393	62.0	S_x	43.3
W200X59	72	228	223	218	211	204	196	308		502	59.6	M_r	131
W8X40	59	214	210	205	200	194	187	252		474	58.5	V_r	77.6
b = 8.07	47	201	197	193	189	184	179	201		441	57.2	L_u	12.3
t = .560	34	186	183	180	177	173	168	145		395	55.2	I_x	146
	22	172	170	167	164	160	156	94.0		336	52.1	S_x	35.4

†No. of studs/beam = 2 x Q_r x percent shear connection/100/q_r (per stud)

*Units — M_r — Ft. Kips L_u — Ft.   b — In.
        V_r — Kips I_x — In.⁴   t — In.
                S_x — In.³

Note: The SI designation in bold face type is the one preferred for use in Canada.

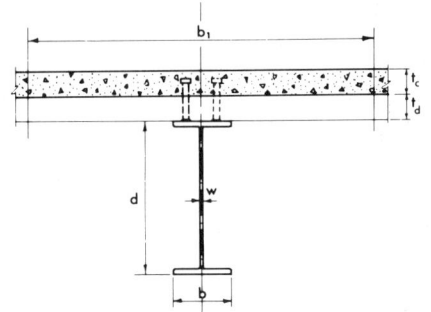

COMPOSITE BEAMS
Trial Selection Tables

G40.21 – 44W
3 Ksi Concrete

1½ Inch Deck with 2½ Inch Slab
$\phi = 0.90$, $\phi_C = 0.67$, $\phi_{SC} = 0.80$

Steel Shape	Composite Beam										Steel Shape Data*	
		Factored Resistances							Properties			
	b_1	M_{rc} in foot Kips for various percentages of shear connection						Q_r† for 100%	I_1	S_{s_1}		
	In.	100%	90%	80%	70%	60%	50%	Kips	In.⁴	In.³		
W200X52	72	208	203	198	192	185	177	308	450	52.8	M_r	115
W8X35	59	194	190	186	180	175	168	252	426	51.9	V_r	65.8
b = 8.02	47	181	178	174	170	165	160	201	398	50.8	L_u	11.7
t = .495	34	167	164	161	158	155	150	145	358	49.1	I_x	127
	22	153	151	149	146	143	139	94.0	306	46.6	S_x	31.3
W200X46	72	191	186	181	175	168	161	308	404	46.9	M_r	100
W8X31	59	177	174	169	164	159	152	252	384	46.2	V_r	59.6
b = 7.99	47	165	162	158	154	149	144	201	359	45.3	L_u	11.3
t = .435	34	151	148	146	143	139	135	145	324	43.8	I_x	110
	22	137	136	134	131	128	124	94.0	278	41.6	S_x	27.5
W200X42	71	179	175	170	164	157	150	303	374	42.6	M_r	89.8
W8X28	58	166	162	158	153	147	141	248	355	41.9	V_r	60.0
b = 6.53	46	153	150	147	143	138	133	196	333	41.0	L_u	9.27
t = .465	34	140	138	135	132	129	125	145	303	39.8	I_x	98.0
	21	126	124	122	119	116	113	89.7	256	37.6	S_x	24.3
W200X36	70	159	155	150	144	138	131	280	325	36.7	M_r	76.6
W8X24	58	149	146	142	137	131	125	248	311	36.2	V_r	50.8
b = 6.49	46	137	134	131	127	122	118	196	293	35.5	L_u	8.86
t = .400	33	123	121	119	116	112	109	141	266	34.5	I_x	82.8
	21	110	109	107	105	102	98.9	89.7	228	32.8	S_x	20.9
W200X31	69	144	140	136	130	124	118	244	305	32.7	M_r	67.3
W8X21	57	140	137	133	128	123	117	243	293	32.3	V_r	54.1
b = 5.27	45	128	125	122	118	114	109	192	276	31.7	L_u	6.98
t = .400	33	115	113	111	108	105	101	141	253	30.8	I_x	75.3
	21	102	101	99.1	96.8	94.0	90.7	89.7	219	29.4	S_x	18.2
W200X27	69	125	121	116	111	106	100	208	263	28.0	M_r	56.1
W8X18	57	122	118	114	110	105	99.6	208	253	27.6	V_r	48.9
b = 5.25	45	115	112	109	105	101	96.4	192	239	27.1	L_u	6.70
t = .330	33	102	100	97.9	95.1	92.0	88.6	141	221	26.4	I_x	61.9
	21	89.8	88.4	86.7	84.7	82.2	79.1	89.7	192	25.2	S_x	15.2

†No. of studs/beam = 2 x Q_r x percent shear connection/100/q_r (per stud)
*Units — M_r — Ft. Kips L_u — Ft.   b — In.
       V_r — Kips I_x — In.⁴   t — In.
               S_x — In.³

Note: The SI designation in bold face type is the one preferred for use in Canada.

COMPOSITE BEAMS
Trial Selection Tables

G40.21 – 44W
3 Ksi Concrete

2 Inch Deck with 2½ Inch Slab
$\varnothing = 0.90$, $\varnothing_C = 0.67$, $\varnothing_{SC} = 0.80$

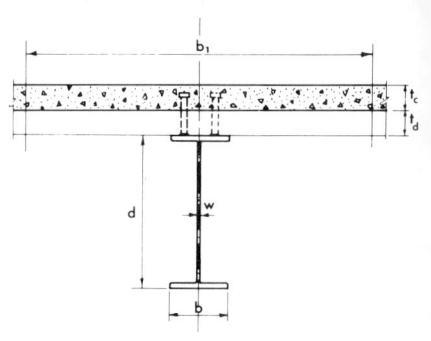

Steel Shape	b₁	Mrc in foot Kips for various percentages of shear connection						Qr† for 100%	I₁	Ss₁	Steel Shape Data*	
		100%	90%	80%	70%	60%	50%	Kips				
	In.	100%	90%	80%	70%	60%	50%	Kips	In.⁴	In.³		
W610X241	85	1920	1890	1860	1830	1800	1760	363	9050	513	Mr	1540
W24X162	70	1860	1840	1810	1790	1760	1720	299	8560	503	Vr	461
b = 12.95	55	1810	1780	1760	1740	1710	1690	235	8000	492	Lu	16.9
t = 1.22	40	1740	1720	1710	1690	1670	1650	171	7370	478	Ix	5170
	25	1670	1660	1650	1630	1620	1610	107	6650	460	Sx	414
W610X217	85	1740	1720	1690	1660	1630	1590	363	8260	463	Mr	1380
W24X146	70	1690	1670	1640	1620	1590	1560	299	7810	455	Vr	420
b = 12.90	55	1630	1610	1590	1570	1550	1520	235	7300	445	Lu	16.5
t = 1.09	40	1570	1550	1540	1520	1500	1480	171	6700	432	Ix	4580
	25	1500	1490	1480	1470	1450	1440	107	6020	415	Sx	370
W610X195	85	1570	1550	1520	1490	1460	1430	363	7500	415	Mr	1220
W24X131	70	1520	1500	1480	1450	1420	1390	299	7090	408	Vr	387
b = 12.85	55	1470	1450	1430	1410	1380	1360	235	6610	399	Lu	16.1
t = .960	40	1410	1390	1380	1360	1340	1320	171	6060	387	Ix	4020
	25	1340	1330	1320	1310	1290	1280	107	5410	371	Sx	328
W610X174	85	1420	1400	1370	1350	1320	1290	363	6820	373	Mr	1080
W24X117	70	1370	1350	1330	1310	1280	1250	299	6450	366	Vr	349
b = 12.80	55	1320	1310	1290	1260	1240	1220	235	6010	358	Lu	15.7
t = .850	40	1270	1250	1230	1220	1200	1180	171	5500	348	Ix	3540
	25	1200	1190	1180	1170	1150	1140	107	4890	333	Sx	292
W610X155	85	1270	1260	1240	1210	1190	1150	363	6190	333	Mr	954
W24X104	70	1240	1220	1200	1180	1150	1120	299	5850	327	Vr	314
b = 12.75	55	1190	1170	1150	1130	1110	1090	235	5450	320	Lu	15.4
t = .750	40	1140	1120	1100	1090	1070	1050	171	4980	310	Ix	3100
	25	1070	1060	1050	1040	1030	1010	107	4400	297	Sx	258
W610X140	81	1160	1140	1120	1090	1060	1030	346	5620	296	Mr	838
W24X94	67	1120	1100	1080	1060	1030	1000	286	5320	291	Vr	327
b = 9.06	53	1070	1050	1040	1010	993	969	226	4960	284	Lu	10.8
t = .875	39	1020	1000	987	971	953	935	167	4530	276	Ix	2700
	24	952	942	931	920	908	896	103	3960	262	Sx	222
W610X125	81	1050	1030	1010	987	961	931	346	5110	265	Mr	739
W24X84	67	1010	994	974	952	928	902	286	4830	261	Vr	296
b = 9.02	53	967	951	933	914	893	870	226	4510	255	Lu	10.6
t = .770	38	912	899	884	868	851	834	162	4080	246	Ix	2370
	24	853	843	832	821	810	798	103	3580	235	Sx	197

†No. of studs/beam = 2 x Qr x percent shear connection/100/qr (per stud)
*Units — Mr — Ft. Kips   Lu — Ft.   b — In.
          Vr — Kips   Ix — In.⁴   t — In.
                     Sx — In.³

Note: The SI designation in bold face type is the one preferred for use in Canada.

2 Inch Deck with 2½ Inch Slab
$\phi = 0.90$, $\phi_C = 0.67$, $\phi_{SC} = 0.80$

Steel Shape	b_1	M_{rc} in foot Kips for various percentages of shear connection						Q_r† for 100%	I_1	S_{s_1}	Steel Shape Data*	
	In.	100%	90%	80%	70%	60%	50%	Kips	In.⁴	In.³		
W610X113	81	957	943	925	904	879	850	346	4680	240	M_r	660
W24X76	67	925	909	891	870	847	821	286	4430	236	V_r	275
b = 8.99	53	884	869	852	833	812	790	226	4140	231	L_u	10.4
t = .680	38	831	818	804	788	772	755	162	3740	223	I_x	2100
	24	773	763	753	742	731	719	103	3270	213	S_x	176
W610X101	81	867	855	839	819	795	768	346	4240	215	M_r	584
W24X68	67	839	824	807	788	765	740	286	4020	211	V_r	257
b = 8.97	53	801	786	770	752	732	710	226	3760	207	L_u	10.1
t = .585	38	750	737	723	708	692	675	162	3400	200	I_x	1830
	24	693	684	673	663	652	640	103	2960	190	S_x	154
W530X138	80	1020	1000	983	960	935	906	342	4480	263	M_r	729
W21X93	66	983	966	947	926	903	878	282	4220	258	V_r	328
b = 8.42	52	940	924	907	889	869	848	222	3920	251	L_u	10.3
t = .930	38	890	877	863	848	832	816	162	3560	242	I_x	2070
	24	833	824	814	804	793	782	103	3120	230	S_x	191
W530X123	80	923	909	891	871	847	820	342	4080	236	M_r	647
W21X83	66	891	876	858	839	817	793	282	3850	231	V_r	288
b = 8.35	52	851	836	821	803	784	764	222	3580	226	L_u	10.1
t = .835	38	804	792	778	764	749	733	162	3250	218	I_x	1830
	24	750	741	731	721	711	700	103	2840	208	S_x	171
W530X109	80	829	818	803	785	763	738	342	3690	210	M_r	568
W21X73	66	802	789	773	755	735	712	282	3490	206	V_r	253
b = 8.30	52	766	753	738	722	704	684	222	3250	201	L_u	9.89
t = .740	38	722	711	698	684	670	654	162	2950	195	I_x	1600
	24	670	662	652	643	633	622	103	2570	185	S_x	151
W530X101	80	777	767	754	738	717	693	342	3480	196	M_r	528
W21X68	66	753	741	727	710	690	668	282	3300	193	V_r	237
b = 8.27	52	720	707	693	678	660	641	222	3070	188	L_u	9.74
t = .685	38	678	667	654	641	627	612	162	2790	182	I_x	1480
	24	628	619	610	600	590	580	103	2420	173	S_x	140
W530X92	80	717	709	697	682	663	640	342	3220	179	M_r	475
W21X62	66	695	685	672	656	637	616	282	3050	176	V_r	219
b = 8.24	52	665	653	640	625	608	589	222	2840	173	L_u	9.59
t = .615	38	625	614	602	589	575	560	162	2580	167	I_x	1330
	24	576	567	558	549	539	529	103	2240	159	S_x	127

†No. of studs/beam = 2 x Q_r x percent shear connection/100/q_r (per stud)
*Units — M_r — Ft. Kips L_u — Ft. b — In.
 V_r — Kips I_x — In.⁴ t — In.
 S_x — In.³

Note: The SI designation in bold face type is the one preferred for use in Canada.

COMPOSITE BEAMS
Trial Selection Tables

G40.21 – 44W
3 Ksi Concrete

2 Inch Deck with 2½ Inch Slab
$\emptyset = 0.90$, $\emptyset_C = 0.67$, $\emptyset_{SC} = 0.80$

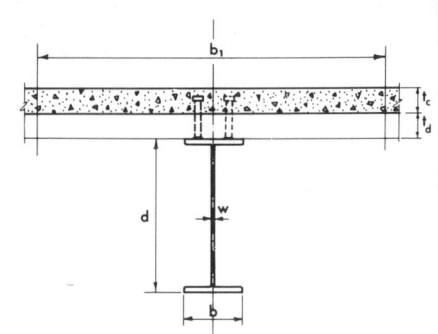

Steel Shape	b_1	Composite Beam									Steel Shape Data*	
		Factored Resistances							Properties			
		M_{rc} in foot Kips for various percentages of shear connection						$Q_r^\dagger$ for 100%	I_1	S_{S_1}		
	In.	100%	90%	80%	70%	60%	50%	Kips	In.⁴	In.³		
W530X82	80	646	639	629	615	598	576	342	2900	159	M_r	416
W21X55	66	627	617	605	590	573	552	282	2750	157	V_r	204
b = 8.22	52	599	588	575	561	544	526	222	2570	153	L_u	9.31
t = .522	38	561	550	539	526	513	498	162	2330	149	I_x	1150
	24	513	505	496	487	477	467	103	2020	141	S_x	111
W460X106	80	710	701	689	674	655	633	342	2840	182	M_r	478
W18X71	66	687	677	663	648	630	610	282	2680	179	V_r	239
b = 7.64	52	657	646	633	619	603	586	222	2490	174	L_u	9.51
t = .810	38	619	608	597	585	573	559	162	2250	168	I_x	1170
	24	573	565	557	549	540	530	103	1950	159	S_x	127
W460X97	80	659	651	641	627	610	590	342	2650	168	M_r	439
W18X65	66	638	629	618	603	587	568	282	2510	165	V_r	216
b = 7.59	52	611	601	589	575	560	544	222	2330	161	L_u	9.35
t = .750	38	575	566	555	543	531	518	162	2110	156	I_x	1070
	24	531	524	516	507	499	489	103	1820	148	S_x	117
W460X89	80	613	606	597	585	570	551	342	2480	156	M_r	406
W18X60	66	594	586	576	564	548	530	282	2350	153	V_r	198
b = 7.56	52	570	561	550	537	523	507	222	2190	150	L_u	9.20
t = .695	38	537	528	518	507	495	482	162	1990	145	I_x	984
	24	495	488	480	472	463	454	103	1720	138	S_x	108
W460X82	80	570	563	554	544	530	512	342	2310	143	M_r	370
W18X55	66	551	545	536	524	509	492	282	2190	141	V_r	185
b = 7.53	52	530	521	511	499	485	470	222	2040	138	L_u	9.02
t = .630	38	498	490	480	469	458	445	162	1850	134	I_x	890
	24	457	450	443	435	426	417	103	1600	127	S_x	98.3
W460X74	79	524	516	508	499	487	471	337	2120	130	M_r	333
W18X50	66	506	500	493	482	469	453	282	2020	129	V_r	167
b = 7.49	52	487	480	470	459	447	432	222	1890	126	L_u	8.89
t = .570	38	459	451	441	431	420	407	162	1720	122	I_x	800
	24	420	413	406	398	390	381	103	1480	116	S_x	88.9
W460X67	79	484	477	469	460	449	434	337	1950	119	M_r	301
W18X45	66	467	461	454	445	432	416	282	1870	117	V_r	156
b = 7.48	52	448	442	433	422	410	395	222	1750	115	L_u	8.65
t = .499	38	421	414	405	395	384	371	162	1590	112	I_x	719
	24	383	377	370	362	353	345	103	1370	106	S_x	80.5

†No. of studs/beam = 2 x Q_r x percent shear connection/100/q_r (per stud)

*Units — M_r — Ft. Kips L_u — Ft.   b — In.
   V_r — Kips I_x — In.⁴   t — In.
         S_x — In.³

Note: The SI designation in bold face type is the one preferred for use in Canada.

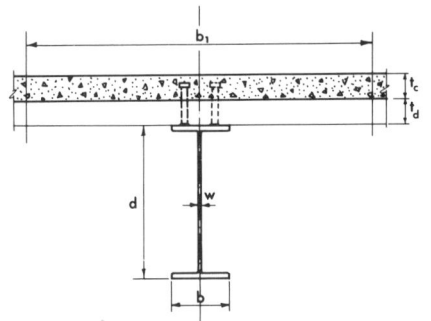

COMPOSITE BEAMS
Trial Selection Tables

G40.21 – 44W
3 Ksi Concrete

2 Inch Deck with 2½ Inch Slab
$\phi = 0.90$, $\phi_C = 0.67$, $\phi_{SC} = 0.80$

Steel Shape		Composite Beam								Properties		Steel Shape Data*	
		Factored Resistances											
	b_1	M_{rc} in foot Kips for various percentages of shear connection						Q_r† for 100%		I_1	S_{s_1}		
	In.	100%	90%	80%	70%	60%	50%	Kips		In.⁴	In.³		
W460X61	79	443	437	429	421	410	395	337		1770	107	M_r	264
W18X41	66	427	421	415	406	394	379	282		1690	105	V_r	148
b = 7.45	52	409	403	395	385	372	358	222		1590	103	L_u	8.40
t = .425	38	383	376	367	358	347	334	162		1440	100	I_x	623
	24	346	340	332	325	316	308	103		1250	95.3	S_x	70.4
W410X85	79	539	531	523	512	499	482	337		2010	137	M_r	346
W16X57	65	520	513	504	492	479	462	278		1900	135	V_r	185
b = 7.12	51	497	489	480	468	455	441	218		1760	132	L_u	8.91
t = .715	38	469	461	452	442	431	419	162		1600	128	I_x	758
	24	431	424	417	409	401	393	103		1380	121	S_x	92.3
W410X74	79	481	474	466	457	446	431	337		1800	121	M_r	304
W16X50	65	463	456	449	440	428	414	278		1710	119	V_r	161
b = 7.07	51	443	437	429	419	407	394	218		1590	116	L_u	8.67
t = .630	38	419	412	404	395	385	373	162		1450	113	I_x	659
	24	384	378	371	364	357	348	103		1250	107	S_x	81.1
W410X67	79	443	436	428	419	409	396	337		1650	110	M_r	272
W16X45	65	425	419	412	404	393	380	278		1570	108	V_r	145
b = 7.03	51	406	401	393	384	373	361	218		1460	106	L_u	8.50
t = .565	38	384	378	370	361	352	340	162		1340	103	I_x	586
	24	351	345	339	332	324	316	103		1150	97.5	S_x	72.7
W410X60	79	402	395	388	379	370	359	337		1490	97.8	M_r	241
W16X40	65	384	378	372	365	356	344	278		1420	96.5	V_r	128
b = 6.99	51	366	361	356	348	339	327	218		1330	94.6	L_u	8.38
t = .505	38	348	342	335	328	318	308	162		1220	92.1	I_x	518
	24	317	312	306	299	292	285	103		1050	87.7	S_x	64.7
W410X54	79	368	362	354	346	337	327	337		1350	87.3	M_r	211
W16X36	65	351	345	339	332	324	313	278		1290	86.2	V_r	122
b = 6.98	51	333	329	324	317	307	296	218		1210	84.5	L_u	8.14
t = .430	38	316	311	304	297	288	278	162		1110	82.3	I_x	448
	24	287	281	276	269	262	254	103		956	78.5	S_x	56.5
W410X46	78	329	323	316	308	299	289	333		1180	75.1	M_r	178
W16X31	64	312	307	301	294	286	276	273		1130	74.2	V_r	114
b = 5.52	50	295	290	285	279	271	260	214		1070	72.8	L_u	6.31
t = .440	37	278	273	267	260	252	242	158		979	70.9	I_x	375
	23	250	245	239	233	227	220	98.2		843	67.5	S_x	47.2

†No. of studs/beam = 2 x Q_r x percent shear connection/100/q_r (per stud)

*Units — M_r — Ft. Kips L_u — Ft.   b — In.
 V_r — Kips I_x — In.⁴   t — In.
                       S_x — In.³

Note: The SI designation in bold face type is the one preferred for use in Canada.

COMPOSITE BEAMS
Trial Selection Tables

G40.21 – 44W
3 Ksi Concrete

2 Inch Deck with 2½ Inch Slab
$\emptyset = 0.90$, $\emptyset_C = 0.67$, $\emptyset_{SC} = 0.80$

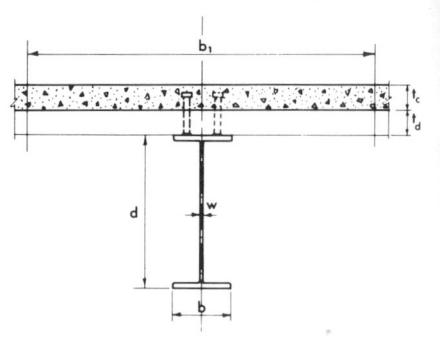

Steel Shape	b_1	Composite Beam								Properties		Steel Shape Data*	
		Factored Resistances											
		M_{rc} in foot Kips for various percentages of shear connection						Q_r† for 100%	I_1	S_{s_1}		
	In.	100%	90%	80%	70%	60%	50%	Kips	In.⁴	In.³		
W410X39	78	284	278	271	264	255	246	304	1010	62.9	M_r	146
W16X26	64	273	268	262	255	248	240	273	966	62.2	V_r	99.1
b = 5.50	50	256	252	247	242	235	225	214	912	61.1	L_u	6.05
t = .345	37	240	236	231	225	217	208	158	843	59.6	I_x	301
	23	215	211	206	200	193	186	98.2	729	56.8	S_x	38.4
W360X79	80	446	439	430	421	411	400	342	1500	116	M_r	287
W14X53	66	427	421	414	406	397	385	282	1420	114	V_r	135
b = 8.06	52	408	403	397	389	379	368	222	1320	112	L_u	10.6
t = .660	38	387	381	375	367	358	348	162	1190	108	I_x	541
	24	357	351	346	339	333	325	103	1020	103	S_x	77.7
W360X72	80	410	403	395	386	377	366	342	1380	106	M_r	259
W14X48	66	392	386	379	372	364	353	282	1310	104	V_r	123
b = 8.03	52	374	369	363	356	347	337	222	1220	102	L_u	10.4
t = .595	38	354	349	343	336	327	318	162	1100	98.7	I_x	485
	24	326	321	316	310	303	296	103	948	93.8	S_x	70.3
W360X64	80	375	368	360	352	342	332	342	1250	94.6	M_r	230
W14X43	66	357	351	345	338	330	320	282	1190	93.3	V_r	109
b = 7.99	52	339	334	329	323	315	305	222	1110	91.5	L_u	10.1
t = .530	38	320	316	311	304	297	287	162	1010	88.8	I_x	428
	24	295	291	285	280	273	266	103	868	84.6	S_x	62.7
W360X57	79	351	344	337	329	319	309	337	1180	85.2	M_r	203
W14X38	65	334	328	322	314	307	297	278	1120	84.0	V_r	114
b = 6.77	51	316	311	306	300	292	282	218	1050	82.3	L_u	8.32
t = .515	37	297	292	287	280	272	263	158	953	79.9	I_x	385
	24	272	268	263	257	250	243	103	826	76.2	S_x	54.6
W360X51	79	322	315	308	300	291	281	337	1070	76.3	M_r	180
W14X34	65	305	299	293	286	279	270	278	1020	75.3	V_r	104
b = 6.74	51	287	283	278	272	265	256	218	957	73.9	L_u	8.16
t = .455	37	269	265	261	255	247	239	158	871	71.8	I_x	340
	24	247	243	238	232	226	220	103	758	68.7	S_x	48.6
W360X45	79	293	287	280	272	264	254	337	951	67.3	M_r	156
W14X30	65	277	272	266	259	252	243	278	910	66.5	V_r	97.7
b = 6.73	51	260	255	250	245	239	230	218	857	65.3	L_u	7.93
t = .385	37	242	239	234	229	222	214	158	783	63.5	I_x	291
	24	222	218	213	208	202	195	103	683	60.8	S_x	42.1

†No. of studs/beam = 2 x Q_r x percent shear connection/100/q_r (per stud)

*Units — M_r — Ft. Kips L_u — Ft.   b — In.
        V_r — Kips I_x — In.⁴   t — In.
                     S_x — In.³

Note: The SI designation in bold face type is the one preferred for use in Canada.

2 Inch Deck with 2½ Inch Slab
$\phi = 0.90$, $\phi_C = 0.67$, $\phi_{SC} = 0.80$

Steel Shape	b_1	Composite Beam									Steel Shape Data*	
		Factored Resistances							Properties			
		M_{rc} in foot Kips for various percentages of shear connection						$Q_r{}^\dagger$ for 100%	I_1	S_{s_1}		
	In.	100%	90%	80%	70%	60%	50%	Kips	In.⁴	In.³		
W360X39	77	261	255	249	241	233	224	305	842	58.4	M_r	133
W14X26	64	250	245	240	233	226	218	273	810	57.7	V_r	92.7
b = 5.02	50	233	229	224	219	213	205	214	764	56.7	L_u	5.83
t = .420	37	217	214	210	205	198	190	158	704	55.3	I_x	245
	23	196	192	187	182	176	170	98.2	608	52.7	S_x	35.2
W360X33	77	223	217	211	204	196	188	257	717	49.1	M_r	110
W14X22	64	218	213	208	202	195	187	257	692	48.6	V_r	82.6
b = 5.00	50	205	201	196	191	185	179	214	656	47.8	L_u	5.60
t = .335	37	189	186	182	178	172	165	158	608	46.7	I_x	199
	23	170	166	162	157	152	146	98.2	529	44.6	S_x	29.0
W310X129	84	608	599	590	580	568	554	359	1850	172	M_r	436
W12X87	69	587	580	572	562	551	537	295	1730	168	V_r	169
b = 12.13	55	567	560	552	543	532	519	235	1600	164	L_u	18.1
t = .810	40	541	534	526	518	508	497	171	1440	158	I_x	740
	25	506	501	495	488	481	474	107	1230	149	S_x	118
W310X118	84	557	549	540	530	520	507	359	1700	156	M_r	393
W12X79	69	537	530	522	514	504	491	295	1600	153	V_r	152
b = 12.08	55	517	512	505	496	486	474	235	1480	150	L_u	17.5
t = .735	40	494	488	480	472	463	453	171	1330	144	I_x	662
	25	461	456	450	444	437	430	107	1130	136	S_x	107
W310X107	84	514	506	497	487	477	465	359	1570	143	M_r	356
W12X72	69	494	487	480	472	462	451	295	1480	140	V_r	138
b = 12.04	55	474	469	463	455	446	434	235	1370	137	L_u	17.0
t = .670	40	453	447	441	433	425	415	171	1230	132	I_x	597
	25	423	418	412	406	400	393	107	1050	125	S_x	97.5
W310X97	84	472	465	456	447	436	425	359	1450	130	M_r	290
W12X65	69	452	446	439	431	422	412	295	1360	128	V_r	124
b = 12.00	55	434	428	423	416	407	397	235	1270	125	L_u	17.5
t = .605	40	413	408	402	395	387	378	171	1140	121	I_x	533
	25	385	380	375	369	363	356	107	971	114	S_x	88.0
W310X86	82	431	424	416	406	396	385	350	1330	117	M_r	285
W12X58	68	413	407	399	392	383	374	290	1260	115	V_r	115
b = 10.01	53	393	388	382	376	368	358	226	1160	112	L_u	13.9
t = .640	39	374	369	364	357	350	341	167	1050	109	I_x	475
	25	349	345	340	334	328	321	107	903	103	S_x	77.9

†No. of studs/beam = 2 x Q_r x percent shear connection/100/q_r (per stud)

*Units — M_r — Ft. Kips $\qquad$ L_u — Ft. $\qquad$ b — In.
$\qquad\quad$ V_r — Kips $\qquad\qquad$ I_x — In.⁴ $\qquad\quad$ t — In.
$\qquad\qquad\qquad\qquad\qquad$ S_x — In.³

Note: The SI designation in bold face type is the one preferred for use in Canada.

COMPOSITE BEAMS
Trial Selection Tables

G40.21 – 44W
3 Ksi Concrete

2 Inch Deck with 2½ Inch Slab
$\emptyset = 0.90$, $\emptyset_C = 0.67$, $\emptyset_{SC} = 0.80$

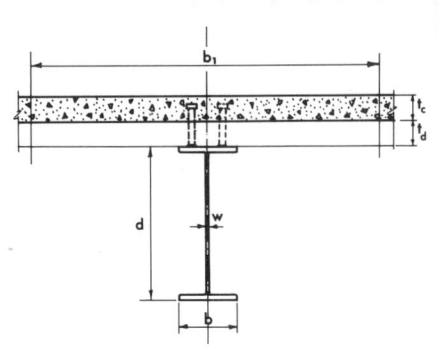

Steel Shape	b₁	Composite Beam — Factored Resistances — M_{rc} in foot Kips for various percentages of shear connection						Q_r† for 100%	Properties I_1	S_{s_1}	Steel Shape Data*	
	In.	100%	90%	80%	70%	60%	50%	Kips	In.⁴	In.³		
W310X79	82	402	394	386	377	367	357	350	1230	107	M_r	257
W12X53	68	383	377	370	363	355	345	290	1160	105	V_r	109
b = 9.99	53	364	359	353	347	340	330	226	1080	103	L_u	13.5
t = .575	39	345	341	336	329	322	313	167	974	99.6	I_x	425
	25	321	317	312	306	300	293	107	836	94.5	S_x	70.5
W310X74	80	384	377	369	360	350	340	342	1170	100	M_r	239
W12X50	66	366	360	353	346	337	327	282	1110	98.7	V_r	118
b = 8.08	52	347	342	337	330	322	312	222	1030	96.5	L_u	11.0
t = .640	38	328	323	318	311	303	294	162	929	93.4	I_x	394
	24	302	297	292	287	281	274	103	792	88.3	S_x	64.6
W310X67	80	353	346	338	330	320	310	342	1070	90.5	M_r	214
W12X45	66	335	329	323	315	307	298	282	1010	89.2	V_r	106
b = 8.05	52	317	312	307	301	294	284	222	945	87.3	L_u	10.7
t = .575	38	298	294	289	283	276	268	162	855	84.6	I_x	350
	24	275	270	266	260	255	248	103	730	80.2	S_x	58.0
W310X60	80	324	317	310	301	292	282	342	972	81.3	M_r	190
W12X40	66	307	301	294	287	279	271	282	925	80.2	V_r	92.1
b = 8.00	52	289	284	279	273	267	258	222	864	78.6	L_u	10.4
t = .515	38	270	267	263	257	251	243	162	784	76.3	I_x	310
	24	249	245	241	236	230	224	103	671	72.5	S_x	51.9
W310X52	79	303	297	290	281	272	262	337	925	73.0	M_r	169
W12X35	65	286	281	274	267	260	251	278	882	72.0	V_r	98.0
b = 6.56	51	269	264	259	253	247	239	218	826	70.6	L_u	8.33
t = .520	37	250	247	243	238	231	224	158	750	68.5	I_x	285
	24	231	227	223	218	212	206	103	649	65.3	S_x	45.6
W310X45	79	270	264	257	249	241	231	337	803	62.4	M_r	142
W12X30	65	254	248	242	236	228	220	278	768	61.6	V_r	83.9
b = 6.52	51	237	232	227	222	216	209	218	723	60.5	L_u	8.09
t = .440	37	219	216	212	208	202	195	158	660	58.9	I_x	238
	24	201	198	194	190	185	179	103	574	56.3	S_x	38.6
W310X39	78	239	233	226	219	211	202	303	708	54.5	M_r	123
W12X26	65	229	224	218	212	205	197	278	681	53.9	V_r	73.5
b = 6.49	51	213	208	204	198	193	186	218	643	53.0	L_u	7.92
t = .380	37	195	192	189	185	180	174	158	590	51.6	I_x	204
	24	179	176	173	169	164	159	103	516	49.5	S_x	33.4

†No. of studs/beam = 2 x Q_r x percent shear connection/100/q_r (per stud)

*Units — M_r — Ft. Kips L_u — Ft.   b — In.
       V_r — Kips I_x — In.⁴   t — In.
                   S_x — In.³

Note: The SI designation in bold face type is the one preferred for use in Canada.

2 Inch Deck with 2½ Inch Slab
$\phi = 0.90, \phi_C = 0.67, \phi_{SC} = 0.80$

Steel Shape	b_1	Mrc in foot Kips for various percentages of shear connection						Q_r† for 100%	I_1	S_{s_1}	Steel Shape Data*	
		100%	90%	80%	70%	60%	50%					
	In.							Kips	In.⁴	In.³		
W250X101	82	428	420	411	402	391	380	350	1160	120	M_r	281
W10X68	68	409	402	395	387	378	367	290	1090	118	V_r	128
b = 10.13	53	388	383	377	370	362	352	226	1000	114	L_u	16.1
t = .770	39	368	363	358	351	344	335	167	895	110	I_x	394
	25	343	339	334	328	323	317	107	760	103	S_x	75.8
W250X89	82	385	378	369	360	350	339	350	1040	106	M_r	246
W10X60	68	367	360	353	345	337	328	290	981	104	V_r	112
b = 10.08	53	347	341	336	330	322	314	226	902	102	L_u	15.2
t = .680	39	327	323	319	313	306	298	167	809	98.0	I_x	341
	25	305	301	297	292	286	280	107	687	92.4	S_x	66.7
W250X80	82	354	347	339	330	320	309	350	951	96.1	M_r	220
W10X54	68	336	330	323	315	307	298	290	899	94.4	V_r	97.6
b = 10.03	53	316	311	305	299	293	285	226	829	92.1	L_u	14.6
t = .615	39	297	293	289	284	278	271	167	745	89.0	I_x	303
	25	277	273	269	264	259	254	107	634	84.0	S_x	60.1
W250X73	82	329	322	314	306	296	285	350	878	87.8	M_r	199
W10X49	68	312	306	299	291	283	275	290	831	86.4	V_r	88.7
b = 10.00	53	292	287	282	276	270	262	226	769	84.4	L_u	14.2
t = .560	39	274	270	266	261	256	249	167	692	81.6	I_x	272
	25	254	251	247	243	238	232	107	589	77.2	S_x	54.5
W250X67	80	312	305	297	288	279	269	342	828	81.2	M_r	181
W10X45	66	294	288	281	274	266	257	282	784	79.8	V_r	92.4
b = 8.02	52	276	271	265	260	253	245	222	728	78.0	L_u	11.6
t = .620	38	257	253	249	244	238	231	162	654	75.4	I_x	248
	24	236	233	229	224	219	214	103	553	71.1	S_x	49.1
W250X58	80	280	273	266	257	248	238	342	728	70.4	M_r	154
W10X39	66	263	257	251	243	236	227	282	691	69.3	V_r	81.7
b = 7.98	52	245	240	235	229	223	216	222	644	67.9	L_u	11.1
t = .530	38	227	223	219	215	209	203	162	581	65.7	I_x	209
	24	207	204	201	196	192	186	103	493	62.2	S_x	42.1
W250X49	80	248	242	235	227	218	208	342	624	59.5	M_r	128
W10X33	66	232	226	220	213	206	197	282	594	58.7	V_r	73.7
b = 7.96	52	214	210	205	199	193	187	222	557	57.5	L_u	10.5
t = .435	38	197	193	189	185	181	175	162	505	55.8	I_x	170
	24	178	176	172	169	164	159	103	431	53.0	S_x	34.9

†No. of studs/beam = 2 x Q_r x percent shear connection/100/q_r (per stud)
*Units — M_r — Ft. Kips L_u — Ft. b — In.
  V_r — Kips I_x — In.⁴ t — In.
  S_x — In.³

Note: The SI designation in bold face type is the one preferred for use in Canada.

COMPOSITE BEAMS
Trial Selection Tables

G40.21 – 44W
3 Ksi Concrete

2 Inch Deck with 2½ Inch Slab
$\emptyset = 0.90$, $\emptyset_C = 0.67$, $\emptyset_{SC} = 0.80$

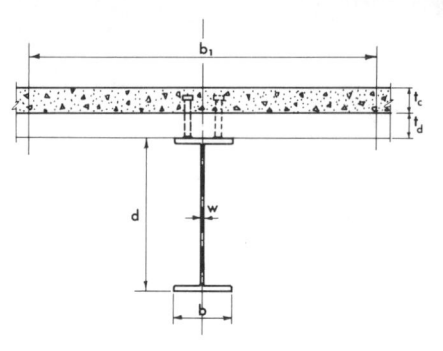

Steel Shape	Composite Beam										Steel Shape Data*	
		Factored Resistances							Properties			
	b_1	M_{rc} in foot Kips for various percentages of shear connection						Q_r† for 100%	I_1	S_{s_1}		
	In.	100%	90%	80%	70%	60%	50%	Kips	In.⁴	In.³		
W250X45	78	243	237	230	222	213	203	333	630	56.2	M_r	121
W10X30	64	226	221	215	208	201	193	273	601	55.3	V_r	82.1
b = 5.81	51	210	206	201	195	189	183	218	566	54.3	L_u	7.63
t = .510	37	192	189	185	181	176	169	158	514	52.7	I_x	170
	23	173	170	167	163	158	153	98.2	437	49.9	S_x	32.5
W250X39	78	214	208	202	194	186	177	301	552	48.6	M_r	103
W10X26	64	204	199	193	186	179	171	273	528	47.9	V_r	70.2
b = 5.77	51	188	184	179	174	168	162	218	499	47.1	L_u	7.38
t = .440	37	171	167	164	160	155	150	158	456	45.8	I_x	144
	23	153	150	147	144	139	135	98.2	390	43.6	S_x	27.9
W250X33	78	185	179	173	166	158	150	257	474	41.4	M_r	85.8
W10X22	64	180	175	170	163	157	149	257	456	40.8	V_r	63.8
b = 5.75	51	168	164	159	154	148	142	218	432	40.2	L_u	7.10
t = .360	37	151	148	144	140	136	131	158	397	39.1	I_x	118
	23	133	131	128	125	121	117	98.2	343	37.3	S_x	23.2
W200X100	80	373	365	356	346	336	324	342	904	106	M_r	232
W8X67	66	353	346	339	331	322	312	282	846	103	V_r	134
b = 8.28	52	333	327	321	315	307	297	222	774	100	L_u	16.3
t = .935	38	312	308	302	296	289	281	162	685	95.5	I_x	272
	24	288	284	279	275	269	264	103	570	88.6	S_x	60.4
W200X86	80	332	325	316	307	297	286	342	796	92.1	M_r	197
W8X58	66	313	307	300	292	283	274	282	747	90.2	V_r	117
b = 8.22	52	294	289	283	276	269	261	222	685	87.6	L_u	14.9
t = .810	38	274	270	265	260	253	246	162	608	83.9	I_x	228
	24	251	248	244	239	234	229	103	506	78.1	S_x	52.1
W200X71	80	287	280	272	263	254	243	342	677	76.9	M_r	162
W8X48	66	269	263	256	249	241	232	282	638	75.4	V_r	88.9
b = 8.11	52	251	246	240	234	228	221	222	589	73.5	L_u	13.4
t = .685	38	232	228	224	219	214	207	162	525	70.7	I_x	184
	24	212	209	205	201	197	192	103	438	66.2	S_x	43.3
W200X59	80	251	244	237	228	219	209	342	571	64.0	M_r	131
W8X40	66	233	228	221	214	206	198	282	541	62.9	V_r	77.6
b = 8.07	52	216	211	206	200	194	187	222	502	61.5	L_u	12.3
t = .560	38	197	194	190	186	181	175	162	450	59.3	I_x	146
	24	179	176	173	169	165	161	103	377	55.8	S_x	35.4

†No. of studs/beam = 2 x Q_r x percent shear connection/100/q_r (per stud)
*Units — M_r — Ft. Kips L_u — Ft.   b — In.
         V_r — Kips I_x — In.⁴   t — In.
                   S_x — In.³

Note: The SI designation in bold face type is the one preferred for use in Canada.

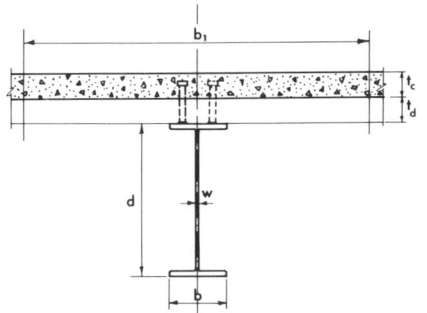

COMPOSITE BEAMS
Trial Selection Tables

G40.21 – 44W
3 Ksi Concrete

2 Inch Deck with 2½ Inch Slab
$\phi = 0.90, \phi_C = 0.67, \phi_{SC} = 0.80$

Steel Shape		Composite Beam										Steel Shape Data*	
		Factored Resistances								Properties			
	b_1	M_{rc} in foot Kips for various percentages of shear connection						$Q_r^\dagger$ for 100%	I_1	S_{s_1}		
	In.	100%	90%	80%	70%	60%	50%	Kips	In.⁴	In.³		
W200X52	80	230	224	217	208	199	189	342	512	56.7	M_r	115
W8X35	66	213	208	202	195	187	179	282	486	55.8	V_r	65.8
b = 8.02	52	196	191	186	181	175	168	222	453	54.6	L_u	11.7
t = .495	38	178	175	171	167	162	157	162	408	52.8	I_x	127
	24	160	157	155	151	148	143	103	344	49.9	S_x	31.3
W200X46	80	213	207	200	192	183	173	342	459	50.4	M_r	100
W8X31	66	196	191	185	178	171	163	282	437	49.7	V_r	59.6
b = 7.99	52	179	175	170	165	159	152	222	409	48.7	L_u	11.3
t = .435	38	162	159	155	151	146	141	162	370	47.2	I_x	110
	24	144	142	139	136	133	129	103	314	44.6	S_x	27.5
W200X42	79	199	193	186	179	170	161	327	425	45.8	M_r	89.8
W8X28	65	185	180	174	167	160	152	278	405	45.1	V_r	60.0
b = 6.53	51	168	163	159	153	147	141	218	379	44.1	L_u	9.27
t = .465	37	150	147	143	139	135	130	158	344	42.8	I_x	98.0
	24	133	131	129	126	122	118	103	295	40.7	S_x	24.3
W200X36	78	173	167	161	154	146	137	280	370	39.5	M_r	76.6
W8X24	65	168	163	157	151	144	136	278	355	39.0	V_r	50.8
b = 6.49	51	151	147	143	137	132	125	218	334	38.2	L_u	8.86
t = .400	37	134	131	128	124	119	115	158	304	37.1	I_x	82.8
	24	118	116	113	111	108	104	103	263	35.4	S_x	20.9
W200X31	77	157	151	145	138	131	124	244	346	35.1	M_r	67.3
W8X21	64	153	148	143	137	130	123	244	333	34.7	V_r	54.1
b = 5.27	50	142	138	133	128	123	117	214	314	34.0	L_u	6.98
t = .400	37	126	123	120	116	112	107	158	289	33.2	I_x	75.3
	23	109	107	104	102	98.5	94.7	98.2	248	31.5	S_x	18.2
W200X27	77	135	130	124	118	112	105	208	298	30.0	M_r	56.1
W8X18	64	132	128	122	117	111	104	208	287	29.7	V_r	48.9
b = 5.25	50	128	124	119	115	109	103	208	272	29.1	L_u	6.70
t = .330	37	113	110	107	103	99.0	94.5	158	252	28.4	I_x	61.9
	23	96.0	94.1	91.9	89.5	86.5	82.9	98.2	218	27.1	S_x	15.2

†No. of studs/beam = 2 x Q_r x percent shear connection/100/q_r (per stud)

*Units — M_r — Ft. Kips L_u — Ft. b — In.
  V_r — Kips I_x — In.⁴ t — In.
  S_x — In.³

Note: The SI designation in bold face type is the one preferred for use in Canada.

COMPOSITE BEAMS
Trial Selection Tables

G40.21 – 44W
3 Ksi Concrete

3 Inch Deck with 2½ Inch Slab
$\varnothing = 0.90$, $\varnothing_C = 0.67$, $\varnothing_{SC} = 0.80$

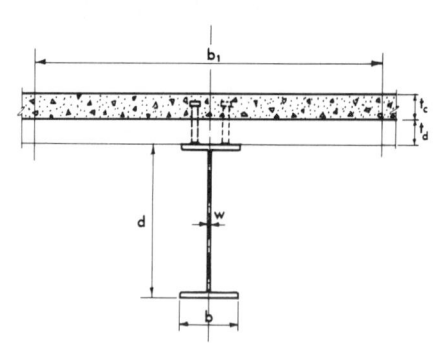

Steel Shape	b_1	Factored Resistances						Q_r† for 100%	I_1	S_{s_1}	Steel Shape Data*	
		M_{rc} in foot Kips for various percentages of shear connection										
	In.	100%	90%	80%	70%	60%	50%	Kips	In.⁴	In.³		
W610X241	101	2000	1970	1940	1900	1860	1820	431	10100	541	M_r	1540
W24X162	83	1940	1910	1880	1850	1810	1770	355	9480	530	V_r	461
b = 12.95	66	1870	1850	1820	1790	1760	1730	282	8840	518	L_u	16.9
t = 1.22	48	1790	1770	1750	1730	1700	1680	205	8050	500	I_x	5170
	30	1700	1690	1670	1660	1640	1630	128	7130	477	S_x	414
W610X217	101	1820	1800	1760	1730	1690	1650	431	9230	489	M_r	1380
W24X146	83	1760	1740	1710	1680	1640	1600	355	8680	480	V_r	420
b = 12.90	66	1700	1680	1650	1620	1590	1560	282	8090	468	L_u	16.5
t = 1.09	48	1620	1600	1580	1560	1540	1510	205	7350	453	I_x	4580
	30	1540	1520	1510	1490	1480	1460	128	6480	431	S_x	370
W610X195	101	1650	1620	1590	1560	1520	1480	431	8390	439	M_r	1220
W24X131	83	1590	1570	1540	1510	1480	1440	355	7900	431	V_r	387
b = 12.85	66	1530	1510	1480	1460	1430	1400	282	7360	421	L_u	16.1
t = .960	48	1460	1440	1420	1400	1370	1350	205	6680	407	I_x	4020
	30	1370	1360	1350	1330	1320	1300	128	5860	387	S_x	328
W610X174	101	1490	1470	1440	1410	1380	1340	431	7650	394	M_r	1080
W24X117	83	1440	1420	1390	1360	1330	1300	355	7210	387	V_r	349
b = 12.80	66	1390	1360	1340	1310	1280	1250	282	6710	378	L_u	15.7
t = .850	48	1310	1300	1280	1250	1230	1210	205	6090	366	I_x	3540
	30	1230	1220	1210	1190	1180	1160	128	5310	348	S_x	292
W610X155	101	1340	1320	1300	1270	1240	1200	431	6950	352	M_r	954
W24X104	83	1300	1280	1260	1230	1200	1160	355	6560	346	V_r	314
b = 12.75	65	1250	1230	1200	1180	1150	1120	278	6080	338	L_u	15.4
t = .750	48	1180	1160	1150	1130	1100	1080	205	5530	327	I_x	3100
	30	1100	1090	1080	1060	1050	1030	128	4810	311	S_x	258
W610X140	97	1230	1210	1180	1150	1120	1080	414	6350	315	M_r	838
W24X94	80	1180	1160	1140	1110	1080	1050	342	5990	309	V_r	327
b = 9.06	63	1130	1110	1080	1060	1030	1000	269	5560	302	L_u	10.8
t = .875	46	1060	1040	1030	1000	983	961	196	5030	291	I_x	2700
	29	985	972	959	944	930	914	124	4360	276	S_x	222
W610X125	97	1110	1090	1070	1050	1020	980	414	5770	282	M_r	739
W24X84	80	1070	1050	1030	1000	976	943	342	5460	277	V_r	296
b = 9.02	63	1020	1000	981	957	932	904	269	5070	271	L_u	10.6
t = .770	46	959	942	924	904	884	862	196	4580	261	I_x	2370
	29	885	873	859	846	831	816	124	3960	248	S_x	197

†No. of studs/beam = 2 x Q_r x percent shear connection/100/q_r (per stud)

*Units — M_r — Ft. Kips L_u — Ft.   b — In.
　　　　 V_r — Kips I_x — In.⁴   t — In.
　　　　　　　　　　 S_x — In.³

Note: The SI designation in bold face type is the one preferred for use in Canada.

3 Inch Deck with 2½ Inch Slab
$$\varnothing = 0.90, \quad \varnothing_C = 0.67, \quad \varnothing_{SC} = 0.80$$

Steel Shape	Composite Beam										Steel Shape Data*	
	b_1	Factored Resistances							Properties			
		M_{rc} in foot Kips for various percentages of shear connection						$Q_r{}^\dagger$ for 100%	I_1	S_{s_1}		
	In.	100%	90%	80%	70%	60%	50%	Kips	In.⁴	In.³		
W610X113	97	1020	1000	985	961	932	898	414	5300	256	M_r	660
W24X76	80	983	966	945	921	893	862	342	5010	251	V_r	275
b = 8.99	63	937	919	898	876	851	824	269	4660	245	L_u	10.4
t = .680	46	877	861	843	824	804	782	196	4220	237	I_x	2100
	29	805	793	780	766	752	737	124	3640	225	S_x	176
W610X101	97	925	912	896	874	847	815	414	4810	229	M_r	584
W24X68	80	894	879	860	837	811	780	342	4560	225	V_r	257
b = 8.97	63	851	834	815	793	769	743	269	4240	220	L_u	10.1
t = .585	46	795	779	762	743	723	702	196	3840	213	I_x	1830
	29	725	713	700	687	673	658	124	3310	201	S_x	154
W530X138	96	1090	1070	1050	1020	989	954	410	5110	281	M_r	729
W21X93	80	1050	1030	1010	980	952	920	342	4830	276	V_r	328
b = 8.42	63	997	978	957	934	909	883	269	4470	269	L_u	10.3
t = .930	46	936	919	902	883	863	842	196	4020	259	I_x	2070
	29	865	853	840	827	814	800	124	3460	244	S_x	191
W530X123	96	985	970	950	927	898	866	410	4660	252	M_r	647
W21X83	79	949	932	911	888	862	832	337	4400	248	V_r	288
b = 8.35	63	905	888	868	847	823	798	269	4090	242	L_u	10.1
t = .835	46	848	833	816	798	779	759	196	3690	233	I_x	1830
	29	780	769	757	744	731	717	124	3170	220	S_x	171
W530X109	96	886	873	858	837	812	782	410	4220	225	M_r	568
W21X73	79	855	841	823	802	778	750	337	3990	221	V_r	253
b = 8.30	63	817	802	784	764	742	718	269	3720	216	L_u	9.89
t = .740	46	765	750	735	718	699	680	196	3360	209	I_x	1600
	29	700	689	678	665	652	639	124	2880	197	S_x	151
W530X101	96	833	820	806	788	765	736	410	3980	210	M_r	528
W21X68	79	804	791	775	755	732	706	337	3770	206	V_r	237
b = 8.27	63	769	754	738	719	698	674	269	3510	202	L_u	9.74
t = .685	46	719	706	690	674	656	637	196	3180	195	I_x	1480
	29	657	646	635	623	610	597	124	2730	185	S_x	140
W530X92	96	773	760	747	731	709	682	410	3680	192	M_r	475
W21X62	79	744	733	718	700	678	653	337	3490	189	V_r	219
b = 8.24	63	712	699	683	665	645	622	269	3260	185	L_u	9.59
t = .615	46	665	652	638	622	604	585	196	2950	179	I_x	1330
	29	605	594	583	571	559	545	124	2530	170	S_x	127

†No. of studs/beam = 2 x Q_r x percent shear connection/100/q_r (per stud)

*Units — M_r — Ft. Kips L_u — Ft.   b — In.
   V_r — Kips I_x — In.⁴   t — In.
   S_x — In.³

Note: The SI designation in bold face type is the one preferred for use in Canada.

COMPOSITE BEAMS
Trial Selection Tables

G40.21 – 44W
3 Ksi Concrete

3 Inch Deck with 2½ Inch Slab
$\emptyset = 0.90$, $\emptyset_C = 0.67$, $\emptyset_{SC} = 0.80$

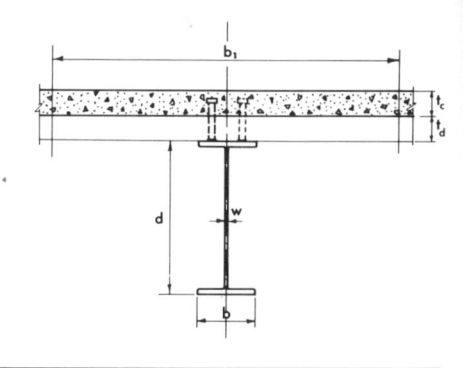

Steel Shape	b_1	\multicolumn{7}{c}{Composite Beam — Factored Resistances}			\multicolumn{2}{c}{Properties}	\multicolumn{2}{c}{Steel Shape Data*}
		\multicolumn{6}{c}{M_{rc} in foot Kips for various percentages of shear connection}	Q_r† for 100%	I_1	S_{S_1}		
		100%	90%	80%	70%	60%	50%	Kips	In.⁴	In.³		
	In.											
W530X82	96	701	689	676	661	642	617	410	3320	171	M_r	416
W21X55	79	673	663	650	633	613	588	337	3150	168	V_r	204
b = 8.22	63	644	632	617	600	580	558	269	2950	165	L_u	9.31
t = .522	46	600	588	574	558	541	523	196	2680	160	I_x	1150
	29	542	531	520	509	496	483	124	2300	151	S_x	111
W460X106	96	767	754	740	723	701	674	410	3290	196	M_r	478
W18X71	79	737	725	710	692	670	646	337	3100	193	V_r	239
b = 7.64	62	701	688	673	655	636	615	265	2870	188	L_u	9.51
t = .810	45	655	642	629	614	598	580	192	2580	181	I_x	1170
	29	600	591	580	569	558	546	124	2210	171	S_x	127
W460X97	96	715	702	689	673	654	629	410	3070	181	M_r	439
W18X65	79	686	675	662	645	625	602	337	2900	178	V_r	216
b = 7.59	62	654	642	628	611	593	572	265	2690	174	L_u	9.35
t = .750	45	610	598	585	571	556	539	192	2420	168	I_x	1070
	29	558	549	539	528	517	505	124	2080	159	S_x	117
W460X89	96	669	657	643	629	611	589	410	2880	168	M_r	406
W18X60	79	640	630	618	604	585	564	337	2720	165	V_r	198
b = 7.56	62	610	600	587	572	555	535	265	2530	162	L_u	9.20
t = .695	45	571	560	547	534	519	503	192	2280	156	I_x	984
	29	521	512	502	492	481	469	124	1960	148	S_x	108
W460X82	96	626	613	600	586	570	549	410	2670	155	M_r	370
W18X55	79	597	587	576	563	546	525	337	2540	152	V_r	185
b = 7.53	62	568	559	547	533	516	497	265	2360	149	L_u	9.02
t = .630	45	531	521	509	496	481	466	192	2130	144	I_x	890
	29	483	475	465	455	444	433	124	1830	137	S_x	98.3
W460X74	95	578	566	553	540	525	506	406	2460	141	M_r	333
W18X50	79	552	542	531	519	504	485	337	2340	139	V_r	167
b = 7.49	62	523	515	505	492	476	458	265	2190	136	L_u	8.89
t = .570	45	490	481	470	457	443	428	192	1980	132	I_x	800
	29	445	437	427	418	407	396	124	1700	125	S_x	88.9
W460X67	95	537	526	514	500	485	468	406	2270	129	M_r	301
W18X45	79	512	502	491	480	466	448	337	2160	127	V_r	156
b = 7.48	62	484	476	466	454	439	422	265	2030	124	L_u	8.65
t = .499	45	452	443	433	421	407	392	192	1840	121	I_x	719
	29	409	400	391	381	371	360	124	1590	115	S_x	80.5

†No. of studs/beam = 2 x Q_r x percent shear connection/100/q_r (per stud)

*Units — M_r — Ft. Kips L_u — Ft. b — In.
  V_r — Kips I_x — In.⁴ t — In.
  S_x — In.³

Note: The SI designation in bold face type is the one preferred for use in Canada.

COMPOSITE BEAMS
Trial Selection Tables

G40.21 – 44W
3 Ksi Concrete

3 Inch Deck with 2½ Inch Slab
$\phi = 0.90$, $\phi_C = 0.67$, $\phi_{SC} = 0.80$

Steel Shape	b₁	\multicolumn{6}{c}{M_{rc} in foot Kips for various percentages of shear connection}	Q_r for 100%	I_1	S_{s_1}	\multicolumn{2}{c}{Steel Shape Data*}

Steel Shape	b_1	\multicolumn{6}{c	}{Factored Resistances — M_{rc} in foot Kips for various percentages of shear connection}	Q_r† for 100%	Properties I_1	Properties S_{s_1}	\multicolumn{2}{c	}{Steel Shape Data*}
	In.	100%	90%	80%	70%	60%	50%	Kips	In.⁴	In.³		
W460X61	95	497	486	473	460	446	429	406	2050	115	M_r	264
W18X41	79	471	462	452	440	427	410	337	1960	114	V_r	148
b = 7.45	62	444	436	427	416	401	384	265	1840	112	L_u	8.40
t = .425	45	414	405	395	383	370	355	192	1670	108	I_x	623
	29	371	363	354	344	334	323	124	1450	103	S_x	70.4
W410X85	95	594	582	569	554	538	518	406	2350	149	M_r	346
W16X57	78	565	555	544	531	514	494	333	2230	147	V_r	185
b = 7.12	62	537	528	517	503	487	469	265	2070	143	L_u	8.91
t = .715	45	501	491	480	468	454	439	192	1860	138	I_x	758
	29	456	447	438	429	419	408	124	1600	131	S_x	92.3
W410X74	95	536	524	511	497	482	465	406	2110	132	M_r	304
W16X50	78	508	498	487	475	462	444	333	2000	130	V_r	161
b = 7.07	62	481	472	463	452	437	421	265	1870	127	L_u	8.67
t = .630	45	449	441	431	420	407	393	192	1690	123	I_x	659
	29	408	400	392	383	373	363	124	1450	116	S_x	81.1
W410X67	95	497	485	473	459	444	428	406	1930	119	M_r	272
W16X45	78	469	459	449	437	425	409	333	1840	117	V_r	145
b = 7.03	62	443	435	426	416	403	387	265	1720	115	L_u	8.50
t = .565	45	413	405	396	386	373	360	192	1560	112	I_x	586
	29	374	367	359	350	341	330	124	1340	106	S_x	72.7
W410X60	95	455	444	432	419	404	389	406	1750	106	M_r	241
W16X40	78	428	419	409	397	385	372	333	1670	105	V_r	128
b = 6.99	62	402	395	386	377	366	352	265	1570	103	L_u	8.38
t = .505	45	374	368	360	351	339	327	192	1430	100	I_x	518
	28	337	331	323	315	306	297	120	1220	95.0	S_x	64.7
W410X54	95	421	410	398	385	371	356	406	1580	95.2	M_r	211
W16X36	78	395	386	376	365	353	340	333	1510	93.9	V_r	122
b = 6.98	62	369	362	354	345	334	321	265	1420	92.3	L_u	8.14
t = .430	45	342	336	328	319	308	296	192	1300	89.7	I_x	448
	28	306	300	293	285	276	266	120	1110	85.2	S_x	56.5
W410X46	94	371	360	349	337	324	310	361	1390	82.0	M_r	178
W16X31	77	355	346	337	326	315	302	329	1330	80.9	V_r	114
b = 5.52	61	330	323	315	306	297	284	261	1260	79.6	L_u	6.31
t = .440	44	303	297	290	282	272	260	188	1150	77.4	I_x	375
	28	271	265	258	251	242	233	120	996	73.8	S_x	47.2

†No. of studs/beam = 2 x Q_r x percent shear connection/100/q_r (per stud)

*Units — M_r — Ft. Kips L_u — Ft.   b — In.
       V_r — Kips I_x — In.⁴   t — In.
               S_x — In.³

Note: The SI designation in bold face type is the one preferred for use in Canada.

COMPOSITE BEAMS
Trial Selection Tables

G40.21 – 44W
3 Ksi Concrete

3 Inch Deck with 2½ Inch Slab
$\phi = 0.90$, $\phi_C = 0.67$, $\phi_{SC} = 0.80$

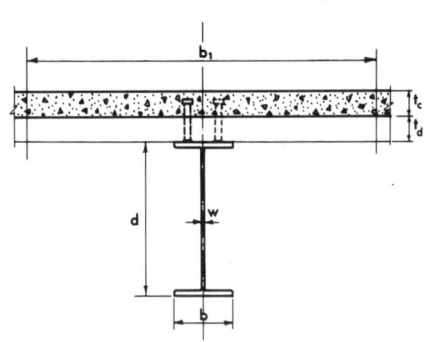

Steel Shape		Composite Beam										Steel Shape Data*	
		Factored Resistances							Properties				
	b_1	M_{rc} in foot Kips for various percentages of shear connection						$Q_r{}^†$ for 100%	I_1	S_{s_1}			
		100%	90%	80%	70%	60%	50%	Kips	In.⁴	In.³			
	In.												
W410X39	94	314	305	295	284	272	260	304	1180	68.7	M_r	146
W16X26	77	309	300	291	281	270	259	304	1130	67.9	V_r	99.1
b = 5.50	61	291	284	276	268	259	248	261	1080	66.9	L_u	6.05
t = .345	44	264	259	253	246	237	226	188	992	65.2	I_x	301
	28	236	230	224	217	209	200	120	864	62.3	S_x	38.4
W360X79	96	501	489	476	462	447	430	410	1780	127	M_r	287
W14X53	79	473	463	452	440	427	413	337	1690	125	V_r	135
b = 8.06	62	444	436	427	417	406	391	265	1570	123	L_u	10.6
t = .660	46	416	410	401	392	380	368	196	1420	119	I_x	541
	29	379	372	365	357	348	339	124	1200	112	S_x	77.7
W360X72	96	465	453	440	427	412	396	410	1640	116	M_r	259
W14X48	79	437	427	417	405	393	379	337	1550	114	V_r	123
b = 8.03	62	409	401	392	383	373	359	265	1450	112	L_u	10.4
t = .595	46	382	376	368	360	349	337	196	1320	108	I_x	485
	29	348	341	334	327	318	309	124	1120	103	S_x	70.3
W360X64	96	429	417	405	392	377	362	410	1490	104	M_r	230
W14X43	79	402	392	382	370	358	345	337	1410	102	V_r	109
b = 7.99	62	374	366	358	349	339	327	265	1320	100	L_u	10.1
t = .530	46	348	342	335	327	318	306	196	1210	97.6	I_x	428
	29	316	310	304	296	288	279	124	1030	92.6	S_x	62.7
W360X57	95	404	393	381	368	354	338	406	1400	93.5	M_r	203
W14X38	78	378	368	358	347	335	322	333	1330	92.2	V_r	114
b = 6.77	62	352	344	336	327	317	305	265	1250	90.5	L_u	8.32
t = .515	45	324	318	311	303	293	282	192	1140	87.9	I_x	385
	28	291	285	279	271	263	255	120	968	83.3	S_x	54.6
W360X51	95	372	361	350	337	323	308	396	1260	83.8	M_r	180
W14X34	78	348	339	329	318	307	294	333	1210	82.7	V_r	104
b = 6.74	62	323	316	307	299	289	278	265	1140	81.3	L_u	8.16
t = .455	45	296	290	284	277	268	257	192	1040	79.1	I_x	340
	28	265	260	254	247	239	231	120	890	75.1	S_x	48.6
W360X45	95	331	321	310	298	286	272	350	1130	73.9	M_r	156
W14X30	78	320	311	301	291	279	267	333	1080	73.0	V_r	97.7
b = 6.73	62	295	288	280	271	262	252	265	1020	71.9	L_u	7.93
t = .385	45	268	263	257	250	242	232	192	938	70.0	I_x	291
	28	239	234	228	222	214	206	120	806	66.7	S_x	42.1

†No. of studs/beam = 2 x Q_r x percent shear connection/100/q_r (per stud)

*Units — M_r — Ft. Kips L_u — Ft.   b — In.
         V_r — Kips I_x — In.⁴   t — In.
                  S_x — In.³

Note: The SI designation in bold face type is the one preferred for use in Canada.

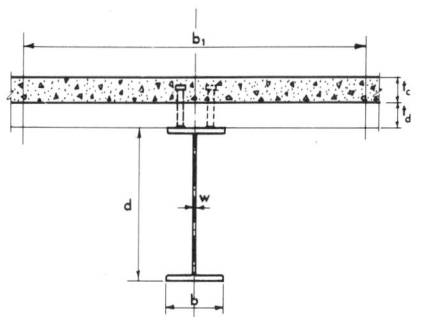

COMPOSITE BEAMS
Trial Selection Tables

G40.21 – 44W
3 Ksi Concrete

3 Inch Deck with 2½ Inch Slab
$\phi = 0.90$, $\phi_C = 0.67$, $\phi_{SC} = 0.80$

Steel Shape		Composite Beam										Steel Shape Data*	
		Factored Resistances							Properties				
	b_1	M_{rc} in foot Kips for various percentages of shear connection						Q_r† for 100%	I_1	S_{s_1}			
	In.	100%	90%	80%	70%	60%	50%	Kips	In.⁴	In.³		
W360X39	93	292	282	272	261	250	238	305	999	64.2	M_r	133
W14X26	77	287	278	269	259	248	237	305	962	63.5	V_r	92.7
b = 5.02	60	267	260	252	244	235	225	256	910	62.4	L_u	5.83
t = .420	44	242	236	230	224	216	206	188	839	60.9	I_x	245
	28	215	210	204	198	191	183	120	729	58.2	S_x	35.2
W360X33	93	248	239	230	220	210	200	257	851	54.1	M_r	110
W14X22	77	244	236	228	219	209	199	257	823	53.6	V_r	82.6
b = 5.00	60	238	231	224	216	207	197	256	782	52.7	L_u	5.60
t = .335	44	213	208	202	196	189	180	188	726	51.5	I_x	199
	28	187	183	178	173	166	158	120	636	49.4	S_x	29.0
W310X129	100	666	652	638	622	606	588	427	2210	189	M_r	436
W12X87	83	636	625	612	599	585	568	355	2080	186	V_r	169
b = 12.13	65	604	595	585	573	559	543	278	1910	180	L_u	18.1
t = .810	48	573	564	554	543	531	518	205	1700	173	I_x	740
	30	529	522	514	506	497	487	128	1430	162	S_x	118
W310X118	100	615	602	588	572	556	539	427	2040	173	M_r	393
W12X79	83	586	575	563	550	536	520	355	1920	169	V_r	152
b = 12.08	65	554	546	536	525	513	497	278	1760	165	L_u	17.5
t = .735	48	524	517	508	497	486	473	205	1580	159	I_x	662
	30	484	477	470	462	453	443	128	1320	149	S_x	107
W310X107	100	570	558	544	529	513	496	427	1890	158	M_r	356
W12X72	83	542	531	520	507	494	479	355	1780	155	V_r	138
b = 12.04	65	511	503	493	483	472	458	278	1640	151	L_u	17.0
t = .670	48	482	475	467	458	447	434	205	1470	146	I_x	597
	30	444	438	431	423	415	406	128	1230	137	S_x	97.5
W310X97	100	528	516	503	488	472	456	427	1740	144	M_r	290
W12X65	83	500	490	479	466	453	439	355	1640	141	V_r	124
b = 12.00	65	470	462	453	443	432	419	278	1520	138	L_u	17.5
t = .605	48	441	435	428	419	409	397	205	1360	133	I_x	533
	30	406	400	394	386	378	369	128	1150	125	S_x	88.0
W310X86	98	487	475	461	447	432	416	419	1600	129	M_r	285
W12X58	81	459	449	437	426	413	399	346	1510	127	V_r	115
b = 10.01	64	430	422	413	403	393	381	273	1400	124	L_u	13.9
t = .640	47	401	395	388	380	371	359	201	1260	120	I_x	475
	29	367	362	355	348	341	332	124	1060	113	S_x	77.9

†No. of studs/beam = 2 x Q_r x percent shear connection/100/q_r (per stud)

*Units — M_r — Ft. Kips L_u — Ft.   b — In.
       V_r — Kips I_x — In.⁴   t — In.
                  S_x — In.³

Note: The SI designation in bold face type is the one preferred for use in Canada.

COMPOSITE BEAMS
Trial Selection Tables

G40.21 – 44W
3 Ksi Concrete

3 Inch Deck with 2½ Inch Slab
$\phi = 0.90, \phi_C = 0.67, \phi_{SC} = 0.80$

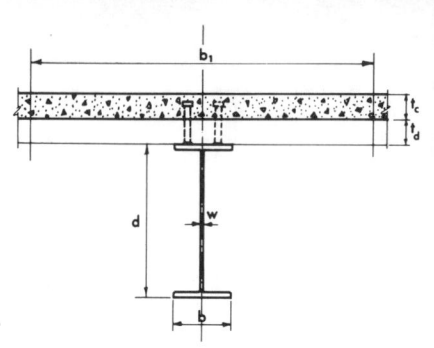

Steel Shape	b₁	Composite Beam									Steel Shape Data*	
		Factored Resistances							Properties			
		M_{rc} in foot Kips for various percentages of shear connection						Q_r† for 100%	I_1	S_{S_1}		
	In.	100%	90%	80%	70%	60%	50%	Kips	In.⁴	In.³		
W310X79	98	457	445	432	418	403	387	419	1480	118	M_r	257
W12X53	81	429	419	408	396	384	370	346	1400	116	V_r	109
b = 9.99	64	401	393	384	375	365	353	273	1300	114	L_u	13.5
t = .575	47	372	366	360	352	342	331	201	1170	110	I_x	425
	29	339	334	327	320	313	304	124	983	104	S_x	70.5
W310X74	96	439	427	414	401	386	370	410	1410	111	M_r	239
W12X50	79	411	401	391	379	366	353	337	1340	109	V_r	118
b = 8.08	62	383	375	366	357	347	334	265	1240	107	L_u	11.0
t = .640	46	356	349	343	334	324	313	196	1120	104	I_x	394
	29	323	317	310	303	295	287	124	948	97.6	S_x	64.6
W310X67	96	407	396	383	370	355	339	410	1290	100	M_r	214
W12X45	79	380	370	360	348	336	323	337	1230	98.8	V_r	106
b = 8.05	62	352	344	336	327	317	306	265	1140	96.7	L_u	10.7
t = .575	46	325	319	313	305	296	286	196	1040	93.8	I_x	350
	29	295	289	283	276	269	261	124	876	88.7	S_x	58.0
W310X60	96	377	366	354	341	327	311	410	1170	90.1	M_r	190
W12X40	79	351	341	331	320	308	295	337	1120	88.9	V_r	92.1
b = 8.00	62	324	316	308	299	289	279	265	1040	87.1	L_u	10.4
t = .515	46	297	291	285	278	270	260	196	951	84.7	I_x	310
	29	268	263	258	251	244	236	124	808	80.3	S_x	51.9
W310X52	95	356	345	334	321	307	291	406	1110	80.7	M_r	169
W12X35	78	330	321	311	300	288	275	333	1060	79.6	V_r	98.0
b = 6.56	61	303	296	287	279	269	259	261	994	78.1	L_u	8.33
t = .520	45	277	271	265	258	250	241	192	908	76.0	I_x	285
	28	248	243	238	231	225	217	120	772	72.0	S_x	45.6
W310X45	95	307	297	286	275	262	249	348	964	69.1	M_r	142
W12X30	78	297	288	278	268	256	244	333	924	68.2	V_r	83.9
b = 6.52	61	271	263	256	247	238	228	261	871	67.1	L_u	8.09
t = .440	45	245	240	234	227	220	212	192	800	65.4	I_x	238
	28	217	213	208	203	197	189	120	685	62.2	S_x	38.6
W310X39	94	269	260	250	239	228	216	303	849	60.3	M_r	123
W12X26	78	264	256	247	237	226	215	303	819	59.6	V_r	73.5
b = 6.49	61	246	239	232	223	214	205	261	775	58.7	L_u	7.92
t = .380	45	221	216	210	204	197	190	192	716	57.3	I_x	204
	28	194	190	186	181	175	169	120	618	54.8	S_x	33.4

†No. of studs/beam = 2 x Q_r x percent shear connection/100/q_r (per stud)

*Units — M_r — Ft. Kips L_u — Ft.   b — In.
         V_r — Kips I_x — In.⁴   t — In.
                 S_x — In.³

Note: The SI designation in bold face type is the one preferred for use in Canada.

3 Inch Deck with 2½ Inch Slab
$\phi = 0.90$, $\phi_C = 0.67$, $\phi_{SC} = 0.80$

Steel Shape	Composite Beam								Properties		Steel Shape Data*	
		Factored Resistances						$Q_r^{\dagger}$ for 100%	Properties			
	b_1	M_{rc} in foot Kips for various percentages of shear connection							I_1	S_{s_1}		
	In.	100%	90%	80%	70%	60%	50%	Kips	In.⁴	In.³		
W250X101	98	484	472	458	443	427	411	419	1430	135	M_r	281
W10X68	81	455	445	433	421	408	394	346	1340	132	V_r	128
b = 10.13	64	426	417	408	398	388	375	273	1230	129	L_u	16.1
t = .770	47	396	390	383	374	364	353	201	1100	123	I_x	394
	29	361	356	349	343	335	327	124	903	115	S_x	75.8
W250X89	98	441	429	416	401	386	369	419	1280	119	M_r	246
W10X60	81	413	403	391	379	366	353	346	1210	117	V_r	112
b = 10.08	64	384	376	367	357	347	336	273	1120	114	L_u	15.2
t = .680	47	355	349	342	335	326	316	201	997	110	I_x	341
	29	322	317	312	305	298	291	124	822	103	S_x	66.7
W250X80	98	409	397	384	370	355	339	419	1170	108	M_r	220
W10X54	81	381	371	360	349	336	323	346	1110	106	V_r	97.6
b = 10.03	64	353	345	336	327	317	306	273	1030	104	L_u	14.6
t = .615	47	325	319	312	305	297	287	201	920	100	I_x	303
	29	293	289	284	278	271	264	124	762	93.6	S_x	60.1
W250X73	98	384	373	360	346	331	315	419	1080	98.7	M_r	199
W10X49	81	357	347	336	325	312	299	346	1030	97.1	V_r	88.7
b = 10.00	64	329	321	313	303	293	283	273	954	94.9	L_u	14.2
t = .560	47	301	295	289	282	274	265	201	857	91.8	I_x	272
	29	270	266	261	256	249	242	124	711	86.1	S_x	54.5
W250X67	96	366	355	342	329	314	298	410	1020	91.3	M_r	181
W10X45	79	339	329	319	307	295	282	337	970	89.8	V_r	92.4
b = 8.02	62	311	303	295	285	276	265	265	900	87.8	L_u	11.6
t = .620	46	284	278	272	265	257	248	196	812	85.0	I_x	248
	29	255	250	245	239	233	225	124	680	79.9	S_x	49.1
W250X58	96	333	322	310	297	283	267	410	900	79.3	M_r	154
W10X39	79	307	297	287	276	264	251	337	856	78.1	V_r	81.7
b = 7.98	62	280	272	264	255	245	235	265	798	76.4	L_u	11.1
t = .530	46	253	248	241	235	227	219	196	724	74.2	I_x	209
	29	225	221	216	211	205	198	124	610	70.1	S_x	42.1
W250X49	96	295	284	272	260	247	232	385	772	67.0	M_r	128
W10X33	79	275	266	256	245	234	221	337	737	66.1	V_r	73.7
b = 7.96	62	249	241	233	225	215	205	265	691	64.9	L_u	10.5
t = .435	46	223	218	211	205	198	190	196	631	63.1	I_x	170
	29	195	192	187	182	177	170	124	536	59.9	S_x	34.9

†No. of studs/beam = 2 x Q_r x percent shear connection/100/q_r (per stud)

*Units — M_r — Ft. Kips L_u — Ft.   b — In.
        V_r — Kips I_x — In.⁴   t — In.
                S_x — In.³

Note: The SI designation in bold face type is the one preferred for use in Canada.

COMPOSITE BEAMS
Trial Selection Tables

G40.21 – 44W
3 Ksi Concrete

3 Inch Deck with 2½ Inch Slab
$\emptyset = 0.90$, $\emptyset_C = 0.67$, $\emptyset_{SC} = 0.80$

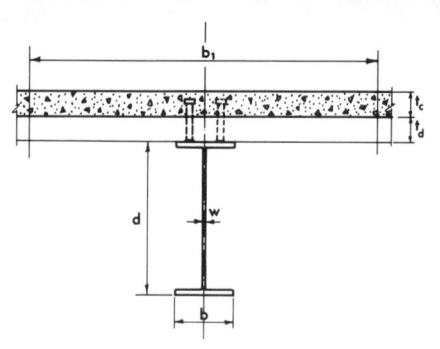

Steel Shape		Composite Beam										Steel Shape Data*	
		Factored Resistances							Properties				
	b_1	M_{rc} in foot Kips for various percentages of shear connection						Q_r† for 100%	I_1	S_{s_1}			
	In.	100%	90%	80%	70%	60%	50%	Kips	In.⁴	In.³			
W250X45	94	281	271	260	248	236	222	350	774	63.0	M_r	121
W10X30	77	269	260	251	240	229	216	329	740	62.2	V_r	82.1
b = 5.81	61	244	237	229	220	211	201	261	698	61.1	L_u	7.63
t = .510	45	219	213	207	200	193	185	192	638	59.4	I_x	170
	28	190	187	182	177	171	164	120	542	56.3	S_x	32.5
W250X39	94	244	235	225	214	203	191	301	677	54.5	M_r	103
W10X26	77	239	231	221	212	201	190	301	650	53.8	V_r	70.2
b = 5.77	61	222	215	207	199	190	180	261	615	52.9	L_u	7.38
t = .440	45	197	191	185	179	172	165	192	566	51.6	I_x	144
	28	169	166	162	157	152	146	120	485	49.2	S_x	27.9
W250X33	94	210	201	192	182	172	162	257	582	46.5	M_r	85.8
W10X22	77	206	198	190	181	171	161	257	561	45.9	V_r	63.8
b = 5.75	61	200	193	186	178	169	160	257	533	45.2	L_u	7.10
t = .360	45	177	171	166	159	153	146	192	494	44.2	I_x	118
	28	150	146	142	138	133	127	120	427	42.2	S_x	23.2
W200X100	96	429	416	403	388	372	355	410	1150	121	M_r	232
W8X67	79	400	389	377	365	351	337	337	1070	118	V_r	134
b = 8.28	63	371	362	353	343	332	320	269	983	115	L_u	16.3
t = .935	46	340	334	327	319	309	299	196	864	109	I_x	272
	29	307	302	296	290	283	275	124	707	101	S_x	60.4
W200X86	96	388	375	362	348	332	316	410	1010	105	M_r	197
W8X58	79	359	349	337	325	313	299	337	948	103	V_r	117
b = 8.22	63	332	323	314	304	294	282	269	874	101	L_u	14.9
t = .810	46	302	295	289	281	273	263	196	772	96.3	I_x	228
	29	271	266	260	254	248	240	124	634	89.3	S_x	52.1
W200X71	96	342	330	317	304	289	273	410	859	87.9	M_r	162
W8X48	79	314	304	294	282	270	256	337	810	86.4	V_r	88.9
b = 8.11	62	286	278	269	260	250	240	265	748	84.2	L_u	13.4
t = .685	46	259	253	246	239	232	223	196	670	81.2	I_x	184
	29	229	225	221	215	210	203	124	554	75.8	S_x	43.3
W200X59	96	304	293	281	268	254	238	410	726	73.3	M_r	131
W8X40	79	278	268	258	247	235	222	337	689	72.1	V_r	77.6
b = 8.07	62	250	243	235	226	216	206	265	639	70.5	L_u	12.3
t = .560	46	224	218	212	205	198	190	196	577	68.2	I_x	146
	29	196	192	188	183	177	171	124	481	64.1	S_x	35.4

†No. of studs/beam = 2 x Q_r x percent shear connection/100/q_r (per stud)
*Units — M_r — Ft. Kips L_u — Ft.   b — In.
        V_r — Kips I_x — In.⁴   t — In.
                      S_x — In.³

Note: The SI designation in bold face type is the one preferred for use in Canada.

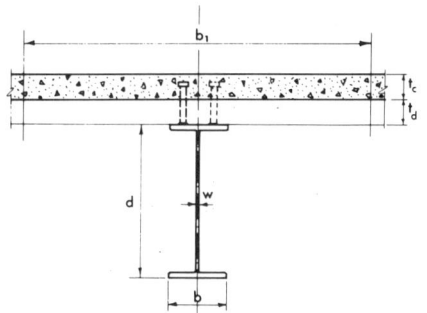

COMPOSITE BEAMS
Trial Selection Tables

G40.21 – 44W
3 Ksi Concrete

3 Inch Deck with 2½ Inch Slab
$\emptyset = 0.90$, $\emptyset_C = 0.67$, $\emptyset_{SC} = 0.80$

Steel Shape		Composite Beam										Steel Shape Data*	
		Factored Resistances							Properties				
	b_1	M_{rc} in foot Kips for various percentages of shear connection						Q_r† for 100%	I_1	S_{s_1}			
	In.	100%	90%	80%	70%	60%	50%	Kips	In.⁴	In.³		
W200X52	96	283	272	260	247	233	218	408	651	64.9	M_r	115
W8X35	79	257	248	238	227	215	203	337	619	64.0	V_r	65.8
b = 8.02	62	230	223	215	206	197	187	265	577	62.6	L_u	11.7
t = .495	46	205	199	193	186	179	172	196	524	60.8	I_x	127
	29	177	173	169	165	160	154	124	440	57.4	S_x	31.3
W200X46	96	253	243	231	219	207	193	362	584	57.8	M_r	100
W8X31	79	240	231	221	211	199	187	337	557	56.9	V_r	59.6
b = 7.99	62	214	206	198	190	181	171	265	522	55.8	L_u	11.3
t = .435	46	188	183	177	170	163	156	196	476	54.3	I_x	110
	29	161	157	153	149	144	139	124	402	51.4	S_x	27.5
W200X42	95	232	222	212	200	188	176	327	540	52.4	M_r	89.8
W8X28	78	226	217	208	197	186	174	327	516	51.7	V_r	60.0
b = 6.53	61	202	195	187	178	169	160	261	484	50.7	L_u	9.27
t = .465	45	176	171	165	159	152	144	192	442	49.3	I_x	98.0
	28	149	145	141	137	133	127	120	374	46.7	S_x	24.3
W200X36	94	201	192	182	172	161	150	280	470	45.2	M_r	76.6
W8X24	78	197	188	179	170	160	149	280	452	44.7	V_r	50.8
b = 6.49	61	185	178	170	162	153	144	261	426	43.8	L_u	8.86
t = .400	45	160	155	149	143	136	129	192	392	42.7	I_x	82.8
	28	133	129	126	122	117	113	120	334	40.7	S_x	20.9
W200X31	93	180	172	163	154	145	135	244	437	40.2	M_r	67.3
W8X21	77	177	169	161	153	144	134	244	421	39.7	V_r	54.1
b = 5.27	61	172	165	158	150	142	133	244	400	39.0	L_u	6.98
t = .400	44	150	145	140	134	127	120	188	368	38.0	I_x	75.3
	28	125	122	118	114	110	104	120	319	36.3	S_x	18.2
W200X27	93	155	147	140	132	123	114	208	377	34.4	M_r	56.1
W8X18	77	152	145	138	130	122	114	208	364	33.9	V_r	48.9
b = 5.25	61	149	142	136	129	121	113	208	347	33.4	L_u	6.70
t = .330	44	137	132	127	121	114	108	188	321	32.6	I_x	61.9
	28	112	109	105	101	97.2	92.5	120	281	31.3	S_x	15.2

†No. of studs/beam = 2 x Q_r x percent shear connection/100/q_r (per stud)

*Units — M_r — Ft. Kips L_u — Ft.   b — In.
       V_r — Kips I_x — In.⁴   t — In.
                S_x — In.³

Note: The SI designation in bold face type is the one preferred for use in Canada.

COMPOSITE BEAMS
Trial Selection Tables

G40.21 – 44W
4 Ksi Concrete

2 Inch Deck with 3¼ Inch Slab
$\emptyset = 0.90$, $\emptyset_C = 0.67$, $\emptyset_{SC} = 0.80$

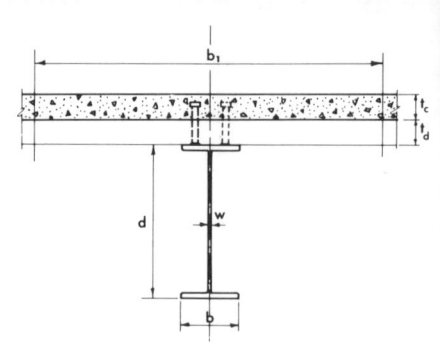

Steel Shape	b₁	\multicolumn{6}{c}{M_{rc} in foot Kips for various percentages of shear connection}	Q_r† for 100%	I₁	S_{s₁}	\multicolumn{2}{c}{Steel Shape Data*}
	In.	100%	90%	80%	70%	60%	50%	Kips	In.⁴	In.³		
W610X241	97	2130	2110	2080	2050	2000	1950	718	9780	530	M_r	1540
W24X162	80	2080	2050	2020	1990	1940	1890	592	9230	520	V_r	461
b = 12.95	63	2010	1980	1950	1910	1870	1830	466	8610	508	L_u	16.9
t = 1.22	46	1910	1890	1860	1830	1790	1760	341	7880	492	I_x	5170
	29	1790	1770	1750	1730	1700	1680	215	7030	471	S_x	414
W610X217	97	1930	1910	1890	1860	1820	1770	718	8940	479	M_r	1380
W24X146	80	1880	1870	1840	1810	1770	1720	592	8440	470	V_r	420
b = 12.90	63	1820	1800	1770	1740	1700	1660	466	7860	459	L_u	16.5
t = 1.09	46	1730	1710	1680	1650	1620	1590	341	7190	445	I_x	4580
	29	1620	1600	1580	1560	1540	1510	215	6380	426	S_x	370
W610X195	97	1750	1730	1710	1680	1650	1600	718	8120	429	M_r	1220
W24X131	80	1700	1680	1660	1630	1600	1550	592	7670	422	V_r	387
b = 12.85	63	1640	1620	1600	1570	1530	1490	466	7140	412	L_u	16.1
t = .960	46	1570	1540	1520	1490	1460	1420	341	6520	400	I_x	4020
	29	1460	1440	1420	1400	1380	1350	215	5760	382	S_x	328
W610X174	97	1580	1560	1540	1520	1490	1450	718	7390	385	M_r	1080
W24X117	80	1530	1520	1500	1480	1440	1400	592	6990	379	V_r	349
b = 12.80	63	1480	1470	1440	1420	1380	1350	466	6510	370	L_u	15.7
t = .850	46	1410	1390	1370	1340	1310	1280	341	5930	359	I_x	3540
	29	1310	1300	1280	1260	1230	1210	215	5220	343	S_x	292
W610X155	97	1420	1410	1390	1370	1340	1310	718	6710	344	M_r	954
W24X104	80	1380	1360	1350	1330	1300	1260	592	6340	338	V_r	314
b = 12.75	63	1330	1320	1300	1280	1250	1210	466	5910	331	L_u	15.4
t = .750	46	1270	1260	1230	1210	1180	1150	341	5380	321	I_x	3100
	29	1180	1160	1150	1130	1110	1080	215	4720	307	S_x	258
W610X140	93	1310	1290	1280	1250	1230	1190	689	6120	307	M_r	838
W24X94	77	1270	1250	1240	1210	1180	1150	570	5790	302	V_r	327
b = 9.06	60	1220	1200	1180	1160	1130	1090	444	5370	295	L_u	10.8
t = .875	44	1160	1140	1110	1090	1060	1030	326	4880	285	I_x	2700
	28	1060	1040	1030	1010	986	963	207	4260	271	S_x	222
W610X125	93	1190	1170	1150	1130	1110	1080	689	5550	275	M_r	739
W24X84	77	1140	1130	1120	1100	1070	1040	570	5260	270	V_r	296
b = 9.02	60	1100	1090	1070	1050	1020	986	444	4890	264	L_u	10.6
t = .770	44	1040	1030	1010	985	959	929	326	4440	256	I_x	2370
	28	958	943	925	907	886	864	207	3870	243	S_x	197

†No. of studs/beam = 2 x Q_r x percent shear connection/100/q_r (per stud)
*Units — M_r — Ft. Kips L_u — Ft. b — In.
V_r — Kips I_x — In.⁴ t — In.
S_x — In.³

#Concrete density = 115 lb./ft.³

Note: The SI designation in bold face type is the one preferred for use in Canada.

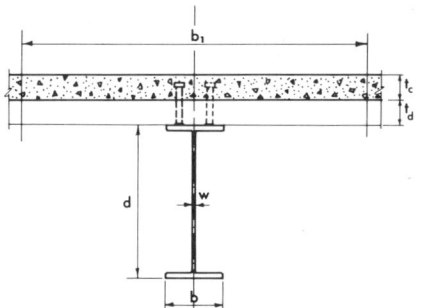

COMPOSITE BEAMS
Trial Selection Tables

G40.21 – 44W
4 Ksi Concrete

2 Inch Deck with 3¼ Inch Slab
$\emptyset = 0.90$, $\emptyset_C = 0.67$, $\emptyset_{SC} = 0.80$

Steel Shape	b₁	Composite Beam								Properties#		Steel Shape Data*	
		Factored Resistances											
		M_{rc} in foot Kips for various percentages of shear connection						Q_r† for 100%		I_1	S_{s_1}		
	In.	100%	90%	80%	70%	60%	50%	Kips	In.⁴	In.³		
W610X113	93	1090	1080	1060	1040	1020	990	689	5090	249	M_r	660
W24X76	77	1050	1040	1020	1010	984	952	570	4830	245	V_r	275
b = 8.99	60	1010	996	982	962	935	903	444	4490	239	L_u	10.4
t = .680	44	957	942	924	902	877	848	326	4080	232	I_x	2100
	28	876	861	844	826	806	785	207	3550	221	S_x	176
W610X101	93	994	981	965	946	926	901	689	4610	223	M_r	584
W24X68	77	956	944	930	915	895	866	570	4380	219	V_r	257
b = 8.97	60	914	904	892	874	850	820	444	4080	214	L_u	10.1
t = .585	44	869	856	839	818	794	767	326	3710	208	I_x	1830
	28	793	779	763	745	726	705	207	3220	197	S_x	154
W530X138	92	1170	1150	1140	1110	1090	1050	681	4900	273	M_r	729
W21X93	76	1130	1110	1100	1080	1050	1010	563	4620	268	V_r	328
b = 8.42	60	1080	1070	1050	1020	995	962	444	4290	262	L_u	10.3
t = .930	44	1020	1000	984	961	935	906	326	3890	253	I_x	2070
	28	934	919	903	885	865	845	207	3380	239	S_x	191
W530X123	92	1060	1050	1030	1010	986	956	681	4460	245	M_r	647
W21X83	76	1020	1010	991	974	950	918	563	4220	241	V_r	288
b = 8.35	60	977	965	950	930	904	873	444	3920	235	L_u	10.1
t = .835	44	925	910	893	872	848	821	326	3560	227	I_x	1830
	28	847	832	817	800	781	761	207	3080	216	S_x	171
W530X109	92	957	943	927	908	887	862	681	4030	218	M_r	568
W21X73	76	918	906	891	875	856	829	563	3820	215	V_r	253
b = 8.30	60	877	867	855	838	816	788	444	3560	210	L_u	9.89
t = .740	44	833	821	805	787	764	739	326	3230	203	I_x	1600
	28	763	750	735	719	701	682	207	2800	193	S_x	151
W530X101	92	902	889	873	854	834	810	681	3800	204	M_r	528
W21X68	76	864	852	838	822	804	780	563	3610	200	V_r	237
b = 8.27	60	824	814	802	788	768	742	444	3360	196	L_u	9.74
t = .685	44	782	771	757	740	719	695	326	3050	190	I_x	1480
	28	717	704	690	675	658	639	207	2650	181	S_x	140
W530X92	92	839	826	811	793	773	750	681	3510	186	M_r	475
W21X62	76	802	791	777	762	744	723	563	3340	183	V_r	219
b = 8.24	60	763	753	742	729	711	687	444	3120	180	L_u	9.59
t = .615	44	722	713	701	685	665	642	326	2840	174	I_x	1330
	28	662	651	637	622	606	587	207	2450	166	S_x	127

†No. of studs/beam = 2 x Q_r x percent shear connection/100/q_r (per stud)   #Concrete density = 115 lb./ft.³

*Units — M_r — Ft. Kips L_u — Ft.   b — In.
V_r — Kips I_x — In.⁴   t — In.
               S_x — In.³

Note: The SI designation in bold face type is the one preferred for use in Canada.

COMPOSITE BEAMS
Trial Selection Tables

G40.21 – 44W
4 Ksi Concrete

2 Inch Deck with 3¼ Inch Slab
$\emptyset = 0.90$, $\emptyset_C = 0.67$, $\emptyset_{SC} = 0.80$

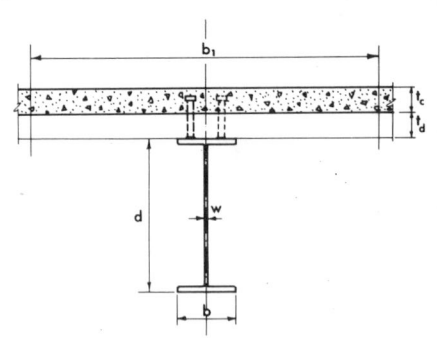

Steel Shape	b_1	Composite Beam									Steel Shape Data*	
		Factored Resistances							Properties#			
		M_{rc} in foot Kips for various percentages of shear connection						Q_r† for 100%	I_1	S_{s_1}		
	In.	100%	90%	80%	70%	60%	50%	Kips	In.⁴	In.³		
W530X82	92	759	746	731	714	695	673	645	3160	166	M_r	416
W21X55	76	729	718	705	690	674	654	563	3010	163	V_r	204
b = 8.22	60	691	682	671	659	643	621	444	2820	160	L_u	9.31
t = .522	44	651	644	633	618	600	577	326	2560	155	I_x	1150
	28	597	586	573	559	542	524	207	2220	148	S_x	111
W460X106	92	838	824	808	789	768	744	681	3120	190	M_r	478
W18X71	76	799	787	772	756	738	715	563	2950	187	V_r	239
b = 7.64	60	758	748	736	722	703	679	444	2750	182	L_u	9.51
t = .810	44	715	705	693	677	657	635	326	2480	176	I_x	1170
	27	650	639	626	612	597	581	200	2110	166	S_x	127
W460X97	92	784	770	755	736	716	692	681	2910	175	M_r	439
W18X65	76	746	734	720	704	686	666	563	2760	172	V_r	216
b = 7.59	60	706	696	684	671	655	633	444	2570	169	L_u	9.35
t = .750	44	664	656	645	630	613	592	326	2330	163	I_x	1070
	27	605	595	583	570	555	539	200	1980	154	S_x	117
W460X89	92	735	723	707	690	669	647	681	2730	162	M_r	406
W18X60	76	698	687	674	658	641	622	563	2590	160	V_r	198
b = 7.56	60	659	650	639	626	612	592	444	2420	157	L_u	9.20
t = .695	43	616	608	599	586	570	551	318	2180	151	I_x	984
	27	565	556	545	532	518	503	200	1870	143	S_x	108
W460X82	92	683	670	655	638	618	597	642	2530	149	M_r	370
W18X55	76	654	643	630	615	598	579	563	2410	147	V_r	185
b = 7.53	59	613	604	593	581	567	549	437	2240	144	L_u	9.02
t = .630	43	573	566	557	546	531	512	318	2030	140	I_x	890
	27	525	517	506	494	481	465	200	1740	132	S_x	98.3
W460X74	91	623	610	596	579	561	541	582	2320	136	M_r	333
W18X50	75	604	594	581	567	551	532	555	2210	134	V_r	167
b = 7.49	59	567	558	548	536	523	507	437	2070	131	L_u	8.89
t = .570	43	528	521	513	503	490	472	318	1880	127	I_x	800
	27	484	476	466	455	442	428	200	1620	121	S_x	88.9
W460X67	91	570	558	544	528	511	492	531	2140	124	M_r	301
W18X45	75	558	548	536	522	506	489	531	2040	122	V_r	156
b = 7.48	59	526	518	508	496	483	468	437	1920	120	L_u	8.65
t = .499	43	488	481	473	464	452	435	318	1750	117	I_x	719
	27	446	438	429	419	406	391	200	1500	111	S_x	80.5

†No. of studs/beam = 2 x Q_r x percent shear connection/100/q_r (per stud)   #Concrete density = 115 lb./ft.³

*Units – M_r – Ft. Kips L_u – Ft.   b – In.
　　　　V_r – Kips I_x – In.⁴   t – In.
　　　　　　　　　　　　　　　 S_x – In.³

Note: The SI designation in bold face type is the one preferred for use in Canada.

2 Inch Deck with 3¼ Inch Slab
$$\phi = 0.90, \quad \phi_C = 0.67, \quad \phi_{SC} = 0.80$$

Steel Shape	b_1	Composite Beam									Steel Shape Data*	
		Factored Resistances							Properties #			
		M_{rc} in foot Kips for various percentages of shear connection						$Q_r^\dagger$ for 100%	I_1	S_{s_1}		
	In.	100%	90%	80%	70%	60%	50%	Kips	In.⁴	In.³		
W460X61	91	517	505	491	476	460	443	479	1940	111	M_r	264
W18X41	75	507	497	485	471	456	440	479	1850	110	V_r	148
b = 7.45	59	485	477	467	456	443	429	437	1740	108	L_u	8.40
t = .425	43	448	441	434	425	413	397	318	1590	105	I_x	623
	27	407	400	391	381	368	354	200	1370	99.5	S_x	70.4
W410X85	91	658	645	630	613	593	571	665	2220	144	M_r	346
W16X57	75	622	611	598	583	566	547	555	2100	141	V_r	185
b = 7.12	59	584	574	563	551	537	519	437	1960	138	L_u	8.91
t = .715	43	543	535	527	516	501	483	318	1770	134	I_x	758
	27	495	487	477	466	453	439	200	1510	126	S_x	92.3
W410X74	91	581	568	554	537	519	498	582	1980	127	M_r	304
W16X50	75	562	552	539	525	508	490	555	1890	125	V_r	161
b = 7.07	59	525	516	505	493	480	465	437	1760	122	L_u	8.67
t = .630	43	485	478	470	461	449	433	318	1600	118	I_x	659
	27	443	436	427	417	406	392	200	1370	112	S_x	81.1
W410X67	91	529	516	502	486	469	450	527	1820	115	M_r	272
W16X45	75	517	506	494	480	465	447	527	1730	113	V_r	145
b = 7.03	59	485	477	467	455	442	428	437	1620	111	L_u	8.50
t = .565	43	447	440	432	423	413	399	318	1470	108	I_x	586
	27	406	400	393	383	372	359	200	1260	102	S_x	72.7
W410X60	91	472	460	447	432	416	399	467	1640	102	M_r	241
W16X40	75	463	452	441	427	413	397	467	1570	101	V_r	128
b = 6.99	59	444	435	426	415	402	388	437	1480	99.2	L_u	8.38
t = .505	43	406	400	392	384	374	362	318	1350	96.4	I_x	518
	27	367	362	356	348	338	326	200	1160	91.8	S_x	64.7
W410X54	91	426	414	401	387	373	357	420	1480	91.5	M_r	211
W16X36	75	418	408	396	384	370	355	420	1420	90.3	V_r	122
b = 6.98	59	406	398	389	378	366	352	420	1340	88.7	L_u	8.14
t = .430	43	373	366	359	351	341	330	318	1220	86.3	I_x	448
	27	334	330	324	316	307	295	200	1050	82.2	S_x	56.5
W410X46	90	370	360	348	335	322	308	361	1300	78.8	M_r	178
W16X31	74	365	355	344	333	320	307	361	1250	77.8	V_r	114
b = 5.52	58	356	348	339	328	317	305	361	1180	76.4	L_u	6.31
t = .440	43	335	329	322	314	304	294	318	1090	74.6	I_x	375
	27	297	293	288	281	272	261	200	944	71.1	S_x	47.2

†No. of studs/beam = 2 x Q_r x percent shear connection/100/q_r (per stud)

*Units — M_r — Ft. Kips L_u — Ft.   b — In.

         V_r — Kips I_x — In.⁴   t — In.

                      S_x — In.³

\# Concrete density = 115 lb./ft.³

Note: The SI designation in bold face type is the one preferred for use in Canada.

COMPOSITE BEAMS
Trial Selection Tables

G40.21 – 44W
4 Ksi Concrete

2 Inch Deck with 3¼ Inch Slab
$\phi = 0.90$, $\phi_C = 0.67$, $\phi_{SC} = 0.80$

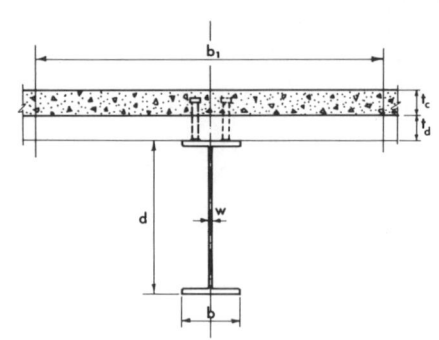

Steel Shape	b_1	M_{rc} in foot Kips for various percentages of shear connection						Q_r† for 100%	I_1	S_{s_1}	Steel Shape Data*	
	In.	100%	90%	80%	70%	60%	50%	Kips	In.⁴	In.³		
W410X39	90	313	303	293	282	270	258	304	1100	66.1	M_r	146
W16X26	74	309	300	290	280	269	257	304	1060	65.3	V_r	99.1
b = 5.50	58	303	295	286	277	267	256	304	1010	64.2	L_u	6.05
t = .345	43	293	287	280	272	263	253	304	936	62.7	I_x	301
	27	258	254	249	244	236	226	200	817	60.0	S_x	38.4
W360X79	92	553	540	525	508	489	468	618	1670	122	M_r	287
W14X53	76	528	517	505	490	473	455	563	1580	120	V_r	135
b = 8.06	60	491	481	471	459	445	430	444	1480	118	L_u	10.6
t = .660	44	451	444	436	427	416	403	326	1340	114	I_x	541
	28	410	405	398	390	380	368	207	1140	108	S_x	77.7
W360X72	92	503	490	476	460	442	422	558	1530	111	M_r	259
W14X48	76	490	480	467	453	437	419	558	1450	109	V_r	123
b = 8.03	60	454	445	435	423	410	396	444	1360	107	L_u	10.4
t = .595	44	416	409	401	392	382	370	326	1240	104	I_x	485
	28	375	371	365	358	348	337	207	1060	98.9	S_x	70.3
W360X64	92	453	440	426	411	395	377	499	1390	99.5	M_r	230
W14X43	76	442	432	420	406	391	374	499	1320	98.1	V_r	109
b = 7.99	60	418	410	400	388	375	361	444	1240	96.3	L_u	10.1
t = .530	44	380	374	366	357	348	337	326	1130	93.6	I_x	428
	28	341	336	331	325	317	306	207	973	89.2	S_x	62.7
W360X57	91	415	403	390	376	360	344	444	1300	89.6	M_r	203
W14X38	75	407	396	384	372	357	342	444	1240	88.4	V_r	114
b = 6.77	59	393	384	375	364	351	337	437	1170	86.7	L_u	8.32
t = .515	43	356	349	342	333	324	313	318	1070	84.3	I_x	385
	27	316	312	307	300	292	281	200	915	80.1	S_x	54.6
W360X51	91	372	361	349	335	321	306	396	1180	80.3	M_r	180
W14X34	75	366	355	344	332	319	305	396	1130	79.3	V_r	104
b = 6.74	59	355	347	338	327	315	302	396	1060	77.9	L_u	8.16
t = .455	43	326	320	313	305	295	285	318	975	75.8	I_x	340
	27	288	284	279	273	266	256	200	840	72.2	S_x	48.6
W360X45	91	331	320	309	296	284	270	350	1050	70.9	M_r	156
W14X30	75	325	316	305	294	282	269	350	1010	70.0	V_r	97.7
b = 6.73	59	317	309	300	290	279	267	350	953	68.8	L_u	7.93
t = .385	43	298	292	285	277	268	258	318	876	67.0	I_x	291
	27	261	257	252	247	239	230	200	759	64.0	S_x	42.1

†No. of studs/beam = 2 x Q_r x percent shear connection/100/q_r (per stud)   #Concrete density = 115 lb./ft.³

*Units — M_r — Ft. Kips L_u — Ft.   b — In.
$\qquad$ V_r — Kips I_x — In.⁴   t — In.
$\qquad\qquad$ S_x — In.³

Note: The SI designation in bold face type is the one preferred for use in Canada.

2 Inch Deck with 3¼ Inch Slab
$\phi = 0.90$, $\phi_C = 0.67$, $\phi_{SC} = 0.80$

Steel Shape	b_1	Composite Beam							Properties#		Steel Shape Data*	
		Factored Resistances						$Q_r^\dagger$ for 100%	I_1	S_{s_1}		
		M_{rc} in foot Kips for various percentages of shear connection										
	In.	100%	90%	80%	70%	60%	50%	Kips	In.⁴	In.³		
W360X39	89	291	281	270	260	248	236	305	930	61.6	M_r	133
W14X26	73	286	277	268	257	247	235	305	894	60.8	V_r	92.7
b = 5.02	58	280	273	264	255	244	233	305	849	59.8	L_u	5.83
t = .420	42	269	264	257	249	240	231	305	782	58.3	I_x	245
	27	236	232	227	222	215	206	200	685	55.8	S_x	35.2
W360X33	89	246	237	228	219	209	198	257	792	52.0	M_r	110
W14X22	73	243	235	226	217	208	197	257	764	51.3	V_r	82.6
b = 5.00	58	239	231	223	215	206	196	257	729	50.5	L_u	5.60
t = .335	42	231	225	218	211	203	194	257	675	49.3	I_x	199
	27	207	203	199	194	188	180	200	596	47.3	S_x	29.0
W310X129	96	740	725	708	688	666	642	711	2070	181	M_r	436
W12X87	79	698	685	670	654	635	615	585	1940	178	V_r	169
b = 12.13	62	655	644	632	619	604	587	459	1790	173	L_u	18.1
t = .810	46	612	604	595	585	573	557	341	1610	167	I_x	740
	29	566	559	551	541	530	517	215	1360	157	S_x	118
W310X118	96	687	672	656	637	615	591	711	1900	165	M_r	393
W12X79	79	646	633	619	603	585	565	585	1790	162	V_r	152
b = 12.08	62	603	593	582	568	554	538	459	1650	158	L_u	17.5
t = .735	46	562	554	545	535	524	510	341	1490	152	I_x	662
	29	517	511	504	495	485	472	215	1260	144	S_x	107
W310X107	96	641	627	611	592	571	548	711	1760	151	M_r	356
W12X72	79	600	588	575	559	541	522	585	1660	148	V_r	138
b = 12.04	62	559	549	538	525	511	495	459	1530	145	L_u	17.0
t = .670	46	519	511	502	493	482	469	341	1380	140	I_x	597
	29	474	469	463	455	445	434	215	1170	132	S_x	97.5
W310X97	96	597	583	568	550	529	506	711	1620	137	M_r	290
W12X65	79	557	546	532	517	500	481	585	1530	135	V_r	124
b = 12.00	62	517	507	496	484	470	455	459	1420	132	L_u	17.5
t = .605	46	477	470	461	452	441	430	341	1280	128	I_x	533
	29	434	429	423	416	407	396	215	1090	121	S_x	88.0
W310X86	94	548	535	520	503	483	461	673	1490	123	M_r	285
W12X58	78	516	505	492	477	460	441	577	1410	121	V_r	115
b = 10.01	61	476	466	456	444	430	415	452	1310	118	L_u	13.9
t = .640	45	436	429	421	412	401	390	333	1180	115	I_x	475
	28	393	388	383	376	368	358	207	999	108	S_x	77.9

†No. of studs/beam = 2 x Q_r x percent shear connection/100/q_r (per stud)

#Concrete density = 115 lb./ft.³

*Units — M_r — Ft. Kips L_u — Ft.   b — In.
  V_r — Kips I_x — In.⁴   t — In.
  S_x — In.³

Note: The SI designation in bold face type is the one preferred for use in Canada.

COMPOSITE BEAMS
Trial Selection Tables

G40.21 – 44W
4 Ksi Concrete

2 Inch Deck with 3¼ Inch Slab
$\emptyset = 0.90$, $\emptyset_C = 0.67$, $\emptyset_{SC} = 0.80$

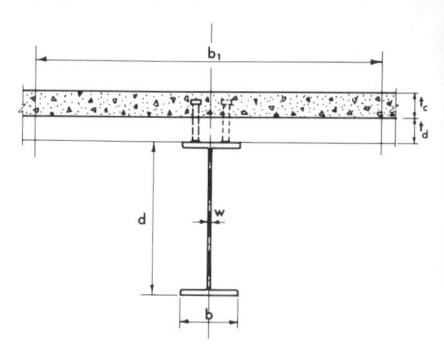

Steel Shape		Composite Beam										Steel Shape Data*	
		Factored Resistances								Properties #			
	b_1	M_{rc} in foot Kips for various percentages of shear connection						$Q_r^\dagger$ for 100%	I_1	S_{s_1}			
	In.	100%	90%	80%	70%	60%	50%	Kips	In.⁴	In.³		
W310X79	94	506	493	478	461	443	422	618	1370	113	M_r	257
W12X53	78	485	474	461	447	430	411	577	1300	111	V_r	109
b = 9.99	61	445	436	426	414	401	386	452	1210	109	L_u	13.5
t = .575	45	407	400	392	383	372	361	333	1100	105	I_x	425
	28	364	360	354	348	340	330	207	928	99.6	S_x	70.5
W310X74	92	483	470	455	439	421	401	582	1310	106	M_r	239
W12X50	76	466	455	443	428	412	394	563	1240	104	V_r	118
b = 8.08	60	429	420	409	397	384	369	444	1160	102	L_u	11.0
t = .640	44	390	383	375	366	356	344	326	1050	98.9	I_x	394
	28	349	344	339	332	323	313	207	894	93.7	S_x	64.6
W310X67	92	437	424	410	395	377	359	523	1200	95.8	M_r	214
W12X45	76	426	415	403	389	373	356	523	1140	94.3	V_r	106
b = 8.05	60	396	388	378	366	353	339	444	1060	92.4	L_u	10.7
t = .575	44	359	352	344	335	325	314	326	964	89.6	I_x	350
	28	319	314	309	303	295	285	207	824	85.0	S_x	58.0
W310X60	92	393	381	368	353	337	320	467	1090	86.1	M_r	190
W12X40	76	384	374	362	349	334	318	467	1040	84.8	V_r	92.1
b = 8.00	60	367	358	349	337	325	311	444	971	83.2	L_u	10.4
t = .515	44	330	323	315	307	297	287	326	884	80.8	I_x	310
	28	291	286	281	275	269	260	207	759	76.9	S_x	51.9
W310X52	91	357	346	333	320	305	290	408	1030	77.2	M_r	169
W12X35	75	350	340	329	316	303	288	408	984	76.1	V_r	98.0
b = 6.56	59	339	331	322	311	299	285	408	926	74.6	L_u	8.33
t = .520	43	308	302	294	286	277	266	318	845	72.5	I_x	285
	27	269	265	260	255	248	239	200	724	69.0	S_x	45.6
W310X45	91	307	296	285	273	260	247	348	893	66.1	M_r	142
W12X30	75	302	292	281	270	258	245	348	857	65.2	V_r	83.9
b = 6.52	59	294	286	276	266	255	243	348	809	64.1	L_u	8.09
t = .440	43	275	269	262	254	245	235	318	742	62.4	I_x	238
	27	238	233	229	223	217	210	200	641	59.5	S_x	38.6
W310X39	90	268	258	248	237	226	214	303	787	57.7	M_r	123
W12X26	75	264	255	246	235	225	213	303	759	57.0	V_r	73.5
b = 6.49	59	258	250	242	232	222	212	303	719	56.1	L_u	7.92
t = .380	43	248	242	235	227	219	209	303	663	54.7	I_x	204
	27	214	210	205	200	194	188	200	577	52.3	S_x	33.4

†No. of studs/beam = 2 x Q_r x percent shear connection/100/q_r (per stud)

*Units — M_r — Ft. Kips L_u — Ft. b — In.
 V_r — Kips I_x — In.⁴ t — In.
 S_x — In.³

#Concrete density = 115 lb./ft.³

Note: The SI designation in bold face type is the one preferred for use in Canada.

2 Inch Deck with 3¼ Inch Slab
$\phi = 0.90$, $\phi_C = 0.67$, $\phi_{SC} = 0.80$

Steel Shape	b_1				Composite Beam						Steel Shape Data*	
		Factored Resistances							Properties#			
		M_{rc} in foot Kips for various percentages of shear connection						Q_r† for 100%	I_1	S_{s_1}		
	In.	100%	90%	80%	70%	60%	50%	Kips	In.⁴	In.³		
W250X101	94	553	539	524	505	485	462	696	1310	128	M_r	281
W10X68	78	515	503	490	474	456	437	577	1240	125	V_r	128
b = 10.13	61	474	464	452	440	426	410	452	1140	122	L_u	16.1
t = .770	45	433	425	417	407	396	384	333	1020	117	I_x	394
	28	388	383	377	370	362	352	207	849	110	S_x	75.8
W250X89	94	507	494	479	461	441	419	696	1180	113	M_r	246
W10X60	78	470	459	446	431	414	395	577	1110	111	V_r	112
b = 10.08	61	430	421	410	398	384	369	452	1030	108	L_u	15.2
t = .680	45	391	383	375	365	355	344	333	922	105	I_x	341
	28	347	342	337	331	323	314	207	771	98.1	S_x	66.7
W250X80	94	461	448	432	415	397	376	626	1080	102	M_r	220
W10X54	78	437	426	414	399	382	364	577	1020	101	V_r	97.6
b = 10.03	61	398	389	378	366	353	338	452	944	98.2	L_u	14.6
t = .615	45	359	352	344	335	325	314	333	850	94.9	I_x	303
	28	316	312	307	301	294	286	207	712	89.2	S_x	60.1
W250X73	94	423	410	396	379	361	342	570	994	93.6	M_r	199
W10X49	78	410	400	387	373	357	339	570	943	92.1	V_r	88.7
b = 10.00	61	373	364	354	342	329	314	452	875	90.0	L_u	14.2
t = .560	45	335	328	320	311	301	290	333	790	87.1	I_x	272
	28	293	288	283	277	271	263	207	663	82.0	S_x	54.5
W250X67	92	397	384	370	354	337	319	527	938	86.6	M_r	181
W10X45	76	385	375	363	349	333	316	527	890	85.2	V_r	92.4
b = 8.02	60	355	347	337	325	312	298	444	829	83.3	L_u	11.6
t = .620	44	317	311	303	294	284	273	326	748	80.5	I_x	248
	28	278	273	268	262	255	247	207	633	76.0	S_x	49.1
W250X58	92	346	334	321	306	291	274	455	824	75.2	M_r	154
W10X39	76	338	327	315	302	288	272	455	784	74.0	V_r	81.7
b = 7.98	60	322	314	305	293	281	267	444	733	72.5	L_u	11.1
t = .530	44	286	279	272	263	253	243	326	665	70.2	I_x	209
	28	247	242	237	232	225	218	207	566	66.5	S_x	42.1
W250X49	92	295	283	271	258	245	230	385	706	63.7	M_r	128
W10X33	76	289	278	267	255	242	229	385	674	62.7	V_r	73.7
b = 7.96	60	279	271	261	251	239	226	385	634	61.5	L_u	10.5
t = .435	44	254	248	241	232	223	213	326	578	59.7	I_x	170
	28	216	212	207	202	196	189	207	495	56.8	S_x	34.9

†No. of studs/beam = 2 x Q_r x percent shear connection/100/q_r (per stud)

*Units — M_r — Ft. Kips L_u — Ft.   b — In.
   V_r — Kips I_x — In.⁴   t — In.
   S_x — In.³

#Concrete density = 115 lb./ft.³

Note: The SI designation in bold face type is the one preferred for use in Canada.

COMPOSITE BEAMS
Trial Selection Tables

G40.21 – 44W
4 Ksi Concrete

2 Inch Deck with 3¼ Inch Slab
$\emptyset = 0.90$, $\emptyset_C = 0.67$, $\emptyset_{SC} = 0.80$

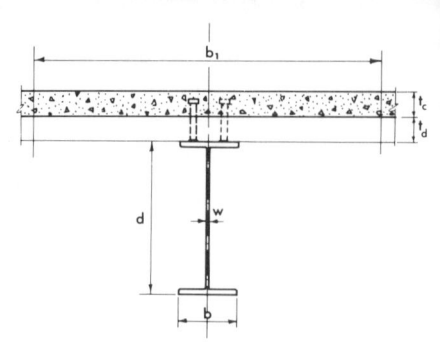

Steel Shape	b₁	Composite Beam — Factored Resistances — M_{rc} in foot Kips for various percentages of shear connection						Q_r for 100%	I_1	S_{s_1}	Steel Shape Data*	
	In.	100%	90%	80%	70%	60%	50%	Kips	In.⁴	In.³		
W250X45	90	281	270	259	247	234	220	350	711	60.0	M_r	121
W10X30	74	276	266	255	244	232	219	350	680	59.1	V_r	82.1
b = 5.81	58	267	259	250	240	229	217	350	639	57.9	L_u	7.63
t = .510	43	249	243	236	228	218	208	318	586	56.3	I_x	170
	27	211	207	202	197	191	184	200	502	53.5	S_x	32.5
W250X39	90	243	233	223	212	201	189	301	622	52.0	M_r	103
W10X26	74	239	230	220	210	199	188	301	596	51.2	V_r	70.2
b = 5.77	58	233	225	217	207	197	186	301	563	50.2	L_u	7.38
t = .440	43	223	217	210	202	194	184	301	519	48.9	I_x	144
	27	189	185	181	175	169	163	200	448	46.6	S_x	27.9
W250X33	90	208	199	190	180	171	160	257	535	44.4	M_r	85.8
W10X22	74	205	197	188	179	170	160	257	514	43.7	V_r	63.8
b = 5.75	58	201	193	185	177	168	158	257	487	42.9	L_u	7.10
t = .360	43	193	187	181	173	165	157	257	452	41.9	I_x	118
	27	169	165	161	156	150	144	200	393	40.0	S_x	23.2
W200X100	92	498	484	468	450	429	406	681	1040	114	M_r	232
W8X67	76	460	448	434	418	400	381	563	976	111	V_r	134
b = 8.28	60	420	410	398	385	371	355	444	895	108	L_u	16.3
t = .935	44	378	370	361	351	340	329	326	793	103	I_x	272
	28	334	329	323	316	308	298	207	657	95.8	S_x	60.4
W200X86	92	452	439	424	407	387	365	677	917	99.2	M_r	197
W8X58	76	416	405	392	377	360	341	563	862	97.2	V_r	117
b = 8.22	60	378	368	357	345	331	316	444	794	94.5	L_u	14.9
t = .810	44	337	330	322	312	302	290	326	705	90.6	I_x	228
	28	295	290	285	278	271	262	207	586	84.4	S_x	52.1
W200X71	92	380	367	353	337	319	299	558	778	82.9	M_r	162
W8X48	76	367	357	344	330	314	296	558	735	81.3	V_r	88.9
b = 8.11	60	331	322	312	300	287	273	444	681	79.3	L_u	13.4
t = .685	44	293	286	278	269	259	248	326	609	76.4	I_x	184
	28	252	248	242	236	230	222	207	510	71.6	S_x	43.3
W200X59	92	319	307	294	279	263	246	463	657	69.1	M_r	131
W8X40	76	310	300	288	275	260	244	463	623	67.9	V_r	77.6
b = 8.07	60	293	285	275	264	252	238	444	581	66.4	L_u	12.3
t = .560	44	256	250	242	234	224	214	326	523	64.1	I_x	146
	28	218	213	208	202	196	189	207	440	60.4	S_x	35.4

†No. of studs/beam = 2 x Q_r x percent shear connection/100/q_r (per stud) #Concrete density = 115 lb./ft.³

*Units — M_r — Ft. Kips L_u — Ft.   b — In.
      V_r — Kips I_x — In.⁴   t — In.
               S_x — In.³

Note: The SI designation in bold face type is the one preferred for use in Canada.

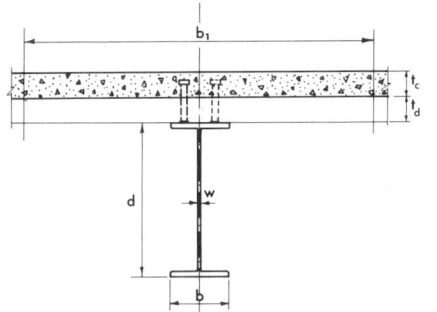

2 Inch Deck with 3¼ Inch Slab
$$\phi = 0.90, \quad \phi_C = 0.67, \quad \phi_{SC} = 0.80$$

Steel Shape	b_1	\multicolumn{6}{c|}{M_{rc} in foot Kips for various percentages of shear connection}						$Q_r^\dagger$ for 100%	I_1	S_{s_1}	\multicolumn{2}{c}{Steel Shape Data*}	
		100%	90%	80%	70%	60%	50%	Kips				
	In.							Kips	In.⁴	In.³		
W200X52	92	283	272	259	246	231	216	408	589	61.3	M_r	115
W8X35	76	276	266	255	242	229	214	408	560	60.3	V_r	65.8
b = 8.02	60	266	257	248	237	225	212	408	524	59.0	L_u	11.7
t = .495	44	236	230	222	214	205	194	326	474	57.1	I_x	127
	28	198	194	189	183	177	170	207	401	54.0	S_x	31.3
W200X46	92	253	242	230	218	205	191	362	528	54.6	M_r	100
W8X31	76	247	237	227	215	203	190	362	504	53.7	V_r	59.6
b = 7.99	60	239	231	221	211	200	187	362	473	52.6	L_u	11.3
t = .435	44	219	213	206	197	188	178	326	430	51.0	I_x	110
	28	182	177	173	167	161	154	207	366	48.3	S_x	27.5
W200X42	91	231	221	210	198	186	174	327	489	49.6	M_r	89.8
W8X28	75	227	217	207	196	185	173	327	467	48.8	V_r	60.0
b = 6.53	59	220	211	203	193	182	171	327	439	47.7	L_u	9.27
t = .465	43	206	200	193	185	176	166	318	399	46.3	I_x	98.0
	27	169	165	160	155	149	143	200	340	43.8	S_x	24.3
W200X36	90	199	190	180	170	159	148	280	426	42.9	M_r	76.6
W8X24	75	196	187	178	169	158	148	280	409	42.3	V_r	50.8
b = 6.49	59	191	183	175	166	156	146	280	386	41.4	L_u	8.86
t = .400	43	182	176	169	162	153	144	280	353	40.2	I_x	82.8
	27	152	149	144	139	133	127	200	303	38.2	S_x	20.9
W200X31	89	179	170	161	152	143	133	244	397	38.2	M_r	67.3
W8X21	74	176	168	160	151	142	132	244	382	37.6	V_r	54.1
b = 5.27	58	172	165	157	149	140	131	244	361	36.8	L_u	6.98
t = .400	42	165	159	153	146	138	130	244	332	35.8	I_x	75.3
	27	144	141	136	131	125	119	200	290	34.2	S_x	18.2
W200X27	89	153	145	138	130	121	113	208	343	32.7	M_r	56.1
W8X18	74	151	144	137	129	121	112	208	331	32.3	V_r	48.9
b = 5.25	58	148	142	135	127	120	112	208	314	31.6	L_u	6.70
t = .330	42	143	137	131	125	118	110	208	290	30.7	I_x	61.9
	27	131	127	123	118	113	106	200	255	29.4	S_x	15.2

†No. of studs/beam = 2 x Q_r x percent shear connection/100/q_r (per stud)

#Concrete density = 115 lb./ft.³

*Units — M_r — Ft. Kips L_u — Ft.   b — In.
       V_r — Kips I_x — In.⁴   t — In.
                S_x — In.³

Note: The SI designation in bold face type is the one preferred for use in Canada.

COMPOSITE BEAMS
Trial Selection Tables

G40.21 – 44W
4 Ksi Concrete

3 Inch Deck with 3¼ Inch Slab
$\varnothing = 0.90$, $\varnothing_C = 0.67$, $\varnothing_{SC} = 0.80$

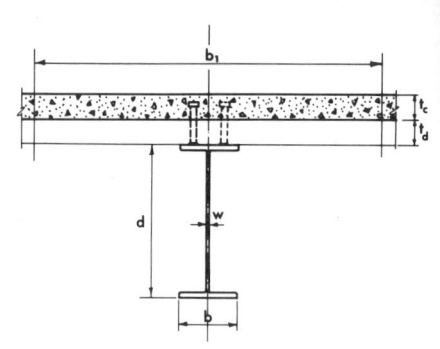

Steel Shape	b_1	Composite Beam — Factored Resistances — M_{rc} in foot Kips for various percentages of shear connection						Q_r† for 100%	Properties# I_1	S_{s_1}	Steel Shape Data*	
	In.	100%	90%	80%	70%	60%	50%	Kips	In.⁴	In.³		
W610X241	113	2250	2220	2180	2150	2100	2040	837	10900	559	M_r	1540
W24X162	93	2170	2150	2120	2080	2030	1970	689	10200	548	V_r	461
b = 12.95	73	2100	2070	2030	1990	1940	1890	540	9470	534	L_u	16.9
t = 1.22	54	1990	1960	1930	1890	1850	1810	400	8630	516	I_x	5170
	34	1850	1830	1800	1770	1740	1710	252	7560	491	S_x	414
W610X217	113	2050	2020	1990	1950	1910	1860	837	9960	506	M_r	1380
W24X146	93	1980	1950	1930	1890	1850	1790	689	9380	496	V_r	420
b = 12.90	73	1910	1880	1850	1810	1770	1720	540	8680	483	L_u	16.5
t = 1.09	54	1810	1780	1750	1720	1680	1640	400	7900	468	I_x	4580
	34	1680	1660	1630	1600	1580	1550	252	6900	444	S_x	370
W610X195	113	1860	1830	1800	1770	1730	1680	837	9070	454	M_r	1220
W24X131	93	1790	1770	1740	1710	1670	1620	689	8540	446	V_r	387
b = 12.85	73	1720	1700	1670	1640	1600	1550	540	7910	435	L_u	16.1
t = .960	54	1640	1610	1580	1550	1510	1470	400	7190	420	I_x	4020
	34	1510	1490	1470	1440	1410	1380	252	6250	399	S_x	328
W610X174	113	1690	1660	1630	1600	1570	1520	837	8270	408	M_r	1080
W24X117	93	1620	1600	1580	1550	1510	1470	689	7790	400	V_r	349
b = 12.80	73	1560	1540	1520	1480	1450	1400	540	7230	391	L_u	15.7
t = .850	54	1480	1460	1430	1400	1370	1330	400	6560	378	I_x	3540
	34	1370	1350	1320	1300	1270	1240	252	5690	359	S_x	292
W610X155	113	1530	1510	1480	1450	1410	1380	837	7510	364	M_r	954
W24X104	93	1470	1450	1420	1400	1370	1330	689	7090	358	V_r	314
b = 12.75	73	1400	1390	1370	1340	1310	1270	540	6580	350	L_u	15.4
t = .750	54	1340	1320	1300	1270	1230	1200	400	5980	339	I_x	3100
	34	1230	1210	1190	1170	1140	1110	252	5170	322	S_x	258
W610X140	109	1420	1390	1370	1340	1300	1260	807	6870	326	M_r	838
W24X94	90	1360	1340	1310	1290	1250	1210	666	6500	320	V_r	327
b = 9.06	71	1290	1280	1260	1230	1190	1150	526	6030	313	L_u	10.8
t = .875	52	1220	1200	1180	1150	1110	1080	385	5450	302	I_x	2700
	33	1110	1090	1070	1050	1020	995	244	4700	286	S_x	222
W610X125	109	1290	1270	1240	1210	1180	1150	807	6240	292	M_r	739
W24X84	90	1230	1210	1190	1170	1140	1100	666	5910	287	V_r	296
b = 9.02	71	1170	1160	1140	1110	1080	1040	526	5500	281	L_u	10.6
t = .770	52	1110	1090	1070	1040	1010	975	385	4980	271	I_x	2370
	33	1010	990	970	947	922	896	244	4290	257	S_x	197

†No. of studs/beam = 2 x Q_r x percent shear connection/100/q_r (per stud)

*Units — M_r — Ft. Kips L_u — Ft.   b — In.
      V_r — Kips I_x — In.⁴   t — In.
                   S_x — In.³

#Concrete density = 115 lb./ft.³

Note: The SI designation in bold face type is the one preferred for use in Canada.

3 Inch Deck with 3¼ Inch Slab
$$\emptyset = 0.90, \ \emptyset_C = 0.67, \ \emptyset_{SC} = 0.80$$

Steel Shape	Composite Beam										Steel Shape Data*	
		Factored Resistances							Properties #			
	b_1	M_{rc} in foot Kips for various percentages of shear connection						Q_r† for 100%	I_1	S_{s_1}		
	In.	100%	90%	80%	70%	60%	50%	Kips	In.⁴	In.³		
W610X113 W24X76 b = 8.99 t = .680	109 90 71 52 33	1190 1140 1080 1020 925	1170 1120 1060 1000 908	1150 1100 1040 981 888	1120 1070 1020 956 866	1090 1050 995 927 842	1050 1010 958 893 816	807 666 526 385 244	5730 5430 5060 4580 3950	265 260 255 246 233	M_r V_r L_u I_x S_x	660 275 10.4 2100 176
W610X101 W24X68 b = 8.97 t = .585	109 90 71 52 33	1100 1040 985 925 841	1070 1020 970 912 824	1050 1000 952 894 805	1020 979 933 871 784	992 954 907 843 761	958 923 873 810 735	796 666 526 385 244	5190 4930 4610 4180 3590	237 233 228 221 209	M_r V_r L_u I_x S_x	584 257 10.1 1830 154
W530X138 W21X93 b = 8.42 t = .930	108 89 70 51 33	1280 1220 1150 1080 985	1250 1200 1140 1060 966	1230 1170 1120 1040 946	1200 1150 1090 1010 924	1160 1110 1050 981 900	1120 1070 1010 947 875	800 659 518 378 244	5560 5240 4850 4360 3760	292 287 279 269 254	M_r V_r L_u I_x S_x	729 328 10.3 2070 191
W530X123 W21X83 b = 8.35 t = .835	108 89 70 51 33	1170 1110 1050 982 895	1140 1090 1030 966 878	1120 1060 1010 945 859	1090 1040 989 921 838	1060 1010 960 892 815	1020 977 924 860 791	800 659 518 378 244	5070 4790 4440 4000 3450	262 258 251 242 229	M_r V_r L_u I_x S_x	647 288 10.1 1830 171
W530X109 W21X73 b = 8.30 t = .740	108 89 70 51 32	1060 1010 946 885 803	1040 986 930 872 788	1010 964 912 855 770	987 940 893 833 751	956 914 868 807 730	922 884 836 777 707	800 659 518 378 237	4580 4340 4040 3640 3110	233 230 224 217 205	M_r V_r L_u I_x S_x	568 253 9.89 1600 151
W530X101 W21X68 b = 8.27 t = .685	108 89 70 51 32	1000 950 892 832 756	982 931 877 820 741	958 910 859 805 725	930 887 840 785 706	900 861 818 761 686	867 833 788 732 663	792 659 518 378 237	4320 4100 3820 3450 2950	218 214 210 203 192	M_r V_r L_u I_x S_x	528 237 9.74 1480 140
W530X92 W21X62 b = 8.24 t = .615	108 89 70 51 32	922 887 831 772 701	901 869 816 760 687	877 849 799 746 671	851 826 780 729 653	823 801 759 706 634	792 773 732 678 611	725 659 518 378 237	3990 3800 3540 3210 2740	199 196 192 186 176	M_r V_r L_u I_x S_x	475 219 9.59 1330 127

†No. of studs/beam = 2 x Q_r x percent shear connection/100/q_r (per stud)

\# Concrete density = 115 lb./ft.³

*Units — M_r — Ft. Kips L_u — Ft.   b — In.
       V_r — Kips I_x — In.⁴   t — In.
                 S_x — In.³

Note: The SI designation in bold face type is the one preferred for use in Canada.

COMPOSITE BEAMS
Trial Selection Tables

G40.21 – 44W
4 Ksi Concrete

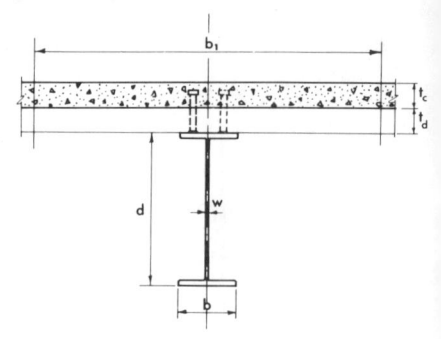

3 Inch Deck with 3¼ Inch Slab
$\phi = 0.90$, $\phi_C = 0.67$, $\phi_{SC} = 0.80$

Steel Shape	b₁	Composite Beam									Steel Shape Data*	

Steel Shape	b₁	M_{rc} in foot Kips for various percentages of shear connection						Q_r† for 100%	I_1	S_{s_1}	Steel Shape Data*	
	In.	100%	90%	80%	70%	60%	50%	Kips	In.⁴	In.³		
W530X82	108	825	805	782	758	731	703	645	3590	177	M_r	416
W21X55	89	810	792	772	750	726	699	645	3420	175	V_r	204
b = 8.22	70	758	743	727	709	689	664	518	3200	171	L_u	9.31
t = .522	51	700	689	676	660	639	613	378	2910	166	I_x	1150
	32	634	621	606	589	570	548	237	2490	157	S_x	111
W460X106	108	942	920	895	868	837	803	800	3590	205	M_r	478
W18X71	89	886	867	845	821	795	766	659	3400	201	V_r	239
b = 7.64	70	827	811	793	774	752	724	518	3160	196	L_u	9.51
t = .810	51	766	753	739	720	698	671	378	2840	190	I_x	1170
	32	692	679	664	647	628	607	237	2410	178	S_x	127
W460X97	108	875	854	830	803	773	741	756	3350	189	M_r	439
W18X65	89	832	813	792	769	743	715	659	3180	186	V_r	216
b = 7.59	70	774	759	741	722	701	676	518	2960	182	L_u	9.35
t = .750	51	714	702	689	672	652	627	378	2670	176	I_x	1070
	32	646	634	619	603	585	565	237	2260	166	S_x	117
W460X89	108	810	789	766	740	712	682	697	3140	175	M_r	406
W18X60	89	784	766	745	722	697	670	659	2980	172	V_r	198
b = 7.56	70	727	712	695	676	656	633	518	2780	169	L_u	9.20
t = .695	51	668	656	643	629	610	587	378	2510	163	I_x	984
	32	604	593	580	565	548	528	237	2140	154	S_x	108
W460X82	108	749	728	706	681	655	627	642	2910	161	M_r	370
W18X55	89	734	716	696	674	650	623	642	2770	159	V_r	185
b = 7.53	70	683	668	652	633	613	591	518	2590	156	L_u	9.02
t = .630	51	625	613	601	587	570	548	378	2350	151	I_x	890
	32	563	553	541	526	510	491	237	2000	143	S_x	98.3
W460X74	107	682	662	641	618	594	568	582	2670	147	M_r	333
W18X50	89	670	653	633	612	589	565	582	2560	145	V_r	167
b = 7.49	70	636	621	605	588	568	546	518	2400	142	L_u	8.89
t = .570	51	579	568	555	542	527	507	378	2180	138	I_x	800
	32	519	511	500	486	471	453	237	1860	131	S_x	88.9
W460X67	107	623	604	584	563	540	516	531	2460	134	M_r	301
W 18X45	89	613	597	578	558	537	514	531	2360	132	V_r	156
b = 7.48	70	595	581	565	547	528	507	518	2220	130	L_u	8.65
t = .499	51	539	528	516	502	488	469	378	2020	126	I_x	719
	32	480	472	462	449	434	416	237	1730	120	S_x	80.5

†No. of studs/beam = 2 x Q_r x percent shear connection/100/q_r (per stud)   #Concrete density = 115 lb./ft.³

*Units — M_r — Ft. Kips L_u — Ft.   b — In.
       V_r — Kips I_x — In.⁴   t — In.
                     S_x — In.³

Note: The SI designation in bold face type is the one preferred for use in Canada.

COMPOSITE BEAMS
Trial Selection Tables

G40.21 – 44W
4 Ksi Concrete

3 Inch Deck with 3¼ Inch Slab
$\phi = 0.90$, $\phi_C = 0.67$, $\phi_{SC} = 0.80$

Steel Shape	b_1	Composite Beam								Properties#		Steel Shape Data*	
		Factored Resistances											
		M_{rc} in foot Kips for various percentages of shear connection						Q_r† for 100%	I_1	S_{s_1}			
	In.	100%	90%	80%	70%	60%	50%	Kips	In.⁴	In.³		
W460X61	107	564	546	527	507	486	464	479	2230	120	M_r	264
W18X41	89	556	540	522	503	484	462	479	2140	119	V_r	148
b = 7.45	70	543	529	514	497	479	459	479	2010	117	L_u	8.40
t = .425	51	498	488	476	463	448	431	378	1840	113	I_x	623
	32	441	433	423	411	396	379	237	1580	108	S_x	70.4
W410X85	107	726	706	683	658	631	602	665	2580	156	M_r	346
W16X57	88	707	689	669	647	622	595	652	2450	154	V_r	185
b = 7.12	70	654	639	622	603	583	561	518	2290	150	L_u	8.91
t = .715	51	595	583	570	556	539	518	378	2060	145	I_x	758
	32	532	523	511	497	481	463	237	1750	137	S_x	92.3
W410X74	107	640	620	599	576	551	525	582	2310	138	M_r	304
W16X50	88	627	610	591	570	547	522	582	2200	135	V_r	161
b = 7.07	70	594	579	563	545	526	504	518	2060	133	L_u	8.67
t = .630	51	537	526	513	499	485	466	378	1870	129	I_x	659
	32	477	469	459	447	433	416	237	1590	122	S_x	81.1
W410X67	107	581	562	542	521	498	474	527	2110	125	M_r	272
W16X45	88	571	554	536	516	494	472	527	2010	123	V_r	145
b = 7.03	70	554	540	524	507	487	466	518	1900	121	L_u	8.50
t = .565	51	498	487	475	461	447	430	378	1720	117	I_x	586
	32	439	432	423	412	398	382	237	1470	111	S_x	72.7
W410X60	107	518	500	482	462	442	420	467	1910	111	M_r	241
W16X40	88	510	494	477	458	439	418	467	1830	110	V_r	128
b = 6.99	70	498	484	469	453	435	415	467	1720	108	L_u	8.38
t = .505	51	457	446	434	421	407	391	378	1580	105	I_x	518
	32	399	392	384	375	363	348	237	1350	99.8	S_x	64.7
W410X54	107	466	450	432	414	396	376	420	1720	99.5	M_r	211
W16X36	88	459	444	428	411	393	374	420	1650	98.2	V_r	122
b = 6.98	70	450	437	422	407	390	372	420	1560	96.6	L_u	8.14
t = .430	51	423	412	401	388	374	359	378	1430	94.0	I_x	448
	32	366	359	352	343	331	317	237	1230	89.6	S_x	56.5
W410X46	106	405	390	375	358	342	324	361	1510	85.8	M_r	178
W16X31	87	400	386	371	356	340	323	361	1450	84.7	V_r	114
b = 5.52	69	392	380	367	353	337	321	361	1380	83.3	L_u	6.31
t = .440	50	379	369	358	346	333	318	361	1270	81.2	I_x	375
	32	329	322	314	306	296	282	237	1110	77.7	S_x	47.2

†No. of studs/beam = 2 x Q_r x percent shear connection/100/q_r (per stud)

#Concrete density = 115 lb./ft.³

*Units — M_r — Ft. Kips L_u — Ft.   b — In.
  V_r — Kips I_x — In.⁴   t — In.
                   S_x — In.³

Note: The SI designation in bold face type is the one preferred for use in Canada.

COMPOSITE BEAMS
Trial Selection Tables

G40.21 – 44W
4 Ksi Concrete

3 Inch Deck with 3¼ Inch Slab
$\emptyset = 0.90$, $\emptyset_C = 0.67$, $\emptyset_{SC} = 0.80$

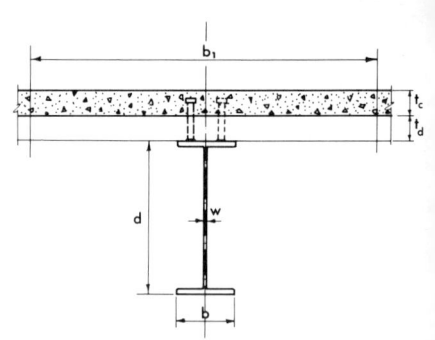

Steel Shape	Composite Beam										Steel Shape Data*	
		Factored Resistances							Properties#			
	b_1	M_{rc} in foot Kips for various percentages of shear connection						$Q_r^\dagger$ for 100%	I_1	S_{s_1}		
	In.	100%	90%	80%	70%	60%	50%	Kips	In.⁴	In.³		
W410X39	106	341	328	315	301	287	272	304	1280	72.0	M_r	146
W16X26	87	338	326	313	299	285	271	304	1240	71.1	V_r	99.1
b = 5.50	69	333	321	309	297	284	270	304	1180	70.1	L_u	6.05
t = .345	50	323	314	304	292	280	267	304	1090	68.4	I_x	301
	32	290	283	276	268	259	247	237	961	65.6	S_x	38.4
W360X79	108	615	595	573	550	524	497	618	1960	134	M_r	287
W14X53	89	602	584	565	543	519	493	618	1870	132	V_r	135
b = 8.06	70	557	543	527	509	489	467	518	1740	129	L_u	10.6
t = .660	51	500	489	476	463	448	432	378	1570	125	I_x	541
	32	440	433	424	414	402	387	237	1330	118	S_x	77.7
W360X72	108	559	540	519	497	473	448	558	1800	121	M_r	259
W14X48	89	548	530	512	491	469	445	558	1720	120	V_r	123
b = 8.03	70	520	506	490	473	454	432	518	1600	117	L_u	10.4
t = .595	51	464	453	441	428	413	397	378	1450	114	I_x	485
	32	405	398	390	381	370	356	237	1230	108	S_x	70.3
W360X64	108	502	484	464	444	422	399	499	1630	109	M_r	230
W14X43	89	493	476	458	439	419	397	499	1560	107	V_r	109
b = 7.99	70	479	465	450	433	414	394	499	1460	105	L_u	10.1
t = .530	51	429	418	406	393	379	363	378	1330	102	I_x	428
	32	371	364	356	347	337	325	237	1140	97.2	S_x	62.7
W360X57	107	458	441	423	404	385	364	444	1530	98.1	M_r	203
W14X38	88	451	435	419	401	382	362	444	1470	96.8	V_r	114
b = 6.77	69	439	426	411	395	378	359	444	1380	95.0	L_u	8.32
t = .515	51	406	395	384	371	356	341	378	1260	92.5	I_x	385
	32	349	342	334	325	315	302	237	1080	87.9	S_x	54.6
W360X51	107	410	394	378	361	343	324	396	1390	87.9	M_r	180
W14X34	88	404	390	374	358	341	323	396	1330	86.8	V_r	104
b = 6.74	69	395	383	369	354	337	320	396	1260	85.3	L_u	8.16
t = .455	51	376	366	355	342	328	313	378	1160	83.1	I_x	340
	32	320	313	306	297	288	276	237	996	79.2	S_x	48.6
W360X45	107	364	349	334	319	303	286	350	1230	77.7	M_r	156
W14X30	88	359	346	331	316	301	285	350	1190	76.7	V_r	97.7
b = 6.73	69	352	340	327	313	298	283	350	1130	75.4	L_u	7.93
t = .385	51	341	331	320	307	294	280	350	1040	73.6	I_x	291
	32	292	286	278	270	261	250	237	901	70.3	S_x	42.1

†No. of studs/beam = 2 x Q_r x percent shear connection/100/q_r (per stud)

*Units — M_r — Ft. Kips L_u — Ft.   b — In.
        V_r — Kips I_x — In.⁴   t — In.
                  S_x — In.³

#Concrete density = 115 lb./ft.³

Note: The SI designation in bold face type is the one preferred for use in Canada.

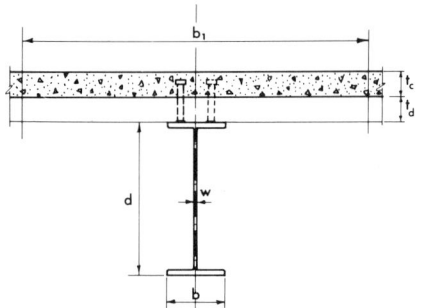

COMPOSITE BEAMS
Trial Selection Tables

G40.21 – 44W
4 Ksi Concrete

3 Inch Deck with 3¼ Inch Slab
$\phi = 0.90$, $\phi_C = 0.67$, $\phi_{SC} = 0.80$

Steel Shape	b₁	Composite Beam								Properties#		Steel Shape Data*	
		Factored Resistances											
		M_{rc} in foot Kips for various percentages of shear connection						$Q_r{}^†$ for 100%		I_1	S_{s_1}		
		100%	90%	80%	70%	60%	50%	Kips		In.⁴	In.³		
	In.												
W360X39	105	319	306	293	279	264	249	305		1090	67.6	M_r	133
W14X26	87	316	303	291	277	263	248	305		1060	66.8	V_r	92.7
b = 5.02	68	310	299	287	274	261	247	305		1000	65.7	L_u	5.83
t = .420	50	301	292	281	270	258	245	305		930	64.1	I_x	245
	32	267	261	253	245	236	226	237		816	61.5	S_x	35.2
W360X33	105	269	258	247	235	222	209	257		932	57.0	M_r	110
W14X22	87	267	256	245	233	221	209	257		902	56.4	V_r	82.6
b = 5.00	68	263	253	243	232	220	208	257		861	55.5	L_u	5.60
t = .335	50	257	248	238	228	218	206	257		803	54.3	I_x	199
	32	238	232	225	217	208	199	237		711	52.2	S_x	29.0
W310X129	112	847	824	798	768	736	702	829		2460	200	M_r	436
W12X87	93	790	770	747	722	695	666	689		2320	196	V_r	169
b = 12.13	73	728	711	693	673	651	628	540		2130	190	L_u	18.1
t = .810	53	664	651	638	623	606	588	392		1890	183	I_x	740
	34	601	593	583	570	556	540	252		1590	171	S_x	118
W310X118	112	793	770	745	716	685	651	829		2270	182	M_r	393
W12X79	92	734	714	693	669	642	614	681		2130	178	V_r	152
b = 12.08	73	676	660	642	622	601	578	540		1970	174	L_u	17.5
t = .735	53	613	601	587	573	557	540	392		1750	167	I_x	662
	34	552	543	534	523	510	495	252		1480	157	S_x	107
W310X107	112	746	724	699	671	640	607	829		2100	166	M_r	356
W12X72	92	688	669	648	624	598	570	681		1980	163	V_r	138
b = 12.04	73	631	615	598	579	558	535	540		1830	160	L_u	17.0
t = .670	53	569	557	544	530	514	498	392		1630	154	I_x	597
	34	509	501	492	482	470	456	252		1380	145	S_x	97.5
W310X97	112	682	661	636	610	581	549	756		1930	151	M_r	290
W12X65	92	644	626	605	582	556	529	681		1820	149	V_r	124
b = 12.00	73	588	573	556	537	516	494	540		1690	145	L_u	17.5
t = .605	53	527	516	503	489	474	457	392		1520	140	I_x	533
	34	468	460	452	442	431	418	252		1280	132	S_x	88.0
W310X86	110	617	596	573	548	521	492	673		1780	136	M_r	285
W12X58	91	601	583	563	541	516	489	673		1680	134	V_r	115
b = 10.01	72	546	531	515	496	476	454	533		1570	131	L_u	13.9
t = .640	52	486	475	462	448	433	417	385		1400	126	I_x	475
	33	426	419	411	402	391	379	244		1180	119	S_x	77.9

†No. of studs/beam = 2 x Q_r x percent shear connection/100/q_r (per stud)

\#Concrete density = 115 lb./ft.³

*Units — M_r — Ft. Kips L_u — Ft.   b — In.
        V_r — Kips I_x — In.⁴   t — In.
                 S_x — In.³

Note: The SI designation in bold face type is the one preferred for use in Canada.

COMPOSITE BEAMS
Trial Selection Tables

G40.21 – 44W
4 Ksi Concrete

3 Inch Deck with 3¼ Inch Slab
$\emptyset = 0.90$, $\emptyset_C = 0.67$, $\emptyset_{SC} = 0.80$

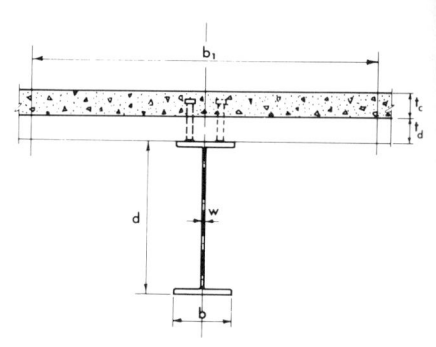

Steel Shape		Composite Beam										Steel Shape Data*	
		Factored Resistances							Properties#				
	b_1	M_{rc} in foot Kips for various percentages of shear connection						Q_r† for 100%	I_1	S_{s_1}			
	In.	100%	90%	80%	70%	60%	50%	Kips	In.⁴	In.³			
W310X79	110	569	548	526	503	477	450	618	1640	125	M_r	257
W12X53	91	555	538	518	496	473	447	618	1560	123	V_r	109
b = 9.99	71	513	498	482	464	444	423	526	1450	120	L_u	13.5
t = .575	52	456	445	432	419	404	388	385	1310	116	I_x	425
	33	397	390	382	373	363	350	244	1100	110	S_x	70.5
W310X74	108	541	522	501	478	453	427	582	1570	117	M_r	239
W12X50	89	529	512	493	472	449	424	582	1490	115	V_r	118
b = 8.08	70	495	481	465	447	428	406	518	1390	113	L_u	11.0
t = .640	51	438	427	415	402	387	371	378	1250	109	I_x	394
	32	379	372	364	355	344	331	237	1050	103	S_x	64.6
W310X67	108	489	470	450	429	406	383	523	1430	106	M_r	214
W12X45	89	479	462	444	424	403	380	523	1360	104	V_r	106
b = 8.05	70	462	449	433	416	396	376	518	1270	102	L_u	10.7
t = .575	51	407	396	384	371	357	341	378	1150	99.0	I_x	350
	32	349	341	334	325	315	304	237	975	93.6	S_x	58.0
W310X60	108	439	421	403	383	363	341	467	1300	95.1	M_r	190
W12X40	89	431	415	398	380	360	339	467	1240	93.7	V_r	92.1
b = 8.00	70	419	405	390	374	356	336	467	1160	91.9	L_u	10.4
t = .515	51	377	367	355	342	328	313	378	1060	89.3	I_x	310
	32	320	313	306	297	288	277	237	900	84.7	S_x	51.9
W310X52	107	396	380	364	346	328	308	408	1230	85.1	M_r	169
W12X35	88	390	375	360	343	325	307	408	1170	83.9	V_r	98.0
b = 6.56	69	381	368	354	338	322	304	408	1110	82.4	L_u	8.33
t = .520	51	358	348	336	323	309	294	378	1010	80.2	I_x	285
	32	301	294	287	278	269	259	237	869	76.3	S_x	45.6
W310X45	107	340	325	310	295	279	262	348	1060	72.9	M_r	142
W12X30	88	335	322	307	293	277	261	348	1020	72.0	V_r	83.9
b = 6.52	69	328	316	303	289	275	259	348	966	70.7	L_u	8.09
t = .440	51	317	307	296	284	271	256	348	892	69.0	I_x	238
	32	269	263	255	247	238	228	237	771	65.9	S_x	38.6
W310X39	106	296	283	270	256	242	227	303	936	63.7	M_r	123
W12X26	88	293	281	268	255	241	227	303	904	62.9	V_r	73.5
b = 6.49	69	288	276	265	252	239	225	303	858	61.9	L_u	7.92
t = .380	51	279	270	259	248	236	223	303	797	60.5	I_x	204
	32	245	239	231	223	215	205	237	694	57.9	S_x	33.4

†No. of studs/beam = 2 x Q_r x percent shear connection/100/q_r (per stud)

\#Concrete density = 115 lb./ft.³

*Units — M_r — Ft. Kips L_u — Ft.   b — In.

V_r — Kips I_x — In.⁴   t — In.

S_x — In.³

Note: The SI designation in bold face type is the one preferred for use in Canada.

3 Inch Deck with 3¼ Inch Slab
$\phi = 0.90$, $\phi_C = 0.67$, $\phi_{SC} = 0.80$

Steel Shape	Composite Beam										Steel
	b_1	Factored Resistances							Properties#		Shape Data*
		M_{rc} in foot Kips for various percentages of shear connection						Q_r† for 100%	I_1	S_{s_1}	
	In.	100%	90%	80%	70%	60%	50%	Kips	In.⁴	In.³	
W250X101	110	651	630	605	578	548	515	792	1610	143	M_r 281
W10X68	91	602	583	562	539	513	485	674	1510	140	V_r 128
b = 10.13	72	545	530	512	493	472	450	533	1400	137	L_u 16.1
t = .770	52	483	471	458	444	428	412	385	1230	131	I_x 394
	33	422	414	405	396	385	372	244	1020	122	S_x 75.8
W250X89	110	579	558	534	509	481	452	697	1440	127	M_r 246
W10X60	91	556	538	518	495	470	443	674	1360	125	V_r 112
b = 10.08	72	501	486	469	450	430	408	533	1260	122	L_u 15.2
t = .680	52	440	429	416	402	387	371	385	1120	117	I_x 341
	33	380	373	364	355	345	334	244	935	110	S_x 66.7
W250X80	110	524	503	481	457	432	405	626	1320	115	M_r 220
W10X54	91	510	492	473	451	427	401	626	1250	113	V_r 97.6
b = 10.03	72	468	453	437	419	399	377	533	1160	110	L_u 14.6
t = .615	52	408	397	385	371	356	340	385	1040	106	I_x 303
	33	350	342	334	325	315	305	244	867	99.9	S_x 60.1
W250X73	110	480	460	439	417	393	368	570	1220	105	M_r 199
W10X49	91	469	451	432	411	389	365	570	1150	103	V_r 88.7
b = 10.00	72	442	428	412	394	374	353	533	1080	101	L_u 14.2
t = .560	52	384	373	361	347	333	317	385	964	97.5	I_x 272
	33	326	318	310	302	292	282	244	810	91.9	S_x 54.5
W250X67	108	449	430	410	389	366	343	527	1150	97.0	M_r 181
W10X45	89	439	422	404	384	363	340	527	1090	95.5	V_r 92.4
b = 8.02	70	421	407	392	374	355	334	518	1020	93.4	L_u 11.6
t = .620	51	366	355	343	330	315	300	378	915	90.3	I_x 248
	32	307	300	292	284	274	264	237	766	85.0	S_x 49.1
W250X58	108	390	373	355	336	316	295	455	1010	84.3	M_r 154
W10X39	89	383	367	350	332	313	293	455	961	83.0	V_r 81.7
b = 7.98	70	371	358	343	326	309	290	455	900	81.3	L_u 11.1
t = .530	51	333	323	311	298	284	269	378	815	78.8	I_x 209
	32	276	269	262	253	244	234	237	688	74.5	S_x 42.1
W250X49	108	331	316	300	283	265	247	385	864	71.4	M_r 128
W10X33	89	326	311	296	280	264	246	385	827	70.4	V_r 73.7
b = 7.96	70	318	305	291	276	261	244	385	778	69.0	L_u 10.5
t = .435	51	301	291	280	268	254	239	378	710	67.1	I_x 170
	32	246	239	232	223	214	205	237	604	63.7	S_x 34.9

†No. of studs/beam = 2 x Q_r x percent shear connection/100/q_r (per stud)

#Concrete density = 115 lb./ft.³

*Units — M_r — Ft. Kips L_u — Ft.   b — In.
          V_r — Kips I_x — In.⁴   t — In.
                       S_x — In.³

Note: The SI designation in bold face type is the one preferred for use in Canada.

COMPOSITE BEAMS
Trial Selection Tables

G40.21 – 44W
4 Ksi Concrete

3 Inch Deck with 3¼ Inch Slab
$\emptyset = 0.90$, $\emptyset_C = 0.67$, $\emptyset_{SC} = 0.80$

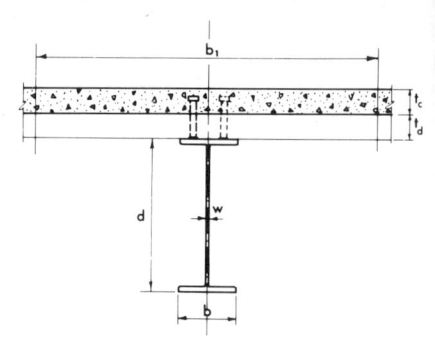

Steel Shape	b_1	\multicolumn{6}{c}{Composite Beam — Factored Resistances — M_{rc} in foot Kips for various percentages of shear connection}	Q_r† for 100%	\multicolumn{2}{c}{Properties#}	\multicolumn{2}{c}{Steel Shape Data*}
		100%	90%	80%	70%	60%	50%	Kips	I_1	S_{s_1}		
	In.								In.⁴	In.³		
W250X45	106	314	300	285	269	253	236	350	864	67.0	M_r	121
W10X30	87	309	296	282	267	251	235	350	828	66.1	V_r	82.1
b = 5.81	69	303	290	277	263	249	233	350	783	64.9	L_u	7.63
t = .510	50	290	280	269	257	244	230	350	716	63.1	I_x	170
	32	243	236	229	220	211	202	237	617	60.1	S_x	32.5
W250X39	106	271	258	245	231	217	202	301	755	58.1	M_r	103
W10X26	87	268	255	243	229	216	201	301	726	57.2	V_r	70.2
b = 5.77	69	263	251	240	227	214	200	301	689	56.3	L_u	7.38
t = .440	50	253	244	234	223	211	198	301	634	54.8	I_x	144
	32	221	214	207	199	190	180	237	552	52.4	S_x	27.9
W250X33	106	231	220	208	196	184	171	257	650	49.6	M_r	85.8
W10X22	87	229	218	207	195	183	171	257	626	48.9	V_r	63.8
b = 5.75	69	225	215	205	193	182	170	257	597	48.1	L_u	7.10
t = .360	50	219	210	200	190	180	168	257	553	46.9	I_x	118
	32	200	194	187	179	170	161	237	485	45.0	S_x	23.2
W200X100	108	596	574	550	523	493	460	780	1300	129	M_r	232
W8X67	89	546	527	506	483	457	429	659	1220	127	V_r	134
b = 8.28	70	488	472	455	436	415	393	518	1120	123	L_u	16.3
t = .935	51	428	416	403	388	373	356	378	986	117	I_x	272
	32	365	357	349	339	329	316	237	803	108	S_x	60.4
W200X86	108	522	501	478	453	426	396	677	1150	113	M_r	197
W8X58	89	501	483	463	440	416	388	659	1080	111	V_r	117
b = 8.22	70	445	430	413	395	375	353	518	996	108	L_u	14.9
t = .810	51	387	375	362	349	333	317	378	881	103	I_x	228
	32	326	318	310	301	291	280	237	722	95.8	S_x	52.1
W200X71	108	436	417	396	374	350	325	558	976	94.2	M_r	162
W8X48	89	424	407	389	368	346	322	558	923	92.5	V_r	88.9
b = 8.11	70	397	383	367	350	330	309	518	856	90.3	L_u	13.4
t = .685	51	341	330	318	305	290	274	378	764	87.0	I_x	184
	32	282	275	267	258	249	239	237	632	81.4	S_x	43.3
W200X59	108	364	347	328	309	289	267	463	825	78.6	M_r	131
W8X40	89	356	341	324	305	286	265	463	784	77.3	V_r	77.6
b = 8.07	70	344	331	316	299	282	262	463	731	75.6	L_u	12.3
t = .560	51	304	294	282	269	255	240	378	658	73.1	I_x	146
	32	247	240	233	224	215	205	237	549	68.8	S_x	35.4

†No. of studs/beam = 2 x Q_r x percent shear connection/100/q_r (per stud)

*Units — M_r — Ft. Kips L_u — Ft.   b — In.
       V_r — Kips I_x — In.⁴   t — In.
                S_x — In.³

#Concrete density = 115 lb./ft.³

Note: The SI designation in bold face type is the one preferred for use in Canada.

G40.21 – 44W
4 Ksi Concrete

3 Inch Deck with 3¼ Inch Slab
$\phi = 0.90$, $\phi_C = 0.67$, $\phi_{SC} = 0.80$

Steel Shape		Composite Beam										Steel Shape Data*	
		Factored Resistances								Properties#			
	b_1	M_{rc} in foot Kips for various percentages of shear connection						Q_r† for 100%		I_1	S_{s_1}		
	In.	100%	90%	80%	70%	60%	50%	Kips		In.⁴	In.³		
W200X52	108	322	306	289	272	254	234	408		738	69.7	M_r	115
W8X35	89	316	301	286	269	251	233	408		704	68.6	V_r	65.8
b = 8.02	70	307	294	280	264	248	231	408		659	67.2	L_u	11.7
t = .495	51	283	273	262	249	235	220	378		597	65.1	I_x	127
	32	227	221	213	205	196	186	237		502	61.5	S_x	31.3
W200X46	108	287	272	257	241	224	207	362		663	62.1	M_r	100
W8X31	89	282	268	254	238	222	206	362		634	61.1	V_r	59.6
b = 7.99	70	275	262	249	235	220	204	362		595	59.9	L_u	11.3
t = .435	51	262	252	241	229	215	201	362		542	58.1	I_x	110
	32	211	204	197	189	180	170	237		460	55.1	S_x	27.5
W200X42	107	262	248	234	219	204	188	327		613	56.4	M_r	89.8
W8X28	88	258	245	231	217	202	187	327		587	55.6	V_r	60.0
b = 6.53	69	252	240	227	214	200	186	327		552	54.4	L_u	9.27
t = .465	51	242	232	221	209	197	183	327		507	52.9	I_x	98.0
	32	200	194	186	178	169	160	237		432	50.3	S_x	24.3
W200X36	106	225	213	201	188	174	161	280		534	48.8	M_r	76.6
W8X24	88	222	211	199	186	173	160	280		514	48.1	V_r	50.8
b = 6.49	69	218	207	196	184	172	159	280		486	47.1	L_u	8.86
t = .400	51	210	201	191	180	169	157	280		448	45.9	I_x	82.8
	32	184	177	170	162	154	144	237		387	43.8	S_x	20.9
W200X31	105	201	190	179	167	156	144	244		495	43.3	M_r	67.3
W8X21	87	199	188	178	166	155	143	244		477	42.7	V_r	54.1
b = 5.27	68	195	185	175	165	154	142	244		453	41.9	L_u	6.98
t = .400	50	189	181	172	162	152	141	244		420	40.8	I_x	75.3
	32	175	169	162	154	146	136	237		367	39.1	S_x	18.2
W200X27	105	172	162	152	142	132	122	208		427	37.2	M_r	56.1
W8X18	87	170	161	151	142	132	122	208		413	36.7	V_r	48.9
b = 5.25	68	167	159	150	140	131	121	208		393	35.9	L_u	6.70
t = .330	50	163	155	147	138	129	120	208		366	35.1	I_x	61.9
	32	154	148	141	134	126	118	208		323	33.7	S_x	15.2

†No. of studs/beam = 2 x Q_r x percent shear connection/100/q_r (per stud)

*Units — M_r — Ft. Kips L_u — Ft.   b — In.
      V_r — Kips I_x — In.⁴   t — In.
             S_x — In.³

#Concrete density = 115 lb./ft.³

Note: The SI designation in bold face type is the one preferred for use in Canada.

NOTES

BEAM SELECTION TABLE

Table

The table on pages 9–144 to 9–155 inclusive lists WWF, W, S, C and the MC460 shapes in order of decreasing factored moment resistance (M_r) for G40.21-44W steel. Shapes not available from Canadian mills are identified by an asterisk in the table. Class 3 sections are identified.

Symbols

J = St. Venant torsional constant, $in.^4$

C_w = warping torsion constant, $in.^6$

b = flange width, in.

L_u = Maximum unsupported length of compression flange for which no reduction in factored moment resistance, M_r, is required, ft. ($\omega = 1.0$)

V_r = factored shear resistance for an unstiffened web for beams analysed elastically, kips. ($V_r = \phi A_w F_s$.)

I_x = moment of inertia about the X–X axis, $in.^4$

M_r = factored moment resistance, $M_r = \phi Z_x F_y$ for Class 1 and 2 sections and $\phi S_x F_y$ for Class 3 sections, ft-kips.

M_r' = factored moment resistance for a beam for a given unbraced length greater than L_u. M_r is computed according to Clauses 13.6.1 and 13.6.2 using the expression

$$\frac{\pi}{L}\sqrt{EI_y\,GJ + \left(\frac{\pi E}{L}\right)^2 I_y C_w} \qquad \text{to determine } M_u, \text{ ft-kips, } (\omega = 1.0)$$

For further information on the factored resistances of beams, refer to page 5–92.

Loads and Reactions

To determine the total uniformly distributed factored load, W_f, in kips, for a laterally supported beam for span, L, in feet, find the factored moment resistance, M_r, from the Beam Selection Table and compute W_f as follows:

$$W_f = \frac{8M_r}{L}$$

$$\text{Reaction, } R_f = \frac{W_f}{2} = \frac{4M_r}{L}$$

The value of N, the length of bearing required to develop V_r, in inches $\approx 0.528d - k$.

The maximum factored end reaction, R, in kips for 3-1/2 inches of bearing = $1.25 \times 0.90 \times F_y \times (3.5 + k) \times w$.

Note: Minor differences in the order of tabulation of beams given in the Tables on pages 9–144 to 9–155 from the order given in the Tables on pages 5–98 to 5–109, result from differences in the rounded values between metric and Imperial properties, dimensions, steel grades, etc.

BEAM SELECTION TABLES

Shape #	Properties							M_r' (Ft.-Kips)		
	J	C_w	††$_b$	L_u	V_r	I_x	M_r	Unbraced Length in Feet		
	In.^{4}	In.^{6}	In.	Feet	Kips	In.^{4}	Ft.-Kips	14	16	18
WWF1200X487	60.1	1390000	21.7	27.3	602	40200	**6170**	....	....	....
WWF1100X458	58.6	1160000	21.7	28.0	461	32700	**5440**	....	....	....
WWF1200X403	27.5	1060000	21.7	26.0	602	32000	**4950**	....	....	....
WWF1000X447	58.4	954000	21.7	28.6	461	26600	4850			
WWF1100X388	36.6	769000	19.7	24.6	461	27000	**4520**	....	....	....
WWF1200X364	21.3	745000	19.7	23.1	602	28000	**4390**	....	....	....
WWF900X417	57.3	762000	21.7	29.5	284	20800	4190	....	....	....
WWF1000X377	36.4	631000	19.7	25.1	461	21900	4030	....	....	....
W920X446*	64.2	399000	16.7	21.8	866	20300	3970	....	....	....
WWF1100X335	19.9	623000	19.7	23.8	461	22600	**3790**	....	....	....
W920X417*	52.6	366000	16.6	21.5	806	18900	3690	....	....	....
WWF900X347	35.2	507000	19.7	26.0	284	17000	3430	....	....	....
WWF1200X302	13.8	343000	15.7	17.6	602	21600	**3430**	....	....	3410
W920X387*	41.5	330000	16.5	21.0	760	17300	3400	....	....	....
WWF1000X324	19.7	513000	19.7	24.2	461	18300	3370	....	....	....
WWF1100X291	16.4	320000	15.7	18.6	461	18700	**3200**	....	....	....
W920X365*	34.6	305000	16.5	20.8	720	16100	3180	....	....	....
W840X359*	35.8	250000	15.9	19.8	741	14200	3100	....	....	....
WWF800X332	34.9	397000	19.7	26.7	235	13100	2970	....	....	....
W920X342*	28.6	282000	16.5	20.6	681	15000	2970	....	....	....
WWF900X293	18.5	413000	19.7	25.0	284	14200	2860	....	....	....
WWF1200X263	11.3	145000	11.8	12.6	602	17400	**2850**	2750	2600	2430
WWF1000X280	16.1	263000	15.7	18.9	461	15100	2830	....	....	....
W920X313*	28.0	128000	12.2	14.3	796	13200	2750	....	2660	2540
WWF1100X255	9.14	254000	15.7	17.8	461	15700	**2710**	....	....	2700
W840X329*	27.5	224000	15.8	20.0	656	12800	2690	....	....	....
W920X289*	22.2	116000	12.1	14.1	730	12100	2530	....	2430	2320
W760X314*	27.9	166000	15.1	19.1	627	10300	2470	....	....	....
WWF800X279	18.2	323000	19.7	25.6	235	10900	2470	....	....	....
W840X299*	20.5	198000	15.7	19.6	601	11500	2430	....	....	....
WWF1000X244	8.92	209000	15.7	18.1	461	12600	**2390**	....	....	....
WWF900X249	15.0	212000	15.7	19.7	284	11600	2370	....	....	....
W920X271*	18.4	107000	12.1	13.9	688	11300	2370	....	2270	2160
WWF1100X220	7.44	107000	11.8	12.7	461	12600	**2230**	2160	2040	1920
W760X284*	20.6	146000	15.0	18.7	569	9170	2220	....	....	....
W920X253*	15.1	98400	12.0	13.8	643	10500	2200	....	2100	2000
W920X238*	12.4	90300	12.0	13.6	612	9750	2060	2040	1950	1850
WWF800X235	14.7	166000	15.7	20.2	235	8890	2030	....	....	....
W760X257*	15.3	129000	15.0	18.4	521	8200	2000	....	....	....
WWF900X213	7.73	168000	15.7	18.9	284	9590	**1970**	....	....	....
W920X223*	10.1	82300	12.0	13.5	586	9040	1920	1900	1810	1710
W690X265*	19.5	98300	14.1	17.8	527	6990	1870	....	....	....
W840X226*	12.3	71800	11.6	13.4	556	8160	1840	1820	1740	1650

* Not available from Canadian mills.
# The SI designation is shown for each shape and is the preferred designation for use in Canada.
†† Rounded to three significant figures. For more precise figures see Part Eight.

Mass kg/m	M_r' (Ft.-Kips) Unbraced Length in Feet										Imperial Designation
	20	22	24	26	28	30	35	40	45	50	
487	....	....	....	....	6120	5990	5640	5260	4850	4430	**WWF(M)47X326**
458	....	....	....	....	....	5340	5040	4730	4400	4060	**WWF(M)43X307**
403	....	....	....	....	4840	4720	4390	4030	3640	3200	**WWF(M)47X270**
447	....	....	....	....	....	4780	4540	4280	4010	3730	WWF(M)39X300
388	....	....	....	4450	4340	4220	3920	3580	3230	2820	**WWF(M)43X260**
364	....	....	4340	4220	4100	3960	3600	3210	2730	2280	**WWF(M)47X244**
417	....	....	....	....	....	4170	3980	3780	3560	3340	WWF(M)35X279
377	....	....	....	3980	3890	3790	3540	3260	2970	2660	WWF(M)39X253
446	....	3960	3860	3770	3660	3560	3300	3030	2760	2440	W36X300
335	....	....	....	3690	3590	3480	3190	2880	2530	2120	**WWF(M)43X225**
417	....	3660	3570	3480	3380	3280	3020	2750	2480	2160	W36X280
347	....	....	....	....	3360	3280	3080	2870	2650	2420	WWF(M)35X233
302	3290	3160	3020	2870	2710	2540	2040	1610	1320	1100	**WWF(M)47X203**
387	....	3360	3270	3180	3080	2980	2730	2460	2170	1870	W36X260
324	....	....	....	3290	3210	3120	2870	2610	2320	1980	WWF(M)39X217
291	3120	3020	2900	2780	2640	2510	2140	1700	1400	1180	**WWF(M)43X195**
365	....	3130	3040	2950	2860	2760	2510	2250	1950	1680	W36X245
359	3090	3000	2920	2820	2730	2630	2380	2120	1810	1570	W33X241
332	....	....	....	....	2940	2880	2720	2550	2380	2200	W36X230
342	....	2910	2830	2740	2650	2560	2310	2060	1750	1500	WWF(M)31X223
293	....	....	....	2830	2760	2690	2500	2300	2080	1820	WWF(M)35X197
263	2240	2050	1810	1570	1380	1220	943	759	632	539	**WWF(M)47X176**
280	2780	2690	2590	2490	2380	2260	1960	1590	1310	1110	**WWF(M)39X188**
313	2420	2300	2170	2030	1900	1740	1390	1160	992	868	W36X210
255	2610	2500	2390	2280	2150	2020	1620	1280	1040	873	**WWF(M)43X171**
329	....	2620	2540	2460	2370	2290	2060	1830	1560	1340	W33X221
289	2210	2080	1960	1830	1700	1530	1220	1010	861	751	W36X194
314	2440	2370	2300	2220	2140	2060	1860	1650	1400	1220	W30X211
279	....	....	....	2460	2400	2340	2190	2030	1860	1680	WWF(M)31X187
299	2420	2350	2270	2200	2110	2030	1810	1570	1320	1130	W33X201
244	2310	2230	2130	2040	1930	1820	1500	1190	972	816	**WWF(M)39X163**
249	2360	2290	2220	2140	2050	1970	1740	1470	1220	1040	W36X182
271	2050	1930	1800	1680	1530	1380	1090	902	767	668	WWF(M)35X167
220	1770	1620	1440	1250	1100	970	745	598	496	421	**WWF(M)43X147**
284	2180	2110	2040	1970	1890	1810	1610	1380	1170	1020	W30X191
253	1890	1770	1650	1530	1380	1240	975	803	681	591	W36X170
238	1750	1630	1520	1390	1240	1110	873	716	605	524	W36X160
235	....	1980	1920	1860	1790	1720	1540	1360	1130	971	WWF(M)31X157
257	1950	1880	1820	1740	1670	1600	1400	1170	987	851	W30X173
213	1940	1880	1800	1730	1650	1570	1340	1080	882	743	**WWF(M)35X142**
223	1610	1500	1380	1260	1110	991	776	634	535	462	W36X150
265	1810	1750	1690	1630	1560	1500	1330	1140	976	852	W27X178
226	1560	1460	1350	1240	1110	998	792	654	557	485	W33X152

BEAM SELECTION TABLES

Shape#	Properties							M'r (Ft.-Kips)				
	J	Cw	††b	Lu	Vr	Ix	Mr	Unbraced Length in Feet				
	In.⁴	In.⁶	In.	Feet	Kips	In.⁴	Ft.-Kips	10	12	14	16	18
WWF1000X200	5.95	80800	11.8	12.8	461	9470	**1840**	....	....	1790	1690	1590
WWF900X192	8.42	80400	11.8	14.1	284	8310	**1730**	....	....	....	1660	1580
WWF700X222	14.4	126000	15.7	20.9	190	6590	1710	....	....	....	....	....
W840X210*	9.70	64300	11.5	13.2	527	7450	1700	....	....	1670	1590	1500
W690X240*	14.7	87300	14.0	17.5	476	6280	1690	....	....	....	....	1680
W920X201*	6.99	68000	12.0	13.0	557	7800	1680	....	....	1640	1560	1470
WWF800X198	7.43	132000	15.7	19.4	235	7310	1680	....	....	....	....	....
WWF700X203	10.4	113000	15.7	20.4	190	6000	1560	....	....	....	....	....
W610X241	18.5	62600	13.0	16.9	461	5170	**1540**	....	....	....	....	1520
W840X193*	7.37	56600	11.5	12.9	502	6710	1540	....	....	1500	1430	1350
W690X217*	10.9	77200	14.0	17.2	433	5630	1520	....	....	....	....	1500
WWF900X169	4.76	64800	11.8	13.5	284	7040	1470	....	....	1460	1390	1310
W760X196*	9.72	42100	10.5	12.3	487	5770	1440	....	....	1380	1310	1230
WWF700X185	7.20	100000	15.7	20.0	190	5400	1410	....	....	....	....	....
W610X217	13.4	54700	12.9	16.5	420	4580	**1380**	....	....	....	....	1350
W840X176*	5.30	48200	11.5	12.6	472	5900	1370	....	....	1320	1250	1180
W760X185*	7.99	38700	10.5	12.1	461	5360	1350	....	....	1290	1220	1140
WWF800X164	5.72	55800	11.8	14.2	235	5710	1330	....	....	....	1280	1220
W760X173*	6.43	34900	10.5	11.9	443	4930	1250	....	....	1180	1110	1040
WWF800X154	4.45	50900	11.8	13.9	235	5310	1240	....	....	....	1190	1130
W530X219*	15.4	41100	12.5	16.7	415	3630	1230	....	....	....	....	1210
W610X195	9.50	47000	12.9	16.1	387	4020	**1220**	....	....	....	....	1180
WWF700X164	7.89	47700	11.8	15.0	190	4630	1220	....	....	....	1200	1150
W760X161*	4.99	30800	10.5	11.7	425	4470	1140	....	1130	1070	1010	934
W690X170*	7.33	27600	10.1	11.9	407	4090	1130	....	....	1070	1010	949
WWF700X151	5.50	42400	11.8	14.6	190	4190	1110	....	....	....	1080	1030
W530X196*	11.3	36000	12.4	16.3	371	3220	1100	....	....	....	....	1070
W610X174	6.72	40700	12.8	15.7	349	3540	**1080**	....	....	....	1070	1040
W760X147*	3.77	26900	10.4	11.5	403	3990	1030	....	1020	959	895	827
WWF700X141	4.23	38700	11.8	14.4	190	3880	1030	....	....	....	993	947
S610X180*	12.8	11500	8.05	9.1	512	3160	1010	988	928	867	805	743
W530X182*	8.98	32700	12.4	16.0	340	2960	1010	....	....	....	....	979
W690X152*	5.28	24000	10.0	11.7	365	3620	1010	....	998	946	890	829
W610X155	4.72	35200	12.8	15.4	314	3100	**954**	...	...	...	944	907
S610X158*	10.1	10600	7.87	9.0	397	2940	924	898	842	783	723	663
W530X165*	6.83	29200	12.3	15.6	309	2670	921	...	...	...	915	883
W690X140*	4.03	21200	9.99	11.4	345	3270	917	...	905	855	800	741
W460X177*	10.6	20300	11.3	15.4	325	2190	861	...	...	...	853	826
W610X140	5.26	15000	9.06	10.8	327	2700	**838**		813	766	716	663
W530X150*	5.21	26200	12.3	15.4	279	2420	835	...	...	...	827	796
W690X125*	2.81	18000	9.96	11.2	321	2850	805	...	788	742	691	636
S610X149*	7.59	6450	7.25	7.6	467	2390	792	722	659	595	530	452
W460X158*	7.48	17400	11.2	14.9	289	1910	759	...	...	...	744	718

* Not available from Canadian mills.

#The S I designation is shown for each shape and is the preferred designation for use in Canada.

†† Rounded to three significant figures. For more precise figures see Part Eight.

Mass kg/m	M_r' (Ft.-Kips)										Imperial Designation
	Unbraced Length in Feet										
	20	22	24	26	28	30	35	40	45	50	
200	1470	1340	1200	1040	915	811	624	501	416	355	**WWF(M)39X134**
192	1490	1400	1300	1200	1070	954	743	604	507	436	**WWF(M)35X128**
222	....	1690	1640	1590	1540	1490	1360	1220	1060	911	WWF(M)28X149
210	1410	1310	1210	1100	973	872	688	566	480	417	W33X141
240	1620	1570	1510	1450	1380	1320	1160	969	824	717	W27X161
201	1370	1260	1150	1020	894	797	620	504	422	363	W36X135
198	1660	1610	1560	1500	1430	1370	1200	984	811	686	WWF(M)31X133
203	....	1520	1480	1430	1380	1330	1200	1060	893	765	WWF(M)28X136
241	1470	1420	1370	1320	1270	1220	1080	933	805	708	**W24X162**
193	1260	1160	1060	945	836	747	587	480	406	351	W33X130
217	1450	1400	1340	1280	1220	1160	996	817	692	599	W27X146
169	1230	1140	1040	932	817	724	557	448	372	317	WWF(M)35X113
196	1150	1060	975	865	773	698	560	467	401	351	W30X132
185	....	1360	1320	1280	1230	1180	1050	895	743	633	WWF(M)28X124
217	1300	1250	1200	1150	1100	1050	918	767	659	578	**W24X146**
176	1090	1000	903	787	694	619	483	393	330	284	W33X118
185	1060	974	882	777	693	624	499	415	355	310	W30X124
164	1150	1080	1000	927	833	742	577	469	393	338	WWF(M)31X109
173	961	878	780	686	610	549	437	362	308	269	W30X116
154	1060	991	917	839	740	658	509	411	343	294	WWF(M)31X103
219	1170	1130	1090	1050	1010	973	874	761	660	583	W21X147
195	1140	1090	1040	993	943	892	749	622	532	464	**W24X131**
164	1100	1040	984	926	866	803	636	525	446	388	WWF(M)28X110
161	857	776	676	593	526	472	374	308	262	228	W30X108
170	882	813	737	652	584	529	427	357	308	270	W27X114
151	978	925	869	810	750	675	530	434	366	317	WWF(M)28X101
196	1030	995	957	918	879	840	742	627	542	477	W21X132
174	993	949	904	856	808	759	616	508	432	376	**W24X117**
147	753	670	578	505	447	401	315	259	219	190	W30X99
141	898	845	790	732	667	595	464	378	317	273	WWF(M)28X95
180	680	604	542	492	451	416	349	302	265	237	W21X122
182	944	907	870	832	793	754	650	545	469	413	S24X121
152	764	698	617	544	486	438	351	292	250	219	W27X102
155	868	827	783	738	691	643	508	416	352	304	**W24X104**
158	596	527	472	428	391	360	302	260	228	204	S24X106
165	849	813	777	739	701	663	554	462	396	347	W21X111
140	679	613	532	468	416	375	298	247	211	184	W27X94
177	798	770	741	712	684	655	584	501	437	388	W18X119
140	608	548	482	429	386	351	286	241	209	184	**W24X94**
150	763	729	694	658	621	583	475	395	337	294	W21X101
125	576	507	437	383	340	305	241	199	169	146	W27X84
149	395	350	315	286	262	242	203	176	155	138	S24X100
158	691	663	635	607	578	550	471	400	347	308	W18X106

Shape#	J In.^{4}	C$_w$ In.^{6}	††b In.	L$_u$ Feet	V$_r$ Kips	I$_x$ In.^{4}	M$_r$ Ft.-Kips	M$_r'$ (Ft.-Kips) Unbraced Length in Feet 8	10	12	14	16
W610X125	3.70	12800	9.02	10.6	296	2370	**739**	...	...	711	666	619
S610X134*	6.05	6070	7.13	7.5	392	2250	736	724	667	607	544	475
W530X138	6.03	9940	8.42	10.3	328	2070	729	...	...	697	657	614
W460X144*	5.86	15800	11.1	14.6	260	1750	696	...	...	...	...	679
S610X119*	4.88	5720	7.00	7.6	314	2110	676	666	613	556	496	428
W610X113	2.68	11100	8.99	10.4	275	2100	**660**	...	...	629	587	542
S510X143*	8.56	4750	7.20	8.2	424	1680	657	...	621	580	539	497
W410X149*	7.73	11900	10.4	14.5	259	1490	653	...	...	...	...	637
W530X123	4.34	8630	8.35	10.1	288	1830	647	...	...	613	574	533
W360X162*	7.12	20200	14.6	21.3	196	1240	634	...	...	...	...	...
W460X128*	4.10	13600	11.1	14.2	231	1530	614	...	...	...	...	593
S510X128*	6.78	4440	7.06	8.1	350	1580	607	...	570	530	489	448
W610X101	1.87	9430	8.97	10.1	257	1830	**584**	...	...	551	511	467
W410X132*	5.45	10300	10.4	14.0	230	1300	577	...	...	...	...	557
W360X147*	5.37	18000	14.6	20.7	179	1110	571	...	...	...	...	...
W530X109	3.03	7420	8.30	9.9	253	1600	568	...	566	532	496	457
W460X113*	2.83	11700	11.0	13.9	202	1330	538	...	...	...	537	515
W530X101	2.45	6760	8.27	9.7	237	1480	**528**	...	524	492	456	418
S510X112*	4.59	2780	6.39	6.9	332	1280	505	484	443	401	358	308
W610X92*	1.71	4620	7.04	7.6	267	1550	505	498	455	406	352	287
W410X114*	3.57	8570	10.3	13.5	196	1110	495	...	...	...	490	470
W460X106	3.49	4700	7.64	9.5	239	1170	478	...	472	444	415	384
W530X92	1.83	5970	8.24	9.6	219	1330	**475**	...	470	439	405	369
+W360X134*	4.06	16000	14.5	21.3	161	999	472	...	...	...	...	...
S510X98*	3.58	2590	6.26	6.9	264	1190	462	442	403	362	319	270
W360X122*	5.08	6700	10.1	14.3	191	882	459	...	...	...	...	446
W610X82*	1.18	3870	7.00	7.4	243	1350	442	432	392	346	294	234
W460X97	2.73	4240	7.59	9.3	216	1070	439	...	431	404	375	345
W310X129	5.10	8280	12.1	18.1	169	740	436	...	...	...	...	...
W410X100*	2.39	7300	10.2	13.1	169	954	429	...	...	...	422	403
W530X85*	1.77	3190	6.56	7.4	223	1170	426	416	380	339	296	243
W360X110*	3.88	6000	10.1	14.0	167	796	416	...	...	...	...	401
W530X82	1.27	4970	8.22	9.3	204	1150	**416**	...	407	378	346	311
S460X104*	4.15	1840	6.25	6.7	334	928	412	392	359	325	292	253
W460X89	2.17	3860	7.56	9.2	198	984	406	...	396	370	342	312
W310X118	3.84	7320	12.1	17.5	152	662	393	...	...	...	...	...
W360X101*	3.02	5370	10.0	13.6	152	723	379	...	...	...	377	363
W460X82	1.66	3430	7.53	9.0	185	890	**370**	...	358	333	306	277
W530X74*	1.14	2560	6.53	7.2	207	984	363	350	316	278	234	188
W310X107	2.93	6540	12.0	17.0	138	597	356	...	...	...	...	...
S460X81.4*	2.37	1590	6.00	6.5	217	807	346	325	294	261	226	189
W410X85	2.22	2660	7.12	8.9	185	758	346	...	335	313	290	266
W360X91*	2.20	4690	9.99	13.3	136	640	337	...	...	...	332	319
W460X74	1.24	3040	7.49	8.9	167	800	**333**	...	321	297	271	243
W530X66*	.770	2110	6.50	6.9	189	843	315	300	269	232	188	150
W410X74	1.52	2270	7.07	8.7	161	659	**304**	...	291	269	247	223

* Not available from Canadian mills.

\#The SI designation is shown for each shape and is the preferred designation for use in Canada.

†† Rounded to three significant figures. For more precise figures see Part Eight.

Mass kg/m	M'_r (Ft.-Kips)											Imperial Designation
	Unbraced Length in Feet											
	18	20	22	24	26	28	30	35	40	45	50	
125	568	515	451	394	350	314	284	230	193	167	147	**W24X84**
134	403	350	310	278	252	230	212	178	153	135	120	S24X90
138	571	526	480	426	383	348	319	264	226	198	176	W21X93
144	653	627	599	572	544	516	487	407	344	298	263	W18X97
119	362	313	276	247	223	204	188	157	135	118	106	S24X80
113	493	442	378	329	291	260	235	189	158	136	119	**W24X76**
143	456	408	364	330	301	277	256	217	188	166	149	S20X96
149	615	593	570	548	525	503	480	421	360	315	280	W16X100
123	491	447	395	350	314	284	260	214	182	159	141	W21X83
162	...	...	628	615	601	586	572	537	501	466	431	W14X109
128	568	542	516	489	461	434	404	328	275	238	209	W18X86
128	407	357	318	287	262	241	223	188	163	144	129	S20X86
101	420	364	311	269	237	211	190	152	126	108	94.0	**W24X68**
132	535	513	491	469	446	424	402	338	288	251	223	W16X89
147	...	...	562	549	535	521	507	472	437	402	363	W14X99
109	416	372	323	284	254	229	209	171	145	126	111	W21X73
113	492	467	442	416	389	362	328	264	220	189	166	W18X76
101	378	331	286	251	224	202	183	150	126	110	96.7	**W21X68**
112	265	233	208	188	171	157	146	123	107	94.2	84.4	S20X75
92	237	201	174	153	136	123	112	91.0	76.9	66.7	58.9	W24X62
114	450	429	407	386	364	342	316	259	219	191	169	W16X77
106	353	322	283	253	228	208	191	159	137	120	107	W18X71
92	330	283	244	213	189	170	154	125	105	90.8	80.0	**W21X62**
134	...	...	468	457	446	435	423	394	365	336	305	W14X90
98	231	203	180	162	148	136	125	106	91.5	80.6	72.2	S20X66
122	431	416	401	385	370	355	340	300	258	226	201	W14X82
82	192	162	139	122	108	97.3	88.2	71.5	60.1	51.9	45.7	W24X55
97	314	280	245	218	196	179	164	136	116	102	90.5	W18X65
129	...	425	415	404	393	382	371	345	318	292	260	W12X87
100	384	363	343	321	300	276	250	204	171	148	131	W16X67
85	203	174	152	135	121	110	100	83.0	70.8	61.8	54.9	W21X57
110	386	371	356	341	326	311	296	253	217	190	169	W14X74
82	272	228	196	171	151	135	122	98.6	82.5	70.9	62.2	**W21X55**
104	219	194	174	157	144	133	123	104	90.6	80.1	71.8	S18X70
89	282	246	214	190	171	155	142	117	100	87.5	77.7	W18X60
118	390	380	369	358	348	337	326	300	273	243	215	W12X79
101	348	333	318	303	288	273	258	215	184	160	142	W14X68
82	247	210	183	162	145	131	120	98.8	84.1	73.2	64.9	**W18X55**
74	156	133	115	102	90.9	82.2	75.0	61.6	52.3	45.5	40.3	W21X50
107	351	341	331	320	309	299	288	262	234	204	181	W12X72
81.4	162	142	126	114	104	95.4	88.3	74.5	64.5	56.9	50.9	S18X54.7
85	241	213	188	168	152	138	127	106	91.4	80.2	71.5	W16X57
91	305	290	276	261	246	232	214	176	150	130	116	W14X61
74	211	179	156	137	122	110	101	82.4	69.9	60.7	53.7	**W18X50**
66	124	105	90.5	79.6	70.9	63.9	58.1	47.4	40.1	34.7	30.6	W21X44
74	198	171	150	133	120	109	100	83.2	71.3	62.4	55.5	**W16X50**

BEAM SELECTION TABLES

| Shape# | Properties | | | | | | | M'r (Ft.-Kips) | | | | |
| | J | Cw | ††b | Lu | Vr | Ix | Mr | Unbraced Length in Feet | | | | |
	In.4	In.6	In.	Feet	Kips	In.4	Ft.-Kips	8	10	12	14	16
W460X67	.986	2620	7.48	8.6	156	719	**301**	...	287	264	239	212
W460X68*	1.22	1710	6.06	7.1	170	712	299	288	261	231	199	162
†W310X97	2.18	5770	12.0	17.5	124	533	290	...	...	...	...	...
W360X79	1.94	2540	8.06	10.6	135	541	287	...	...	278	263	248
W310X86	2.10	3570	10.0	13.9	115	475	285	...	...	...	284	274
W250X101	3.56	3110	10.1	16.1	128	394	281	...	...	...	...	...
W410X67	1.11	1990	7.03	8.5	145	586	**272**	...	258	238	216	193
W460X61	.696	2190	7.45	8.4	148	623	**264**	...	249	227	203	177
W360X72	1.46	2240	8.03	10.4	123	485	259	...	...	248	234	219
W460X60*	.809	1440	6.01	6.9	147	612	259	247	221	193	160	129
W310X79	1.58	3160	9.99	13.5	109	425	257	...	...	...	255	245
S380X74*	2.12	822	5.64	6.2	216	487	255	236	214	192	169	144
†MC460X86*	2.86	1070	4.20	7.2	329	679	248	241	224	207	190	173
W250X89	2.48	2640	10.1	15.2	112	341	246	...	...	...	...	243
W410X60	.793	1740	6.99	8.4	128	518	**241**	...	227	208	187	165
W310X74	1.78	1880	8.08	11.0	118	394	239	...	...	234	223	211
W200X100	5.06	1440	8.28	16.3	134	272	232	...	...	...	...	...
†MC460X77.2*	2.07	990	4.10	7.0	282	631	231	222	205	187	169	150
W360X64	1.05	1950	7.99	10.1	109	428	230	...	...	218	204	190
S380X64*	1.54	755	5.50	6.2	161	448	229	211	190	168	143	121
W250X80	1.82	2310	10.0	14.6	97.6	303	220	...	...	...	...	215
W460X52*	.505	1140	6.00	6.6	139	510	219	206	182	155	122	98.1
W310X67	1.31	1650	8.05	10.7	106	350	214	...	...	207	196	185
†MC460X68.2*	1.49	903	4.00	6.7	235	582	213	202	184	166	147	125
W410X54	.544	1460	6.98	8.1	122	448	**211**	...	196	178	159	136
†MC460X63.5*	1.26	858	3.95	6.7	212	558	204	193	175	157	138	116
W360X57	.798	1230	6.77	8.3	114	385	203	...	191	176	160	143
S310X74*	2.82	511	5.48	7.0	215	306	202	196	184	172	160	148
W250X73	1.39	2070	10.0	14.2	88.7	272	199	...	...	...	...	193
W200X86	3.34	1180	8.22	14.9	117	228	197	...	...	...	...	195
W310X60	.953	1440	8.00	10.4	92.1	310	190	...	...	182	172	161
W250X67	1.51	1200	8.02	11.6	92.4	248	181	...	...	180	173	165
W360X51	.569	1070	6.74	8.2	104	340	**180**	...	168	154	138	121
W410X46	.460	739	5.52	6.3	114	375	**178**	163	143	121	94.2	76.5
†C380X74	2.67	492	3.72	6.6	281	404	178	170	159	147	136	125
S310X60.7*	1.75	444	5.25	6.6	145	273	176	167	154	142	129	117
W310X52	.741	879	6.56	8.3	98.0	285	169	...	160	148	135	122
W200X71	1.96	930	8.11	13.4	88.9	184	162	...	...	...	160	156
W360X45	.380	887	6.73	7.9	97.7	291	**156**	...	144	130	115	97.3
W250X58	.976	992	7.98	11.1	81.7	209	154	...	...	151	144	137
†C380X50	1.46	411	3.52	6.1	204	349	153	142	129	116	103	88.7
S310X52	1.08	328	5.08	5.8	134	230	148	134	121	108	93.1	79.4
W410X39	.261	565	5.50	6.0	99.1	301	**146**	131	112	89.1	68.6	55.1
W310X45	.457	719	6.52	8.1	83.9	238	142	...	132	121	109	96.4
S310X47	.900	311	5.00	5.8	110	219	139	125	112	99.0	84.1	71.4
†C380X50	1.02	358	3.40	5.8	157	315	139	125	112	98.6	83.5	71.0

† Class 3 Section.

*Not available from Canadian mills.

#The S I designation is shown for each shape and is the preferred designation for use in Canada.

††Rounded to three significant figures. For more precise figures see Part Eight.

Mass kg/m	M_r' (Ft.-Kips)										Imperial Designation
	Unbraced Length in Feet										
	18	20	22	24	26	28	30	35	40	45	
67	180	152	132	116	103	93.2	84.8	69.2	58.6	50.8	**W18X45**
68	136	117	103	91.9	82.9	75.5	69.3	57.7	49.4	43.3	W18X46
97	288	280	272	263	255	246	238	216	194	169	W12X65
79	232	217	201	184	166	151	139	116	99.4	87.1	W14X53
86	264	253	242	231	221	210	199	168	143	125	W12X58
101	275	267	260	253	246	239	232	214	197	177	W10X68
67	166	142	124	110	99.0	89.8	82.3	68.0	58.0	50.6	**W16X45**
61	146	123	106	93.0	82.6	74.3	67.4	54.8	46.1	39.8	**W18X41**
72	204	188	173	154	139	126	116	96.1	82.3	72.0	W14X48
60	108	92.6	80.8	71.7	64.4	58.5	53.5	44.3	37.8	33.0	W18X40
79	235	224	214	203	192	181	170	140	119	104	W12X53
74	125	110	99.0	89.8	82.3	75.9	70.5	59.8	52.0	46.0	S15X50
86	154	136	122	111	102	93.9	87.2	74.1	64.5	57.1	MC18X58
89	236	229	222	215	208	201	194	176	157	138	W10X60
60	139	118	103	90.9	81.3	73.6	67.2	55.2	46.9	40.8	**W16X40**
74	200	189	177	166	153	140	129	108	92.9	81.6	W12X50
100	227	223	218	213	208	203	199	187	175	163	W8X67
77.2	130	115	103	93.2	85.2	78.5	72.8	61.7	53.6	47.4	MC18X51.9
64	175	160	143	127	114	103	94.4	77.9	66.4	58.0	W14X43
64	104	91.9	82.2	74.4	68.0	62.7	58.1	49.2	42.7	37.8	S15X42.9
80	208	201	194	187	180	173	166	149	128	113	W10X54
52	81.4	69.3	60.1	53.1	47.5	42.9	39.2	32.2	27.3	23.7	W18X35
67	174	163	152	140	126	115	106	88.3	75.8	66.5	W12X45
68.2	108	94.9	84.7	76.6	69.9	64.3	59.5	50.3	43.6	38.5	MC18X45.8
54	112	95.2	82.3	72.4	64.5	58.2	52.9	43.2	36.5	31.7	**W16X36**
63.5	99.8	87.5	78.0	70.4	64.1	58.9	54.6	46.0	39.9	35.2	MC18X42.7
57	123	105	92.4	82.2	74.0	67.3	61.7	51.2	43.8	38.4	W14X38
74	136	122	110	101	92.5	85.6	79.7	68.0	...	...	S12X50
73	187	180	173	166	159	152	145	126	108	94.5	W10X49
86	190	185	180	176	171	166	161	150	138	125	W8X58
60	151	140	129	115	104	94.3	86.5	71.8	61.5	53.8	W12X40
67	158	151	144	136	129	122	113	95.1	82.2	72.4	W10X45
51	102	86.8	75.7	67.1	60.2	54.6	50.0	41.2	35.1	30.7	**W14X34**
46	64.1	55.0	48.2	42.8	38.5	35.0	32.1	26.6	22.8	19.9	**W16X31**
74	112	99.8	90.1	82.2	75.6	69.9	65.1	55.5	48.4	43.0	C15X50
60.7	102	91.0	82.0	74.6	68.5	63.3	58.9	50.2	...	...	S12X40.8
52	107	92.6	81.6	72.9	66.0	60.2	55.4	46.3	39.8	34.9	W12X35
71	151	146	141	137	132	128	123	112	98.3	86.9	W8X48
45	80.7	68.6	59.5	52.5	46.9	42.4	38.7	31.7	26.9	23.4	**W14X30**
58	130	123	116	109	101	92.2	85.0	71.2	61.3	53.9	W10X39
60	77.4	68.8	61.9	56.3	51.7	47.8	44.4	37.8	32.9	29.2	C15X40
52	69.2	61.5	55.3	50.3	46.1	42.6	39.6	33.7	...	...	S12X35
39	45.8	39.0	33.9	30.0	26.8	24.3	22.2	18.2	15.5	13.5	**W16X26**
45	81.3	69.9	61.2	54.4	49.0	44.5	40.8	33.9	29.0	25.3	W12X30
47	62.2	55.1	49.5	45.0	41.2	38.0	35.3	30.0	...	...	S12X31.8
50	61.8	54.7	49.1	44.6	40.9	37.8	35.1	29.8	25.9	22.9	C15X33.9

Shape#	Properties							M_r' (Ft.-Kips)				
	J	C_w	††b	L_u	V_r	I_x	M_r	Unbraced Length in Feet				
	In.^{4}	In.^{6}	In.	Feet	Kips	In.^{4}	Ft.-Kips	5	6	8	10	12
W360X39	.358	405	5.02	5.8	92.7	245	**133**	...	132	117	101	81.2
W200X59	1.12	726	8.07	12.3	77.6	146	131	...	...	...	...	...
W250X49	.583	791	7.96	10.5	73.7	170	128	...	...	...	...	123
W310X39	.300	606	6.49	7.9	73.5	204	**123**	...	...	122	113	102
W250X45	.622	414	5.81	7.6	82.1	170	121	...	...	119	111	102
S250X52	1.29	191	4.94	6.1	155	147	117	...	...	109	101	92.7
W200X52	.771	619	8.02	11.7	65.8	127	115	...	...	...	...	114
W360X33	.208	314	5.00	5.6	82.6	199	**110**	...	107	94.1	78.7	60.0
W250X39	.402	345	5.77	7.4	70.2	144	103	...	...	101	93.0	84.5
W200X46	.538	531	7.99	11.3	59.6	110	100	...	...	...	...	98.8
W310X33*	.293	165	4.03	4.7	83.7	156	96.7	94.9	88.7	74.7	58.2	44.6
S250X38	.603	156	4.66	5.6	81.3	124	93.7	...	92.1	83.7	75.1	66.5
W200X42	.538	313	6.53	9.3	60.0	98.0	89.8	...	...	...	88.1	83.5
†C310X45	.870	151	3.17	5.5	160	162	89.1	...	87.4	80.0	72.5	65.1
W250X33	.239	274	5.75	7.1	63.8	118	**85.8**	...	...	82.8	75.3	67.2
W310X28*	.180	131	4.00	4.5	74.7	130	81.5	78.9	73.1	59.8	43.9	33.3
†C310X37	.544	130	3.05	5.2	121	144	79.2	...	76.2	68.3	60.4	52.2
W200X36	.347	259	6.49	8.9	50.8	82.8	76.6	...	...	...	74.1	69.6
W250X28*	.233	104	4.02	4.8	66.9	96.3	71.3	70.6	66.4	57.1	47.1	36.5
†C310X31	.372	112	2.94	5.0	88.4	129	**70.9**	...	67.1	59.1	50.8	41.4
†C250X45*	1.23	79.3	3.03	6.1	176	103	68.0	...	...	64.0	60.0	56.0
W200X31	.282	152	5.27	7.0	54.1	75.3	**67.3**	...	...	64.8	59.6	54.2
W310X24*	.103	96.9	3.99	4.3	68.9	103	66.3	62.9	57.5	44.9	31.1	23.3
S200X34	.550	62.4	4.17	5.2	92.2	64.9	63.7	...	61.7	56.5	51.3	46.2
W150X37	.461	150	6.08	9.5	53.4	53.4	62.4	...	...	...	61.6	58.9
W250X25*	.156	85.1	4.01	4.6	63.4	81.9	61.7	60.4	56.4	47.4	36.8	28.3
†C250X37	.694	68.4	2.89	5.3	137	91.2	60.1	...	58.5	53.8	49.1	44.6
W310X21*	.070	80.6	3.97	4.2	62.3	88.6	57.4	53.8	48.9	36.8	25.0	18.6
W200X27	.172	122	5.25	6.7	48.9	61.9	**56.1**	...	...	53.1	48.2	43.0
S200X27	.335	54.1	4.00	5.0	56.7	57.7	**54.8**	54.7	52.1	46.7	41.4	36.0
W250X22*	.104	68.3	4.00	4.5	60.1	68.9	52.8	51.0	47.2	38.6	28.4	21.6
†C250X30	.372	57.0	2.74	4.8	99.1	79.0	52.1	51.6	49.0	43.7	38.4	32.7
W150X30	.240	113	6.02	8.7	42.1	41.4	49.2	...	...	...	47.4	44.7
S180X30*	.451	34.9	3.86	5.1	82.3	42.5	47.8	...	46.1	42.3	38.6	35.0
W200X22*	.137	51.8	4.01	4.9	51.9	48.0	44.9	44.6	42.1	36.6	30.8	24.3
†C230X30	.431	39.5	2.65	4.9	105	61.0	44.9	44.6	42.7	38.8	34.9	31.1
†C250X23	.211	45.6	2.60	4.4	62.7	67.4	**44.5**	43.1	40.4	34.7	28.8	23.0
W250X18*	.055	50.9	3.96	4.3	49.0	53.8	41.6	39.5	36.2	28.5	19.8	14.9
S180X22.8*	.241	29.1	3.66	4.6	46.1	36.8	39.9	39.3	37.3	33.3	29.4	25.2
W150X24*	.223	38.2	4.03	5.8	42.7	32.1	38.6	...	38.3	35.4	32.4	29.4
W200X19*	.087	40.8	4.00	4.7	48.0	39.6	37.6	36.9	34.5	29.3	23.2	18.0
†C230X22	.210	31.1	2.48	4.3	67.0	51.1	**37.6**	36.2	34.0	29.6	25.2	20.3
†C200X28	.439	25.1	2.53	5.0	102	44.0	36.3	...	34.9	32.2	29.5	26.8
S150X26	.374	18.5	3.57	5.1	72.9	26.4	35.0	...	33.8	31.2	28.7	26.2

† Class 3 Section.

* Not available from Canadian mills.

\# The S I designation is shown for each shape and is the preferred designation for use in Canada.

†† Rounded to three significant figures. For more precise figures see Part Eight.

Mass kg/m	M_r' (Ft.-Kips)										Imperial Designation
	Unbraced Length in Feet										
	14	16	18	20	22	24	26	28	30	35	
39	63.9	52.5	44.4	38.5	34.0	30.4	27.5	25.1	23.1	19.3	**W14X26**
59	127	123	118	113	109	104	99.8	95.3	90.8	77.8	W8X40
49	117	110	103	95.9	88.8	80.6	72.7	66.3	60.9	50.7	W10X33
39	90.9	77.8	64.7	55.2	48.1	42.5	38.1	34.5	31.6	26.0	**W12X26**
45	93.1	84.0	73.5	64.5	57.4	51.8	47.2	43.4	40.1	33.8	W10X30
52	84.6	76.1	66.9	59.8	54.1	49.4	45.4	42.1	39.2	...	S10X35
52	109	105	100	95.7	91.1	86.6	82.1	77.7	72.2	60.7	W8X35
33	46.7	38.0	31.9	27.4	24.1	21.4	19.3	17.5	16.1	13.4	**W14X22**
39	75.7	66.1	56.4	49.2	43.6	39.2	35.6	32.6	30.1	25.3	W10X26
46	94.4	90.0	85.5	81.0	76.5	72.0	67.5	62.0	57.2	47.9	W8X31
33	36.1	30.3	26.1	22.9	20.5	18.5	16.9	15.6	14.4	12.2	W12X22
38	56.8	48.5	42.4	37.7	34.0	30.9	28.4	26.3	24.4	...	S10X25.4
42	78.8	74.1	69.4	64.7	60.1	54.3	49.5	45.6	42.2	35.7	W8X28
45	57.3	49.3	43.3	38.7	34.9	31.9	29.3	27.1	25.2	21.5	C12X30
33	58.7	48.7	41.2	35.7	31.4	28.1	25.4	23.2	21.4	17.9	**W10X22**
28	26.6	22.2	19.0	16.6	14.8	13.3	12.1	11.1	10.3	8.7	W12X19
37	43.3	37.1	32.5	28.9	26.1	23.7	21.8	20.2	18.7	16.0	C12X25
36	65.0	60.4	55.7	51.1	45.4	40.9	37.2	34.2	31.6	26.6	W8X24
28	29.8	25.1	21.8	19.2	17.2	15.6	14.3	13.2	12.2	10.3	W10X19
31	34.2	29.1	25.4	22.6	20.3	18.5	16.9	15.6	14.5	12.4	**C12X20.7**
45	52.1	48.1	43.8	39.3	35.6	32.6	30.1	27.9	26.0	...	C10X30
31	48.7	42.7	36.9	32.5	29.0	26.2	23.9	22.0	20.4	17.3	**W8X21**
24	18.4	15.2	13.0	11.3	10.0	9.0	8.1	7.4	6.9	5.8	W12X16
34	40.7	35.2	31.1	27.8	25.2	23.0	...	...	...	...	S8X23
37	56.1	53.4	50.7	48.0	45.3	42.6	39.5	36.5	33.9	28.8	W6X25
25	22.9	19.2	16.6	14.6	13.0	11.8	10.8	9.9	9.2	7.8	W10X17
37	40.1	34.7	30.6	27.4	24.9	22.7	20.9	19.4	18.1	...	C10X25
21	14.6	12.0	10.2	8.8	7.8	6.9	6.3	5.7	5.3	4.4	W12X14
27	37.6	31.4	26.9	23.6	21.0	18.9	17.2	15.8	14.6	12.3	**W8X18**
27	30.2	26.0	22.9	20.4	18.4	16.8	...	...	...	...	**S8X18.4**
22	17.4	14.5	12.5	10.9	9.7	8.8	8.0	7.4	6.8	5.7	W10X15
30	27.5	23.7	20.8	18.6	16.8	15.3	14.1	13.1	12.2	...	C10X20
30	42.0	39.3	36.6	34.0	30.9	28.0	25.6	23.6	21.8	18.5	W6X20
30	31.1	27.0	23.9	21.4	...	...	...	...	...	...	S7X20
22	19.9	16.9	14.7	13.0	11.6	10.6	9.7	8.9	8.3	7.0	W8X15
30	26.8	23.2	20.5	18.4	16.6	15.2	14.0	...	...	...	C9X20
23	19.1	16.4	14.4	12.8	11.5	10.5	9.7	8.9	8.3	...	**C10X15.3**
18	11.8	9.7	8.3	7.2	6.4	5.7	5.2	4.8	4.4	3.7	W10X12
22.8	21.2	18.3	16.1	14.4	...	...	...	...	...	...	S7X15.3
24	26.5	23.1	20.3	18.1	16.3	14.9	13.7	12.7	11.8	10.1	W6X16
19	14.6	12.3	10.7	9.4	8.4	7.6	7.0	6.4	6.0	5.0	W8X13
22	17.0	14.7	12.9	11.6	10.5	9.5	8.8	...	...	...	**C9X15**
28	24.1	20.9	18.5	16.6	15.1	13.8	...	...	...	...	C8X18.75
26	23.7	20.8	18.4	...	...	...	...	...	...	...	S6X17.25

| Shape # | Properties | | | | | | | M_r' (Ft.-Kips) | | | |
| | J | C_w | ††b | L_u | V_r | I_x | M_r | Unbraced Length in Feet | | | |
	In.^{4}	In.^{6}	In.	Feet	Kips	In.^{4}	Ft.-Kips	4	5	6	8
†C230X20	.170	28.2	2.43	4.2	54.8	47.9	**35.0**	...	33.3	31.2	26.7
†W150X22	.101	76.5	5.99	8.4	36.0	29.1	32.1	...	...	...	...
†C200X21	.188	19.3	2.34	4.2	63.4	36.2	29.9	...	28.6	26.9	23.6
W200X15*	.043	30.9	3.94	4.5	35.1	30.8	29.3	...	28.4	26.3	21.6
S150X19	.168	14.7	3.33	4.4	36.4	22.2	**28.0**	...	27.2	25.8	23.0
W150X18*	.090	24.7	4.00	5.2	36.2	22.1	27.4	...	...	26.3	23.5
†C200X17	.131	16.5	2.26	4.0	46.0	32.6	**26.9**	26.8	25.2	23.5	20.0
†C180X22*	.270	13.2	2.30	4.6	76.7	27.3	25.7	...	25.3	24.3	22.2
S130X22	.323	9.18	3.28	5.3	64.6	15.2	24.5	...	...	24.0	22.4
†C180X18	.162	11.2	2.19	4.1	57.4	24.3	22.9	...	21.8	20.6	18.3
W150X14*	.040	17.7	3.94	4.9	26.2	16.4	20.6	...	20.4	19.3	16.7
†C180X15	.101	9.18	2.09	3.8	38.4	21.3	**20.1**	19.8	18.5	17.2	14.7
†C150X19	.243	7.22	2.16	4.8	68.5	17.4	19.1	...	19.0	18.3	16.9
S130X15	.114	6.72	3.00	4.1	28.0	12.3	**18.7**	...	17.9	17.0	15.2
†C150X16	.132	5.95	2.03	4.1	49.2	15.2	16.7	...	16.0	15.1	13.5
†C150X12	.076	4.72	1.92	3.6	31.4	13.1	**14.4**	14.0	13.1	12.2	10.5
†C130X17	.233	3.69	2.03	5.4	61.7	10.4	13.7	...	...	13.5	12.7
S100X14.1*	.120	3.13	2.80	4.5	34.1	6.8	13.4	...	13.1	12.6	11.5
†C130X13	.111	2.93	1.88	4.2	42.5	8.9	11.7	...	11.3	10.8	9.8
S100X11	.073	2.65	2.66	4.0	20.2	6.1	**11.6**	...	11.0	10.5	9.4
†C130X10	.056	2.22	1.75	3.4	24.8	7.5	**9.9**	9.6	9.0	8.4	7.2
S75X11	.091	1.11	2.51	5.1	27.4	2.9	7.8	...	...	7.6	7.1
†C100X11	.083	1.24	1.72	4.4	33.6	4.6	7.6	...	7.4	7.1	6.5
†C100X9	.056	1.08	1.65	3.8	25.8	4.2	**6.9**	6.9	6.5	6.2	5.6
S75X8	.044	.863	2.33	4.0	13.3	2.5	**6.5**	6.5	6.2	5.9	5.3
†C100X8	.040	.921	1.58	3.4	19.2	3.8	**6.3**	6.1	5.8	5.4	4.8
†C75X9	.074	.462	1.60	5.5	27.9	2.1	4.5	...	...	4.5	4.2
†C75X7	.043	.379	1.50	4.4	20.2	1.8	**4.1**	...	4.0	3.8	3.5
†C75X6	.027	.309	1.41	3.5	13.3	1.7	**3.7**	3.6	3.4	3.2	2.9

† Class 3 Section.
* Not available from Canadian mills.
# The SI designation is shown for each shape and is the preferred designation for use in Canada.
†† Rounded to three significant figures. For more precise figures see Part Eight.

Mass kg/m	M_r' (Ft.-Kips)										Imperial Designation
	Unbraced Length in Feet										
	10	12	14	16	18	20	22	24	26	28	
20	22.0	17.7	14.8	12.7	11.2	10.0	9.0	8.2	7.6	...	**C9X13.4**
22	30.6	28.5	26.4	24.3	22.2	19.7	17.5	15.8	14.4	13.2	W6X15
21	20.4	16.7	14.1	12.2	10.8	9.6	8.7	8.0	...	...	C8X13.75
15	15.9	12.1	9.7	8.0	6.9	6.0	5.4	4.8	4.4	4.0	W8X10
19	20.2	17.2	14.5	12.6	11.1	...	...	...	...	...	**S6X12.5**
18	20.7	17.6	14.6	12.4	10.9	9.7	8.7	7.9	7.3	6.7	W6X12
17	16.2	13.1	11.0	9.5	8.4	7.5	6.8	6.2	...	...	**C8X11.5**
22	20.1	18.0	15.7	13.7	12.1	10.9	...	...	...	...	C7X14.75
22	20.9	19.4	17.8	...	...	...	...	...	...	...	S5X14.75
18	16.0	13.3	11.3	9.8	8.7	7.8	...	...	...	...	C7X12.25
14	13.9	10.8	8.8	7.5	6.5	5.7	5.1	4.6	4.2	3.9	W6X9
15	11.9	9.7	8.2	7.1	6.3	5.6	...	...	...	...	**C7X9.8**
19	15.6	14.2	12.9	11.2	10.0	...	...	...	...	...	C6X13
15	13.4	11.3	9.6	...	...	...	...	...	...	...	**S5X10**
16	12.0	10.2	8.7	7.6	6.7	...	...	...	...	...	C6X10.5
12	8.5	7.0	5.9	5.2	4.6	...	...	...	...	...	**C6X8.2**
17	11.9	11.1	10.3	...	...	...	...	...	...	...	C5X11.5
14,1	10.5	9.5	...	...	...	...	...	...	...	...	S4X9.5
13	8.9	7.9	6.7	...	...	...	...	...	...	...	C5X9
11	8.3	7.1	...	...	...	...	...	...	...	...	**S4X7.7**
10	6.0	4.9	4.2	...	...	...	...	...	...	...	**C5X6.7**
11	...	...	...	...	...	...	...	...	...	...	S3X7.5
11	6.0	5.4	...	...	...	...	...	...	...	...	C4X7.25
9	5.0	4.3	...	...	...	...	...	...	...	...	**C4X6.25**
8	...	...	...	...	...	...	...	...	...	...	**S3X5.7**
8	4.1	3.4	...	...	...	...	...	...	...	...	**C4X5.4**
9	...	...	...	...	...	...	...	...	...	...	C3X6
7	...	...	...	...	...	...	...	...	...	...	**C3X5**
6	...	...	...	...	...	...	...	...	...	...	**C3X4.1**

IMP

PART TEN
GENERAL INDEX

Amplification Factors (U) 4-32
Anchor Bolts 1-88; 4-149
Angles, Double
    Connections, Beam 3-54
    Factored Axial Compressive Resistances 4-122
    Properties and Dimensions, SI 6-72
    Properties and Dimensions, Imperial 8-40
Angles, Single
    Comparison Tables 6-28
    Gauge Distances 6-125
    Permissible Variations in Sectional Dimensions 6-15
    Properties and Dimensions, SI 6-68
    Properties and Dimensions, Imperial 8-36
    Shape Size Groupings 6-6
    Sources 6-19
Areas of Circles, length for Unit Radius 7-55
Area
    Bars, Square and Round 6-110
    Fastener Holes 3-91
    Surface, of Structural Shapes (See Properties and Dimensions)
Availability of Structural Sections 6-17
Bars
    Abbreviations vii
    Area 6-110
    General Information 6-103
    Mass 6-110
Base Plates for Columns 1-88; 4-144
Beams
    Bearing Plates 5-151
    Camber 1-23; 6-12
    Classes of Sections in Bending 1-30; 5-5
    Composite 1-66; 5-18
    Connections 1-76; 3-52
    Deflections 1-23; 5-88
    Diagrams and Formulas 5-132
    Factored Load Tables 5-110
        WWF Shapes 5-110
        W Shapes 5-116
        S Shapes 5-124
        HSS 5-126
    M Shapes (See M Shapes)
    Selection Tables
        CSA G40.21-M 300W (SI) 5-98
        CSA G40.21 − 44W (Imperial) 9-143
    S Shapes (See S Shapes)
    Trial Selection Tables, Composite Beam (See Composite Beams)
    W Shapes (See W Shapes)
    Web Holes, Beams with 5-155
    WWF Shapes (See WWF Shapes)

Beam-Columns 4-96
Bearing Piles, HP Shapes, SI 6-54
Bearing Piles, HP Shapes, Imperial 8-22
Bearing Plates, Beams 5-151
    Design Chart 5-153
Bearing Resistances, Factored, SI 1-43; 3-9
Bearing Resistances, Factored, Imperial 9-7
Bearing-Type Connections, SI 1-44; 3-7
Bearing-Type Connections, Imperial 9-6
Bending Coefficient (ω) for Beam-Columns 4-30
Bending Factors (B_x, B_y), Approximate 4-27
Bolts
    ASTM A307 .... 1-79; 6-122
    ASTM A325 1-81
    ASTM A325M 6-117; 6-119
    ASTM A490 1-81
    ASTM A490M 6-117
    Data — SI 3-5
    Data — Imperial 9-5
    Erection Clearances 6-126
    Inspection 1-84
    Installation 1-83
    Joints 1-81
    Factored Shear and Tension 3-13; 3-17
    Factored Shear Resistance, SI 1-44; 3-8
    Factored Shear Resistance, Imperial 9-6
    Factored Tensile Resistance, SI 1-44; 3-8
    Factored Tensile Resistance, Imperial 9-6
    Slip Resistance, SI 1-44; 3-15
    Slip Resistance, Imperial 9-8
    Tension and Prying Action, in.................................. 3-18
Bracing Formulas 7-54
Bracing Requirements 1-75
Building Materials 7-28
Built-Up Sections 1-72; 6-95
C Shapes (See Channels)
Camber 1-23; 6-12
Channels
    Comparison Tables 6-27
    Miscellaneous (MC), Principal Sources 6-18
    Miscellaneous (MC), Properties and Dimensions, SI 6-64
    Miscellaneous (MC), Properties and Dimensions, Imperial 8-32
    Permissible Variations in Sectional Dimensions 6-14
    Shape Size Grouping 6-6
    Standard (C), Principal Sources 6-18
    Standard (C), Properties and Dimensions, SI 6-62
    Standard (C), Properties and Dimensions, Imperial 8-30
Chemical Composition (Heat Analysis), Structural Steels 6-8
Circle, Properties of 7-49
Circular Arcs, Length for Unit Radius 7-55
Classes of Sections in Bending 5-5
Code of Standard Practice for Structural Steel 7-3
Coefficients of Thermal Expansion 7-33
Colour Code, Steel Marking 6-9

Columns

Amplification Factors (U) 4-32
Base Plates 4-144
Beam-Columns 4-96
Bending Factors 4-27
Biaxial Bending 1-41; 4-108
Effective Lengths 1-29; 4-22
Euler Buckling Load per Unit Area 4-31
Factored Axial Compressive Resistances 4-33
    Double Angle Struts 4-122
    HSS, Class C, SI 4-48
    HSS, Class C, Imperial................................... 9-32
    HSS, Class H, SI 4-72
    HSS, Class H, Imperial 9-56
    W Shapes, SI 4-41
    W Shapes, Imperial 9-25
    WWF Shapes, SI 4-36
    WWF Shapes, Imperial 9-20
Factored Moment Resistances 4-117
HSS Properties and Dimensions, SI 6-85
HSS Properties and Dimensions, Imperial 8-46
M Shape, Properties and Dimensions, SI 6-56
M Shape, Properties and Dimensions, Imperial 8-24
Pipe, Properties and Dimensions 6-87
Stability Effects 1-28; 4-14
Unit Factored Compressive Resistances, SI 4-8
Unit Factored Compressive Resistances, Imperial 9-12
Unit Factored Compressive Resistances for Class H HSS, SI 4-13
Unit Factored Compressive Resistances for Class H HSS, Imperial 9-16
W Shapes, Properties and Dimensions, SI 6-40
W Shapes, Properties and Dimensions, Imperial 8-8
Width-Thickness Ratios 1-30; 4-5
WWF Shapes, Properties and Dimensions, SI 6-33
WWF Shapes, Properties and Dimensions, Imperial 8-4

Commentary on CSA Standard CAN3-S16.1-M78 2-3

Composite Beams

Requirements of CAN3-S16.1-M78 1-66
Composite Design Trial Selection Tables
    130 mm Solid Slab 5-28
    38 mm Deck + 65 mm Slab 5-38
    51 mm Deck + 65 mm Slab 5-48
    76 mm Deck + 65 mm Slab 5-58
    51 mm Deck + 85 mm Slab 5-68
    76 mm Deck + 85 mm Slab 5-78
    5" Solid Slab 9-82
    1-1/2" Deck + 2-1/2" Slab 9-92
    2" Deck + 2-1/2" Slab 9-102
    3" Deck + 2-1/2" Slab 9-112
    2" Deck + 3-1/4" Slab 9-122
    3" Deck + 3-1/4" Slab 9-132

Composite Truss 5-23
Compression Members (See Columns)

Connections

    Double Angle 3-54

    End Plate 3-60

    HSS Connections 3-80

    Moment 3-72

    Requirements of CAN3-S16.1-M78 1-76

    Seated 3-66

    Single Angle 3-62

    Stiffened Seated 3-70

Continuous Spans, Formulas and Flexure Diagrams 5-146

Conversion Factors, Imperial — SI — Imperial 7-60

Crane Rails 6-111

CSA G40.20-M and G40.21-M 6-3

CSSBI Standards 7-25

Cutting Tolerances 6-13

Definitions of Section Properties 7-38

Deflections 1-23

    Graph 5-90

    Recommended Maximum Values 1-99

    Table 5-91

Deformations, Permanent 1-24

Designations vii

Detailing Practices (gauge distances) 6-125

Dimensions, see specific items

Distance, Centre to Centre between Staggered Fasteners 6-124

Double Angle Beam Connections 3-54

Double Angles, Properties and Dimensions, SI 6-72

Double Angles, Properties and Dimensions, Imperial 8-40

Double Angle Struts

    Factored Axial Compressive Resistances 4-122

Double Channels, Properties and Dimensions, Toe-to-Toe 6-96

Double Channels, Properties and Dimensions, Back-to-Back 6-97

Dynamic Effects 1-23

Eccentric Loads

    On Bolt Groups 3-24

    On Weld Groups 3-38

Effect of Factored Loads 1-26

Effective Lengths of Compression Members 1-29; 4-2

Effective Slab Width 1-67; 5-19

Electronic Aids 7-34

Ellipse, Properties of 7-50

End Distance 1-80

End Plate Connections 3-60

Equal Leg Angles, Properties of, SI 6-68

Equal Leg Angles, Properties of, Imperial 8-36

Equivalent Uniform Bending Coefficients 4-30

Erection 1-92

    Erection Clearances, Bolts 6-126

Euler Buckling Load per Unit Area, SI 4-31

Euler Buckling Load per Unit Area, Imperial 9-17

Expansion, Coefficients of 7-33

Factored

    Axial Compressive Resistances, SI 1-35; 4-33

    Axial Compressive Resistances, Imperial 9-19

Bearing Resistances, SI 1-43; 3-9
Bearing Resistances, Imperial 9-7
Moment Resistances, Flexural Members, SI 1-38; 5-92
Moment Resistances, Flexural Members, Imperial 9-143
Moment Resistances, Columns 4-117
Resistance of Welds, SI 1-45; 3-37
Resistance of Welds, Imperial 9-9
Shear Resistance, Bolts, SI 1-44; 3-8
Shear Resistance, Bolts, Imperial 9-6
Tensile Resistance, Bolts, SI 1-44; 3-8
Tensile Resistance, Bolts, Imperial 9-6
Ultimate Shear Stress, Girder Webs 1-36; 5-8
Unit Compressive Resistances, SI 4-8
Unit Compressive Resistances, Imperial 9-11
Factors
Bending 4-27
Load 1-16; 1-26
Load Combination 1-16; 1-26
Importance Factor 1-16; 1-26
Performance 1-16; 1-34; 1-44; 1-68; 1-70; 2-6; 2-8
Fasteners (See Bolts, Welds)
Fatigue 1-47
Flexural Members (See Beams: Girders)
Formulas
Beam 5-132
Bracing 7-54
Properties of Geometric Sections 7-38
Trigonometric 7-53
Friction-Type Connections (See Slip-Resistant Connections)
Gauges, Usual 6-125
General Nomenclature viii
General Requirements for Built-up Members 1-72
Geometric Sections, Properties of 7-38
Girders, Plate
Design 5-11
Factored Shear Stress in Web 5-8
Requirements of CAN3-S16.1-M78 1-51
HP Shapes
Comparison Table 6-26
Permissible Variations in Sectional Dimensions 6-13
Properties and Dimensions, SI 6-54
Properties and Dimensions, Imperial 8-22
Shape Size Groupings 6-6
Source, Principal 6-17
High Strength Bolts (See Bolts)
Holes
Area of Fastener Holes 3-91
Staggered Net Width 3-92
Hollow Structural Sections (HSS)
Beam Load Tables 5-126
Comparison Table 6-30
Connections 3-80
Factored Compressive Resistances, Class C, SI 4-48
Factored Compressive Resistances, Class C, Imperial 9-31

    Factored Compressive Resistances, Class H, SI 4-72
    Factored Compressive Resistances, Class H, Imperial 9-56
    Permissible Variations in Sectional Dimensions 6-15
    Properties and Dimensions, SI 6-85
    Properties and Dimensions, Imperial 8-46
    Sources, Principal 6-20
    Unit Factored Compressive Resistances, Class C, SI 4-8
    Unit Factored Compressive Resistances, Class C, Imperial 9-11
    Unit Factored Compressive Resistances, Class H, SI 4-13
    Unit Factored Compressive Resistances, Class H, Imperial 9-16
I-Shapes (See S Shapes)
Importance Factor 1-16; 1-26
Indexes for
    CAN3-S16.1-M78 1-3
    CISC Code of Standard Practice 7-4
    Compression Members 4-1
    Connections and Tension Members 3-1
    Flexural Members 5-1
    Limit States Design Tables in Imperial 9-1
    Properties and Dimensions, SI 6-1
    Properties and Dimensions, Imperial 8-1
Initial Out-of-Straightness 2-20
Interaction Equations (Beam-Columns) 1-41; 4-108
Joists 1-55; 2-45
Junior Beams (See Beams, M Shapes)
Junior Channels (See Channels, Miscellaneous)
K-Factors 1-29; 4-14; 4-25
L Shapes (See Angles)
Lateral Bracing 1-40; 1-75
Length of Circular Arcs for Unit Radius 7-55
Light Beams (See Beams, W Shapes)
Limit States 1-16; 1-23
Load Factors 1-16; 1-25
Load Combination Factor 1-16; 1-25
M Shapes
    Comparison Table 6-26
    Properties and Dimensions, SI 6-56
    Properties and Dimensions, Imperial 8-24
    Shape Size Groupings 6-6
    Sources, Principal 6-17
MC Shapes (See Channels)
Materials, Mass and Forces 7-28
Mechanical, Properties Summary 6-7
Metric Conversion (See SI Summary)
Mill Practice, Standard 6-11
Miscellaneous Channels (See Channels)
Moment Connections 1-77; 3-72
Moment Diagrams for Beams 5-132
Moment Resistances, Factored
    Beams, SI 1-38; 5-98
    Beams, Imperial 9-143
    Columns 4-117
    Composite Beams, SI 1-66; 5-28
    Composite Beams, Imperial 9-82

Moving Concentrated Loads 5-143
M/D Ratios 7-30
Net Area of Tension Members 1-31
Nomenclature, General viii
Nuts
    Dimensions, A325M, A490M 6-117
    Dimensions, A307 6-122
    Rotation 1-86
Open Web Steel Joists 1-55; 2-45
Parabola, Properties of 7-50
Parallel Bracing Formulas 7-54
Performance Factor 1-16; 1-34; 1-44; 1-68; 1-70; 2-6; 2-8
Permanent Deformations 1-24
Piles (See HP Shapes)
Plastic Analysis 1-28
Plate Girders
    Design 5-11
    Factored Shear Stress in Web 5-8
    Requirements of CAN3-S16.1-M78 1-51
Plates
    Beam Bearing 5-151
    Column Base 4-144
    General Information 6-103
    Mass 6-105
Properties of Geometric Sections 7-38
Properties of Sections, Definitions 7-38
Prying Action, Bolts in Tension and 3-18
P△ Effect 1-28; 4-14
Rectangular Hollow Structural Sections (See Hollow Structural Sections)
Reduction of Area for Holes 3-91
Residual Stress 2-20
Resistances (see Factored Resistances)
Rolled Structural Shapes 6-38
Roof Deck, Steel 7-25
Round Bars, Properties of 6-110
S Shapes
    Comparison Table 6-26
    Permissible Variations in Sectional Dimensions 6-14
    Properties and Dimensions, SI 6-58
    Properties and Dimensions, Imperial 8-26
    Shape Size Groupings 6-6
    Sources, Principal 6-17
Safety Index (β) 2-6
Seated Beam Shear Connections 3-66
Selection Tables
    Beams, SI 5-98
    Beams, Imperial 9-143
    Composite Beams (See Composite Beams)
Shape Size Groupings 6-6
Shear
    Factored Ultimate Shear Stress 1-36; 5-5
    Resistance, Bolts in Bearing-Type Connections 1-44; 3-8; 9-5
Shear and Moment in Girders 1-38; 2-25; 5-17

Shear and Tension in Bolts
    Bearing-Type Connections 1-44; 3-13
    Slip-Resistant Connections 1-45; 3-17
Shear Connections for Composite Beams 1-68
Sheet Steel Products 7-25
SI Summary 7-56
Single Angle Beam Connections 3-62
Source, Principal, of Sections 6-17
Square Bars, Properties of 6-110
Square Hollow Structural Sectional (See Hollow Structural Sections)
Stability Effects 1-28; 4-14
Staggered Holes in Tension Members 3-92
Standard Beams (See S Shapes)
Standard Channels (See Channels)
Standard Mill Practice 6-11
Standard Practice, Code of 7-3
Starred Angles
    Factored Axial Compressive Resistances 4-139
Stiffened Seated Beam Connections 3-70
Stiffeners 1-52; 1-77; 3-76; 5-15
Structural Shapes
    General Information 6-11
    Source, Principal 6-17
Structural Steels 6-3
Structural Tees, (See Tees)
Struts, Double Angle
    Factored Axial Compressive Resistances 4-122
Sweep 1-17; 6-11
Symbols, Welds 6-133
Tees, Properties and Dimensions 6-78
Temperature, Coefficients of Expansion 7-33
Tensile Strengths (Mechanical Properties) 6-7
Tension and Prying Action, Bolts in 3-18
Tension and Shear (See Shear and Tension)
Tension Members 1-34; 3-89
Transverse Stiffeners 1-52
Truss, Composite 5-23
Truss Connections 3-83
Two Angles (See Double Angles)
Two Channels, Properties and Dimensions 6-96
Unequal Leg Angles
    Factored Axial Compressive Resistances 4-127
    Properties and Dimensions, SI 6-70
    Properties and Dimensions, Imperial 8-38
Usual Gauges 6-125
Vibrations, Guide for Floor 5-169
W Shapes
    Beam Load Tables 5-116
    Beam Selection Tables, SI 5-98
    Beam Selection Tables, Imperial 9-143
    Comparison Table 9-24
    Factored Axial Compressive Resistance, SI 4-41
    Factored Axial Compressive Resistance, Imperial 9-25
    Permissible Variations in Sectional Dimensions 6-13

    Properties and Dimensions, SI 6-40

    Properties and Dimensions, Imperial 8-8

    Shape Size Groupings 6-6

    Sources, Principal 6-17

WWF Shapes

    Beam Load Tables 5-110

    Beam Selection Tables, SI 5-98

    Beam Selection Tables, Imperial 9-143

    Comparison Table 6-23

    Factored Axial Compressive Resistances, SI 4-36

    Factored Axial Compressive Resistances, Imperial 9-20

    Permissible Variations in Sectional Dimensions 6-12

    Properties and Dimensions, SI 6-33

    Properties and Dimensions, Imperial 8-4

    Source, Principal 6-17

Web Crippling 1-54

Web Holes, Beams with 5-155

Welded Wide Flange Shapes (See WWF Shapes)

Welds

    Eccentric Loads on Weld Groups 3-38

    Factored Resistances, SI 1-45; 3-37

    Factored Resistances, Imperial 9-9

    General Information 6-127

    Symbols 6-133

Width-Thickness Limits 1-30; 4-5

Yield Strengths (Mechanical Properties) 6-7

Yield Points, Mechanical Properties 6-7

NOTES